IFC®

CODE AND COMMENTARY

VOLUME 1

The complete **IFC** with corresponding commentary after each section.

2018 IFC® Code and Commentary—Volume 1

First Printing: August 2018

ISBN: 978-1-60983-769-3 (soft-cover edition)

T023335

PRINTED IN THE USA

PREFACE

The principal purpose of the Commentary is to provide a basic volume of knowledge and facts relating to building construction as it pertains to the regulations set forth in the 2018 *International Fire Code*. The person who is serious about effectively designing, constructing and regulating buildings and structures will find the Commentary to be a reliable data source and reference to almost all components of the built environment.

As a follow-up to the *International Fire Code*, we offer a companion document, the *IFC® Code and Commentary—Volume 1*. Volume 1 covers Chapters 1 through 19 of the 2018 *International Fire Code*. The basic appeal of the Commentary is thus: it provides in a small package and at reasonable cost thorough coverage of many issues likely to be dealt with when using the *International Fire Code*—and then supplements that coverage with historical and technical background. Reference lists, information sources and bibliographies are also included.

Throughout all of this, effort has been made to keep the vast quantity of material accessible and its method of presentation useful. With a comprehensive yet concise summary of each section, the Commentary provides a convenient reference for regulations applicable to the construction of buildings and structures. In the chapters that follow, discussions focus on the full meaning and implications of the code text. Guidelines suggest the most effective method of application, and the consequences of not adhering to the code text. Illustrations are provided to aid understanding; they do not necessarily illustrate the only methods of achieving code compliance.

The format of the Commentary includes the full text of each section, table and figure in the code, followed immediately by the commentary applicable to that text. At the time of printing, the Commentary reflects the most up-to-date text of the 2018 *International Fire Code*. Each section's narrative includes a statement of its objective and intent, and usually includes a discussion about why the requirement commands the conditions set forth. Code text and commentary text are easily distinguished from each other. All code text is shown as it appears in the *International Fire Code*, and all commentary is indented below the code text and begins with the symbol ❖.

Readers should note that the Commentary is to be used in conjunction with the *International Fire Code* and not as a substitute for the code. The Commentary is advisory only; the code official alone possesses the authority and responsibility for interpreting the code.

Comments and recommendations are encouraged, for through your input, we can improve future editions. Please direct your comments to the Codes and Standards Development Department at the Chicago District Office.

The International Code Council would like to extend its thanks to the following individuals for their contributions to the technical content of this commentary:

Zack Adams
Robert Davidson
Steve Forrester
Ray Grill
Traci Harvey
Don Havener
Howard Hopper
Jeff Hugo
Chris Jeleniwicz
Richard Kluge
Pat McLaughlin
Mark Murray
Ray Reynolds
Greg Rogers
Bruce Swiecicki
Carl Wren

For the complete errata history of this code, please visit: https://www.iccsafe.org/errata-central/

Arrangement and Format of the 2018 IFC

Before applying the requirements of the IFC it is beneficial to understand its arrangement and format. The IFC, like other codes published by the International Code Council, is arranged and organized to follow sequential steps that generally occur during a plan review or inspection. In the 2012 edition, the IFC was reorganized into seven parts, as illustrated in the tables below. Each part represents a broad subject matter and includes the chapters that logically fit under the subject matter of each part. It is also foreseeable that additional chapters will need to be added in the future as regulations for new processes or operations are developed. Accordingly, the reorganization was designed to accommodate such future chapters by providing reserved (unused) chapters in several of the parts. This will allow the subject matter parts to be conveniently and logically expanded without requiring a major renumbering of the IFC chapters.

2018 ORGANIZATION OF THE IFC	
Parts and Chapters	**Subject Matter**
Part I – Chapters 1 and 2	Administrative and definitions
Part II – Chapters 3 and 4	General safety provisions
Part III – Chapters 5 through 12	Building and equipment design features
Part III – Chapters 13 through 19	Reserved for future use
Part IV – Chapters 20 through 39	Special occupancies and operations
Part IV – Chapters 40 through 49, 52	Reserved for future use
Part V – Chapters 50, 51 and 53 through 67	Hazardous materials
Part V – Chapters 68 through 79	Reserved for future use
Part VI – Chapter 80	Referenced standards
Part VII – Appendices A through N	Adoptable and informational appendices

The IFC requirements for fire-resistive construction, interior finish, fire protection systems, means of egress and construction safeguards are directly correlated to the chapters containing parallel requirements in the IBC, as follows:

IFC Chapter	Subject
7	Fire and smoke protection features
8	Interior finish, decorative materials and furnishings
9	Fire protection and life safety systems
10	Means of egress
33	Fire safety during construction and demolition

TABLE OF CONTENTS

Part I—Administrative

Chapter 1: Scope and Administration

General Comments

This chapter addresses the administration and enforcement of the code. The objectives and mandate for enforcement are beyond the scope of this chapter. Before adopting the code, a state or local government must establish an agency with staff trained to administer and enforce the code. The administrative relationships, designation of the enforcement authority (fire code official), funding, training and certification of inspectors and scope of the enforcement program are determined by the adopting body.

Management personnel generally perform functions, such as planning, organizing, directing, controlling, analyzing and budgeting. Though the code administrator's duties may include all of these functions, this chapter takes a much narrower view of the code administrative function, dealing mainly with technical and legal areas. Fire prevention code administration must be considered in the context of a complex environment containing political, social, economic, technical and legal aspects. Enforcement, too, is a broad term that includes a range of activities aimed at identifying and eliminating hazards; in this case, hazards causing or contributing to a fire or impairing life safety.

Four functions are commonly associated with enforcement: inspecting, detecting, notifying and reporting [see Commentary Figure 1(1)]. This chapter describes the technical and legal requirements associated with administering a code enforcement program to achieve these functions. The examination of these concepts specifically provides a better understanding of the fire code official's authority, duties and liabilities.

Two main duties of the fire code official are administration and enforcement. In administration, the following concepts are most important:

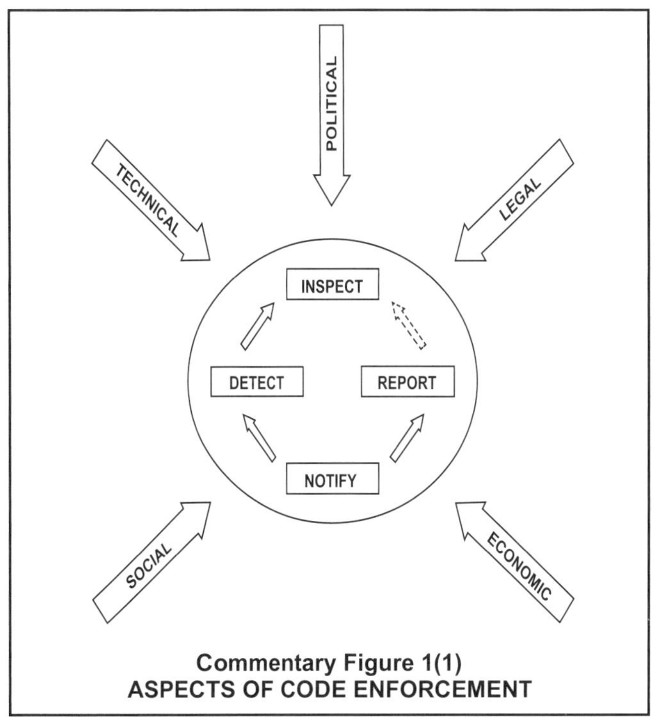

Commentary Figure 1(1)
ASPECTS OF CODE ENFORCEMENT

Code Administrative Environment

Many administrative or management functions are not addressed in the code. Before the provisions of this document can be of any use, many basic questions must be answered. Jurisdictions adopting a code enforcement program are using discretionary powers to fulfill a community need. The need in the community must be clearly identified, the program mission clearly established and the most appropriate delivery system selected. To address the technical and legal demands of the code administrative environment, the code assumes that jurisdictions adopting the document are interested in protecting the health, safety and welfare of its citizens from the effects of fires and explosions. Additionally, the code assumes that these jurisdictions are authorized to use the police power of the state to receive these benefits. Finally, the code assigns principal responsibility for enforcing this document to the department or agency (fire department or fire prevention bureau) most frequently available to perform this mission.

The particular objectives and social or political mandate of a code enforcement program are not considered in the context of this document. These items, however, are often cited as the most frustrating problems faced by code administrators. Code enforcers often complain of being overwhelmed by demands for leniency or special consideration based on the economic, social or political effects of their decisions.

As stated, this chapter establishes ground rules for enforcing the code; however, these ground rules are only the technical and legal requirements binding both fire code officials and the general public. For guidance on the political, social and economic considerations associated with code enforcement activities, adopting authorities must turn elsewhere; however, none of this is intended to imply that these considerations are absent from the code process. To the contrary, by establishing these requirements as "minimums," the ICC voting membership (see ICC Board of Directors Policy CP-28) has, through a democratic process of public hearings and debate, attempted to weigh these considerations carefully when deliberating, modifying and adopting the provisions appearing in this document. In the end, each jurisdiction must give careful consideration to how these requirements should be adopted; who should be responsible for enforcing them; how enforcement personnel should be trained; how the operation will be financed; and when and how to modify or change operations, if necessary. These considerations deserve careful, thorough public attention before a decision is made to adopt and enforce the code.

Scope and Applicability of the Code

The code applies to new and existing structures and premises as prescribed in Sections 102.1 and 102.2, in matters related to occupancy and maintenance for the protection of lives and property from fire. Conditions related to fire spread, occupant hazard protection and maintenance are regulated as follows:

Retroactivity: Because the code applies to both new and existing structures and premises as prescribed in Sections 102.1 and 102.2, the existing building provisions may be considered retroactive. Existing structures and premises built in compliance with the codes and standards in effect at the time of their original construction or alteration are not in all cases exempt from code compliance.

Other codes and standards: The code relies heavily on other codes and standards to specify a means of complying with its provisions, including, among others, the *International Building Code*® (IBC®), the *International Mechanical Code*® (IMC®), the *International Fuel Gas Code*® (IFGC®) and the standards referenced in the text. Additionally, other federal, state and local codes and ordinances may establish certain requirements related to fire protection and life safety. Code requirements are intended to complement other regulations. Where conflicts arise between code provisions and the referenced standards, the code provisions apply. Where a standard provides additional technical detail or guidance beyond that provided in the related code text, the fire code official must use judgment when applying these provisions to prevent conflicts with the code provisions. If a conflict arises, it is the fire code official's duty to determine which provisions secure the code's intent. When a conflict between codes or other legal action causes a portion of this document to be "struck down," such action is not intended to invalidate the remaining code provisions. The severability of code provisions, however, does not imply that these same provisions should be considered or applied outside of their context as a part of the code.

Fire Code Official's Judgment

The code relies heavily not only on other codes and standards but also on the judgment and experience of the fire code official.

Approval: The code details occupancy and maintenance requirements; however, it relies heavily on performance criteria, as opposed to detailed specifications, to accomplish this task. The fire code official, therefore, must exercise judgment when approving or permitting operations, processes and procedures required by the code. Proof of compliance may include certification or labeling by independent testing laboratories; however, regardless of the conclusions of these external agencies and authorities, the fire code official remains the sole judge of what fulfills the intent of the code. This becomes particularly important when the fire code official is asked to evaluate equivalent methods and materials. Having piles of data may seem helpful, but the data may prove to be meaningless when it is considered in the context of the code's intent. Data in support of alternative methods and materials must demonstrate not only compliance with the code's intent but also relevance to the issues at hand. Evidence, such as a label or an independent laboratory test report, may sometimes be used inappropriately to support an application for recognition of equivalency. The fire code official must evaluate all submitted evidence to make sure it applies to its intended use, as well as to the code's intent. In an increasingly technical and litigious society, learning how to make such judgments may be the biggest challenge facing fire code officials. Relying on strict interpretations of intent or the "letter" of the code may be the conservative way, but conservative approaches may simply increase the social and political pressures confronting fire code officials. Decision-making aids employing contemporary computer technology permit a designer to propose more innovative and creative responses to complex problems. Fire code officials must begin to recognize, use and interpret these tools and data to maintain effective protection.These models permit designers to quickly and easily evaluate the relationships and performance of a variety of complex variables.

Another model that does not rely on a computer is NFPA 550 [see Commentary Figure 1(2)]. This model requires little training to use or understand and is an all-inclusive representation of the variables contributing to fire safety. The model may, therefore, serve as a useful tool for qualitatively evaluating the contribution of various approaches to an overall fire safety system. Once equivalent alternative methods have been identified using the Fire Safety Concepts Tree (see "General Comments" in Chapter 3), quantitative (cost/benefit) analyses may be applied.

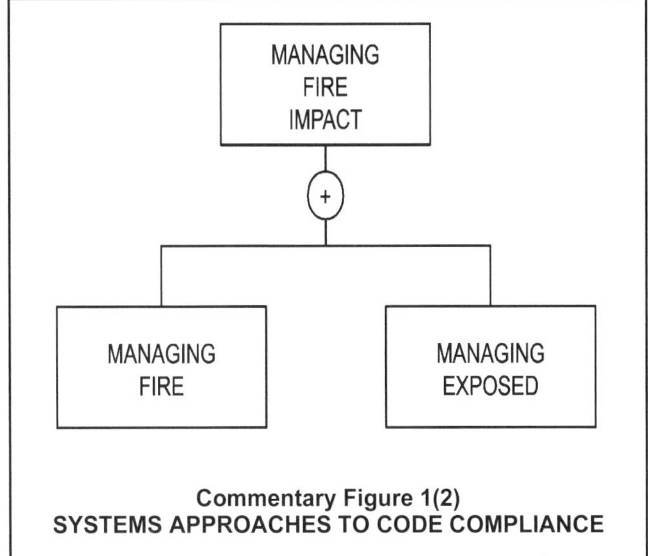

Commentary Figure 1(2)
SYSTEMS APPROACHES TO CODE COMPLIANCE

Fire Code Officials and Liability

Like all professionals, fire code officials are subject to legal action. The two most common legal actions that may be pursued against fire code officials are breach of contract lawsuits and tort claims. Tort claims, by far, are the most common lawsuits. These lawsuits allege that some damage, injury or harm (a tort) resulted from the actions of the fire code official. A successful tort claim must prove that the plaintiff was injured or harmed; that the fire code official had a legal duty or obligation to perform with respect to the plaintiff and that the cause of the plaintiff's injury was the fire code official's actions or inactions while performing these duties.

The Law of Torts includes the following:

The tort: Damages arising from the acts of fire code officials fall into two broad categories: property and personal [see Commentary Figure 1(3)]. Property torts involve the control, use, operation or ownership of personal and real property by private individuals. Personal torts involve physical, verbal or written assaults on the character, person, psyche or privacy of individuals. Such assaults or invasions may involve actual contact or threat of harm. For example, fire code officials' acts of commission may restrain business or trade activity, while acts of omission may fail to recognize that hazards need to be corrected, thus resulting in life or property losses.

PROPERTY	PERSONAL
Trespass Conversion Nuisance	Assault and Battery False Arrest or Imprisonment Defamation, Slander and Libel

Source: Rosenbauer, D.L., *Introduction to Fire Protection Law*.

Commentary Figure 1(3)
TYPES OF TORTS

Two actions dominate lawsuits filed against enforcement authorities: Most lawsuits either allege improper acts by the fire code official (acts of commission) or failure to fulfill specified or implied legal obligations (acts of omission). In the former, plaintiffs usually seek temporary or permanent relief from a fire code official's decision. In these actions, plaintiffs usually allege improper interpretation or application of the code or its intent. Other lawsuits usually allege failure to exercise a reasonable standard of care in the performance of duties of the fire code official. In either type of lawsuit, and often in the case of omissions, plaintiffs seek compensatory and even punitive damages. Infringements on constitutional protections may be, though occurring infrequently, the basis for lawsuits against fire code officials. Common constitutional issues raised in lawsuits against fire code officials include violations of the Fourth Amendment's protection against unreasonable searches and seizures, the Sixth Amendment's due process protections and the Fourteenth Amendment's equal protection provisions. First Amendment rights guaranteed under freedom of association protections may be raised in cases involving public assembly occupancies, especially churches.

Condition of negligence: To prevail in a tort claim action, a plaintiff must demonstrate negligence on the part of the defendant. Negligence may be simple—a failure to exercise reasonable or adequate care when performing assigned duties (commonly known as misfeasance)—or it may be gross—represented by wanton, willful, reckless or malicious disregard for public safety. Criminal activities, including dereliction (nonfeasance) or the failure to perform required assigned duties, may be cause for claims of gross negligence. Likewise, malfeasance, the willful or malicious violation of a legal duty, may constitute grossly negligent behavior. The following three elements must be proven to sustain a claim of negligence: the defendant had a duty to act, the defendant failed to exercise the required standard of care in the performance of that duty and, as a result of that failure, damage was in incurred or harm was suffered by the plaintiff.

Duty to act: The code establishes few duties of the fire code official; instead, it places greatest emphasis on the responsibility of structure or premises owners and operators to perform their duties with adequate regard for public health, safety and welfare. The duties owed to the public by the fire code official fall under the following categories: approvals, enforcement, personnel, inspections, investigations, reports and record keeping. Other duties may be assumed by fire code officials through the performance of their official duties. Recently, some courts have ruled that failure to perform timely reinspections or exhaust legal remedies against violators in fire code cases creates a special relationship between the fire code official and the occupants of properties in violation of the code, especially when the occupants do not own the property and are not responsible for code compliance. Some court rulings have even implied that conducting inspections not otherwise required by the code constitutes an *ultra vires* (beyond the authority of) liability. Fire code officials should consult their jurisdiction's legal counsel to determine how these decisions, the jurisdiction's enforcement policies and the code provisions combined affect their enforcement program and jurisdictional and personal liabilities.

Standard of care: Taken together, the fire code official's duties are the basis for determining his or her standard of care. When assessing whether fire code officials have met this standard, judges and juries must determine whether they performed the required duties as reasonable, comparably trained and experienced fire code officials. Failure to meet the appropriate standard of care may be classified in three ways: nonfeasance, misfeasance or malfeasance. Nonfeasance is the failure to perform a required duty. Improper performance of a required duty constitutes misfeasance, and malicious or willful violation of a required duty is malfeasance. Of the three, misfeasance or simple negligence is the most common cause of action. The code and most tort claims either hold the government immune from specific claims of misfeasance or severely limit damage awards in such cases. For all purposes, sovereign immunity—the doctrine inherited from British common law mandating that "the King can do no wrong"—is obsolete. Similarly, courts in many states have abandoned the public duty doctrine, which states that a duty to all is a duty to no one. Holding that most code provisions and governmental regulations secure benefits for select groups, some state courts recognize that specific enforcement activities secure greater benefits for some members of the public than others. Such judicial reasoning holds that the inspector's duty applies to the individual who may be injured as a result of failure to detect a hazard or diligently pursue compliance. Moreover, this duty may include acts of omission, such as failure to perform required inspections. With courts today recognizing only limited immunity for government officials, fire code officials must become more aware of their duties and liabilities. Although tort claim acts limit damage awards, they still permit lawsuits to proceed against governmental officials and agencies to determine their responsibility for negligent acts. Claims of gross negligence arising from nonfeasance or malfeasance are less common than misfeasance actions but are predictably harder to defend. The code provides no relief from liability where the fire code official either fails to perform a required duty or acts *ultra vires*; that is, beyond his or her authority. The jurisdiction is generally immune from claims when its agents perform acts beyond the scope of their authority, unless such acts were implicitly endorsed by the government (explicit endorsement may constitute a discretionary governmental act and, similarly, immunize the government). Nonfeasance is considered a criminal offense in many jurisdictions. An employee's dereliction of duty exempts the jurisdiction from immunity under most circumstances, unless the employee's failure to perform was the direct result of explicit instructions from governmental superiors; however, the employee may be held criminally liable.

In addition to the Law of Torts, the following have an impact on fire code officials and liability:

Awards: Lawsuits may seek declarative judgments (injunctive relief or monetary awards) in favor of the plaintiff. Monetary awards fall into four categories: nominal, special, compensatory and punitive. The first purpose of monetary awards should be to the claimant or plaintiff for real losses. This is the purpose of compensatory and special damages. Compensatory awards reimburse the claimant or plaintiff for the direct costs resulting from the defendant's negligence or carelessness. Many times, a plaintiff will also seek additional compensation for the indirect results of the defendant's acts. Such special damage claims may result in additional compensation beyond that provided by compensatory damages. Punitive awards are intended to punish the defendant for the misdeed and discourage him or her from future unlawful activity. These awards are often held up as examples to the community as a whole and are a way to discourage unlawful activities by others. Nominal damage awards serve to assign blame in intentional tort cases when the facts of the case do not merit a substantial settlement.

- **You cannot prevent someone from filing a lawsuit against you.**
- **Do not take the lawsuit personally.**
- **Understand your risk exposure or exposures.**
- **Be professional.**
- **You are not an insurer.**
- **Do not make stupid mistakes.**

Commentary Figure 1(4)
MARKMAN'S SIX RULES

Protection: The best protection against a lawsuit is professional conduct and preparation; that is, training, education and research. Lawsuits filed against public officials have become commonplace and are probably inevitable. In 1983, H. M. Markman suggested six rules to manage legal liability [see Commentary Figure 1(4)].

Although no single rule should be considered more important than another, the last one is perhaps the best to remember. Everyone makes mistakes, so strive to learn from the mistakes rather than repeat them. Nonetheless, every mistake may be potential exposure. Acting professionally helps minimize exposure to error, especially when training, and common sense is encouraged. Using common sense, exercising reasonable care and acting professionally are no insurance against a lawsuit, but they all may provide considerable protection in the event a lawsuit is filed. No matter how hard someone may try to avoid a lawsuit, someone may sue. When a lawsuit is filed, the most important things to remember are not to take it personally and not to forget the other five rules.

Enforcement

The enforcement duty of the fire code official's position is composed of four distinct functions: inspection, detection, notification and reporting. All four functions define phases in the enforcement process duties of fire code officials.

During the code enforcement process, structures or premises requiring inspections are identified. Inspectors are assigned and inspections are performed. During these inspections, any code violations found are usually noted. Then, the owner or occupant is verbally advised or notified that the deficiencies noted are code violations. To promote code compliance, the inspector may suggest remedial actions that may be taken to establish compliance. Finally, a written violation notice serving as further notice to the owner or occupant is issued. The written notice also serves as a permanent record or report of the inspection.

Inspection

Inspections are careful examinations of plans or premises for the presence of fire and life safety hazards. Upon observing a hazardous condition, the fire code official begins a process directed at correcting the situation. This may be accomplished by removing or eliminating the hazardous condition or providing some countermeasure designed to lessen its effects on the property, occupants or neighbors. Inspections should demonstrate a systematic method that keeps the inspection process in a proper perspective and recognizes that code enforcement is limited to legal and technical means of pursuing fire safety. Achieving fire safety objectives means using a balanced approach composed of some elements seeking to prevent ignitions and others attempting to control fire effects. Fire safety objectives are not defined by the code but rather by the users. Each jurisdiction must establish what risks and costs are reasonable while pursuing fire safety.

There may be as many different methods of conducting inspections as there are inspectors. No single method is necessarily the correct one; however, each method probably has some strong and weak points. The following three approaches can form the basis for any number of different inspection techniques.

Outside to inside: Beginning outside is not only logical but necessary. Inspectors too often neglect hazards and clues outside the building that suggest significant danger to the occupants. An inspector must ask the following question: "Do the things I see outside match those I see inside?" For example:

- •Do doors identified as exits inside actually discharge outside to acceptable refuge areas or the public way?
- •Are trash receptacles or other obstructions outside located so the effectiveness of exits is not reduced, or do receptacles alone pose a fire hazard?
- •Does the site permit sufficient access for firefighter rescue operations and fire suppression?

Top to bottom: Once inside a structure, deciding where to start is more than a matter of preference. One question inspectors may ask is: "If completeness is the principal criterion, why not start at the bottom and work up?" The answer to this question is that walking down stairs is easier than walking up stairs. This easier path of travel allows the inspector to concentrate more completely on the inspection itself. After performing many inspections, there will not be a need for additional exercise obtained from beginning at the bottom.

General to specific: Without constructing a detailed inspection framework, many fire code officials find it helpful to move from the general to the specific when evaluating occupancies and hazards. This helps keep the whole problem in focus while preserving attention to detail. The inspector can focus on a specific problem without losing sight of the "big picture."

Detection

Systematic inspection procedures, like those described, should aid in the detection of code violations. By keeping the premises, processes or objectives in clear focus, the inspector keeps the task in context. A systematic inspection process implies not only organization but an understanding of the entire process. Achieving fire safety objectives means understanding how structures, premises, occupants and fire interact [see Commentary Figure 1(5)]. More specifically, each aspect affects another. Human behavior affects the likelihood of fire and how humans react to fire. The type of facility will have an impact on the types of fires and

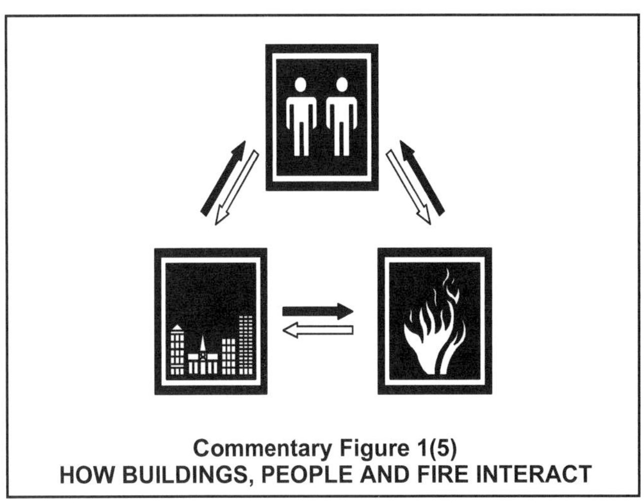

Commentary Figure 1(5)
HOW BUILDINGS, PEOPLE AND FIRE INTERACT

types and characteristics of occupants. To keep the system in balance and prevent uncontrolled fires means understanding how people use structures and premises.

In such a context, a fire hazard is anything that either fails to prevent an uncontrolled fire or permits a fire to spread unchecked. Similarly, hazardous conditions are those preventing occupants from escaping or fire fighters from entering a structure and premises to control a fire.

Notification

Inspection programs cannot identify and abate all hazards. Code enforcement alone cannot secure absolute protection for people and property. Further, many code requirements maintain or reinforce features not intended to prevent a fire but rather to minimize a fire's effects should one occur. Every inspection program, therefore, should consider the benefits of educating building owners and occupants about the hazards endangering their lives and property. Not only do such efforts help secure compliance with code requirements, but they are likely to secure long-term commitments to fire safety as well. Another equally apt metaphor describes the fire prevention process as the "Three E's": engineering, education and enforcement. A balanced approach composed of these three elements can be an especially effective way of achieving desired fire safety objectives.

Reporting

The first three elements of the code enforcement process are directed at identifying and eliminating hazards at their source. Reporting is intended to help document and reinforce the lessons learned from the previous three phases. The words, "If it's not written down, it didn't happen!" reinforce the message that reporting is just as important as any of the other three elements of the code enforcement system. Few people enjoy paperwork and data entry. Without documentation, however, prosecuting an effective code enforcement program becomes nearly impossible. Accurate, concise and timely records are essential for both legal and historical reasons. Documenting the inspection and violation history of a particular premises or owner is essential when prosecuting criminal actions under the code provisions.

Commentary Figure 1(6) illustrates a systems approach using data generated by fire incidents and inspections to direct code enforcement, public education activities or code development. This approach is equivalent to the one typically used to make ordinary decisions about problems with many competing solutions, to plan for the future and to consider the cost and benefits of these decisions.

This system is used mostly to solve everyday problems, weigh costs and benefits of alternatives, and plan responses to problems. It is also a helpful tool for responding to fire protection problems. As an example, fire data suggest the emergence of a trend toward more fires caused by misuse of auxiliary heating appliances. Alternative solutions include:

- A public education campaign on safe use of heaters.
- A targeted inspection program to identify and correct improper heating practices in homes and businesses.
- Doing nothing but hoping for warm weather.

The evaluation must consider a variety of complex factors and methods of measuring the success of each approach. Once an approach is selected and implemented, it must be evaluated to examine whether the desired reduction in fires occurs. If not, perhaps one of the other alternatives should be reexamined, or the problem should be redefined.

Understanding the code administration process and the environment influencing it allows the fire code official to be more effective. Adhering to the provisions of Chapter 1 not only minimizes the fire code official's liability, but also provides an effective code enforcement program. Just as owners and occupants have obligations under the code, so does the fire code official. Following these procedures enables him or her to identify and respond to the community's needs, thus reducing the community's fire risk.

Purpose

Chapter 1 establishes provisions to ensure that code administration and enforcement is reasonable, appropriate and fair. This chapter outlines the duties and powers of the fire code official; the scope of the fire code official's authority to enforce the code; the applicability of the document and proofs of compliance; the means of securing compliance with its provisions and procedures for protecting due process rights of applicants, owners, occupants and others affected by the code provisions; and the enforcement activities of the fire code official.

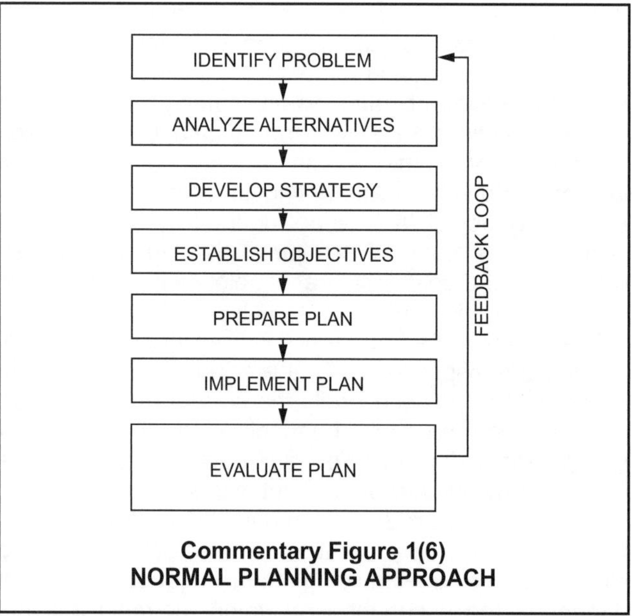

Commentary Figure 1(6)
NORMAL PLANNING APPROACH

PART 1—GENERAL PROVISIONS

SECTION 101
SCOPE AND GENERAL REQUIREMENTS

[A] 101.1 Title. These regulations shall be known as the *Fire Code* of **[NAME OF JURISDICTION]**, hereinafter referred to as "this code."

❖ This section identifies jurisdictional applicability in legal terms. The local jurisdiction is to insert its name into this section by including a modification to the code in the adopting ordinance. This will make the code applicable to the local jurisdiction.

[A] 101.2 Scope. This code establishes regulations affecting or relating to structures, processes, premises and safeguards regarding all of the following:

1. The hazard of fire and explosion arising from the storage, handling or use of structures, materials or devices.
2. Conditions hazardous to life, property or public welfare in the occupancy of structures or premises.
3. Fire hazards in the structure or on the premises from occupancy or operation.
4. Matters related to the construction, extension, repair, alteration or removal of fire suppression or alarm systems.
5. Conditions affecting the safety of fire fighters and emergency responders during emergency operations.

❖ The code does not attempt to achieve perfection by requiring every conceivable or available safeguard for every structure, premises or operation within the scope of the code; rather, the code seeks to establish a minimum acceptable safety level to balance the many factors that must be considered, including loss statistics, relative hazard and the economic and social impact. The code is maintained through the use of a democratic code development process so that everyone affected by these minimum requirements has an equal opportunity to present his or her concern, both for and against any of the requirements.

The question is often asked, "Does the code apply only to buildings and facilities, or does it cover vehicles as well?" Though the scope text does not specifically mention vehicles, vehicles are intended to be covered by the terms of "... use of... devices..." and "... occupancy of... structures or premises..." in Items 1 and 2 of the section. It is clear that the code specifically intends to regulate vehicles because, in some cases, there are regulations in the code that are specific to vehicles, such as those in Sections 309, 319, 5706 and 5707. However, in most cases, unless vehicles are specifically mentioned, provisions in the code would not apply to them (see also Section 904.12).

[A] 101.2.1 Appendices. Provisions in the appendices shall not apply unless specifically adopted.

❖ The code has several appendices, which provide additional information regarding the provisions in the code and additional regulations that are available for adoption if desired by the adopting jurisdiction. If the jurisdiction decides to include any of the appendices as part of the code, each of the appendices to be adopted must be specifically listed in the adoption ordinance for the code.

[A] 101.3 Intent. The purpose of this code is to establish the minimum requirements consistent with nationally recognized good practice for providing a reasonable level of life safety and property protection from the hazards of fire, explosion or dangerous conditions in new and existing buildings, structures and premises, and to provide a reasonable level of safety to fire fighters and emergency responders during emergency operations.

❖ Code requirements regulate conditions that are likely to cause or contribute to fires or explosions, endanger life or property if a fire occurs or contribute to the spread of a fire. The code is intended to regulate conditions related to the health, safety and welfare of the public, fire fighters and other emergency responders called on to conduct emergency operations in or on any building, structure or premises. Note that the code requirements are minimum (see commentary, Section 101.2 for a discussion on minimum requirements).

While the code does serve as a maintenance code for buildings constructed in accordance with the IBC, it has provisions that go far beyond maintenance of construction regulations for buildings. Much of the code prescribes construction regulations of several sorts, which can be seen throughout the code in the general provisions for safety and in special occupancies, processes and equipment. These regulations supplement the construction regulations in the IBC for cases where special hazards exist.

A common question that arises is, "Is it the intent of the code to apply to noncommercial structures?" Yes. The code applies to all structures within a jurisdiction, including residential occupancies, unless such occupancies are specifically excluded within the text of a particular code section. For example, Sections 503.1.1 and 507.1 require that all occupancies, including residential occupancies, be provided with fire apparatus access and a water supply for fire fighting. Though it is true that there are many provisions in the code that would not normally be applicable to a residential occupancy based on the scope of the particular provision, the overall application of the code is not limited to commercial structures (see the commentaries to Section 503.1.1 and Appendix D107.1 for further discussion of this topic).

[A] 101.4 Severability. If a section, subsection, sentence, clause or phrase of this code is, for any reason, held to be unconstitutional, such decision shall not affect the validity of the remaining portions of this code.

❖ All sections of the code not invalidated by legal action remain in effect. While a dispute over a particular issue (such as hazardous materials quantity limitation) may have caused litigation that resulted in the provision being found unconstitutional, the remainder of the code is still applicable.

[A] 101.5 Validity. In the event any part or provision of this code is held to be illegal or void, this shall not have the effect of making void or illegal any of the other parts or provisions hereof, which are determined to be legal; and it shall be presumed that this code would have been adopted without such illegal or invalid parts or provisions.

❖ The code provisions are intended to be construed as severable. If any part of the code is ruled invalid by a court of competent jurisdiction, the remaining sections of the code are intended to stand as though the invalid section never existed. Fire code officials and adopting bodies should carefully and promptly evaluate the impact of any such ruling on ongoing enforcement activities and the remaining code provisions. Such changes that are necessary to preserve and protect the enforcement authority of the jurisdiction and the public should be instituted through legislative action as soon as practical. Additionally, the International Code Council® (ICC®) should be advised of court actions invalidating any code provisions. For the same reason local officials must evaluate the effects of court decisions, the influence of court decisions on the remainder of the code must be evaluated for national impact.

SECTION 102
APPLICABILITY

[A] 102.1 Construction and design provisions. The construction and design provisions of this code shall apply to:

1. Structures, facilities and conditions arising after the adoption of this code.
2. Existing structures, facilities and conditions not legally in existence at the time of adoption of this code.
3. Existing structures, facilities and conditions where required in Chapter 11.
4. Existing structures, facilities and conditions that, in the opinion of the *fire code official*, constitute a distinct hazard to life or property.

❖ This section establishes the scope of application of the code provisions that regulate construction and design. Construction and design requirements include, but are not limited to, the installation of fire protection systems; drainage and secondary containment facilities for hazardous materials; fire-resistive construction and the activities stated in Section 105.7 for which a construction permit is required.

Item 1 specifies that construction and design code requirements apply to new construction that occurs following the adoption of the code.

Item 2 means that construction and design code requirements are to apply to existing structures that did not have a certificate of occupancy at the time the code was adopted. An example would be a building that was built when there was no adopted construction code in the jurisdiction.

Item 3 refers to Chapter 11, "Construction Requirements for Existing Buildings," which was added in the 2009 edition of the code to assemble in a single location all of the construction and design code requirements that specifically target existing structures, facilities and conditions for retroactive application, which had previously been scattered throughout the code.

Item 4 generally requires the fire code official to determine that a "distinct hazard to life or property" exists prior to enforcing a construction and design code provision retroactively. Simply claiming that a violation exists because a building does not comply with the most recent edition of the code does not necessarily establish that a hazard actually exists. The fire code official should be prepared to demonstrate, based on evidence or case histories that would be defensible in a court of law, that a distinct hazard exists. This would be especially true where enforcement would result in substantial expense to the property owner or when a building has remained in compliance with the edition of the code under which it was originally constructed.

Further legal counsel should be consulted prior to the retroactive application of the code in order to establish the defensibility of the fire code official's determination in a court of law. Also, similar occupancies in the jurisdiction should be treated equally using a written policy to avoid the possibility of charges of selective enforcement.

[A] 102.2 Administrative, operational and maintenance provisions. The administrative, operational and maintenance provisions of this code shall apply to:

1. Conditions and operations arising after the adoption of this code.
2. Existing conditions and operations.

❖ This section specifies that the administrative, operational and maintenance requirements of the code apply to conditions and operations that exist when the code is adopted and new conditions and operations that begin after the code is adopted. Although Sections 102.1 and 102.2 are the controlling sections for retroactive application of the code to existing buildings, they do not provide for retroactive code application solely on the basis of a change in ownership or the occupying tenant. If a change in the occupancy group or the character of use occurs, the current edition of the code becomes enforceable. In such cases, Section 102.3 also applies.

[A] 102.3 Change of use or occupancy. A change of occupancy shall not be made unless the use or occupancy is made to comply with the requirements of this code and the *International Existing Building Code*.

Exception: Where approved by the *fire code official*, a change of occupancy shall be permitted without complying with the requirements of this code and the *International Existing Building Code*, provided that the new or proposed use or occupancy is less hazardous, based on life and fire risk, than the existing use or occupancy.

❖ A change of occupancy in an existing structure may change the level of inherent hazards, and a different code section may be applicable to the new occupancy. This section addresses both a change of occupancy from one group to another or a change in the level of use of an occupancy; for example, a Group A-2 restaurant being changed to a nightclub. Another example relative to the code would be a Group S-1 warehouse that is adding high-piled combustible storage or changing the classification to a higher hazard storage commodity.

This section requires that the building comply with this code and the *International Existing Building Code*® (IEBC®). Three different options for compliance are provided within the IEBC: the prescriptive method, the work area method or the performance method. In the 2012 IBC, Chapter 34 addressed existing buildings and this code referred to the IBC for change of occupancy. This criterion from Chapter 34 of the IBC was repeated in the IEBC as Chapter 4, Prescriptive Compliance Methods, and Chapter 14 (what is now chapter 13), Performance Compliance Methods. Now this information is only available in the IEBC.

The exception acknowledges that compliance with this code and the IEBC is not necessary where the proposed use or occupancy would decrease the hazard level; for example, where a Group A-2 nightclub is changed to a Group A-2 restaurant. Note that the IEBC may need to be reviewed due to possible compliance with repair requirements or any alterations that are being addressed. In addition, the IEBC may be administered by another entity, typically the building department.

[A] 102.4 Application of building code. The design and construction of new structures shall comply with the *International Building Code*, and any *alterations*, additions, changes in use or changes in structures required by this code, which are within the scope of the *International Building Code*, shall be made in accordance therewith.

❖ The code is the companion fire and life safety maintenance code to the IBC. Maintenance of other building features is governed by other International Codes® (I-Codes®). When existing buildings change occupancy group or are altered, increased in area or demolished, the IBC provisions must apply. When compliance with the code requires alterations, additions or modifications within the scope of the IBC, the IBC regulations and the building official's authority must prevail. This makes it essential that the code officials responsible for enforcing the building and fire codes establish a sound working relationship. Clear communication is essential to achieve compliance with the respective code officials' orders.

[A] 102.5 Application of residential code. Where structures are designed and constructed in accordance with the *International Residential Code*, the provisions of this code shall apply as follows:

1. Construction and design provisions of this code pertaining to the exterior of the structure shall apply including, but not limited to, premises identification, fire apparatus access and water supplies. Where interior or exterior systems or devices are installed, construction permits required by Section 105.7 shall apply.
2. Administrative, operational and maintenance provisions of this code shall apply.

❖ This section clarifies the extent to which the *International Residential Code*® (IRC®) and the code are interrelated and how the provisions of the code apply to the development of one- and two-family dwelling projects built under the IRC.

The IRC is designed and intended for use as a stand-alone code for the construction of detached one- and two-family dwellings and townhouses not more than three stories in height. As such, the construction of detached one- and two-family dwellings and townhouses is regulated exclusively by the IRC and not subject to the provisions of any other I-Codes other than to the extent specifically referenced. Although the IRC regulates the construction of detached one- and two-family dwellings and townhouse structures, it does not regulate the design and construction of emergency access to and community fire protection for residential developments containing such dwelling structures. Accordingly, where the code is adopted, the design, construction, regulation and maintenance of fire apparatus access roads for servicing such residential developments must comply with the provisions of Section 503 and, if adopted, Appendix D. Also, the design, construction, regulation and maintenance of fire protection water supplies for servicing such residential developments must comply with the provisions of Section 507 and, if adopted, Appendices B and C. These specific requirements of the code are applicable because they include design and construction regulations that provide necessary emergency access and community fire protection for residential developments containing structures that are regulated within the scope of the IRC.

[A] 102.6 Historic buildings. The provisions of this code relating to the construction, *alteration*, repair, enlargement, restoration, relocation or moving of buildings or structures shall not be mandatory for existing buildings or structures identified and classified by the state or local jurisdiction as historic buildings where such buildings or structures do not constitute a distinct hazard to life or property. Fire protection in designated historic buildings shall be provided with an *approved* fire protection plan as required in Section 1103.1.1.

❖ This section provides a blanket exception from code requirements when the building in question has historic value. The most important criterion for application of this section is that the building must be recognized by a qualified party or agency as having historic significance. Usually this is done by a state or local authority after considerable scrutiny of the historical value of the building. Most, if not all, states have such authorities, as do many local jurisdictions. The agencies with such authority can be located at the state or local government level or through the local chapter of the American Institute of Architects (AIA). This section requires an approved fire protection plan. More specifically, reference is made to Section 1103.1.1, which provides some minimal requirements. Section 1103.1.1 requires a plan to be developed in accordance with NFPA 914. The reference to NFPA 914 provides specific guidance to code officials, design professionals and building owners as to the provisions that are applicable to fire protection plans for historic buildings in order to provide a reasonable level of building and life safety provisions. Note that the IEBC also addresses historic buildings undergoing repairs, alterations and changes of occupancy.

[A] 102.7 Referenced codes and standards. The codes and standards referenced in this code shall be those that are listed in Chapter 80, and such codes and standards shall be considered to be part of the requirements of this code to the prescribed extent of each such reference and as further regulated in Sections 102.7.1 and 102.7.2.

❖ The use of referenced codes and standards to cover certain aspects of various occupancies and operations rather than write parallel or competing requirements into the code is a long-standing and successful code development principle. Often, however, questions and potential conflicts in the use of referenced codes and standards can arise, which can lead to inconsistent enforcement of the code. This section establishes the relationship between the code and the codes or standards that it references. A referenced code or standard or portion thereof is to be considered an enforceable extension of the code as if the specified content of the referenced code or standard were included in the body of the code. The extent to which the provisions of a referenced standard may be enforced is limited to those portions of the standard that are specifically identified in the code section that makes the reference. As an example of such limiting references, in regard to Chapter 57, "Flammable and Combustible Liquids," the question has been posed as to whether the entire referenced standard, NFPA 30, is applicable since it is referenced 30 times in Chapter 57. The answer is no. The applicability of NFPA 30 content would be limited to only the specific content indicated in the code section making the reference. For example, Section 5703.6.2 limits the applicable NFPA 30 content to only Chapter 27 of that document; Section 5704.2.7 limits the applicable NFPA 30 content to only the tank design, fabrication and construction provisions of Chapters 21 and 22 or 23 of that document; and various other code sections, such as Sections 5704.2.7.8 and 5704.2.7.9, limit the reference to specifically enumerated sections of NFPA 30.

[A] 102.7.1 Conflicts. Where conflicts occur between provisions of this code and referenced codes and standards, the provisions of this code shall apply.

❖ Where a code section referencing a standard contains no content limitation, any applicable provisions of the standard may be applied to the extent that they do not conflict with similar provisions in the code or other I-Codes. See the commentary to Section 102.7.2 for further discussion of conflicting provisions.

[A] 102.7.2 Provisions in referenced codes and standards. Where the extent of the reference to a referenced code or standard includes subject matter that is within the scope of this code, the provisions of this code, as applicable, shall take precedence over the provisions in the referenced code or standard.

❖ This new section expands on the provisions of Section 102.7.1 by making it clear that, even if a referenced standard contains requirements that parallel the code (or the other referenced I-Codes) in the standard's own duly referenced section(s), the provisions of the code (or the other referenced I-Codes) will always take precedence. One of the most common examples of such conflicting provisions is that many referenced standards contain building construction requirements that may differ from the requirements of the IBC, the applicability of which is established in Section 102.4 of the code. In such cases, the IBC would supersede the standard.

[A] 102.8 Subjects not regulated by this code. Where applicable standards or requirements are not set forth in this code, or are contained within other laws, codes, regulations, ordinances or bylaws adopted by the jurisdiction, compliance with applicable standards of the National Fire Protection Association or other nationally recognized fire safety standards, as *approved,* shall be deemed as prima facie evidence of compliance with the intent of this code. Nothing herein shall derogate from the authority of the *fire code official* to determine compliance with codes or standards for those activities or installations within the *fire code official's* jurisdiction or responsibility.

❖ This section provides guidance for situations in which no specific standard is designated in the code or otherwise adopted by the jurisdiction. In this instance, compliance with the requirements of a standard of the NFPA or other nationally recognized standards can be approved by the fire code official.

[A] 102.9 Matters not provided for. Requirements that are essential for the public safety of an existing or proposed activity, building or structure, or for the safety of the occupants thereof, that are not specifically provided for by this code, shall be determined by the *fire code official.*

❖ Evolving technology in our society will sometimes result in a situation or circumstance that the code does not cover. The reasonable application of the code to such hazardous, unforeseen conditions is provided in this section. Clearly, such a section is needed and the fire code official's experience and judgment must be used. The section, however, does not override requirements that may be preferred when the code provides alternative methods. Additionally, the section can be used to implement the general performance-oriented language of the code in specific enforcement situations.

[A] 102.10 Conflicting provisions. Where there is a conflict between a general requirement and a specific requirement, the specific requirement shall be applicable. Where, in a specific case, different sections of this code specify different materials, methods of construction or other requirements, the most restrictive shall govern.

❖ The provisions of this section provide guidance to both fire code officials and other code users on the application of the code when different sections specify different materials, methods of construction or other requirements.

The importance of this section should not be understated. It resolves the question of how to handle conflicts between general and specific provisions found in the code, and those instances where different sections specify different requirements. This section provides a necessary hierarchy for application of code provisions and clarifies code applications that would otherwise leave persistent questions and lead to debate. The code requires that where different sections of the code apply but contain different requirements, the most restrictive provisions shall govern. The code also resolves conflicts between the general requirements of any particular issue with any specific requirements of the same issue by indicating that the specific requirements take precedence over the general requirements.

[A] 102.11 Other laws. The provisions of this code shall not be deemed to nullify any provisions of local, state or federal law.

❖ Compliance with the requirements of the code does not entail authorization, approval or permission to violate the regulations of other local, state or federal laws. Other laws, ordinances and regulations not regulated or enforced by the fire code official could be in existence and enforced by another authority having jurisdiction over those provisions. Although the requirements may have similar provisions to those of the code, the work must be in conformance with the other regulations.

[A] 102.12 Application of references. References to chapter or section numbers, or to provisions not specifically identified by number, shall be construed to refer to such chapter, section or provision of this code.

❖ There are many instances in the code where a reference is merely a chapter number, section number or, in some cases, a provision not specified by number. In all such situations, these references are to the content of the code and not some other code or publication.

PART 2—ADMINISTRATIVE PROVISIONS

SECTION 103 DEPARTMENT OF FIRE PREVENTION

[A] 103.1 General. The department of fire prevention is established within the jurisdiction under the direction of the *fire code official.* The function of the department shall be the implementation, administration and enforcement of the provisions of this code.

❖ The traditional enforcement agency for the code is the fire department or fire prevention bureau of a state, county or municipal government. Such agencies usually perform administrative functions and provide public safety services related to fire protection; however, a variety of less-traditional arrangements have also been used to enforce the code, including private corporations, such as fire districts and fire companies employed by a local government to act as its agent; police and other law enforcement agencies; building, housing or zoning authorities; and community and economic development departments. Regardless of who is designated by the legislative or administrative authority to adopt and enforce the code, this section establishes the legal duty of the fire code official to enforce the code.

[A] 103.2 Appointment. The *fire code official* shall be appointed by the chief appointing authority of the jurisdiction; and the *fire code official* shall not be removed from office except for cause and after full opportunity to be heard on specific and relevant charges by and before the appointing authority.

❖ A fire code official's independence is essential so that public safety decisions are not based on political, economic or social expediency. This is not to say that social, political and economic considerations should not matter when deciding some code questions, but the interests of public health, safety and welfare must not be compromised to achieve such objectives. Protection of officials from removal from office without cause helps ensure that reasonable and competent professionals will be willing to serve.

[A] 103.3 Deputies. In accordance with the prescribed procedures of this jurisdiction and with the concurrence of the appointing authority, the *fire code official* shall have the authority to appoint a deputy *fire code official,* other related technical officers, inspectors and other employees.

❖ Most jurisdictions require more than one official to enforce the code. With the technical and legal demands on code enforcers increasing, additional personnel will certainly be required in this area to serve adequately the public interest. Though the professional qualifications of fire code officials are not detailed in the code, individuals appointed to code enforcement positions should be technically competent, motivated, well-adapted and possess good written and oral communication skills.

Many jurisdictions find it helpful, if not essential, to appoint an individual who is second-in-command and who would assume leadership of the organization in the absence of the chief code enforcement official.

[A] 103.4 Liability. The *fire code official*, member of the board of appeals, officer or employee charged with the enforcement of this code, while acting for the jurisdiction, in good faith and without malice in the discharge of the duties required by this code or other pertinent law or ordinance, shall not thereby be rendered civilly or criminally liable personally, and is hereby relieved from all personal liability for any damage accruing to persons or property as a result of an act or by reason of an act or omission in the discharge of official duties.

❖ The fire code official, other department employees and members of the appeals board are not intended to be held liable, civilly or criminally, for those actions performed in accordance with the code in a reasonable and lawful manner. However, the responsibility of the fire code official in this regard is subject to local, state and federal laws that may supersede this provision. This section further establishes that fire code officials (or subordinates) must not be liable for costs in any legal action instituted in response to the performance of lawful duties. Section 103.4.1 states that those costs are to be borne by the state, county or municipality, as applicable. The best way to be certain that the fire code official's action is a "lawful duty" is always to cite the applicable code section on which the enforcement action is based.

[A] 103.4.1 Legal defense. Any suit or criminal complaint instituted against any officer or employee because of an act performed by that officer or employee in the lawful discharge of duties and under the provisions of this code shall be defended by the legal representatives of the jurisdiction until the final termination of the proceedings. The *fire code official* or any subordinate shall not be liable for costs in an action, suit or proceeding that is instituted in pursuance of the provisions of this code; and any officer of the department of fire prevention, acting in good faith and without malice, shall be free from liability for acts performed under any of its provisions or by reason of any act or omission in the performance of official duties in connection therewith.

❖ Section 103.4 establishes that fire code officials or subordinates must not be liable for costs in any legal action, whether criminal or civil in nature, in response to the performance of lawful duties. This section states that these costs must be borne by the state or municipality. The best way to be certain that the fire code official's action is a lawful duty is to always cite the applicable code section substantiating the action.

SECTION 104 GENERAL AUTHORITY AND RESPONSIBILITIES

[A] 104.1 General. The *fire code official* is hereby authorized to enforce the provisions of this code. The *fire code official* shall have the authority to render interpretations of this code and to adopt policies, procedures, rules and regulations in order to clarify the application of its provisions. Such interpretations, policies, procedures, rules and regulations shall be in compliance with the intent and purpose of this code. Such policies, procedures, rules and regulations shall not have the effect of waiving requirements specifically provided for in this code.

❖ The duty of the fire code official is to enforce the code. Because the fire code official must also act on all questions related to this responsibility, except as specifically exempted by statutory requirements or elsewhere in the code, the fire code official is the "authority having jurisdiction" for all matters relating to the code and its enforcement.

This section also gives the fire code official interpretation authority. Note, however, that the interpretations are to be consistent with the intent and purpose of the code and are not allowed to set aside any specific requirement in the code.

[A] 104.2 Applications and permits. The *fire code official* is authorized to receive applications, review *construction documents* and issue permits for construction regulated by this code, issue permits for operations regulated by this code, inspect the premises for which such permits have been issued and enforce compliance with the provisions of this code.

❖ The fire code official is obligated to receive, review and act on permit applications required by the code as detailed in Section 105. All permitted premises must be inspected either before or after the permit is issued to determine compliance with the code provisions and terms of the permit.

[A] 104.3 Right of entry. Where it is necessary to make an inspection to enforce the provisions of this code, or where the *fire code official* has reasonable cause to believe that there exists in a building or on any premises any conditions or violations of this code that make the building or premises unsafe, dangerous or hazardous, the *fire code official* shall have the authority to enter the building or premises at all reasonable times to inspect or to perform the duties imposed on the *fire code official* by this code. If such building or premises is occupied, the *fire code official* shall present credentials to the occupant and request entry. If such building or premises is unoccupied, the *fire code official* shall first make a reasonable effort to locate the *owner*, the owner's authorized agent or other person having charge or control of the building or premises and request entry. If entry is refused, the *fire code* *official* has recourse to every remedy provided by law to secure entry.

❖ This section establishes the right of the fire code official to enter the premises to make the permit inspections required by Section 105.2.2. Permit application forms typically include a statement in the certification signed by the applicant (who is the owner or owner's authorized agent) granting the fire code official the authority to enter areas covered by the permit to enforce related code provisions.

The right to enter other structures or premises is more limited. First, to protect the right of privacy, the owner or occupant must grant the building official permission before an interior inspection of the property can be conducted. Permission is not required for inspections that can be accomplished from within the public right-of-way. Second, such access may be denied by the owner or occupant. Unless the inspector has reasonable cause to believe that a violation of the code exists, access may be unattainable. Third, fire code officials must present proper identification (see Section 104.4) and request admittance during reasonable hours—usually the normal business hours of the establishment—to be admitted. Fourth, inspections must be aimed at securing or determining compliance with the provisions and intent of the regulations that are specifically within the established scope of the fire code official's authority.

Searches to gather information for the purpose of enforcing other codes, ordinances or regulations are considered unreasonable and are prohibited by the Fourth Amendment to the U.S. Constitution. "Reasonable cause" in the context of this section must be distinguished from "probable cause," which is required to gain access to property in criminal cases. The burden of proof establishing reasonable cause may vary among jurisdictions. Usually, an inspector must show that the property is subject to inspection under the provisions of the code; that the interests of the public health, safety and welfare outweigh the individual's right to maintain privacy and that such an inspection is required solely to determine compliance with the provisions of the code.

Many jurisdictions do not recognize the concept of an administrative warrant and may require the fire code official to prove probable cause in order to gain access upon refusal. This burden of proof is usually more substantial, often requiring the fire code official to stipulate in advance why access is needed (usually access is restricted to gathering evidence for seeking an indictment or making an arrest); what specific item or information is sought; its relevance to the case against the individual subject; how knowledge of the relevance of the information or items sought was obtained; and how the evidence sought will be used. In all such cases, the right to privacy must always be weighed against the right of the fire code official to conduct an inspection to verify that public health, safety and welfare are not in jeopardy. Such important and complex constitutional issues should be discussed with the jurisdiction's legal counsel. Jurisdictions should establish procedures for securing the necessary court orders where an inspection is deemed necessary following a refusal.

[A] 104.3.1 Warrant. Where the *fire code official* has first obtained a proper inspection warrant or other remedy provided by law to secure entry, an *owner*, the *owner's* authorized agent or occupant or person having charge, care or control of the building or premises shall not fail or neglect, after proper request is made as herein provided, to permit entry therein by the *fire code official* for the purpose of inspection and examination pursuant to this code.

❖ Very simply, the requirements in this section specify that where the fire code official has obtained a warrant to inspect the property, the owner, owner's authorized agent or occupant is to allow the fire code official entry to do the inspection (see commentary, Section 104.3).

[A] 104.4 Identification. The *fire code official* shall carry proper identification when inspecting structures or premises in the performance of duties under this code.

❖ This section requires the fire code official (including, by definition, all authorized designees) to carry appropriate official identification in the course of conducting the duties of the position. Such official identification may take the form of a badge, an identification card or both and removes any question as to the purpose and authority of the inspector.

[A] 104.5 Notices and orders. The *fire code official* is authorized to issue such notices or orders as are required to affect compliance with this code in accordance with Sections 110.1 and 110.2.

❖ The fire code official is required to issue orders to abate illegal or hazardous conditions and to pursue correction or abatement of hazardous conditions by issuing legal notices and orders as described by the code. Courts are increasingly ruling that failure to follow up and pursue appropriate legal remedies promptly exposes both the fire code official and the jurisdiction to a liability in tort.

[A] 104.6 Official records. The *fire code official* shall keep official records as required by Sections 104.6.1 through 104.6.4. Such official records shall be retained for not less than 5 years or for as long as the structure or activity to which such records relate remains in existence, unless otherwise provided by other regulations.

❖ In keeping with the need for an efficiently conducted business practice, the fire code official must keep official records. Such documentation provides a valuable resource of information if questions arise throughout the life of the building and its occupants. The code requires that the construction documents be kept until the project is complete or for at least 5 years, whichever is longer.

[A] 104.6.1 Approvals. A record of approvals shall be maintained by the *fire code official* and shall be available for public inspection during business hours in accordance with applicable laws.

❖ Records of prior approvals may be needed to determine the status of an existing operation or for future validation of a specific condition.

[A] 104.6.2 Inspections. The *fire code official* shall keep a record of each inspection made, including notices and orders issued, showing the findings and disposition of each.

❖ Records of inspections are needed to support the issuance of a certificate of occupancy. The inspection records should document any code violations that were subsequently corrected.

104.6.3 Fire records. The fire department shall keep a record of fires occurring within its jurisdiction and of facts concerning the same, including statistics as to the extent of such fires and the damage caused thereby, together with other information as required by the *fire code official.*

❖ Fire records provide a history of the fire experience of a facility and a cumulative record for all of the facilities of a jurisdiction. Fire records support consideration for construction code requirements based on the need to prevent additional fire occurrences.

[A] 104.6.4 Administrative. Application for modification, alternative methods or materials and the final decision of the *fire code official* shall be in writing and shall be officially recorded in the permanent records of the *fire code official.*

❖ The written approval of modifications or alternative materials and methods of construction or operation are needed to support the approval of these items in the future. This file could be used to verify that an existing condition had been previously approved.

[A] 104.7 Approved materials and equipment. Materials, equipment and devices *approved* by the *fire code official* shall be constructed and installed in accordance with such approval.

❖ The code is a compilation of criteria with which materials, equipment, devices and systems must comply to be acceptable for a particular application. The fire code official has a duty to evaluate such materials, equipment, devices and systems for code compliance and, when compliance is determined, approve them for use. As a result of this approval, the material, equipment, device or system must be constructed and installed in compliance with that approval, and with all the conditions and limitations considered as a basis for that approval. For example, the manufacturer's instructions and recommendations are to be followed if the approval of the material was based, even in part, on those instructions and recommendations.

The approval authority given to the fire code official is a significant responsibility and is a key to code compliance. The approval process is first technical and then administrative and must be approached that way. For example, if data to determine code compliance are required, such data should be in the form of test reports or engineering analyses—not simply taken from a sales brochure.

[A] 104.7.1 Material and equipment reuse. Materials, equipment and devices shall not be reused or reinstalled unless such elements have been reconditioned, tested and placed in good and proper working condition and *approved.*

❖ Used materials, equipment and devices are considered to have completed their life span; however, adequate substitutes are occasionally not available for existing items that still serve a useful and practical purpose. In such cases, existing used equipment should be approved, provided that the application is consistent with the purpose for which the equipment was designed; the function is the same as a "new" item, if one were available; and the intended use can be demonstrated as not compromising the public's safety.

[A] 104.7.2 Technical assistance. To determine the acceptability of technologies, processes, products, facilities, materials and uses attending the design, operation or use of a building or premises subject to inspection by the *fire code official*, the *fire code official* is authorized to require the *owner* or owner's authorized agent to provide, without charge to the jurisdiction, a technical opinion and report. The opinion and report shall be prepared by a qualified engineer, specialist, laboratory or fire safety specialty organization acceptable to the *fire code official* and shall analyze the fire safety properties of the design, operation or use of the building or premises and the facilities and appurtenances situated thereon, to recommend necessary changes. The *fire code official* is authorized to require design submittals to be prepared by, and bear the stamp of, a registered design professional.

❖ No one person has the technical knowledge to evaluate all of the various operations and uses from a safety standpoint. This section provides the fire code official the authority to require the owner or owner's authorized agent to provide a technical opinion safety report. The report is to be prepared by parties that have the technical ability to evaluate the design of the facility or the operational process in question. A registered design professional is commonly used for these services. It is critical that the preparer of the report have the proper background and experience for the project since the credibility of the report depends on these qualifications.

[A] 104.8 Modifications. Where there are practical difficulties involved in carrying out the provisions of this code, the *fire code official* shall have the authority to grant modifications for individual cases, provided that the *fire code official* shall first find that special individual reason makes the strict letter of this code impractical and the modification is in compliance with the intent and purpose of this code and that such modification does not lessen health, life and fire safety requirements. The details of action granting modifications shall be recorded and entered in the files of the department of fire prevention.

❖ The fire code official may amend or make exceptions to the code as needed to respond to "practical difficulties" in work on new or existing buildings. Consideration of a particular difficulty is to be based on the application of the owner and a demonstration that the intent of the code is satisfied. This section is not intended to allow a code provision to be set aside or ignored; rather, it is intended to provide for the acceptance of equivalent protection. Such modifications do not, however, extend to actions that are necessary to correct violations of the code. In other words, a code violation or the expense of correcting a code violation cannot constitute a practical difficulty.

Comprehensive written records are an essential part of an effective administrative system. Unless clearly written records of the considerations and documentation used in the modification process are created and maintained, subsequent enforcement action cannot be supported.

[A] 104.9 Alternative materials, design and methods of construction and equipment. The provisions of this code are not intended to prevent the installation of any material or to prohibit any design or method of construction not specifically prescribed by this code, provided that any such alternative has been *approved*. An alternative material, design or method of construction shall be approved where the *fire code official* finds that the proposed design is satisfactory and complies with the intent of the provisions of this code, and that the material, method or work offered is, for the purpose intended, not less than the equivalent of that prescribed in this code in quality, strength, effectiveness, *fire resistance*, durability and safety. Where the alternative material, design or method of construction is not approved, the *fire code official* shall respond in writing, stating the reasons why the alternative was not approved.

❖ Performance requirements have replaced detailed specifications to permit ready substitution and integration of new technologies in the marketplace. The code is not intended to restrict or prevent the development or application of new technologies or applications of existing technologies, provided they meet the intent of the code to protect public health, safety and welfare. When new methods or materials are developed, they should be evaluated.

Alternative methods, materials and designs are permitted where the fire code official approves such approaches. The approach is required to maintain the level of protection required by the code. One of the most frequent criticisms of codes is that their provisions apply too broadly to classes of occupancies and, therefore, are incapable of recognizing the inherent dissimilarities within occupancy groups. While some criticism may be justified, it is the fire code official's duty to evaluate scrupulously the conditions in each case, as well as judge whether the intent of the code (to provide the minimum acceptable level of protection to life and property) is met. Fire code officials should, therefore, be prepared to use decision aids, the appeals process and outside experts as needed to show that code requirements are met.

The last sentence is similar to that included in Section 105.2.1 when a permit application is rejected. The reason for this additional level of communication is that the nonapproval of an alternative method is not the same as the nonapproval of a permit. In other words, the permit application may have been approved but an alternative method might not be approved until a later date. However, the reasons for responding to the applicant in writing are the same. In order to ensure effective communication and due process of law, the reasons for denial are required to be in writing. Similar language is found in all of the I-Codes.

[A] 104.9.1 Research reports. Supporting data, where necessary to assist in the approval of materials or assemblies not specifically provided for in this code, shall consist of valid research reports from *approved* sources.

❖ When an alternative material or method is proposed for construction, it is incumbent upon the fire code official to determine whether the alternative is, in fact, equivalent to the methods prescribed by the code. Reports providing evidence of this equivalency are required to be supplied by an approved source, meaning a source that the fire code official finds to be reliable and accurate. The ICC Evaluation Service (ICC-ES) is an example of an agency that provides research reports for alternative materials and methods.

[A] 104.9.2 Tests. Where there is insufficient evidence of compliance with the provisions of this code, or evidence that a material or method does not conform to the requirements of this code, or in order to substantiate claims for alternative materials or methods, the *fire code official* shall have the authority to require tests as evidence of compliance to be made without expense to the jurisdiction. Test methods shall be as specified in this code or by other recognized test standards. In the absence of recognized and accepted test methods, the *fire code official* shall approve the testing procedures. Tests shall be performed by an *approved* agency. Reports of such tests shall be retained by the *fire code official* for the period required for retention of public records.

❖ To provide the basis on which the fire code official can make a decision regarding an alternative material or method, sufficient technical data, test reports and documentation must be provided for evaluation. If evidence satisfactory to the fire code official indicates that the alternative material or construction method is equivalent to that required by the code, he or she may approve it. Any such approval cannot have the effect of waiving any requirements of the code. The burden of proof of equivalence lies with the applicant who proposes the use of alternative materials or methods.

The fire code official must require the submission of any appropriate information and data to assist in the determination of equivalency. This information must be submitted before a permit can be issued. The type of information required includes test data in accordance with referenced standards, evidence of compliance with the referenced standard specifications and design calculations. A research report issued by an authoritative agency is particularly useful in providing the fire code official with the technical basis for evaluation and approval of new and innovative materials and methods of construction. The use of authoritative research reports can greatly assist the fire code official by reducing the time-consuming engineering analysis necessary to review these materials and methods. Failure to substantiate adequately a request for the use of an alternative is a valid reason for the building official to deny a request. Any tests submitted in support of an application must have been performed by an agency approved by the fire code official based on evidence that the agency has the technical expertise, equipment and quality assurance to properly conduct and report the necessary testing. The test reports submitted to the fire code official must be retained in accordance with the requirements of Section 104.6.

104.10 Fire investigations. The *fire code official*, the fire department or other responsible authority shall have the authority to investigate the cause, origin and circumstances of any fire, explosion or other hazardous condition. Information that could be related to trade secrets or processes shall not be made part of the public record, except as directed by a court of law.

❖ The prompt and thorough investigation of fires is important for many reasons, not the least of which are the identification of incendiary fires and prosecution of arsonists. In such cases, the duty of the fire code official is clear—evidence must be preserved and leads pursued through criminal prosecution, if possible. However, a more important and frequently overlooked aspect of fire investigation is loss analysis. Whether or not the fire code official has jurisdiction to investigate incendiary fires and prosecute arsonists, it is extremely important that the enforcement agency be involved in the process of determining why fires occur, what can be done to prevent fires, how their effects can be lessened and how people behave once fires occur. Such lessons gleaned from past tragedies have influenced the code-development efforts of various organizations across the country. The second sentence recognizes the sensitivity of trade secrets that may be involved. This section cautions that such information not be released unless permitted by the court.

104.10.1 Assistance from other agencies. Police and other enforcement agencies shall have authority to render necessary assistance in the investigation of fires when requested to do so.

❖ When needed, the fire code official has the authority to ask for assistance from the police department or other enforcement agencies, such as fire code officials in nearby jurisdictions, to investigate fires.

104.11 Authority at fires and other emergencies. The fire chief or officer of the fire department in charge at the scene of a fire or other emergency involving the protection of life or property, or any part thereof, shall have the authority to direct such operation as necessary to extinguish or control any fire, perform any rescue operation, investigate the existence of suspected or reported fires, gas leaks or other hazardous conditions or situations, or take any other action necessary in the reasonable performance of duty. In the exercise of such power, the fire chief is authorized to prohibit any person, vehicle, vessel or thing from approaching the scene, and is authorized to remove, or cause to be removed or kept away from the scene, any vehicle, vessel or thing that could impede or interfere with the operations of the fire department and, in the judgment of the fire chief, any person not actually and usefully employed in the extinguishing of such fire or in the preservation of property in the vicinity thereof.

❖ This section describes the specific conditions of authority that are granted to the fire code official at a fire or other emergencies. The first half of the paragraph simply describes the fire code official's authority to carry out the fire operation at the site. The fire code official also needs to be able to control who and what are allowed to be at the site so that emergency operations are not hampered.

104.11.1 Barricades. The fire chief or officer of the fire department in charge at the scene of an emergency is authorized to place ropes, guards, barricades or other obstructions across any street, alley, place or private property in the vicinity of such operation so as to prevent accidents or interference with the lawful efforts of the fire department to manage and control the situation and to handle fire apparatus.

❖ This section gives the fire code official the authority to control access to the emergency site so that fire-fighting operations can occur without interference. This authority is also addressed in Section 104.11.

104.11.2 Obstructing operations. Persons shall not obstruct the operations of the fire department in connection with extinguishment or control of any fire, or actions relative to other emergencies, or disobey any lawful command of the fire chief or officer of the fire department in charge of the emergency, or any part thereof, or any lawful order of a police officer assisting the fire department.

❖ This section requires that fire department operations not be obstructed and that directions from the fire department official in command at the emergency site be carried out. This is necessary for efficient emergency operations.

104.11.3 Systems and devices. Persons shall not render a system or device inoperative during an emergency unless by direction of the fire chief or fire department official in charge of the incident.

❖ This section is an extension of the requirements in Section 104.11. The fire department official is in complete charge of the fire-fighting operation at the site. No person is to tamper with the equipment needed for the emergency.

SECTION 105
PERMITS

[A] 105.1 General. Permits shall be in accordance with Sections 105.1.1 through 105.7.25.

❖ This section includes the regulations covering permits, including a comprehensive list of the kinds of activities that require permits.

[A] 105.1.1 Permits required. A property owner or owner's authorized agent who intends to conduct an operation or business, or install or modify systems and equipment that are regulated by this code, or to cause any such work to be performed, shall first make application to the *fire code official* and obtain the required permit.

❖ This section identifies that the property owner or an owner's authorized agent is required to make application for and obtain a permit. It is important that the owner or an owner's authorized agent performs this function to confirm that they are aware of and give consent for permitted operations that may include hazardous materials that could pollute or contaminate the property. See the commentary for permit fees (Section 106.1) and keeping permits on the premises and available for inspection (Section 105.3.5).

105.1.2 Types of permits. There shall be two types of permits as follows:

1. Operational permit. An operational permit allows the applicant to conduct an operation or a business for which a permit is required by Section 105.6 for either:
    1.1. A prescribed period.
    1.2. Until renewed or revoked.
2. Construction permit. A construction permit allows the applicant to install or modify systems and equipment for which a permit is required by Section 105.7.

❖ The types of activities that require an operational permit are listed in Section 105.6. Construction activities that require a permit are listed in Section 105.7.

105.1.3 Multiple permits for the same location. Where more than one permit is required for the same location, the *fire code official* is authorized to consolidate such permits into a single permit provided that each provision is listed in the permit.

❖ The code allows for a number of activities to be included on a single permit in order to decrease the paperwork for all concerned. In this instance, the permit must list in detail the activities that are covered by the combined permit.

[A] 105.1.4 Emergency repairs. Where equipment replacement and repairs must be performed in an emergency situation, the permit application shall be submitted within the next working business day to the *fire code official.*

❖ This section recognizes that, in some cases, emergency replacement and repair work must be done as quickly as possible, so it is not practical to take the necessary time to apply for and obtain approval. A permit for the work must be obtained the next day that the building department is open for business. Any work performed before the permit is issued must be done in accordance with the code and corrected if not approved by the fire code official. For example, if a concealed trap failed on a Sunday, the plumber could replace the trap at that time, but he would have to apply for a permit on Monday and have the repair pass an inspection.

[A] 105.1.5 Repairs. Application or notice to the *fire code official* is not required for ordinary repairs to structures, equipment or systems. Such repairs shall not include the cutting away of any wall, partition or portion thereof, the removal or change of any required *means of egress*, or rearrangement of parts of a structure affecting the egress requirements; nor shall any repairs include addition to, alteration of, replacement or relocation of any standpipe, fire protection water supply, *automatic sprinkler system*, fire alarm system or other work affecting fire protection or life safety.

❖ This section distinguishes between alterations, wherein the code is to be applicable, and ordinary repairs, which are maintenance activities that do not require a permit.

[A] 105.1.6 Annual permit. Instead of an individual construction permit for each alteration to an already *approved* system or equipment installation, the *fire code official* is authorized to issue an annual permit on application therefor to any person, firm or corporation regularly employing one or more qualified tradespersons in the building, structure or on the premises owned or operated by the applicant for the permit.

❖ Some large buildings or industrial facilities require repair, replacement or alteration of systems and equipment on a frequent basis. This section allows the fire code official to issue an annual permit for such work. This relieves both the fire department and the owners of such facilities from the burden of filing and processing individual applications for this activity; however, there are restrictions on who is entitled to these permits. They can be issued only for work on a previously approved installation and only to an individual or corporation that employs persons specifically qualified in the trade for which the permit is issued. If tradespeople who perform the work involved are required to be licensed in the jurisdiction, only those persons would be permitted to perform the work. If trade licensing is not required, the fire code official must review and approve the qualifications of the persons who will perform the work. The annual permit can apply only to the individual property that is owned or operated by the applicant.

[A] 105.1.6.1 Annual permit records. The person to whom an annual permit is issued shall keep a detailed record of alterations made under such annual permit. The *fire code official* shall have access to such records at all times or such records shall be filed with the *fire code official* as designated.

❖ The work performed in accordance with an annual permit must be inspected by the fire code official, so it is necessary to know when and where such work was performed. This can be accomplished by having records of the work available to the building official either at the premises or in the official's office, as determined by the official.

[A] 105.2 Application. Application for a permit required by this code shall be made to the *fire code official* in such form and detail as prescribed by the *fire code official*. Applications for permits shall be accompanied by such plans as prescribed by the *fire code official*.

❖ Applications provided by the jurisdiction should be complete, concise and relevant. Though the burden of proof is on the applicant to supply all necessary information to determine compliance with the code provisions, it is the fire code official's duty to request sufficient information to make a reasonable and informed judgment prior to approving a permit.

[A] 105.2.1 Refusal to issue permit. If the application for a permit describes a use that does not conform to the requirements of this code and other pertinent laws and ordinances, the *fire code official* shall not issue a permit, but shall return the application to the applicant with the refusal to issue such permit. Such refusal shall, where requested, be in writing and shall contain the reasons for refusal.

❖ This section directs the fire code official not to issue a permit if the application describes a use that does not conform to the requirements of the code. Note that this direction is not advisory. The fire code official would be in violation of the code if a permit were issued in such circumstances. Similar to Section 104.9, where requested by the applicant, this section requires the reason for refusal.

[A] 105.2.2 Inspection authorized. Before a new operational permit is *approved*, the *fire code official* is authorized to inspect the receptacles, vehicles, buildings, devices, premises, storage spaces or areas to be used to determine compliance with this code or any operational constraints required.

❖ The inspections described in this section are necessary for the fire code official to determine that the application for an operational permit complies with the code prior to issuing that permit. Operations may not proceed without an operational permit.

[A] 105.2.3 Time limitation of application. An application for a permit for any proposed work or operation shall be deemed to have been abandoned 180 days after the date of filing, unless such application has been diligently prosecuted or a permit shall have been issued; except that the *fire code official* is authorized to grant one or more extensions of time for additional periods not exceeding 90 days each. The extension shall be requested in writing and justifiable cause demonstrated.

❖ Permit applications lingering indefinitely in an incomplete condition can be an administrative nuisance to the fire code official, while also overburdening the filing system. This section establishes 180 days as the time limit for the permit applicant to provide the fire code official with sufficient information to evaluate the application and take appropriate action. That period should normally be more than enough time for an applicant to satisfy code requirements for submittal of construction documents and all other required information.

There may be circumstances, however, that could cause an application to age beyond 180 days prior to permit issuance, such as awaiting issuance of a report by a quality assurance agency. If the fire code official is satisfied that every effort is being made by the applicant to pursue the application, an extension of time would be acceptable.

[A] 105.2.4 Action on application. The *fire code official* shall examine or cause to be examined applications for permits and amendments thereto within a reasonable time after filing. If the application or the *construction documents* do not conform to the requirements of pertinent laws, the *fire code official* shall reject such application in writing, stating the reasons therefor. If the *fire code official* is satisfied that the proposed work or operation conforms to the requirements of this code and laws and ordinances applicable thereto, the *fire code official* shall issue a permit therefor as soon as practicable.

❖ While the fire code official has the duty to take all necessary and prudent actions to determine the applicant's compliance with the code, the evaluation must be completed promptly. Once the fire code official's review of the application is complete, either a permit will be issued or a written disapproval notice will be given. The disapproval notice must outline the reasons for rejection and should include a list of applicable code sections with which the applicant must comply to obtain approval.

[A] 105.3 Conditions of a permit. A permit shall constitute permission to maintain, store or handle materials; or to conduct processes that produce conditions hazardous to life or property; or to install equipment utilized in connection with such activities; or to install or modify any *fire protection system* or equipment or any other construction, equipment installation or modification in accordance with the provisions of this code where a permit is required by Section 105.6 or 105.7. Such permission shall not be construed as authority to violate, cancel or set aside any of the provisions of this code or other applicable regulations or laws of the jurisdiction.

❖ In effect, a permit is a contract or covenant between the jurisdiction and the applicant, allowing the applicant to operate, perform, conduct or direct a hazardous operation, process or occupancy. As with all contracts, the terms remain binding for a finite period. This process allows continual review of the applicant's compliance with the contract's terms. Failure to meet the terms of the contract may result in the applicant's forfeiture of the right to conduct or operate the process, operation or occupancy, and subsequently the fire code official may revoke the permit without further notice.

This section also states the fundamental premise that the permit is only a license to proceed with the work. It is not a license to violate, cancel or set aside any provisions of the code. This is significant because, even if there are errors or oversights in the permit approval process, the permit applicant, not the fire code official, is responsible for code compliance.

[A] 105.3.1 Expiration. An operational permit shall remain in effect until reissued, renewed or revoked, or for such a period of time as specified in the permit. Construction permits shall automatically become invalid unless the work authorized by such permit is commenced within 180 days after its issuance, or if the work authorized by such permit is suspended or abandoned for a period of 180 days after the time the work is commenced. Before such work recommences, a new permit shall be first obtained and the fee to recommence work, if any, shall be one-half the amount required for a new permit for such work, provided that changes have not been made and will not be made in the original construction documents for such work, and provided further that such suspension or abandonment has not exceeded one year. Permits are not transferable and any change in occupancy, operation, tenancy or ownership shall require that a new permit be issued.

❖ A construction permit is invalid when 180 days go by without any of the authorized work being done. The permit holder should be notified in writing that the permit is invalid, including the reasons why.

Permits are neither transferable nor assignable because they are agreements between two specific parties: the fire code official, who is acting for the jurisdiction, and the applicant. Any changes amending the application or terms of the original agreement will require a new application and permit approval.

[A] 105.3.2 Extensions. A permittee holding an unexpired permit shall have the right to apply for an extension of the time within which the permittee will commence work under that permit where work is unable to be commenced within the time required by this section for good and satisfactory reasons. The *fire code official* is authorized to grant, in writing, one or more extensions of the time period of a permit for periods of not more than 180 days each. Such extensions shall be requested by the permit holder in writing and justifiable cause demonstrated.

❖ The significant issue in this section is that an extension of time is to be granted when justifiable cause is demonstrated by the permit applicant. For example, a construction permit might be granted for certain equipment installation, but the equipment might not be received at the site until after the installation permit expires. To get a time extension, the applicant is to submit a request in writing to the fire code official, including a written explanation of why the work did not proceed within the permit time frame.

[A] 105.3.3 Occupancy prohibited before approval. The building or structure shall not be occupied prior to the *fire code official* issuing a permit and conducting associated inspections indicating the applicable provisions of this code have been met.

❖ The owner of an existing structure may request that the fire code official issue a certificate of occupancy for the structure, provided that there are no pending violations. A final inspection is usually done to verify that the work covered by the permit has been completed in accordance with the code.

[A] 105.3.4 Conditional permits. Where permits are required and on the request of a permit applicant, the *fire code official* is authorized to issue a conditional permit to occupy the premises or portion thereof before the entire work or operations on the premises is completed, provided that such portion or portions will be occupied safely prior to full completion or installation of equipment and operations without endangering life or public welfare. The *fire code official* shall notify the permit applicant in writing of any limitations or restrictions necessary to keep the permit area safe. The holder of a conditional permit shall proceed only to the point for which approval has been given, at the permit holder's own risk and without assurance that approval for the occupancy or the utilization of the entire premises, equipment or operations will be granted.

❖ The fire code official is allowed to issue a conditional permit prior to the completion of all work. Such a permit is to be issued only when the building or structure is available for safe occupancy prior to full completion. The permit is intended to acknowledge that some building features may not be completed even though the building is safe for occupancy.

[A] 105.3.5 Posting the permit. Issued permits shall be kept on the premises designated therein at all times and shall be readily available for inspection by the *fire code official*.

❖ Note that this section does not require the permit to be posted, but it is to be kept on site at all times for inspection by the fire code official.

[A] 105.3.6 Compliance with code. The issuance or granting of a permit shall not be construed to be a permit for, or an approval of, any violation of any of the provisions of this code or of any other ordinance of the jurisdiction. Permits presuming to give authority to violate or cancel the provisions of this code or other ordinances of the jurisdiction shall not be valid. The issuance of a permit based on *construction documents* and other data shall not prevent the *fire code official* from requiring the correction of errors in the *construction documents* and other data. Any addition to or alteration of *approved construction documents* shall be *approved* in advance by the *fire code official*, as evidenced by the issuance of a new or amended permit.

❖ This section includes an important principle regarding construction documents. The fire code official has the authority to require that errors in construction be corrected, even if the construction is based on documents that were part of the applicant's submittal for a construction permit. Thus, the code requirements are not set aside by approved drawings that may include noncomplying items of construction. Any changes amending the application or construction of the original agreement will require a new application and permit approval.

[A] 105.3.7 Information on the permit. The *fire code official* shall issue all permits required by this code on an *approved* form furnished for that purpose. The permit shall contain a general description of the operation or occupancy and its location and any other information required by the *fire code official*. Issued permits shall bear the signature of the *fire code official* or other *approved* legal authorization.

❖ This section describes the form of the permit and requires that it be either signed by the fire code official or otherwise reflect the legal authorization of the jurisdiction. In many jurisdictions, permits are electronically generated and do not require a traditional signature.

[A] 105.3.8 Validity of permit. The issuance or granting of a permit shall not be construed to be a permit for, or an approval of, any violation of any of the provisions of this code or of any other ordinances of the jurisdiction. Permits presuming to give authority to violate or cancel the provisions of this code or other ordinances of the jurisdiction shall not be valid. The issuance of a permit based on *construction documents*, operational documents and other data shall not prevent the *fire code official* from requiring correction of errors in the documents or other data.

❖ This section states the fundamental premise that the permit is only a license to proceed with the work. It is not a license to violate, cancel or set aside any provisions of the code. This is significant because it means that despite any errors or oversights in the approval process, the permit applicant, not the fire code official, is responsible for code compliance. Also, the permit can be revoked in accordance with Section 105.5.

[A] 105.4 Construction documents. *Construction documents* shall be in accordance with Sections 105.4.1 through 105.4.6.

❖ This section states the scope of the sections covering construction documents.

[A] 105.4.1 Submittals. *Construction documents* and supporting data shall be submitted in two or more sets with each application for a permit and in such form and detail as required by the *fire code official*. The *construction documents* shall be prepared by a registered design professional where required by the statutes of the jurisdiction in which the project is to be constructed.

Exception: The *fire code official* is authorized to waive the submission of *construction documents* and supporting data not required to be prepared by a registered design professional if it is found that the nature of the work applied for is such that review of *construction documents* is not necessary to obtain compliance with this code.

A detailed description of the work for which an application is made must be submitted in the form and detail required by the fire code official. Construction documents are to be prepared by a registered design professional where required by state laws in effect in the jurisdiction. States have professional registration laws that specify the type of construction documents to be prepared by a registered design professional. The code relies on these state laws to determine where a registered design professional is required.

The requirement for the preparation of construction documents and the submittal of calculations is specified by the code in several chapters. For example, Section 901.2 specifies that construction documents and calculations are to be submitted for fire protection systems when required by the fire code official.

[A] 105.4.1.1 Examination of documents. The *fire code official* shall examine or cause to be examined the accompanying *construction documents* and shall ascertain by such examinations whether the work indicated and described is in accordance with the requirements of this code.

❖ The requirements of this section are related to those found in Section 105.2.4 regarding the action of the fire code official in response to a permit application. The fire code official can delegate review of the construction documents to subordinates as provided for in Section 103.3.

[A] 105.4.2 Information on construction documents. *Construction documents* shall be drawn to scale on suitable material. Electronic media documents are allowed to be submitted where *approved* by the *fire code official*. *Construction documents* shall be of sufficient clarity to indicate the location, nature and extent of the work proposed and show in detail that it will conform to the provisions of this code and relevant laws, ordinances, rules and regulations as determined by the *fire code official*.

❖ Construction documents are not sketches. They are comprehensive drawings, drawn to scale, that provide the details to verify the work will comply with the code. The permit applicant must be familiar with code requirements to prepare code-compliant construction documents. If the applicant is not familiar with the code, the construction documents will most likely not have sufficient detail to determine compliance and, thus, not be satisfactory as the basis for a permit.

[A] 105.4.2.1 Fire protection system shop drawings. Shop drawings for the fire protection system(s) shall be submitted to indicate compliance with this code and the *construction documents*, and shall be *approved* prior to the start of installation. Shop drawings shall contain all information as required by the referenced installation standards in Chapter 9.

❖ It is common that fire protection contractor(s) for a project will not have been selected at the time a permit is issued; thus, detailed shop drawings for fire protection systems would not be available. Because they provide the information necessary to determine code compliance, as specified in the appropriate referenced standard in Chapter 9, detailed shop drawings for fire protection systems must be submitted and approved by the fire code official before the contractor can begin installing the system. For example, the professional responsible for the design of an automatic sprinkler system should determine that the water supply is adequate, but will not be able to prepare a final set of hydraulic calculations if the specific materials and pipe sizes, lengths and arrangements have not been identified. Once the installing contractor is selected, specific hydraulic calculations can be prepared. Factors such as classification of the hazard, amount of water supply available and the density or concentration to be achieved by the system are to be included with the submission of the shop drawings. Specific data sheets identifying sprinklers, pipe dimensions, power requirements for smoke detectors, etc., should also be included with the submission.

[A] 105.4.3 Applicant responsibility. It shall be the responsibility of the applicant to ensure that the *construction documents* include all of the fire protection requirements and the shop drawings are complete and in compliance with the applicable codes and standards.

❖ This requirement is similar to the one in Section 901.2 regarding construction documents for fire protection systems.

The requirement in this section regarding shop drawings applies to all types of shop drawings, not just those for fire protection systems. The permit applicant is responsible for the review of the shop drawings, not the fire code official. The permit applicant is also responsible for seeing that the work on the job site complies with the code. Since a lot of the construction work is done in accordance with shop drawings, the applicant should review those drawings for code compliance to make sure field construction complies with the code.

[A] 105.4.4 Approved documents. *Construction documents approved* by the *fire code official* are *approved* with the intent that such *construction documents* comply in all respects with this code. Review and approval by the *fire code official* shall not relieve the applicant of the responsibility of compliance with this code.

❖ The applicant is responsible for making sure that construction complies with the code. If approved drawings include errors that do not comply with the code, the fire code official still has the authority to require that the errors be corrected. Thus, it is important that the permit applicant is familiar with code requirements to prevent preparation of construction documents that do not meet the code.

[A] 105.4.4.1 Phased approval. The *fire code official* is authorized to issue a permit for the construction of part of a structure, system or operation before the *construction documents* for the whole structure, system or operation have been submitted, provided that adequate information and detailed statements have been filed complying with pertinent requirements of this code. The holder of such permit for parts of a structure, system or operation shall proceed at the holder's own risk with the building operation and without assurance that a permit for the entire structure, system or operation will be granted.

❖ The fire code official has the authority to issue a partial permit to allow for the practice of "fast tracking" a job. Any construction under a partial permit is, as stated in the code, "at the holder's own risk" and "without assurance that a permit for the entire structure, system or operation will be granted." The fire code official is under no obligation to accept work or issue a complete permit in violation of the code, ordinances or statutes simply because a partial permit has been issued. "Fast tracking" puts an unusual administrative and technical burden on the fire code official. The purpose is to proceed with construction while the design continues for other aspects of the work. Coordinating and correlating the code aspects into the project in phases requires attention to detail and project tracking so that all code issues are addressed.

[A] 105.4.5 Amended construction documents. Work shall be installed in accordance with the *approved construction documents*, and any changes made during construction that are not in compliance with the *approved construction documents* shall be resubmitted for approval as an amended set of *construction documents*.

❖ Any amendments to the approved construction documents must be filed before constructing the amended item. In the broadest sense, amendments include all addenda, change orders, revised drawings and marked-up shop drawings. Fire code officials should maintain a policy that all amendments be submitted for review. Otherwise, a significant amendment may not be submitted, resulting in an activity that is not approved and that causes a needless delay in obtaining approval of the finished work.

[A] 105.4.6 Retention of construction documents. One set of *construction documents* shall be retained by the *fire code official* for a period of not less than 180 days from date of completion of the permitted work, or as required by state or local laws. One set of *approved construction documents* shall be returned to the applicant, and said set shall be kept on the site of the building or work at all times during which the work authorized thereby is in progress.

❖ It is important that a complete, current set of construction documents be kept on the job site at all times. Another set of construction documents is to be kept by the fire code official until final approval of the completed work. It is not unusual for state laws to establish records-retention criteria, and this section is intended to not only make the code consistent with such laws but also to provide a minimum post-construction retention period since the months immediately following construction completion are typically when most disputes arise that depend on the construction documents for resolution. The construction documents are part of the official records of the department and should be kept in accordance with Section 104.6.

[A] 105.5 Revocation. The *fire code official* is authorized to revoke a permit issued under the provisions of this code where it is found by inspection or otherwise that there has been a false statement or misrepresentation as to the material facts in the application or *construction documents* on which the permit or approval was based including, but not limited to, any one of the following:

1. The permit is used for a location or establishment other than that for which it was issued.
2. The permit is used for a condition or activity other than that listed in the permit.
3. Conditions and limitations set forth in the permit have been violated.
4. There have been any false statements or misrepresentations as to the material fact in the application for permit or plans submitted or a condition of the permit.
5. The permit is used by a different person or firm than the name for which it was issued.
6. The permittee failed, refused or neglected to comply with orders or notices duly served in accordance with the provisions of this code within the time provided therein.
7. The permit was issued in error or in violation of an ordinance, regulation or this code.

❖ The fire code official must revoke all permits shown to be based, all or in part, on any false statement or misinterpretation of fact. An applicant may subsequently reapply for a permit. The code specifies seven specific conditions that allow the fire code official to revoke a permit.

105.6 Required operational permits. The *fire code official* is authorized to issue operational permits for the operations set forth in Sections 105.6.1 through 105.6.50.

❖ Sections 105.6.1 through 105.6.50 list the conditions requiring operational permits. Many of the items are stated in general terms, in which case the fire code official is to determine whether a specific operation is a significant hazard that requires a permit.

105.6.1 Aerosol products. An operational permit is required to manufacture, store or handle an aggregate quantity of Level 2 or Level 3 aerosol products in excess of 500 pounds (227 kg) net weight.

❖ See Chapter 51 for code requirements covering aerosol products (see commentary, Section 105.6).

105.6.2 Amusement buildings. An operational permit is required to operate a special amusement building.

❖ For requirements that apply to special amusement buildings, see Sections 202, 907.2.11 and 914.7, and Section 411 of the IBC (see commentary, Section 105.6).

105.6.3 Aviation facilities. An operational permit is required to use a Group H or Group S occupancy for aircraft servicing or repair and aircraft fuel-servicing vehicles. Additional permits required by other sections of this code include, but are not limited to, hot work, hazardous materials and flammable or combustible finishes.

❖ See Chapter 20 for aviation facility requirements (see commentary, Section 105.6).

105.6.4 Carnivals and fairs. An operational permit is required to conduct a carnival or fair.

❖ See Section 3103.3 for carnival requirements (see commentary, Section 105.6).

105.6.5 Cellulose nitrate film. An operational permit is required to store, handle or use cellulose nitrate film in a Group A occupancy.

❖ Although cellulose nitrate film is no longer in general use, there are a small number of locations in which this type of film is archived or restored for historical purposes. This section applies to those few locations (see Section 306 for cellulose nitrate film requirements).

105.6.6 Combustible dust-producing operations. An operational permit is required to operate a grain elevator, flour starch mill, feed mill, or a plant pulverizing aluminum, coal, cocoa, magnesium, spices or sugar, or other operations producing *combustible dusts* as defined in Chapter 2.

❖ See Chapter 22 for combustible dust-producing operations (see commentary, Section 105.6).

105.6.7 Combustible fibers. An operational permit is required for the storage and handling of *combustible fibers* in quantities greater than 100 cubic feet (2.8 m^3).

Exception: A permit is not required for agricultural storage.

❖ See Chapter 37 for combustible fiber requirements. The exception is for agricultural storage facilities where the hazard to persons is minimal (see Section 105.6).

105.6.8 Compressed gases. An operational permit is required for the storage, use or handling at *normal temperature and pressure* (NTP) of *compressed gases* in excess of the amounts listed in Table 105.6.8.

Exception: Vehicles equipped for and using *compressed gas* as a fuel for propelling the vehicle.

❖ See Chapter 53 for compressed gas requirements. The exception exempts vehicles equipped for compressed gas, since the code requirements for compressed gases do not apply to them.

TABLE 105.6.8
PERMIT AMOUNTS FOR COMPRESSED GASES

TYPE OF GAS	AMOUNT (cubic feet at NTP)
Carbon dioxide used in carbon dioxide enrichment systems	875 (100 lbs.)
Carbon dioxide used in insulated liquid carbon dioxide beverage dispensing applications	875 (100 lbs.)
Corrosive	200
Flammable (except cryogenic fluids and liquefied petroleum gases)	200
Highly toxic	Any Amount
Inert and simple asphyxiant	6,000
Oxidizing (including oxygen)	504
Pyrophoric	Any Amount
Toxic	Any Amount

For SI: 1 cubic foot = 0.02832 m^3.

❖ When the use of compressed gases exceeds the amounts indicated in Table 105.6.8, an operational permit is required. The quantities in the table are at normal temperature and pressure (NTP) (see Chapter 53 for compressed gas requirements).

105.6.9 Covered and open mall buildings. An operational permit is required for:

1. The placement of retail fixtures and displays, concession equipment, displays of highly combustible goods and similar items in the mall.
2. The display of liquid- or gas-fired equipment in the mall.
3. The use of open-flame or flame-producing equipment in the mall.

❖ The listed operations in a covered or open mall building require an operational permit, since they involve a significant hazard to the occupants. See Section 308 for open-flame regulations (see Section 105.6).

105.6.10 Cryogenic fluids. An operational permit is required to produce, store, transport on site, use, handle or dispense *cryogenic fluids* in excess of the amounts listed in Table 105.6.10.

Exception: Permits are not required for vehicles equipped for and using *cryogenic fluids* as a fuel for propelling the vehicle or for refrigerating the lading.

❖ See Chapter 55 for requirements regarding cryogenic fluids. The exception exempts vehicles using cryogenic fluids, since the code requirements do not apply to them.

TABLE 105.6.10
PERMIT AMOUNTS FOR CRYOGENIC FLUIDS

TYPE OF CRYOGENIC FLUID	INSIDE BUILDING (gallons)	OUTSIDE BUILDING (gallons)
Flammable	More than 1	60
Inert	60	500
Oxidizing (includes oxygen)	10	50
Physical or health hazard not indicated above	Any Amount	Any Amount

For SI: 1 gallon = 3.785 L.

❖ Where cryogenic fluids are used in excess of the amounts shown in Table 105.6.10, an operational permit is required. The listed amounts are significantly different inside or outside of a building, since the hazard is greatly reduced if a leak occurs outdoors.

105.6.11 Cutting and welding. An operational permit is required to conduct cutting or welding operations within the jurisdiction.

❖ See Chapter 35 for welding requirements (see commentary, Section 105.6).

105.6.12 Dry cleaning. An operational permit is required to engage in the business of dry cleaning or to change to a more hazardous cleaning solvent used in existing dry cleaning equipment.

❖ See Chapter 21 for dry cleaning regulations (see commentary, Section 105.6).

105.6.13 Exhibits and trade shows. An operational permit is required to operate exhibits and trade shows.

❖ The primary concern is to identify hazardous and highly flammable materials that could be involved in an exhibit or booth (see commentary, Section 105.6).

105.6.14 Explosives. An operational permit is required for the manufacture, storage, handling, sale or use of any quantity of *explosives*, *explosive materials*, fireworks or pyrotechnic special effects within the scope of Chapter 56.

Exception: Storage in Group R-3 occupancies of smokeless propellant, black powder and small arms primers for personal use, not for resale and in accordance with Section 5606.

❖ See Chapter 56 for requirements for explosives and fireworks (see commentary, Section 105.6 and Chapter 56).

The exception correlates the permit requirements for the possession, storage or use of smokeless propellant, black powder and small arms primers for personal use in Group R-3 residential occupancies with the scope of Chapter 56, as stated in Section 5601.1,

Exception 4 and Section 5606.4. The exception is also consistent with NFPA 495, referenced in Chapter 56, which limits quantities allowed in residences, but allows for quantities in residences outside the scope of Chapter 56 to be regulated without a permit.

105.6.15 Fire hydrants and valves. An operational permit is required to use or operate fire hydrants or valves intended for fire suppression purposes that are installed on water systems and provided with ready access from a fire apparatus access road that is open to or generally used by the public.

Exception: A permit is not required for authorized employees of the water company that supplies the system or the fire department to use or operate fire hydrants or valves.

❖ An operational permit is required for persons other than authorized employees of the water company or the fire department to operate fire hydrants or valves. This restriction is intended to make sure that the use will not result in a lack of water supply and pressure that may be needed for fire-fighting purposes. The exception allows water company employees or the fire department to use fire hydrants or valves without a permit. Such use is common in order to flush out the piping periodically. When fire departments or fire districts interact with water districts, they should communicate the need for the fire department to use the hydrants and valves for nonemergency situations, such as training. A notification procedure is needed to let the water district know of this planned use.

105.6.16 Flammable and combustible liquids. An operational permit is required:

1. To use or operate a pipeline for the transportation within facilities of flammable or *combustible liquids*. This requirement shall not apply to the off-site transportation in pipelines regulated by the Department of Transportation (DOTn) nor does it apply to piping systems.
2. To store, handle or use Class I liquids in excess of 5 gallons (19 L) in a building or in excess of 10 gallons (37.9 L) outside of a building, except that a permit is not required for the following:
   2.1. The storage or use of Class I liquids in the fuel tank of a motor vehicle, aircraft, motorboat, mobile power plant or mobile heating plant, unless such storage, in the opinion of the *fire code official*, would cause an unsafe condition.
   2.2. The storage or use of paints, oils, varnishes or similar flammable mixtures where such liquids are stored for maintenance, painting or similar purposes for a period of not more than 30 days.
3. To store, handle or use Class II or Class IIIA liquids in excess of 25 gallons (95 L) in a building or in excess of 60 gallons (227 L) outside a building, except for fuel oil used in connection with oil-burning equipment.
4. To store, handle or use Class IIIB liquids in tanks or portable tanks for fueling motor vehicles at motor fuel-dispensing facilities or where connected to fuel-burning equipment.

   Exception: Fuel oil and used motor oil used for space heating or water heating.
5. To remove Class I or II liquids from an underground storage tank used for fueling motor vehicles by any means other than the *approved*, stationary on-site pumps normally used for dispensing purposes.
6. To operate tank vehicles, equipment, tanks, plants, terminals, wells, fuel-dispensing stations, refineries, distilleries and similar facilities where flammable and *combustible liquids* are produced, processed, transported, stored, dispensed or used.
7. To place temporarily out of service (for more than 90 days) an underground, protected above-ground or above-ground flammable or *combustible liquid* tank.
8. To change the type of contents stored in a flammable or *combustible liquid* tank to a material that poses a greater hazard than that for which the tank was designed and constructed.
9. To manufacture, process, blend or refine flammable or *combustible liquids*.
10. To engage in the dispensing of liquid fuels into the fuel tanks of motor vehicles at commercial, industrial, governmental or manufacturing establishments in accordance with Section 5706.5.4 or to engage in on-demand mobile fueling operations in accordance with Section 5707.
11. To utilize a site for the dispensing of liquid fuels from tank vehicles into the fuel tanks of motor vehicles, marine craft and other special equipment at commercial, industrial, governmental or manufacturing establishments in accordance with Section 5706.5.4 or, where required by the fire code official, to utilize a site for on-demand mobile fueling operations in accordance with Section 5707.

❖ See Chapter 57 for regulations regarding flammable and combustible liquids (see commentary, Section 105.6).

105.6.17 Floor finishing. An operational permit is required for floor finishing or surfacing operations exceeding 350 square feet (33 m^2) using Class I or Class II liquids.

❖ The concern of this section is the proper use and handling of Class I or II liquids that are used in the floor-finishing process. If such liquids are not used, an operational permit is not required for floor finishing.

105.6.18 Fruit and crop ripening. An operational permit is required to operate a fruit- or crop-ripening facility or conduct a fruit-ripening process using ethylene gas.

❖ See Chapter 25 for regulations for fruit- and crop-ripening processes where ethylene gas is used (see commentary, Section 105.6).

105.6.19 Fumigation and insecticidal fogging. An operational permit is required to operate a business of fumigation or insecticidal fogging, and to maintain a room, vault or chamber in which a toxic or flammable fumigant is used.

❖ See Chapter 26 for fumigation and insecticidal fogging regulations within structures (see commentary, Section 105.6).

105.6.20 Hazardous materials. An operational permit is required to store, transport on site, dispense, use or handle hazardous materials in excess of the amounts listed in Table 105.6.20.

❖ See Chapter 50 for the general provisions regarding hazardous materials. Also see Chapters 51 through 67 for regulations regarding a specific hazardous material (see commentary, Section 105.6).

TABLE 105.6.20. See page 1-26.

❖ Where the amounts of hazardous materials in the table are exceeded, an operational permit is required. This applies to the storage, transportation on site, dispensing, use or handling of the hazardous materials that are listed in the table.

Table Notes a and b create parity for Class 3 oxidizer permit amounts with the adjustments to the maximum allowable quantity per control area (MAQ) specified in Table 5003.1.1(1), Note k. This eliminates the need for small apartment complexes and similar occupancies with swimming pools to obtain permits for normal pool maintenance using relatively small amounts of material.

05.6.21 HPM facilities. An operational permit is required to store, handle or use hazardous production materials.

❖ See Chapter 27 for regulations regarding semiconductor fabrication facilities (see commentary, Section 105.6).

105.6.22 High-piled storage. An operational permit is required to use a building or portion thereof with more than 500 square feet (46 m^2), including aisles, of *high-piled storage*.

❖ See Chapter 32 for high-piled storage provisions (see commentary, Section 105.6).

105.6.23 Hot work operations. An operational permit is required for hot work including, but not limited to:

1. Public exhibitions and demonstrations where hot work is conducted.
2. Use of portable hot work equipment inside a structure.

   Exception: Work that is conducted under a construction permit.
3. Fixed-site hot work equipment, such as welding booths.
4. Hot work conducted within a wildfire risk area.
5. Application of roof coverings with the use of an open-flame device.
6. Where *approved*, the *fire code official* shall issue a permit to carry out a hot work program. This program allows *approved* personnel to regulate their facility's hot work operations. The *approved* personnel shall be trained in the fire safety aspects denoted in this chapter and shall be responsible for issuing permits requiring compliance with the requirements found in Chapter 35. These permits shall be issued only to their employees or hot work operations under their supervision.

❖ See Chapter 35 for hot work regulations. The exception to Item 2 in this section recognizes that work done under a construction permit is already covered by that permit so an operational permit is not required (see commentary, Section 105.6).

105.6.24 Industrial ovens. An operational permit is required for operation of industrial ovens regulated by Chapter 30.

❖ See Chapter 30 for regulations regarding industrial ovens (see commentary, Section 105.6).

105.6.25 Lumber yards and woodworking plants. An operational permit is required for the storage or processing of lumber exceeding 100,000 board feet (8,333 ft^3) (236 m^3).

❖ See Chapter 28 for provisions for lumber yards and woodworking plants (see commentary, Section 105.6).

105.6.26 Liquid- or gas-fueled vehicles or equipment in assembly buildings. An operational permit is required to display, operate or demonstrate liquid- or gas-fueled vehicles or equipment in assembly buildings.

❖ See Section 314.4 for requirements regarding liquid- or gas-fueled vehicles inside buildings (see commentary, Section 105.6).

105.6.27 LP-gas. An operational permit is required for:

1. Storage and use of LP-gas.

   Exception: A permit is not required for individual containers with a 500-gallon (1893 L) water capacity or less or multiple container systems having an aggregate quantity not exceeding 500 gallons (1893 L), serving occupancies in Group R-3.
2. Operation of cargo tankers that transport LP-gas.

❖ See Chapter 61 for liquefied petroleum gas (LP-gas) regulations. The exception to Item 1 in this section exempts small tanks with an individual capacity of 500 gallons (1893 L) or multiple small tanks with an aggregate capacity of 500 gallons (1893 L) commonly found in residential service. A permit is required where the aggregate quantity of multiple small LP-gas containers exceeds 500 gallons (1893 L). It has become commonplace for LP-gas distributors to install LP-gas systems exceeding 500 gallons (1893 L) that consist of multiple containers in series with individual containers that do not exceed 500 gallons (1893 L), thereby avoiding the permit requirement. It is appropriate to require a permit at these locations given the significant hazard associated with these quantities. Item 2 covers cargo tankers, since they transport LP-gas onto premises covered by the code and, therefore, represent a potential hazard.

TABLE 105.6.20
PERMIT AMOUNTS FOR HAZARDOUS MATERIALS

TYPE OF MATERIAL	AMOUNT
Combustible liquids	See Section 105.6.16
Corrosive materials	
Gases	See Section 105.6.8
Liquids	55 gallons
Solids	1000 pounds
Explosive materials	See Section 105.6.14
Flammable materials	
Gases	See Section 105.6.8
Liquids	See Section 105.6.16
Solids	100 pounds
Highly toxic materials	
Gases	See Section 105.6.8
Liquids	Any Amount
Solids	Any Amount
Organic peroxides	
Liquids	
Class I	Any Amount
Class II	Any Amount
Class III	1 gallon
Class IV	2 gallons
Class V	No Permit Required
Solids	
Class I	Any Amount
Class II	Any Amount
Class III	10 pounds
Class IV	20 pounds
Class V	No Permit Required
Oxidizing materials	
Gases	See Section 105.6.8
Liquids	
Class 4	Any Amount
Class 3	1 gallon[a]
Class 2	10 gallons
Class 1	55 gallons
Solids	
Class 4	Any Amount
Class 3	10 pounds[b]
Class 2	100 pounds
Class1	500 pounds
Pyrophoric materials	
Gases	Any Amount
Liquids	Any Amount
Solids	Any Amount
Toxic materials	
Gases	See Section 105.6.8
Liquids	10 gallons
Solids	100 pounds
Unstable (reactive) materials	
Liquids	
Class 4	Any Amount
Class 3	Any Amount
Class 2	5 gallons
Class 1	10 gallons
Solids	
Class 4	Any Amount
Class 3	Any Amount
Class 2	50 pounds
Class 1	100 pounds

(continued)

TABLE 105.6.20—continued
PERMIT AMOUNTS FOR HAZARDOUS MATERIALS

TYPE OF MATERIAL	AMOUNT
Water-reactive materials	
Liquids	
Class 3	Any Amount
Class 2	5 gallons
Class 1	55 gallons
Solids	
Class 3	Any Amount
Class 2	50 pounds
Class 1	500 pounds

For SI: 1 gallon = 3.785 L, 1 pound = 0.454 kg.

a. 20 gallons where Table 5003.1.1(1) Note k applies and hazard identification signs in accordance with Section 5003.5 are provided for quantities of 20 gallons or less.

b. 200 pounds where Table 5003.1.1(1) Note k applies and hazard identification signs in accordance with Section 5003.5 are provided for quantities of 200 pounds or less.

105.6.28 Magnesium. An operational permit is required to melt, cast, heat treat or grind more than 10 pounds (4.54 kg) of magnesium.

❖ See Section 5906 for the code requirements for magnesium (see commentary, Section 105.6).

105.6.29 Miscellaneous combustible storage. An operational permit is required to store in any building or on any premises in excess of 2,500 cubic feet (71 m3) gross volume of combustible empty packing cases, boxes, barrels or similar containers, combustible pallets, rubber tires, rubber, cork or similar combustible material.

❖ See Section 315 for requirements for miscellaneous combustible material storage (see commentary, Section 105.6).

105.6.30 Mobile food preparation vehicles. A permit is required for mobile food preparation vehicles equipped with appliances that produce smoke or grease-laden vapors.

❖ See Section 319 for requirements for mobile food preparation vehicles (see commentary, Section 105.6).

105.6.31 Motor fuel-dispensing facilities. An operational permit is required for the operation of automotive, marine and fleet motor fuel-dispensing facilities.

❖ See Chapter 23 for requirements for motor fuel-dispensing facilities (see commentary, Section 105.6).

105.6.32 Open burning. An operational permit is required for the kindling or maintaining of an open fire or a fire on any public street, alley, road, or other public or private ground. Instructions and stipulations of the permit shall be adhered to.

Exception: *Recreational fires.*

❖ See Section 307 for open burning provisions. Section 202 includes the definition of "Open burning." The exception exempts recreational fires, which are also defined in Section 202.

105.6.33 Open flames and torches. An operational permit is required to remove paint with a torch; or to use a torch or open-flame device in a wildfire risk area.

❖ See Section 308 for regulations regarding open flames (see commentary, Section 105.6).

105.6.34 Open flames and candles. An operational permit is required to use open flames or candles in connection with assembly areas, dining areas of restaurants or drinking establishments.

❖ See Section 308 for regulations regarding open flames (see commentary, Section 105.6).

105.6.35 Organic coatings. An operational permit is required for any organic-coating manufacturing operation producing more than 1 gallon (4 L) of an organic coating in one day.

❖ The manufacture of organic coatings is addressed in Chapter 29 (see commentary, Section 105.6).

105.6.36 Outdoor assembly event. An operational permit is required to conduct an *outdoor assembly event* where planned attendance exceeds 1,000 persons.

❖ See Section 3106 for requirements regarding outdoor assembly events (see commentary, Section 105.6).

105.6.37 Places of assembly. An operational permit is required to operate a place of assembly.

❖ Because of the higher occupant loads found in Group A occupancies, such occupancies justify an increased level of scrutiny, such as is provided through the permit process.

105.6.38 Plant extraction systems. An operational permit is required to use plant extraction systems.

❖ See Chapter 39 for regulations regarding plant extraction systems. More specifically, this chapter addresses the processing and extraction of oils from plants (see commentary, Section 105.6).

105.6.39 Private fire hydrants. An operational permit is required for the removal from service, use or operation of private fire hydrants.

Exception: A permit is not required for private industry with trained maintenance personnel, private fire brigade or fire departments to maintain, test and use private hydrants.

❖ The purpose of an operational permit for the removal of private fire hydrants is to see that adequate fire hydrants are maintained for use during a fire. The exception allows testing and use of private fire hydrants by trained private industry personnel without an operational permit.

105.6.40 Pyrotechnic special effects material. An operational permit is required for use and handling of pyrotechnic special effects material.

❖ See Chapter 56 for fireworks regulations. The definition of "Pyrotechnic special-effect material" is found in Section 202 (see commentary, Section 105.6).

105.6.41 Pyroxylin plastics. An operational permit is required for storage or handling of more than 25 pounds (11 kg) of cellulose nitrate (pyroxylin) plastics, and for the assembly or manufacture of articles involving pyroxylin plastics.

❖ See Chapter 65 for requirements regarding pyroxylin (cellulose nitrate) plastics (see commentary, Section 105.6).

105.6.42 Refrigeration equipment. An operational permit is required to operate a mechanical refrigeration unit or system regulated by Chapter 6.

❖ See Section 605 for mechanical refrigeration regulations (see commentary, Section 105.6).

105.6.43 Repair garages and motor fuel-dispensing facilities. An operational permit is required for operation of repair garages.

❖ See Chapter 23 for requirements for repair garages (see commentary, Section 105.6).

105.6.44 Rooftop heliports. An operational permit is required for the operation of a rooftop heliport.

❖ See Chapter 20 for aviation facility requirements. Section 2007 contains helistop and heliport requirements (see commentary, Section 105.6).

105.6.45 Spraying or dipping. An operational permit is required to conduct a spraying or dipping operation utilizing flammable or *combustible liquids*, or the application of combustible powders regulated by Chapter 24.

❖ See Chapter 24 for flammable finish requirements. Section 2404 contains the spray finishing provisions, Section 2405 addresses dipping operations and Section 2406 includes powder coating regulations (see commentary, Section 105.6).

105.6.46 Storage of scrap tires and tire byproducts. An operational permit is required to establish, conduct or maintain storage of scrap tires and tire byproducts that exceeds 2,500 cubic feet (71 m^3) of total volume of scrap tires, and for indoor storage of tires and tire byproducts.

❖ See Chapter 34 for regulations regarding tire rebuilding and tire storage (see Section 105.6).

105.6.47 Temporary membrane structures and tents. An operational permit is required to operate an air-supported temporary membrane structure, a temporary *special event structure* or a tent having an area in excess of 400 square feet (37 m^2).

Exceptions:

1. Tents used exclusively for recreational camping purposes.
2. Tents open on all sides, which comply with all of the following:
   2.1. Individual tents having a maximum size of 700 square feet (65 m^2).
   2.2. The aggregate area of multiple tents placed side by side without a fire break clearance

of not less than 12 feet (3658 mm) shall not exceed 700 square feet (65 m^2) total.

2.3. A minimum clearance of 12 feet (3658 mm) to structures and other tents shall be provided.

❖ See Chapter 31 for requirements for tents and other membrane structures. The first exception in this section exempts recreational camping tents, since they are small, temporary and have few occupants. The second exception exempts relatively small tents that are very low hazard, since they are spaced at least 12 feet (3658 mm) apart (see also commentary, Section 3103.2).

105.6.48 Tire-rebuilding plants. An operational permit is required for the operation and maintenance of a tire-rebuilding plant.

❖ See Chapter 34 for regulations regarding tire rebuilding and tire storage (see Section 105.6).

105.6.49 Waste handling. An operational permit is required for the operation of wrecking yards, junk yards and waste material-handling facilities.

❖ See Section 315 for miscellaneous combustible materials storage requirements, Section 5004 for provisions regarding the storage of hazardous materials and Section 2808 for provisions regarding yard waste and recycling facilities (see commentary, Section 105.6).

105.6.50 Wood products. An operational permit is required to store chips, hogged material, lumber or plywood in excess of 200 cubic feet (6 m^3).

❖ See Section 2808 for requirements regarding the storage and handling of wood chips, hogged material, fines, compost and raw product in association with yard waste and recycling facilities (see commentary, Section 105.6).

[A] 105.7 Required construction permits. The *fire code official* is authorized to issue construction permits for work as set forth in Sections 105.7.1 through 105.7.25.

❖ This section addresses conditions requiring a construction permit (see Section 105.6). Generally, a construction permit is required when a safety-related system or hazardous material storage is installed or an existing system or facility is modified. Other sections of the code may also apply.

In some cases, the requirements in Sections 105.7.1 through 105.7.25 are stated in only general terms. In these instances, the fire code official is to evaluate the scope of work involved for the modification or installation and determine whether a construction permit is required for the specific project.

[A] 105.7.1 Automatic fire-extinguishing systems. A construction permit is required for installation of or modification to an automatic fire-extinguishing system. Maintenance performed in accordance with this code is not considered to be a modification and does not require a permit.

❖ See Chapter 9 for fire protection system requirements. A construction permit is required for the installation or modification of an automatic fire-extinguishing system so that the work can be verified to meet the code requirements, since the system is obviously safety related (see commentary, Section 105.7).

[A] 105.7.2 Battery systems. A construction permit is required to install stationary storage battery systems regulated by Section 1206.2.

❖ See Sections 1206.2 for battery system requirements (see commentary, Section 105.7).

[A] 105.7.3 Capacitor energy storage systems. A construction permit is required to install capacitor energy storage systems regulated by Section 1206.3.

❖ See Section 1206.3 for capacitor storage systems requirements (see commentary, Section 105.7).

[A] 105.7.4 Compressed gases. Where the compressed gases in use or storage exceed the amounts listed in Table 105.6.8, a construction permit is required to install, repair damage to, abandon, remove, place temporarily out of service, or close or substantially modify a *compressed gas* system.

Exceptions:

1. Routine maintenance.
2. For emergency repair work performed on an emergency basis, application for permit shall be made within two working days of commencement of work.

❖ See Chapter 53 for the requirements for compressed gas systems. Where the volume of the compressed gas presents a significant health hazard and the quantity exceeds the allowed amounts in Table 105.6.8, a permit is needed to trigger construction document submittal, document review and inspections of the work on the system. The exceptions exempt maintenance work and allow emergency work to proceed immediately.

[A] 105.7.5 Cryogenic fluids. A construction permit is required for installation of or *alteration* to outdoor stationary *cryogenic fluid* storage systems where the system capacity exceeds the amounts listed in Table 105.6.10. Maintenance performed in accordance with this code is not considered to be an *alteration* and does not require a construction permit.

❖ See Chapter 55 for the requirements for cryogenic fluids and Chapter 58 for the requirements for flammable cryogenic fluids. The application for a construction permit for cryogenic fluids is intended to trigger a plan review that will examine constraints on location and the requirements of Chapters 55 and 58.

[A] 105.7.6 Emergency responder radio coverage system. A construction permit is required for installation of or modification to emergency responder radio coverage systems and related equipment. Maintenance performed in accordance with this code is not considered to be a modification and does not require a construction permit.

❖ This section establishes that a permit must be obtained for the installation or modification of the emergency responder radio coverage system (ERRCS) to ensure that the work is done correctly and that any parts replacement will be compatible with the existing system components. Since the normal maintenance of a system typically would not involve alteration of the system, it would not require a permit.

[A] 105.7.7 Fire alarm and detection systems and related equipment. A construction permit is required for installation of or modification to fire alarm and detection systems and related equipment. Maintenance performed in accordance with this code is not considered to be a modification and does not require a construction permit.

❖ See Section 907 for fire alarm and detection requirements. A construction permit is required for installation or modification of these systems since they are obviously safety related. A permit is not required for maintenance when no modifications are made to the systems (see commentary, Section 105.7).

[A] 105.7.8 Fire pumps and related equipment. A construction permit is required for installation of or modification to fire pumps and related fuel tanks, jockey pumps, controllers and generators. Maintenance performed in accordance with this code is not considered to be a modification and does not require a construction permit.

❖ See Section 913 for requirements regarding fire pumps. A construction permit is required for modification or installation of equipment that is necessary to serve the sprinkler or standpipe system. This construction work must be monitored since these are safety-related systems (see commentary, Section 105.7).

[A] 105.7.9 Flammable and combustible liquids. A construction permit is required:

1. To install, repair or modify a pipeline for the transportation of flammable or *combustible liquids*.
2. To install, construct or alter tank vehicles, equipment, tanks, plants, terminals, wells, fuel-dispensing stations, refineries, distilleries and similar facilities where flammable and *combustible liquids* are produced, processed, transported, stored, dispensed or used.
3. To install, alter, remove, abandon or otherwise dispose of a flammable or *combustible liquid* tank.

❖ See Chapter 57 for provisions for flammable and combustible liquids. This section requires a construction permit for any of the three activities listed, since flammable and combustible liquids are a significant hazard (see commentary, Section 105.7).

[A] 105.7.10 Fuel cell power systems. A construction permit is required to install *stationary fuel cell power systems*.

❖ See Section 1205 for requirements regarding fuel cell power systems (see commentary, Section 105.7).

[A] 105.7.11 Gas detection systems. A construction permit is required for the installation of or modification to gas detection systems. Maintenance performed in accordance with this code is not considered a modification and shall not require a permit.

❖ Gas detection systems are required throughout the IFC and are addressed as a life safety system in Section 916 such as for CO_2 systems and toxic and highly toxic gases. See Section 916 for general requirements for gas detection systems (see commentary, Section 105.7).

[A] 105.7.12 Gates and barricades across fire apparatus access roads. A construction permit is required for the installation of or modification to a gate or barricade across a fire apparatus access road.

❖ The permit gives the fire code official the ability to ensure that access requirements are met.

Current code requirements for gates and barricades include an approved method of locking/securing, proper dimensions and opening width, and proper devices for operation. See the commentaries to Sections 503.5 and 503.6.

[A] 105.7.13 Hazardous materials. A construction permit is required to install, repair damage to, abandon, remove, place temporarily out of service, or close or substantially modify a storage facility or other area regulated by Chapter 50 where the hazardous materials in use or storage exceed the amounts listed in Table 105.6.20.

Exceptions:

1. Routine maintenance.
2. For repair work performed on an emergency basis, application for permit shall be made within two working days of commencement of work.

❖ A construction permit is needed for hazardous-material-related construction to ensure submittal of construction documents, document review and inspection of the work for code compliance. The exceptions provide exemptions for maintenance work and allow emergency work to proceed immediately, provided the permit application is submitted within two working days of starting the job.

[A] 105.7.14 High-piled combustible storage. A construction permit is required for the installation of or modification to a structure exceeding 500 square feet (46 m2), including aisles, for high-piled combustible storage. Maintenance performed in accordance with this code is not considered to be a modification and does not require a construction permit.

❖ See Chapter 32 and Section 3201.3 regarding high-piled combustible storage and the requirements for a construction permit (see commentary, Section 105.7).

[A] 105.7.15 Industrial ovens. A construction permit is required for installation of industrial ovens covered by Chapter 30.

Exceptions:

1. Routine maintenance.

2. For repair work performed on an emergency basis, application for permit shall be made within two working days of commencement of work.

❖ A construction permit is required for industrial oven installation so that the requirements in Chapter 30 for industrial ovens can be verified. The exceptions provide exemptions for maintenance work and allow emergency work to proceed immediately, provided that the permit is applied for within two working days after work begins.

[A] 105.7.16 LP-gas. A construction permit is required for installation of or modification to an LP-gas system. Maintenance performed in accordance with this code is not considered to be a modification and does not require a permit.

❖ See Chapter 61 for the requirements for LP-gas systems (see commentary, Section 105.7). Ordinary maintenance that does not involve modifications to the system does not require a construction permit.

[A] 105.7.17 Motor vehicle repair rooms and booths. A construction permit is required to install or modify a motor vehicle repair room or booth. Maintenance performed in accordance with this code is not considered to be a modification and does not require a permit.

❖ See Sections 2311.8.3 and 2311.8.4 for the requirements for motor vehicle repair rooms and booths, respectively (see commentary, Section 105.7).

[A] 105.7.18 Plant extraction systems. A construction permit is required for installation of or modification to plant extraction systems. Maintenance performed in accordance with this code is not considered to be a modification and does not require a permit.

❖ See Chapter 39 for requirements for plant extraction systems. Note that this chapter deals specifically with the processing and extraction of oils from plants. (see commentary, Section 105.7).

[A] 105.7.19 Private fire hydrants. A construction permit is required for the installation or modification of private fire hydrants. Maintenance performed in accordance with this code is not considered to be a modification and does not require a permit.

❖ A construction permit is needed for the installation or modification of private fire hydrants so that they remain in service for fire protection purposes. The water flow rate and pressure capability must be maintained. Ordinary maintenance that does not involve modifications does not require a construction permit.

[A] 105.7.20 Smoke control or smoke exhaust systems. Construction permits are required for installation of or alteration to smoke control or smoke exhaust systems. Maintenance performed in accordance with this code is not considered to be an alteration and does not require a permit.

❖ Smoke control and smoke exhaust systems are required fire protection systems by Chapter 9. A permit is necessary to ensure proper design and installation. Ordinary maintenance that does not involve modifications to the system does not require a construction permit.

[A] 105.7.21 Solar photovoltaic power systems. A construction permit is required to install or modify solar photovoltaic power systems. Maintenance performed in accordance with this code is not considered to be a modification and does not require a permit.

❖ Section 1204 regulates solar photovoltaic power system installations on buildings. Because of the unique electrical and physical hazards they present to fire fighters and the impact such systems have on fire suppression operations, a permit is required. Ordinary maintenance that does not involve modifications to the system does not require a construction permit.

[A] 105.7.22 Special event structure. A single construction permit is required to erect and take down a *temporary special event structure*.

❖ See Section 3105 for specific requirements for temporary special event structures (see commentary, Section 105.7).

[A] 105.7.23 Spraying or dipping. A construction permit is required to install or modify a spray room, dip tank or booth. Maintenance performed in accordance with this code is not considered to be a modification and does not require a permit.

❖ See Chapter 24 for flammable finish requirements. The spray finishing requirements are in Section 2404, while dipping operations regulations are in Section 2405 (see commentary, Section 105.7). Ordinary maintenance that does not involve modifications does not require a construction permit.

[A] 105.7.24 Standpipe systems. A construction permit is required for the installation, modification or removal from service of a standpipe system. Maintenance performed in accordance with this code is not considered to be a modification and does not require a permit.

❖ See Section 905 for standpipe system requirements. Construction permits are required for standpipe systems because they are safety-related fire protection systems. Ordinary maintenance that does not involve modifications to the system does not require a construction permit.

[A] 105.7.25 Temporary membrane structures and tents. A construction permit is required to erect an air-supported temporary membrane structure, a temporary stage canopy or a tent having an area in excess of 400 square feet (37 m^2).

Exceptions:

1. Tents used exclusively for recreational camping purposes.
2. Funeral tents and curtains, or extensions attached thereto, when used for funeral services.
3. Tents and awnings open on all sides, which comply with all of the following:
   3.1. Individual tents shall have a maximum size of 700 square feet (65 m^2).

3.2. The aggregate area of multiple tents placed side by side without a fire break clearance of not less than 12 feet (3658 mm) shall not exceed 700 square feet (65 m^2) total.

3.3. A minimum clearance of 12 feet (3658 mm) to structures and other tents shall be maintained.

❖ See Chapter 31 for requirements regarding tents and other membrane structures. The exceptions are for tents where the hazard is very low. They provide needed exemptions for tents used for recreational camping and funerals. Relatively small tents and awnings that are open on all sides and are located a minimum of 12 feet (3658 mm) apart are also exempt (see commentary, Section 3103.2).

SECTION 106
FEES

[A] 106.1 Fees. A permit shall not be issued until the fees have been paid, nor shall an amendment to a permit be released until the additional fee, if any, has been paid.

❖ The code anticipates that jurisdictions will establish their own fee schedules. It is the intent that the fees collected by the department for permit issuance, plan review and inspection be adequate to cover the costs to the department in these areas. If the department has additional duties, then its budget will need to be supplemented from the general fund. This section requires that all fees be paid prior to permit issuance or release of an amendment to a permit. Since department operations are intended to be supported by fees paid by the user of department activities, it is important that these fees are received before incurring any expense. This philosophy has resulted in some departments having fees paid prior to the performance of two areas of work: plan review and inspection.

[A] 106.2 Schedule of permit fees. A fee for each permit shall be paid as required, in accordance with the schedule as established by the applicable governing authority.

❖ The jurisdiction is responsible for promulgating a schedule of fees to be charged for operational or construction permits. Permit fees should be established by law, such as in an ordinance adopting the code, a separate ordinance or a legally promulgated regulation, as required by state or local law. Fee schedules for operational permits should be based on an analysis of the amount of time and resources to be expended by the jurisdiction in administering the permit. Fee schedules for construction permits are often based on a valuation of the work to be performed. This concept is based on the proposition that the valuation of a project is related to the amount of work to be expended in plan review, inspections and administering the permit, plus an excess to cover the department overhead.

[A] 106.3 Work commencing before permit issuance. A person who commences any work, activity or operation regulated by this code before obtaining the necessary permits shall be subject to an additional fee established by the applicable governing authority, which shall be in addition to the required permit fees.

❖ The fire code official will incur certain costs (i.e., inspection time and administrative) when investigating and citing a person who has commenced work, activity or operation without having obtained a permit. The fire code official is, therefore, entitled to recover these costs by establishing a fee, in addition to that collected when the required permit is issued, to be imposed on the responsible party. Note that this is not a penalty, as described in Section 110.4, for which the person can also be liable.

[A] 106.4 Related fees. The payment of the fee for the construction, *alteration*, removal or demolition of work done in connection to or concurrently with the work or activity authorized by a permit shall not relieve the applicant or holder of the permit from the payment of other fees that are prescribed by law.

❖ The fees for a permit may be in addition to other fees required by the jurisdiction or others for related items, such as sewer connections, water service taps, driveways and signs and others. It cannot be construed that the fire code permit fee includes these other items.

[A] 106.5 Refunds. The applicable governing authority is authorized to establish a refund policy.

❖ This section allows for a refund of fees, which may be full or partial, typically resulting from the revocation, abandonment or discontinuance of a project or operation for which a permit has been issued and fees have been collected. The refund of fees should be related to the cost of enforcement services not provided because of the termination of the project or operation. The fire code official, when authorizing a fee refund, is authorizing the disbursement of public funds; therefore, the request for a refund should be in writing and for good cause.

SECTION 107
INSPECTIONS

[A] 107.1 Inspection authority. The *fire code official* is authorized to enter and examine any building, structure, marine vessel, vehicle or premises in accordance with Section 104.3 for the purpose of enforcing this code.

❖ The first part of this section establishes the right of the fire code official to enter the premises to make the permit inspections required by Section 104. Permit application forms typically include a statement in the certification signed by the applicant (who is the owner or owner's agent) granting the fire code official the authority to enter areas covered by the permit to enforce code provisions related to the permit.

The right to enter other structures or premises is more limited. First, to protect the right of privacy, the owner or occupant must grant the fire code official permission before the interior of the property can be inspected. Permission is not required for inspections that can be accomplished from within the public right-of-way. Second, such access may be denied by the owner or occupant. Unless the inspector has "reasonable cause" to believe that a violation of the code exists, access may be unattainable. Third, fire code officials must present proper identification (see Section 104.4) and request admittance during reasonable hours—usually the normal business hours of the establishment—to be admitted. Fourth, inspections must be aimed at securing or determining compliance with the provisions and intent of the regulations that are specifically within the established scope of the fire code official's authority. Searches to gather information for the purpose of enforcing other codes, ordinances or regulations are considered unreasonable and are prohibited by the Fourth Amendment to the U.S. Constitution.

Reasonable cause in the context of this section must be distinguished from probable cause, which is required to gain access to property in criminal cases. The burden of proof for establishing reasonable cause may vary among jurisdictions. Usually, an inspector must show that the property is subject to inspection under the provisions of the code (see Section 104), that the interests of the public health, safety and welfare outweigh the individual's right to maintain privacy and that such an inspection is required solely to determine compliance with the provisions of the code. Many jurisdictions do not recognize the concept of an administrative warrant, and may require the fire code official to prove probable cause in order to gain access upon refusal. This burden of proof is usually more substantial, often requiring the fire code official to stipulate in advance why access is needed (usually access is restricted to gathering evidence for seeking an indictment or making an arrest); what specific item or information is sought; its relevance to the case against the individual subject; how knowledge of the relevance of the information or items sought was obtained; and how the evidence sought will be used. In all such cases, the right to privacy must always be weighed against the right of the fire code official to conduct an inspection to determine whether the health, safety or welfare of the public is in jeopardy. Such important and complex constitutional issues should be discussed with the jurisdiction's legal counsel. Jurisdictions should establish procedures for securing the necessary court orders when an inspection is considered necessary following a refusal.

[A] 107.2 Inspections. The *fire code official* is authorized to conduct such inspections as are deemed necessary to determine the extent of compliance with the provisions of this code and to approve reports of inspection by *approved* agencies or individuals. Reports of such inspections shall be prepared and submitted in writing for review and approval. Inspection reports shall be certified by a responsible officer of such *approved* agency or by the responsible individual. The *fire code official* is authorized to engage such expert opinion as deemed necessary to report on unusual, detailed or complex technical issues subject to the approval of the governing body.

❖ This section establishes the fire code official's authority to inspect buildings, structures or premises to verify that the requirements of the code are met or to accept written reports of inspections by an approved agency. The code does not, however, establish the frequency of inspections or even require that inspections be conducted, since the code does not presume to interpret or influence the adopting jurisdiction's political, social and economic priorities. Jurisdictions may establish their inspection priorities and frequencies based on a variety of factors, including the availability of inspection resources; the level of available fire suppression services; the value of premises to the community; or the potential disruption to community services or stability if a fire occurs. In summary, each community determines and assumes its own acceptable risk level.

In order to expand the available resources for inspection purposes, the fire code official is also authorized to approve a third-party agency that is regularly engaged in conducting relevant tests or furnishing inspection services. Approval of such an agency may be acquired through review of the résumés and references of the agency and its personnel, and analyzing the capacity and capability of the agency to perform the work. Additional guidance can be obtained by reviewing the provisions of Sections 1703 and 1704 of the IBC.

When unusual, extraordinary or complex technical issues arise relative to building safety, the fire code official has the authority to seek the opinion and advice of experts. Since this usually involves the expenditure of funds, the approval of the jurisdiction's chief administrative authority must be obtained.

[A] 107.2.1 Inspection requests. It shall be the duty of the holder of the permit or their duly authorized agent to notify the *fire code official* when work is ready for inspection. It shall be the duty of the permit holder to provide access to and means for inspections of such work that are required by this code.

❖ It is the responsibility of the permit holder or other authorized person, such as the contractor performing the work, to arrange for the required inspections when completed work is ready and to allow for sufficient time for the fire code official to schedule a visit to the site to prevent work from being concealed prior to being inspected. Access to the work to be inspected must be provided, including any special means such as a ladder to gain access.

[A] 107.2.2 Approval required. Work shall not be done beyond the point indicated in each successive inspection without first obtaining the approval of the *fire code official.*

The *fire code official,* on notification, shall make the requested inspections and shall either indicate the portion of the construction that is satisfactory as completed, or notify the permit holder or his or her agent wherein the same fails to comply with this code. Any portions that do not comply shall be corrected, and such portion shall not be covered or concealed until authorized by the *fire code official.*

❖ This section establishes that work cannot progress beyond the point of a required inspection without the fire code official's approval. Upon making the inspection, the fire code official must either approve the completed work or notify the permit holder or other responsible party of that which does not comply with the code. Approvals and notices of noncompliance must be in writing, as required by Section 110.3, to avoid any misunderstanding as to what is required. Any item not approved cannot be covered or concealed until it has been corrected and approved by the fire code official.

[A] 107.3 Concealed work. It shall be the duty of the permit applicant to cause the work to remain visible and able to be accessed for inspection purposes. Where any installation subject to inspection prior to use is covered or concealed without having first been inspected, the *fire code official* shall have the authority to require that such work be made visible and able to be accessed for inspection. Neither the *fire code official* nor the jurisdiction shall be liable for expense entailed in the removal or replacement of any material required to allow inspection.

❖ This section addresses the procedure that is available to the fire code official for inspection of concealed work. In many jurisdictions, the contractor or permit holder of an operation or a construction project is to contact the local fire inspection authority when work is completed but still exposed to allow inspection. The section requires that any work to be concealed upon completion must remain exposed until an inspection is made. If the work requiring inspection is covered up before the inspection takes place, the fire code official has the authority to require removal of the concealing construction. The section also makes it clear that any expense incurred in removing or replacing material that conceals an item to be inspected is not the responsibility of either the fire code official or the jurisdiction. Obviously, this can be a time-consuming and expensive procedure that can be eliminated by good communication and cooperation between the contractor or permit holder and the fire code official.

[A] 107.4 Approvals. Approval as the result of an inspection shall not be construed to be an approval of a violation of the provisions of this code or of other ordinances of the jurisdiction. Inspections presuming to give authority to violate or cancel provisions of this code or of other ordinances of the jurisdiction shall not be valid.

❖ As with the issuance of permits (see commentary, Section 105.3), approval as a result of an inspection is not a license to violate the code. Further, approval in violation of the code does not relieve the applicant from complying with the code and is not valid. This is significant because even if there are errors or oversights in the approval process, the permit applicant or other recipient of the inspection, not the fire code official, is still responsible for code compliance.

SECTION 108 MAINTENANCE

[A] 108.1 Maintenance of safeguards. Where any device, equipment, system, condition, arrangement, level of protection, or any other feature is required for compliance with the provisions of this code, or otherwise installed, such device, equipment, system, condition, arrangement, level of protection, or other feature shall thereafter be continuously maintained in accordance with this code and applicable referenced standards.

❖ This section does not identify who is responsible for maintenance because that determination should be made in accordance with the legal documents created between owners and occupants, such as a lease. The owner of a structure or premises, however, is usually primarily responsible for its maintenance, since the owner stands to gain the most from a well-maintained property. One of the underlying assumptions is that maintaining a commercial property in good condition allows the owner to recoup a substantial portion of his or her investment in maintenance. There are three factors that may influence owners to comply with code requirements:

- Code compliance requires only a small additional investment in the property.
- The owner has a long-term interest in the property.
- The owner expects profitability after incurring the additional expense of complying with the code.

While all these factors represent economic incentives, fire code officials should be equally aware of potential disincentives to compliance, such as assessable value, expiring tax credits or historic, architectural or aesthetic criteria. The fire code official need not belabor the justifications for compliance, but should be prepared to acknowledge the owner's rationalizations for failure to comply.

This section also emphasizes that any "otherwise installed" system that currently exists must be maintained. For example, an existing fire protection system cannot be removed from a building just because it is not required in new or existing buildings by current codes.

[A] 108.2 Testing and operation. Equipment requiring periodic testing or operation to ensure maintenance shall be tested or operated as specified in this code.

❖ This section addresses periodic testing or operation to verify that the equipment can be expected to operate when needed. For example, see Section 901.6 for inspection and testing requirements for fire protection systems.

Test and inspection records must be available to the fire code official for verification that the tests and inspections required by the code and the referenced standards are in compliance.

If the fire code official requests, such records must be filed with the jurisdictional office.

[A] 108.2.1 Reinspection and testing. Where any work or installation does not pass an initial test or inspection, the necessary corrections shall be made so as to achieve compliance with this code. The work or installation shall then be resubmitted to the *fire code official* for inspection and testing.

❖ This section simply requires an installation to be of such quality that it will pass any tests or inspections required by the code. For example, if a fire alarm system did not pass the installation test upon completion of the system, the system is to be reworked until it passes the test.

[A] 108.3 Recordkeeping. A record of periodic inspections, tests, servicing and other operations and maintenance shall be maintained on the premises or other *approved* location for not less than 3 years, or a different period of time where specified in this code or referenced standards. Records shall be made available for inspection by the *fire code official,* and a copy of the records shall be provided to the *fire code official* on request.

The *fire code official* is authorized to prescribe the form and format of such recordkeeping. The *fire code official* is authorized to require that certain required records be filed with the *fire code official.*

❖ Recordkeeping of testing, inspections, servicing and other operations and maintenance are critical to the successful application of this code. Proper and consistent recordkeeping will increase the safety to both building occupants and fire fighters. This section also makes it clear that records must be provided to the fire code official upon request and maintained for a period of not less than 3 years unless a different time interval is specified in the code or a referenced standard. Also, the fire code official is authorized to prescribe the form and format of such records. The recordkeeping requirements throughout the code have been specifically coordinated with this section.

[A] 108.4 Supervision. Maintenance and testing shall be under the supervision of a responsible person who shall ensure that such maintenance and testing are conducted at specified intervals in accordance with this code.

❖ Maintenance supervision is needed to verify that testing and general supervision is done regularly. Section 901.6 states code requirements regarding testing and maintenance of the fire protection systems.

108.5 Rendering equipment inoperable. Portable or fixed fire-extinguishing systems or devices, and fire-warning systems, shall be provided with ready access and shall not be rendered inoperative, except as necessary during emergencies, maintenance, repairs, *alterations,* drills or prescribed testing.

❖ If fire protection systems are going to be effective when needed, they must be in good operating condition. This section specifies those circumstances when they are allowed to be temporarily out of service. See Section 901.6 for code requirements regarding testing and maintenance of the fire protection systems.

[A] 108.6 Overcrowding. Overcrowding or admittance of any person beyond the *approved* capacity of a building or a portion thereof shall not be allowed. The *fire code official,* on finding any overcrowding conditions or obstructions in *aisles,* passageways or other *means of egress,* or on finding any condition that constitutes a life safety hazard, shall be authorized to cause the event to be stopped until such condition or obstruction is corrected.

❖ The key to enforcing this provision successfully is good judgment. Rarely is it possible to count accurately the number of people in any given place of public assembly. Usually, the proprietors or operators of such events have no accurate estimate of the crowd size or they are unwilling to provide an estimate. Despite these difficulties, when the number of people is too large to permit aisles and required egress elements to remain clear or at least flow smoothly, remedies must be sought. In many instances, overcrowding can be remedied by simply preventing any more occupants from entering, thus limiting the potential hazard to those occupants already inside. If the fire code official determines that preventing further access will be insufficient in itself, he or she is authorized to order the owner or operator to stop the event until the hazardous condition is abated, the approved occupant load is reestablished and resumption of the event is authorized by the fire code official.

SECTION 109
BOARD OF APPEALS

[A] 109.1 Board of appeals established. In order to hear and decide appeals of orders, decisions or determinations made by the *fire code official* relative to the application and interpretation of this code, there shall be and is hereby created a board of appeals. The board of appeals shall be appointed by the governing body and shall hold office at its pleasure. The *fire code official* shall be an ex officio member of said board but shall not have a vote on any matter before the board. The board shall adopt rules of procedure for conducting its business, and shall render all decisions and findings in writing to the appellant with a duplicate copy to the *fire code official.*

❖ This section provides an objective forum for settling disputes regarding the application or interpretation of code requirements. The board is required to issue a written decision to the appellant who brought the matter before the board and to the fire code official. Note that the fire code official is a nonvoting member of the board. The board of appeals is an effective decision-making body that is commonly used when the owner or owner's agent and the fire code official do not agree on a matter relating to the application of the code.

[A] 109.2 Limitations on authority. An application for appeal shall be based on a claim that the intent of this code or the rules legally adopted hereunder have been incorrectly interpreted, the provisions of this code do not fully apply, or an equivalent method of protection or safety is proposed. The board shall not have authority to waive requirements of this code.

❖ This section states the scope of the issues that are to be addressed by the board of appeals and limits its authority to ruling on these issues. Commonly, the issues relate to the applicability of the code or the interpretation of the code to a given situation. The board listens to both the person who filed the appeal and to the fire code official before ruling on the matter.

This section specifically states that the board does not have the authority to waive code requirements; however, the board has the authority to accept an alternative method of protection or safety if, in its view, it is equivalent to the specific requirement in the code.

[A] 109.3 Qualifications. The board of appeals shall consist of members who are qualified by experience and training to pass on matters pertaining to hazards of fire, explosions, hazardous conditions or *fire protection systems*, and are not employees of the jurisdiction.

❖ It is important that the decisions of the board of appeals are based purely on the technical merits involved in an appeal; it is not the place for policy or political deliberations. The members of the board of appeals are, therefore, expected to have experience in matters within the scope of the code and must be of the highest character, competence and status in their professions and the community at large. Appendix A of the code provides more detailed qualifications for board of appeals members and can be adopted by jurisdictions desiring that level of expertise (see commentary, Appendix A).

SECTION 110 VIOLATIONS

[A] 110.1 Unlawful acts. It shall be unlawful for a person, firm or corporation to erect, construct, alter, repair, remove, demolish or utilize a building, occupancy, premises or system regulated by this code, or cause same to be done, in conflict with or in violation of any of the provisions of this code.

❖ Section 110 establishes that compliance with the code is required, and what measures are to be taken for noncompliance.

[A] 110.2 Owner/occupant responsibility. Correction and abatement of violations of this code shall be the responsibility of the *owner* or the owner's authorized agent. Where an occupant creates, or allows to be created, hazardous conditions in violation of this code, the occupant shall be held responsible for the abatement of such hazardous conditions.

❖ Hazards related to use and occupancy, and not those related to fixed equipment or installations, fall within the scope of the occupants' responsibility. Owners or the owner's authorized agent, however, may become liable if they allow the unlawful operation or continuation of a public nuisance on a property under their control, especially if they knowingly or willfully lease the property in violation of fire, zoning or building regulations.

The simple rule for determining what is the responsibility of the owner or owner's authorized agents and what is the occupants' responsibility is whether the issue involves fixed equipment installations or if the structure is separate from those items related to occupancy. The owner or owner's authorized agent is usually responsible for the physical maintenance of the building or structure and its utilities and appurtenances (that is, building services and systems).

[A] 110.3 Notice of violation. Where the *fire code official* finds a building, premises, vehicle, storage facility or outdoor area that is in violation of this code, the *fire code official* is authorized to prepare a written notice of violation describing the conditions deemed unsafe and, where compliance is not immediate, specifying a time for reinspection.

❖ The fire code official has a duty to supply owners, agents or occupants with a written notice of code violations on the premises under their control. When possible, both the owner and the occupants should be made aware of hazardous conditions. Such notices constitute the first of several steps in the due process procedure. Violation notices must clearly indicate the defect, its location, the code section being violated, what must be done to correct the violation and the date of the reinspection. Owners, agents or occupants should also be supplied with information regarding penalties, permit applications and appeal procedures. The notice or order must be signed by the fire code official who issued it and should provide a space for the owner, agent or occupants' signature to acknowledge receipt of the document. If possible, duplicate or triplicate copies should be prepared, with the original notice issued to the responsible party. Other copies should be maintained by the inspector and the departmental record keeper.

[A] 110.3.1 Service. A notice of violation issued pursuant to this code shall be served on the *owner*, the owner's authorized agent, operator, occupant or other person responsible for the condition or violation, either by personal service, mail or by delivering the same to, and leaving it with, some person of responsibility on the premises. For unattended or abandoned locations, a copy of such notice of violation shall be posted on the premises in a conspicuous place at or near the entrance to such premises and the notice of violation shall be mailed by certified mail with return receipt requested or a certificate of mailing, to the last known address of the *owner*, the owner's authorized agent, or occupant.

❖ Service methods are listed by order or preference. The first and best method is to personally serve the owner, owner's authorized agent or the occupant, in that order, at the premises cited, with a signature acknowledging receipt. The next-most desirable method is service to these same parties in the order indicated at their place of business when it is not the premises cited.

While post office delivery by ordinary first-class mail is acceptable, most jurisdictions prefer certified mail with return receipt, followed by a certificate of mailing; however, owners or owner's authorized agents familiar with the legal process will often refuse to accept certified mail. As a result, many jurisdictions follow up returned certified mail with a request for a certificate of mailing. A certificate of mailing includes certification by the mail carrier or post office that the item was physically delivered to the address indicated, but does not verify that the addressee actually took possession of the item. The least-desirable method of service is physically posting the premises with the violation notice. When service proves difficult, many jurisdictions pursue the mailing and posting service options simultaneously to exhaust all service methods. Jurisdictions should consult legal counsel about case law regarding legal service in their communities. The following methods are most common:

- Personal to violator.
- Personal to party at premises.
- Certified mail with return receipt.
- First-class mail with certificate of mailing.
- Posting at the premises.

[A] 110.3.2 Compliance with orders and notices. A notice of violation issued or served as provided by this code shall be complied with by the *owner*, the owner's authorized agent, operator, occupant or other person responsible for the condition or violation to which the notice of violation pertains.

❖ The party responsible for the condition that is in noncompliance is required by this section to bring the property into code compliance. See the remainder of Section 110 for what is to be done if this does not occur.

[A] 110.3.3 Prosecution of violations. If the notice of violation is not complied with promptly, the *fire code official* is authorized to request the legal counsel of the jurisdiction to institute the appropriate legal proceedings at law or in equity to restrain, correct or abate such violation or to require removal or termination of the unlawful occupancy of the structure in violation of the provisions of this code or of the order or direction made pursuant hereto.

❖ The duty to pursue legal remedies through judicial due process is established by this section. Local prosecutors and fire code officials should establish policies covering the following issues regarding judicial due process proceedings:

- Length of compliance period for representative violations.
- Quality or quantity of progress toward compliance warranting an extension or representing reasonable intent to comply.
- Whether court filings should be sought during the appeal application period.
- Rules for obtaining arrest warrants for code violations.
- Rules for obtaining administrative and criminal search warrants.

The cooperation of the police department and other law enforcement agencies should be coordinated in advance. When necessary to enforce code provisions, arrangements should be made to have police or other law enforcement personnel make arrests for code violations or ignoring lawful orders of the fire code official.

[A] 110.3.4 Unauthorized tampering. Signs, tags or seals posted or affixed by the *fire code official* shall not be mutilated, destroyed or tampered with, or removed, without authorization from the *fire code official*.

❖ This section states that tampering with signs, seals or tags posted at the property is a violation of the code. The safety of occupants may depend on warning signs posted by the fire code official remaining in place.

[A] 110.4 Violation penalties. Persons who shall violate a provision of this code or shall fail to comply with any of the requirements thereof or who shall erect, install, alter, repair or do work in violation of the *approved construction documents* or directive of the *fire code official*, or of a permit or certificate used under provisions of this code, shall be guilty of a **[SPECIFY OFFENSE]**, punishable by a fine of not more than **[AMOUNT]** dollars or by imprisonment not exceeding **[NUMBER OF DAYS]**, or both such fine and imprisonment. Each day that a violation continues after due notice has been served shall be deemed a separate offense.

❖ Penalties for code violations must be established in adopting legislation. The offense, dollar amount for the fine and maximum number of days of imprisonment are to be specific in the adopting ordinance of the jurisdiction.

The code does not establish penalties for violations. The jurisdiction's judicial and legislative bodies should work with the fire code official to establish reasonable and equitable penalties for violators. The penalties set for individual violations should be representative of the severity of the act committed and the culpability of the violator. Once served with a violation notice, the violator becomes guilty of a separate offense for each day the violation continues to exist; however, most prosecutors and courts are reluctant to impose this penalty for days during the compliance period. Many violators wrongly assume that the Seventh Amendment of the U.S. Constitution, which offers protection against double jeopardy, exempts them from compliance once they have paid or served their sentence for a previous fire code violation. This is certainly not the case. Most courts reinforce the compliance requirement in such cases by making compliance a condition for completing the sentence. Failure to comply with the judge's order mandating compliance may result in a contempt of court charge.

[A] 110.4.1 Abatement of violation. In addition to the imposition of the penalties herein described, the *fire code official* is authorized to institute appropriate action to prevent unlawful construction or to restrain, correct or abate a violation; or to prevent illegal occupancy of a structure or premises; or to stop an illegal act, conduct of business or occupancy of a structure on or about any premises.

❖ Even though the person who violated the code has paid any fine and served any sentence that may be imposed for the jurisdiction under Section 110.4, the fire code official has the right to require that the code violation be removed. If the violation is not abated, the fire code official has the right to prevent occupancy until the violation is addressed. Usually, the court will require that the violation be corrected as part of the sentence of noncompliance prior to the occupancy of the building.

SECTION 111 UNSAFE BUILDINGS

[A] 111.1 General. If during the inspection of a premises, a building or structure, or any building system, in whole or in part, constitutes a clear and inimical threat to human life, safety or health, the *fire code official* shall issue such notice or orders to remove or remedy the conditions as shall be deemed necessary in accordance with this section, and shall refer the building to the building department for any repairs, *alterations*, remodeling, removing or demolition required.

❖ The fire code official is required to order the correction or abatement of hazardous conditions within the scope of the code and to refer the building to the building department for those operations that are within the scope of that department. The conditions listed in Section 111.1.1 represent many of the most common hazardous conditions encountered. Specific requirements supporting each of these objectives are found throughout the code.

[A] 111.1.1 Unsafe conditions. Structures or existing equipment that are or hereafter become unsafe or deficient because of inadequate *means of egress*, that constitute a fire hazard, are otherwise dangerous to human life or the public welfare, or involve illegal or improper occupancy or inadequate maintenance, shall be deemed an unsafe condition. A vacant structure that is not secured against unauthorized entry as required by Section 311 shall be deemed unsafe.

❖ Courts have continually upheld the right of states and their authorized subdivisions to abate public nuisances, even by demolition, and bill or assess the property owner through a tax lien for their expenses. However, care must be exercised to maintain compliance with the due process and equal protection doctrines of the Fourth and Fourteenth Amendments of the U.S. Constitution. Jurisdictions should consult legal counsel and adopt appropriate guidelines before engaging in a nuisance abatement program.

Uninhabited or abandoned buildings that are not secured against unauthorized entry as required by Section 311 have a very high probability of intentionally set fires. When fires occur in these buildings, they present a host of unusual hazards to fire fighters. Since the buildings are uninhabited, fires may develop for significant periods of time before they are detected and reported. Accordingly, such unsecured buildings are declared by this section to be unsafe and therefore subject to remediation as provided in Section 111 (see commentary, Section 311).

[A] 111.1.2 Structural hazards. Where an apparent structural hazard is caused by the faulty installation, operation or malfunction of any of the items or devices governed by this code, the *fire code official* shall immediately notify the building code official in accordance with Section 110.1.

❖ The fire code official is required to report structurally unsafe buildings to the building official to secure abatement of unsafe conditions. Courts have continually upheld the right of states and their authorized subdivisions to abate public nuisances, even by demolition, and bill or assess the property owner through a tax lien for their expenses. However, care must be exercised to maintain compliance with the due process and equal protection doctrines of the Fourth and Fourteenth Amendments of the U.S. Constitution.

[A] 111.2 Evacuation. The *fire code official* or the fire department official in charge of an incident shall be authorized to order the immediate evacuation of any occupied building deemed unsafe where such building has hazardous conditions that present imminent danger to building occupants. Persons so notified shall immediately leave the structure or premises and shall not enter or re-enter until authorized to do so by the *fire code official* or the fire department official in charge of the incident.

❖ The fire code official must immediately order the evacuation of any premises posing a clear and imminent threat to life or property. Building occupants who are warned must comply with the evacuation order without delay. Upon leaving the building, occupants may not reenter until authorization is given by the fire code official. Severe and immediate danger anticipated in this section dictates such extreme measures to protect public health, safety and welfare.

[A] 111.3 Summary abatement. Where conditions exist that are deemed hazardous to life and property, the *fire code official* or fire department official in charge of the incident is authorized to abate summarily such hazardous conditions that are in violation of this code.

❖ As indicated in the commentary to Section 111.1.1, the fire code official is authorized to seek abatement action by the building department and bill the owner for abatement costs. Obviously, this is an extreme measure and should be done only when the owner, operator or occupant does not take such measures under the requirements of Section 111.4.

[A] 111.4 Abatement. The *owner*, the owner's authorized agent, operator or occupant of a building or premises deemed unsafe by the *fire code official* shall abate or cause to be abated or corrected such unsafe conditions either by repair, rehabilitation, demolition or other *approved* corrective action.

❖ This section describes the usual circumstance in which a building has such critical violations that it is declared unsafe by the fire code official. The owner, owner's authorized agent, operator or occupant should take abatement measures to correct the unsafe condition. If this is not done promptly, the fire code official has the authority to directly abate the unsafe conditions and bill the owner for the abatement work in accordance with Sections 111.1.1 and 111.3.

SECTION 112 STOP WORK ORDER

[A] 112.1 Order. Where the *fire code official* finds any work regulated by this code being performed in a manner contrary to the provisions of this code, or in a dangerous or unsafe manner, the *fire code official* is authorized to issue a stop work order.

❖ The fire code official is authorized to issue a stop work order when the work does not comply with the code. Obviously, this is an extreme and costly measure that should be reserved for situations in which the violation is a serious safety hazard.

[A] 112.2 Issuance. A stop work order shall be in writing and shall be given to the *owner* of the property, or to the *owner's* authorized agent, or to the person doing the work. Upon issuance of a stop work order, the cited work shall immediately cease. The stop work order shall state the reason for the order, and the conditions under which the cited work is authorized to resume.

❖ The stop work order is to be in writing and must cite the reason for issuing the order.

Upon receipt of a violation notice from the fire code official, all construction activities identified in the notice must immediately cease, except as expressly permitted to correct the violation.

Construction activities that are outside of the scope of the issue involved with the stop work order are not affected and need not stop; thus, the scope of the order must be clearly stated.

[A] 112.3 Emergencies. Where an emergency exists, the *fire code official* shall not be required to give a written notice prior to stopping the work.

❖ This section gives the fire code official the authority to stop the work in dispute immediately when, in his or her opinion, there is an unsafe emergency condition that has been created by the work. The need for the written notice is suspended for this situation so that the work can be stopped immediately. After the work is stopped, immediate measures should be taken to correct the work at issue.

[A] 112.4 Failure to comply. Any person who shall continue any work after having been served with a stop work order, except such work as that person is directed to perform to remove a violation or unsafe condition, shall be liable to a fine of not less than **[AMOUNT]** dollars or more than **[AMOUNT]** dollars.

❖ The local jurisdiction is to designate the fine that is to apply to any person who continues work that is at issue, other than abatement work. The dollar amounts for the minimum and maximum fines are to be specified in the adopting ordinance.

SECTION 113 SERVICE UTILITIES

[A] 113.1 Authority to disconnect service utilities. The *fire code official* shall have the authority to authorize disconnection of utility service to the building, structure or system in order to safely execute emergency operations or to eliminate an immediate hazard. The *fire code official* shall notify the serving utility and, where possible, the *owner* or the owner's authorized agent and the occupant of the building, structure or service system of the decision to disconnect prior to taking such action. If not notified prior to disconnection, then the *owner*, the owner's authorized agent or occupant of the building, structure or service system shall be notified in writing as soon as practical thereafter.

❖ This section authorizes the fire code official to order the disconnection of building utilities that interfere with emergency operations or contribute to a public safety hazard. This section also provides that such an action must be preceded by written notice to the utility and the owner or owner's authorized agent and occupants of the building. When the hazard to the public health, safety or welfare is so imminent as to mandate immediate disconnection, this section makes it clear that the fire code official has the authority and even the obligation to cause disconnection without notice.

Bibliography

The following resource materials were used in the preparation of the commentary for this chapter of the code:

2009 International Code Interpretations. Washington, DC: International Code Council, 2009.

Complete Revision History to the 2018 I-Codes: Successful Changes and Public Comments. Washington, DC: International Code Council, 2017.

NFPA 550—17, *Fire Safety Concepts Tree*. Quincy, MA: National Fire Protection Association, 2017.

Robertson, J. C. and W.E. Koffel, Jr. *Fire Prevention Organization and Management. Course Guide.* Emmitsburg, MD: Executive Office of the President, U.S. Federal Emergency Management Agency, U.S. Fire Administration, National Fire Academy and Open Learning Fire Service Program, 1990.

Rosenbauer, D. L. *Introduction to Fire Protection Law*. Quincy, MA: National Fire Protection Association, 1978.

Chapter 2: Definitions

General Comments

All terms used in the code and their definitions are listed alphabetically in Chapter 2. While a defined term may be used in one chapter or another, the meaning provided in Chapter 2 is applicable throughout the code.

Where understanding of a term's definition is especially key to or necessary for understanding a particular code provision, the term is shown in italics. This is true only for those terms that have a meaning that is unique to the code. In other words, the generally understood meaning of a term or phrase might not be sufficient or consistent with the meaning prescribed by the code; therefore, it is essential that the code-defined meaning be known.

Guidance regarding tense, gender and plurality of defined terms as well as terms not defined in the code is also provided.

Purpose

Codes, by their very nature, are technical documents. Every word, term and punctuation mark can alter a sentence's meaning and, if misused, muddy its intent.

Further, the code, with its broad scope of applicability, includes terms that have a different meaning than the generally accepted meaning of the term. Additionally, these terms can have multiple meanings depending on the context or discipline in which they are being used.

For these reasons, maintaining a consensus on the specific meaning of terms contained in the code is essential. Chapter 2 performs this function by stating clearly what specific terms mean for the purpose of the code.

SECTION 201 GENERAL

201.1 Scope. Unless otherwise expressly stated, the following words and terms shall, for the purposes of this code, have the meanings shown in this chapter.

❖ This section contains the definitions for application of the code. The use of the words and terms is governed by the provisions of this section. This includes code-defined terms as well as those terms that are not defined in the code, as addressed in Section 201.3.

201.2 Interchangeability. Words used in the present tense include the future; words stated in the masculine gender include the feminine and neuter; the singular number includes the plural and the plural, the singular.

❖ While the definitions are to be taken literally, gender and tense are to be considered interchangeable.

201.3 Terms defined in other codes. Where terms are not defined in this code and are defined in the *International Building Code*, *International Fuel Gas Code*, *International Mechanical Code* or *International Plumbing Code*, such terms shall have the meanings ascribed to them as in those codes.

❖ If a term is not defined in the code but is defined in another volume of the International Codes® (I-Codes®), the definition applies in this code. This adds consistency to the application of the codes.

201.4 Terms not defined. Where terms are not defined through the methods authorized by this section, such terms shall have ordinarily accepted meanings such as the context implies. *Merriam Webster's Collegiate Dictionary, 11th Edition*, shall be considered as providing ordinarily accepted meanings.

❖ Another resource for defining words or terms not defined within the code or other I-Codes is simply their "ordinarily accepted meaning." With some words, a dictionary definition may be sufficient, if the definition is applied within an appropriate context. Not all dictionaries, however, define words the same and not all regions of the world apply the same meanings to all words. The dictionary referenced in this section provides a standardized resource for defining terms and establishing "ordinarily accepted" meanings of words, thus reducing the likelihood of inconsistent enforcement of the code.

Some terms used throughout the code may not be defined in Chapter 2 or in a dictionary. In those cases, the user should first turn to the definitions contained in the referenced standards (see Chapter 80) and then refer to published textbooks on the subject in question.

SECTION 202 GENERAL DEFINITIONS

[BG] 24-HOUR BASIS. The actual time that a person is an occupant within a facility for the purpose of receiving care. It shall not include a facility that is open for 24 hours and is capable of providing care to someone visiting the facility during any segment of the 24 hours.

❖ Care offered over a 24-hour basis is used to differentiate groups and levels of protection between institutional facilities that typically house patients for more than a day, such as hospitals, detoxification facilities, foster care and nursing homes, from other care facilities that keep patients for only part of a day, such as day cares, clinics, day surgery centers and outpatient facilities. To better understand how these concepts work together, see the definitions for "Ambulatory care facility," "Custodial care," "Medical care," "Personal care service" and "Incapable of self-preservation." Facilities that have patients/residents/customers who typically stay for 24 hours or more are considered to be providing care on a 24-hour basis. However, a facility such as a day care or an urgent care facility that operates 24 hours a day would not be considered as providing care on a 24-hour basis if the clients did not stay 24 hours, but instead were in and out of the facility similar to one that closed for the night.

[M]ACCESS (TO). That which enables a device, appliance or equipment to be reached by ready access or by a means that first requires the removal or movement of a panel, door or similar obstruction [see also "Ready access (to)"].

❖ Providing access to devices, appliances and equipment is necessary for facility inspection, observation, maintenance, adjustment, repair or replacement. Access to equipment means that the equipment can be physically reached without having to remove a permanent portion of the structure. It is acceptable, for example, to install equipment in an interstitial space that would require lay-in suspended ceiling panels to be removed to gain access. Devices, appliances and equipment would not be considered as being provided with access if it were necessary to remove or open any portion of a structure other than panels, doors, covers or similar obstructions intended to be removed or opened. Also, see the definition of "Ready access (to)."

Access can be described as the capability of being reached or approached for the purpose of inspection, observation, maintenance, adjustment, repair or replacement. Achieving access may first require the removal or opening of a panel, door or similar obstruction and may require the overcoming of an obstacle such as elevation.

[BE] ACCESSIBLE MEANS OF EGRESS. A continuous and unobstructed way of egress travel from any *accessible* point in a building or facility to a *public way*.

❖ Accessible means of egress requirements are needed to provide those persons with physical disabilities or mobility impairments a means of egress to exit the building. Because of physical limitations, some occupants may need assistance to exit a building. See Section 1009 for requirements establishing areas where people can safely wait for assisted rescue. Chapter 4 also includes requirements in the fire safety and evacuation plans for specific planning to address occupants who may need assistance in evacuation during emergencies. In addition, Chapter 9 of the code includes requirements for emergency evacuation notification for persons with hearing and vision disabilities.

The accessible means of egress requirements may not be the same route as that required for ingress into the building [see Sections 1104 and 1105 of the *International Building Code*® (IBC®)]. For example, a two-story building requires one accessible route to connect all accessible spaces within the building. The accessible route to the second level is typically by an elevator. During a fire emergency, persons with mobility impairments on the second level would move to the exit stairways for assisted rescue, not back the way they entered the level, via the elevator.

[BE] ACCESSIBLE ROUTE. A continuous, unobstructed path that complies with Chapter 11 of the *International Building Code*.

❖ There are typically more physical barriers in the built environment to people with a mobility impairment than in any other category of disability. An accessible route enables a person with a mobility impairment to approach and utilize a facility's accessible fixtures and features. While there are a variety of mobility devices, the design and construction of an accessible route is based predominantly on provisions necessary for accessibility to a person using a wheelchair. Accessible routes are required for both ingress and egress (see Sections 1009 and 1104).

An accessible route must also be safe and usable by people with other disabilities and those without disabilities. Requirements set forth in consideration of those needs include restrictions on objects that protrude into a circulation path in consideration of a person with a visual impairment as well as the possibility of smoke limiting visibility during an emergency.

AEROSOL CONTAINER. A metal can or plastic container up to a maximum size of 33.8 fluid ounces (1000 ml) or a glass bottle up to a maximum size of 4 fluid ounces (118 ml) designed and intended to dispense an aerosol.

❖ All design criteria for the aerosol container, including the maximum size and minimum strength, are set by the US Department of Transportation (DOTn 49 CFR). Section 5103 classifies the different types of aerosol for the purposes of the application of Chapter 51. The DOT container regulations are necessary for the safe transportation of aerosol products. Section 5101.4 emphasizes these size criteria as well.

AEROSOL COOKING SPRAY PRODUCTS. Aerosol cooking spray products are those aerosol products designed to deliver a vegetable oil or a solid or nonflammable liquid to reduce sticking on cooking and baking surfaces, or to be applied to food, or both. These products have a chemical heat of combustion that is greater than 8600 Btu/lb. (20 kJ/g) and contain no more than 18 percent by weight of flammable propellant.

❖ Aerosol cooking sprays have a have a high flash point and were typically addressed as a Class III commodity based on early testing of aerosols by Factory Mutual. However, later tests on this type of commodity showed that protection as a Class III commodity was not sufficient and that the product required protection as a Level 2 or 3 aerosol. Note that the testing did show that it was somewhat less hazardous than a Level 2 aerosol. Due to this, such cooking sprays are specifically defined and have specific requirements in Chapter 51.

AEROSOL PRODUCT. A combination of a container, a propellant and a material that is dispensed. Aerosol products shall be classified by means of the calculation of their chemical heats of combustion and shall be designated Level 1, Level 2 or Level 3.

Level 1 aerosol products. Those with a total chemical heat of combustion that is less than or equal to 8,600 British thermal units per pound (Btu/lb) (20 kJ/g).

Level 2 aerosol products. Those with a total chemical heat of combustion that is greater than 8,600 Btu/lb (20 kJ/g), but less than or equal to 13,000 Btu/lb (30 kJ/g).

Level 3 aerosol products. Those with a total chemical heat of combustion that is greater than 13,000 Btu/lb (30 kJ/g).

❖ The code is intended to regulate those aerosol products that contain a flammable propellant such as butane, isobutane or propane and cannot be protected easily. An aerosol product such as whipped cream is a water-based material with a nonflammable propellant (nitrous oxide) and would, therefore, not be regulated as a hazardous material. Many aerosols are water based and, while containing some flammable material, do not produce a threat to standard commodity protection scenarios. The contents of an aerosol container may be dispensed in the form of a mist, spray, foam, gel or aerated powder.

Because of the wide range of flammability of aerosol products, a classification system was established to determine the required level of fire protection. Categories are defined according to the aerosol's chemical heat of combustion expressed in Btus per pound (Btu/lb). Aerosol category classifications of Levels 1, 2 and 3 are used to avoid confusion with flammable liquid classifications.

Examples of Level 1 aerosol products are air fresheners, shaving gel and whipped cream. Level 1 aerosols are not regulated as a hazardous material and are essentially exempt from the requirements of Sections 307 and 414 of the IBC. Examples of Level 2 aerosols include some hair sprays and insect repellents. Level 3 aerosols include carburetor cleaner and other petroleum-based aerosols.

While aerosols are defined as hazardous materials, note that they are not listed in Table 5003.1.1(1) or 5003.1.1(2) [IBC Table 307.1(1) or 307.1(2)] as having a maximum allowable quantity per control area. As stated in IBC Section 307.1.1, Item 12, a building or structure used for aerosol product storage is classified as Group S-1, provided the requirements of Chapter 51 of the code are satisfied. Therefore, the Group H classification is not utilized since the design must satisfy Chapter 51 of the code in order to be in compliance.

It is important to note that, in dealing with aerosols, the designation of "flammable" on an aerosol can is strictly a consumer warning labeling and must not be confused with the aerosol level printed on the carton. This is important because there are instances where a Level 3 aerosol product requiring the highest level of sprinkler protection will not be flammable for consumer use, and conversely there are instances where a flammable aerosol may be a Level 1 aerosol product and could require only Class III commodity protection in accordance with NFPA 13.

AEROSOL PRODUCT WAREHOUSE. A building used for warehousing aerosol products.

❖ Any building used primarily for storing large quantities of aerosol products would be considered an aerosol warehouse and would be subject to fire safety requirements that are consistent with the types of aerosol products stored and their known hazards. Commodities other than aerosol products are allowed to be stored in an aerosol product warehouse in accordance with Chapter 51 (see Section 5104.4).

AGENCY. Any emergency responder department within the jurisdiction that utilizes radio frequencies for communication. This could include, but not be limited to, various public safety agencies such as fire departments, emergency medical services and law enforcement.

❖ This definition provides clarification as to the primary emergency responders that are intended to be included in the term, but does not rule out other responders who might also need the use of the emergency responders radio coverage system (ERRCS), based on the needs and policies of the adopting jurisdiction.

AGENT. A person who shall have charge, care or control of any structure as *owner*, or agent of the *owner*, or as executor, executrix, administrator, administratrix, trustee or guardian of the estate of the *owner*. Any such person representing the actual *owner* shall be bound to comply with the provisions of this code to the same extent as if that person was the *owner*.

❖ An agent, for purposes of the code, is a person who has full authority under the law to act for or represent the owner of a building subject to the provisions of the code. An agent acts by the authority of the person he or she represents and generally has the same powers as the person represented. It is commonplace for building owners to retain the services of management agents to conduct all affairs pertinent to their building, including code compliance.

[BG] AGRICULTURAL BUILDING. A structure designed and constructed to house farm implements, hay, grain, poultry, livestock or other horticultural products. This structure shall not be a place of human habitation or a place of employment where agricultural products are processed, treated or packaged, nor shall it be a place used by the public.

❖ This definition is needed for the proper application of the utility and miscellaneous occupancy group provisions. The use of the building is quite restricted such that buildings that include habitable or public spaces are not agricultural buildings by definition.

AGRO-INDUSTRIAL. A facility, or portion thereof, housing operations involving the transforming of raw agricultural products into intermediate or consumable products.

❖ This definition coordinates with the requirements in Chapter 28 that have been scoped to address facilities addressing the creation of these products. Providing this definition helps to understand what types of facilities are regulated by Sections 2808 and 2809.

[BG] AIR-INFLATED STRUCTURE. A structure that uses air-pressurized membrane beams, arches or other elements to enclose space. Occupants of such a structure do not occupy the pressurized areas used to support the structure.

❖ This type of membrane structure is characterized by multiple layers arranged such that air-pressurized membrane beams, arches or similar elements are formed. These elements are pressurized with air and form the membrane structure. Note that the occupants of the structure are not subjected to the pressurized areas, because the pressurization is in the structural elements, not within the space used by the occupants. This type of structure is generally much smaller than an air-supported structure and differs in that it depends for support on the inflation of balloon-like sections over, under or around the occupants. The occupants normally are found within a surrounding structure consisting of these inflated sections. Possibly the most common example of this kind of structure is the "Moonwalk" children's entertainment structure, which has an inflated floor structure for children to play on and also inflated columns that support an overhead canopy and plastic mesh walls. Commentary Figure 202-A1 illustrates an air-inflated structure.

[BG] AIR-SUPPORTED STRUCTURE. A structure wherein the shape of the structure is attained by air pressure, and occupants of the structure are within the elevated pressure area. Air supported structures are of two basic types:

❖ An air-supported structure identifies those membrane structures that are completely pressurized for the purposes of supporting the membrane covering. Most "domed" sports arenas use air pressure within the structure to support the membrane covering. The membrane covering can consist of one layer or multiple layers; thus, air-supported structures are classified as either "single skin" or "double skin." Commentary Figure 202-A2 illustrates an air-supported structure.

Double skin. Similar to a single skin, but with an attached liner that is separated from the outer skin and provides an airspace which serves for insulation, acoustic, aesthetic or similar purposes.

❖ A double-skin, air-supported structure contains multiple layers of membrane sheathing. The membranes are usually separated by enough distance to allow for pressurized air or other materials to be inserted between the plies. The pressurized air or other materials usually serve to increase the insulating and acoustical properties.

Single skin. Where there is only the single outer skin and the air pressure is directly against that skin.

❖ A single-skin, air-supported structure consists of just one membrane covering that is directly supported by the interior pressurized air. No other membranes are provided for insulating or acoustical purposes. If the membrane covering consists of several laminated plies, such an arrangement is still considered a single-skin, air-supported structure.

Commentary Figure 202-A1
EXAMPLE OF AIR-INFLATED MEMBRANE STRUCTURE

AIRCRAFT MOTOR-VEHICLE FUEL-DISPENSING FACILITY. That portion of property where flammable or *combustible liquids* or gases used as motor fuels are stored and dispensed from fixed automotive-type equipment into the fuel tanks of aircraft.

❖ Since the first edition of the code, Sections 2003.5 and 2006.1 have required that aircraft motor-vehicle fuel-dispensing facilities comply with Chapter 23. This definition, in addition to the scope statement in Section 2301.1, provides correlation with Chapter 20, making it clear that Chapter 23 does, in fact, apply to aircraft motor-vehicle fuel-dispensing facilities. While the text does not specify limitations on the types of aircraft involved, the typical aircraft that might be brought to a fixed fueling station using equipment similar to that used at automotive service stations, rather than fueling from hydrants or fuel tanker trucks that are used on larger aircraft, would likely be small, general aviation-type aircraft.

AIRCRAFT OPERATION AREA (AOA). Any area used or intended for use for the parking, taxiing, takeoff, landing or other ground-based aircraft activity.

❖ Any area involving aircraft, whether moving or stationary, is known as the aircraft operating area. This area has special operating procedures and hazards.

AIRPORT. An area of land or structural surface that is used, or intended for use, for the landing and taking off of aircraft with an overall length greater than 39 feet (11 887 mm) and an overall exterior fuselage width greater than 6.6 feet (2012 mm), and any appurtenant areas that are used or intended for use for airport buildings and other airport facilities.

❖ Those structures and operations included in an airport are terminal buildings; maintenance hangars; runways; taxiways; loading and unloading of passengers, luggage and freight; and control towers with all the land involved in performing these functions.

[BE] AISLE. An unenclosed *exit access* component that defines and provides a path of egress travel.

❖ Aisles and aisle accessways are both utilized as part of the means of egress in facilities where tables, seats, displays or other furniture may limit the path of travel. The aisle accessways lead to the main aisles that lead to the exits from the space and building (see Commentary Figure 202-A3). While both may result in a confined path of travel, an aisle is an unenclosed component, while a corridor would be an enclosed component of the means of egress. See Sections 1018 and 1029 for requirements for aisles.

[BE] AISLE ACCESSWAY. That portion of an *exit access* that leads to an *aisle*.

❖ As illustrated in Commentary Figure 202-A3, an aisle accessway is intended for one-way travel or limited two-way travel. The space between tables, seats, displays or other furniture (i.e., aisle accessway) utilized for means of egress will lead to a main aisle. See Sections 1018 and 1029 for requirements for aisle accessways.

ALARM, NUISANCE. See "Nuisance alarm."

ALARM DEVICE, MULTIPLE STATION. See "Multiple-station alarm device."

ALARM NOTIFICATION APPLIANCE. A fire alarm system component such as a bell, horn, speaker, light or text display that provides audible, tactile or visible outputs, or any combination thereof. See also "Audible alarm notification appliance" or "Visible alarm notification appliance."

❖ The code requires that fire alarm systems be equipped with approved alarm notification appliances so that in an emergency, the fire alarm system will notify the occupants of the need for evacuation or implementation of the fire emergency plan. Alarm notification devices required by the code are of two general types: visible and audible. Except for emergency voice/alarm communication systems, once the fire alarm system has been activated, all visible and audible communication alarms are required to activate. Emergency voice/alarm communication systems are special signaling systems that are activated selectively in response to specific emergency conditions but have the capability to be activated throughout the building if necessary.

Commentary Figure 202-A2
AIR-SUPPORTED MEMBRANE STRUCTURE—SWIMMING POOL COVER

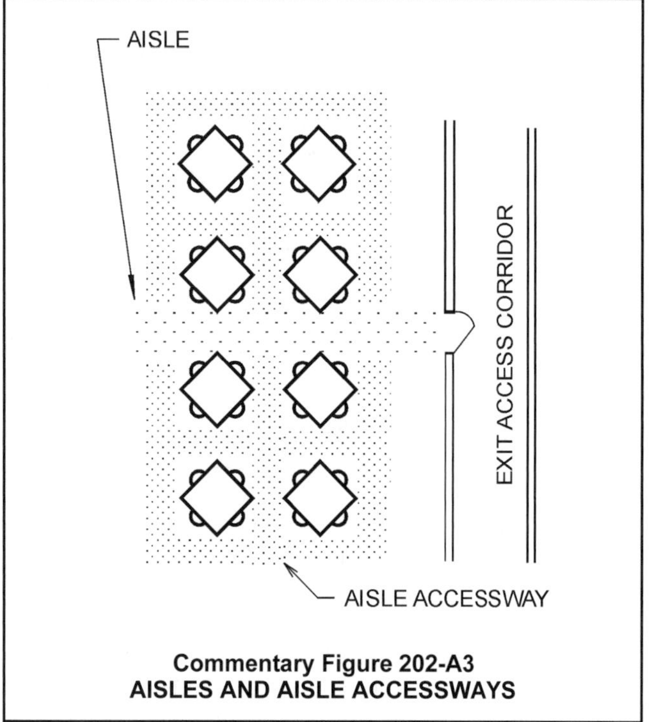

Commentary Figure 202-A3
AISLES AND AISLE ACCESSWAYS

ALARM SIGNAL. A signal indicating an emergency requiring immediate action, such as a signal indicative of fire.

❖ This is a general term for all types of supervisory and trouble signals. An example would be a supervisory (tamper) switch on a sprinkler control valve. It could also be the response to a specific device that is not part of the alarm notification system but causes a specific function, such as a smoke detector for elevator recall. The activation of the device does not necessarily indicate that there is a fire; however, the level of protection may have been compromised (see also the definitions of "Fire alarm signal" and "Supervisory signal").

ALARM VERIFICATION FEATURE. A feature of automatic fire detection and alarm systems to reduce unwanted alarms wherein smoke detectors report alarm conditions for a minimum period of time, or confirm alarm conditions within a given time period, after being automatically reset, in order to be accepted as a valid alarm-initiation signal.

❖ False fire (evacuation) alarms are a nuisance. For this reason the code specifies that alarms activated by smoke detectors are not to be sounded until the alarm signal is verified by cross-zoned detectors in a single protected area or by system features that will retard the alarm until the signal is determined to be valid. Valid alarm initiation signals can be determined by detectors that report alarm conditions for a minimum period of time or, after being reset, continue to report an alarm condition. The alarm verification feature may not retard signal activation for a period of more than 60 seconds and must not apply to alarm-initiating devices other than smoke detectors (which may be connected to the same circuit). Alarm verification is not the same as presignal features that delay an alarm signal for more than 1 minute and that are allowed only where specifically permitted by the authority having jurisdiction.

ALCOHOL-BASED HAND RUB. An alcohol-containing preparation designed for application to the hands for reducing the number of viable microorganisms on the hands and containing ethanol or isopropanol in an amount not exceeding 95-percent by volume.

❖ Alcohol-based hand rub solutions are typically packaged in pump bottles or nonrefillable soft bladders for insertion into a wall-mounted pump dispenser. They are typically closed to the atmosphere with no mixing or refilling of containers, which makes the ignition of fugitive vapors very unlikely. See the commentary to Sections 5705.5 and 5705.5.1 for further information.

As part of ongoing research to control the outbreak of multiple-drug resistant bacteria, such as methicillin-resistant Staphylococcus aureus (MRSA) and vancoymin-resistant Enterococcus (VRE) and similar "super bugs," which are highly resistant to antibiotics, the US Centers for Disease Control (CDC) and Food and Drug Administration (FDA) have continued to study the performance of alcohol-based hand rubs. As a result of their research, both agencies now recommend that the concentration of ethanol or isopropanol in alcohol-based hand rubs be increased to 95 percent by volume. The research found that a higher alcohol concentration offers much more virucidal activity when compared to alcohol-based hand rubs formulated with 70-percent alcohol by volume. To help protect health care workers, hospital patients and long-term care residents against health care-acquired infections, the definition of 11 alcohol-based hand rubs was revised in the 2012 edition of the code to increase the permissible volume of ethyl or isopropyl alcohol from 70 to 95 percent. It should be noted that alcohol-based hand rubs formulated at this concentration are classified as Class IB flammable liquids.

Because of the increased volume of alcohol in alcohol-based hand rubs, and to supplement the original fire test and modeling findings, the heat release rate and burning time of 95-percent ethanol were calculated using formulae found in the *SFPE Handbook of Fire Protection Engineering* and compared to weaker solutions found in older alcohol-based hand rubs. The calculations confirmed that 95-percent ethanol will exhibit the highest heat release (282 kW) when compared to more dilute ethanol/water solutions (146-240 kW) but also exhibits the shortest duration pool fire (83 seconds versus 95 to 119 seconds) because the lack of water allowed quicker volatilization of the fuel.

ALCOHOL-BLENDED FUELS. Flammable liquids consisting of greater than 10 percent, by volume, ethanol or other alcohols blended with gasoline.

❖ Alcohols are polar compounds that exhibit increased moisture absorption, water solubility, polar solvency and solution conductivity relative to gasoline. Alcohol-gasoline blended fuels have unique properties that may affect dispensing equipment and hardware material compatibility and fire response. The most common alcohol blended fuel is E85, which consists of nominally 85-percent ethanol and 15-percent unleaded gasoline. The blending is usually done at the processing plant, or may be accomplished by filling the delivery tanker with the designated percentage of each fuel. In cold climates, the fuel blend may include more gasoline to improve vehicle performance. The properties of E85 are listed in Commentary Figure 202-A4. Ethanol is a flammable, colorless liquid with a faint alcohol odor. The color of ethanol fuel blends depends on the color of the gasoline in the blend. Blends may also have a gasoline-like odor. See the commentary to Section 2306.8 for a more detailed discussion of the hazards presented by these alternative fuels.

[A] ALTERATION. Any construction or renovation to an existing structure other than a repair or addition.

❖ The code utilizes this term to reflect construction operations intended for an existing building but not within the scope of an addition or repair [see the definitions of "Addition" and "Repair" in the *International Existing Building Code*® (IEBC®)]. See IBC Section 101.4.7 for a reference to the IEBC.

[BE] ALTERNATING TREAD DEVICE. A device that has a series of steps between 50 and 70 degrees (0.87 and 1.22 rad) from horizontal, usually attached to a center support rail in an alternating manner so that the user does not have both feet on the same level at the same time.

❖ An alternating tread device is commonly used in areas that would otherwise be provided with a ladder where there is not adequate space for a full stairway. Where these devices are permitted is specifically listed (e.g., Section 1006.2.2.1). The device is used extensively in industrial facilities for worker access to platforms or equipment. Requirements are found in Section 1011.14

[BG] AMBULATORY CARE FACILITY. Buildings or portions thereof used to provide medical, surgical, psychiatric, nursing or similar care on a less-than-24-hour basis to persons who are rendered *incapable of self-preservation* by the services provided or staff has accepted responsibility for care recipients already incapable.

❖ The code provides different requirements for outpatient clinics, ambulatory care facilities and hospitals. Ambulatory care facilities, while still classified as a Group B occupancy, have additional standards above those of an outpatient clinic because its patients are temporarily unable to respond to emergencies due to treatment processes or staff has taken charge of a person who cannot self-evacuate (see commentary, Section 422 of the IBC and the definition for "Incapable of self-preservation"). Ambulatory care facilities include day surgery centers and similar facilities where patients may receive fairly intensive treatment, but do not stay at the facility more than a few hours. If patients are receiving care on a 24-hour basis, such facilities would be defined as hospitals (see definition, "24-hour basis").

Vapor density	Ethanol vapor, like gasoline vapor, is denser than air and tends to settle in low areas. However, ethanol vapor disperses rapidly.
Solubility in water	Fuel ethanol will mix with water, but at high enough concentrations of water, the ethanol will separate from the water.
Energy content	For identical volumes, ethanol contains less energy than gasoline. On an energy basis, 1.0 gallon of E85 is equivalent to 0.72 gallons of gasoline.
Flame visibility	A fuel ethanol flame is less bright than a gasoline flame but is easily visible in daylight.
Specific gravity	Pure ethanol and ethanol blends are heavier than gasoline.
Conductivity	Ethanol and ethanol blends conduct electricity. Gasoline, by contrast, is an electrical insulator.
Toxicity	Ethanol is less toxic than gasoline or methanol. Carcinogenic compounds are not present in pure ethanol; however, because gasoline is used in the blend, E85 is considered to be potentially carcinogenic.
Flammability	At low temperatures, the vapor concentration in an E85 tank can fall into the flammable range. The temperature for flammable E85 vapors depends on the E85 volatility. Although less likely than with E85, gasoline tanks can also contain flammable vapors at extremely low temperature.
Fire fighting	Fuel ethanol fires, like all fires, should be taken seriously. An E85 fire should be handled like a gasoline fire. Use a CO_2 or dry chemical extinguisher that is marked B, BC or ABC. An alcohol-type or alcohol-resistant (ARF) foam may be used to effectively combat fuel ethanol fires. Never use water to control a fire involving high-concentration fuel ethanol such as E85.

For SI: 1 gallon = 3.785 L.

Commentary Figure 202-A4
PROPERTIES OF FUEL ETHANOL

AMMONIUM NITRATE. A chemical compound represented by the formula NH_4NO_3.

❖ Ammonium nitrate is a fairly simple compound (NH_4NO_3), but one that has an extremely complex set of reactions in a fire. The history of ammonium nitrate has been marked by major fires and explosions. Certain characteristics have caused or contributed to these fires and explosions. The following properties of ammonium nitrate are similar to those of other nitrates:

1. It is an oxidizing agent—it contains available oxygen that can make ignition easier and cause a fire to burn with surprising intensity.
2. It is hygroscopic, absorbing moisture from the air or from substances it touches.
3. It is deliquescent—as it absorbs moisture, a portion will liquefy and nearby combustibles can become impregnated with an oxidizing salt.

ANNUNCIATOR. A unit containing one or more indicator lamps, alphanumeric displays or other equivalent means in which each indication provides status information about a circuit, condition or location.

❖ This refers to the panel that displays the status of the monitored fire protection systems and devices. It is not the fire alarm control unit; however, the control panel may function as an annunciator.

[A] APPROVED. Acceptable to the *fire code official*.

❖ As related to the process of acceptance of building installations, including materials, equipment and construction systems, this definition identifies where the ultimate authority rests. Whenever this term is used, it intends that only the enforcing authority can accept a specific installation or component as complying with the code. For the IBC and *International Residential Code*® (IRC®), the "building official" is identified as the person responsible for administering its provisions. For the *International Fire Code*® (IFC®), the "fire code official" is identified as the person responsible for administering IFC provisions. For the *International Energy Conservation Code*® (IECC®), *International Fuel Gas Code*® (IFGC®), *International Green Construction Code*® (IgCC®), *International Mechanical Code*® (IMC®), *International Plumbing Code*® (IPC®), *International Property Maintenance Code*® (IPMC®), *International Swimming Pool and Spa Code*® (ISPSC®) and *International Wildfire-Urban Interface Code*® (IWUIC®), the "code official" is identified as the person responsible.

[BG] AREA, BUILDING. The area included within surrounding *exterior walls* (or *exterior walls* and *fire walls*) exclusive of vent shafts and *courts*. Areas of the building not provided with surrounding walls shall be included in the building area if such areas are included within the horizontal projection of the roof or floor above.

❖ Allowable building areas (as established by the provisions of Chapter 5 and Table 506.2 of the IBC) are a function of the potential fire hazard and the level of fire endurance of the building's structural elements, as defined by the types of construction in Chapter 6 of the IBC. A building area is the "footprint" of the building; that is, the area measured within the perimeter formed by the inside surface of the exterior walls. This excludes spaces that are inside this perimeter and open to the outside atmosphere at the top, such as open shafts and courts (see Section 1205 of the IBC). Where a portion of the building has no exterior walls, the area regulated by Chapter 5 of the IBC is defined by the projection of the roof or floor above [see IBC Commentary Figure 202(5)]. The roof overhang on portions of a building where there are exterior enclosure walls does not add to the building area because the area is defined by exterior walls.

[BE] AREA OF REFUGE. An area where persons unable to use *stairways* can remain temporarily to await instructions or assistance during emergency evacuation.

❖ The area of refuge is a temporary waiting area used during emergency evacuations for persons who are unable to exit the building using the stairways. The fire safety plans (in accordance with Section 404) include the locations of areas of refuge so that the fire department will know where people may be waiting for rescue assistance. See Section 1009 for where areas of refuge are required at stairways and elevators. Areas of refuge have requirements for separation, size, signage, instructional information and two-way communication systems.

ARRAY. The configuration of storage. Characteristics considered in defining an array include the type of packaging, flue spaces, height of storage and compactness of storage.

❖ This term defines the configuration of storage, with its essential components being the manner in which the commodity is packaged (stored either in piled formation or on a rack storage system); the amount of flue space between formations of the commodity; height, width and length of any one array; and compactness.

ARRAY, CLOSED. A storage configuration having a 6-inch (152 mm) or smaller width vertical flue space that restricts air movement through the stored commodity.

❖ The term "closed array" was effectively defined as the result of a number of fire tests. These tests were conducted with the sample test assembly array employing 6-inch-wide (152 mm) longitudinal flues and no transverse flues.

[BG] ATRIUM. An opening connecting two or more stories other than enclosed *stairways*, elevators, hoistways, escalators, plumbing, electrical, air-conditioning or other equipment, which is closed at the top and not defined as a mall. Stories, as used in this definition, do not include balconies within assembly groups or mezzanines that comply with Section 505 of the *International Building Code*.

❖ The definition identifies that an atrium is a floor opening or a series of floor openings that connect the environments of adjacent stories. The definition of "Atrium" excludes enclosed stairways, elevators, hoistways and other similar openings in order to clarify that those elements would not fall under the purview as to what is considered an atrium and, therefore, the associated requirements found in Section 404 of the IBC would not apply. What this does not preclude is the inclusion of elevators and open stairways within atriums. Such elements would need to be entirely within the atrium to meet the separation requirements found in Section 404.6 of the IBC. Building features, such as stairways, elevators, hoistways, escalators, plumbing, electrical, air conditioning or other equipment openings, are required to be enclosed in fire-resistance-rated shafts in accordance with Sections 712 and 713 of the IBC. Atriums are specified in Section 712.1.7 of the IBC to address openings in horizontal assemblies. An atrium is not defined by size or use. A series of floor openings that are enclosed with exterior walls, yet open at the roof, would be considered a court and would be exempt from the requirements of Section 404 of the IBC. Balconies associated with assembly occupancies and mezzanines are not considered individual stories that would contribute to the classification of a space as an atrium.

[BG] ATTIC. The space between the ceiling framing of the top *story* and the underside of the roof.

❖ This definition identifies the portion of a building or structure that must meet the requirements specific to attics, such as ventilation (see Section 1202 of the IBC) and draftstopping (see Section 718 of the IBC). Additionally, the IBC has access requirements (see Section 1208 of the IBC) and uniformly distributed live load requirements (see Table 1607.1 of the IBC) for attics. An attic is considered the space or area located immediately below the roof sheathing within the roof framing system of a building. Pitched roof systems, such as gabled, hip, sawtoothed or curved roofs, all create spaces between the roof sheathing and ceiling membrane, which are considered attics.

AUDIBLE ALARM NOTIFICATION APPLIANCE. A notification appliance that alerts by the sense of hearing.

❖ Audible alarms that are part of a fire alarm system must be loud enough to be heard in every occupied space of a building. Section 907.5.2.1.1 prescribes the minimum sound pressure level for all audible alarm notification appliances depending on the occupancy of the building and the function of the space.

AUTOMATED RACK STORAGE. Automated rack storage is a stocking method whereby the movement of pallets, products, apparatus or systems are automatically controlled by mechanical or electronic devices.

❖ This definition for automated rack storage systems applies to storage and retrieval systems designed for movement of palletized loads commonly used in warehouses containing extra-high-rack storage of Class I-IV commodities over 40 feet (12 192 mm) in height or high-hazard commodities over 30 feet (9144 mm) in height. Conventional material-handling equipment such as forklifts generally cannot be used above this height to safely retrieve or store palletized loads. It is not uncommon for these systems to be used in buildings with roof heights over 100 feet (30 480 mm). NFPA 13 has no limit on the height of storage racks. See also the commentary to Section 3209.4.

AUTOMATIC. As applied to fire protection devices, a device or system providing an emergency function without the necessity for human intervention and activated as a result of a predetermined temperature rise, rate of temperature rise or combustion products.

❖ This term, when used in conjunction with fire protection systems or devices, means that the system or device will perform its intended function without a person being present or performing any task in its control or operation. The device or system has the inherent capability to detect a developing fire condition and perform some predetermined function.

AUTOMATIC FIRE-EXTINGUISHING SYSTEM. An *approved* system of devices and equipment which automatically detects a fire and discharges an *approved* fire-extinguishing agent onto or in the area of a fire.

❖ This term is the generic name for all types of automatic fire-extinguishing systems, including the most common type—the automatic sprinkler system. See Section 904 for requirements for particular alternative automatic fire-extinguishing systems, such as wet-chemical, dry-chemical, foam, carbon dioxide, Halon, clean-agent systems and automatic water mist.

AUTOMATIC SMOKE DETECTION SYSTEM. A fire alarm system that has initiation devices that utilize smoke detectors for protection of an area such as a room or space with detectors to provide early warning of fire.

❖ Chapter 9 provides requirements for various automatic fire protection systems including automatic fire detection system, automatic sprinkler system, automatic fire alarm system, and automatic smoke detection system. Automatic smoke detection systems are required for various occupancies as specified in Section 907. They are required to increase the likelihood that fire is detected and occupants of the building are given an early warning of danger.

AUTOMATIC SPRINKLER SYSTEM. An *automatic sprinkler system*, for fire protection purposes, is an integrated system of underground and overhead piping designed in accordance with fire protection engineering standards. The system includes a suitable water supply. The portion of the system above the ground is a network of specially sized or hydraulically designed piping installed in a structure or area, generally overhead, and to which automatic sprinklers are connected in a systematic pattern. The system is usually activated by heat from a fire and discharges water over the fire area.

❖ An automatic sprinkler system is one type of automatic fire-extinguishing system. Automatic sprinkler systems are the most common, and their life safety attributes are widely recognized. The code specifies three types of automatic sprinkler systems: one installed in accordance with NFPA 13, one in accordance with NFPA 13R and the other in accordance with NFPA 13D. To be considered for most code design alternatives, a building automatic sprinkler system must be installed throughout in accordance with NFPA 13 (see Section 903.3.1.1).

In a fire, sprinklers automatically open and discharge water onto the fire in a spray pattern that is designed to contain or extinguish the fire. Originally, automatic sprinkler systems were developed just for the protection of buildings and their contents. Because of the development and improvements in sprinkler head response time and water distribution, however, automatic sprinkler systems are now also considered a life safety system. Proper operation of an automatic sprinkler system requires careful selection of the sprinkler heads so that water in sufficient quantity at adequate pressure and properly distributed will be available to suppress the fire. Note that the use of the term "fire area" in the last sentence of the definition refers to the area in which the fire is occurring, not to the defined term "fire area."

There are many different types of automatic sprinkler systems—wet pipe, dry pipe, preaction, antifreeze and various combinations. Sprinklers can be pendant, upright or sidewall and can be designed for standard or extended coverage. Additional information can be found in NFPA 13.

AUTOMATIC WATER MIST SYSTEM. A system consisting of a water supply, a pressure source and a distribution piping system with attached nozzles which, at or above a minimum operating pressure, defined by its listing, discharges water in fine droplets meeting the requirements of NFPA 750 for the purpose of the control, suppression or extinguishment of a fire. Such systems include wet-pipe, dry-pipe and pre-action types. The systems are designed as engineered, preengineered, local-application or total flooding systems.

❖ The code recognizes water mist systems as an alternative extinguishing system to automatic sprinkler systems. However, no exceptions, reductions or tradeoffs for water mist systems are granted or permitted by the code because such systems are not considered to be equivalent to automatic sprinkler systems. Automatic water mist systems have been approved by FM Global for occupancies similar to a Light Hazard Group (as defined by NFPA 13) and listed by UL for occupancies similar to Ordinary Hazard Group I (as defined by NFPA 13). These listings permit automatic water mist systems to be installed as the primary suppression systems in a variety of occupancy classifications.

Water mist systems create a heat absorbent vapor consisting of water droplets with a size of less than 1,000 microns at the discharge nozzle. These systems are typically used where water damage may be an issue or where water supplies are limited. The droplet size can be controlled by adjusting the discharge pressure through the nozzle. Creating a mist and an equal volume of water will create a larger total service area exposed to the fire and thus better facilitate the absorption of heat, allowing more water droplets to turn to steam more quickly and thus more effectively cool the room.

AUTOMOTIVE MOTOR FUEL-DISPENSING FACILITY. That portion of property where flammable or *combustible liquids* or gases used as motor fuels are stored and dispensed from fixed equipment into the fuel tanks of motor vehicles.

❖ Automotive motor fuel-dispensing facilities may be attended or unattended and they may take the form of the conventional motor fuel-dispensing facility, convenience store or other location that transfers fuel from a storage tank to the fuel tank of some type of motorized equipment. Motor fuel-dispensing facilities are classified in occupancy Group M by the IBC.

AVERAGE AMBIENT SOUND LEVEL. The root mean square, A-weighted sound pressure level measured over a 24-hour period, or the time any person is present, whichever time period is less.

❖ The ambient noise that can be expected depends on the occupancy of the building. To attract the attention of the occupants, audible alarm devices must be heard above the ambient noise in the space. For this reason, the alarm devices must have minimum sound pressure levels above the average ambient sound level. Section 907.5.2.1.1 prescribes the minimum sound pressure levels for audible alarm notification appliances for all occupancy conditions.

Although it is possible to measure the ambient sound within an occupied space, alarm notification devices are usually designed and installed before buildings are occupied, thus it is typically a careful analysis of the types of uses within a space that will determine the average ambient sound level. If, after the building is occupied, the alarm notification devices are below expected audibility, a field measurement may be necessary to determine whether the design assumptions were correct.

[BG] AWNING. An architectural projection that provides weather protection, identity or decoration and is partially or wholly supported by the building to which it is attached. An awning is comprised of a lightweight frame structure over which a covering is attached.

❖ Similar to a canopy, an awning typically provides weather protection, signage or decoration. Its distinguishing characteristic is the lightweight frame structure. It is also supported, at least in part, by the building from which it projects. See Section 3105 of the IBC for general requirements and Section 3202 of the IBC for encroachment requirements. This definition helps to clarify the applicability of roof loads in Section 1607.13.4 of the IBC. Also see the definitions of "Retractable awning," "Canopy" and "Marquee" in the IBC.

[BE] BALANCED DOOR. A door equipped with double-pivoted hardware so designed as to cause a semicounter balanced swing action when opening.

❖ Balanced doors are commonly used to decrease the force necessary to open the door or to reduce the length of the door swing. Balanced doors typically reduce the clear opening width more than normally hinged doors (see Commentary Figure 202-B1 and Section 1010.1.10.2).

BALED COTTON. See "Cotton."

BALED COTTON, DENSELY PACKED. See "Cotton."

BARRICADE. A structure that consists of a combination of walls, floor and roof, which is designed to withstand the rapid release of energy in an explosion and which is fully confined, partially vented or fully vented; or other effective method of shielding from *explosive materials* by a natural or artificial barrier.

Artificial barricade. An artificial mound or revetment with a minimum thickness of 3 feet (914 mm).

Natural barricade. Natural features of the ground, such as hills, or timber of sufficient density that the surrounding exposures that require protection cannot be seen from the magazine or building containing *explosives* when the trees are bare of leaves.

❖ The definition describes the effective screening of a building containing explosives by means of a natural or artificial barrier from a magazine, another building, a railway or a highway.

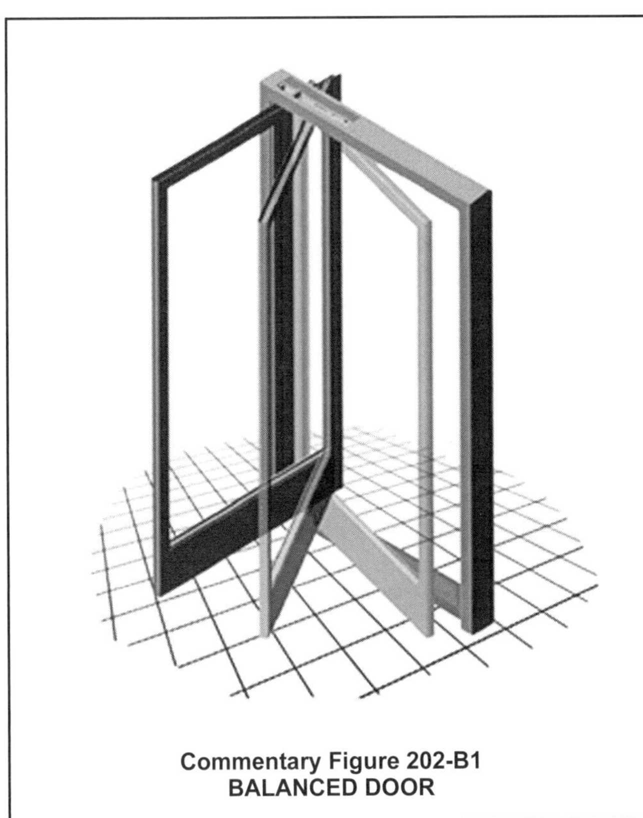

Commentary Figure 202-B1
BALANCED DOOR

Native land features capable of protecting adjacent buildings, people and property from blast effects if an explosion in a magazine occurs may qualify as reduced separation distances permitted by Table 5604.5.2(2). Trees and other ground cover must be thick enough for effective visual screening for the magazine when the branches are bare of leaves or other seasonal foliage.

BARRICADED. The effective screening of a building containing *explosive materials* from the magazine or other building, railway or highway by a natural or an artificial barrier. A straight line from the top of any sidewall of the building containing *explosive materials* to the eave line of any magazine or other building or to a point 12 feet (3658 mm) above the center of a railway or highway shall pass through such barrier.

❖ Natural or artificial barriers must exist or be constructed to qualify for the separation distance reductions allowed in Table 5604.5.2(1). These barriers are intended to provide protection for people and property equivalent to the larger separation distances by absorbing or deflecting blast effects and debris from explosions involving magazines. Commentary Figure 202-B2 illustrates the arrangement of natural and artificial barricades for protection from two 2,000-pound (908 kg) Type 1 magazines.

[BG] BASEMENT. A story that is not a story above grade plane.

❖ A basement is now defined as a story that has its floor surface below the adjoining ground level and that does not qualify as a story above grade plane (see the commentary to the definition of "Story above grade plane"). IBC Commentary Figure 202.2(7) illustrates the application of the definition of "Story above grade plane." Since a basement is not a story above grade, it does not contribute to the height of the building for the purpose of applying the allowable building height in stories from Table 504.4 of the IBC.

BATTERY SYSTEM, STATIONARY STORAGE. A rechargeable energy storage system consisting of electrochemical storage batteries, battery chargers, controls and associated electrical equipment designed to provide electrical power to a building. The system is typically used to provide standby or emergency power, an uninterruptable power supply, load shedding, load sharing or similar capabilities.

❖ This describes generally what is regulated in Section 1206.2. There are many types of stationary battery systems and they are used for a variety of reasons. Historically used for standby power, emergency power or uninterruptable power supplies, such systems are now also used in a variety of other applications, such as load shedding or sharing. Because of these applications, stationary battery systems are being installed in a much wider variety of locations than in the past.

BATTERY TYPES.

Flow battery. A type of storage battery that includes chemical components dissolved in two different liquids. Ion exchange, which provides the flow of electrical current, occurs through the membrane while both liquids circulate in their respective spaces. The electrolyte is a carbonate mixture or a gelled polymer. The lithium ions are the charge carriers of the battery.

❖ Flow batteries use two different chemicals dissolved in liquids separated by a membrane. These batteries have the possibility of releasing hydrogen and therefore require ventilation. Spill control and neutralization must be addressed as there are liquids involved in these types of batteries. There are various combinations of chemicals used for flow batteries.

Lead-acid battery. A storage battery that is comprised of lead electrodes immersed in sulphuric acid electrolyte.

❖ Lead-acid batteries were one of the original types of batteries specifically regulated by the code. These have been historically used for the telecommunications industry as a backup power supply. Lead-acid batteries contain plates of lead and lead oxide in sulfuric acid solution. The reaction occurs between the lead oxide and lead plate, creating an electrical current. There are generally two types, which are described here:

- **Valve-regulated lead-acid (VRLA) battery.** A lead-acid battery consisting of sealed cells furnished with a valve that opens to vent the battery whenever the internal pressure of the battery exceeds the ambient pressure by a set amount. In VRLA batteries, the liquid electrolyte in the cells is immobilized in an absorptive glass mat (AGM cells or batteries) or by the addition of a gelling agent (gel cells or gelled batteries).

  Valve-regulated lead-acid (VRLA) batteries (sometimes referred to as "gel cells") differ substantially from flooded batteries in design, operation and potential hazard. VRLA-type batteries are uniquely different from traditional liquid electrolyte lead-acid batteries in that they have no liquid electrolyte to flow from the container if it were to break. Also, VRLA batteries do not vent their off-gases to the atmosphere but rather implement an oxygen recombination cycle that minimizes the emissions of gas from the batteries during overcharging. Though these batteries are considered sealed, their design includes spring-controlled valves that vent gases at a pressure threshold of 2 to 5 psig (14 to 34 kPa). These batteries are sometimes mistakenly called "maintenance free"; however, they should be maintained in accordance with the manufacturer's instructions.

- **Vented (flooded) lead-acid battery.** A lead-acid battery consisting of cells that have electrodes immersed in liquid electrolyte. Flooded lead-acid batteries have a provision for the user to add water to the cell and are equipped with a flame-arresting vent, which permits the escape of hydrogen and oxygen gas from the cell in a diffused manner such that a spark or other ignition source outside the cell will not ignite the gases inside the cell.

  There are basically two types of lead-acid storage batteries, which are based on how they are constructed and vented: vented (flooded) or sealed. Vented (flooded) and sealed batteries differ in how they dispose of the hydrogen (explosive in air at 4 percent by volume) and oxygen produced by electrolysis during recharging (off-gassing). In a vented (flooded) battery, these gases are allowed to escape to the atmosphere. In a sealed battery, the gases are contained within the battery cell(s) and recombined with the electrolyte. Because the gases created during battery charging are vented to the atmosphere, distilled water must

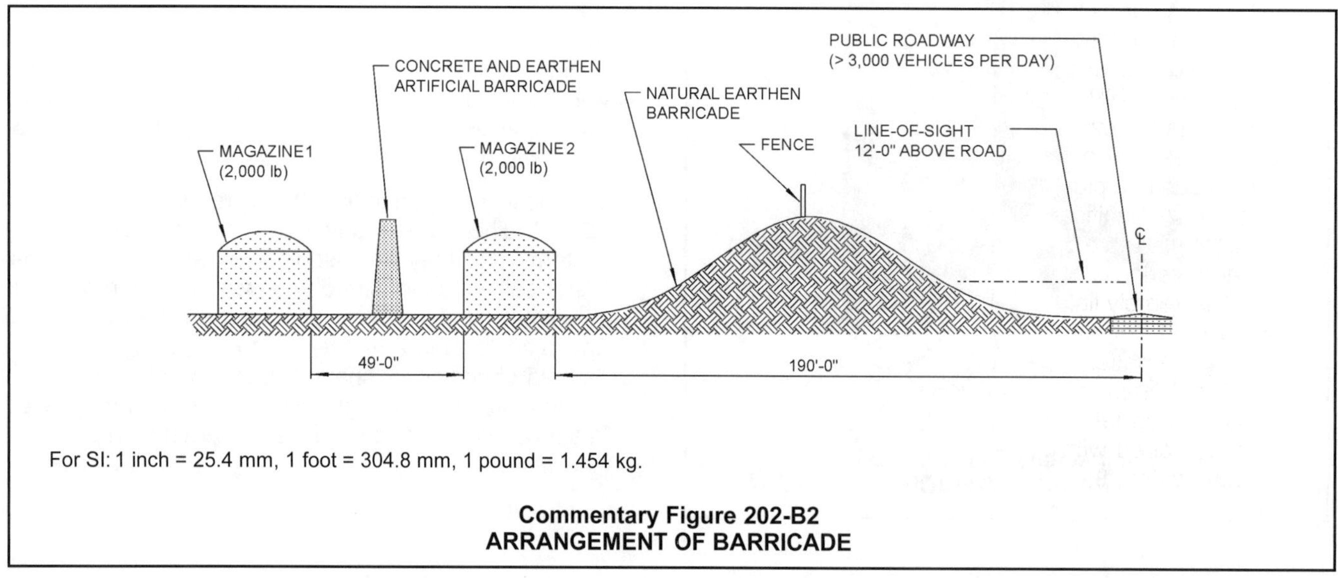

For SI: 1 inch = 25.4 mm, 1 foot = 304.8 mm, 1 pound = 1.454 kg.

Commentary Figure 202-B2
ARRANGEMENT OF BARRICADE

be added periodically to bring the electrolyte level back to that required by the battery specifications. One of the most common types of vented (flooded) lead-acid batteries is the automobile battery.

Lithium-ion battery. A storage battery with lithium ions serving as the charge carriers of the battery. The electrolyte is a polymer mixture of carbonates with an inorganic salt and can be in a liquid or a gelled polymer form. Lithiated metal oxide is typically a cathode and forms of carbon or graphite typically form the anode.

❖ This definition describes a specific type of sealed, nonventing, recombinant storage battery similar to nickel-metal hydride batteries, although not as durable. Lithium-ion batteries, also commonly known as "Li-ion" batteries, are typically lighter than other comparably sized types of rechargeable batteries, which makes them a popular choice for portable devices and automotive applications. They hold their charge well, are generally durable and may be recharged many times. Like other types of sealed batteries with a high-viscocity, immobilized electrolyte, Li-ion batteries have the advantage of not requiring spill control safeguards and also pose a reduced fugitive gas hazard. Lithium-ion batteries, when exposed to prolonged hot conditions with inadequate ventilation, can rupture, ignite, or explode. Li-ion batteries were the subject of a massive battery recall initiative by several computer and cell phone manufacturers due to the Li-ion batteries used in their products overheating from internal contamination defects and causing fires or burn injuries.

Lithium metal polymer battery. A storage battery that is similar to the lithium ion battery except that it has a lithium metal anode in the place of the traditional carbon or graphite anode.

❖ This definition describes lithium metal polymer (LMP) batteries, a specific type of sealed, nonventing storage battery similar to lithium-ion batteries. The LMP battery is similar to the Lithium-ion type in its characteristics (light, energy-dense, no liquid electrolyte, etc.). This technology is becoming more popular for deployment in outdoor cabinets and in buildings as well. Like lithium-ion batteries, LMP batteries use lithium ions as the charge carrier. However, LMP batteries have more lithium because their anode is a solid, thin foil of pure lithium encased in a plastic-like polymer that serves as the electrolyte. A significant advantage of LMP batteries is that they store more energy per unit of weight compared to other batteries using nickel or lead anodes. Lithium is also an extremely light-weight metal when compared to other cathode or anode materials, which results in a rechargeable battery with high energy density.

LMP batteries are constructed with an internal means of thermal runaway management. Each battery is equipped with an internal heating system that is located within the electrochemical stack of anodes and cathodes. This heating element ensures that the battery temperature limits are not exceeded when the battery is being charged or discharged.

These batteries contain no liquid electrolytes or electrolytes suspended in a gel or similar liquids. The electrolyte is a solid lithium-ion that is normally mixed with a rubber polymer that is located between the cathode and anode. Since these batteries do not contain any liquid, the code does not require spill control or a means of neutralization.

While LMP batteries do not have the potential for spills or discharging of hydrogen or oxygen, they still present a potential fire threat if they are somehow overheated and can be a threat to fire fighters because they will be connected to an energized circuit.

Nickel-cadmium (Ni-Cd) battery. An alkaline storage battery in which the positive active material is nickel oxide, the negative contains cadmium and the electrolyte is potassium hydroxide.

❖ This definition describes a specific type of nonrecombinant storage battery. Nickel-cadmium (Ni-Cd) batteries are durable and may be recharged many times. One of the hazards of storage batteries is overcharging. In the case of Ni-Cd batteries, overcharging can produce either hydrogen gas or oxygen that could result in a rupture of the cell casing. Ni-Cd cells are, therefore, provided with safety venting caps to allow the generated gas to escape from inside the cell. See the commentary to Section 1206.2.10.6 for further discussion of vents.

Preengineered stationary storage battery system. An energy storage system consisting of batteries, a battery management system, components and modules that are produced in a factory, designed to comprise the system when assembled on the job site.

❖ These types of battery systems can consist of various technologies but are designed as package with a specific listing. Section 1206.2 addresses these two types of battery systems differently than individual technologies. Prepackaged and preengineered systems must be listed in accordance with UL 9540 which includes compliance with UL 1973. Preengineered and prepacked systems have been approved more as a system versus components and carry with them listings as a system. The rest of the definitions discuss a specific type of battery technology. A preengineered system needs more specific approvals at the site than prepackaged, which is ready to be used once delivered.

Prepackaged stationary storage battery system. An energy storage system consisting of batteries, a battery management system, components and modules that is factory assembled and shipped as a complete unit for installation at the job site.

❖ See definition for "Preengineered stationary storage battery system."

Sodium-beta storage battery. A storage battery, also referred to as a Na-beta battery or NBB, which uses a solid beta-alumina electrolyte membrane that selectively allows sodium ion transport between a positive electrode such as metal halide and a negative sodium electrode.

❖ These batteries contain sodium and thus are potentially water reactive. Sodium beta storage batteries require ventilation due to concerns regarding the production of hydrogen and shouldn't normally be protected with an automatic sprinkler system. Some sodium-based battery systems have designs such that metallic sodium as a separate element will never exist in a case where it could be exposed to water, and thus these types of batteries could potentially be installed in a space where automatic sprinklers are installed.

Stationary storage battery. A group of electrochemical cells interconnected to supply a nominal voltage of DC power to a suitably connected electrical load, designed for service in a permanent location.

❖ The term "stationary storage battery" applies to all battery types made up of multiple electrochemical cells interconnected to supply a nominal voltage of direct current (DC) power. This is a general term used to describe the fact that such installations are stationary versus portable. As the definition of "Battery system, stationary storage" denotes, these are used for a variety of reasons including standby or emergency power, an uninterruptable power supply, load shedding, load sharing or similar capabilities.

BIN BOX. A five-sided container with the open side facing an aisle. Bin boxes are self-supporting or supported by a structure designed so that little or no horizontal or vertical space exists around the boxes.

❖ Proprietary storage systems, such as bin box storage, are common in warehousing and manufacturing industries, such as automotive assembly plants and mail-order mercantile operations. Many bin box systems rely on the rigidity of adjacent bins and interlocking design for stability. Provisions for fastening the self-supporting units together to permit higher stacking are typical in most designs. Other bin box systems are designed in conjunction with a supporting rack system to minimize unusable space between bins. Bin boxes can be constructed of combustible materials, such as wood or cardboard, or of noncombustible materials such as metal.

BIOMASS. Plant- or animal-based material of biological origin excluding material embedded in geologic formations or transformed into fossils.

❖ This term is provided to coordinate with the requirements in Chapter 28 and the inclusion of these materials in the commodity classifications for high-piled combustible storage found in Chapter 32. These materials are becoming more prevalent and guidance is needed in terms of the hazards they pose and how they should be regulated.

BLAST AREA. The area including the blast site and the immediate adjacent area within the influence of flying rock, missiles and concussion.

❖ The area of a blast is affected by flying rock missiles, gases and concussion and also includes the blast site and the immediately adjacent area that is owned, leased or controlled by the blast operator.

BLAST SITE. The area in which *explosive materials* are being or have been loaded and which includes all holes loaded or to be loaded for the same blast and a distance of 50 feet (15 240 mm) in all directions.

❖ The area where explosive material is handled during loading, which includes 50 feet (15 240 mm) in all directions from loaded blast holes or holes to be loaded.

BLASTER. A person qualified in accordance with Section 3301.4 to be in charge of and responsible for the loading and firing of a blast.

❖ In general, the blaster should be qualified, experienced and of sound judgment when performing the duties of blasting. This person is authorized to use explosives for blasting purposes. The blaster is trained and experienced in the use of explosives and licensed by the department.

BLASTING AGENT. A material or mixture consisting of fuel and oxidizer, intended for blasting provided that the finished product, as mixed for use or shipment, cannot be detonated by means of a No. 8 test detonator when unconfined. Blasting agents are labeled and placarded as Class 1.5 material by US DOTn.

❖ This definition is derived from federal explosive regulations and is intended to distinguish blasting agents from more dangerous explosive materials on the basis of their propensity to mass detonate by initiation using a standard device.

[BE] BLEACHERS. Tiered seating supported on a dedicated structural system and two or more rows high and is not a building element (see "*Grandstand*").

❖ Bleachers, folding and telescopic seating and grandstands are essentially unique forms of tiered seating that are supported on a dedicated structural system. All types are addressed in ICC 300, *Standard on Bleachers, Folding and Telescopic Seating and Grandstands*, the safety standard for these types of seating arrangements (see Section 1029.1.1). Bleachers can have backrests or just seatboards. The term "building element" used in Section 1029.1.1 is a defined term in the IBC, which is primarily used in conjunction with the structural elements regulated in Table 601 of the IBC. Bleachers have a separate structural system and are not considered a building element of the building or structure in which they are located. An individual bench seat directly attached to a floor system is not a bleacher. The terms "bleacher" and "grandstand" are basically interchangeable. There is no cut-off in size or number of seats that separates bleachers and grandstands.

[BG] BOARDING HOUSE. A building arranged or used for lodging for compensation, with or without meals, and not occupied as a single-family unit.

❖ A boarding house is a structure where the occupants are provided sleeping accommodations or meals and accommodations for a fee. The individual rooms used usually do not contain all of the permanent living provisions of a dwelling unit (e.g., permanent cooking facilities). Most often, the term "boarding house" describes a facility that is primarily for transient occupants; however, these facilities might also be used for nontransient purposes. Depending on the extent of transiency, a boarding house could be classified as Group R-1 when an occupant typically stays for not more than 30 days or Group R-2 when the length of stay is greater than 30 days. Boarding houses are distinct from lodging houses. Lodging houses allow transient guests within a residence that is also occupied by the owner or primary residents of the dwelling unit. Lodging houses are classified as Group R-3 occupancies.

BOILING POINT. The temperature at which the vapor pressure of a liquid equals the atmospheric pressure of 14.7 pounds per square inch absolute (psia) (101 kPa) or 760 mm of mercury. Where an accurate boiling point is unavailable for the material in question, or for mixtures which do not have a constant boiling point, for the purposes of this classification, the 20-percent evaporated point of a distillation performed in accordance with ASTM D86 shall be used as the boiling point of the liquid.

❖ The purpose of the boiling point is to assist in classifying flammable liquids. The classification of flammable liquids is based on the flash point and the boiling point. When one compares a Class IA liquid and a Class IB liquid, the only difference in their definitions is the boiling point. The lower the boiling point of a flammable liquid, the greater the hazard due to increased vapor pressure at NTP. This information will be found in the safety data sheet (SDS) and must be evaluated by the fire code official.

BONFIRE. An outdoor fire utilized for ceremonial purposes.

❖ Bonfires are usually very large and are associated with a crowd activity. Failure to follow good safety practices with these fires can lead to serious injuries and property damage.

[BE] BREAKOUT. For revolving doors, a process whereby wings or door panels can be pushed open manually for *means of egress* travel.

❖ In addition to swinging doors in the immediate area, revolving doors have a breakout feature as an additional safety requirement. The panels in the door can be operated manually to collapse or fold in the direction of egress during an emergency. This should increase the number of people that could exit per minute compared to using the revolving door in the standard manner.

BRITISH THERMAL UNIT (BTU). The heat necessary to raise the temperature of 1 pound (0.454 kg) of water by 1°F (0.5565°C).

❖ This definition describes the English unit of heat used throughout the document. A British thermal unit (Btu) is used as a way to describe the heat content of combustibles. The metric equivalent of a Btu is a joule. This term should not be confused with heat release rate. Heat release rate would be described as Btu per second (joule per second = watt).

[A] BUILDING. Any structure utilized or intended for supporting or sheltering any occupancy.

❖ The code uses this term to identify those structures that provide shelter for a function or activity. See the definition for "Area, building" for situations when a single structure may be two or more "Buildings" created by fire walls.

BUILDING AREA. See "Area, building."

BUILDING HEIGHT. See "Height, building."

[A] BUILDING OFFICIAL. The officer or other designated authority charged with the administration and enforcement of the *International Building Code*, or a duly authorized representative.

❖ The statutory power to enforce the building code is normally vested in a building department of a state, county or municipality that has a designated enforcement officer termed the "building official" (see Section 103.1 of the IBC).

BULK OXYGEN SYSTEM. An assembly of equipment, such as oxygen storage containers, pressure regulators, safety devices, vaporizers, manifolds and interconnecting piping, that has a storage capacity of more than 20,000 cubic feet (566 m^3) of oxygen at *normal temperature and pressure (NTP)* including unconnected reserves on hand at the site. The bulk oxygen system terminates at the point where oxygen at service pressure first enters the supply line. The oxygen containers can be stationary or movable, and the oxygen can be stored as a gas or liquid.

❖ As indicated in Section 6301.1, NFPA 55 contains installation and maintenance requirements for bulk oxygen systems. NFPA 55 also has the requirements for the protection of bulk oxygen systems from potential fire exposures. Oxygen storage systems with less than the capacities indicated in the definition are not required to comply with NFPA 55, but are regulated by this chapter.

BULK PLANT OR TERMINAL. That portion of a property where flammable or *combustible liquids* are received by tank vessel, pipelines, tank car or tank vehicle and are stored or blended in bulk for the purpose of distributing such liquids by tank vessel, pipeline, tank car, tank vehicle, portable tank or container.

❖ All of us have seen the large storage tanks surrounded by containment berms that constitute what is commonly called a "tank farm." A facility of this kind may consist of one tank or several tanks and typically receives, stores and dispenses anywhere from thousands of gallons to hundreds of thousands of gallons of flammable or combustible liquids daily.

BULK TRANSFER. The loading or unloading of flammable or *combustible liquids* from or between tank vehicles, tank cars or storage tanks.

❖ This term refers to the loading or unloading of a flammable or combustible liquid from or between storage tanks, tank vehicles or tank cars or any combination thereof. See also the definition of "Process transfer" and Section 5706.5. This transfer is for the storage or transportation of flammable or combustible liquids.

BULLET RESISTANT. Constructed so as to resist penetration of a bullet of 150-grain M2 ball ammunition having a nominal muzzle velocity of 2,700 feet per second (fps) (824 mps) when fired from a 30-caliber rifle at a distance of 100 feet (30 480 mm), measured perpendicular to the target.

❖ Tests to determine bullet resistance are to be conducted on test panels or empty magazines. The panels or magazines are to resist a penetration of five out of five shots placed independently of each other in an area at least 3 feet by 3 feet (0.9 m by 0.9 m). If hardwood or softwood is used, its water content is not to exceed 15 percent.

Where a magazine roof or ceiling is required to be bullet resistant, it must be constructed of materials comparable to the sidewalls or of other materials that can withstand the penetration of bullets fired at an angle of 45 degrees (0.79 rad) from perpendicular.

CANOPY. A structure or architectural projection of rigid construction over which a covering is attached that provides weather protection, identity or decoration, and may be structurally independent or supported by attachment to a building on one end and by not less than one stanchion on the outer end.

❖ A canopy can be either an architectural projection from a building, or it can be an independent structure. Examples of the former might be found covering entrance walkways in front of hotels, apartment buildings or upscale restaurants. An example of the latter is a canopy built over fuel pumps at a gasoline station. This definition distinguishes a canopy from an awning, which consists of a lightweight frame that is supported by the building from which it projects. In doing so, the definition clarifies the applicability of roof loads in Section 1607.13.4 of the IBC. See Section 3105 of the IBC for general requirements and Section 3202 of the IBC for encroachment requirements. Commentary Figures 202-C1, 202-C2 and 202-C3 illustrate types of canopies.

CAPACITOR ARRAY. An arrangement of individual capacitor modules in close proximity to each other, mounted on storage racks or in cabinets or other enclosures.

❖ Chapter 12 addresses energy storage systems. Among the specific systems addressed are capacitor energy storage systems. Included in the require-

Commentary Figure 202-C1
EXAMPLE OF A FREE-STANDING MEMBRANE-COVERED CANOPY

Commentary Figure 202-C2
EXAMPLE OF A CANOPY SUPPORTED BY A BUILDING AND STANCHION

Commentary Figure 202-C3
EXAMPLE OF A FREE-STANDING MOTOR FUEL-DISPENSING FACILITY CANOPY

ments associated with such systems as part of the risk management approach is the spacing of capacitor arrays from one another. Each array is limited by Section 1206.3.2.3 to 50 kWh.

CAPACITOR ENERGY STORAGE SYSTEM. A stationary, rechargeable energy storage system consisting of capacitors, chargers, controls and associated electrical equipment designed to provide electrical power to a building or facility. The system is typically used to provide standby or emergency power, an uninterruptable power supply, load shedding, load sharing or similar capabilities.

Preengineered capacitor energy storage system. A capacitor energy storage system consisting of capacitors, an energy management system, components and modules that are produced in a factory, designed to comprise the system when assembled on the job site.

Prepackaged capacitor energy storage system. A capacitor energy storage system consisting of capacitors, an energy management system, components and modules that is factory assembled and then shipped as a complete unit for installation at the job site.

❖ Capacitor energy storage systems are addressed in Section 1206.3 of this code where the capacity exceeds 3 kWh. Chapter 12 addresses stationary battery systems and stationary fuel cell power systems as well. This definition makes clear what specifically is being regulated. These types of systems are of concern without regulation due to the amount of energy they store and how they may be a source of a fire or contribute to a fire and pose a risk to fire fighters. These systems are being installed in new and existing buildings. See commentary for Section 1206.3.

Based on specific allowances and requirements for preengineered and prepackaged capacitor energy storage systems, definitions are provided. Both are assembled in a factory. Preengineered systems are capacitor energy storage systems designed as a complete unit. Prepackaged are also assembled in a factory but are made up of separate manufactured components. These two types of systems require listing in accordance with UL 9540 in addition to the requirements of Section 1206.3.

CARBON DIOXIDE ENRICHMENT SYSTEM. A system where carbon dioxide gas is intentionally introduced into an indoor environment, typically for the purpose of stimulating plant growth.

❖ This term is provided to correlate with the requirements in Section 5307.4. Such systems are prevalent in greenhouses where the introduction of CO_2 enhances the growing process. The concern is that CO_2 is an asphyxiant; therefore, such systems must provide certain safety controls to protect occupants. One of the key elements of these controls includes gas detection to address slow leaks causing long-term effects and larger releases that cause acute life safety hazards. See the commentaries to Sections 5307.4 through 5307.4.7.

CARBON DIOXIDE EXTINGUISHING SYSTEM. A system supplying carbon dioxide (CO_2) from a pressurized vessel through fixed pipes and nozzles. The system includes a manual- or automatic-actuating mechanism.

❖ Carbon dioxide (CO_2) extinguishing systems are useful in extinguishing fires in specific hazards or equipment in occupancies where an inert electrically nonconductive medium is essential or desirable and where cleanup of other extinguishing agents, such as dry-chemical residue, presents a problem. The system works by displacing the oxygen in an enclosed area by flooding the space with carbon dioxide. To effectively flood the enclosure, automatic door and window closers and control dampers for the mechanical ventilation system must be installed.

These types of gaseous extinguishing systems have some inherent disadvantages that should be considered before selection. Because the oxygen is being displaced, occupants should not be in the space for a period after discharge, depending on the concentration of CO_2 to be achieved. Additionally, the discharge rate can result in a rapid increase in pressure within the space where the system is discharged. Where water is not a desired means of suppression, carbon dioxide and other gaseous suppression systems can be very effective. NFPA 12 contains minimum requirements for the design, installation, testing, inspection, approval, operation and maintenance of carbon dioxide extinguishing systems.

CARBON MONOXIDE ALARM. A single- or multiple-station alarm intended to detect carbon monoxide gas and alert occupants by a distinct audible signal. It incorporates a sensor, control components and an alarm notification appliance in a single unit.

❖ The definitions of "Carbon monoxide alarm" and "Carbon monoxide detector" are provided to differentiate between the two types of detection devices. Both terms are used in Section 915 and are addressed by different standards. Alarms must comply with UL 2034, whereas detectors that are part of a larger system and are simply sensors that transmit a signal to the system are required to comply with UL 2075.

CARBON MONOXIDE DETECTOR. A device with an integral sensor to detect carbon monoxide gas and transmit an alarm signal to a connected alarm control unit.

❖ See the commentary to the definition of "Carbon monoxide alarm." Also note that carbon monoxide detection systems are required by Section 915.5.1 to comply with NFPA 720.

[BG] CARE SUITE. In Group I-2 occupancies, a group of treatment rooms, care recipient sleeping rooms and the support rooms or spaces and circulation space within the suite where staff are in attendance for supervision of all care recipients within the suite, and the suite is in compliance with the requirements of Section 407.4.4 of the *International Building Code*.

❖ Care suites are designed to allow for a group of rooms to function as a unit in the treatment and care of patients. Suites provide flexibility in reaching an exit access. Use of suites is a particularly useful tool at intensive care units and emergency departments in patient treatment areas. Suites allow staff to have clear and unobstructed supervision of patients/care recipients in specific treatment and sleeping rooms through the elimination of corridor width or rating requirements. The term is not intended to apply to day rooms or business sections of the hospital. This term is only applicable to suites of patient rooms in Group I-2 occupancies, and should not be confused with similar layouts in other parts of the hospital or within other occupancies that may be referred to as a "suite." Care suites are to meet the requirements of Section 407 of the IBC.

CARTON. A cardboard or fiberboard box enclosing a product.

❖ This term is commonly used when applying the high-piled storage requirements of Chapter 32 and also for packaging of aerosols in Chapter 51. This definition provides a consistent understanding of a word often used to describe packaging.

CEILING LIMIT. The maximum concentration of an airborne contaminant to which one may be exposed. The ceiling limits utilized are those published in DOL 29 CFR Part 1910.1000. The ceiling Recommended Exposure Limit (REL-C) concentrations published by the US National Institute for Occupational Safety and Health (NIOSH), Threshold Limit Value-Ceiling (TLV-C) concentrations published by the American Conference of Governmental Industrial Hygienists (ACGIH), Ceiling Workplace Environmental Exposure Level (WEEL-Ceiling) Guides published by the American Industrial Hygiene Association (AIHA), and other *approved*, consistent measures are allowed as surrogates for hazardous substances not listed in DOL 29 CFR Part 1910.1000.

❖ This limit is the concentration at which immediate irritation to skin, respiratory system or both will occur. This is an important level for emergency personnel and workers to be aware of. Mechanical ventilation may be used to assist in keeping the working environment below these levels.

[A] CHANGE OF OCCUPANCY. A change in the use of a building or a portion of a building that results in any of the following:

1. A change of occupancy classification.
2. A change from one group to another group within an occupancy classification.
3. Any change in use within a group for which there is a change in the application of the requirements of this code.

❖ This term describes the condition when an existing building or structure is used for a different use or the same use with an increase in the level of activity (see Section 101.4.7 for a reference to the IEBC). This term is only applicable to existing buildings, never new ones. For example, Group B includes both beauty parlors and post offices. If a beauty shop moved into an old post office, while remaining a Group B building, there would be a change in the level of activity; therefore, this would be considered a change of occupancy.

CHEMICAL. An element, chemical compound or mixture of elements or compounds or both.

❖ Chemicals may be hazardous, in which case the buildings, processes and storage that use them are regulated, or they may be nonhazardous, in which case their storage is regulated. These regulations are typically found in the IBC, IMC, IPC, IFGC and the code.

CHEMICAL FUME HOOD. A ventilated enclosure designed to contain and exhaust fumes, gases, vapors, mists and particulate matter generated within the hood.

❖ This term is used within Chapter 38 regarding higher education laboratories. More specifically, this concept is used for the increases allowed in existing nonsprinklered laboratories. The use of a chemical fume hood is required to allow use of these restricted materials. The specific restricted materials are pyrophorics and Class 4 oxidizers.

CHEMICAL NAME. The scientific designation of a chemical in accordance with the nomenclature system developed by the International Union of Pure and Applied Chemistry, the Chemical Abstracts Service rules of nomenclature, or a name which will clearly identify a chemical for the purpose of conducting an evaluation.

❖ This name can be used to research the product in resource manuals to determine the hazard characteristics of the product. Some examples of resources are: National Toxicology Program (NTP), Chemical Hazards Response Information System (CHRIS) manual, Emergency Response Guidebook (ERG) and SDS.

[M] CHIMNEY. A primarily vertical structure containing one or more flues for the purpose of carrying gaseous products of combustion and air from a fuel-burning appliance to the outdoor atmosphere.

❖ The IFGC and the IMC address the installation of chimneys and venting systems that are required to convey products of combustion from fuel-burning appliances to the atmosphere. The code regulates the maintenance of masonry chimneys in Section 603.6.1. Chimneys differ from metal vents in the materials from which they are constructed and the type of appliance they are designed to serve. Chimneys can vent much hotter flue gases than metal vents.

Factory-built chimney. A listed and labeled chimney composed of factory-made components, assembled in the field in accordance with manufacturer's instructions and the conditions of the listing.

❖ A factory-built chimney is a manufactured listed and labeled chimney that has been tested by an approved agency to determine its performance characteristics.

Factory-built chimneys are manufactured in two basic designs: either a double-wall insulated design or a triple-wall air-cooled design. Both designs use stainless steel inner liners to resist the corrosive effects of combustion products.

Masonry chimney. A field-constructed chimney composed of solid masonry units, bricks, stones, or concrete.

❖ Masonry chimneys can have one or more flues within them, and are field constructed of brick, stone, concrete or fire-clay materials. Masonry chimneys can stand alone or be part of a masonry fireplace.

Metal chimney. A field-constructed chimney of metal.

❖ A metal chimney is an unlisted chimney constructed and installed in accordance with NFPA 211 and is sometimes referred to as a "smokestack." Metal chimneys are typically field constructed and installed in industrial structures.

CLEAN AGENT. Electrically nonconducting, volatile or gaseous fire extinguishant that does not leave a residue upon evaporation.

❖ The two categories of clean agents are halocarbon compounds and inert gas agents. Halocarbon compounds include bromine, carbon, chloride, fluorine, hydrogen and iodine. Halocarbon compounds suppress the fire through a combination of breaking the chemical chain reaction of the fire, reducing the ambient oxygen supporting the fire and reducing the ambient temperature of the fire origin to reduce the propagation of fire. The clean agents that are inert gas agents contain primary components consisting of helium, neon or argon, or a combination of all three. Inert gases work by reducing the oxygen concentration around the fire origin to a level that does not support combustion (see commentary, Section 904.10).

[BG] CLINIC, OUTPATIENT. Buildings or portions thereof used to provide medical care on a less-than-24-hour basis to persons who are not rendered incapable of self-preservation by the services provided.

❖ Outpatient clinics generally consist of doctors' offices where various medical services can be provided. These clinics typically function during normal business hours (i.e., less than 24 hours) and, unlike ambulatory care facilities, the patients are generally ambulatory and capable of self-preservation. This definition clarifies the difference between ambulatory surgery centers (ambulatory care facilities) and the typical doctor's office. In many cities, outpatient clinics are open at all hours to be available to people who work a variety of shifts. The term "urgent care" is often used to describe such facilities. An outpatient facility that is open 24/7 may still be classified as a Group B occupancy, provided that all patients are outpatients and individual patients are not treated for periods in excess of 24 hours. The latter would describe a Group I-2 hospital. See the commentaries to Sections 407 and 422 of the IBC.

CLOSED CONTAINER. A container sealed by means of a lid or other device such that liquid, vapor or dusts will not escape from it under ordinary conditions of use or handling.

❖ A closed container is one that is sealed so that no vapors or dust can escape. An open container is more dangerous and calls for more safety requirements. The fire tetrahedron is made up of fuel, heat, oxygen and a chain reaction. In a closed container, there is only the fuel part of the tetrahedron; an open container provides fuel and oxygen. In this case, a closed container is less hazardous than an open container unless there is a leak.

CLOSED SYSTEM. The use of a solid or liquid hazardous material involving a closed vessel or system that remains closed during normal operations where vapors emitted by the product are not liberated outside of the vessel or system and the product is not exposed to the atmosphere during normal operations; and all uses of *compressed gases*. Examples of closed systems for solids and liquids include product conveyed through a piping system into a closed vessel, system or piece of equipment.

❖ This definition is used primarily with regard to hazardous materials. The difference between a closed system and an open system is whether the hazardous material involved in the process is exposed to the atmosphere. A closed system is inherently less hazardous than an open system due to the fact that vapors, dusts or similar materials are not normally released from closed systems. Because closed systems are less hazardous than open systems, credit is typically given to increase the maximum allowable quantities (MAQ) when systems are considered closed. Materials in closed or open systems are assumed to be "in use" as opposed to "in storage." Gases are always assumed to be in closed systems since they would be immediately dispersed in an open system if exposed to the atmosphere without some means of containment (see the definition of "Open system").

COLD DECK. A pile of unfinished cut logs.

❖ A cold deck is a pile of ranked logs that have different lengths. The lengths are usually greater than 8 feet (2438 mm) and up to 50 feet (15 240 mm) long.

COMBUSTIBLE DUST. Finely divided solid material which is 420 microns or less in diameter and which, when dispersed in air in the proper proportions, could be ignited by a flame, spark or other source of ignition. Combustible dust will pass through a U.S. No. 40 standard sieve.

❖ Combustible dusts are combustible solids in a finely divided state that are suspended in the air. An explosion hazard exists when the concentration of the combustible dust is within the explosive limits and exposed to an ignition source of sufficient energy and duration to initiate self-sustained combustion. A review of the occupancy classification for Group H-2 in Chapter 2 (based on IBC Section 307.4) indicates that combustible dusts are classified in that occupancy group. That section is intended to ensure that, where engineering analysis determines that the dispersion and proportion of combustible dust are such that the dust can be ignited by an ignition source, then the deflagration hazard is sufficient to classify the occupancy in Group H-2. Combustible dust, as a material, that does not rise to that defined level of hazard in a particular building would not cause the building or portion thereof housing the hazard to be classified in Group H-2, but rather in the group that is most appropriate for the particular operation.

The original tabular MAQ per control area for combustible dust, included in the legacy building and fire codes, was deleted because of its questionable value, given the complexities of dust explosion hazards. In the 2012 edition of the code, a row for combustible dust was added to Table 5003.1.1(1) along with a new Note q. The note reinforces the fact that determining a theoretical MAQ of combustible dust and the potential for a dust explosion requires a thorough evaluation and technical report based on the provisions of Section 104.7.2. Such determination is complex and requires evaluation far beyond the simple 1 pound per 1,000 cubic feet (16 g/m^3) MAQ previously used by the legacy codes. Critical factors, such as particle size, material density, humidity and oxygen concentration, play a major role in the evaluation of the dust hazard and are much too complex to be simply addressed.

COMBUSTIBLE FIBERS. Readily ignitable and free-burning materials in a fibrous or shredded form, such as cocoa fiber, cloth, cotton, excelsior, hay, hemp, henequen, istle, jute, kapok, oakum, rags, sisal, Spanish moss, straw, tow, wastepaper, certain synthetic fibers or other like materials. This definition does not include densely packed baled cotton.

❖ Operations involving combustible fibers are typically associated with paper milling, recycling, cloth manufacturing, carpet and textile mills and agricultural operations, among others. The primary hazards associated with such operations involve the abundance of materials and their ready ignitability. Many organic fibers are prone to spontaneous ignition if improperly dried and kept in areas without sufficient ventilation.

The basic component of all textiles is fibers. Fibers may be either natural or man-made. Cellulosic, protein and mineral fibers are considered natural fibers. Fibers produced by chemical processes (nylon, rayon, Orlon, etc.) are considered man-made. The definition clarifies that densely packed baled cotton is not to be considered a hazardous material. The density and packaging arrangements of cotton fibers meeting the definition of "Baled cotton, densely packed" in this section reduce the hazard of the material such that the hazardous materials provisions of the code need no longer apply.

COMBUSTIBLE GAS DETECTOR. An instrument that samples the local atmosphere and indicates the presence of ignitable vapors or gases within the flammable or explosive range expressed as a volume percent in air.

❖ This definition coordinates with the requirements in Section 3510 that provide procedures for undertaking hot work on tanks that have contained flammable or combustible liquids. One of the procedures required is the use of a combustible gas detector to evaluate the conditions of the space while hot work is occurring.

COMBUSTIBLE LIQUID. A liquid having a closed cup flash point at or above 100°F (38°C). Combustible liquids shall be subdivided as follows:

Class II. Liquids having a closed cup flash point at or above 100°F (38°C) and below 140°F (60°C).

Class IIIA. Liquids having a closed cup flash point at or above 140°F (60°C) and below 200°F (93°C).

Class IIIB. Liquids having closed cup *flash points* at or above 200°F (93°C).

The category of combustible liquids does not include *compressed gases* or *cryogenic fluids*.

❖ Combustible liquids differ from flammable liquids in that the closed-cup flash point of all combustible liquids is at or above 100°F (38°C) (see the definition of "Flash point"). The three classes of combustible liquids are dictated by the range of their closed-cup flash point. The flash point range of 100°F (38°C) to 140°F (60°C) for Class II liquids was based on a possible indoor ambient temperature exceeding 100°F (38°C). Only a moderate degree of heating would be required to bring the liquid to its flash point at this temperature. Class III liquids, which have flash points higher than 140°F (60°C), would require a significant heat source above ambient temperature to reach their flash point (see the definition of "Flammable liquid"). Class IIIA has a closed-cup flash point range of 140°F (60°C) to 200°F (93°C). Class IIIB has a closed-cup flash point at or above 200°F (93°C). The term "combustible liquid" does not include liquefied compressed gases or cryogenic fluids. Compressed gases are regulated in Chapter 53 and cryogenic fluids are regulated in Chapter 55.

[M] COMMERCIAL COOKING APPLIANCES. Appliances used in a commercial food service establishment for heating or cooking food and which produce grease vapors, steam, fumes, smoke or odors that are required to be removed through a local exhaust ventilation system. Such appliances include deep fat fryers, upright broilers, griddles, broilers, steam-jacketed kettles, hot-top ranges, under-fired broilers (charbroilers), ovens, barbecues, rotisseries, and similar appliances. For the purpose of this definition, a food service establishment shall include any building or a portion thereof used for the preparation and serving of food.

❖ This definition is important in the application of Section 607, which requires a commercial kitchen hood above commercial cooking appliances. A definition of "Food service establishment" is included within this definition. "Food service" includes operations, such as preparing, handling, cleaning, cooking and packaging food items of any kind.

COMMERCIAL MOTOR VEHICLE. A motor vehicle used to transport passengers or property where the motor vehicle:

1. Has a gross vehicle weight rating of 10,000 pounds (454 kg) or more; or
2. Is designed to transport 16 or more passengers, including the driver.

❖ This definition clarifies what constitutes a "commercial vehicle." This term has often been misinterpreted in previous editions. These criteria are from the DOTn 49 CFR Part 390.5, and correlate with IBC Section 1607.7. Where vehicles of this size are present in buildings greater than 5,000 square feet (464 m^2) in area, the code requires an automatic sprinkler system be provided in repair garages, commercial parking garages and in Group S-1 storage occupancies (see Section 903.2).

COMMODITY. A combination of products, packing materials and containers.

❖ Commodity is a term used to identify the product being stored, its container or housing and the type of stackable mechanism (with or without pallet). Commodities and their containers are generally identified as classes, with each classification identifying the combustibility (potential fire hazard). The quantity and locations of each type of commodity will define the type of general and special fire protection and life safety requirements necessary for the building or structure. See the commentary for the various commodities in Section 3203.

[BE] COMMON PATH OF EGRESS TRAVEL. That portion of *exit access* travel distance measured from the most remote point of each room, area or space to that point where the occupants have separate and distinct access to two *exits* or *exit access* doorways.

❖ The common path of egress travel is a concept used to refine travel distance criteria. A common path of travel is the route an occupant will travel where the one way in is also the one way out, similar to a dead-end corridor or single exit suite. Once occupants reach a point where two different routes are available, and the two different routes continue to two separate exits, then common path of travel is finished. The length of a common path of egress travel is limited so that the means of egress path of travel provides a choice before the occupant has traveled an excessive distance (see Section 1006). This reduces the possibility that, although the exits are remote from one another, a single fire condition will render both paths unavailable. The common path of egress travel is part of the overall exit access travel distance. To be compliant, the path of egress must meet criteria for both common path of egress travel and exit access travel distance.

[BE] COMMON USE. Interior or exterior circulation paths, rooms, spaces or elements that are not for public use and are made available for the shared use of two or more people.

❖ Some buildings include areas that are restricted to employees only or where public access is limited. Common-use spaces may be part of employee work areas but do not include public-use spaces. Any space that is shared by two or more persons, such as copy areas, break rooms, toilet rooms or circulation paths, are common use areas. A grade school classroom would be another example of a common-use space (see also the commentaries for the definition of "Public-use areas" and "Employee work area").

COMPRESSED GAS. A material, or mixture of materials that:

1. Is a gas at 68°F (20°C) or less at 14.7 psia (101 kPa) of pressure; and
2. Has a *boiling point* of 68°F (20°C) or less at 14.7 psia (101 kPa) which is either liquefied, nonliquefied or in solution, except those gases which have no other health- or physical-hazard properties are not considered to be compressed until the pressure in the packaging exceeds 41 psia (282 kPa) at 68°F (20°C).

The states of a compressed gas are categorized as follows:

1. Nonliquefied compressed gases are gases, other than those in solution, which are in a packaging under the charged pressure and are entirely gaseous at a temperature of 68°F (20°C).
2. Liquefied compressed gases are gases that, in a packaging under the charged pressure, are partially liquid at a temperature of 68°F (20°C).
3. Compressed gases in solution are nonliquefied gases that are dissolved in a solvent.
4. Compressed gas mixtures consist of a mixture of two or more compressed gases contained in a packaging, the hazard properties of which are represented by the properties of the mixture as a whole.

❖ This term refers to all types of gases that are under pressure at normal room or outdoor temperatures inside their containers, including, but not limited to, flammable, nonflammable, highly toxic, toxic, cryogenic and liquefied gases. The vapor pressure limitations provide the distinction between a liquid and a gas.

COMPRESSED GAS CONTAINER. A pressure vessel designed to hold *compressed gases* at pressures greater than one atmosphere at 68°F (20°C) and includes cylinders, containers and tanks.

❖ Containers covered by this definition range from the small compressed air tanks carried by some road service trucks to the very large storage tanks mounted on permanent bases at industrial plants. Designs vary considerably depending on the gases they are intended to hold, whether they are designed for upright or horizontal mounting and the environment they will be used in.

COMPRESSED GAS SYSTEM. An assembly of equipment designed to contain, distribute or transport *compressed gases*. It can consist of a *compressed gas* container or containers, reactors and appurtenances, including pumps, compressors and connecting piping and tubing.

❖ This definition is intended to include every component used to convey the gas to or from manufacturing, storage and use facilities. System designs will vary widely depending on their intended use.

[BG] CONGREGATE LIVING FACILITIES. A building or part thereof that contains sleeping units where residents share bathroom and/or kitchen facilities.

❖ Congregate living facilities are those pertaining to group housing (i.e., dormitories, fraternities, convents) that combine individual sleeping quarters with communal facilities for food, care, sanitation and recreation. The number of occupants in the facility determines the appropriate occupancy classification. There are two thresholds: 10 and 16. A congregate living facility with 16 or fewer nontransient residents falls in the R-3 classification. For more than 16 nontransient residents, the classification is R-2. For transient residents, if there are 10 or fewer in the facility, it is also in the R-3 classification. If over 10 transient residents, it is an R-1 occupancy.

CONSTANTLY ATTENDED LOCATION. A designated location at a facility staffed by trained personnel on a continuous basis where alarm or supervisory signals are monitored and facilities are provided for notification of the fire department or other emergency services.

❖ These locations are intended to receive trouble, supervisory and fire alarm signals transmitted by the fire protection equipment installed in a protected facility. The code is intended to have both an approved location and personnel who are acceptable to the fire code official responsible for actions taken when the fire protection system requires attention. The term "constantly attended" implies 24-hour surveillance of the system, at the designated location.

[A] CONSTRUCTION DOCUMENTS. The written, graphic and pictorial documents prepared or assembled for describing the design, location and physical characteristics of the elements of the project necessary for obtaining a permit.

❖ To determine whether proposed construction is in compliance with code requirements, sufficient information must be submitted to the fire code official for review. This definition describes in general which items are to be included in that documentation. This typically will include drawings (floor plans, elevations, sections, details, etc.), specifications and product information describing the proposed work. In the past, these documents were referred to as "plans and specifications." Those terms are not broad enough to include all information, such as calculations or graphs.

CONTAINER. A vessel of 60 gallons (227 L) or less in capacity used for transporting or storing hazardous materials. Pipes, piping systems, engines and engine fuel tanks are not considered to be containers.

❖ This definition establishes the intended capacity of the container to avoid confusion with portable or stationary tanks. A container could include typical 55-gallon (208 L) drums or 2-ounce (59 ml) cans. It is important to note the size difference between a drum and a barrel. A drum has a capacity of 55 US gallons (208 L) and a barrel has a capacity of 42 US gallons (158 L). These terms are sometimes reported incorrectly when determining the amount of storage in a facility.

CONTAINMENT SYSTEM. A gas-tight recovery system comprised of equipment or devices which can be placed over a leak in a *compressed gas* container, thereby stopping or controlling the escape of gas from the leaking container.

❖ A containment system consists of various components that will capture gases from a leaking container by being placed at the source of the leak.

CONTAINMENT VESSEL. A gas-tight recovery vessel designed so that a leaking *compressed gas* container can be placed within its confines thereby encapsulating the leaking container.

❖ A containment vessel is a closed unit in which a leaking container can be placed to fully contain any unwanted release.

CONTROL AREA. Spaces within a building where quantities of hazardous materials not exceeding the *maximum allowable quantities per control area* are stored, dispensed, used or handled. See also the definition of "Outdoor control area."

❖ The use of control areas allows for the use and storage of hazardous materials without classifying the building or structure as a high-hazard Group H occupancy where the total quantity of hazardous materials in the entire building might exceed the MAQ. This concept is based on regulating the allowable quantities of hazardous materials in each control area by giving credit for further compartmentation through the use of fire barriers having a minimum fire-resistance rating of 1 hour. Maximum quantities of hazardous materials within each control area cannot exceed the MAQ for a given material. Thus, the quantities in each control area will be less than the MAQ, while the overall quantity in the entire building could exceed the MAQ (see commentary, Section 5003.8.3).

[BE] CORRIDOR. An enclosed *exit access* component that defines and provides a path of egress travel.

❖ Corridors are regulated in the code because they serve as principal elements of travel in many means of egress systems within buildings. Typically, corridors have walls that extend from the floor to the ceiling. They need not extend above the ceiling or have doors in their openings unless a fire-resistance rating is required (see Section 1020).

While both aisles and corridors may result in a confined path of travel, an aisle is an unenclosed component, while a corridor would be an enclosed component of the means of egress. The enclosed character of the corridor restricts the sensory perception of the user. A fire located on the other side of the corridor wall, for example, may not be as readily seen, heard or smelled by the occupants traveling through the egress corridor. The code does not specifically state what is considered "enclosed" where corridors are not fire-resistance rated. Where an egress path is bounded by partial-height walls, such as work-station partitions in an office, issues would be if the walls provided a confined path of travel and limited fire recognition in adjacent spaces by restricting line of sight, hearing and smell.

CORRIDOR, OPEN-ENDED. See "Open-ended corridor."

CORROSIVE. A chemical that causes visible destruction of, or irreversible alterations in, living tissue by chemical action at the point of contact. A chemical shall be considered corrosive if, when tested on the intact skin of albino rabbits by the method described in DOTn 49 CFR 173.137, such chemical destroys or changes irreversibly the structure of the tissue at the point of contact following an exposure period of 4 hours. This term does not refer to action on inanimate surfaces.

❖ This definition is derived from DOTn 49 CFR Part 173. While corrosive materials may not pose a fire, explosion or reactivity hazard, they do pose a handling and storage problem. Corrosive materials, therefore, are primarily considered a health hazard, and an occupancy containing such materials in excess of the maximum allowable quantity per control area (MAQ) is classified in Group H-4. It should be noted that many corrosive chemicals are also strong oxidizing agents that would require review as a multiple-hazard material in accordance with Section 5001.1.

COTTON.

Baled cotton. A natural seed fiber wrapped in and secured with industry-accepted materials, usually consisting of burlap, woven polypropylene, polyethylene or cotton or sheet polyethylene, and secured with steel, synthetic or wire bands, or wire; also includes linters (lint removed from the cottonseed) and motes (residual materials from the ginning process).

❖ Since Section 3705 deals with baled fibers, this definition of standard "Baled cotton" is being included only to distinguish it from "Baled cotton, densely packed" (see commentary to the definition of "Baled cotton, densely packed"). The Joint Cotton Industry Bale Packaging Committee (JCIBPC) is a committee that represents all parts of the cotton industry and sets standards and specifications for packaging of cotton bales that include bale density. The JCIBPC specifications for baling of cotton require that all cotton bales be secured with fixed-length wire bands, polyester plastic strapping or cold-rolled high tensile steel strapping and then covered in fully coated woven polyolefin, polyethylene film or burlap.

Baled cotton, densely packed. Cotton, made into banded bales, with a packing density of not less than 22 pounds per cubic foot (360 kg/m^3), and dimensions complying with the following: a length of 55 inches (1397 mm), a width of 21 inches (533.4 mm) and a height of 27.6 to 35.4 inches (701 to 899 mm).

❖ Currently, over 99 percent of all US cotton is pressed and stored as densely packed baled cotton, with bales meeting the weight and dimension requirements of ISO 8115. Because such bales are very difficult to ignite, the industry is able to transport them without being labeled as "flammable solids" or "dangerous goods" by the national or international transport authorities. This definition should be used to distinguish such bales from other combustible fibers.

In order to counteract some erroneous information regarding the combustibility characteristics of densely packed cotton bales, flammability research was conducted on baled cotton. The research demonstrated that densely packed baled cotton meeting the size and weight requirements of ISO 8115 is not a hazardous material. In view of that data, the US Department of Transportation (DOT) (US Coast Guard), the United Nations (U.N.) and the International Maritime Organization (IMO) have all removed baled cotton from the list of hazardous materials and flammable solids, provided that the cotton bales are the densely packed type that meet the standard noted above. The research conclusions were:

1. Standard cotton fiber "passed" the DOT spontaneous combustion test: the cotton did not exceed the oven temperature and was not classified as self-heating.
2. Cotton, as densely packed baled cotton, did not cause sustained smoldering propagation: an electric heater placed within the bale was unable to cause sustained smoldering propagation, due to the lack of oxygen inside the densely packed bale.
3. Cotton, as densely packed baled cotton, was exposed to ignition from a cigarette and a match and performed very well: no propagating combustion with either.
4. Cotton, as densely packed baled cotton, was exposed to ignition from the gas burner source in ASTM E1590 (also known as California Technical Bulletin 129) 12 L/min of propane gas for 180 seconds and passed all the criteria, including mass loss of less than 1.36 kg (3 pounds), heat release rate less than 100 kW and total heat release of less than 25 MJ in the first 10 minutes of the test.

Seed cotton. Perishable raw agricultural commodity consisting of cotton fiber (lint) attached to the seed of the cotton plant, which requires ginning to become a commercial product.

❖ Before cotton can be spun into yarn or thread and woven into cloth, the fibers must be separated from their seeds by a cotton gin (short for "cotton engine") in a process called "cotton ginning," which takes seed cotton and converts it into cotton fibers that are then stored in bales. Thus, seed cotton is a perishable raw material without commercial value that is not stored, but exists simply as a step on the way from the cotton field to the gin plant. Seed cotton is held in modules on the way from the harvest to the ginning factory, and is neither a loose cotton fiber (it has not been converted into fibers yet) nor densely packed baled cotton. As such, it is still a perishable agricultural product.

In the typical harvesting process (for example, grain harvesting), threshing machines are used to separate the raw agricultural product into a product that can then be stored and marketed, such as use as food or animal feed, and a byproduct that is usually left in the field. The cotton ginning process is essentially the same as the grain harvesting process in that a raw agricultural product (seed cotton) is converted by specially designed equipment into products with commercial value. These products are: cotton fiber (that exits the ginning process packaged as densely packed cotton bales and is either stored in a cotton warehouse or shipped to a textile mill) and cottonseeds (that go either to cottonseed oil mills or are fed directly to dairy cattle).

[BG] COURT. An open, uncovered space, unobstructed to the sky, bounded on three or more sides by exterior building walls or other enclosing devices.

❖ The provisions in the code for courts (Section 1205 of the IBC) are only applicable to those areas created by the arrangement of exterior walls and used to provide natural light or ventilation. See Section 1205.1 of the IBC and the definition of "Yard." See also the definition of "Egress court" for courts that are utilized for exit discharge.

[BG] COVERED MALL BUILDING. A single building enclosing a number of tenants and occupants such as retail stores, drinking and dining establishments, entertainment and amusement facilities, passenger transportation terminals, offices, and other similar uses wherein two or more tenants have a main entrance into one or more malls. Anchor buildings shall not be considered as a part of the covered mall building. The term "covered mall building" shall include open mall buildings as defined below.

Mall. A roofed or covered common pedestrian area within a covered mall building that serves as access for two or more tenants and not to exceed three levels that are open to each other. The term "mall" shall include open malls as defined below.

❖ The covered mall building is the entire area of the building (area of mall plus gross leasable area), excluding the anchor buildings. Passenger transportation terminals frequently are developed as wide concourses with small shops along the sides. For this reason, passenger transportation facilities are included. Transportation facilities used for freight or other purposes are not to be considered a covered mall building.

Open mall. An unroofed common pedestrian way serving a number of tenants not exceeding three levels. Circulation at levels above grade shall be permitted to include open exterior balconies leading to *exits* discharging at grade.

❖ A mall is an interior, climate-controlled pedestrian way that is open to the tenant spaces within the mall building and typically connects to the anchor buildings. The term "mall" also includes open mall. Unless noted otherwise, an open mall must comply with all the provisions for a mall.

Open mall building. Several structures housing a number of tenants such as retail stores, drinking and dining establishments, entertainment and amusement facilities, offices, and other similar uses wherein two or more tenants have a main entrance into one or more open malls. Anchor buildings are not considered as a part of the open mall building.

❖ An open mall building includes all of the buildings housing a number of tenants wherein two or more tenants have a main entrance into one or more open malls. Because the open mall is characterized by there not being a roof connecting one side of the pedestrian mall to the other, the covered mall "building" may actually be a collection of separate buildings which all rely on a shared pedestrian concourse for egress. Similar to the covered mall building, the open mall "building" does not include the anchor buildings. Unless noted otherwise, open mall buildings must comply with all the provisions for covered mall buildings.

CRITICAL CIRCUIT. A circuit that requires continuous operation to ensure safety of the structure and occupants.

❖ The purpose of this definition is to clarify the applicability of the provisions of Section 1203.3. Critical circuits are those electrical circuits supplying power to systems and equipment that are vital to the safety of building occupants and to the operational continuity of safety systems such as fire alarm systems, security systems, emergency communication systems and similar systems identified throughout the code, most notably in sections pertaining to emergency power. Although the term "critical circuit" is used widely throughout many industry standards, there is no specific definition for the term. As such, this definition was created based on definitions found in NFPA 70 and is similar to the definition of "Critical Operations Power Systems (COPS)" in that standard (see commentary, Section 1203.3).

CRYOGENIC CONTAINER. A cryogenic vessel of any size used for the transportation, handling or storage of *cryogenic fluids*.

❖ This definition is necessary to differentiate containers that hold cryogenic fluids from those that are used for ordinary compressed gases as addressed in Chapter 53, flammable and combustible liquids as addressed in Chapter 57 or other liquid or gaseous hazardous materials. Because of the extreme pressures and temperatures, these containers are unique in construction (see also commentary for the definition of "Container").

CRYOGENIC FLUID. A fluid having a *boiling point* lower than -130°F (-89.9°C) at 14.7 pounds per square inch atmosphere (psia) (an absolute pressure of 101.3 kPa).

❖ This definition contains the criteria for determining whether Chapter 55 is applicable. If a fluid falls outside of these criteria, it would likely be treated as a compressed gas and addressed within Chapter 53 (see also the definition for "Compressed gas").

CRYOGENIC VESSEL. A pressure vessel, low-pressure tank or atmospheric tank designed to contain a *cryogenic fluid* on which venting, insulation, refrigeration or a combination of these is used in order to maintain the operating pressure within the design pressure and the contents in a liquid phase.

❖ Cryogenic vessels differ from basic containers in that they are designed for use as either a pressure vessel, a low-pressure tank or an atmospheric tank that regulates the operating pressure to maintain the fluid as a liquid. Such vessels not only contain the fluids but also play an active role in regulating the state of the fluids.

[BG] CUSTODIAL CARE. Assistance with day-to-day living tasks; such as assistance with cooking, taking medication, bathing, using toilet facilities and other tasks of daily living. Custodial care includes persons receiving care who have the ability to respond to emergency situations and evacuate at a slower rate and/or who have mental and psychiatric complications.

❖ Care facilities encompass a full spectrum of occupant acuity and support services and span a wide range of occupancy types, including Groups E, I, and R. There are three types of care defined in the IBC and IFC: personal, custodial, and medical.

- Personal care is on one end of the care spectrum. It occurs in Group E occupancies for child day care services for persons over $2^1/_2$ years of age. Occupants are supervised but do not need custodial or medical care.
- Custodial care occurs in Groups I-1, I-4 and R-4, where occupants may be elderly or impaired, or require adult or child day care of any age. Care recipients may need daily living assistance such as cooking, cleaning, bathing or help with taking medications. Persons who receive custodial care may or may not require assistance with evacuation depending on the occupancy and the "condition" in the occupancy. See also the commentary to the definitions of Groups I-1, I-4 and R-4.
- Medical care occurs in Group I-2 occupancies on the opposite end of the spectrum, where care recipients are incapable of self-preservation. They may be completely bedridden, meaning bed movement may be required during emergencies, and may be dependent on life support systems such as medical gases and emergency power to maintain life. This level of acuity is not allowed in custodial care or personal care.

There are two other key defining aspects of custodial care that also differentiate it from medical care. The first is the evacuation capability of custodial care recipients. Custodial care recipients' evacuation capabilities are limited by the occupancy classification criteria or the occupancy condition in which care occurs. Group I-1, Condition 1 and Group R-4, Condition 1 only includes occupants with the ability to self-evacuate. Group I-1, Condition 2 and Group R-4, Condition 2 includes limited assistance with evacuation. The second differentiating aspect is that Group I-1 and R-4 custodial care recipients also participate in fire drills in accordance with the code, versus Group I-2 medical care that implements defend-in-place strategies during emergencies.

The level of care provided describes the condition and capabilities of an occupant, which then indicates the appropriate standards for protection systems, both active and passive. See also the definitions of "24-hour basis," "Ambulatory care facility," "Detoxification facilities," "Foster care facilities," "Group home," "Hospitals and psychiatric hospitals," "Incapable of self-preservation," "Medical care," "Nursing homes" and "Personal care service."

CYLINDER. A pressure vessel designed for pressures higher than 40 psia (275.6 kPa) and having a circular cross section. It does not include a portable tank, multiunit tank car tank, cargo tank or tank car.

❖ As referenced in the code, cylinders are vessels containing flammable or nonflammable compressed gases. Gas cylinders are fabricated to comply with regulations specified by DOTn and are generally limited to a capacity equivalent to the volume of 1,000 pounds (454 kg) of water.

DAMPER. See "Fire damper" and "Smoke damper."

DAY BOX. A portable magazine designed to hold *explosive* materials and constructed in accordance with the requirements for a Type 3 magazine as defined and classified in Chapter 56.

❖ Day boxes are basically Type 3 magazines used to isolate in-process material from a workstation as a means to minimize the potential for involvement should an event occur within the immediate vicinity of the work area. See the commentary to Section 5604.5.1.3 for a more complete discussion of the use of day boxes.

DECORATIVE MATERIALS. All materials applied over the building interior finish for decorative, acoustical or other effect including, but not limited to, curtains, draperies, fabrics, streamers and all other materials utilized for decorative effect including, but not limited to, bulletin boards, artwork, posters, photographs, paintings, batting, cloth, cotton, hay, stalks, straw, vines, leaves, trees, moss and similar items, foam plastics and materials containing foam plastics. Decorative materials do not include wall coverings, ceiling coverings, floor coverings, ordinary window shades, interior finish and materials 0.025 inch (0.64 mm) or less in thickness applied directly to and adhering tightly to a substrate.

❖ Decorative materials have historically been characterized by easily ignitable materials that burn very rapidly and contribute to fire spread. In order to properly classify decorative materials, it is important to define the term and this definition captures the essential elements. The significance of this definition is that it details items that are not regulated as decorative materials in the application of code requirements. While any dictionary would define floor coverings, window shades and wallpaper as being "decorative" in a building interior, they are not considered decorative materials subject to code-required flame-resistance testing.

DEFLAGRATION. An exothermic reaction, such as the extremely rapid oxidation of a flammable dust or vapor in air, in which the reaction progresses through the unburned material at a rate less than the velocity of sound. A deflagration can have an explosive effect.

❖ Materials posing a deflagration hazard usually burn very quickly with an energy release from a chemical reaction in the form of intense heat. Confined deflagration hazards under pressure can result in an explosion. Most hazardous materials posing a severe deflagration hazard are classified as Group H-2.

DELUGE SYSTEM. A sprinkler system employing open sprinklers attached to a piping system connected to a water supply through a valve that is opened by the operation of a detection system installed in the same area as the sprinklers. When this valve opens, water flows into the piping system and discharges from all sprinklers attached thereto.

❖ A deluge system applies large quantities of water or foam throughout the protected area by means of a system of open sprinklers. In a fire, the system is activated by a fire detection system that makes it possible to apply water to a fire more quickly and to cover a larger area than with a conventional automatic sprinkler system, which depends on sprinklers being activated individually as the fire spreads. As the definition indicates, the sprinklers are open. There is no fusible link so when water is admitted into the system by the fire detection system, it flows through the piping and is immediately discharged through the sprinkler heads.

Deluge systems are particularly beneficial in hazardous areas where the fuel loads (combustible contents) are of such a nature that fire may grow with exceptional rapidity and possibly flash ahead of the operations of conventional automatic sprinklers.

DESIGN PRESSURE. The maximum gauge pressure that a pressure vessel, device, component or system is designed to withstand safely under the temperature and conditions of use expected.

❖ A container that is subjected to an internal pressure higher than its design pressure faces a high failure rate. If the container is used to store flammable liquids or gases, a boiling liquid expanding vapor explosion (BLEVE), which is a form of pressure-releasing explosion, may occur.

DESOLVENTIZING. The act of removing a solvent from a material.

❖ This definition is associated with Chapter 39, addressing the processing and extraction of oils from a plant. This definition describes the part of the process where the solvent used to extract the oil from a plant is removed from the oils collected.

DETACHED BUILDING. A separate single-story building, without a *basement* or crawl space, used for the storage or use of hazardous materials and located an *approved* distance from all structures.

❖ This term refers to the type of structure that the code recognizes for using and storing Group H materials exceeding MAQ. A detached storage building is required only for Group H, as indicated in Table 5003.8.2 of the code or Table 415.6.2 of the IBC, and as may be required in Chapters 50 through 67 of the code.

DETEARING. A process for rapidly removing excess wet coating material from a dipped or coated object or material by passing it through an electrostatic field.

❖ Detearing applies to dip tank operations. It is the process of rapidly removing excess wet coating materials from an object.

DETECTOR, HEAT. A fire detector that senses heat, either abnormally high temperature or rate of rise, or both.

❖ Heat detectors include fixed temperature detectors, rate compensation detectors and rate-of-rise detectors. The code requires all automatic fire detectors to be smoke detectors, except that heat detectors tested and approved in accordance with NFPA 72 may be used as an alternative to smoke detectors in rooms and spaces where, during normal operation, products of combustion are present in sufficient quantity to actuate a smoke detector.

DETONATING CORD. A flexible cord containing a center core of high *explosive* used to initiate other *explosives*.

❖ Outwardly, detonating cord, or primacord, is somewhat similar to a safety fuse in size and appearance. But instead of being filled with black powder, detonating cord generally contains pentaerythritoltetranitrate (PETN). Like other explosives, primacord is generally set off by a blasting cap. It propagates a detonation at a rate of 9,000 yards per second (8.23 km/s), a little over 5 miles per second (8.05 km/s). A length of detonating cord stretching from San Francisco to New York will explode over its entire length of 3,000 miles (4828.03 km) in about 10 minutes.

DETONATION. An exothermic reaction characterized by the presence of a shock wave in the material which establishes and maintains the reaction. The reaction zone progresses through the material at a rate greater than the velocity of sound. The principal heating mechanism is one of shock compression. *Detonations* have an *explosive* effect.

❖ Detonations are distinguished from deflagrations, which are produced by explosive gases, dusts, vapors and mists, by the speed with which they propagate a blast effect. Both detonations and deflagrations may produce explosive results when they occur in a confined space.

DETONATOR. A device containing any initiating or primary *explosive* that is used for initiating *detonation*. A detonator shall not contain more than 154.32 grains (10 grams) of total *explosives* by weight, excluding ignition or delay charges. The term includes, but is not limited to, electric blasting caps of instantaneous and delay types, blasting caps for use with safety fuses, detonating cord delay connectors, and noninstantaneous and delay blasting caps which use detonating cord, shock tube or any other replacement for electric leg wires. All types of detonators in strengths through No. 8 cap should be rated at $1^1/_2$ pounds (0.68 kg) of explosives per 1,000 caps. For strengths higher than No. 8 cap, consult the manufacturer.

❖ These devices contain a primary explosive charge and are used to initiate other explosives. Detonators include, but are not limited to:

1. Electric detonators of instantaneous and delay types.
2. Detonators for use with safety fuses, detonating cord delay connectors and nonelectric instantaneous delay detonators that use detonating cord, shock tube or any other replacement for electric leg wires.

[BG] DETOXIFICATION FACILITIES. Facilities that provide treatment for substance abuse serving care recipients who are incapable of self-preservation or who are harmful to themselves or others.

❖ Persons in detoxification facilities may be physically incapable of self-preservation, or they may be confined within an area of a building for care or security purposes. See the commentary for the definition of "Occupancy Group I-2" and Section 407 of the IBC.

Care facilities encompass a full spectrum of acuity and support services and span a wide range of occupancy types including Groups B, E, I and R. The level of care provided describes the condition and capabilities of an occupant which, in turn, indicates appropriate standards for protection systems, both passive and active. See also the definitions for "24-hour basis," "Ambulatory care facility," "Group home," "Hospitals and psychiatric hospitals," "Incapable of self-preservation," "Medical care," "Nursing homes" and "Personal care service."

DIP TANK. A tank, vat or container of flammable or combustible liquid in which articles or materials are immersed for the purpose of coating, finishing, treating and similar processes.

❖ Dip tanks can be almost any size, depending on the size of the work pieces to be immersed. They may be equipped with a fire suppression system, as well as overflow and drain pipes, all of which are based on the tank size. Regardless of size, dip tanks must be constructed of noncombustible materials, equipped with an approved self-closing cover and properly ventilated (see Commentary Figure 202-D1).

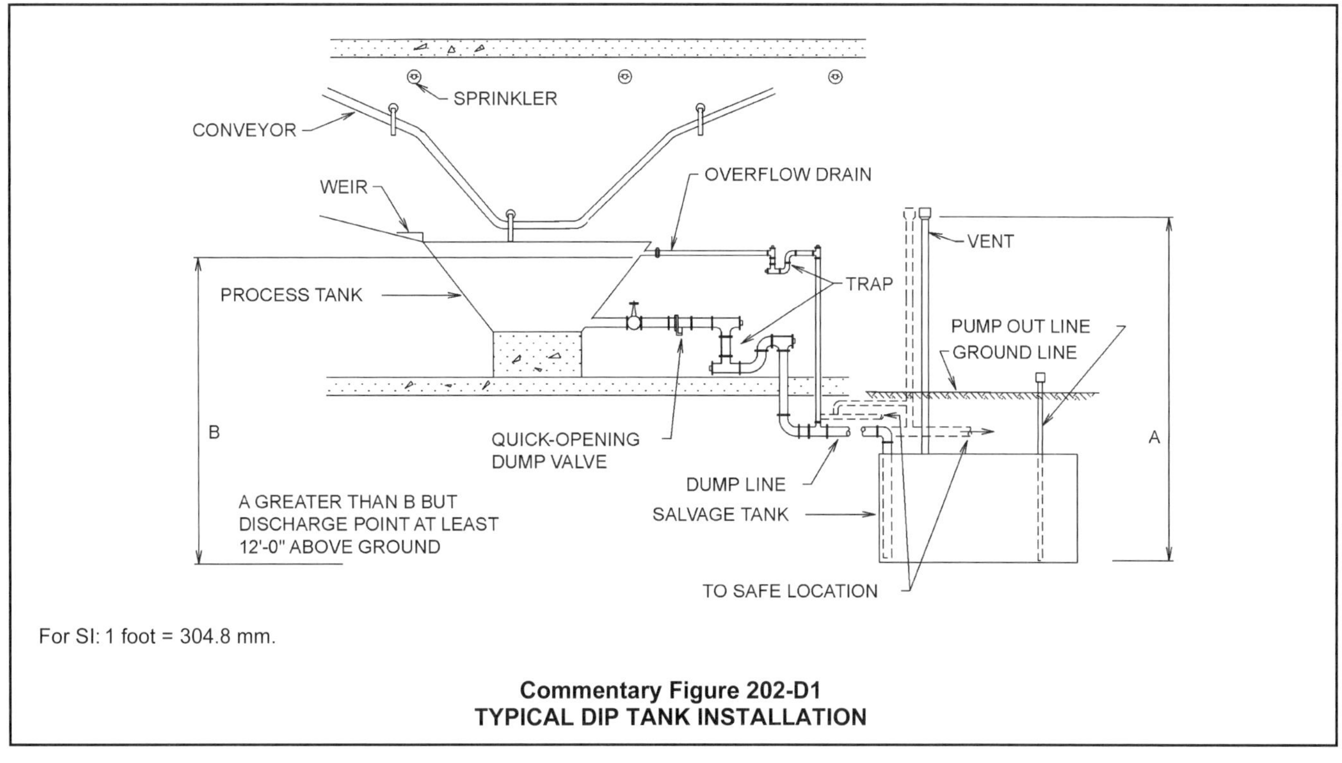

Commentary Figure 202-D1
TYPICAL DIP TANK INSTALLATION

DISCHARGE SITE. The immediate area surrounding the fireworks mortars used for an outdoor fireworks display.

❖ The area selected for the discharge of aerial shells must be located so that the trajectory of the shells does not come within 25 feet (7620 mm) of any overhead object. Ground display pieces must be located a minimum distance of 75 feet (22 860 mm) from spectator viewing areas and parking areas.

DISPENSING. The pouring or transferring of any material from a container, tank or similar vessel, whereby vapors, dusts, fumes, mists or gases are liberated to the atmosphere.

❖ This term refers to any transfer of a hazardous material from one container to another that is open to the atmosphere where liberation of the material in the forms listed in the definition occurs. See also the definitions for "Closed system" and "Handling."

DISPENSING DEVICE, OVERHEAD TYPE. A dispensing device that consists of one or more individual units intended for installation in conjunction with each other, mounted above a dispensing area typically within the motor fuel-dispensing facility canopy structure, and characterized by the use of an overhead hose reel.

❖ Dispensing devices are approved pieces of fixed equipment that control the dispensing of fuel through the dispensing hose connected to them. An overhead-type dispensing device is not to be confused with the conventional dispenser, often referred to as a "high-hose" dispenser, that is equipped with a dispensing hose connected at the top of the dispenser frame. This provision is intended to identify the overhead hose reel that has special requirements for the classification of electrical equipment in the vicinity of the reel in accordance with Chapter 8 of NFPA 30A.

DISPLAY SITE. The immediate area where a fireworks display is conducted. The display area includes the discharge site, the fallout area and the required separation distance from the mortars to spectator viewing areas. The display area does not include spectator viewing areas or vehicle parking areas.

❖ Where added safety precautions have been taken, or particularly favorable conditions exist, the fire code official can decrease the required separation distances upon demonstration that the hazard has been reduced or the risk has been properly protected. Where unusual or safety-threatening conditions exist, he or she can also increase the required separation distances as he or she deems necessary.

DOOR, BALANCED. See "Balanced door."

❖ See the commentary to the definition of "Balanced door."

DOOR, DUTCH. See "Dutch door."

❖ See the commentary to the definition of "Dutch door."

DOOR, LOW ENERGY POWER-OPERATED. See "Low energy power-operated door."

❖ See the commentary to the definition of "Low energy power-operated door."

DOOR, POWER-ASSISTED. See "Power-assisted door."

❖ See the commentary to the definition of "Power-assisted door."

DOOR, POWER-OPERATED. See "Power-operated door."

❖ See the commentary to the definition of "Power-operated door."

DOORWAY, EXIT ACCESS. See "Exit access doorway."

❖ See the commentary to the definition of "Exit access doorway."

[BG] DORMITORY. A space in a building where group sleeping accommodations are provided in one room, or in a series of closely associated rooms, for persons not members of the same family group, under joint occupancy and single management, as in college dormitories or fraternity houses.

❖ Dormitories typically consist of a large room serving as a community sleeping room or many smaller rooms grouped together and serving as private or semiprivate sleeping rooms (sleeping units). A typical setting for dormitories is on college campuses; however, sleeping areas of a fire station and similar lodging facilities for occupants not of the same family group are also considered dormitories. Dormitories most often are not the permanent residence of the occupants. They are typically occupied only for a designated period of time, such as a school year. Though limited, the period of occupancy is usually more than 30 days, which provides the occupant with a familiarity of the structure such that the occupancy is not considered transient. A dormitory is classified as Group R-2 (see the commentary to the definition of "Occupancy Group R-2").

Structures containing a dormitory often have a cafeteria or central eating area and common recreational areas. When such conditions exist, the structure must comply with the mixed occupancy provisions of Section 508 of the IBC. See also the definition of "Sleeping unit"

DRAFT CURTAIN. A structure arranged to limit the spread of smoke and heat along the underside of the ceiling or roof.

❖ A draft curtain restricts the passage of smoke at roof or ceiling level. Located at the roof or ceiling, draft curtains are designed to compartmentalize the roof or ceiling area in order to limit the passage of smoke to a defined area and hinder its spread throughout the entire storage area. It has also been argued that such curtains help the activation of smoke and heat vents. They are not intended to have a fire-resistance rating. Draft curtains are often termed "curtain boards."

[BF] DRAFTSTOP. A material, device or construction installed to restrict the movement of air within open spaces of concealed areas of building components such as crawl spaces, floor/ceiling assemblies, roof/ceiling assemblies and attics.

❖ Draftstopping is required in concealed combustible spaces to limit the movement of air, smoke and other products of combustion. Draftstopping materials are permitted to be combustible based on the rationale that a large and thick enough combustible material will act as a hindrance against the free movement of air, flame/fire and products of combustion [see Commentary Figures 202-D2 and 202-D3 for typical draftstopping applications (also see Section 718 of the IBC)].

Although the term "draftstopping" would seem to imply that its primary purpose is to hinder the circulation of air within the space, its intended purpose is to stop the movement of fire and products of combustion, as evidenced by the fact that draftstopping can be omitted in some cases when appropriate automatic sprinkler protection is installed (see Sections 718.3 and 718.4 of the IBC).

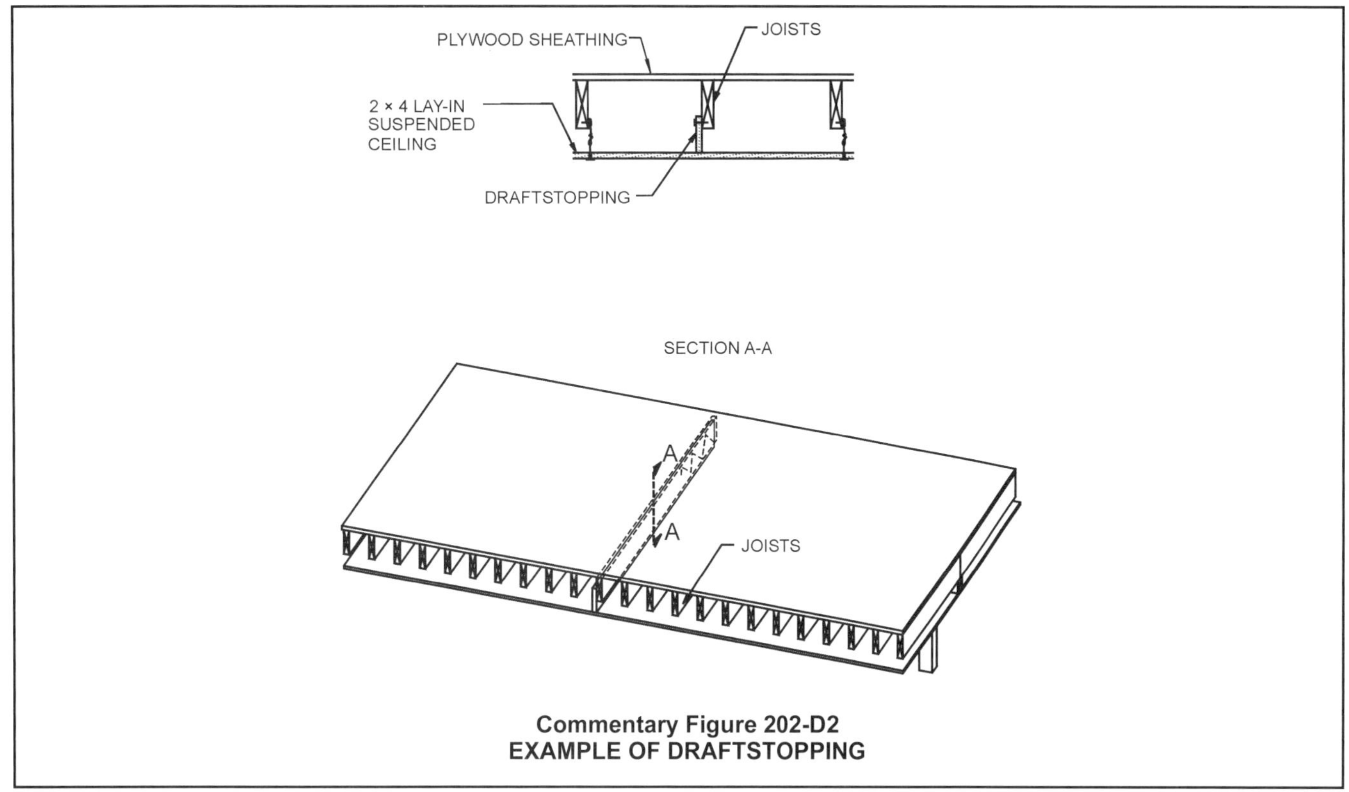

Commentary Figure 202-D2
EXAMPLE OF DRAFTSTOPPING

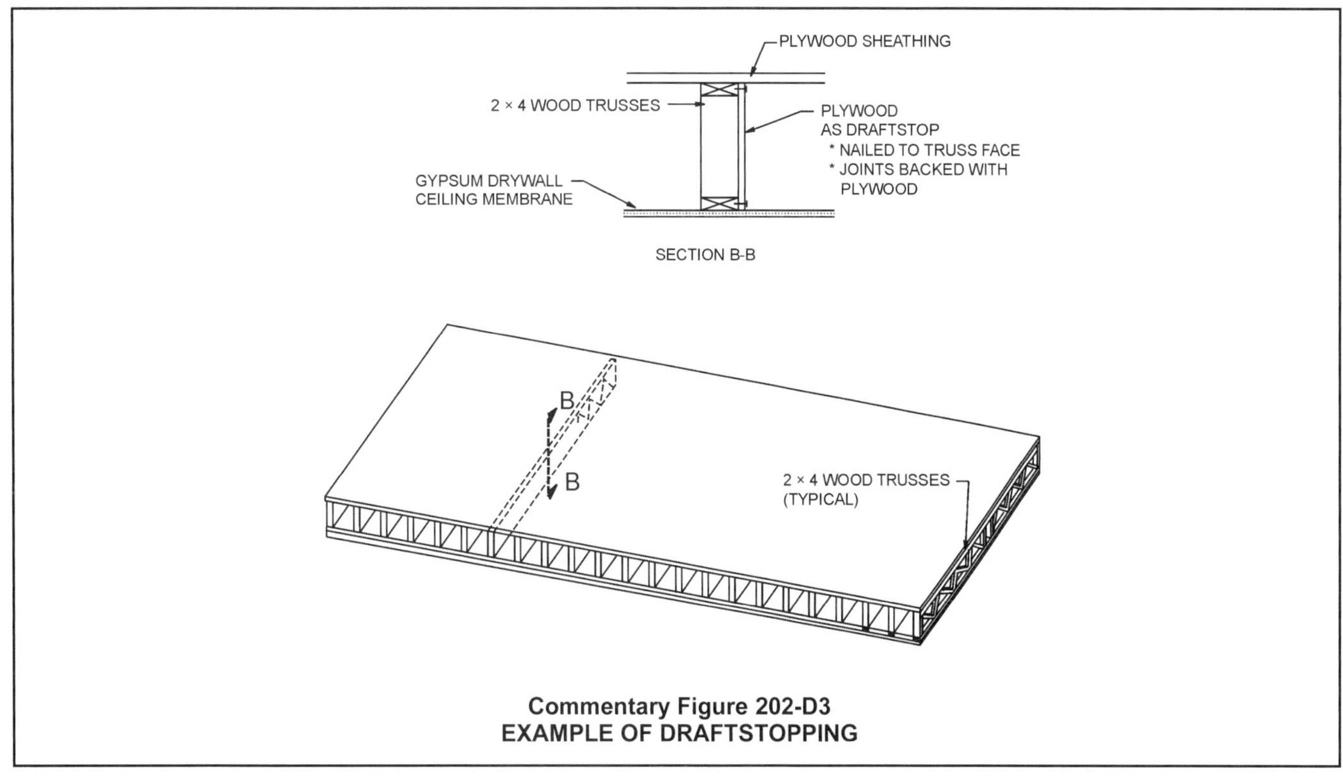

Commentary Figure 202-D3
EXAMPLE OF DRAFTSTOPPING

DRY-CHEMICAL EXTINGUISHING AGENT. A powder composed of small particles, usually of sodium bicarbonate, potassium bicarbonate, urea-potassium-based bicarbonate, potassium chloride or monoammonium phosphate, with added particulate material supplemented by special treatment to provide resistance to packing, resistance to moisture absorption (caking) and the proper flow capabilities.

❖ A dry-chemical system extinguishes a fire by placing a chemical barrier between the fire and oxygen, thus smothering a fire. This system is best known for protection for commercial ranges, commercial fryers and exhaust hoods. Wet-chemical extinguishing systems, however, are more commonly used for new installations in commercial cooking equipment.

The type of dry chemical to be used in the extinguishing system is a function of the hazard expected. The type of dry chemical used in a system must not be changed, unless it has been proven changeable by a testing laboratory; is recommended by the manufacturer of the equipment and is acceptable to the fire code official for the hazard expected. Additional guidance on the use of various dry-chemical agents can be found in NFPA 17, which gives minimum requirements for the design, installation, testing, inspection, approval, operation and maintenance of dry-chemical extinguishing systems.

DRY CLEANING. The process of removing dirt, grease, paints and other stains from such items as wearing apparel, textiles, fabrics and rugs by use of nonaqueous liquids (solvents).

❖ Dry cleaning is the process of cleaning textile-based items in a closed machine using solvents that are not water based; hence, the term "dry." This process generally consists of a "wash cycle" in which the item or items to be cleaned are placed in the machine with the dry cleaning solvent and tumbled for a predetermined length of time, followed by an "extraction cycle" in which the solvent is centrifugally removed from the clean items, not unlike the "spin" cycle of a washing machine. Recovery of remaining solvent and solvent vapors in the cleaned articles is accomplished in a "reclamation cycle," which involves heating the cleaned articles to vaporize the remaining solvent, which is then collected and condensed. Finally, an "aeration" or drying cycle occurs where warm air dries and deodorizes the cleaned articles. The dry cleaning process can also include the manual application of solvent and spotting compounds prior to the main cleaning process. See also the definitions of "Dry cleaning plant" and "Solvent or liquid classifications."

DRY CLEANING PLANT. A facility in which dry cleaning and associated operations are conducted, including the office, receiving area and storage rooms.

❖ The type of construction, occupancy group classification and other building requirements are determined by the type of solvent and machinery used in the cleaning process. The main hazards in a dry cleaning plant are the fire hazards of the flammable and combustible solvents and the health hazards of the chlorinated hydrocarbon solvents. See also the definitions of "Dry cleaning" and "Solvent or liquid classifications."

DRY CLEANING ROOM. An occupiable space within a building used for performing dry cleaning operations, the installation of solvent-handling equipment or the storage of dry cleaning solvents.

❖ The IBC defines an occupiable space as "a room or enclosed space designed for human occupancy ... in which occupants are engaged at labor ..." Within the context of Chapter 21, a dry cleaning room is primarily the room or space in which the actual dry cleaning process is conducted. Depending on the scope of the dry cleaning establishment, it could be a room or space within a large plant or could encompass the entire plant in smaller operations. Note that the focus of the term is on the presence of the dry cleaning solvent, whether it is in the cleaning process, being stored for future use within the room or space, or being transferred from storage containers to the dry cleaning machines. See also the definitions of "Dry cleaning," "Dry cleaning plant" and "Solvent or liquid classifications."

DRY CLEANING SYSTEM. Machinery or equipment in which textiles are immersed or agitated in solvent or in which dry cleaning solvent is extracted from textiles.

❖ This term focuses on the actual dry cleaning machines and solvent extractors that use or recover dry cleaning solvent. Systems are classified according to the hazards of the solvent they use. See the commentary to Sections 2103.2 and 2105 for additional discussion of dry cleaning system classification and operation, respectively. See also the definition of "Solvent or liquid classifications."

DUTCH DOOR. A door divided horizontally so that the top can be operated independently from the bottom.

❖ This definition is associated with the requirements in Section 1105.5.4.2.3 for existing Group I-2 occupancies. Dutch doors have been used in health care facilities for many years for various necessary operational reasons. Existing language in the IBC does not specifically address dutch doors. Their use is not prohibited, but if used they must meet the requirements contained in IBC Section 407.3, including positive latching and limiting the transfer of smoke. The definition is provided for additional clarity as to what is considered a "dutch door."

[BG] DWELLING. A building that contains one or two *dwelling units* used, intended or designed to be used, rented, leased, let or hired out to be occupied for living purposes.

❖ Dwellings are buildings intended to serve as residences for one or two families. Dwellings can be owner-occupied or rented. The term "dwelling," which refers to the building itself, is defined to distinguish it from the term "dwelling unit," which is a single living unit within a building. See also the definition for "Townhouse."

[BG] DWELLING UNIT. A single unit providing complete, independent living facilities for one or more persons, including permanent provisions for living, sleeping, eating, cooking and sanitation.

❖ A dwelling unit, as stated, is a residential unit that contains all of the necessary facilities for independent living. This provides a single, independent unit that serves a single family or single group of individuals. This terminology is used throughout the code for the determination of the application of various provisions. A dwelling unit is also distinguished from a sleeping unit, which does not have all of the features of a dwelling unit and must comply with a different set of requirements (see the definition for "Sleeping unit"). A building containing one or more dwelling units is a "dwelling" (see the definitions for "Dwelling" and "Townhouse"). A building containing three or more dwelling units is regulated as a Group R-2 occupancy. The most common term used for such a building is an apartment house or condominium. To be considered a Group R-3, the structure must have one or two dwelling units, or be subdivided by fire walls between every unit or every two units.

EARLY SUPPRESSION FAST-RESPONSE (ESFR) SPRINKLER. A sprinkler *listed* for early suppression fast-response performance.

❖ The early suppression fast-response (ESFR) sprinkler head was originally designed to provide fire suppression for heat and fire situations that required a lower thermal response to activate the sprinkler head earlier than the standard sprinkler head. The ESFR sprinkler heads have a response time index (RTI) of 50 (meters-seconds) $^1/_2$ or less, compared to a standard sprinkler head, which has an RTI of 80 (meters-seconds) $^1/_2$ or more. ESFR sprinkler design requires the same concepts of sprinkler system design for it to react and suppress a fire when needed. The important difference is that ESFR systems are specifically designed to suppress a high-challenge fire versus simply controlling its growth.

[BE] EGRESS COURT. A court or *yard* which provides access to a *public way* for one or more *exits*.

❖ The egress court requirements address situations where the exit discharge portion of the means of egress passes through confined areas near the building and therefore faces a hazard not normally found in the exit discharge (see Section 1028.4).

ELECTROSTATIC FLUIDIZED BED. A container holding powder coating material that is aerated from below so as to form an air-supported expanded cloud of such material that is electrically charged with a charge opposite to that of the object to be coated. Such object is transported through the container immediately above the charged and aerated materials in order to be coated.

❖ Because the powder used in the electrostatic fluidized bed is not as finely divided as that used in electrostatic spray methods, it is not likely to create a dust explosion potential. Electrostatic fluidized beds allow for the coating of materials that then must be cured in a baking oven (see also Chapter 30). This method of coating is typically used for small pieces [dimensions less than 4 inches (102 mm)].

ELEVATOR GROUP. A grouping of elevators in a building located adjacent or directly across from one another that respond to a common hall call button(s).

❖ This definition clarifies the application of emergency voice/alarm communication system requirements in Section 907.5.2.2 as to the locations, called "paging zones," where system speakers are required (see commentary, Section 907.5.2.2).

EMERGENCY ALARM SYSTEM. A system to provide indication and warning of emergency situations involving hazardous materials.

❖ Because of the potentially volatile nature of hazardous materials, an emergency alarm system is required outside of interior building rooms or areas containing hazardous materials in excess of the maximum allowable quantities permitted in Tables 5003.1.1(1) and 5003.1.1(2). The emergency alarm, upon actuation by an alarm-initiating device, is intended to alert the occupants to an emergency condition involving hazardous materials. The initiation of the emergency alarm can be by manual or automatic means depending on the hazard and the specific requirements for the type of hazard (see commentaries, Sections 908, 5004.9 and 5005.4.4).

EMERGENCY CONTROL STATION. An *approved* location on the premises where signals from emergency equipment are received and which is staffed by trained personnel.

❖ This definition identifies the room or area located in the HPM facility that is used to receive various alarms and signals. The smoke detectors located in the building's recirculation ventilation ducts, the gas-monitoring/detection system and the telephone/fire protective signaling systems located outside of HPM storage rooms must all be connected to the emergency control station. The location of this station must be approved by the fire code official. An approved location should be based on personnel being able to adequately monitor the necessary alarms and signals and on the fire department being able to gain access quickly when responding to emergency situations. Additionally, the room must be occupied by persons who are trained to respond to the various alarms and signals.

[BE] EMERGENCY ESCAPE AND RESCUE OPENING. An operable window, door or other similar device that provides for a means of escape and access for rescue in the event of an emergency.

❖ These are typically windows that are sized and located such that they can be used to exit a building directly from a basement or bedroom during an emergency condition. The openings are also used by emergency personnel to rescue the occupants in a building (see Section 1030). Windows are never considered to be exit or exit access components for purposes of meeting minimum number of exit requirements. An emergency escape and rescue opening could be a type of door, such as a basement door with direct access to an exterior stairway or a door to a balcony. Bulkhead-style cellar doors could also be evaluated as possible emergency escape and rescue openings.

EMERGENCY EVACUATION DRILL. An exercise performed to train staff and occupants and to evaluate their efficiency and effectiveness in carrying out emergency evacuation procedures.

❖ This definition provides a consistent explanation of the purpose and extent of such activities. Without drilling the staff and occupants in the emergency procedures for which they have been trained, neither management nor the staff or occupants can adequately gauge their readiness to perform in a crisis mode.

EMERGENCY POWER SYSTEM. A source of automatic electric power of a required capacity and duration to operate required life safety, fire alarm, detection and ventilation systems in the event of a failure of the primary power. Emergency power systems are required for electrical loads where interruption of the primary power could result in loss of human life or serious injuries.

❖ This definition is intended to provide clarity for the fire code official as to exactly what systems are considered to be emergency power systems and is consistent with the definitions in NFPA 110 and NFPA 111. However, since the list of systems in the definition is not exhaustive, reference must be made to Section 1203 of the code, which establishes the "where required" provisions. When the normal power supply to any of the indicated systems, or other systems designated by the code, fails, the emergency power system is to provide a specified degree and duration of illumination or power for systems and equipment that are essential for life safety. See the commentary to Section 1203 for more detailed discussion on the difference between standby and emergency power.

EMERGENCY SHUTOFF VALVE. A valve designed to shut off the flow of gases or liquids.

❖ See the commentary following the definition of "Emergency shutoff valve, manual."

EMERGENCY SHUTOFF VALVE, AUTOMATIC. A fail-safe automatic-closing valve designed to shut off the flow of gases or liquids initiated by a control system that is activated by automatic means.

❖ See the commentary following the definition of "Emergency shutoff valve, manual."

EMERGENCY SHUTOFF VALVE, MANUAL. A manually operated valve designed to shut off the flow of gases or liquids.

❖ The term "emergency shutoff valve" has historically been used inconsistently throughout various sections in the code. There are fundamentally two types of shutoff valves commonly employed: manually operated or automatically operated. Those that are automatic can either fail open or fail closed. A valve that fails in the closed position is said to be "fail-safe." Automatic valves are actuated by a control system that may activate the valves either automatically or manually. The code requires the manual activation of controls that are used to operate automatic valves.

Three definitions are now provided for emergency valves to include the function of the valve itself and the two subsets that describe the two types encountered (e.g., manual or automatic). See also the commentary to the definitions of "Fail-safe" and "Remotely located, manually activated shutdown control."

EMERGENCY VOICE/ALARM COMMUNICATIONS. Dedicated manual or automatic facilities for originating and distributing voice instructions, as well as alert and evacuation signals pertaining to a fire emergency, to the occupants of a building.

❖ An emergency voice/alarm communication system is a special feature of fire alarm systems in buildings with special evacuation considerations, such as a high-rise building or a large assembly space. Emergency voice/alarm communication systems automatically communicate a fire emergency message to all occupants of a building on a general or selective basis. Such systems also enable the fire service to manually transmit voice instructions to the building occupants about a fire emergency condition and the action to be taken for evacuation or movement to another area of the building. Although most systems use prerecorded messages, some now use computer-synthesized voices to communicate customized messages that are unique to the facility.

[BE] EMPLOYEE WORK AREA. All or any portion of a space used only by employees and only for work. *Corridors*, toilet rooms, kitchenettes and break rooms are not employee work areas.

❖ An employee work area is different in an office versus on a factory line. An employee work area will most likely expand past the station or desk where an employee performs his or her job. An employee work area could include common use spaces, but not public use spaces. Depending on the duties of the employee, it may also include copy areas, stockrooms, filing areas, an assembly line, etc. (see also the commentaries for the definitions of "Common use" and "Public-use areas").

Note that not all employee-only areas are considered part of employee work areas (e.g., bathrooms, corridors, breakrooms).

ENERGY MANAGEMENT SYSTEMS. An electronic system that protects stationary storage batteries from operating outside their safe operating parameters, and generates an alarm and trouble signal for off normal conditions.

❖ This definition is associated with the requirements for stationary battery systems and capacitor energy storage systems. Energy management systems are an essential part of such systems' operating safety. These systems monitor and balance cell voltages, currents and temperatures within the manufacturer's specifications. The requirements of Section 1206 require the energy management system to transmit an alarm signal to an approved location if potentially hazardous temperatures or other conditions such as short circuits, over voltage or under voltage are detected.

[BG] EQUIPMENT PLATFORM. An unoccupied, elevated platform used exclusively for mechanical systems or industrial process equipment, including the associated elevated walkways, *stairways*, *alternating tread devices* and ladders necessary to access the platform (see Section 505.3 of the *International Building Code*).

❖ A distinction is made between equipment platforms and mezzanines by way of this definition. Equipment platforms, covered in Section 505.3 of the IBC, are unoccupied and used exclusively for housing equipment and providing access thereto, and are not subject to the requirements for mezzanines. Their purpose could also be to allow access for maintenance, repair or modification of elevated or very large equipment. Equipment platforms allow efficient use of high bay areas by locating infrequently accessed equipment or processes overhead without the occupant load or increasing the hazard to occupants in the room. Elevated floor areas that do not meet this definition would be subject to the requirements for mezzanines or may be considered additional stories, depending on the circumstances.

EXCESS FLOW CONTROL. A fail-safe system or other *approved* means designed to shut off flow caused by a rupture in pressurized piping systems.

❖ This refers to a fail-safe valve or other approved device that is required on pressurized piping systems to prevent the uncontrolled release of excess quantities of hazardous liquids and gases if piping or valve failure occurs. To safeguard as much piping as practical, the device must be installed as close to the supply container as possible.

EXCESS FLOW VALVE. A valve inserted into a *compressed gas* cylinder, portable tank or stationary tank that is designed to positively shut off the flow of gas in the event that its predetermined flow is exceeded.

❖ Such a valve has the ability to shut down flow when the intended flow rate has been exceeded. Quite often, when the predetermined flow has been exceeded, a failure will occur.

EXHAUSTED ENCLOSURE. An appliance or piece of equipment which consists of a top, a back and two sides providing a means of local exhaust for capturing gases, fumes, vapors and mists. Such enclosures include laboratory hoods, exhaust fume hoods and similar appliances and equipment used to retain and exhaust locally the gases, fumes, vapors and mists that could be released. Rooms or areas provided with general ventilation, in themselves, are not exhausted enclosures.

❖ When a hazardous chemical is being dispensed or used, an exhausted enclosure can be used to reduce the exposure of personnel to a toxic or hazardous atmosphere. These enclosures have special requirements for protection (see Section 5003.8.5).

EXISTING. Buildings, facilities or conditions that are already in existence, constructed or officially authorized prior to the adoption of this code.

❖ This term is specifically defined to reduce any confusion regarding the application of the code to existing buildings, facilities and conditions. This definition would include anything that has already been in use, is already constructed or has been approved by the jurisdiction prior to the adoption of the code. If an occupancy changes use significantly, it may be considered new in some cases.

[BE] EXIT. That portion of a *means of egress* system between the *exit access* and the *exit discharge* or *public way*. Exit components include exterior exit doors at the *level of exit discharge*, *interior exit stairways* and *ramps*, *exit passageways*, *exterior exit stairways* and *ramps* and *horizontal exits*.

❖ Exits are the critical element of the means of egress system that the building occupants travel through to reach the exterior at the level of exit discharge. Exit stairways and ramps from upper and lower stories must be separated from adjacent areas with fire-resistance-rated construction. The fire-resistance-rated construction serves as a barrier between the fire and the means of egress and protects the occupants while they travel through the exit. Separation by fire-resistance-rated construction is not required, however, where the exit leads directly to the exterior at the level of exit discharge (e.g., exterior door at grade). Commentary Figure 202-E1 illustrates three different types of exits: interior exit stairway, exterior exit stairway and exterior exit door.

A horizontal exit, while not discharging to the outside, does discharge to another building or refuge area. The door to the refuge area is through a fire wall or fire barrier (see the definition for "Horizontal exit" and Section 1026).

[BE] EXIT ACCESS. That portion of a *means of egress* system that leads from any occupied portion of a building or structure to an *exit*.

❖ The exit access portion of the means of egress consists of all floor areas that lead from usable spaces within the building to the exit or exits serving that floor area. Crawl spaces and concealed attic and roof spaces are not considered to be part of the exit access. As shown in Commentary Figure 202-E2, the exit access begins at the furthest points within each room or space and ends at the entrance to the exit.

[BE] EXIT ACCESS DOORWAY. A door or access point along the path of egress travel from an occupied room, area or space where the path of egress enters an intervening room, *corridor*, *exit access stairway* or *ramp*.

❖ Exit access doorways are used to design many critical aspects of the means of egress including arrangement, number, separation, opening protection and exit sign placement. The term "doorway" has traditionally been limited to those situations where an actual opening, either with or without a door, is present. The presence of the phrase "access point" clarifies that the definition includes specific points in the means of egress that may not include a "door," such as when an unenclosed exit access stairway is used in the egress path.

[BE] EXIT ACCESS RAMP. A *ramp* within the *exit access* portion of the *means of egress* system.

❖ Unenclosed ramps may serve as part of the route for exit access where floor levels have changes in elevation. For the limited situations where exit access ramps can be used between stories, see Sections 1006.3 and 1019. Exit access elements are included in the travel distance requirements unless specifically exempted (e.g., open parking garages, open air assembly seating) (see Section 1017.3.1).

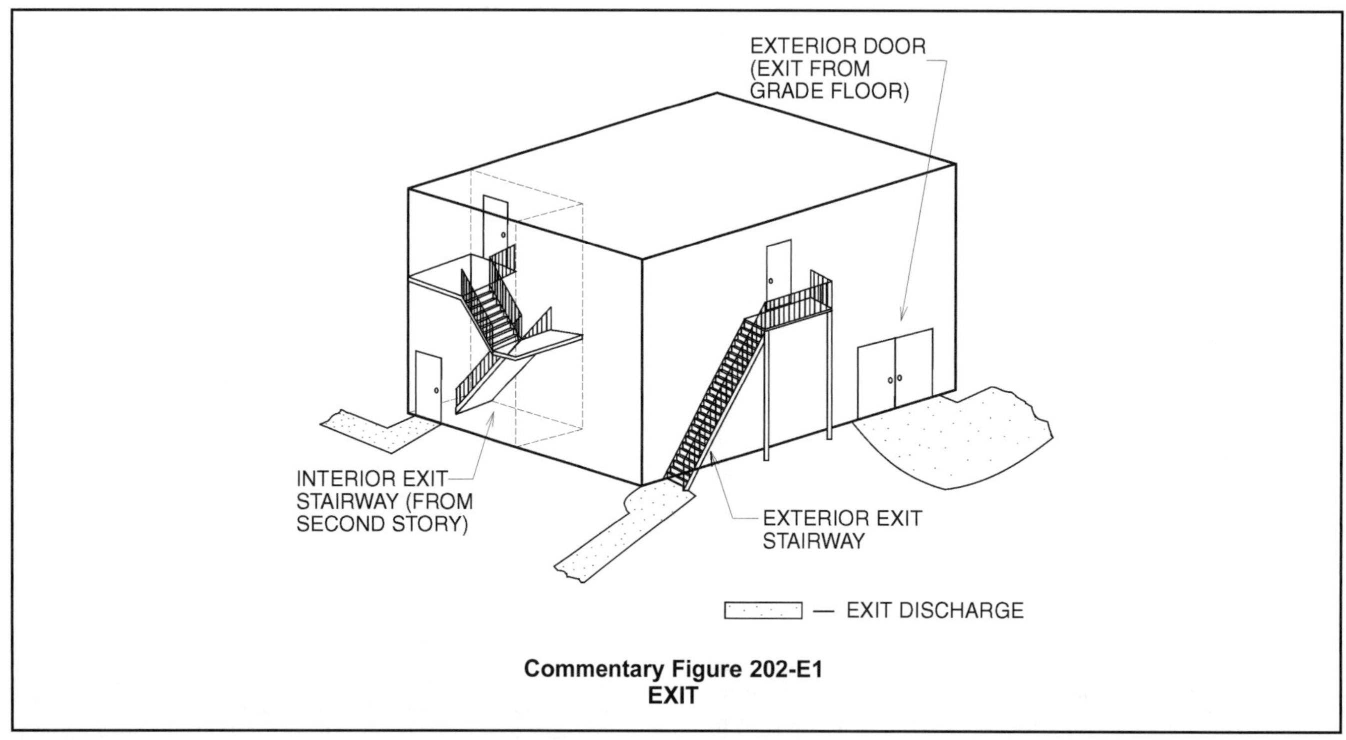

Commentary Figure 202-E1
EXIT

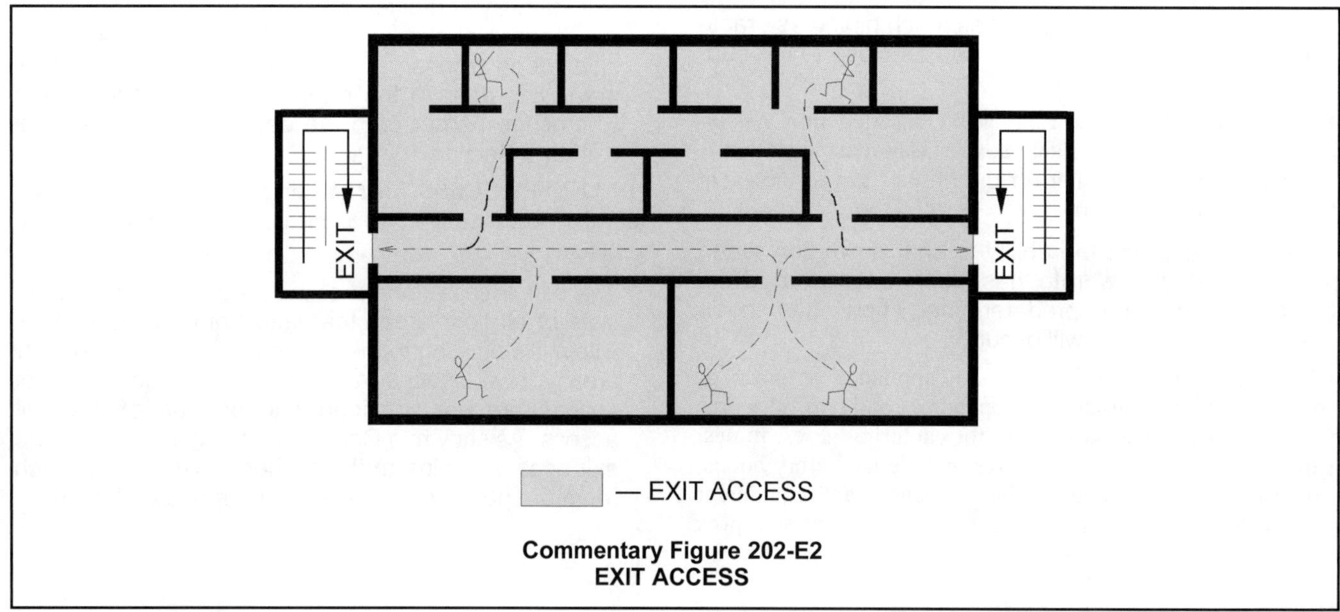

Commentary Figure 202-E2
EXIT ACCESS

[BE] EXIT ACCESS STAIRWAY. A *stairway* within the *exit access* portion of the *means of egress* system.

❖ Unenclosed steps and stairways may serve as part of the route for exit access when floor levels have changes in elevation. For the limited situations where exit access stairways can be used between stories, see Sections 1006.3 and 1019. Exit access elements are included in the travel distance requirements unless specifically exempted (e.g., open parking garages, open air assembly seating) (see Section 1017.3.1).

[BE] EXIT DISCHARGE. That portion of a *means of egress* system between the termination of an *exit* and a *public way*.

❖ The exit discharge will typically begin where the building occupants reach the exterior at or very near grade level. It provides occupants with a path of travel away from the building. All components between the building and the public way are considered to be the exit discharge, regardless of the distance. In areas of sloping terrain, it is possible to have steps or stairs in the exit discharge leading to the public way. The exit discharge is part of the means of egress and, therefore, its components are subject to the requirements of the code (see Commentary Figures 202-E1 and 202-E3 and Section 1028).

[BE] EXIT DISCHARGE, LEVEL OF. The *story* at the point at which an *exit* terminates and an *exit discharge* begins.

❖ The term is intended to describe the story where the transition from exit to exit discharge occurs. At this level, the occupant needs only to move in a substantially horizontal path to move along exit discharge (see Commentary Figure 202-E4). Since the level is a volume rather than a horizontal plane, exterior exit steps may be part of the exit discharge where they provide access to the level that is closest to grade.

[BE] EXIT PASSAGEWAY. An *exit* component that is separated from other interior spaces of a building or structure by fire-resistance-rated construction and opening protectives, and provides for a protected path of egress travel in a horizontal direction to the *exit discharge*.

❖ This term refers to a horizontal portion of the means of egress that serves as an exit element. Since an exit passageway is considered an exit element, it must be protected and separated as required by the code for exits (see Section 1024). Exit passageways between a vertical exit enclosure and an exterior exit door are typically found on the level of exit discharge

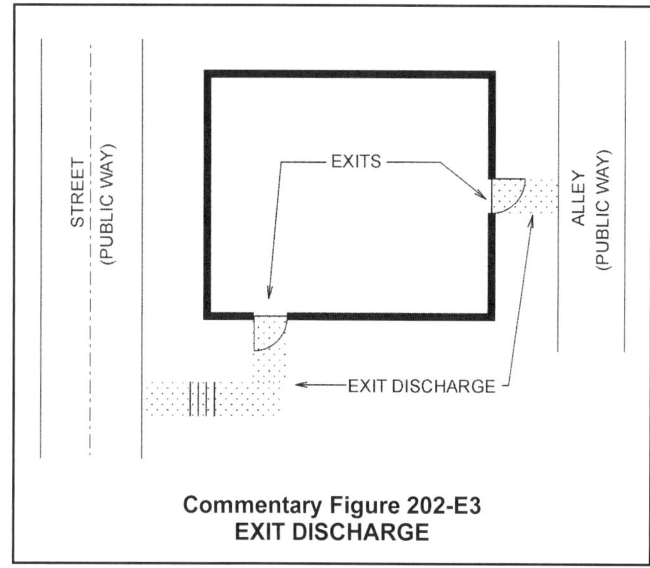

Commentary Figure 202-E3
EXIT DISCHARGE

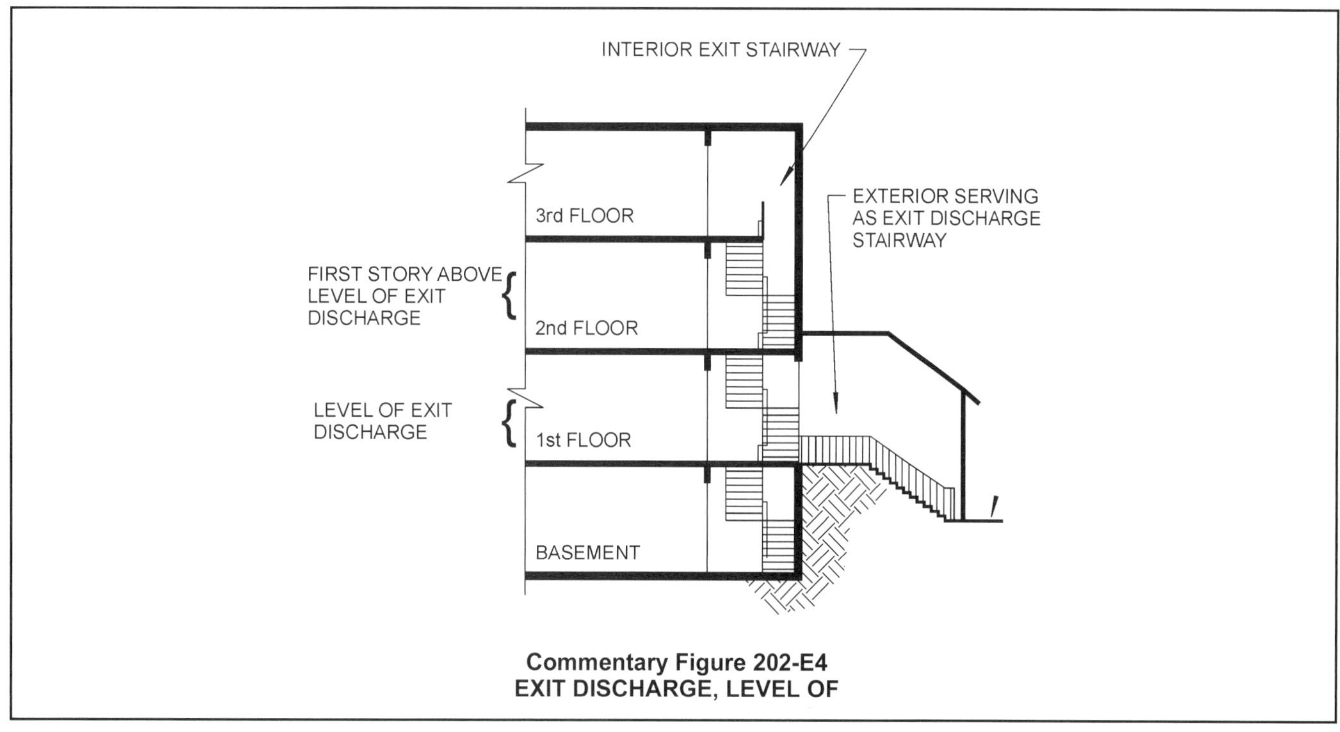

Commentary Figure 202-E4
EXIT DISCHARGE, LEVEL OF

to provide a protected path from a centrally located exit stairway to the exit discharge. In taller buildings that reduce floor sizes as they move up (sometimes called a wedding cake building), exit passageways are sometimes utilized at "transfer floors" where stairway shaft locations shift outward as the floor size increases. Exit passageways that lead to an exterior exit door are commonly used in malls to satisfy the travel distance in buildings having a large floor area.

EXPANDED PLASTIC. A foam or cellular plastic material having a reduced density based on the presence of numerous small cavities or cells dispersed throughout the material.

❖ Expanded plastic is a synthetic or natural organic material that, under high temperatures or pressures, can be shaped, formed and molded into any shape and maintain that shape at ambient temperatures. Plastics are combustible materials, some of which will give off toxic gases when exposed to fire. The most commonly recognized expanded plastic product is a disposable coffee cup. When plastic is expanded, it becomes much more susceptible to combustion due to the larger surface area of the material per unit weight.

EXPLOSION. An effect produced by the sudden violent expansion of gases, which may be accompanied by a shock wave or disruption, or both, of enclosing materials or structures. An explosion could result from any of the following:

1. Chemical changes such as rapid oxidation, *deflagration* or *detonation*, decomposition of molecules and runaway polymerization (usually *detonations*).
2. Physical changes such as pressure tank ruptures.
3. Atomic changes (nuclear fission or fusion).

❖ Buildings containing materials that pose a threat of explosion are classified as Group H-1 where such materials are present in quantities exceeding the MAQ in Table 5003.1.1(1). Such buildings are required to be a detached storage building meeting the requirements of Section 415.7 of the IBC and Chapter 56 of the code.

EXPLOSIVE. A chemical compound, mixture or device, the primary or common purpose of which is to function by explosion. The term includes, but is not limited to, dynamite, black powder, pellet powder, initiating explosives, detonators, safety fuses, squibs, detonating cord, igniter cord and igniters.

The term "Explosive" includes any material determined to be within the scope of USC Title 18: Chapter 40 and also includes any material classified as an explosive by the *hazardous materials* regulations of DOTn 49 CFR Parts 100-185.

❖ Explosives either detonate or deflagrate, rather than burn, when initiated by either heat, shock or electric current. Although these materials are normally designed and intended to be initiated by detonators under controlled conditions, heat, shock and electric current from uncontrolled sources may initiate these materials to produce an explosion.

High explosive. *Explosive material*, such as dynamite, which can be caused to detonate by means of a No. 8 test blasting cap where unconfined.

❖ High explosives can also deflagrate, but they are capable of even more. Before any appreciable amount of gas can escape and reduce the pressure, the body of the explosive is completely vaporized. The strength of a particular explosive depends on the amount of gas and heat it produces. At the very instant of their formation, the gases in a high-explosive state occupy only the original volume of the explosive material. Gas pressures can soar above 1 million pounds per square inch (psi); temperatures of 6,000°F (3316°C) and higher are common. Rapid expansion must occur and pressure waves move out at enormous velocities, often supersonic, doing tremendous damage.

Low explosive. *Explosive material* that will burn or deflagrate when ignited. It is characterized by a rate of reaction that is less than the speed of sound. Examples of low *explosives* include, but are not limited to, black powder, safety fuse, igniters, igniter cord, fuse lighters, fireworks and propellants, 1.3C.

❖ In low-explosive materials the burning rate is rapid but the created gases still have time to escape as the explosive is consumed. Gunpowder, for example, burns extremely rapidly and the gases are put to work, projecting an object out of a gun barrel. Pressures remain relatively low when the explosive is unconfined. Low explosive, like black powder, will deflagrate (burn intensely), producing a visible flame, such as a muzzle flash, but they do not ordinarily detonate.

Mass-detonating explosives. Division 1.1, 1.2 and 1.5 *explosives* alone or in combination, or loaded into various types of ammunition or containers, most of which can be expected to explode virtually instantaneously when a small portion is subjected to fire, severe concussion, impact, the impulse of an initiating agent or the effect of a considerable discharge of energy from without. Materials that react in this manner represent a mass explosion hazard. Such an *explosive* will normally cause severe structural damage to adjacent objects. Explosive propagation could occur immediately to other items of ammunition and *explosives* stored sufficiently close to and not adequately protected from the initially exploding pile with a time interval short enough so that two or more quantities must be considered as one for quantity-distance purposes.

❖ Mass-detonating explosives (typically stored in occupancies classified as Group H-1 by the IBC) present a detonation hazard, as do high explosives, and present a greater threat to adjacent objects and structures. The code, therefore, contains provisions in Table 5605.3 to deal with the separation distances for mass-explosion hazards.

UN/DOTn Class 1 explosives. The former classification system used by DOTn included the terms "high" and "low" *explosives* as defined herein. The following terms further define *explosives* under the current system applied by DOTn for all *explosive materials* defined as hazard Class 1 materials. Compatibility group letters are used in concert with the division to specify further limitations on each division noted (for example, the letter G identifies the material as a pyrotechnic substance or article containing a pyrotechnic substance and similar materials).

❖ The Department of Transportation (DOT) issued new regulations in 1991 based on the United Nations *Recommendations on the Transport of Dangerous Goods* for the transportation of hazardous materials. DOT's hazardous materials requirements with respect to hazard communications, classifications and packaging of explosives were revised by the new regulations.

Division 1.1. *Explosives* that have a mass explosion hazard. A mass explosion is one which affects almost the entire load instantaneously.

Division 1.2. *Explosives* that have a projection hazard but not a mass explosion hazard.

Division 1.3. *Explosives* that have a fire hazard and either a minor blast hazard or a minor projection hazard or both, but not a mass explosion hazard.

Division 1.4. *Explosives* that pose a minor explosion hazard. The explosive effects are largely confined to the package and no projection of fragments of appreciable size or range is to be expected. An external fire must not cause virtually instantaneous explosion of almost the entire contents of the package.

Division 1.5. Very insensitive *explosives*. This division is comprised of substances that have a mass explosion hazard but which are so insensitive that there is very little probability of initiation or of transition from burning to *detonation* under normal conditions of transport.

Division 1.6. Extremely insensitive articles which do not have a mass explosion hazard. This division is comprised of articles that contain only extremely insensitive detonating substances and which demonstrate a negligible probability of accidental initiation or propagation.

❖ The DOT puts explosives in six classes according to the degree of hazard posed by the material (see Commentary Figure 202-E5). The most dangerous of these materials is capable of almost simultaneous detonation of all of the material in a single load or store. The least sensitive explosives produce blasts limited to the packages in which they are transported. This definition of "Explosive" includes materials such as: detonators, blasting agents and water gels. Examples of these materials are listed in DOTy 27, CFR 55.23.

EXPLOSIVE MATERIAL. The term "explosive" material means *explosives*, blasting agents and detonators.

❖ A list of explosive materials is maintained by the ATF pursuant to 18 USC, Chapter 40. This list (ATF Publication 5400.8) is available at no cost from the ATF Distribution Center, 7943 Angus Court, Springfield, VA 22153.

[BE] EXTERIOR EXIT RAMP. An *exit* component that serves to meet one or more *means of egress* design requirements, such as required number of *exits* or *exit access* travel distance, and is open to yards, courts or *public ways*.

❖ Requirements for an exterior exit ramp are different from those for an interior exit ramp. Exterior exit ramps are typically outside of the building, provide exits from levels above or below the level of exit discharge, and are exposed to at least some elements of weather. The protection requirements therefore are for the exterior walls between the building and the ramp, rather than interior walls. For the ramp requirements, see Section 1012. For specifics for exterior exit ramps, see Section 1027.

[BE] EXTERIOR EXIT STAIRWAY. An *exit* component that serves to meet one or more *means of egress* design requirements, such as required number of *exits* or *exit access* travel distance, and is open to yards, courts or *public ways*.

❖ Requirements for an exterior exit stairway are different from those for an interior exit stairway. Exterior exit stairways are typically outside of the building, provide exits from above or below the level of exit discharge, and are exposed to at least some elements of weather. The protection requirements therefore are for the exterior walls between the building and the stairway, rather than interior walls. For the stairway

BATF	OLD DOTn[a]	NEW DOTn[b, c]	Description
High Explosives	Class A Explosives	Division 1.1	Mass Explosion Potential
		Division 1.2	Projectile Hazard
Low Explosives	Class B Explosives	Division 1.3	Predominantly a Fire Hazard
	Class C Explosives	Division 1.4	No Significant Blast Hazard
Blasting Agents	Blasting Agents	Division 1.5	Very Sensitive Explosives
	Dangerous	Division 1.6	Extremely Insensitive Detonating Substances

a. Prior to September 30, 1991.

b. Effective October 1, 1991.

c. *International Fire Code* and new DOT classifications correlate.

Commentary Figure 202-E5
COMPARISON OF CLASSIFICATION SYSTEMS FOR EXPLOSIVE MATERIALS

requirements, see Section 1011. For specifics for exterior exit stairways, see Section 1027.

[BF] EXTERIOR WALL. A wall, bearing or nonbearing, that is used as an enclosing wall for a building, other than a *fire wall*, and that has a slope of 60 degrees (1.05 rad) or greater with the horizontal plane.

❖ A wall is defined as an exterior element that encloses a structure and that has a slope equal to or greater than 60 degrees (1.05 rad) from the horizontal plane. Exterior enclosing elements with slopes less than this are generally subjected to more severe weather exposure than vertical surfaces and thus may experience a greater amount of water intrusion. These sloped surfaces, which may include elements such as inset windowsills, sloped parapets and other architectural elements, should be designed to resist water penetration in a manner similar to a roof.

EXTRA-HIGH-RACK COMBUSTIBLE STORAGE. Storage on racks of Class I, II, III or IV commodities that exceed 40 feet (12 192 mm) in height and storage on racks of high-hazard commodities that exceed 30 feet (9144 mm) in height.

❖ This term was generated to address those storage areas that were of unusual height, and where that height would have an influence on the building or structure, the contents and the safeguards from the hazards of a fire or explosion. Extra-high-rack combustible storage is common to building occupancies that require a substantial amount of storage of commodities (supply) necessary to ensure that the process remains operational. An example of this type of storage is an automotive assembly plant where the rack storage contains a sufficient amount of material to service the assembly plant operation for several days or weeks.

FABRICATION AREA. An area within a semiconductor fabrication facility and related research and development areas in which there are processes using hazardous production materials. Such areas are allowed to include ancillary rooms or areas such as dressing rooms and offices that are directly related to the fabrication area processes.

❖ This definition describes the basic component of a Hazardous Production Materials (HPM) facility. The code uses this definition to set certain material limitations based on both quantity and density, and to require enclosure of the fabrication areas with fire-barrier assemblies in accordance with Section 707 of the IBC, or horizontal assemblies in accordance with Section 711 of the IBC. The fabrication area of an HPM facility is the area where the hazardous materials are actively handled and processed. The fabrication area includes accessory rooms and spaces, such as workstations and employee dressing rooms.

[A] FACILITY. A building or use in a fixed location including exterior storage areas for flammable and combustible substances and hazardous materials, piers, wharves, tank farms and similar uses. This term includes recreational vehicles, mobile home and manufactured housing parks, sales and storage lots.

❖ The scope of a fire code is broader than the scope of a building code, in that it addresses outdoor storage, tank farms, fire department access and similar activities. The term "facility" helps to more clearly define this scope to clarify the application of this code. As noted in the definition, a building would be included in the definition for "Facility." This definition differs from that used in Chapter 11 of the IBC, which addresses the topic of accessibility for those with disabilities.

FAIL-SAFE. A design condition incorporating a feature for automatically counteracting the effect of an anticipated possible source of failure; also, a design condition eliminating or mitigating a hazardous condition by compensating automatically for a failure or malfunction.

❖ This definition provides consistency of terminology among the 10 sections of the code that use the term. A fail-safe design can include an automatic emergency shutoff valve that is designed to close upon loss of power or a process upset condition. It may include an excess flow control valve or feature which is designed to stop the flow of a gas or liquid when a preset flow rate is exceeded. In most cases, the fail-safe condition would stop the movement or processing of hazardous materials. The definition is based on a combination of definitions from *Webster's Third New International Dictionary of the English Language, Unabridged* and NFPA 70E.

FALLOUT AREA. The area over which aerial shells are fired. The shells burst over the area, and unsafe debris and malfunctioning aerial shells fall into this area. The fallout area is the location where a typical aerial shell dud falls to the ground depending on the wind and the angle of mortar placement.

❖ The area described by this definition is a large, unoccupied open space that functions as a "safety zone" between the fireworks display launch area and the spectator areas and is included in the display site definition in this section. The layout of the fallout area is usually centered around the location of, and takes into account the launch angle of, the mortars used to launch the aerial displays. Local weather wind direction and speed forecasts may also affect the layout of the area. The fallout area provides a relatively safe area in which display debris and dud or malfunctioned shells may fall and is the starting point for the post-display inspection required by Section 5608.9. Within the fallout area, no spectators or vehicles should be allowed, and the area should be free of combustible materials that could be ignited by falling debris. In reviewing the fallout area site plan, the presence and location of trees, brush and other vegetation that could "hide" undetonated shells or be a fire ignition hazard should be considered. In some cases, it may be necessary to wet down the fallout area to further reduce the ignition hazard to vegetation by falling hot debris.

FALSE ALARM. The willful and knowing initiation or transmission of a signal, message or other notification of an event of fire when no such danger exists.

❖ The term "false alarm" can have several meanings beyond what this particular definition provides. This definition states that for the purposes of the code a false alarm is an unnecessary, intentional activation of a fire alarm system, signal or message. It would not include alarm activation as a result of a malfunctioning detector.

FINES. Small pieces or splinters of wood byproducts that will pass through a 0.25-inch (6.4 mm) screen.

❖ Fines range in size from sawdust to chips and are usually accumulated in piles.

FIRE ALARM. The giving, signaling or transmission to any public fire station, or company or to any officer or employee thereof, whether by telephone, spoken word or otherwise, of information to the effect that there is a fire at or near the place indicated by the person giving, signaling or transmitting such information.

❖ This is a general definition intended to clarify that a fire alarm is not simply a fire alarm system. This definition would allow a person's actions to be considered part of the fire alarm. The key is that a fire alarm notifies the correct persons or group of persons, such as the fire department or a central station, of a fire.

FIRE ALARM BOX, MANUAL. See "Manual fire alarm box."

FIRE ALARM CONTROL UNIT. A system component that receives inputs from automatic and manual fire alarm devices and may be capable of supplying power to detection devices and transponder(s) or off-premises transmitter(s). The control unit may be capable of providing a transfer of power to the notification appliances and transfer of condition to relays or devices.

❖ The fire alarm control unit (panel) acts as a point where all signals initiated within the protected building are received before the signal is transmitted to a constantly attended location. As the name implies, it also contains controls to test and manually activate or silence systems.

FIRE ALARM SIGNAL. A signal initiated by a fire alarm-initiating device such as a manual fire alarm box, automatic fire detector, waterflow switch or other device whose activation is indicative of the presence of a fire or fire signature.

❖ This signal is transmitted to a fire alarm control unit as a warning that requires immediate action. The personnel at the constantly attended location are trained to immediately respond to a fire alarm signal, which indicates the presence of a fire. A fire alarm signal assumes an actual fire has been detected (see the definition of "Alarm signal"). The fire alarm signal is not the signal used to notify the occupants of an emergency condition. Such an action would involve the audible alarm, visual alarm or emergency voice/alarm notification appliances.

FIRE ALARM SYSTEM. A system or portion of a combination system consisting of components and circuits arranged to monitor and annunciate the status of fire alarm or supervisory signal-initiating devices and to initiate the appropriate response to those signals.

❖ Fire alarm systems are installed in buildings to limit fire casualties and property losses by notifying the occupants of the building, the local fire department or both of an emergency condition. The alarm notification appliances associated with fire alarm systems are intended to be evacuation alarms. All fire alarm systems must be designed and installed to comply with NFPA 72. The term is among the most generic terms used in the code. It does not necessarily imply an automatic or manual system, nor does it identify what type of notification, if any, should be provided. The definition only indicates that an appropriate response must be provided but does not indicate what that response must be. The appropriate responses are identified within the respective sections of Section 907.

FIRE APPARATUS ACCESS ROAD. A road that provides fire apparatus access from a fire station to a facility, building or portion thereof. This is a general term inclusive of all other terms such as *fire lane*, public street, private street, parking lot lane and access roadway.

❖ Fire apparatus access roads are required to be all-weather surfaced roadways that are designed for the weight and type of emergency vehicle that may use the road. No specific surface material is required for a fire apparatus access roadway. It is up to the fire code official to decide whether the surface will support the load of the anticipated emergency vehicles in accordance with Section 503.2.3.

It should be noted that this is a general term intended to include any private roadway providing the required access to a building. As such, private driveways could be included and subject to the provisions of Section 503.

[BF] FIRE AREA. The aggregate floor area enclosed and bounded by *fire walls*, *fire barriers*, *exterior walls* or *horizontal assemblies* of a building. Areas of the building not provided with surrounding walls shall be included in the fire area if such areas are included within the horizontal projection of the roof or floor next above.

❖ This term is used to describe a specific and controlled area within a building that may consist of a portion of the floor area within a single story, one entire story or the combined floor area of several stories, depending on how these areas are enclosed and separated from other floor areas. Where a fire barrier with a fire-resistance rating in accordance with Section 707.3.10 of the IBC divides the floor area of a one-story building, the floor area on each side of the wall would constitute a separate fire area. Where a horizontal assembly separating the two stories in a two-story building is fire-resistance rated in accordance with Section 711.2.4 of the IBC, each story would be a separate fire area. In cases where mezzanines are present, the floor area of the mezzanine is included in the fire area calculations, even though the area of the mezzanine does not contribute to the building area calculations. See the commentary to Sections 707.3.10 and 711.2.4 of the IBC for further information. Note that, while fire walls are one way of creating fire areas, they are typically used to create separate buildings.

[BF] FIRE BARRIER. A fire-resistance-rated wall assembly of materials designed to restrict the spread of fire in which continuity is maintained.

❖ The term represents wall assemblies with a fire-resistance rating that are constructed in accordance with Section 707 of the IBC. Even though the definition applies to walls, horizontal assemblies can be fire barriers, also. See the definition of "Horizontal assembly" and the requirements in Section 711 of the IBC that apply to floor and roof assemblies designed to restrict the spread of fire.

FIRE CHIEF. The chief officer of the fire department serving the jurisdiction, or a duly authorized representative.

❖ This definition is necessary to note that when the term "fire chief" is used within the text of the code it is specifically referring to the chief officer of a fire department. This position can be delegated as necessary but must be appropriately authorized.

FIRE CODE OFFICIAL. The fire chief or other designated authority charged with the administration and enforcement of the code, or a duly authorized representative.

❖ Whoever holds the statutory power to enforce the fire code is termed the "fire code official." Normally, responsibility for this enforcement is assigned to a fire prevention bureau or related code enforcement department of the state, county or municipality. In the case of a fire department, the role of fire code official is most often given to the fire chief, the fire marshal or the fire inspector. Often with regard to the fire code, the fire code official will be the fire marshal or fire chief. In some cases, direct reference will be made to the fire chief within the code because some situations are specific to the actions of the fire department, such as authority at fire scenes.

FIRE COMMAND CENTER. The principal attended or unattended location where the status of detection, alarm communications and control systems is displayed, and from which the system(s) can be manually controlled.

❖ Fire command centers are communication centers, typically in high-rise buildings, where dedicated manual and automatic facilities are located for the origination, control and transmission of information and instructions pertaining to a fire emergency to the occupants (including fire department personnel) of the building. Fire command centers must provide facilities for the control and display of the status of all fire protection (detection, signaling, etc.) systems as well as critical building systems. These fire command centers must be located in secure areas as approved by the fire code official. Often, this is a location near the primary building entrance. Fire command centers may also be combined with other building operations and security facilities, where allowed by the fire code official; however, operating controls for use by the fire department must be clearly marked and not subject to tampering by unauthorized persons (see the commentary to Section 508.1 for further discussion).

[BF] FIRE DAMPER. A *listed* device installed in ducts and air transfer openings designed to close automatically upon detection of heat and resist the passage of flame. Fire dampers are classified for use in either static systems that will automatically shut down in the event of a fire, or in dynamic systems that continue to operate during a fire. A dynamic fire damper is tested and rated for closure under elevated temperature airflow.

❖ Fire dampers are used primarily in heating, ventilating and air-conditioning (HVAC) duct systems that pass through fire-resistance-rated walls or floors. Dampers may also be installed in rated walls independent of HVAC duct systems. Dampers are provided to maintain the fire-resistance rating of the penetrated assembly. Fire dampers are regulated by UL 555. See also the commentary to the definitions of "Damper" and "Smoke damper."

FIRE DEPARTMENT MASTER KEY. A limited issue key of special or controlled design to be carried by fire department officials in command which will open key boxes on specified properties.

❖ Several companies market emergency rapid entry systems and other accessories that use fire department master keys. These keys are used to open key boxes and entry gates, and turn on/off special switches that control electric gates and certain building functions, such as smoke control systems, fans and special processes. These keys are highly secure in their design and very difficult, if not impossible, to duplicate other than by the manufacturer.

FIRE DETECTOR, AUTOMATIC. A device designed to detect the presence of a fire signature and to initiate action.

❖ Automatic fire detectors include all approved devices designed to detect the presence of a fire and automatically initiate emergency action. These include smoke-sensing fire detectors, heat-sensing fire detectors, flame-sensing fire detectors, gas-sensing fire detectors and other fire detectors that operate on other principles as approved by the fire code official. Automatic fire detectors must be selected based on the type and size of fire to be detected and the response required. The automatic fire detector sends a signal to a processing unit to initiate some predetermined action. The processing unit may be internal to the device, as is the case with single-station smoke detectors, or it may be an external unit, as in the case of a fire alarm control unit. Automatic fire detectors must be approved, installed and tested to comply with the code and NFPA 72.

[BF] FIRE DOOR. The door component of a fire door assembly.

❖ A fire door is the primary component of a fire door assembly. The fire protection rating assigned to a tested fire door is only valid if the door is installed in a labeled frame with appropriate hardware. Installation requirements within the code reference NFPA 80, *Standard for Fire Doors and Other Opening Protectives*. Door ratings are expressed in minutes or hours. Field modification of doors are primarily limited to the mounting of listed hardware.

[BF] FIRE DOOR ASSEMBLY. Any combination of a fire door, frame, hardware and other accessories that together provide a specific degree of fire protection to the opening.

❖ Fire door assemblies, (door, frame and hardware) are required to be tested using the appropriate standard and then installed in accordance with NFPA 80. Side-hinged doors, hardware and frames are often manufactured separately with manufacturers and listing agencies defining acceptable combinations of assembly components that have been tested together.

[BF] FIRE EXIT HARDWARE. Panic hardware that is *listed* for use on *fire door assemblies*.

❖ Where a door that is required to be of fire-resistance-rated construction also has panic hardware, the hardware is required to be listed for use on the fire door. Thus, fire door hardware has been tested to function properly where exposed to the effects of a fire (see the definition for "Panic hardware" and Section 1010.1.10).

FIRE LANE. A road or other passageway developed to allow the passage of fire apparatus. A fire lane is not necessarily intended for vehicular traffic other than fire apparatus.

❖ The term "fire lane" is synonymous with "fire apparatus access road"; however, the driving surface may not be the same as for a public road.

[BF] FIRE PARTITION. A vertical assembly of materials designed to restrict the spread of fire in which openings are protected.

❖ Fire partitions are used as wall assemblies to separate adjacent tenant spaces in covered mall buildings, dwelling units and sleeping rooms, and to enclose corridors and elevator lobbies. Section 708 of the IBC establishes the construction requirements for fire partitions. The fire-resistance ratings, continuity requirements and opening protective requirements for fire partitions are usually less restrictive than those for fire barriers.

FIRE POINT. The lowest temperature at which a liquid will ignite and achieve sustained burning when exposed to a test flame in accordance with ASTM D92.

❖ The fire point is the lowest temperature at which a liquid will ignite and sustain burning for a minimum of 5 seconds (fire point) when exposed to the test flame under a specific barometric pressure according to ASTM D92.

[BF] FIRE PROTECTION RATING. The period of time that an opening protective assembly will maintain the ability to confine a fire as determined by tests prescribed in Section 716 of the *International Building Code*. Ratings are stated in hours or minutes.

❖ The term "fire protection rating" applies to the fire performance of an opening protective, such as a fire door, which is determined through tests performed in accordance with NFPA 252 or UL 10C.

FIRE PROTECTION SYSTEM. *Approved* devices, equipment and systems or combinations of systems used to detect a fire, activate an alarm, extinguish or control a fire, control or manage smoke and products of a fire or any combination thereof.

❖ A fire protection system is any approved device or equipment used singly or in combination, either manually or automatically, that is intended to detect a fire, notify the building occupants of a fire or suppress the fire. Fire protection systems include fire suppression systems, standpipe systems, fire alarm systems, fire detection systems, smoke control systems and smoke vents. All fire protection systems must be approved by the fire code official and tested in accordance with the referenced standards and Section 901.6.

[BF] FIRE RESISTANCE. That property of materials or their assemblies that prevents or retards the passage of excessive heat, hot gases or flames under conditions of use.

❖ All materials offer some degree of fire resistance. A sheet of plywood has a low level of fire resistance as compared to a concrete block, which has a higher level of fire resistance. The fire resistance of a material or an assembly is evaluated by testing performed in accordance with ASTM E119. Tested materials will be assigned a fire-resistance rating consistent with the demonstrated performance.

FIRE SAFETY FUNCTIONS. Building and fire control functions that are intended to increase the level of life safety for occupants or to control the spread of the harmful effects of fire.

❖ In many cases, automatic fire detectors are installed even in buildings not required to have a fire alarm system. These fire detectors perform specific functions, such as releasing door hold-open devices, activating elevator recall, smoke damper activation or air distribution system shutdown (see Section 907.3).

[BF] FIRE SEPARATION DISTANCE. The distance measured from the building face to one of the following:

1. The closest interior *lot line*.
2. To the centerline of a street, an alley or *public way*.
3. To an imaginary line between two buildings on the lot.

The distance shall be measured at right angles from the face of the wall.

❖ Fire separation distance is the distance from the exterior wall of the building to one of the three following locations, measured perpendicular to the exterior wall face: an interior lot line; the centerline of a street or public way; or an imaginary line between two buildings on the same property. The imaginary line can be located anywhere between the two buildings; it is the designer's choice, but once established, the location of the line applies to both buildings and cannot be revised.

The distance can vary with irregular-shaped lots and buildings. When applying the exterior wall requirements of Table 602 of the IBC, the required exterior wall fire-resistance rating might vary along a building side; for example, where the lot line is not parallel to the exterior wall. For further information, see Chapter 7 of the *IBC® Code and Commentary*.

[BF] FIRE WALL. A fire-resistance-rated wall having protected openings, which restricts the spread of fire and extends continuously from the foundation to or through the roof, with sufficient structural stability under fire conditions to allow collapse of construction on either side without collapse of the wall.

❖ Fire walls must meet the construction requirements in Section 706 of the IBC. The requirements for fire walls are much more restrictive than for fire barriers or fire partitions. The material constituting the fire wall must be noncombustible in all construction types except Type V. The vertical and horizontal continuity requirements are much more restrictive as are the opening protectives. A fire wall also has stringent requirements for continuity and for protection of any openings through it. A fire wall, unlike the fire barrier and fire partition, must be built so it will remain in place if the construction on either side of it collapses. However, the fire wall is not required to remain in place if construction on both sides of it collapses (i.e., the fire wall is not required to be a free-standing or cantilevered wall). Fire walls are used to divide a structure into separate buildings (see the definition of "Area, building"). To be considered separate buildings, the division must be vertical. The term "fire wall" applies to vertically constructed assemblies only and not to horizontal assemblies.

FIRE WATCH. A temporary measure intended to ensure continuous and systematic surveillance of a building or portion thereof by one or more qualified individuals for the purposes of identifying and controlling fire hazards, detecting early signs of unwanted fire, raising an alarm of fire and notifying the fire department.

❖ This term is used in several places throughout the code. A fire watch, sometimes referred to as standby personnel, provides temporary fire safety where there are potential hazards, such as during hot work operations or when fire protection systems are out of service. A fire watch is not simply to watch for a fire but also to prevent fire by identifying and controlling fire hazards, such as the separation of combustibles from areas where welding is to occur. A fire watch also provides a method of notifying the fire department if a fire should occur.

[BF] FIREBLOCKING. Building materials, or materials *approved* for use as fireblocking, installed to resist the free passage of flame to other areas of the building through concealed spaces.

❖ Fireblocking is required to hinder the concealed spread of flame, heat and other products of combustion within hollow spaces inside of walls or floor/ceiling assemblies. This is done by periodically subdividing that space, as indicated in Section 718.2 of the IBC, using construction materials that have some resistance to fire and by sealing the openings around penetrations through those materials.

Some fireblocking materials are permitted to be combustible based on the rationale that a substantial combustible material will provide a barrier adequate to perform the intended function (also see Section 718 of the IBC).

[BF] FIRE-RESISTANCE RATING. The period of time a building element, component or assembly maintains the ability to confine a fire, continues to perform a given structural function, or both, as determined by the tests, or the methods based on tests, prescribed in Section 703 of the *International Building Code*.

❖ This refers to the period of time a building element, component or assembly maintains the ability to confine a fire, continues to perform a given structural function, or both, as determined by tests or the methods based on tests, prescribed in Section 703 of the IBC.

The fire-resistance rating is developed using standardized test methods (i.e., ASTM E119, etc.). Assemblies rated under these tests are deemed to be able to perform their function for a specified period of time under specific fire conditions (standard time-temperature curve).

The fire-resistance rating is not intended to be a prediction of the actual length of time that an assembly will perform its intended function under actual fire conditions. Although the time-temperature curves of standardized fire test methods are usually selected to approximate at least some real-life fire conditions, the very wide range of actual fire conditions makes the listed fire-resistance rating more of a nominal, comparative index than a predictor of fire-resistance time in any given fire incident.

[BF] FIRE-RESISTANT JOINT SYSTEM. An assemblage of specific materials or products that are designed, tested and fire-resistance rated in accordance with either ASTM E1966 or UL 2079 to resist for a prescribed period of time the passage of fire through joints made in or between fire-resistance-rated assemblies.

❖ In order to maintain the fire-resistant integrity of fire-resistance-rated assemblies, joints that occur within an assembly or between adjacent assemblies must be protected through an installation that has been tested in accordance with ASTM E1966 or UL 2079. Some common examples of applications where a fire-resistant joint system would be required are expansion joints in fire-resistance-rated floors or walls and the junction between fire-resistance-rated floors and walls (see Commentary Figure 202-F1 for examples). The regular joints that occur within a uniform assembly are most often tested as part of fire testing (e.g., in accordance with ASTM E119) for that entire assembly. The required details for these joints are specified in the listings for the underlying assembly. These joints do not need additional testing in accordance with ASTM E1966 or UL 2079. An example of such joints is the joints between individual sheets of gypsum board in a gypsum-sheathed stud wall. Consequently, other than the joints covering or filling the gaps within an assembly, the need for ASTM E1966 or UL 2079 tested joint systems is usually for the joints between dissimilar or adjacent assemblies.

FIREWORKS. Any composition or device for the purpose of producing a visible or an audible effect for entertainment purposes by combustion, *deflagration* or *detonation* that meets the definition of 1.3G fireworks or 1.4G fireworks.

❖ This term refers to any device, other than a novelty or theatrical pyrotechnic article, intended to produce visible or audible effects by combustion, deflagration or detonation and any chemical compound or mechanically mixed preparation of an explosive or inflammable nature that is used for the purpose of making any manufactured fireworks and is not included in any other class of explosives.

Fireworks, 1.3G. Large fireworks devices, which are *explosive materials*, intended for use in fireworks displays and designed to produce audible or visible effects by combustion, *deflagration* or *detonation*. Such 1.3G fireworks include, but are not limited to, firecrackers containing more than 130 milligrams (2 grains) of explosive composition, aerial shells containing more than 40 grams of pyrotechnic composition and other display pieces which exceed the limits for classification as 1.4G fireworks. Such 1.3G fireworks are also described as Fireworks, UN 0335 by the DOTn.

❖ This category of fireworks represents a considerable life safety hazard in comparison to the consumer 1.4G fireworks. This definition reflects the construction, chemical composition and labeling requirements of the CPSC, found in Title 16, Code of Federal Regulations, Parts 1500 and 1507.

Fireworks, 1.4G. Small fireworks devices containing restricted amounts of pyrotechnic composition designed primarily to produce visible or audible effects by combustion or deflagration that complies with the construction, chemical composition and labeling regulations of the DOTn for Fireworks, UN 0336, and the U.S. Consumer Product Safety Commission as set forth in CPSC 16 CFR Parts 1500 and 1507.

❖ The requirements for storage, display and labeling depend on the correct application of this definition. This definition reflects the construction, chemical

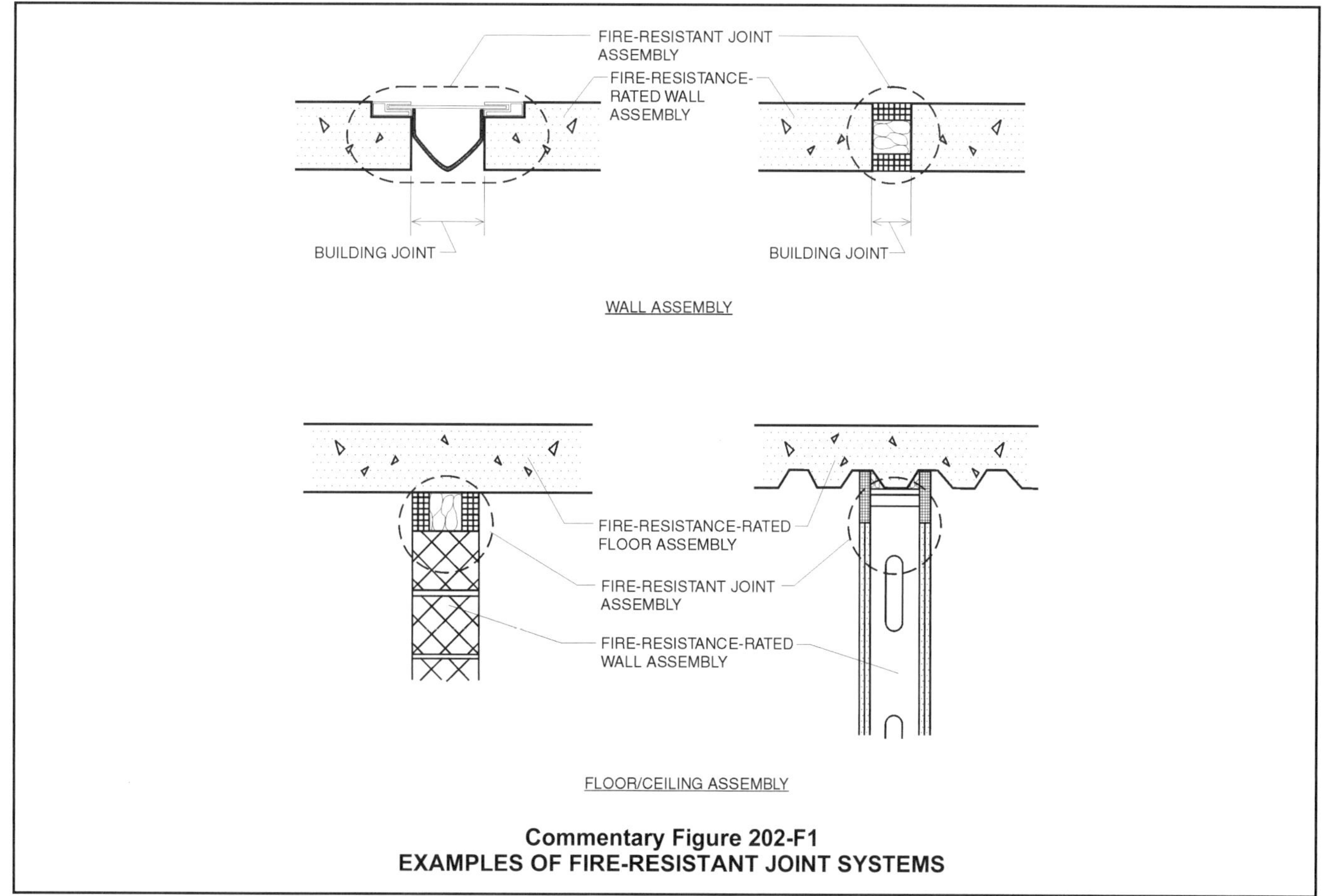

Commentary Figure 202-F1
EXAMPLES OF FIRE-RESISTANT JOINT SYSTEMS

composition and labeling requirements of the US Consumer Product Safety Commission (CPSC), found in Title 16, Code of Federal Regulations, Parts 1500 and 1507.

FIREWORKS DISPLAY. A presentation of fireworks for a public or private gathering.

❖ The areas selected for the discharge site, spectator viewing area, parking areas and the fallout area must be inspected and approved by the authority having jurisdiction.

[BG] FIXED BASE OPERATOR (FBO). A commercial business granted the right by the airport sponsor to operate on an airport and provide aeronautical services such as fueling, hangaring, tie-down and parking, aircraft rental, aircraft maintenance and flight instruction.

❖ Fixed base operator is a term of the aviation industry used to describe a firm that is permanently based at an airport and providing a variety of aircraft services. It is used in conjunction with Section 914.8.3 in the context of determining the appropriate level of fire suppression required in various aircraft hangars that will be found at an airport (see the commentary, Section 914.8.3).

[BE] FIXED SEATING. Furniture or fixtures designed and installed for the use of sitting and secured in place including bench-type seats and seats with or without back or arm rests.

❖ Fixed seating is secured to the floor or is a part of a seating system. Some of the varieties are bench seating, such as in bleachers, which can come with or without back rests; theater seating with arms for each viewer and seats that flip up; lecture halls with individual seats with tablet arms that are fixed or retractable; pew-type seating in courtrooms or churches; or booths in a restaurant. To allow appropriate egress from these spaces the occupant load tables allow for the individual seats to be counted to determine occupant load for the space. Space between the seats (i.e., aisle accessways) and aisles leading to the exits for these types of seating are addressed in Section 1029. Given their unique issues, bleachers, folding and telescopic seating and grandstands are referenced to ICC 300 in Section 1029.1.1.

[BF] FLAME SPREAD. The propagation of flame over a surface.

❖ The rate at which flames travel along the surface of a combustible finish material directly impacts the speed with which a fire spreads within a room or space, and is, therefore, regulated by Chapter 8.

[BF] FLAME SPREAD INDEX. A comparative measure, expressed as a dimensionless number, derived from visual measurements of the spread of flame versus time for a material tested in accordance with ASTM E84 or UL 723.

❖ The ASTM E84 (or UL 723) test method renders measurements of surface flame spread (and smoke density) in comparison with test results obtained by using select red oak as a control material. Red oak is used as a control material for furnace calibration because it is a fairly uniform grade of lumber that is readily available nationally, is uniform in thickness and moisture content, and generally gives consistent and reproducible results. The results of this test simply provide a relative understanding of flame spread potential. The flame spread index is sometimes abbreviated as FSI.

FLAMMABLE CRYOGENIC FLUID. A *cryogenic fluid* that is flammable in its vapor state.

❖ These fluids are flammable in a vapor stage or are to be considered as flammable. It may be possible for a fluid to be nonflammable in the liquid phase but flammable in the vapor stage. The vapor phase would be the more hazardous form of the material. Again, similar to the definition of "Cryogenic fluid," this describes the applicability of the code requirements. Flammability is dealt with in Chapter 58.

FLAMMABLE FINISHES. Coatings to articles or materials in which the material being applied is a flammable liquid, combustible liquid, combustible powder, fiberglass resin or flammable or combustible gel coating.

❖ This general definition is used to describe all the operations regulated in this chapter including spray applications, dip tank operations and powder-coating operations.

Refer to the definitions of "Combustible dust," "Combustible liquid" and "Flammable liquid." Note that although "combustible powder" is not defined in the code, the terms "combustible dust" and "combustible powder" have been used interchangeably. Also, the terms "gel" and "combustible gel" are not defined by the code. Gels or pastes and liquids are classified as liquids when classifying hazardous materials. For example, the flash point of a gel, paste or liquid determines the flammable or combustible classification of the product.

FLAMMABLE GAS. A material which is a gas at 68°F (20°C) or less at 14.7 pounds per square inch atmosphere (psia) (101 kPa) of pressure [a material that has a *boiling point* of 68°F (20°C) or less at 14.7 psia (101 kPa)] which:

1. Is ignitable at 14.7 psia (101 kPa) when in a mixture of 13 percent or less by volume with air; or
2. Has a flammable range at 14.7 psia (101 kPa) with air of not less than 12 percent, regardless of the lower limit.

The limits specified shall be determined at 14.7 psi (101 kPa) of pressure and a temperature of 68°F (20°C) in accordance with ASTM E681.

❖ The ASTM E681 test method covers the determination of the lower and upper concentration limits of chemicals having sufficient vapor pressure to form flammable mixtures in air at atmospheric pressure at the test temperature. The flammability limits depend on the test temperature and pressure. This test method is limited to an initial pressure of the local ambient or less, with a practical lower pressure limit of approximately 13 kPa (100 mm Hg). The maximum practical operating temperature of this equipment is approximately 302°F (150°C).

FLAMMABLE LIQUEFIED GAS. A liquefied *compressed gas* which, under a charged pressure, is partially liquid at a temperature of 68°F (20°C) and which is flammable.

❖ Flammable liqueified gases are widely useful because of their properties, including high heat output in combustion for most gases, high reactivity in chemical processing with other gases, extremely low temperatures available from some gases and the economy of handling them all in a compact form at high pressure or low temperature.

FLAMMABLE LIQUID. A liquid having a closed cup flash point below 100°F (38°C). Flammable liquids are further categorized into a group known as Class I liquids. The Class I category is subdivided as follows:

Class IA. Liquids having a flash point below 73°F (23°C) and having a *boiling point* below 100°F (38°C).

Class IB. Liquids having a *flash point* below 73°F (23°C) and having a *boiling point* at or above 100°F (38°C).

Class IC. Liquids having a *flash point* at or above 73°F (23°C) and below 100°F (38°C).

The category of flammable liquids does not include *compressed gases* or *cryogenic fluids*.

❖ Flammable liquids have a closed-cup flash point less than 100°F (38°C); the classification of Class I liquid into three classes is dependent on their flash point. The 100°F (38°C) flash point limitation for flammable liquids assumes possible indoor ambient temperature conditions of 100°F (38°C). The vapor pressure limitation of 40 pounds per square inch absolute (psia) (276 kPa) at 100°F (38°C) is the threshold for the definition of what constitutes a liquid for the purposes of classifying the material as a flammable or combustible liquid. Flammable liquids are classified into three classes based on a combination of their flash point and boiling point. Class IA has a flash point below 73°F (23°C) and a boiling point below 100°F (38°C). Class IB has a flash point below 73°F (23°C) and a boiling point at or above 100°F (38°C). Class IC has a flash point above 73°F (23°C) and below 100°F (38°C). Flammable liquids do not include compressed gases or cryogenic fluids. Compressed gases are regulated in Chapter 53 and cryogenic fluids are regulated in Chapter 55.

FLAMMABLE MATERIAL. A material capable of being readily ignited from common sources of heat or at a temperature of 600°F (316°C) or less.

❖ The primary focus of this term is to classify solid materials that are more hazardous than normal combustibles because of their susceptibility to ignition as flammable materials. Additionally, any material that will readily ignite at or below 600°F (316°C) would be considered flammable. The term "flammable materials" should not be confused with combustible materials.

FLAMMABLE SOLID. A solid, other than a blasting agent or *explosive*, that is capable of causing fire through friction, absorption of moisture, spontaneous chemical change or retained heat from manufacturing or processing, or which has an ignition temperature below 212°F (100°C) or which burns so vigorously and persistently when ignited as to create a serious hazard. A chemical shall be considered a flammable solid as determined in accordance with the test method of CPSC 16 CFR Part 1500.44, if it ignites and burns with a self-sustained flame at a rate greater than 0.0866 inch (2.2 mm) per second along its major axis.

❖ Flammable solids include various materials that either ignite readily, burn vigorously or are difficult to extinguish. Materials that may not ignite easily or burn vigorously in bulk form may do so in finely divided form. This is especially true of most flammable metals. Ignition sources for flammable solids include frictional heat from machining or cutting operations; absorption of moisture from air (as opposed to water-reactive materials forming flammable vapors when mixed with water); spontaneous chemical changes such as sublimation (the chemical process through which solids emit vapors without first changing phase to liquids); and heat absorbed during manufacturing processes such as oil quenching or heat treating. Solid materials with ignition temperatures below 212°F (100°C) that ignite before melting are also considered flammable solids, as are materials burning robustly and persistently when ignited, including magnesium and coal. CPSC has developed a standard test method (CPSC 16 CFR 1500.44) that is referenced for determining when a material complies with the definition. Commentary Figure 202-F2 depicts the equipment and test method. A material burning at a rate greater than 0.1 inch (2.5 mm) per second is considered a flammable solid for the purpose of applying the requirements of this chapter.

Commentary Figure 202-F3 lists both the melting points and ignition temperatures for several pure metals in bulk form. These materials may ignite at much lower temperatures when finely divided. Moreover, many metals, such as calcium, hafnium, plutonium, sodium, thorium and zirconium, will ignite in air under certain conditions. Thorium and plutonium will release radiation when they burn. Likewise, many metals react with each other in finely divided form. For example, iron or steel filings and fine magnesium particles, combined with frictional heat or cutting oil, can ignite in a thermite reaction. Aluminum, iron and steel are not usually recognized as combustible metals; however, aluminum, iron and steel can be ignited in powdered form. Rather than producing an open flame, both iron and steel produce a vigorous sparking reaction when ignited. On the other hand, aluminum may burn with explosive force.

Although the definition of "Flammable solid" could be literally interpreted as being applicable to a much wider variety of common materials (e.g., plastics, household items, toys, etc.) because ordinary combustible materials could fail the CPSC test, the defini-

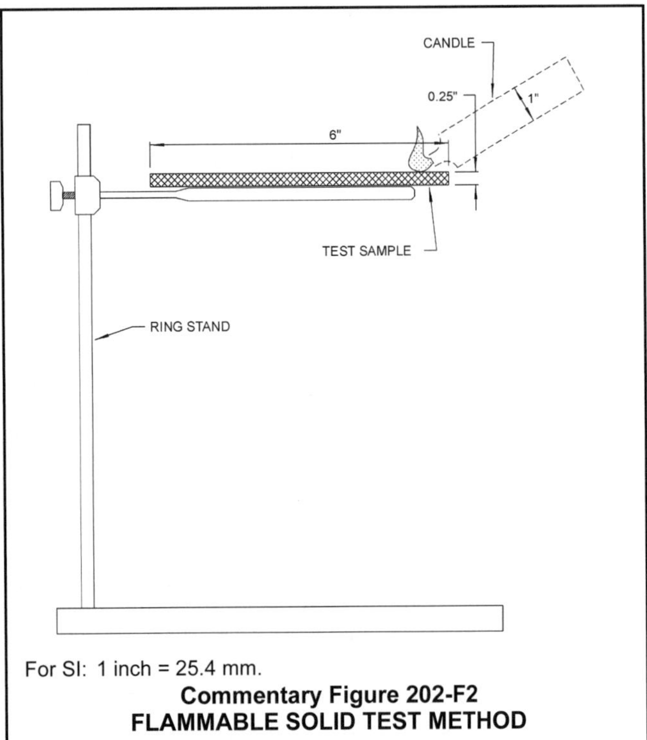

For SI: 1 inch = 25.4 mm.

Commentary Figure 202-F2
FLAMMABLE SOLID TEST METHOD

tion text clearly limits its application to "chemicals." This chapter is not intended to regulate such common-place materials or items because, practically speaking, such a sweeping application could result in many buildings, including Group R buildings, being classified or reclassified in Group H-3, which is certainly not the intent of the code. Commentary Figure 202-F4 describes fire hazards of selected common flammable solids that are regulated by this chapter.

FLAMMABLE VAPOR AREA. An area in which the concentration of flammable constituents (vapor, gas, fume, mist or dust) in air exceeds 25 percent of their lower flammable limit (LFL) because of the flammable finish processes operation. It shall include:

1. The interior of spray booths.
2. The interior of ducts exhausting from spraying processes.
3. Any area in the direct path of spray or any area containing dangerous quantities of air-suspended powder, combustible residue, dust, deposits, vapor or mists as a result of spraying operations.
4. The area in the vicinity of dip tanks, drain boards or associated drying, conveying or other equipment during operation or shutdown periods.

Material	Melting point (°F)	Ignition temperature (°F)
Aluminum[a]	1,220	1,832
Barium	1,337	347
Calcium	1,548	1,300
Hafnium	4,032	—
Iron[b]	2,795	1,706
Lithium	367	356
Magnesium	1,202	1,153
Plutonium	1,184	1,112
Potassium[c]	144	156
Sodium	208	239
Strontium	1,425	1,328
Thorium	3,353	932
Titanium	3,140	2,900
Uranium[d]	2,070	6,900
Zinc	786	1,652
Zinconium	3,326	2,552

For SI: °C = [(°F)-32]/1.8.

a. Above indicated temperature.

b. Ignition in oxygen.

c. Spontaneous ignition in moist air.

d. Below indicated temperature.

Commentary Figure 202-F3
MELTING AND IGNITION TEMPERATURES OF SELECTED PURE METALS IN SOLID FORM

The *fire code official* is authorized to determine the extent of the flammable vapor area, taking into consideration the material characteristics of the flammable materials, the degree of sustained ventilation and the nature of the operations.

❖ The extent of the flammable vapor area should be determined by the fire code official based on an evaluation of the coating process, the liquid being used, the ventilation rate in the area and other variables that might increase the hazard.

FLAMMABLE VAPORS OR FUMES. The concentration of flammable constituents in air that exceeds 25 percent of their lower flammable limit (LFL).

❖ Vapors or fumes are only considered flammable where there is a high enough concentration for an ignition to occur if exposed to an ignition source. The code specifically defines "Flammable" as being greater than 25 percent of the LFL.

FLASH POINT. The minimum temperature in degrees Fahrenheit at which a liquid will give off sufficient vapors to form an ignitable mixture with air near the surface or in the container, but will not sustain combustion. The flash point of a liquid shall be determined by appropriate test procedure and apparatus as specified in ASTM D56, ASTM D93 or ASTM D3278.

❖ The flash point is the characteristic used in the classification of flammable and combustible liquids. The flash point is the minimum temperature of a liquid at which it gives off sufficient vapor to form an ignitable mixture with air above its surface. The Tag Closed Tester (ASTM D56), the Pensky-Martens Closed

Material	Description
Carbon	
Carbon black	Carbon black is formed by combustion of certain gaseous hydrocarbons and hydrocarbon cracking. It is most hazardous after manufacture when particles may still be hot. Carbon black absorbs oxygen while cooling and smoldering may develop. After cooling, the material is not subject to spontaneous heating. A mixture of carbon black and oxidizable oils may produce heating.
Lamp black	Lamp black, a type of carbon black, is formed by incomplete burning of carbonaceous oils. It absorbs gases to some degree and has a strong affinity for liquids. It heats when in contact with drying oils and may ignite spontaneously soon after bagging begins.
Lead sulfocyanate	Burns slowly and decomposes to form flammable and toxic hydrogen disulfide and toxic carbon disulfide when heated.
Nitroaniline	Melts at 295°F with a flash point of 390°F. When in contact with organic materials, it may produce spontaneous ignition.
Nitrochlorobenzene	A solid material giving off flammable vapors when heated (sublimation).
Sulfides	
Antimony pentasulfide	Antimony pentasulfide is readily ignited when in contact with oxidizing materials and yields flammable and toxic hydrogen sulfide when in contact with strong acids.
Phosphorus pentasulfide	Phosphorus pentasulfide ignites readily and is subject to spontaneous heating in the presence of moisture. The ignition temperature is 287°F. Phosphorus pentasulfide produces toxic sulfur dioxide and phosphorus pentoxide when it burns, as well as flammable and toxic hydrogen sulfide when in contact with water.
Phosphorus sesquisulfide	Phosphorus sesquisulfide is highly flammable and ignites at 212°F to produce toxic sulfur dioxide.
Potassium and sodium sulfides	Both potassium and sodium sulfide are moderately flammable and they produce sulfur dioxide when burning and hydrogen sulfide comes in contact with acids.
Sulfur	The melting point is 234°F and the boiling point is 832°F with a flash point of 405°F. Sulfur vapors are highly flammable in air. Sulfur dust is a severe explosion hazard with ignition temperatures in the range of 274°F.
Naphthalene	Combustible in both solid and liquid form. Vapors and dusts form explosive mixtures in air.

For SI: °C = [(°F) - 32]/1.8.

Commentary Figure 202-F4
COMMON FLAMMABLE SOLIDS AND THEIR PROPERTIES

Tester (ASTM D93) and the Small Scale Closed-Cup Apparatus (ASTM D3278) are the referenced test procedures for determining the flash points of liquids. The applicability of the three test methods depends on the viscosity of the test liquid and the expected flash point.

FLEET VEHICLE MOTOR FUEL-DISPENSING FACILITY. That portion of a commercial, industrial, governmental or manufacturing property where liquids used as fuels are stored and dispensed into the fuel tanks of motor vehicles that are used in connection with such businesses, by persons within the employ of such businesses.

❖ This is sometimes referred to as a "you own the tanks, you own the vehicles" motor fuel-dispensing facility. The intent is to allow greater fuel storage tank capacities and reduced separation distances between the dispenser and above-ground tanks when the operator has control of the entire operation, including the vehicles being fueled. In other words, the person dispensing the fuel is an employee of the facility operator. Motor fuel-dispensing facilities are classified in occupancy Group M by the IBC.

[BE] FLIGHT. A continuous run of rectangular treads, *winders* or combination thereof from one landing to another.

❖ Two points of clarification for stairways are addressed by the definition of "Flight." First, a flight is made up of the treads and risers that occur between landings. Therefore, a stairway connecting two stories that includes an intermediate landing consists of two flights. Secondly, the inclusion of winders within a stairway does not create multiple flights. Winders are simply treads within a flight and are often combined with rectangular treads within the same flight.

FLOAT. A floating structure normally used as a point of transfer for passengers and goods, or both, for mooring purposes.

❖ A float is a deck section that lays on top of or is attached to (or both) a buoyant material in the water. The sections are attached to each other and held in place by methods that are designed to keep the floats in place.

[BE] FLOOR AREA, GROSS. The floor area within the inside perimeter of the *exterior walls* of the building under consideration, exclusive of vent shafts and courts, without deduction for *corridors*, *stairways*, *ramps*, closets, the thickness of interior walls, columns or other features. The floor area of a building, or portion thereof, not provided with surrounding *exterior walls* shall be the usable area under the horizontal projection of the roof or floor above. The *gross floor area* shall not include shafts with no openings or interior courts.

❖ Gross floor area is that area measured within the perimeter formed by the inside surface of the exterior walls. The area of all occupiable and nonoccupiable spaces, including mechanical and elevator shafts, toilet rooms, closets, and mechanical equipment rooms, are included in the gross floor area. This area could also include any covered porches, carports or other exterior space intended to be used as part of the building's occupiable space. This gross and net floor areas are primarily used for the determination of occupant load in accordance with Table 1004.1.2.

[BE] FLOOR AREA, NET. The actual occupied area not including unoccupied accessory areas such as corridors, *stairways*, *ramps*, toilet rooms, mechanical rooms and closets.

❖ This net area is intended to be only the room areas that are used for specific occupancy purposes and does not include circulation areas, such as corridors, ramps or stairways, and service and utility spaces, such as toilet rooms and mechanical and electrical equipment rooms. Net floor area is typically measured between inside faces of walls within a room. Net and gross floor areas are utilized in Table 1004.5 to determine occupant load for a space.

FLUE SPACES.

Longitudinal flue space. The flue space between rows of storage perpendicular to the direction of loading.

❖ The longitudinal flue space is a continuous open area between a double-row- or multiple-row-type rack storage system. The flue space is to be clear for a set dimension, as required in Table 3208.3, from the floor to the top of the highest commodity for the entire length of the rack system. The flue spaces are an important feature for automatic sprinkler systems to effectively suppress and potentially control the fire. Reducing or eliminating such spaces will potentially reduce, if not eliminate, sprinkler effectiveness (see Commentary Figure 202-F5).

Transverse flue space. The space between rows of storage parallel to the direction of loading.

❖ The transverse flue space is a continuous open area between commodities in single-row-, double-row- and multiple-row-type rack storage systems. The flue space is to be clear for a set dimension, as required in Table 3208.3, from the floor to the top of the highest commodity for the entire width of the rack system. The flue spaces are an important feature for automatic sprinkler systems to effectively suppress and potentially control the fire. Reducing or eliminating such spaces will potentially reduce, if not eliminate, sprinkler effectiveness (see Commentary Figure 202-F5).

FLUIDIZED BED. A container holding powder coating material that is aerated from below so as to form an air-supported expanded cloud of such material through which the preheated object to be coated is immersed and transported.

❖ A fluidized bed differs from an electrostatic fluidized bed in that the fluidized bed uses an air stream instead of electrostatic charge. The air stream behaves like a fluid as the object is passed through it. Additionally, the object is preheated. In an electrostatic fluidized bed, the object is heated/cured in an oven after the coating process.

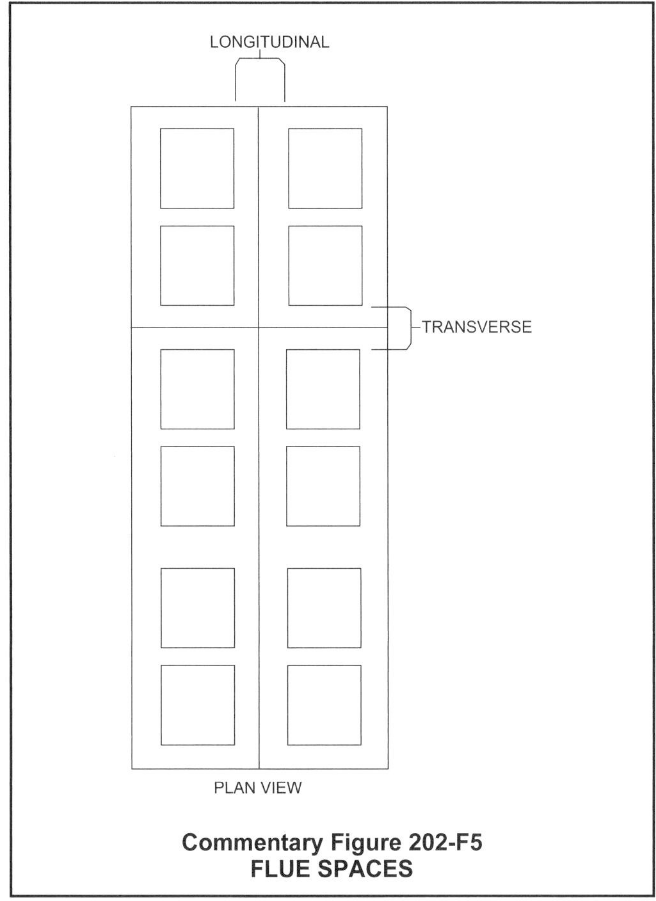

Commentary Figure 202-F5
FLUE SPACES

FOAM-EXTINGUISHING SYSTEM. A special system discharging a foam made from concentrates, either mechanically or chemically, over the area to be protected.

❖ Foam-extinguishing systems must be of an approved type and installed and tested to comply with NFPA 11, 11A and 16. All foams are intended to exclude oxygen from the fire, cool the area of the fire and insulate adjoining surfaces from heat caused by the fire. Foam systems are commonly used to extinguish flammable or combustible liquid fires (see commentary, Section 904.7). While water applied by an automatic sprinkler system can only act horizontally on the surface that it reaches, foam-extinguishing agents have the ability to act vertically in addition to horizontally; and, unlike gaseous extinguishing agents, foam does not dissipate rapidly where there is no confined space. Thus, foam systems are also used where there is a need to fill a nonconfined space with extinguishing material as in the case of certain industrial applications.

[BE] FOLDING AND TELESCOPIC SEATING. Tiered seating having an overall shape and size that is capable of being reduced for purposes of moving or storing and is not a building element.

❖ Bleachers, folding and telescopic seating and grandstands are essentially unique forms of tiered seating that are supported on a dedicated structural system. All types are addressed in ICC 300, the safety standard for these types of seating arrangements. Folding and telescopic seating are commonly used in gymnasiums and sports arenas where the seating can be configured in a variety of ways for various types of events. "Building element" is a defined term in the IBC that is primarily used in conjunction with the structural elements regulated in Table 601 of the IBC. While telescopic seating may be attached to a wall, the system when pulled out or folded includes its main support system. Such seating is not considered a building element of the building or structure in which it is located (see Section 1029.1.1).

[BG] FOSTER CARE FACILITIES. Facilities that provide care to more than five children, $2^1/_2$ years of age or less.

❖ Foster care facilities are group homes where children live. They are not day care facilities. Children under $2^1/_2$ years of age are assumed not capable of self-preservation; thus there is a need for higher levels of active and passive protection in the building (see the commentary to Occupancy Group I-2). Group homes with children over $2^1/_2$ years of age would be Group R-4 or I-1, depending on the number of children housed in the facility. The "more than five children" is intended to clarify that a foster care family would not be considered a Group I-2 facility. See also the definitions for "24-hour basis," "Custodial care," "Group home," "Incapable of self-preservation" and "Personal care service."

FUEL CELL POWER SYSTEM, STATIONARY. A stationary energy generation system that converts the chemical energy of a fuel and oxidant to electric energy (DC or AC electricity) by an electrochemical process.

Field-fabricated fuel cell power system. A *stationary fuel cell power system* that is assembled at the job site and is not a preengineered or prepackaged factory-assembled fuel cell power system.

Preengineered fuel cell power system. A *stationary fuel cell power system* consisting of components and modules that are produced in a factory, and shipped to the job site for assembly.

Prepackaged fuel cell power system. A *stationary fuel cell power system* that is factory assembled as a single, complete unit and shipped as a complete unit for installation at the job site.

❖ This definition is provided for the application of Section 1205. Fuel cell power systems are being used in ever-increasing numbers to meet facility energy needs. Stationary fuel cell power systems generate power through an electrochemical process that combines hydrogen and oxygen to produce electricity. The hydrogen comes from a direct hydrogen source or from any hydrocarbon fuel such as natural gas, gasoline, diesel, or methanol if the fuel cell power system includes integral reforming. The oxygen comes from air around the fuel cell. There are several types of fuel cell systems, which are addressed in more detail within Section 1205. The type of fuel cell will vary the application of the requirements.

FUEL LIMIT SWITCH. A mechanism, located on a tank vehicle, that limits the quantity of product dispensed at one time.

❖ This definition pertains to mobile fueling operations regulated by Section 5706.5.4.5 and describes a limit control that prevents more than a specified amount of liquid fuel from being dispensed at one time from a tank vehicle used in the mobile fueling operation (see commentary, Section 5706.5.4.5).

FUMIGANT. A substance which by itself or in combination with any other substance emits or liberates a gas, fume or vapor utilized for the destruction or control of insects, fungi, vermin, germs, rats or other pests, and shall be distinguished from insecticides and disinfectants which are essentially effective in the solid or liquid phases. Examples are methyl bromide, ethylene dibromide, hydrogen cyanide, carbon disulfide and sulfuryl fluoride.

❖ Pesticides that are applied in gaseous form within a closed space and kill by inhalation are termed "fumigants." The basic fumigant material may be a volatile solid, liquid or gas. An example of a volatile solid fumigant is paradichlorobenzene. This substance, by the process of sublimation, fills a closed space with gas. It is marketed either as moth balls or moth cakes. Sublimation refers to the changing state from a solid to a gas without entering a liquid state. Many fumigants are flammable or combustible and all are toxic, posing health hazards that range from simply hazardous to deadly with minimal exposure.

FUMIGATION. The utilization within an enclosed space of a fumigant in concentrations that are hazardous or acutely toxic to humans.

❖ Fumigation sites are usually contained within a building but may also be at an outdoor location, aboard a vessel or in a vehicle. Soil fumigation can also be successful. The key to any fumigation is applying the appropriate fumigant for the correct duration, usually at least 8 hours for proper soaking to occur. The fumigant gas must penetrate every nook and cranny of the fumigation space or area; therefore, proper enclosure and sealing of the space or area is critical. Rooms can be sealed easily by caulking or taping doors, windows and ventilation openings. Entire structures can be sealed by encapsulation in plastic sheeting. Even trees can be isolated with an air-tight tent and soils can be fumigated by covering the area with plastic covers. Other sections of this commentary discuss operational safeguards for fumigation operations.

FURNACE CLASS A. An oven or furnace that has heat utilization equipment operating at approximately atmospheric pressure wherein there is a potential explosion or fire hazard that could be occasioned by the presence of flammable volatiles or combustible materials processed or heated in the furnace.

Note: Such flammable volatiles or combustible materials can, for instance, originate from the following:

1. Paints, powders, inks, and adhesives from finishing processes, such as dipped, coated, sprayed and impregnated materials.
2. The substrate material.
3. Wood, paper and plastic pallets, spacers or packaging materials.
4. Polymerization or other molecular rearrangements.

Potentially flammable materials, such as quench oil, waterborne finishes, cooling oil or cooking oils, that present a hazard are ventilated according to Class A standards.

❖ Ovens may also use a low-oxygen atmosphere to evaporate solvent. This kind of equipment has potential hazards involving the process material and heat generation.

FURNACE CLASS B. An oven or furnace that has heat utilization equipment operating at approximately atmospheric pressure wherein there are no flammable volatiles or combustible materials being heated.

❖ Even though no flammable, volatile or combustible materials are heated in this kind of oven, the process can still be a serious fire and explosion hazard.

FURNACE CLASS C. An oven or furnace that has a potential hazard due to a flammable or other special atmosphere being used for treatment of material in process. This type of furnace can use any type of heating system and includes a special atmosphere supply system. Also included in the Class C classification are integral quench furnaces and molten salt bath furnaces.

❖ These are units in which there is an explosion hazard because a special flammable atmosphere is being used for treatment of material in process. Within this class, an integral quench tank is used, which is a container that holds a quench medium into which a metalwork is immersed for various heat treatment processes. A molten bath furnace is a heated container that holds a melt or fusion into which metalwork is immersed for various heat treatment processes.

FURNACE CLASS D. An oven or furnace that operates at temperatures from above ambient to over 5,000°F (2760°C) and at pressures normally below atmospheric using any type of heating system. These furnaces can include the use of special processing atmospheres.

❖ These are generally referred to as vacuum furnaces because they operate below normal atmospheric pressure. Vacuum furnaces are described as cold-wall furnaces, hot-wall furnaces or furnaces used for casting or melting of metal at temperatures up to 5,000°F (2760°C) or higher.

GAS CABINET. A fully enclosed, ventilated, noncombustible enclosure used to provide an isolated environment for *compressed gas* cylinders in storage or use. Doors and access ports for exchanging cylinders and accessing pressure-regulating controls are allowed to be included.

❖ This term refers to an assembly constructed and designed to protect compressed gas cylinders and associated equipment. Gas cabinets are used to provide adequate control for escaping gas in the event of a leaking cylinder of compressed gases. Gas cabinets are commonly used when dealing with highly toxic and toxic compressed gases. Sections 5003.8.6 and 6004.1.2 provide additional construction and ventilation requirements for gas cabinets.

GAS DETECTION SYSTEM. A system or portion of a combination system that utilizes one or more stationary sensors to detect the presence of a specified gas at a specified concentration and initiate one or more responses required by this code, such as notifying a responsible person, activating an alarm signal, or activating or deactivating equipment. A self-contained gas detection and alarm device is not classified as a gas detection system.

❖ The code refers to gas detection systems throughout for various applications such as for toxic and highly toxic gases, hydrogen, ozone and CO_2. The way in which the systems function vary based on the specific detection needs of the hazard and are addressed in material specific sections such as Section 5307.4.3 for carbon dioxide enrichment. The overall requirements for gas detection systems are found in Section 916. Section 916 focuses on determination of sensor location, gas sampling methods, system activation requirements, signage and connection to the fire alarm system. See the commentary to Section 916.

GAS ROOM. A separately ventilated, fully enclosed room in which only *compressed gases* and associated equipment and supplies are stored or used.

❖ Gas rooms are used exclusively for the storage or use of hazardous gases in excess of the maximum allowable quantities. Gas rooms are commonly used as alternative storage areas for HPM gases in Group H-5 facilities. A gas room is a site-built room that meets the construction requirements of the IBC. This room will require separation based on the amount of gases stored in the room.

GAS ROOM, HYDROGEN FUEL. See "Hydrogen fuel gas room."

❖ See the commentary to "Hydrogen fuel gas room.

GASEOUS HYDROGEN SYSTEM. An assembly of piping, devices and apparatus designed to generate, store, contain, distribute or transport a nontoxic, gaseous hydrogen-containing mixture having not less than 95-percent hydrogen gas by volume and not more than 1-percent oxygen by volume. Gaseous hydrogen systems consist of items such as *compressed gas* containers, reactors and appurtenances, including pressure regulators, pressure relief devices, manifolds, pumps, compressors and interconnecting piping and tubing and controls.

❖ This term includes the source of hydrogen and all piping and devices between the source and the equipment being used. The gas in a hydrogen system is above the upper flammable limit (UFL) and is therefore "too rich" to burn. Any leakage, however, can quickly create conditions that will be explosive under ambient conditions.

GLOVE BOX. A sealed enclosure in which items inside the box are handled exclusively using long gloves sealed to ports in the enclosure.

❖ This term is associated with Chapter 38 addressing university laboratories. In particular this term describes a tool used to reduce risk when using certain restricted materials in laboratories where an automatic sprinkler system is not installed. It is an alternative to storage in hazardous materials storage cabinets. As the definition notes, the glove box is a sealed enclosure.

[BG] GRADE FLOOR OPENING. A window or other opening located such that the sill height of the opening is not more than 44 inches (1118 mm) above or below the finished ground level adjacent to the opening.

❖ Openings used for emergency escape or rescue are clearly easier to use the closer they are to grade. This definition specifies that the maximum sill height above the exterior adjacent grade must be no more than 44 inches (1118 mm) for an opening to qualify as a grade floor emergency escape and rescue opening (see Section 1030.3).

[BG] GRADE PLANE. A reference plane representing the average of finished ground level adjoining the building at exterior walls. Where the finished ground level slopes away from the exterior walls, the reference plane shall be established by the lowest points within the area between the building and the *lot line* or, where the *lot line* is more than 6 feet (1829 mm) from the building, between the building and a point 6 feet (1829 mm) from the building.

❖ This term is used in the definitions of "Basement" and "Story above grade plane." It is critical in determining the height of a building and the number of stories above grade, which are regulated by Chapter 5 of the IBC, and in determining fire protection system requirements in Chapter 9. Since the finished ground surface adjacent to the building may vary (depending on site conditions), the mean average taken at various points around the building constitutes the grade plane.

Situations may arise where the ground adjacent to the building slopes away from the building because of site or landscaping considerations. In this case, the lowest finished ground level at any point between the building's exterior wall and a point 6 feet (1829 mm) from the building [or the lot line, if closer than 6 feet (1829 mm)] comes under consideration.

In the context of the code, the term "grade" means the finished ground level at the exterior walls. While the grade plane is a hypothetical horizontal plane derived as indicated above, the grade is that which actually exists or is intended to exist at the completion of site work. The only situation where the grade plane and the grade are identical is when the site is perfectly level for a distance of 6 feet (1829 mm) from all exterior walls. See the commentary to this definition in Chapters 2 and 5 of the IBC for a more detailed discussion and illustrations of sloping grade scenarios.

[BE] GRANDSTAND. Tiered seating supported on a dedicated structural system and two or more rows high and is not a building element (see "*Bleachers*").

❖ Bleachers, folding and telescopic seating and grandstands are essentially unique forms of tiered seating that are supported on a dedicated structural system. All types are addressed in the safety standard for these types of seating arrangements, ICC 300. Grandstands can be found at a county fairground, along a parade route or within indoor facilities. Examples are sports arenas and public auditoriums, as well as places of religious worship and gallery-type lecture halls. "Building element" is a defined term in the IBC that is primarily used in conjunction with the structural elements regulated in Table 601 of the IBC. Grandstands have a separate structural system. Individual bench seats directly attached to a floor system are not a grandstand. The terms "bleacher" and "grandstand" are basically interchangeable. There is no cutoff in size or number of seats that separates bleachers and grandstands (see Section 1029.1.1).

[BG] GROUP HOME. A facility for social rehabilitation, substance abuse or mental health problems that contains a group housing arrangement that provides custodial care but does not provide medical care.

❖ The term "group home" is listed under Group I-1 and R-4 occupancies. See the commentary under "Custodial care." The number of occupants would differentiate which occupancy classification is applicable to the facility. Residents live in a supervised living arrangement. Facilities can be for persons with developmental, emotional, mental or physical difficulties or for persons recovering from drugs or alcohol abuse. These facilities are intended to promote recovery, community integration and improved quality of life. While there may be security restrictions, occupants are not restrained (see the definition of Occupancy Group I-3 for restrained conditions). The focus is the increase in an individual's capacity to be successful in living, working, learning and social environments to the best of their ability. See also the commentary to "24-hour basis," "Custodial care," "Foster care facilities," "Incapable of self-preservation," "Nursing homes" and "Personal care services."

[BE] GUARD. A building component or a system of building components located at or near the open sides of elevated walking surfaces that minimizes the possibility of a fall from the walking surface to a lower level.

❖ Guards are sometimes mistakenly referred to as "guardrails." In actuality, the guard consists of the entire vertical portion of the barrier, not just the top rail (see commentary, "Handrail" and Section 1015). The purpose of guards is to minimize the potential for falls at dropoffs adjacent to walking surfaces. Loading requirements for guards are located in Section 1607.8 of the IBC.

[BG] GUESTROOM. A room used or intended to be used by one or more guests for living or sleeping purposes.

❖ Lodging houses with five or fewer guest rooms are allowed by the IBC as Group R-3 occupancies. They are also permitted under the IRC. See the definitions of "Lodging house" and "Residential Group R-3" occupancies.

[BS] GYPSUM BOARD. Gypsum wallboard, gypsum sheathing, gypsum base for gypsum veneer plaster, exterior gypsum soffit board, predecorated gypsum board or water-resistant gypsum backing board complying with the standards listed in Tables 2506.2 and 2507.2 and Chapter 35 of the *International Building Code*.

❖ Gypsum board is the most commonly used material for interior wall covering. Gypsum board is also used for exterior sheathing, plaster lath and ceiling covering. Because it is installed in sheet form, it is less labor intensive and generally considered more cost effective than other wall and ceiling materials, such as plaster. Gypsum board requires a minimal amount of finishing and will readily accept paint, wallpaper, vinyl fabric, special textured paint and similar surface finish materials.

Gypsum board will be subject to severe failure where placed in direct contact with water or continuous moisture. For this reason, the code does not allow gypsum board to be used in wet areas unless it is provided with a finish material impervious to moisture.

[BG] HABITABLE SPACE. A space in a building for living, sleeping, eating or cooking. Bathrooms, toilet rooms, closets, halls, storage or utility spaces and similar areas are not considered habitable spaces.

❖ These spaces are normally considered inhabited in the course of residential living and provide the four basic characteristics associated with it: living, sleeping, eating and cooking. All habitable spaces are considered occupiable spaces, though other occupiable spaces, such as halls or utility rooms, are not considered habitable (see the definition of "Occupiable space" in the IBC).

HALOGENATED EXTINGUISHING SYSTEM. A fire-extinguishing system using one or more atoms of an element from the halogen chemical series: fluorine, chlorine, bromine and iodine.

❖ Halon is a colorless, odorless gas that inhibits the chemical reaction of fire. Halon extinguishing systems are useful in occupancies such as computer rooms, where an electrically nonconductive medium is essential or desirable and where cleanup of other extinguishing agents presents a problem. The halon extinguishing system must to be of an approved type and installed and tested to comply with NFPA 12A.

Halon extinguishing agents have been identified as a source of emissions resulting in the depletion of the stratospheric ozone layer. For this reason, production of new supplies of halon has been phased out. Alternative gaseous extinguishing agents, such as clean agents, have been developed as alternatives to halon.

HANDLING. The deliberate transport by any means to a point of storage or use.

❖ The term "handling" pertains to the transport or movement of hazardous materials within a building. Handling presents a level of hazard less than that of use or dispensing operations but greater than storage. Material is handled only when it is transported from one point to another; it is the act of conveyance.

[BE] HANDRAIL. A horizontal or sloping rail intended for grasping by the hand for guidance or support.

❖ Handrails are provided along walking surfaces that lead from one elevation to another, such as ramps and stairways. Handrails may be any shape in cross section provided that they can be gripped by hand for support and guidance and for checking possible falls on the adjacent walking surface. In addition to being necessary in normal day-to-day use, handrails are especially needed in times of emergency when the pace of egress travel is hurried and the probability for occupant instability while traveling along the sloped or stepped walking surface is greater. Handrails, by themselves, are not intended to be used in place of guards to limit falls at drop-offs. Where guards and handrails are used together, the handrail is a separate element typically attached to the inside surface of the guard. The top guard cannot be used as a required handrail, except within dwelling units and limited areas in assembly seating (see Section 1014). See the commentary to the definition of "Guard." For loading on handrails, see Section 1607.8 of the IBC.

HAZARDOUS MATERIALS. Those chemicals or substances which are *physical hazards* or *health hazards* as defined and classified in this chapter, whether the materials are in usable or waste condition.

❖ The term "hazardous materials" refers to materials posing either a physical or health hazard.

An occupancy containing greater than the maximum allowable quantities per control area of these materials, as indicated in Tables 5003.1.1(1) and 5003.1.1(2), is classified in one of the four high-hazard occupancy classifications by the IBC. The MAQs within this code also drive various requirements when exceeded. Section 307.1.1 of the IBC provides 17 instances where, under specific conditions of handling, use, storage or packaging, the presence of one or more hazardous substances does not result in an occupancy being classified one of the Group H occupancies.

HAZARDOUS PRODUCTION MATERIAL (HPM). A solid, liquid or gas associated with semiconductor manufacturing that has a degree-of-hazard rating in health, flammability or instability of Class 3 or 4 as ranked by NFPA 704 and which is used directly in research, laboratory or production processes which have, as their end product, materials that are not hazardous.

❖ This definition identifies those specific materials that can be contained within an HPM facility. The restriction in the definition for only hazardous materials with a Class 3 or 4 rating is not intended to exclude materials that are less hazardous, but to clarify that materials of the indicated higher ranking are still permitted in an HPM facility without classifying the building as Groups H-1 through H-4. NFPA 704 is referenced to establish the degree of hazard ratings for all materials as related to health, flammability and instability risks. See Commentary Figure 202-H1 for a list of commonly used HPM and their hazard classifications.

HEALTH HAZARD. A classification of a chemical for which there is statistically significant evidence that acute or chronic health effects are capable of occurring in exposed persons. The term "health hazard" includes chemicals that are toxic, highly toxic and *corrosive*.

❖ Materials that pose risks to people from handling or exposure are considered health hazards. Even though the materials may also be flammable, those classified as health hazards either will not burn or will not pose a fire hazard similar to that of ordinary combustible materials. Materials that pose a health hazard may also pose a physical hazard and must comply with the requirements of the code applicable to both hazards. Toxins that attack specific organs are indicative of the other health-hazard materials regulated by this chapter. Hepatotoxins, such as carbon tetrachloride, are capable of causing liver damage and nephrotoxins, such as halogenated hydrocarbons, can cause kidney damage. Neurotoxins include mercury and calcium disulfide, which may produce toxic effects on the nervous system. Although the definition of "Health hazard" includes a reference to carcinogens, this chapter is not intended to regulate carcinogens that are not otherwise classified as an irritant, sensitizer or other known health hazard, such as a target organ toxin. Federal regulations address the permitted workplace exposure conditions to known carcinogens.

HEAT DETECTOR. See "Detector, heat."

[BG] HEIGHT, BUILDING. The vertical distance from grade plane to the average height of the highest roof surface.

❖ This definition establishes the two points of measurement that determine the height of a building. This measurement is used to determine compliance with the building height limitations of Sections 503.1 and 504 and Tables 504.3 and 504.4, which limit building height both in terms of the number of stories and the number of feet between the two points of measurement.

The lower point of measurement is the grade plane (see the definition of “Grade plane”). The upper point of measurement is the roof surface of the building, with consideration given to sloped roofs (such as a hip or gable roof). In the case of sloped roofs, the average height would be used as the upper point of measurement, rather than the eave line or the ridge line. The average height of the roof is the mid-height between the roof eave and the roof ridge, regardless of the shape of the roof.

This definition also indicates that building height is measured to the highest roof surface. In the case of a building with multiple roof levels, the highest of the various roof levels must be used to determine the building height. Where the highest of the various roof

		NFPA 704 Hazard Classification			
Material	Description or Use	Health	Flammability	Reactivity	Other
Acetic acid	Corrosive liquid used for wet etching (metal)	2	2	1	
Acetone	Flammable liquid used for wafer cleaning	1	3	0	
Ammonium fluoride	Corrosive for wet etching (oxide)	3	0	0	
Arsenic trichloride	Diffusion	3	0	1	W̶
Arsenic trioxide	Diffusion	4	0	0	
Arsine	Poison flammable gas used for epitaxial growth, diffusion and ion implanation	4	4	3	
Boron tribromide	Corrosive liquid used for diffusion	4	0	3	W̶
Boron trichloride	Nonflammable corrosive gas used for diffusion	4	0	1	W̶
Chlorine	Poison gas used for dry etching	3	0	0	OXY
Diborane	Highly reactive flammable gas used for diffusion	3	4	3	W̶
Dichlorosilane	Flammable liquefied gas used for epitaxial growth	4	4	4	
Gallium	Reactive metal used as a semiconductor crystal material	1	0	3	
Gallium arsenide	Reactive metal salt used as a semiconductor crystal material	3	0	0	
Gallium arsenide phosphide	Reactive metal salt used as a semiconductor crystal material	3	0	0	
Germanium	Reactive metal used as a semiconductor crystal material	0	0	3	
Hydrofluoric acid	Highly corrosive liquid or gas used for wet etching (oxide)	4	0	0	
Hydrogen peroxide[a]	Organic peroxide used for wafer cleaning	2	0	1	OXY
Isopropanol	Flammable liquid used for wafer cleaning	1	3	0	
Methanol	Flammable liquid used for wafer cleaning	1	3	0	
Nitric acid	Corrosive liquid used for wet etching (metal)	3	0	0	OXY
Oxygen (liquid)	Oxidizing gas used for oxidation	3	0	0	OXY
Phosphine	Flammable liquefied poison gas used for diffusion and ion implantation	4	4	4	
Phosphoric acid	Corrosive liquid used for wet etching (metal)	2	0	0	
Phosphorus oxychloride	Corrosive liquid used for diffusion	4	0	3	W̶
Phosphorus pentoxide	Corrosive solid sublimed for use in diffusion	4	0	3	W̶
Phosphorus tribromide	Corrosive liquid used for diffusion	4	0	3	W̶
Silane	Pyrophoric gas used for oxidation	2	4	4	
Silicon	Flammable solid (metal) used as a semiconductor crystal material	2	4	2	W̶
1, 1, 1-Trichloroethane	Mildly flammable solvent (difficult to ignite) used or wafer cleaning	2	1	0	
Tetrachlorosilane	Flammable liquid used for epitaxial growth	3	4	2	W̶

a. NFPA 704 values for 35 to 52 percent by weight (the most concentration) are listed. The reactivity hazard increases to 3 at concentrations above 52 percent.

Commentary Figure 202-H1
HAZARDOUS PRODUCTION MATERIALS (HPM) USED IN THE MANUFACTURE OF SEMICONDUCTORS

levels is a sloped roof, then the average height of that sloped roof must be used. The average height of multiple roof levels is not to be used to determine the building height. Where structures are divided into multiple buildings by fire walls, building height is determinable for each building separately.

The distance that a building extends above ground also determines the relative hazards of that building. Simply stated, a taller building presents relatively greater safety hazards than a shorter building for several reasons, including fire service access and time for occupant egress. The code specifically defines how building height is measured to enable various code requirements, such as type of construction and fire suppression, to be consistent with those relative hazards.

The term "height" is also used frequently in the code for other limitations related to, and sometimes not related to, "building height." For example, Section 1510 of the IBC limits the height of a penthouse above the top of the roof. Since a "Penthouse" is defined as a structure that is built above the roof of a building, it is above the point to which "Building height" is measured. Therefore, a penthouse would not affect the measurement of building height and can be located above the maximum allowed roof height, provided that it complies with the limitations of Section 1510 of the IBC. Other provisions, such as Section 1013 of the IBC, specify requirements based on height, but such height is usually measured from a location other than grade plane and is not intended to be building height.

HELIPORT. An area of land or water or a structural surface that is used, or intended for use, for the landing and taking off of helicopters, and any appurtenant areas which are used, or intended for use, for heliport buildings and other heliport facilities.

❖ Heliports present special problems because they are frequently located in congested areas of cities, on roofs of buildings, near hospitals and on piers adjacent to water.

HELISTOP. The same as "Heliport," except that fueling, defueling, maintenance, repairs or storage of helicopters is not permitted.

❖ A helistop is a place for landing and taking off for helicopters with no procedures or operations occurring other than loading or off-loading of passengers or freight.

HI-BOY. A cart used to transport hot roofing materials on a roof.

❖ A hi-boy, also known as a hot carrier, is a wheeled tank used on the roof deck to move hot asphalt around the work area. Hi-boys are available in either insulated or noninsulated models, and typically hold either 30 or 55 gallons (114 or 208 L).

HIGHER EDUCATION LABORATORY. Laboratories in Group B occupancies used for educational purposes above the 12th grade. Storage, use and handling of chemicals in such laboratories shall be limited to purposes related to testing, analysis, teaching, research or developmental activities on a nonproduction basis.

❖ This definition sets the scope of the provisions in Chapter 38 for laboratories. This chapter provides requirements that are customized to address the needs of university laboratories including laboratory suites and special allowances for existing laboratories. Without the concept of laboratory suites, such labs would be classified as Group H. Note that the IBC addresses higher education laboratories in Section 428. The provisions in the IBC are limited to laboratory suites for new construction. See the commentary to Chapter 38.

HIGHLY TOXIC. A material which produces a lethal dose or lethal concentration which falls within any of the following categories:

1. A chemical that has a median lethal dose (LD_{50}) of 50 milligrams or less per kilogram of body weight when administered orally to albino rats weighing between 200 and 300 grams each.
2. A chemical that has a median lethal dose (LD_{50}) of 200 milligrams or less per kilogram of body weight when administered by continuous contact for 24 hours (or less if death occurs within 24 hours) with the bare skin of albino rabbits weighing between 2 and 3 kilograms each.
3. A chemical that has a median lethal concentration (LC_{50}) in air of 200 parts per million by volume or less of gas or vapor, or 2 milligrams per liter or less of mist, fume or dust, when administered by continuous inhalation for one hour (or less if death occurs within 1 hour) to albino rats weighing between 200 and 300 grams each.

Mixtures of these materials with ordinary materials, such as water, might not warrant classification as highly toxic. While this system is basically simple in application, any hazard evaluation that is required for the precise categorization of this type of material shall be performed by experienced, technically competent persons.

❖ The definition is derived from DOL 29 CFR, Part 1910.1200. These materials are considered dangerous to humans when inhaled, absorbed or injected through the skin or ingested orally. Highly toxic materials present a health hazard and are subsequently listed as Group H-4 in Section 307.6 of the IBC. Examples of highly toxic materials include gases such as arsine, fluorine and hydrogen cyanide, liquid acrylic acid and calcium cyanide in solid form.

Mixtures of these materials with ordinary materials, such as water, might not warrant a highly toxic classification. While this system is basically simple in application, any hazard evaluation that is required for the precise categorization of this type of material is to be performed by experienced, technically competent persons.

This definition, as does the definition of "Toxic," gives very specific criteria in the form of lethal doses and lethal concentrations as administered to albino rats and albino rabbits. The lethal dosages are related to the ingestion and skin contact with materials, generally liquids and solids. The lethal concentrations are related to vapors, dusts, gases or mists as inhaled by albino rats. Inhalation can occur from either a gas, vapor or mist that is generated from highly toxic or toxic liquids. In some cases, a liquid may be considered highly toxic or toxic if ingested or if skin contact occurs, but vapors are not an inhalation hazard according to the criteria. These definitions give criteria to help determine what materials are regulated by Chapters 50 and 60 and whether a building may warrant a Group H-4 occupancy classification. Often, materials are listed as toxic or highly toxic on an SDS, but may not necessarily meet these criteria. Instead, the terminology may be used to describe irritant characteristics of the material. For a list of common highly toxic materials, see Commentary Figure 202-H2.

HIGHLY VOLATILE LIQUID. A liquefied *compressed gas* with a *boiling point* of less than 68°F (20°C).

❖ This definition provides criteria for the classification of a material as being highly volatile, and provides correlation with the defined terms "Liquid" and "Cryogenic fluid." Basically, if the boiling point of a material is at room temperature or lower it would be considered volatile. The concern usually associated with highly volatile liquids is the volume of vapors released to the atmosphere. These vapors could be harmless, but many liquids, for example, may be corrosive, toxic or flammable. Additionally, vapors are more susceptible to ignition than liquids.

HIGH-PILED COMBUSTIBLE STORAGE. Storage of combustible materials in closely packed piles or combustible materials on pallets, in racks or on shelves where the top of storage is greater than 12 feet (3658 mm) in height. Where required by the *fire code official*, *high-piled combustible storage* also includes certain high-hazard commodities, such as rubber tires, Group A plastics, flammable liquids, idle pallets and similar commodities, where the top of storage is greater than 6 feet (1829 mm) in height.

❖ High-piled combustible storage has two distinct features not common to other storage areas: the large quantity of commodities (or products) and storage in a compact arrangement (density). The height values

Material	Health	Flammability	Reactivity	Other	TLV/TWA Value[a]
Acrolein (CH_2:CHCHO)	3	3	2		0.1 ppm TLV/TWA
Adiponitrile (NC[CH_2]4CN)	4	2	0		
Allyl Alcohol (CH_2:$CHCH_2OH$)	3	3	2		2 ppm TLV/TWA
Benzotrifluoride ($C_6H_5CF_3$)	4	3	0		
Beryllium (Be)	4	1	0		2 mcg/m^3 TLV/TWA
Bromine (Br)	4	0	0	OXY	0.3 ppm TLV/TWA
Bromine Pentafluoride (BF_5)	4	0	3	OXY/~~W~~	0.1 ppm TLV/TWA
Chloropicrin (CCl_3NO_2)	4	0	3		0.1 ppm TLV/TWA
Cyanogen (NCCN)	4	4	2		10 ppm TLV/TWA
Dimethyl Sulfate ($CH_3OSO_2OCH_3$)	4	2	0		0.1 ppm TLV/TWA (skin—suspected carcinogen)
Ethylamine ($C_2H_5NH_2$)	3	4	0		10 ppm TLV/TWA
Epichlorhydrin (chloromethyl or oxirane) ([OCH_2CH]CH_2Cl)	3	3	2		0.1 ppm TLV/TWA (skin)
Hydrazine, anhydrous (H_2NNH_2)	3	3	2		0.1 ppm TLV/TWA (skin—suspected carcinogen)
Hydrogen Cyanide, anhydrous (HCN)	4	4	2		10 ppm TLV-C
Hydrogen Fluoride (HF)	4	0	0		3 ppm TLV-C
Parathion ([C_2H_5O]$_2PSOC_6H_4NO_2$)	4	1	2		0.1 mg/m^3 TLV/TWA
Phenol (C_6H_5OH)	3	2	0		5 ppm TLV/TWA (skin)
Sodium Hydride (NaH)	3	3	2	~~W~~	
Sodium Peroxide (Na_2O_2)	3	0	2	~~W~~	
1,1,2-Trichloroethane ($CHCl_2CH_2Cl$)—Not to be confused with 1,1,1-Trichloroethane	3	1	0		10 ppm TLV/TWA (skin)

a. TLV/TWA means Threshold Limit Value/Time-weighted Average. See definition in Chapter 2 of the *International Mechanical Code*.

Commentary Figure 202-H2
COMMON HIGHLY TOXIC MATERIALS AND THEIR HAZARDS

used to distinguish high-piled storage from general or incidental storage were largely based on fire tests [12 feet (3638 mm) for Class I–IV and 6 feet (1829 mm) for high hazard]. These tests were conducted to determine the effects of various configurations, quantities and classes of commodities as well as various fire protection features.

HIGH-PILED STORAGE AREA. An area within a building which is designated, intended, proposed or actually used for *high-piled combustible storage,* including operating aisles.

❖ This term defines the area or space where the combustible commodity is actually located. The intent of defining this area is to differentiate such a space from any of the other more traditionally defined occupancies (for example, business, factory, etc.) and the amount of fire protection that is required in these unique spaces. Spaces not actually containing high-piled storage are not considered part of the high-piled storage area; thus, those areas would not need to be added into the aggregate area when applying Table 3206.2.

The definition includes aisles specifically associated with the storage. Section 3206.10 has several requirements related to aisles that are focused primarily on access to exits and fire department access. NFPA 13, however, has specific aisle dimensions for rack storage, which are provided based on testing of actual storage commodities and the performance of sprinkler systems. These aisles serve more as "fire breaks" to slow the spread of fire from storage array to storage array. Therefore, any aisles required by NFPA 13 would be required to be included when determining the actual high-piled storage area involving rack storage. See the commentaries to Sections 3206.10 and 3206.3.2.1 for further discussion.

[BG] HIGH-RISE BUILDING. A building with an occupied floor located more than 75 feet (22 860 mm) above the lowest level of fire department vehicle access.

❖ Determining what qualifies as a high-rise building is a fairly unique measurement of height and is not based on the definition of "Building height." The critical measurement is from the lowest ground location where a fire department will be able to set its fire-fighting equipment to a floor level of occupied floors as shown in Commentary Figure 202-H3. It is not a measurement from grade plane to top of the building. The basis of the measurement is analyzing the capability of fighting a fire and rescuing occupants from the outside of the building. Once past a height of 75 feet (22 860 mm) above ground level, ground-based fire fighting will not be sufficient. High-rise buildings must comply with the requirements of Section 403. High-rise buildings with floors over 120 feet and over 420 feet are subject to additional regulations and elevator requirements. Certain buildings such as airport traffic control towers are exempt from Section 403, but similar provisions apply in each case.

HIGH-VOLTAGE TRANSMISSION LINE. An electrical power transmission line operating at or above 66 kilovolts.

❖ High-voltage transmission lines are used to carry large amounts of electrical power (66,000 volts or more) over long distances, usually from a main power generation station to main substations, because the line losses are much smaller than with lower-voltage lines. They may also be used for electric power transmission from one central station to another for load sharing. The term "high voltage transmission line" as used in the context of the code is referring only to overhead conductors that are made of either copper or aluminum. In other contexts, the term could include underground lines as well.

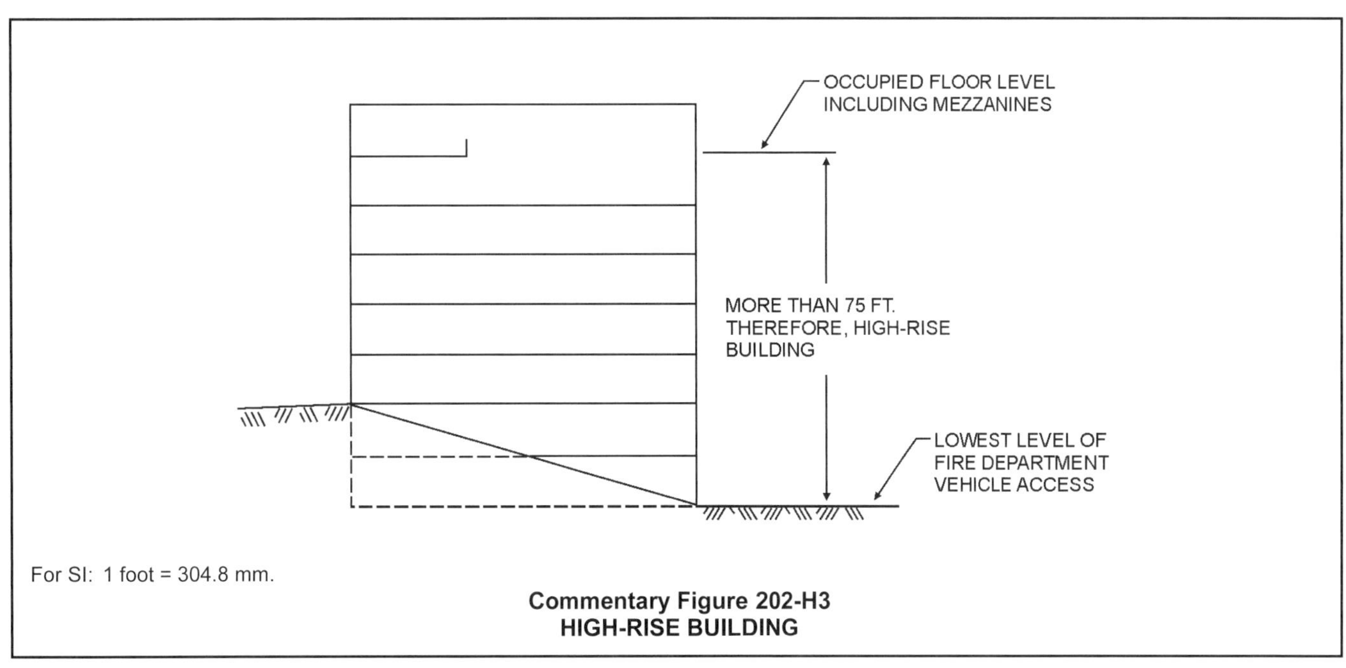

Commentary Figure 202-H3
HIGH-RISE BUILDING

HIGHWAY. A public street, public alley or public road.

❖ Roads, alleys and similar thoroughfares or vehicular accessways on private property are not included in this definition. However, when private roadways adjacent to an explosives magazine or blasting site are commonly used for vehicular traffic by the public, the separation required should be the same as that required for public rights-of-way or public access should be suspended.

[A] HISTORIC BUILDINGS. Any building or structure that is one or more of the following:

1. Listed, or certified as eligible for listing by the state historic preservation officer or the Keeper of the National Register of Historic Places, in the National Register of Historic Places.
2. Designated as historic under an applicable state or local law.
3. Certified as a contributing resource within a national register, state designated or locally designated historic district.

❖ Buildings technically considered historic must be designated as such through a federal, state or local law. In addition, there are buildings that have been reviewed for eligibility to be listed as a national historic building. Those listed as eligible for national listing also are considered historic for the purposes of the code. Buildings that are within a historic district are not necessarily, themselves, historic buildings. The determination of their designation as historic would depend on the specifics of the listing of the historic area. The IEBC provides specific provisions applying to historic buildings.

HOGGED MATERIALS. Wood waste materials produced from the lumber production process.

❖ This term refers to mill waste that may include a mixture of bark, chips or dust along with other byproducts of trees. Material designated as hogged fuel is included in this category.

[M] HOOD. An air-intake device used to capture by entrapment, impingement, adhesion or similar means, grease and similar contaminants before they enter a duct system.

Type I. A kitchen hood for collecting and removing grease vapors and smoke.

❖ A kitchen exhaust system, which includes the hood serving a commercial cooking appliance, is a specialized exhaust system. A commercial cooking appliance can generate large quantities of air contaminants, such as grease vapors, smoke and combustion byproducts. The descriptor "Type I" used in conjunction with the term "hood" refers to an exhaust system that is required for all cooking appliances that are used for commercial purposes and that produce grease-laden vapors or smoke.

Type II. A general kitchen hood for collecting and removing steam vapor, heat, odors and products of combustion.

❖ A Type II exhaust hood is considered a light-duty hood that would typically be installed over steam kettles, conventional ovens, food warmers, some types of enclosed pizza ovens, steam tables and dishwashing machines. A Type II hood is not intended for grease or smoke removal. The primary purpose of a Type II hood is to capture and remove water vapor, waste heat and any products of combustion that might be associated with the heating of the appliance, such as from fuel gas combustion.

[BF] HORIZONTAL ASSEMBLY. A fire-resistance-rated floor or roof assembly of materials designed to restrict the spread of fire in which continuity is maintained.

❖ A horizontal assembly is a component for completing compartmentation. Horizontal assemblies have all openings and penetrations protected equal to the rating for the fire-resistance-rated floor or roof assembly. Horizontal assemblies are regulated by Section 711 of the IBC.

[BE] HORIZONTAL EXIT. An *exit* component consisting of fire-resistance-rated construction and opening protectives intended to compartmentalize portions of a building thereby creating refuge areas that afford safety from fire and smoke from the area of fire origin.

❖ This term refers to a fire-resistance-rated wall that subdivides a structure into multiple compartments and provides an effective barrier to protect occupants from a fire condition within one of the compartments. After occupants pass through a horizontal exit, they must be provided not only with sufficient space to gather but also with access to another exit, such as an exterior door or exit stairway, through which they can exit the building. Commentary Figure 202-H4 depicts the exits serving a single building that is subdivided with a fire-resistance-rated wall (see Section 1026).

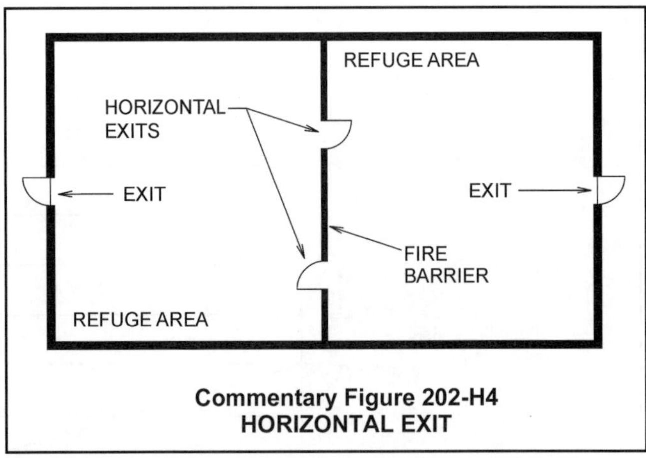

Commentary Figure 202-H4
HORIZONTAL EXIT

[BG] HOSPITALS AND PSYCHIATRIC HOSPITALS. Facilities that provide care or treatment for the medical, psychiatric, obstetrical, or surgical treatment of inpatient care recipients that are incapable of self-preservation.

❖ Persons in hospital facilities may be physically incapable of self-preservation or at least extremely limited in their ability to evacuate. In psychiatric hospitals they may be confined within an area of a building for care or security purposes. In consideration of occupants' health, as well as safety, hospitals and nursing homes at least partially rely on defend-in-place strategies. See the commentary to Occupancy Group I-2 and Section 407 of the IBC.

Care facilities are used by patients of varying acuity seeking a broad spectrum of available support services. These facilities span a wide range of occupancy types, including Groups E, I and R. The level of care provided is based on the condition and capabilities of an occupant, which, in turn, indicate appropriate standards for protection systems, both passive and active. See also the definitions for "24-hour basis," "Care suite," "Custodial care," "Detoxification facilities," "Incapable of self-preservation," "Medical care" and "Nursing homes."

HOT WORK. Operations including cutting, welding, Thermit welding, brazing, soldering, grinding, thermal spraying, thawing pipe, installation of torch-applied roof systems or any other similar activity.

❖ This term describes the scope of what would be considered hot work as it is regulated in this chapter. The scope is broad and would include any activity that produces sparks, slag or other waste products. This would include both gas and electric methods. Torch-applied roof systems are also included.

HOT WORK AREA. The area exposed to sparks, hot slag, radiant heat, or convective heat as a result of the hot work.

❖ This definition helps to locate which areas would be considered part of the hot work area to better understand the level of susceptibility to ignition.

HOT WORK EQUIPMENT. Electric or gas welding or cutting equipment used for hot work.

❖ In the past, chapters dealing with hot work focused primarily on gas welding. Electric welding, though it does not deal with oxygen and fuel gases, still presents ignition hazards (see Commentary Figure 202-H5).

HOT WORK PERMITS. Permits issued by the responsible person at the facility under the hot work permit program permitting welding or other hot work to be done in locations referred to in Section 3503.3 and prepermitted by the *fire code official.*

❖ As applied in Chapter 35, this permit differs from a typical permit in that it is not directly issued by the fire code official. Instead, a hot work operations facility is given permission to designate a person, perhaps the safety officer, to issue permits as needed. This results in flexibility for facilities where hot work is a common occurrence. These permits are issued under what is called a hot work program, which is also defined in this section.

HOT WORK PROGRAM. A permitted program, carried out by *approved* facilities-designated personnel, allowing them to oversee and issue permits for hot work conducted by their personnel or at their facility. The intent is to have trained, on-site, responsible personnel ensure that required hot work safety measures are taken to prevent fires and fire spread.

❖ This kind of program is described in the definition for "Hot work permits." This program allows someone on site to control the issuing of permits for hot work. The person who is charged with this responsibility must be trained in hot work operations and have the necessary authority. Having such a program at a facility encourages a better understanding of fire safety and perhaps more incentive to play an active role in the prevention of fires. This program reduces the administrative burden on the fire department and ensures that hot work operations can proceed as needed.

HPM. See "Hazardous Production Material."

HPM FACILITY. See "Semiconductor fabrication facility."

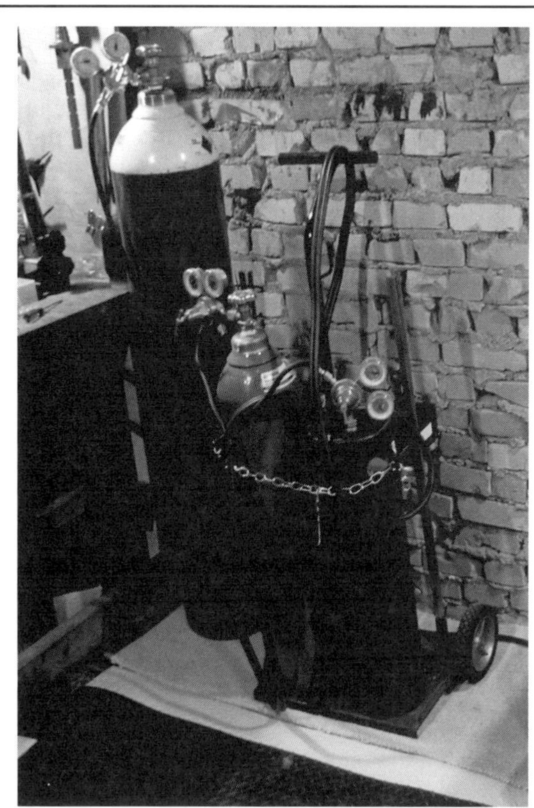

Commentary Figure 202-H5
TYPICAL WELDING CART

HPM ROOM. A room used in conjunction with or serving a Group H-5 occupancy, where HPM is stored or used and which is classified as a Group H-2, H-3 or H-4 occupancy.

❖ An HPM room in a Group H-5 facility is used for the storage and use of HPM in excess of the MAQs permitted in Table 5003.1.1(1) or (2). The room is, therefore, considered a Group H-2, H-3 or H-4 occupancy, depending on the type of hazardous material (see Commentary Figure 202-S3).

HYDROGEN FUEL GAS ROOM. A room or space that is intended exclusively to house a *gaseous hydrogen system*.

❖ This term refers to an enclosed space used exclusively for a gaseous hydrogen system that requires construction and protection that are unique to the hazards associated with this use. The room itself may be considered as an incidental accessory occupancy or a Group H occupancy, depending on the amount of hydrogen in such rooms. The definition itself should not be interpreted to prevent hydrogen piping systems from serving distributed hydrogen-using equipment and appliances located elsewhere on site or in the building; however, the amount of hydrogen within such piping needs to be evaluated with respect to the MAQs in Table 5003.1.1(1).

IMMEDIATELY DANGEROUS TO LIFE AND HEALTH (IDLH). The concentration of airborne contaminants that poses a threat of death, immediate or delayed permanent adverse health effects, or effects that could prevent escape from such an environment. This contaminant concentration level is established by the National Institute of Occupational Safety and Health (NIOSH) based on both toxicity and flammability. It generally is expressed in parts per million by volume (ppm v/v) or milligrams per cubic meter (mg/m^3). Where adequate data do not exist for precise establishment of IDLH concentrations, an independent certified industrial hygienist, industrial toxicologist, appropriate regulatory agency or other source *approved* by the *fire code official* shall make such determination.

❖ There are three general atmospheres that make up an IDLH toxic condition. These are toxic, flammable and oxygen deficient. In the absence of an IDLH value, the fire code official may consider using an estimated IDLH of 10 times the lower explosive limit (LEL) while an IDLH oxygen-deficient atmosphere is 19.5-percent oxygen or lower. The EPA has determined that 10 percent of the IDLH value is an acceptable level of concern for evaluating hazmat release concentrations and public protective options.

IMPAIRMENT COORDINATOR. The person responsible for the maintenance of a particular *fire protection system*.

❖ To minimize the time a fire protection system is out of service, the building owner or other designee is required to monitor impairment procedures (see commentary Section 901.7.1). This person has the responsibility for performing the actions necessary during the impairment and is the single point of contact for issues relating to the impairment; thus, it should be a person who has both authority and knowledge of the facility under consideration.

[BG] INCAPABLE OF SELF-PRESERVATION. Persons who, because of age, physical limitations, mental limitations, chemical dependency or medical treatment, cannot respond as an individual to an emergency situation.

❖ Patients/residents of nursing homes and hospitals may be in situations where they are unable to self-evacuate due to physical limitations arising from, for example, medication, operation, injury or connection to medical equipment.

Care facilities encompass a full spectrum of acuity and support services and span a wide range of occupancy types including Groups E, I and R. There are three types of care defined in the codes: personal, custodial and medical. The level of care provided is based on the condition and capabilities of an occupant, which, in turn, indicate appropriate standards for protection systems, both active and passive. See also the definitions for "24-hour basis," "Custodial care," "Detoxification facilities," "Foster care facilities," "Group home," "Hospitals and psychiatric hospitals," "Medical care," "Nursing home" and "Personal care services."

INCOMPATIBLE MATERIALS. Materials that, when mixed, have the potential to react in a manner which generates heat, fumes, gases or byproducts which are hazardous to life or property.

❖ Incompatible materials constitute a dangerous chemical combination whether in storage or in use. Determining which chemicals in combination pose a hazard is not always easy. SDS may not provide all of the necessary information. When in doubt, the fire code official should seek additional information from the manufacturer of the chemicals involved, the building owner or experts who are knowledgeable in industrial hygiene or chemistry. NFPA's *Fire Protection Guide to Hazardous Materials* also contains useful information on hazardous chemical reactions.

INERT GAS. A gas that is capable of reacting with other materials only under abnormal conditions such as high temperatures, pressures and similar extrinsic physical forces. Within the context of the code, inert gases do not exhibit either physical or *health hazard* properties as defined (other than acting as a simple asphyxiant) or hazard properties other than those of a *compressed gas*. Some of the more common inert gases include argon, helium, krypton, neon, nitrogen and xenon.

❖ The term "inert gas" is used in a number of sections throughout the code. For example, it is used in the exception to Section 2501.1, in Section 2906.4 and in Chapters 50, 53 and 57. The term "inert gas" is also used in the IMC and the IFGC without definition. This definition is not in conflict with the provisions found in either of these companion codes.

While inert gases do not present a physical hazard or health hazard as regulated by Chapter 50, inert gases are hazardous materials in the sense that they are simple asphyxiants that can cause injury or death by displacing oxygen. Any atmosphere containing 19.5 percent or less by volume of oxygen is considered oxygen deficient and inert gases can create such an environment. Inert gases are colorless, odorless, tasteless and are not irritating. As a result, the only means of detecting an oxygen-deficient atmosphere is through the use of gas detection equipment. Inert gases include argon, nitrogen, helium and carbon dioxide. Inert compressed gases and cryogenic fluids have other hazards, such as the potential energy within their containers. Because of these hazards, the provisions in Chapter 53 for compressed gases and Chapter 55 for cryogenic fluids are applicable regardless of whether the stored gas or cryogenic fluid is inert.

The definition includes an explanatory sentence intended to inform the user that inert gases do not react readily with other materials under normal temperatures and pressures, but it is possible for a reaction to occur. For example, even nitrogen combines with some of the more active metals such as lithium and magnesium to form nitrides, and at high temperatures it will also combine with hydrogen, oxygen and other elements. The inert gases neon, krypton and xenon are considered rare due to their scarcity. Although these gases are commonly referred to as inert gases, the formation of compounds is possible. For example, xenon combines with fluorine to form various fluorides, and with oxygen to form oxides. The compounds thus formed are crystalline solids.

By defining the term, the likelihood of using gases that are not inert, including carbon dioxide, will be reduced.

INHABITED BUILDING. A building regularly occupied in whole or in part as a habitation for people, or any place of religious worship, schoolhouse, railroad station, store or other structure where people are accustomed to assemble, except any building or structure occupied in connection with the manufacture, transportation, storage or use of *explosive materials*.

❖ Building use need not conform to regular intervals or schedules to be considered inhabited if people routinely occupy the building. Those buildings at a storage or blasting site used for the manufacture, transportation or storage of explosive materials must be considered as magazines rather than inhabited buildings for the purpose of applying the provisions of Section 5604.

INITIATING DEVICE. A system component that originates transmission of a change-of-state condition, such as in a smoke detector, manual fire alarm box, or supervisory switch.

❖ All fire protection systems consist of devices that, upon use or actuation, will initiate the intended operation. A manual fire alarm box, for example, will transmit a fire alarm signal upon actuation. In the case of a single-station device, the initiating device and the notification appliance are one in the same.

INSECTICIDAL FOGGING. The utilization of insecticidal liquids passed through fog-generating units where, by means of pressure and turbulence, with or without the application of heat, such liquids are transformed and discharged in the form of fog or mist blown into an area to be treated.

❖ Insecticidal fogging as a means of pest control was developed during World War II as part of a program to use smoke-screen techniques for control of malaria-bearing mosquitos. The product of the fog-generating process is an aerosol, which is a suspension of liquid particles in air. Many insecticides used in the fogging process are flammable and pose a fire hazard requiring safeguards, such as the securing of all ignition sources during fogging and for up to 24 hours afterward.

Aerosol insecticides also pose a toxicity hazard; therefore, proper entry precautions for the fogged area should be observed.

INTEGRATED TESTING (FIRE PROTECTION AND LIFE SAFETY SYSTEM). A testing procedure to establish the operational status, interaction and coordination of two or more fire protection and safety systems.

❖ This definition helps to explain what is being addressed in Section 901.6.2. This type of testing is important where life safety systems are within a building and need close coordination to work appropriately. Integrated testing could apply to many buildings but is only necessary for more complex buildings. Section 901.6.2 only applies to high-rise buildings and buildings with smoke control systems. Integrated testing is required to comply with NFPA 4. See also the definition of "Subordinate (fire protection and life safety system)."

[BE] INTERIOR EXIT RAMP. An exit component that serves to meet one or more means of egress design requirements, such as required number of exits or exit access travel distance, and provides for a protected path of egress travel to the exit discharge or public way.

❖ To qualify as an interior exit ramp the ramp must be enclosed with a fire-resistance-rated enclosure in order to provide a protected path between the exit access and exit discharge. This enclosure must extend directly to the exterior at grade; extend through an exit passageway to grade; or comply with one of the allowances for exit discharge through a lobby, vestibule or horizontal exit. Travel distance is measured to the entrance to the enclosure for the interior exit ramp. Ramps that are utilized by occupants for evacuation, but do not meet the provisions for exits, are considered exit access elements (see "Exit access ramp"). For exterior exit ramp requirements, see Section 1027.

[BE] INTERIOR EXIT STAIRWAY. An exit component that serves to meet one or more means of egress design requirements, such as required number of exits or exit access travel distance, and provides for a protected path of egress travel to the exit discharge or public way.

❖ To qualify as an interior exit stairway, the ramp must be enclosed with a fire-resistance-rated enclosure in order to provide a protected path between the exit access and exit discharge. This enclosure must extend directly to the exterior at grade; extend through an exit passageway to grade; or comply with one of the allowances for exit discharge through a lobby, vestibule or horizontal exit. Travel distance is measured to the entrance to the enclosure for the interior exit stairway. Stairways that are utilized by occupants for evacuation, but do not meet the provisions for exits, are considered exit access elements (see "Exit access stairway"). For exterior exit stairway requirements, see Section 1027.

[BG] INTERIOR FINISH. Interior finish includes interior wall and ceiling finish and interior floor finish.

❖ This is a more general term that addresses all exposed surfaces, which includes walls, ceilings and floors. Interior finish material is exposed to the interior space enclosed by these building elements.

[BG] INTERIOR FLOOR-WALL BASE. Interior floor finish trim used to provide a functional or decorative border at the intersection of walls and floors.

❖ This definition, which addresses interior floor-wall base trim materials, provides an understanding and clarification of these types of products versus other interior trim materials. In many cases, floor covering material is just seamlessly turned up or used at the intersection of the floor and the wall, thus becoming the floor-wall base trim. Because of their location at the floor line, floor-wall base materials are not likely to be involved in a fire until the floor covering is also involved, usually at room flashover. See also the commentary to Section 804.4.

[BG] INTERIOR WALL AND CEILING FINISH. The exposed interior surfaces of buildings, including but not limited to: fixed or movable walls and partitions; toilet room privacy partitions; columns; ceilings; and interior wainscoting, paneling or other finish applied structurally or for decoration, acoustical correction, surface insulation, structural *fire resistance* or similar purposes, but not including trim.

❖ This definition describes a material that is applied to ceilings as well as walls, columns, partitions (including the privacy partitions in bathrooms that could pose a significant threat in larger bathrooms where unrated) and other vertical interior surfaces whether fixed or movable. The application of this material may be for structural, decorative, acoustical, structural fire resistance and other similar reasons. Trim, such as baseboard, door or window casing, is not considered interior wall and ceiling finish. Interior wall and ceiling finish is regulated by Section 803.

IRRITANT. A chemical which is not *corrosive*, but which causes a reversible inflammatory effect on living tissue by chemical action at the site of contact. A chemical is a skin irritant if, when tested on the intact skin of albino rabbits by the methods of CPSC 16 CFR Part 1500.41 for an exposure of four or more hours or by other appropriate techniques, it results in an empirical score of 5 or more. A chemical is classified as an eye irritant if so determined under the procedure listed in CPSC 16 CFR Part 1500.42 or other *approved* techniques.

❖ Materials classified as irritants include a wide range of materials that pose a health hazard with acute effects caused by short-term exposure. Exposure to irritants may result in a minor, troublesome injury at the point of contact; however, the injury usually heals without leaving a scar. In comparison, corrosives can cause permanent destruction of tissue at the point of contact—with a scar the likely result. Many household insecticides and pesticides are common irritants. The definition is derived from DOL 29 CFR 1910.1200.

[A] JURISDICTION. The governmental unit that has adopted this code.

❖ The governmental unit such as a town, township, county or state that has the legal authority under state statutes to adopt a building code.

KEY BOX. A secure device with a lock operable only by a fire department master key, and containing building entry keys and other keys that may be required for access in an emergency.

❖ The key box is part of an emergency entry system. The building owner/manager places a key box or key vault in an approved location on the exterior of the building or at the entrance to a facility, placing keys, access cards or security codes inside the box. The emergency responders can use their special fire department master key to enter the box, retrieve the contents and gain access to the building or facility. There are several different brands of highly secure key boxes available that are tested and listed as anti-theft devices. See the commentary to the definition of "Fire department master key" and Section 506.1 for further discussion.

[A] LABELED. Equipment, materials or products to which have been affixed a label, seal, symbol or other identifying mark of a nationally recognized testing laboratory, *approved* agency or other organization concerned with product evaluation that maintains periodic inspection of the production of such labeled items and whose labeling indicates either that the equipment, material or product meets identified standards or has been tested and found suitable for a specified purpose.

❖ The term "labeled" is not to be confused with the term "listed." A label is a marking or other identifying mark that indicates approval from a nationally recognized testing laboratory, approved agency or other organization that evaluates products. A label is used to identify materials and assemblies that must bear the identification of the manufacturer, as well as a third-party quality control agency. The quality control agency allows the use of its label based on the results of periodic audits and inspections of the manufacturer's plant. This is one form of quality control. The code often requires labeled equipment and systems (see the definition for "Listed").

LABORATORY SUITE. A fire-rated enclosed laboratory area that will provide one or more laboratory spaces, within a Group B educational occupancy, that are permitted to include ancillary uses such as offices, bathrooms and corridors that are contiguous with the laboratory area, and are constructed in accordance with Chapter 38.

❖ This concept is one used in Chapter 38 similar to control areas, but instead facilitates the needs of laboratories, which often very easily exceed MAQs where several laboratories are located in a single control area. This concept allows such amounts to be broken into several separated and protected spaces using the concept of laboratory suites.

This concept, detailed in Chapter 38, is similar to that of control areas but is specific to the needs of one or more laboratories and related facilities sharing a single control area. Laboratories in such arrangement normally would exceed the MAQs. This concept allows such amounts to be broken into several separated and protected spaces.

LEVEL OF EXIT DISCHARGE. See "Exit discharge, level of."

LIMITED SPRAYING SPACE. An area in which operations for touch-up or spot painting of a surface area of 9 square feet (0.84 m^2) or less are conducted.

❖ This definition is applicable only to small touch-up-type operations. The requirements in this chapter for limited spraying operations are for an occasional user of flammable/combustible liquids, as opposed to an area used continuously for spraying. An example of such an operation is a furniture distributor that uses a limited spraying space to touch up scratches on products before sale. The limited application method could utilize dedicated spray-finishing equipment or simply an aerosol can (see commentary, Section 2404.9).

LIQUEFIED NATURAL GAS (LNG). A fluid in the liquid state composed predominantly of methane and which may contain minor quantities of ethane, propane, nitrogen or other components normally found in natural gas.

❖ Liquefied natural gas (LNG) for motor vehicle fuel comes from the same source as compressed natural gas (CNG). Unlike liquefied petroleum gas (LP-gas), which changes from vapor to a liquid at room temperature by application of pressure, LNG has to be cooled for it to liquefy. LNG is usually in a liquid state at the dispensing station (see Section 2308).

LIQUEFIED PETROLEUM GAS (LP-gas). A material which is composed predominantly of the following hydrocarbons or mixtures of them: propane, propylene, butane (normal butane or isobutane) and butylenes.

❖ The definition of LP-gas is consistent with that found in NFPA 58, with one exception: NFPA 58 requires that the vapor pressure of an LP-gas mixture be less than or equal to that of commercial propane.

The most prevalent liquefied petroleum gases in the United States are propane and butane, but others such as propylene are also used. The specification for LP-gas is ASTM D1835, Standard Specification for LP-Gases. This standard provides allowable concentrations of various compounds and also vapor pressure limitations on the various gases.

LIQUID. A material having a melting point that is equal to or less than 68°F (20°C) and a *boiling point* which is greater than 68°F (20°C) at 14.7 pounds per square inch absolute (psia) (101 kPa). Where not otherwise identified, the term "liquid" includes both flammable and *combustible liquids*.

❖ This definition specifies the criteria to establish when material is considered a liquid based on its melting and boiling points. Where the term "liquid" is referred to, it is intended to include both flammable and combustible liquids. In dealing with liquids, two areas are important to check on the SDS:

1. What is the specific gravity of the liquid? The specific gravity is the chemical's weight compared to the weight of an equal volume of water. If the specific gravity is lower than 1.0 (which is the specific gravity of water), the chemical will float. If it is higher than 1.0, it will sink. A flammable liquid that has a specific gravity lower than 1.0 will float on top of any fire-fighting water that is applied. It can then become a running fire as it floats on top of the water that is running off from the scene.
2. Will the chemical mix with water? If a chemical will mix with water, it limits the fire-fighting ability of water and another method of extinguishment should be considered.

LIQUID OXYGEN AMBULATORY CONTAINER. A container used for liquid oxygen not exceeding 0.396 gallons (1.5 liters) specifically designed for use as a medical device as defined by 21 USC Chapter 9 that is intended for portable therapeutic use and to be filled from its companion base unit, a liquid oxygen home care container.

❖ These containers are a smaller, portable version of the liquid oxygen (LOX) home care container defined elsewhere in this section. They are used by patients in need of continuous oxygen therapy to enhance their mobility and, thus, improve their lifestyle. See the commentary to the definition of "Liquid oxygen home care container" for a technical description of LOX containers. A key aspect in this definition is that these containers are considered medical devices by the US Food and Drug Administration under the Code of Federal Regulations, Title 21—Federal Food, Drug and Cosmetic Act. LOX containers used as medical devices are unique in that they are intended for therapeutic use only and not for use in industrial applications. These containers include in their design all appurtenances, such as regulators, gauges, piping and controls, and require no external piping other than the application of disposable breathing apparatus (see Commentary Figure 202-L1).

LIQUID OXYGEN HOME CARE CONTAINER. A container used for liquid oxygen not exceeding 15.8 gallons (60 liters) specifically designed for use as a medical device as defined by 21 USC Chapter 9 that is intended to deliver gaseous oxygen for therapeutic use in a home environment.

❖ A LOX home care container is a cryogenic container equipped with a vaporizer, a pressure control system and a means of pressure relief. The container is constructed similar to a thermos bottle with the inner container generally constructed of stainless steel and installed within an outer container constructed of carbon steel or aluminum. The space between the inner and outer vessel is filled with an insulating material or may be placed in a negative pressure (vacuum). The insulation and space limit the heat transfer to the inner container. A vaporizer converts the LOX to oxygen gas, which flows through a pressure control system so the flow rate of oxygen is regulated. These containers can be used for stationary home oxygen therapy or, as indicated in the definition of "Liquid oxygen ambulatory container," to refill the LOX ambulatory container. A key aspect in this definition is that these containers are also considered medical devices by the US Food and Drug Administration under the Code of Federal Regulations, Title 21—Federal Food, Drug and Cosmetic Act. LOX containers used as medical devices are unique in that they are intended for therapeutic use only and not for use in industrial applications (see Commentary Figure 202-L2).

LIQUID STORAGE ROOM. A room classified as a Group H-3 occupancy used for the storage of flammable or *combustible liquids* in a closed condition.

❖ Liquid storage rooms are utilized exclusively for the storage of flammable and combustible liquids in closed containers in excess of the maximum allowable quantities permitted by Tables 5003.1.1(1) and 5003.1.1(2). The Group H-3 occupancy classification for storage of flammable or combustible liquids in closed containers recognizes the hazardous nature of these materials.

LIQUID STORAGE WAREHOUSE. A building classified as a Group H-2 or H-3 occupancy used for the storage of flammable or *combustible liquids* in a closed condition.

❖ This definition clarifies both the occupancy group (Group H-2 or H-3, depending on the pressure of vessels stored) and that a liquid storage warehouse is a building as described in Section 5704.3.8. The term "liquid storage warehouse" is used in the code in Tables 903.2.11.6, 5704.3.6.3(2) and 5704.3.6.3(3) and Sections 2306.2.2, 5104.6, 5704.3.4.3. Note that the term "liquid storage warehouse" is not used in the IBC. See the commentary to Section 5704.8.3 for further information on these unique buildings.

[A] LISTED. Equipment, materials, products or services included in a list published by an organization acceptable to the *fire code official* and concerned with evaluation of products or services that maintains periodic inspection of production of listed equipment or materials or periodic evaluation of services and whose listing states either that the equipment, material, product or service meets identified standards or has been tested and found suitable for a specified purpose.

❖ The term "listed," which is not to be confused with "labeled," is a form of quality control. Essentially, a particular product, piece of equipment or system is evaluated or tested and the results are published in a list by agencies, such as approved testing laborato-

Commentary Figure 202-L1
LIQUID OXYGEN AMBULATORY CONTAINER
Copyright 2008 Chart Industries, Inc.
Used by permission, all rights reserved.

Commentary Figure 202-L2
LIQUID OXYGEN HOME CARE CONTAINER
Copyright 2008 Chart Industries, Inc.
Used by permission, all rights reserved.

ries and inspection agencies. Listed products and equipment are periodically inspected to maintain the listing. The code often requires listed equipment or systems (see also the definition for "Labeled").

The question is often asked whether the listing of a product can be voided or violated. The use of a listing mark applied to a product is authorized by the listing agency and is a "statement" by the product manufacturer that the product, as manufactured, met all appropriate requirements (such as the criteria contained in a test standard) at the time of manufacture and shipment to a point-of-use or point-of-sale. After that point in time, any alteration or modification may make it difficult for the fire code official or the listing agency to determine if the product meets the criteria by which its listing was originally attained. Listed products are subject to the review and approval of the fire code official. Where the fire code official determines that a field modification or alteration to the product is significant enough to call its impact on the listing into question, an evaluation in the field by the listing agency may be required in order to verify the compliance of the product with the original listing criteria. Such field evaluations or tests would be the responsibility of the owner with no expense to the jurisdiction (see the commentary to Section 104.9.2).

LOCKDOWN. An emergency situation, in other than a Group I-3 occupancy, requiring that the occupants be sheltered and secured in place within a building when normal evacuation would put occupants at risk.

❖ Buildings are developing "lockdown" plans in response to such security threats as terrorist attacks and active shooter situations, such as the events that occurred at Columbine High School; Virginia Tech; Sandy Hook; Parkland, Florida; and other venues. In such incidents, security authorities recommend that building occupants be kept inside of the building behind locked doors until authorized to move by safety authorities. Sometimes, lockdown procedures can work in direct opposition to traditional life safety safeguards, particularly as pertains to maintaining a viable means of egress. Requirements have been added to the code on lockdown plans, lockdown drills and lockdown operations, not only in schools, but in all buildings where a lockdown plan is desired in order to reduce the conflicts between security and life safety (see Section 404.2.3).

[BG] LODGING HOUSE. A one-family dwelling where one or more occupants are primarily permanent in nature and rent is paid for guestrooms.

❖ The code establishes a lodging house as a Group R-3 occupancy where there are five or fewer guest rooms. This definition provides a distinction from Group R-1 occupancies where the occupants are expected to be transient. A lodging house has one or more occupants who are permanent; this is their home.

LONGITUDINAL FLUE SPACE. See "Flue space—longitudinal."

[A] LOT. A portion or parcel of land considered as a unit.

❖ A lot is a legally recorded parcel of land, the boundaries of which are described on a deed. When code requirements are based on some element of a lot (such as yard area or lot line location), it is the physical attributes of the parcel of land that the code is addressing, not issues of ownership. Adjacent lots owned by the same party are treated as if they were owned by different parties because ownership can change at any time. However, a group of platted lots or subdivision lots could be joined together and "considered as a unit" for the purposes of the code. For example, a collection of platted lots could be used as a single building lot for the construction of a covered mall and its associated anchor buildings. Local jurisdictions may require for taxing or other purposes that the lots be legally joined, or merged, as well.

A condominium form of building ownership, whether a residential or a commercial condominium, does not create separate lots (i.e., parcels of land) and such unit owners are treated as separate tenants, not separate lot owners. The lines separating one part of a condominium from another are not lot lines but lines indicating the limits of ownership. As such, walls constructed on lines separating condominium ownership would not need to be fire (or party) walls.

Legal property lines do not always constitute site boundaries (i.e., malls, condominiums, townhouses). A site could contain multiple legal "lot" divisions.

[A] LOT LINE. A line dividing one lot from another, or from a street or any public place.

❖ Lot lines are legally recorded divisions between two adjacent land parcels or lots. They are the reference point for the location of buildings for exterior separation and other code purposes (see the definition of "Lot").

[BE] LOW ENERGY POWER-OPERATED DOOR. Swinging, sliding or folding door which opens automatically upon an action by a pedestrian such as pressing a push plate or waving a hand in front of a sensor. The door closes automatically, and operates with decreased forces and decreased speeds. See also "Power-assisted door" and "Power-operated door."

❖ There are basically three different doors that provide some type of power assistance for entry—low energy power-operated doors, power-assisted doors and power-operated doors. The low energy power-operated door is typically a side-swinging door that also operates as a manual door. However, the door has the additional feature of automatic operation when a person pushes on a plate or sensor located on a wall or post near the door [See IBC Commentary Figures 202(31), 202(32) and 202(33)]. The low energy power-assisted door and power-assisted door are operated by the user touching something; therefore, they both must comply with BMHA156.19.

LOWER EXPLOSIVE LIMIT (LEL). See "Lower flammable limit."

❖ See the commentary for the definition of "Lower flammable limit (LFL)."

LOWER FLAMMABLE LIMIT (LFL). The minimum concentration of vapor in air at which propagation of flame will occur in the presence of an ignition source. The LFL is sometimes referred to as LEL or lower explosive limit.

❖ LFL or LEL is the bottom limit on a flammability range, which is the range in which a flammable vapor is mixed with air in just the right percentages to allow combustion. This is an important concept because the requirement for ventilation is based on keeping the vapor concentrations outside of the flammability range. The upper portion of the range is called the UEL, or upper explosive limit; another term that carries the same meaning is UFL, or upper flammable limit. As long as flammable vapors are not within the range between UFL and LFL, combustion is unlikely.

LOW-PRESSURE TANK. A storage tank designed to withstand an internal pressure greater than 0.5 pound per square inch gauge (psig) (3.4 kPa) but not greater than 15 psig (103.4 kPa).

❖ This definition makes a differentiation between what is considered a low-pressure tank and what is considered a high-pressure tank. Low-pressure tanks are generally less hazardous than high-pressure tanks because the rate of release of cryogenic fluids is much lower.

LP-GAS CONTAINER. Any vessel, including cylinders, tanks, portable tanks and cargo tanks, used for transporting or storing LP-gases.

❖ The definition of LP-gas container provides consistency with NFPA 58 and makes it clear that the containers being regulated in Chapter 61 of the code are specifically those used for the storage or transport of LP-gas, not the generic, 60 gallon (227.1 L) or less containers defined in Section 202 of the code.

An LP-gas container can be constructed as a cylinder, portable tank, stationary tank or as a cargo tank vehicle. Cylinders are generally constructed to the requirements of the DOT while stationary tanks, portable tanks and cargo tanks are generally constructed to the requirements of the ASME *Boiler and Pressure Vessel Code* for unfired pressure vessels. In addition to these requirements, LP-gas containers must also be constructed in accordance with the requirements in NFPA 58.

All LP-gas containers must meet the requirements contained in Chapter 5 of NFPA 58, which addresses all components used in the construction of container assemblies or complete LP-gas systems. These requirements include general provisions that are applicable to all containers, visual inspection requirements for DOT cylinders in stationary service, container service pressures, required openings for DOT cylinders and ASME containers, container markings and container appurtenances. A container appurtenance is a device installed in container openings for safety, control, or operating purposes. Appurtenances include a pressure relief device, one or more pressure regulators, an overfill prevention device, a manual shutoff valve, and a means of gauging the liquid level and the pressure inside the container. The types of appurtenances required for LP-gas containers are based on whether the container is constructed as a cylinder or tank. For stationary tanks, its volumetric capacity will dictate the required container appurtenances.

MAGAZINE. A building, structure or container, other than an operating building, *approved* for storage of *explosive materials*.

❖ Structures for the storage of explosive materials are not considered inhabited buildings for the purpose of applying Section 5604. Explosives, a necessary part of our industrialized society, must be transported from places of manufacture to a location of use. Somewhere along the line, they will probably have to be stored. This type of storage place is called a magazine.

Indoor. A portable structure, such as a box, bin or other container, constructed as required for Type 2, 4 or 5 magazines in accordance with NFPA 495, NFPA 1124 or DOTy 27 CFR Part 555 so as to be fire resistant and theft resistant.

❖ These magazines are sometimes found inside warehouses, wholesale houses and retail establishments on wheels or casters to allow easy movement when needed.

Type 1. A permanent structure, such as a building or igloo, that is bullet resistant, fire resistant, theft resistant, weather resistant and ventilated in accordance with the requirements of NFPA 495, NFPA 1124 or DOTy 27 CFR Part 555.

❖ The walls of a Type 1 magazine should be constructed of either masonry, metal or wood. The foundation should consist of brick, concrete, cement, block, stone or wood post. The floors should be constructed of nonsparking material and be strong enough to bear the weight of the maximum quantity to be stored. The listed standards give the sizes of material for each type of construction material.

Type 2. A portable or mobile structure, such as a box, skid-magazine, trailer or semitrailer, constructed in accordance with the requirements of NFPA 495, NFPA 1124 or DOTy 27 CFR Part 555 that is fire resistant, theft resistant, weather resistant and ventilated. If used outdoors, a Type 2 magazine is also bullet resistant.

❖ Construction of a Type 2 magazine may be either:

1. Wood [having sides, bottoms, and covers or doors constructed of 2-inch (51 mm) hardwood, well braced at corners and covered with sheet metal (not less than 26 gauge) with exposed nails countersunk].
2. Metal [having sides, bottoms and covers or doors constructed of 12-gauge (0.1046 inch)

metal and lined inside with a nonsparking material. Edges of metal shall overlap sides at least 1 inch (25 mm)].

Type 3. A fire resistant, theft resistant and weather resistant "day box" or portable structure constructed in accordance with NFPA 495, NFPA 1124 or DOTy 27 CFR Part 555 used for the temporary storage of *explosive materials*.

❖ Construction of a Type 3 magazine may be of not less than 12-gauge (0.1046 inch) steel, lined with $^1/_2$-inch (12.7 mm) plywood or $^1/_2$-inch (12.7 mm) hardboard. The door or lid must overlap the door opening by at least 1 inch (25 mm).

Type 4. A permanent, portable or mobile structure such as a building, igloo, box, semitrailer or other mobile container that is fire resistant, theft resistant and weather resistant and constructed in accordance with NFPA 495, NFPA 1124 or DOTy 27 CFR Part 555.

❖ Construction of a Type 4 magazine may be of masonry, metal-covered wood, fabricated metal or a combination of these materials.

Type 5. A permanent, portable or mobile structure such as a building, igloo, box, bin, tank, semitrailer, bulk trailer, tank trailer, bulk truck, tank truck or other mobile container that is theft resistant, which is constructed in accordance with NFPA 495, NFPA 1124 or DOTy 27 CFR Part 555.

❖ In Type 5 outdoor storage facilities, ground around the storage facility must slope away for drainage. Wheels must be removed from vehicles used as unattended storage facilities or they must be immobilized by kingpin locking devices.

In Type 5 indoor storage facilities, blasting agents are not to be stored in any kind of indoor storage facility in a residence or dwelling.

MAGNESIUM. The pure metal and alloys, of which the major part is magnesium.

❖ Magnesium is a silvery-white combustible metal weighing only two-thirds as much as aluminum and having good structural properties when suitably alloyed. For this reason, magnesium alloys are used to a great extent in the construction of aircraft, automobiles and trucks, household appliances, furniture, office equipment, machine parts and numerous other applications. Powdered magnesium is used in signal flares and other fireworks to produce an intense white light.

The melting point of pure magnesium is 1,202°F (650°C). The ignition temperature is generally considered to be very close to the melting point, but ignition of magnesium in certain forms may occur at lower air temperatures. Magnesium ribbon and fine magnesium shavings can be ignited under some conditions at temperatures of 950°F (510°C), and very finely divided magnesium powder has been ignited at an air temperature below 900°F (482°C).

The ease of ignition of magnesium depends to a large extent on the size and shape of the material as well as the intensity of the ignition source. The flame of a match may be sufficient to ignite magnesium ribbon, shavings or chips with thin feather edges, and a spark will ignite fine dust such as is produced in grinding operations. Heavier pieces, such as ingots or thick-walled castings, are difficult to ignite because heat is rapidly conducted away from a localized ignition source. If the entire piece of metal can be raised to the ignition temperature, however, self-sustained burning will occur.

Because the melting point of magnesium is low, the metal melts as it burns and, after some minutes of burning, produces puddles of molten magnesium. The production of molten metal will depend to a considerable extent on the physical condition of the material. Finely divided magnesium, such as shavings, dust and small scraps, will burn more rapidly and produce less molten metal than will an equal quantity of magnesium in the more solid form of ingots or castings.

Metal products marketed under a variety of trade names and designations and commonly referred to as "magnesium" may, in fact, be one of a large number of alloys containing widely differing percentages of magnesium, aluminum, zinc and manganese. Some of these alloys have melting points and ignition temperatures considerably lower than that of pure magnesium.

MALL. See "Covered mall building."

MANUAL FIRE ALARM BOX. A manually operated device used to initiate an alarm signal.

❖ Manual fire alarm boxes are commonly known as pull stations. Manual fire alarm boxes include all manual devices used to activate a manual fire alarm system and have many configurations, depending on the manufacturer. All manual fire alarm devices, however, must be approved and installed in accordance with NFPA 72 for the particular application. Manual fire alarm boxes may be combined in guard tour boxes.

MANUAL STOCKING METHODS. Stocking methods utilizing ladders or other nonmechanical equipment to move stock.

❖ Manual stocking methods do not require the use of mechanical means to stock and retrieve commodities. Commodities may be stocked or retrieved on foot where the commodity is accessible from a floor or landing, or through the use of a portable ladder or portable stair.

MARINA. Any portion of the ocean or inland water, either naturally or artificially protected, for the mooring, servicing or safety of vessels and shall include artificially protected works, the public or private lands ashore, and structures or facilities provided within the enclosed body of water and ashore for the mooring or servicing of vessels or the servicing of their crews or passengers.

❖ A marina is a protected area where the mooring of marine vessels occurs along with the associated operations to service the vessels, such as fueling, maintenance and repair facilities, ship chandlers, stores and restaurants, the launching of vessels and the loading of vessels with cargo or persons. Marine vessels moored in a marina are usually in close proximity to each other with floats of minimal widths, usually enough for people to walk on, and small carts to carry supplies that are to be loaded onto the vessels. The marina may offer out-of-water-storage, which is useful out of season and important in climates susceptible to freezing waters. Dry storage or "dry stacking" boat storage stores boats vertically in double, triple or even quadruple rack systems. Boats are placed into and retrieved from the storage racks with a forklift.

MARINE MOTOR FUEL-DISPENSING FACILITY. That portion of property where flammable or *combustible liquids* or gases used as fuel for watercraft are stored and dispensed from fixed equipment on shore, piers, wharves, floats or barges into the fuel tanks of watercraft and shall include all other facilities used in connection therewith.

❖ A marine motor fuel-dispensing facility is not to be confused with a bulk marine terminal, which transfers fuel by way of flange-to-flange connections. A marine motor fuel-dispensing facility uses automotive-type dispensing equipment. Motor fuel-dispensing facilities are classified in Occupancy Group M by the IBC.

MAXIMUM ALLOWABLE QUANTITY PER CONTROL AREA. The maximum amount of a hazardous material allowed to be stored or used within a *control area* inside a building or an outdoor control area. The maximum allowable quantity per control area is based on the material state (solid, liquid or gas) and the material storage or use conditions.

❖ Exceeding this amount, also referred to as the MAQ, will place the use area or building into a hazardous occupancy classification. See Tables 5003.1.1(1), 5003.1.1(2), 5003.1.1(3), 5003.1.1(4) and 5003.8.3.2.

[BE] MEANS OF EGRESS. A continuous and unobstructed path of vertical and horizontal egress travel from any occupied portion of a building or structure to a *public way*. A means of egress consists of three separate and distinct parts: the *exit access*, the *exit* and the *exit discharge*.

❖ The means of egress is the path traveled by building occupants to leave the building and the site on which it is located. It includes all interior and exterior elements that the occupants must utilize as they make their way from every room and usable space within the building to a public way such as a street or alley. The elements that make up the means of egress create the lifeline that occupants utilize to travel out of the structure and to a safe distance from the structure. The means of egress provisions of the code strive to provide a reasonable level of life safety in every structure. The means of egress provisions are subdivided into three distinct portions (see the definitions of "Exit access," "Exit" and "Exit discharge").

MECHANICAL STOCKING METHODS. Stocking methods utilizing motorized vehicles or hydraulic jacks to move stock.

❖ Mechanical stocking methods are generally associated with rack storage. The mass of the commodity, the height of the rack storage or the shear quantity of commodity on any one pallet will normally put stocking or retrieval beyond human reach or strength. Methods commonly employed for this type of operation are manned forklifts or unmanned mechanized storage and retrieval systems.

[BG] MEDICAL CARE. Care involving medical or surgical procedures, nursing or for psychiatric purposes.

❖ Persons who need medical care are likely to be incapable of self-preservation or at least extremely limited in their ability to evacuate. In consideration of occupants' health as well as safety, hospitals and nursing homes at least partially rely on defend-in-place strategies rather than evacuation. See also the commentary to Occupancy Group I-2.

Care facilities encompass a full spectrum of occupant acuity and support services, and span a wide range of occupancy types, including Groups E, I and R. There are three types of care defined in the codes: personal, custodial and medical. On the lower end of the care spectrum (i.e., personal care) is where occupants are supervised but do not need custodial or medical care. Where occupants may be elderly or impaired (i.e., custodial care), they may need occasional daily living assistance, such as cooking and cleaning. Persons who receive custodial care may or may not require assistance with evacuation depending on the occupancy and conditions of the occupancy. On the opposite end of the care spectrum, persons receiving care may be completely bedridden and dependent on medical gases and emergency power to maintain life (i.e., medical care). The level of care provided is based on the condition and capabilities of an occupant, which, in turn, indicate appropriate standards for protection systems, both active and passive. See also the definitions for "24-hour basis," "Custodial care," "Detoxification facilities," "Foster care facilities," "Group home," "Hospitals and psychiatric hospitals," "Incapable of self-preservation," "Nursing homes" and "Personal care services."

MEMBRANE STRUCTURE. An air-inflated, air-supported, cable or frame-covered structure as defined by the *International Building Code* and not otherwise defined as a tent. See Chapter 31 of the *International Building Code*.

❖ This definition is broadly inclusive of all types of membrane structures, regardless of the supporting mechanism or structure, defined in Chapter 2 of the IBC as "Air-inflated structure," "Air-supported structure," "Cable-restrained, air supported structure," "Membrane-covered cable structure" and "Membrane-covered frame structure." Note that tents are not included. See the definitions of "Air-inflated structure," "Air-supported structure" and "Tent."

[BF] MEMBRANE-PENETRATION FIRESTOP SYSTEM. An assemblage consisting of a fire-resistance-rated floor-ceiling, roof-ceiling or wall assembly, one or more penetrating items installed into or passing through the breach in one side of the assembly and the materials or devices, or both, installed to resist the spread of fire into the assembly for a prescribed period of time.

❖ Membrane-penetration firestop systems maintain the required protection from the spread of fire, passage of hot gases and transfer of heat. A firestop usually refers to a single item, where a system is a combination of elements. See also the commentary to the definition of "Through-penetration firestop system."

[BE] MERCHANDISE PAD. A merchandise pad is an area for display of merchandise surrounded by *aisles*, permanent fixtures or walls. Merchandise pads contain elements such as nonfixed and moveable fixtures, cases, racks, counters and partitions as indicated in Section 105.2 of the *International Building Code* from which customers browse or shop.

❖ Merchandise pads would most likely be found in large stores with changing displays of clothes or furniture. This is not a raised display-only area. These areas allow customers to move between displays or racks. In regards to means of egress, merchandise pads could be considered analogous to areas of fixed seating or groups of tables. The aisle accessways are within the merchandise pad and lead to the aisles on the outside edges of the merchandise pads. Not all stores will contain merchandise pads (e.g., a typical grocery store with fixed shelves and aisles).

METAL HYDRIDE. A generic name for compounds composed of metallic element(s) and hydrogen.

❖ Hydride is the name given to the negative ion of hydrogen. With the exception of inert gases, every element in the Periodic Table of Elements can form a hydride. The hazards of hydrides will vary based on the elemental molecule to which the -H ion attaches itself.

A metal hydride is a metallic alloy that will adsorb and release hydrogen molecules. (The term "adsorb" means a taking up by physical or chemical forces of the molecules of hydrogen gas by the surfaces of solids with which they are in contact.) With metal hydrides, adsorption occurs when the hydrogen molecules accumulate on the surface of metal. Many of the metals used in metal hydride storage systems (MHSS) are designed to be reversible, meaning they can adsorb and release hydrogen from the system. The adsorption and release occurs when heat is transferred within the MHSS, which upsets the equilibrium condition between the hydrogen, the hydrogen-adsorbing alloy and the metal hydride system.

METAL HYDRIDE STORAGE SYSTEM. A *closed system* consisting of a group of components assembled as a package to contain metal-hydrogen compounds for which there exists an equilibrium condition where the hydrogen-absorbing metal alloy(s), hydrogen gas and the metal-hydrogen compound(s) coexist and where only hydrogen gas is released from the system in normal use.

❖ Metal hydride storage systems (MHSS) are another technological advancement in fuel-cell technology that is becoming a commonly used method for storing hydrogen and is an alternative to traditional compressed or cryogenic fluid storage methods for supplying hydrogen to fuel cells. An MHSS will release or adsorb hydrogen gas when the equilibrium condition is changed. Changes in the equilibrium condition cause the system to either release heat (exothermic) or absorb heat (endothermic). MHSSs designed in compliance with Section 5807 are designed so only hydrogen is released from or introduced into the system during its discharge or filling. The requirements in Section 5807 provide guidance to fire code officials and design professionals in the design, construction, inspection and testing of systems and components used as an MHSS (see Commentary Figure 202-M1).

[BG] MEZZANINE. An intermediate level or levels between the floor and ceiling of any story and in accordance with Section 505 of the *International Building Code*.

❖ A common design feature in factories, warehouses and mercantile buildings is an intermediate loft, or platform, between the story levels of a building. This type of feature, or mezzanine, can be found in buildings of all occupancies. The IBC must be used to determine whether this intermediate level is another story of the building or whether it can simply be treated as part of the story in which it is contained. The basic rule is that the intermediate level must be less than one-third of the area of the story below (of the room in which it is located) in order to be considered a mezzanine. However a variety of exceptions are provided by the IBC. Requirements for mezzanines are found in Section 505 of the IBC.

MISCELLA. A mixture, in any proportion, of the extracted oil or fat and the extracting solvent.

❖ This definition is specifically related to Chapter 39 dealing with processing and extraction facilities. The processing and extraction being address is related to the removal of oils and fats associated with various plants. This process involves the use of solvents to separate oil and proteins. The material leaving the solvent extractor is the miscella. From there the miscella must be distilled to remove remaining solvents. See the commentary to Chapter 39.

Commentary Figure 202-M1
METAL HYDRIDE STORAGE CONTAINER AND ITS METAL HYDRIDE CONTENT
Photo courtesy of Ovanics Hydrogen Systems, LLC

MOBILE FOOD PREPARATION VEHICLES. Vehicles that contain cooking equipment that produce smoke or grease-laden vapors for the purpose of preparing and serving food to the public. Vehicles intended for private recreation shall not be considered mobile food preparation vehicles.

❖ This definition is provided in support of Section 319 addressing mobile food preparation vehicles (food trucks and their associated hazards). The definition helps to clarify what types of trucks are being regulated. The definition is focused only on trucks that have food preparation operations producing smoke and grease-laden vapors. It also scopes out private recreation vehicles. Concerns with food preparation vehicles are the fire hazards associated with the actual preparation, including cooking oils, and the cooking fuel and associated connections to the equipment.

MOBILE FUELING. The operation of dispensing liquid fuels from tank vehicles into the fuel tanks of motor vehicles. Mobile fueling may also be known by the terms “Mobile fleet fueling,” “Wet fueling” and “Wet hosing.”

❖ This definition pertains to the fueling process regulated by Section 5706.5.4.5, wherein fuel is dispensed from the tank vehicle directly to the fuel tank of a vehicle. Also note the requirements in Section 5707 for on-demand mobile fueling (see commentaries, Section 5706.5.4.5 and 5707).

MORTAR. A tube from which fireworks shells are fired into the air.

❖ Mortars must be inspected carefully for defects, such as dents, bent ends, damaged interiors and damaged plugs, prior to placement and use. Defective mortars must not be used. Careful inspection of mortars is of particular importance for paper mortars that can sustain undetected damage to their interiors that can result in serious malfunctions.

MULTIPLE-STATION ALARM DEVICE. Two or more single-station alarm devices that can be interconnected such that actuation of one causes all integral or separate audible alarms to operate. A multiple-station alarm device can consist of one single-station alarm device having connections to other detectors or to a manual fire alarm box.

❖ This definition refers to a combination of similar or different types of alarm devices that could be interconnected. The actuation of any two devices, whether a smoke detector or manual fire alarm box, will activate the required audible alarms at all interconnected devices.

MULTIPLE-STATION SMOKE ALARM. Two or more single-station alarm devices that are capable of interconnection such that actuation of one causes the appropriate alarm signal to operate in all interconnected alarms.

❖ In occupancies with sleeping areas, occupants must be notified in a fire so that they can promptly evacuate the premises. In accordance with the requirements of NFPA 72, multiple-station smoke alarms are self-contained, smoke-activated alarm devices built in accordance with UL 217 that can be interconnected with other devices so that all integral or separate alarms will operate when any one device is activated.

NESTING. A method of securing flat-bottomed *compressed gas* cylinders upright in a tight mass using a contiguous three-point contact system whereby all cylinders within a group have not less than three points of contact with other cylinders, walls or bracing.

❖ Nesting is the placement of cylinders in tightly packed groups in which three sides of the group are composed of walls or barriers and each cylinder is in contact with a wall or another cylinder in at least three places. It is generally considered an alternative to chaining or otherwise physically securing compressed gas cylinders (as required by Section 5303.5.3) under conditions of occupancy where cylinders must be readily moveable, such as in a filling plant.

Placing cylinders in multipoint contact with one another can reduce cylinder instability while affording the ready mobility required by an operation being conducted by trained personnel. Such a configuration is relatively secure for all cylinders involved because even those cylinders on the open side would have to be displaced from behind, i.e., an area within the nest itself. This reduces the potential for damage to the cylinder valve since a knockdown of the cylinder could result in leakage of hazardous gas or create a projectile situation.

One safety precaution that could reduce the likelihood of a cylinder on the face of the nest having a valve sheared is maintaining an open space in front of the nest, free of shelves, counters or other projections, which could act to break the valve on an overturning cylinder. Additionally, valve protection caps should be in place on the cylinders at all times when the cylinder is not connected, being filled or emptied (see Commentary Figure 202-N1).

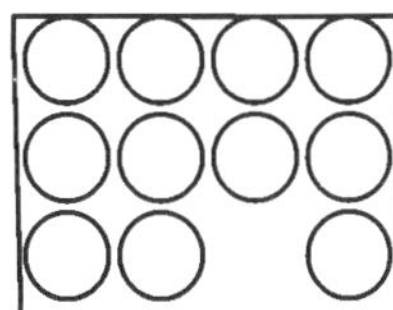

Cylinders aligned but not nested

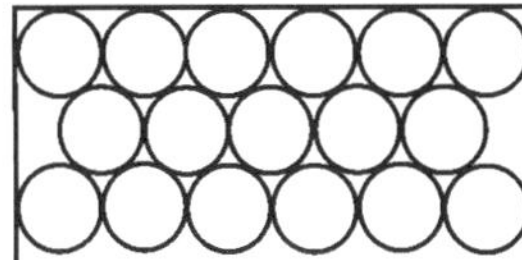

Cylinders nested

Commentary Figure 202-N1
NESTING OF CYLINDERS

NET EXPLOSIVE WEIGHT (net weight). The weight of *explosive material* expressed in pounds. The net explosive weight is the aggregate amount of *explosive material* contained within buildings, magazines, structures or portions thereof, used to establish quantity-distance relationships.

❖ This definition is included to correlate the use of the provisions of this chapter. The definition is based on Department of Defense (DOD) concepts; however, prescriptive requirements have been removed from the DOD definition and placed into the body of the code. The net explosive weight may vary depending on building construction; for example, in cases where appropriate barrier walls or appropriate distances have been employed to avoid propagation.

NORMAL TEMPERATURE AND PRESSURE (NTP). A temperature of 70°F (21°C) and a pressure of 1 atmosphere [14.7 psia (101 kPa)].

❖ Reaction by some chemicals is based on temperature and pressure. Understanding this relationship to normal room temperature and pressure (elevation) can provide information on the hazards for the chemical being considered.

[BE] NOSING. The leading edge of treads of *stairs* and of landings at the top of *stairway flights*.

❖ The front edge of the tread that is exposed to the user's foot provides the visual clue for the placement of the foot in both ascent and descent. The nosings of a stair are a reference point for the measurement of the tread depth and riser height. The line connecting the nosings serves as the reference for the measurement of handrail and guard heights as well as headroom. The code ensures their uniformity by limiting the projection of the tread and landing nosings, resulting in a stairway that is easy to use. Where too large, nosings are a tripping hazard when walking up a stair. Where too small in relation to tread depth, the effective tread depth required for heel clearance in descent is minimized. The code provides limits for both minimum and maximum nosing projections and establishes a minimum tread depth where no projection is required. An exception to these limits exists in the requirements for both alternating tread devices and ships ladders where an exaggerated projected tread depth, required to provide for reasonable foot room, is unique to the steeper gradient and functional use of these devices.

NOTIFICATION ZONE. See "Zone, notification."

NUISANCE ALARM. An alarm caused by mechanical failure, malfunction, improper installation or lack of proper maintenance, or an alarm activated by a cause that cannot be determined.

❖ A nuisance alarm is essentially any alarm that occurs as a result of a condition that does not arise during the normal operation of the equipment. A nuisance alarm is not the same as a false alarm. A person who intentionally initiates an alarm by using a manual pull station or a person who accidentally initiates a smoke detector is not initiating a nuisance alarm. A nuisance alarm is, by nature, a factor of the system itself. See commentary to the definition of "False alarm."

[BG] NURSING HOMES. Facilities that provide care, including both intermediate care facilities and skilled nursing facilities, where any of the persons are incapable of self-preservation.

❖ Persons in nursing homes may be physically incapable of self-preservation or at least extremely limited in their ability to evacuate. In dementia wards, they may be confined within an area of a building for care or security purposes. In consideration of occupants' health as well as safety, hospitals and nursing homes at least partially rely on defend-in-place strategies. See the commentaries for Occupancy Group I-2 and Section 407 of the IBC.

Care facilities are used by patients of varying acuity seeking a broad spectrum of available support services. These facilities span a wide range of occupancy types, including Groups B, E, I and R. The level of care provided is based on the condition and capabilities of an occupant, which, in turn, indicate appropriate standards for protection systems, both passive and active. See also the definitions for "24-hour basis," "Care suite," "Custodial care," "Detoxification facilities," "Hospitals and psychiatric hospitals," "Incapable of self-preservation" and "Medical care."

OCCUPANCY CLASSIFICATION. For the purposes of this code, certain occupancies are defined as follows:

❖ The provisions of Sections 302 through 312 of the IBC control the classification of buildings and structures as to their use and occupancy. The purpose of those provisions is to provide rational criteria for the classification of various occupancies into groups based on their relative fire hazard and life safety properties. This is necessary because the IBC, as well as many provisions of the code, utilize occupancy group classification as a fundamental principle for differentiating code requirements related to fire and life safety protection. By organizing occupancies with similar fire hazard and life safety properties into occupancy groups, the IBC and the code have adopted the means to differentiate occupancies such that various fire protection and life safety requirements can be rationally organized and applied. Each specific group has an individual classification and represents a different characteristic and level of fire hazard that requires special code provisions to lessen the associated risks. See Chapter 3 of the IBC commentary for further discussion of occupancy groups and examples of how they are applied.

[BG] Assembly Group A. Assembly Group A occupancy includes, among others, the use of a building or structure, or a portion thereof, for the gathering of persons for purposes such as civic, social or religious functions; recreation, food or drink consumption; or awaiting transportation.

❖ Because of the arrangement and density of the occupant load associated with occupancies classified in the Group A assembly category, the potential for multiple fatalities and injuries from fire is comparatively high. For example, no other use listed in Section 302.1 of the IBC contemplates occupant loads as dense as 5 square feet (0.46 m^2) per person (see Table 1004.5). Darkened spaces in theaters, nightclubs and the like serve to increase hazards. In sudden emergencies, the congestion caused by large numbers of people rushing to exits can cause panic conditions. For these and many other reasons, there is a relatively high degree of hazard to life safety in assembly facilities. The relative hazards of assembly occupancies are reflected in the height and area limitations of Tables 504.3, 504.4 and 506.2 that are, in comparison, generally more restrictive than for buildings in other group classifications.

A room or space with an occupant load of 50 or more persons should not be automatically classified as a Group A; however, if a room or space is used for assembly purposes as detailed in IBC Section 303.1 (i.e., gathering of persons for purposes such as civic, social or religious functions; recreation, food or drink consumption; or awaiting transportation) and the occupant load is 50 or more, Group A is likely to be the appropriate designation. Other uses can have an occupant load of more than 50 in a space or room; for example, a large office space, a grocery store or the main floor of a major retail business, but these are not assembly occupancies.

There are five specific assembly group classifications, Groups A-1 through A-5, described in IBC Section 303.1. Where used in the code, the general term "Group A" is intended to include all five classifications.

The fundamental characteristics of all assembly occupancies are identified in this section. Structures that are designed or occupied for assembly purposes must be placed in one of the assembly group classifications. There are buildings and spaces which are used for assembly purposes, but are not classified as Assembly occupancies. These "exceptions" to this rule include small assembly buildings, tenant spaces and assembly spaces in mixed-use buildings. These exceptions to the Group A classification are addressed below.

[BG] Small buildings and tenant spaces. A building or tenant space used for assembly purposes with an *occupant load* of less than 50 persons shall be classified as a Group B occupancy.

❖ There are often small establishments that serve food, have a few seats and technically meet the definition of an assembly Group A occupancy, but due to the low occupant load, pose a lower risk than a typical assembly occupancy. These types of buildings and tenant spaces are to be considered as Group B occupancies where the occupant load is determined to be less than 50 persons. Examples of this include small "fast-food" establishments and small "mom-and-pop" cafes or coffee shops.

[BG] Small assembly spaces. The following rooms and spaces shall not be classified as assembly occupancies:

1. A room or space used for assembly purposes with an *occupant load* of less than 50 persons and accessory to another occupancy shall be classified as a Group B occupancy or as part of that occupancy.
2. A room or space used for assembly purposes that is less than 750 square feet (70 m^2) in area and accessory to another occupancy shall be classified as a Group B occupancy or as part of that occupancy.

❖ Assembly rooms or spaces within larger buildings that house other uses are classified based on their occupant loads. Where the occupant load of the assembly space is less than 50, or where the floor area of the space used for assembly purposes is less than 750 square feet (65 m^2), a classification of other than Group A is permitted. In both cases, the purpose of the assembly space must be accessory to the principal occupancy of the structure (i.e., the activities in the assembly space are subordinate and secondary to the primary occupancy). If either the occupant load or floor area requirement is satisfied and the purpose of the assembly space is accessory to the principal occupancy, the space is permitted to either be classified as a Group B occupancy or as part of the principal occupancy. In either case, the assembly space is not required to be less than 10 percent of the area of the story on which it is located, as is specified for accessory occupancies in Section 508.2 of the IBC (IBC Interpretation No. 20-04).

The allowances given to assembly spaces in buildings containing multiple uses are a practical code consideration that permits a mixed-use condition to exist without requiring compliance with the provisions for mixed occupancies (see Section 508 of the IBC). Although the term "accessory" is used in describing the relationship of the uses, the term here is intended to convey that the use of the space is related to, or part of, the main use of the space. These exceptions are not limited by the accessory use requirements found in Section 508.2 of the IBC.

Example 1: An office building, classified as a Group B occupancy, has a conference room used for staff meetings with an occupant load of 40 (see Commentary Figure 202-O1). The occupancy classification of a conference room is generally considered a Group A-3. Since the occupant load of the conference room is less than 50 and its function is clearly accessory to the business area, the room is permitted to be classified the same as the main occupancy, Group B.

Example 2: A 749-square-foot (70 m^2) assembly area is located adjacent to a mercantile floor area of 5,000 square feet (465 m^2) (see Commentary Figure 202-O2). Although the assembly use area occupies 15 percent of the 5,000-square-foot (465 m^2) floor area, it does not exceed 750 square feet (70 m^2) and is not considered a Group A occupancy, but rather is classified as part of the Group M occupancy.

[BG] Associated with Group E occupancies. A room or space used for assembly purposes that is associated with a Group E occupancy is not considered a separate occupancy.

❖ A typical educational facility for students in the 12th grade and below invariably contains many types of assembly spaces other than classrooms, such as auditoriums, cafeterias, gymnasiums and libraries.

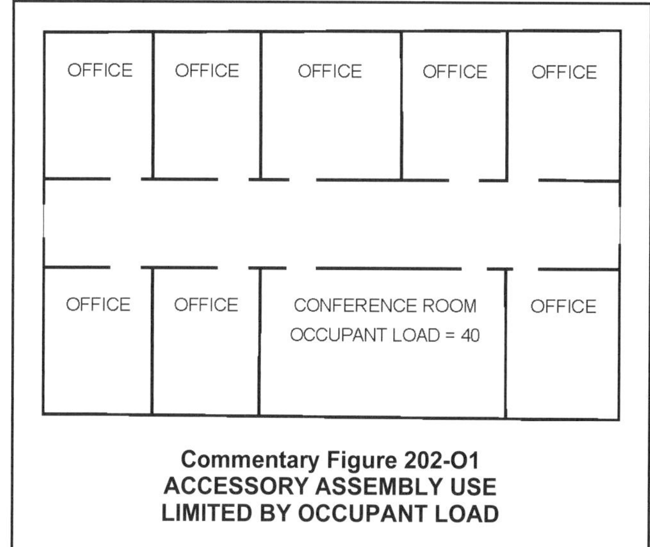

**Commentary Figure 202-O1
ACCESSORY ASSEMBLY USE
LIMITED BY OCCUPANT LOAD**

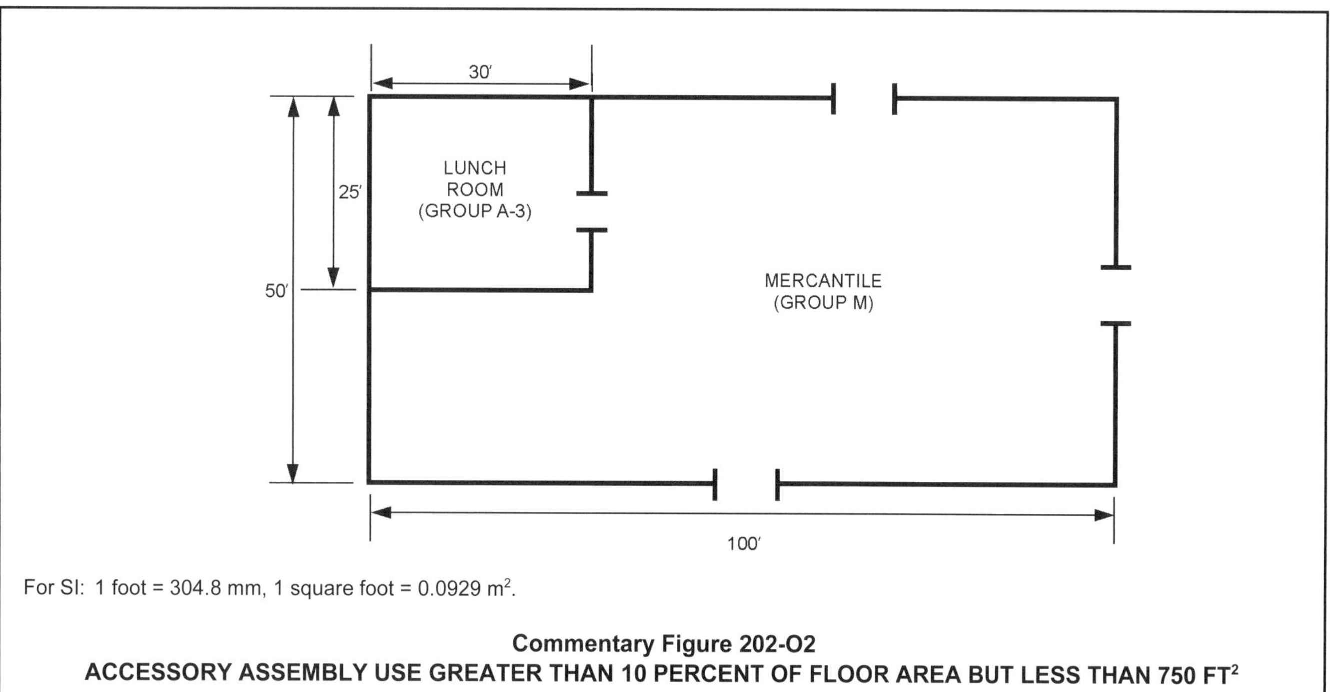

For SI: 1 foot = 304.8 mm, 1 square foot = 0.0929 m^2.

**Commentary Figure 202-O2
ACCESSORY ASSEMBLY USE GREATER THAN 10 PERCENT OF FLOOR AREA BUT LESS THAN 750 FT^2**

Such assembly spaces in a Group E building are not intended to be regulated as separate Group A occupancies, regardless of their floor area, but rather an extension of the Group E classification. It is worth mentioning that, for such assembly functions to be considered part of the primary Group E occupancy, the assembly functions must be ancillary and supportive to the educational operation of the building. Otherwise, they would be classified into the appropriate Group A occupancy based on their specific function. These assembly spaces, where classified as a portion of the Group E occupancy, are still considered as assembly in nature and must comply with assembly space requirements specified for accessibility and means of egress. However, often such school facilities are used for other functions, such as a meeting of a community service organization or a community crafts fair. These types of uses fall outside of the intent of this section and, therefore, such assembly spaces would need to be classified as Group A.

[BG] Accessory with places of religious worship. Accessory religious educational rooms and religious auditoriums with *occupant loads* of less than 100 per room or space are not considered separate occupancies

❖ Places of religious worship are listed as Group A-3 occupancies. In addition to the worship hall, it is common for such facilities to contain smaller rooms used for educational activities. This provision allows such spaces to be considered as part of the Group A-3 classification rather than create a mixed-occupancy condition. For example, classrooms are normally classified as Group E if occupied by persons of ages through the 12th grade, or as Group B if the education is provided to adults. These types of classrooms could be considered as a part of the Group A-3 occupancy under the provisions of this section. Where such rooms at certain times have uses other than as a religious auditorium or for religious education, Section 302 of the IBC requires that the requirements of each occupancy be applied.

[BG] Assembly Group A-1. Group A occupancy includes assembly uses, usually with fixed seating, intended for the production and viewing of performing arts or motion pictures including, but not limited to:

Motion picture theaters
Symphony and concert halls
Television and radio studios admitting an audience
Theaters

❖ Some of the characteristics of Group A-1 occupancies are large, concentrated occupant loads; low lighting levels; above-normal sound levels; and a moderate fuel load.

Group A-1 is characterized by two basic types of activities. The first type is one in which the facility is occupied for the production and viewing of theatrical or operatic performances. Facilities of this type ordinarily have fixed seating; a permanent raised stage; a proscenium wall and curtain; fixed or portable scenery drops; lighting devices; dressing rooms; mechanical appliances or other theatrical accessories and equipment (see Commentary Figure 202-O3).

The second type is one in which the structure is primarily occupied for the viewing of motion pictures. Facilities of this type ordinarily have fixed seating, no stage, a viewing screen, motion picture projection booths and equipment (see Commentary Figure 202-O4).

Group A-1 presents a significant potential life safety hazard because of the large occupant loads and the concentration of people within confined spaces. The means of egress is an important factor in the design of such facilities. Theaters for the performing arts that require stages are considered particularly hazardous because of the amount of combustibles, such as curtains, drops, scenery, construction materials and other accessories normally associated with stage operation. As such, special protection requirements applicable to stages and platforms are provided in Section 410 of the IBC and Chapter 10 of the code.

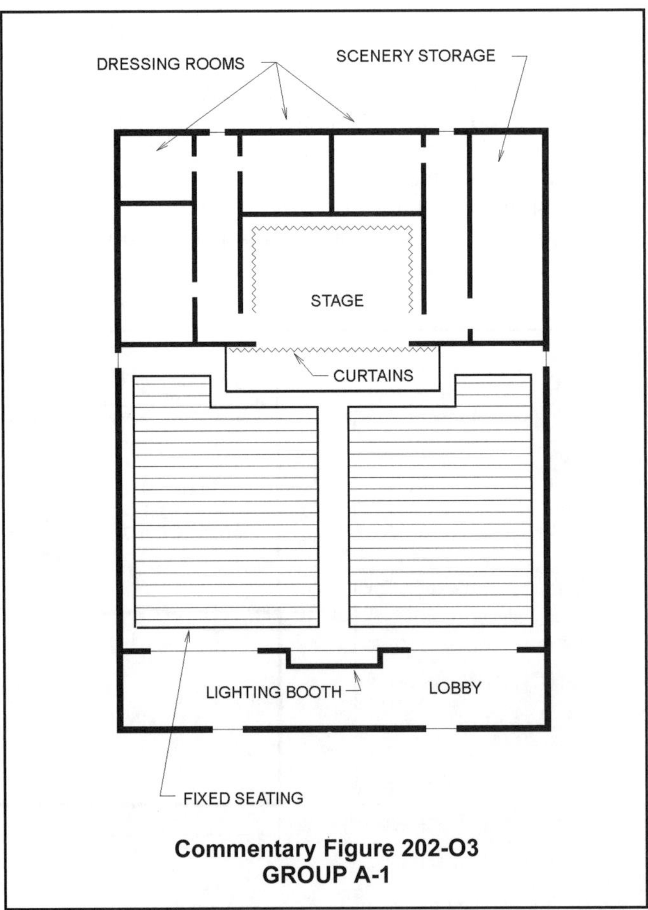

Commentary Figure 202-O3
GROUP A-1

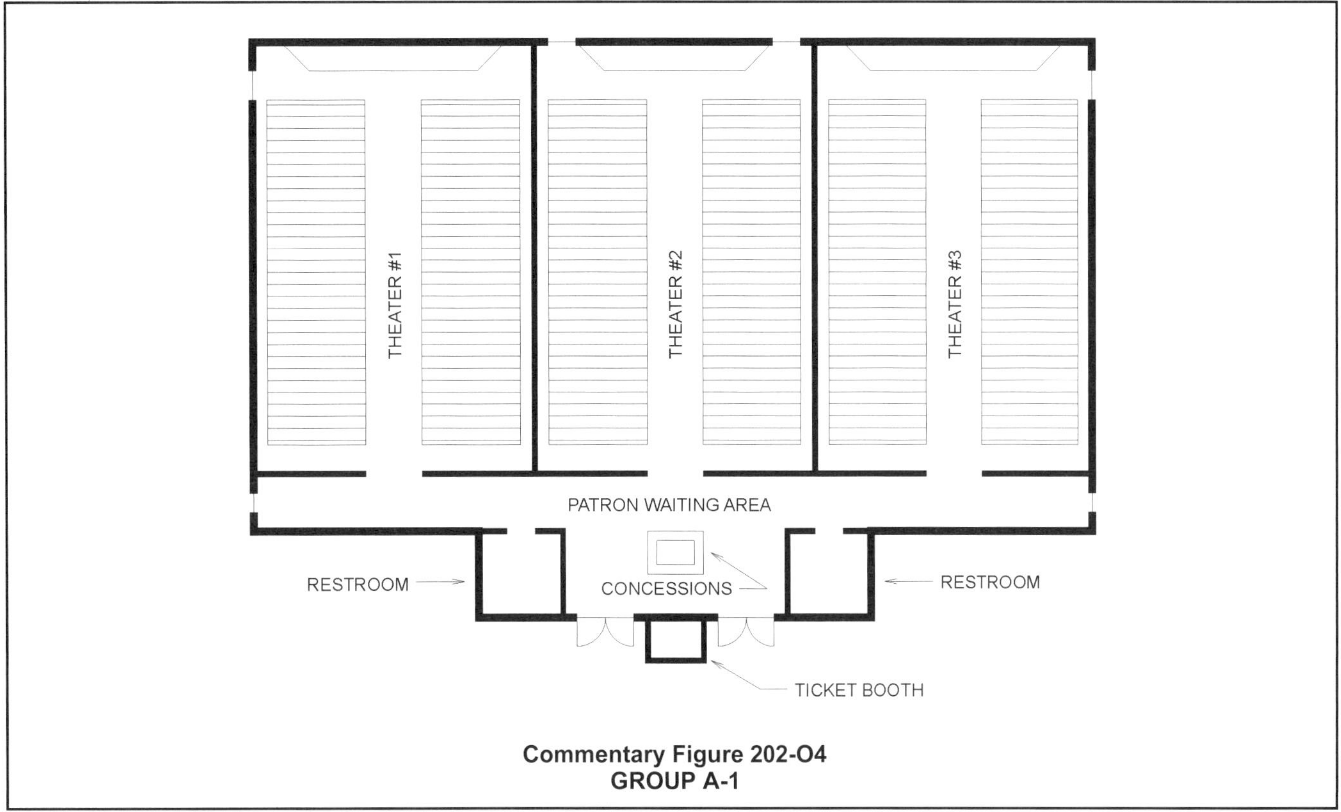

Commentary Figure 202-O4
GROUP A-1

[BG] Assembly Group A-2. Group A-2 occupancy includes assembly uses intended for food and/or drink consumption including, but not limited to:

Banquet halls
Casinos (gaming areas)
Night clubs
Restaurants, cafeterias and similar dining facilities (including associated commercial kitchens)
Taverns and bars

❖ Group A-2 includes occupancies in which people congregate in high densities for social entertainment, such as drinking and dancing (e.g., nightclubs, dance halls, banquet halls, cabarets, etc.) and food and drink consumption (e.g., restaurants). The uniqueness of these occupancies is characterized by some or all of the following:

- Low lighting levels.
- Entertainment by a live band or recorded music generating above-normal sound levels.
- No theatrical stage accessories.
- Later-than-average operating hours.
- Tables and seating arranged or positioned so as to create ill-defined aisles.
- A specific area designated for dancing.
- Service facilities for alcoholic beverages and food.
- High occupant load density.

The fire records are very clear in identifying that the characteristics listed above often cause a delayed awareness of a fire situation and confuse the appropriate response, resulting in an increased egress time and sometimes panic. Together, these factors may result in extensive life and property losses. These characteristics are only advisory in determining whether Group A-2 is the appropriate classification. Often, there are additional characteristics that are unique to a project, which also must be taken into consideration when a classification is made.

Example: The Downtown Club, a popular local nightclub/dance hall, features a different band every weekend (see Commentary Figure 202-O5). It is equipped with a bar and basic kitchen facilities so that beverages and appetizers can be served. There is a platform for a band to perform, a dance floor in front of the platform and numerous cocktail tables and chairs. The tables and chairs are not fixed, resulting in a hazardous arrangement because there are no distinct aisles. When the band performs, the house lights are dimmed and spotlights are keyed in on the performers. The club is equipped with a sound system that can be used at loud levels. The club is open until 3:00 a.m., the latest time the local jurisdiction will allow.

From this description of the Downtown Club, one can readily see that the appropriate classification is Group A-2. Sometimes, however, it is not this easy to determine the appropriate classification. In such cases, the building official must seek additional information regarding the functions of the building and each area within the building.

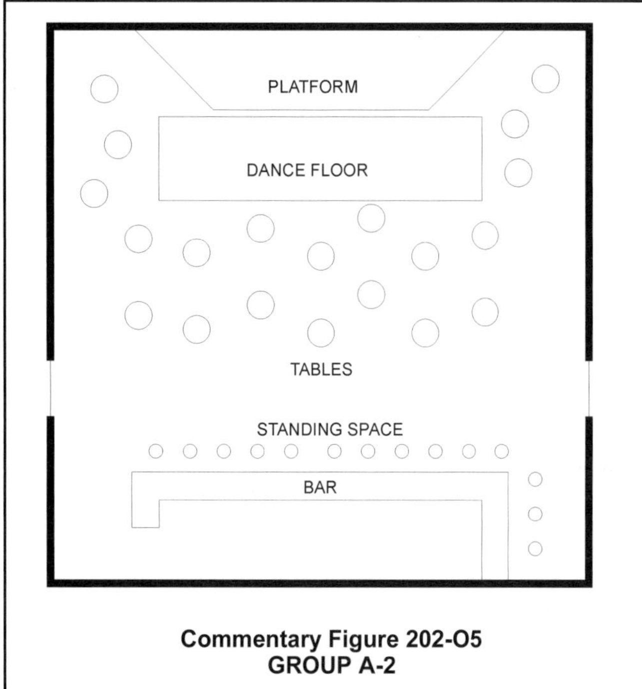

Commentary Figure 202-O5
GROUP A-2

Two of the specific uses listed as Group A-2 occupancies are typically not considered as facilities primarily used for food and/or drink consumption, however, their classification as such has been deemed appropriate for varying reasons. The placement of casino gaming areas in the Group A-2 classification is because they share many hazard characteristics with night clubs and, to some extent, the other uses in the category. The presence of distracting lights, sounds and decorations, along with the potential for alcohol consumption, create an assembly environment that is best addressed under the Group A-2 provisions. The classification is specific to the gaming areas of a casino, therefore, other related uses, such as administrative, storage and lodging areas are to be individually classified based on their specific use.

Although commercial kitchens do not pose the same conditions and concerns as the other uses classified as Group A-2, their classification as such recognizes the relationship that exists between the dining and cooking areas. Providing a physical fire-resistive separation between the kitchen and the dining area that it serves is often found to be impractical. Assigning a single occupancy classification for both the commercial kitchen and its associated dining area eliminates any potential for an unnecessary mixed-occupancy condition. This single classification approach can also be applied where the occupant load of the dining area is below 50, allowing for a Group B classification. Under such circumstances, the kitchen would be considered an extension of the Group B dining facility.

[BG] Assembly Group A-3. Group A-3 occupancy includes assembly uses intended for worship, recreation or amusement and other assembly uses not classified elsewhere in Group A, including, but not limited to:

Amusement arcades
Art galleries
Bowling alleys
Community halls
Courtrooms
Dance halls (not including food or drink consumption)
Exhibition halls
Funeral parlors
Greenhouses with public access for the conservation and exhibition of plants
Gymnasiums (without spectator seating)
Indoor swimming pools (without spectator seating)
Indoor tennis courts (without spectator seating)
Lecture halls
Libraries
Museums
Places of religious worship
Pool and billiard parlors
Waiting areas in transportation terminals

❖ Structures in which people assemble for the purpose of social activities (such as entertainment, recreation and amusement) that are neither classified in Group A-1 or A-2 nor appropriately classified in Group A-4 or A-5 are to be classified in Group A-3. Exhibition halls, libraries, dance halls (not including food and drink), places of religious worship, museums, gymnasiums, recreation centers, health clubs, fellowship halls, indoor shooting galleries, bowling centers and billiard halls are among the facilities often classified in Group A-3. Also, since they most nearly resemble this occupancy classification, public and private spaces used for assembly are often classified in Group A-3. These include large courtrooms, meeting rooms and conference centers. Similarly, lecture rooms located in colleges, universities or in schools for students above the 12th grade that have an occupant load of 50 or more are also classified in Group A-3, as well as structures in which people gather exclusively for worship and other religious purposes. Although such worship and religious purposes are without restriction to any particular sect or creed, the code is intended to limit Group A-3 classification to occupancies that are specifically related to worship services, devotions and religious rituals.

"Greenhouse" is often a term describing a type of structure. Its group classification is based on how the greenhouse is used. Where the use is display and conservation of plants, as opposed to cultivation or retail sale, then the use is similar to a museum and therefore a Group A-3.

The fire hazard in terms of combustible contents (fuel load) in structures classified in Group A-3 is most often expected to be moderate to low. Since structures classified in Group A-3 vary widely as to the purpose for which they are used, the range of fuel load varies widely. For example, the fuel load in a library or an exhibition hall usually is considerably greater than that normally found in a gymnasium. While the code specifically addresses kitchens associated with Group A-2 restaurants and similar dining facilities, it is silent regarding accessory kitchens one might find associated with community centers or a fellowship hall of a place of religious worship. These kitchens should be considered carefully by the building official. Each facility and its use will be unique. The intensity and frequency of the use of the space for serving of food as well as the type of cooking equipment installed are important factors. The occasional use of the fellowship hall for a fundraising dinner where food is brought in and warmed is one end of the spectrum and may warrant keeping a Group A-3 classification. But when the same hall becomes a daily charity "soup" kitchen, then Group A-2 classification is more appropriate.

[BG] Assembly Group A-4. Group A-4 occupancy includes assembly uses intended for viewing of indoor sporting events and activities with spectator seating including, but not limited to:

Arenas
Skating rinks
Swimming pools
Tennis courts

❖ Structures provided with spectator seating in which people assemble to watch an indoor sporting event are to be classified as Group A-4. Arenas, skating rinks, swimming pools and tennis courts are among the facilities often classified as Group A-4 occupancies, though this is not an exhaustive list. Every 2 years, the Olympics remind us that other sports such as badminton, curling, wrestling and gymnastics will occur in indoor sport venues. The distinguishing factor between Group A-4 and A-5 structures is whether the event is indoors or outdoors. Group A-4 facilities are limited to indoor structures only. The distinguishing factor between Group A-3 and A-4 facilities is the presence of a defined seating area. While Group A-3 facilities are indoors (e.g., tennis courts, swimming pools), they typically do not have a defined seating area in which to view the event. Only facilities that are both indoors and have a defined seating area are to be classified as Group A-4.

[BG] Assembly Group A-5. Group A-5 occupancy includes assembly uses intended for participation in or viewing outdoor activities including, but not limited to:

Amusement park structures
Bleachers
Grandstands
Stadiums

❖ Structures classified in Group A-5 are outdoor facilities where people assemble to view or participate in social and recreational activities (e.g., stadiums, grandstands, bleachers, coliseums). In order to qualify as an outdoor facility, the structure must be one where the products of combustion are freely and rapidly vented to the atmosphere (i.e., a structure without enclosures that would prevent the free movement of smoke from the occupied area to the outside). Any recreation facility that has exterior walls that enclose the facility and a roof that fully covers the area would not be classified in Group A-5, but rather in Group A-3 or A-4 depending on whether a seating area has been provided. In the case of a structure with a retractable roof, the more stringent occupancy classification (i.e., Group A-4) would be required.

Since occupancies classified in Group A-5 are primarily viewing and sports participation areas, the fuel load associated with them is very low (i.e., the structure itself and seats). Since the fuel load present is relatively low and the expectation is that smoke will be quickly evacuated from the structure, the relative fire hazard of occupancies classified in Group A-5 is expected to be low. The life safety hazard from panic that might occur in an emergency, however, is a serious concern; hence, the capability of large crowds to exit the structure quickly and orderly during emergencies is an important design consideration (see Section 1029).

Both A-4 and A-5 occupancies will include a variety of uses that support the viewing of sports and similar activities. There will likely be luxury seating suites, locker rooms, toilet facilities and press boxes, which are clearly part of the overall uses of the facility. There may also be offices, food concession stands and merchandise stands which by their use are different occupancies, but are probably within the accessory occupancy limits established in Section 508.2 of the IBC. Because of the multitiered design of most Group A-4 and A-5 occupancies, the limit for accessory occupancies of 10 percent of the story will need to be creatively applied. There may be full-fledged restaurants that are in the same building, but may be open to guests not limited to those attending an event. A Group A-2 occupancy designation is likely the most appropriate classification, and the mixed occupancy conditions would most typically be addressed under the accessory occupancy provisions of Section 508.2 of the IBC.

[BG] Business Group B. Business Group B occupancy includes, among others, the use of a building or structure, or a portion thereof, for office, professional or service-type transactions, including storage of records and accounts. Business occupancies shall include, but not be limited to, the following:

Airport traffic control towers
Ambulatory care facilities
Animal hospitals, kennels and pounds
Banks
Barber and beauty shops
Car wash
Civic administration
Clinic-outpatient
Dry cleaning and laundries: pick-up and delivery stations and self-service

Educational occupancies for students above the 12th grade
Electronic data processing
Food processing establishments and commercial kitchens not associated with restaurants, cafeterias and similar dining facilities not more than 2,500 square feet (232 m^2) in area.
Laboratories: testing and research
Motor vehicle showrooms
Post offices
Print shops
Professional services (architects, attorneys, dentists, physicians, engineers, etc.)
Radio and television stations
Telephone exchanges
Training and skill development not in a school or academic program (This shall include, but not be limited to, tutoring centers, martial arts studios, gymnastics and similar uses regardless of the ages served, and where not classified as a Group A occupancy).

❖ The risks to life safety in the business occupancy classification are relatively low. Exposure to the potential effects of fire is limited because business-type facilities most often have low fuel loads, are normally occupied only during the daytime and, with some exceptions, are usually occupied for a set number of hours. The occupants, because of the nature of the use, are typically alert, ambulatory, conscious, aware of their surroundings and generally familiar with the building's features, particularly the means of egress. Historically, this occupancy has one of the better fire safety records for the protection of life and property.

This section identifies the general characteristics and lists examples of occupancies that are classified in Group B. Note that the general description of the occupancy recognizes the need for limited storage spaces that are incidental to Group B occupancies. In addition, Section 311.1.1 of the IBC allows accessory storages to be classified as part of the principal occupancy. Colleges (educational occupancies for students above grade 12) may have spaces that have an occupant load of more than 50 in a room, but are ancillary to the place of education and used only for programs directly associated with training and education programs (see Section 303.4 of the IBC). For college buildings, similar to other office buildings, if there are spaces with occupant loads of greater than 50, such as cafeterias or lecture halls, by the character of the space and the level of fire hazard, they would be appropriately classified as Group A-2 or A-3, respectively (see IBC Section 302.1). Where lecture facilities for large groups (i.e., occupant load of 50 or more) are located within the same building where classrooms with an occupant load less than 50 are found, the building is a mixed occupancy (Groups A-3 and B) and is subject to the provisions of Section 508.

College- and university-level laboratories that comply with Section 428 of the IBC and Chapter 38 of this code will also be classified as Group B (Section 307.1.1 of the IBC).

While civic administration covers a broad range of state and local government buildings, many such buildings will have a variety of uses and need to be considered under mixed occupancy provisions. Frequently, police stations will include jails or holding cells. Fire stations will be a mix of offices, parking and maintenance facilities for the fire engines and living spaces for the fire fighters. Often, a meeting room that is open to the public is also included. This type of facility is a mix of Group A, B, R and S occupancies.

Ambulatory care facilities are those that provide medical, or similar care, on less than a 24-hour basis to patients who are rendered incapable of self-preservation (see the definition of that term). Frequently called "day surgery centers" or "ambulatory surgical centers," ambulatory care facilities are where procedures are performed that render care recipients (patients) temporarily incapable of self-preservation due to the use of nerve blocks, sedation or anesthesia. Due to the condition of the care recipients, the need for medical staff to stabilize the patients before evacuation and the use of medical gases such as oxygen and nitrous oxide, these types of facilities pose greater fire and life safety hazards than other business occupancies. Accordingly, additional fire protection and means of egress requirements specific to ambulatory care are provided in Section 422 of the IBC.

Facilities that provide medical services for inpatient care where the care recipients (patients) stay for more than 24 hours would be classified as Group I-2. Buildings used as sleep clinics would be classified as Group B since these spaces are not typical dwelling or sleeping units where people live, the occupants are assumed to be capable of self-preservation and the occupants are not living in a supervised environment. Although the patients in a sleep clinic may be sleeping, they can be easily awakened and alerted to an emergency as compared to the patients at an ambulatory care facility.

The code distinguishes between food processing operations that are not directly associated with a restaurant based on size. Those operations 2,500 square feet or smaller fall under the Group B classification. A small catering business would fall under this classification. Other food-related businesses that don't provide a space for their product to be eaten on site, such as a take-out pizza store and neighborhood bakery, would also fall under this classification. A commercial kitchen or food processing facility larger than 2,500 square feet would be classified as a Group F occupancy.

Training and skill development is classified as a Group B occupancy due to the similarity in use of spaces to education above the 12th grade and with professional consultation. Often, unions provide training facilities for their members so they can keep up with new materials and updates of regulations. Other facilities can provide one-on-one tutoring such as remedial reading or math skills for students. Training or skill development can include those whose ages are typically associated with grades 12 or earlier. The determination of the appropriate classification requires the building official to consider whether the training is given as part of a traditional educational program. Examples provided by the code allow a range of size in the numbers receiving the training from a one-on-one tutoring situation to large classes of children learning martial arts or ballet. The presence of children does not automatically mean a classification as a Group E. Where the occupant load of a training classroom or space exceeds 50 occupants, a Group A classification may be appropriate for the space, especially if the space is to be used for different activities at different times. If the training room is used for a martial arts competition, with spectators, on an evening or weekend, then a Group A designation should also be considered.

[BG] Educational Group E. Educational Group E occupancy includes, among others, the use of a building or structure, or a portion thereof, by six or more persons at any one time for educational purposes through the 12th grade.

❖ The risks to life safety in this occupancy vary with the composition of the facilities and also with the ages of the occupants. In general, children require more safeguards than do older, more mature persons.

This section identifies the criteria for classification of a building in Group E. The two fundamental characteristics of a Group E facility are as follows:

1. The facility is occupied by more than five persons (excluding the instructor).
2. The purpose of the facility is for educating persons at the 12th-grade level and below, but not including more than five occupants $2^1/_2$ years of age or younger.

It is common for a school to also have gymnasiums (Group A-3), auditoriums (Group A-1), libraries (Group A-3) and offices (Group B). Storage rooms might be classified as either a Group S-1 occupancy or Group E (see Section 311.1.1 of the IBC). When this occurs, the building is considered as a mixed occupancy condition and is subject to the provisions of Section 508. In accordance with Section 303.1.3 of the IBC, assembly spaces, such as the gymnasium, auditorium, library and cafeteria, do not have to be considered separate occupancies if used for school purposes (see commentary below). For such assembly functions to be considered part of the primary Group E occupancy, the assembly functions must be ancillary and supportive to the educational operation of the building.

Occupancies used for the education of persons above the 12th grade level are not included in Group E but are classified as Group B. These facilities are occupied by adults who are not expected to require special supervision, direction or instruction in a fire or other emergency.

[BG] Accessory to places of religious worship. Religious educational rooms and religious auditoriums, which are accessory to places of religious worship in accordance with Section 303.1.4 of the *International Building Code* and have *occupant loads* of less than 100 per room or space shall be classified as Group A-3 occupancies.

❖ In places of religious worship, worship halls, religious educational rooms and religious auditoriums are often all provided in the same building complex. Such religious educational rooms and auditoriums are not to be considered separate occupancies (i.e., Group E). Where such rooms at certain times have uses other than as a religious auditorium or for religious education, Section 302 of the IBC requires that the requirements of each occupancy be applied.

[BG] Group E, day care facilities. This group includes buildings and structures or portions thereof occupied by more than five children older than $2^1/_2$ years of age who receive educational, supervision or *personal care services* for less than 24 hours per day.

❖ Group E day care occupancies include facilities intended to be used for the care and supervision of more than five children older than $2^1/_2$ years of age where individual care is for a period of less than 24 hours per day. Day care centers are a special concern since they are generally occupied by preschool children who are less capable of responding to an emergency. The hazards found in a day care center are far greater than in normal educational facilities, not so much because of the occupant or fuel load, but because of the inability of the occupants to respond.

Children $2^1/_2$ years of age or younger usually are not able to recognize an emergency situation, respond appropriately or simply be able to egress without assistance; thus, facilities that have more than five children $2^1/_2$ years of age or younger are classified as child care facilities and considered to be Group I-4 unless the provisions of one of the subclassifications of that group allow for a different classification.

Locations where child care may be provided that would not be considered Group E, I-4 or I-2 are addressed in Sections 305.2.1 through 305.2.3 of the IBC.

[BG] Within places of worship. Rooms and spaces within places of worship providing such care during religious functions shall be classified as part of the primary occupancy.

❖ Cry rooms and other types of child care areas within places of worship that are used for this purpose during a religious function need not be classified as Group E day care facilities. Such rooms and spaces may take on the classification of the primary occupancy, which in most cases would be Group A-3. The limited occupant load makes the need for classification as a Group E occupancy unnecessary. If the child care areas are used when there is not a service or other religious function going on simultaneously, such as for child day care during the week, the religious facility would be a mixed use building (see commentary, IBC Section 303.5.2 or 308.5).

[BG] Five or fewer children. A facility having five or fewer children receiving such care shall be classified as part of the primary occupancy.

❖ Where a child care facility has no more than five children receiving care at any one time, the classification of the main occupancy may extend to the child care use. The limited number of occupants requiring care services does not warrant classification as a separate and distinct occupancy from that of the major use.

[BG] Five or fewer children in a dwelling unit. A facility such as the above within a dwelling unit and having five or fewer children receiving such care shall be classified as a Group R-3 occupancy or shall comply with the *International Residential Code.*

❖ Where the child care services are performed within a single-family dwelling or within a dwelling unit of a two-family dwelling, residential provisions are applicable provided that the number of children receiving care does not exceed five. The facility may be classified under the IBC as a Group R-3 occupancy or may be regulated under the provisions of the IRC. Where such a use occurs within a dwelling unit of a Group R-2 multi-family building, it is expected that the child care facility be considered as an extension of the primary Group R-2 classification as with five or fewer children.

[BG] Factory Industrial Group F. Factory Industrial Group F occupancy includes, among others, the use of a building or structure, or a portion thereof, for assembling, disassembling, fabricating, finishing, manufacturing, packaging, repair or processing operations that are not classified as a Group H high-hazard or Group S storage occupancy.

❖ The purpose of this definition is to identify the characteristics of occupancies that are classified in the factory industrial group and to differentiate Groups F-1 and F-2. Because of the vast number of diverse manufacturing and processing operations in the industrial community, it is more practical to classify such facilities by their level of hazard rather than by their function. In industrial facilities, experience has shown that the loss of life or property is most directly related to fire hazards, particularly the fuel load contributed by the materials being fabricated, assembled or processed.

Statistics show that property losses are comparatively high in factory and industrial occupancies, but the record of fatalities and injuries from fire has been remarkably low. This excellent life safety record can, in part, be attributed to fire protection requirements of the code.

This definition requires that all structures that are used for fabricating, finishing, manufacturing, packaging, assembling or processing products or materials are to be classified in either Group F-1 (moderate hazard) or F-2 (low hazard). These classifications are based on the relative level of hazard for the types of materials that are fabricated, assembled or processed. Where the products and materials in a factory present an extreme fire, explosion or health hazard, such facilities are classified in Group H. It should be noted that the term "Group F" is not a specific occupancy, but is a term that collectively applies to Groups F-1 and F-2.

[BG] Factory Industrial F-1 Moderate-hazard occupancy. Factory industrial uses that are not classified as Factory Industrial F-2 Low Hazard shall be classified as F-1 Moderate Hazard and shall include, but not be limited to, the following:

Aircraft (manufacturing, not to include repair)
Appliances
Athletic equipment
Automobiles and other motor vehicles
Bakeries
Beverages; over 16-percent alcohol content
Bicycles
Boats
Brooms or brushes
Business machines
Cameras and photo equipment
Canvas or similar fabric
Carpets and rugs (includes cleaning)
Clothing
Construction and agricultural machinery
Disinfectants
Dry cleaning and dyeing
Electric generation plants
Electronics
Engines (including rebuilding)
Food processing and commercial kitchens not associated with restaurants, cafeterias and similar dining facilities more than 2,500 square feet (232 m^2) in area.
Furniture
Hemp products
Jute products
Laundries
Leather products
Machinery
Metals
Millwork (sash and door)
Motion pictures and television filming (without spectators)
Musical instruments
Optical goods
Paper mills or products
Photographic film
Plastic products
Printing or publishing
Refuse incineration
Shoes

Soaps and detergents
Textiles
Tobacco
Trailers
Upholstering
Wood; distillation
Woodworking (cabinet)

❖ Structures classified in Group F-1 (moderate hazard) are occupied for the purpose of the fabrication, finishing, manufacturing, packaging, assembly or processing of materials that are combustible or that use combustible products in the production process. Food processing facilities and commercial kitchens that are 2,500 square feet or smaller in area fall under the Group B occupancy category (see Section 304.1 of the IBC).

[BG] Factory Industrial F-2 Low-hazard Occupancy. Factory industrial uses involving the fabrication or manufacturing of noncombustible materials that, during finishing, packaging or processing do not involve a significant fire hazard, shall be classified as Group F-2 occupancies and shall include, but not be limited to, the following:

Beverages; up to and including 16-percent alcohol content
Brick and masonry
Ceramic products
Foundries
Glass products
Gypsum
Ice
Metal products (fabrication and assembly)

❖ Structures classified in Group F-2 (low hazard) are occupied for the purpose of the fabrication, manufacturing or processing of noncombustible materials. It is acceptable for noncombustible products to be packaged in a combustible material, provided that the fuel load contributed by the packaging is negligible when compared to the amount of noncombustible product. The use of a significant amount of combustible material to package or finish a noncombustible product, however, will result in a Group F-1 (moderate-hazard factory and industrial) classification.

To distinguish when the presence of combustible packaging constitutes a significant fuel load, possibly requiring the reclassification of the building or structure as Group F-1, a reasonable guideline to follow is the "single-thickness" rule, which is when a noncombustible product is put in one layer of packaging material.

Examples of acceptable conditions in Group F-2 include:

- Vehicle engines placed on wood pallets for transportation after assembly.
- Washing machines in corrugated cardboard boxes.
- Soft-drink glass bottles packaged in pressed paper boxes.

Occupancies involving noncombustible items packaged in more than one layer of combustible packaging material are most appropriately classified in Group F-1.

Typical examples of packaging that would result in a Group F-1 classification include:

- Chinaware wrapped in corrugated paper and placed in cardboard boxes.
- Glassware set in expanded foam forms and placed in cardboard boxes.
- Fuel filters individually packed in pressed paper boxes, placed by the gross in a cardboard box and stacked on a pallet for transportation.

Factories and industrial facilities often have offices and areas where large quantities of materials are kept in the same building as manufacturing operations, fabrication processes and assembly processes. The stock areas are classified as either Group S-1 or S-2, depending on the combustibility of the materials stored. Areas used for offices that do not qualify as accessory occupancies (see Section 508.2 of the IBC) are classified in Group B. When these combinations of occupancies occur, as well as other combinations of occupancies, the building is subject to the mixed occupancy provisions in Section 508 of the IBC.

High-hazard Group H. High-hazard Group H occupancy includes, among others, the use of a building or structure, or a portion thereof, that involves the manufacturing, processing, generation or storage of materials that constitute a physical or *health hazard* in quantities in excess of those allowed in *control areas* complying with Section 5003.8.3, based on the maximum allowable quantity limits for *control areas* set forth in Tables 5003.1.1(1) and 5003.1.1(2). Hazardous occupancies are classified in Groups H-1, H-2, H-3, H-4 and H-5 and shall be in accordance with this code and the requirements of Section 415 of the *International Building Code*. Hazardous materials stored or used on top of roofs or canopies shall be classified as outdoor storage or use and shall comply with this code.

❖ This occupancy classification identifies the various types of facilities contained in the high-hazard occupancy groups, e.g., those facilities where the storage of materials or the operations are deemed to be extremely hazardous to life and property, especially when they involve the use of significant amounts of highly combustible, flammable or explosive materials, regardless of their composition (i.e., solids, liquids, gases or dust). Although they are not explosive or highly flammable, other hazardous materials, such as corrosive liquids, highly toxic materials and poisonous gases, still present an extreme hazard to life. Many materials possess multiple hazards, whether physical or health related.

There is a wide range of high-hazard operations in the industrial community; therefore, it is more practical to categorize such facilities in terms of the degree of hazard they present, rather than attempt to define a facility in terms of its function. This method is similar to that used to categorize Group F factory and Group S storage occupancies.

Group H is handled as a separate classification because it represents an unusually high degree of hazard that is not found in the other occupancies. It is important to isolate those industrial or storage operations that pose the greatest dangers to life and property and to reduce such hazards by providing systems or elements of protection through the regulatory provisions of building codes. There are numerous provisions and exceptions throughout the code that cannot be used when one or more Group H occupancies are present.

Operations that, because of the materials utilized or stored, cause a building or portion of a building to be classified as a high-hazard occupancy are identified in this section. While buildings classified as Group H may not have a large occupant load, the unstable chemical properties of the materials contained on the premises constitute an above-average fuel load and serve as a potential danger to the surrounding area.

The dangers created by the high-hazard materials require special consideration for the abatement of the danger. The classification of a material as high hazard is based on information derived from National Fire Protection Association (NFPA) standards and the Code of Federal Regulations (DOL 29 CFR).

The wide range of materials utilized or stored in buildings creates an equally wide range of hazards to the occupants of the building, the building proper and the surrounding area. Since these hazards range from explosive to corrosive conditions, the high-hazard occupancy has been broken into four subclassifications: Groups H-1 through H-4. A fifth category, Group H-5, is used to represent structures that contain hazardous production material (HPM) facilities. Each of these subclassifications addresses materials that have similar characteristics. The protection requirements attempt to address the hazard involved. These subclassifications are defined by the properties of the materials involved with only occasional reference to specific materials. This performance-based criterion may involve additional research to identify a hazard, but it is the only way to remain current in a rapidly changing field. SDS will be a major source for information.

Additional information on hazardous materials can be found in Section 415 of the IBC as well as the commentaries to Chapters 50 through 67.

This definition and Section 307.1 of the IBC acknowledge that a building is not classified as a high-hazard occupancy unless the MAQs per control area as prescribed in Tables 5003.1.1(1) and 5003.1.1(2) [IBC Tables 307.1(1) and 307.1(2)] are exceeded, subject to the applicable control area provisions of Section 5003.8.3 (IBC Section 414.2). The maximum quantity limitations per control area prescribed in Tables 5003.1.1(1) and 5003.1.1(2) [IBC Tables 307.1(1) and 307.1(2)] have been determined to be relatively safe when maintained in accordance with the code. Therefore, a building containing less than the MAQs specified would not be classified as a Group H occupancy but, rather, as the occupancy group it most nearly resembles. The materials in these tables are defined in detail in this chapter.

Section 5003.8.3 (IBC Section 414.2) establishes the control area concept for regulating hazardous materials. This concept would allow the maximum allowable quantities of hazardous materials per control area in Tables 5003.1.1(1) and 5003.1.1(2) [IBC Tables 307.1(1) and 307.1(2)] to be exceeded within a given building without classifying the building as a high-hazard occupancy by utilizing a multiple control area approach. The permitted number of control areas, maximum percentage of allowable quantities of hazardous materials per control area and degree of fire separation between control areas are regulated by Section 5003.8.3 (IBC Section 414.2) (see the definition of "Control area" and the commentary to Section 5003.8.3).

This definition and Section 307.1 of the IBC also clarify that hazardous materials outside of the building envelope should be classified as outdoor storage. As such, hazardous material quantities on roofs or canopies are not included in evaluating the occupancy classification of a building or structure. Canopies used to support gaseous hydrogen systems must comply with Section 406.7.2.1 of the IBC.

Uses other than Group H. The storage, use or handling of hazardous materials as described in one or more of the following items shall not cause the occupancy to be classified as Group H, but it shall be classified as the occupancy that it most nearly resembles:

1. Buildings and structures occupied for the application of flammable finishes, provided that such buildings or areas conform to the requirements of Chapter 24 of this code and Section 416 of the *International Building Code*.
2. Wholesale and retail sales and storage of flammable and *combustible liquids* in mercantile occupancies conforming to Chapter 57.
3. Closed piping system containing flammable or *combustible liquids* or gases utilized for the operation of machinery or equipment.
4. Cleaning establishments that utilize *combustible liquid* solvents having a *flash point* of 140°F (60°C) or higher in *closed systems* employing equipment *listed* by an *approved* testing agency, provided that this occupancy is separated from all other areas of the building by 1-hour *fire barriers* in accordance with Section 707 of the *International Building Code* or 1-hour *horizontal assemblies* in accordance with Section 711 of the *International Building Code*, or both.

5. Cleaning establishments that utilize a liquid solvent having a *flash point* at or above 200°F (93°C).
6. Liquor stores and distributors without bulk storage.
7. Refrigeration systems.
8. The storage or utilization of materials for agricultural purposes on the premises.
9. Stationary storage battery systems installed in accordance with Section 1206.2.
10. *Corrosive* personal or household products in their original packaging used in retail display.
11. Commonly used *corrosive* building materials.
12. Buildings and structures occupied for aerosol product storage shall be classified as Group S-1, provided that such buildings conform to the requirements of Chapter 51.
13. Display and storage of nonflammable solid and nonflammable or noncombustible liquid hazardous materials in quantities not exceeding the *maximum allowable quantity per control area* in Group M or S occupancies complying with Section 5003.8.3.5.1.
14. The storage of black powder, smokeless propellant and small arms primers in Groups M and R-3 and special industrial explosive devices in Groups B, F, M and S, provided such storage conforms to the quantity limits and requirements of this code.
15. Stationary fuel cell power systems installed in accordance with this code.
16. *Capacitor energy storage systems* in accordance with this code.
17. Group B higher education laboratory occupancies complying with Section 428 of the *International Building Code* and Chapter 38 of this code.

❖ The IBC provides 17 cases where facilities would not be classified as Group H because of the specific type of material, how it is expected to be used or stored, or both; the building's construction and use; the packaging of materials; the quantity of materials; or the precautions taken to prevent fire. Even if a high-hazard material meets one of these 17 cases, its storage and use must comply with the applicable provisions of Section 414 of the IBC and this code.

Item 1 exempts spray painting and similar operations within buildings from being classified as a high-hazard occupancy. This exception requires that all such operations, as well as the handling of flammable finishes, are in accordance with the provisions of Section 416 of the IBC and Chapter 24 of this code; therefore, an adequately protected typical paint spray booth in a factory (Group F-1) would not result in a high-hazard occupancy classification for either the building or the paint spray area.

Item 2 relies on the provisions of Section 5704.3.4.1 to regulate the storage of flammable and combustible liquids for wholesale and retail sales and storage in mercantile occupancies. The overall permitted amount of flammable and combustible liquids is dependent on the class of liquid, storage arrangement, container size and level of sprinkler protection. For nonsprinklered buildings, the maximum allowable quantity per control area permitted by Table 5704.3.4.1 is 1,600 gallons (6057 L) of Class IB, IC, II, and IIIA liquids with a maximum of 60 gallons (227 L) of Class IA liquids. Depending on storage and ceiling heights, buildings equipped with a sprinkler system with a minimum design density for an Ordinary Hazard Group 2 occupancy may have an aggregate total of 7,500 gallons (28 391 L) of Class IB, IC, II and IIIA liquids with a maximum of 60 gallons (227 L) of Class IA liquids. The quantities of Class IB, IC, II and IIA liquids could be further increased depending on the potential storage conditions and enhanced degree of sprinkler protection (see Section 5703.3.4.1 for additional design information). Again, it should be noted that, despite increased quantities that far exceed the base quantity limitations of Table 5003.1.1(1) [IBC Table 307.1(1)], compliance with this item would result in the building not being classified as a Group H occupancy.

Item 3 exempts from Group H classification closed systems that are used exclusively for the operation of machinery or equipment. The closed piping systems, which are essentially not open to the atmosphere, keep flammable or combustible liquids from direct exposure to external sources of ignition as well as prevent the users from coming in direct contact with liquids or harmful vapors. This item would include systems such as oil-burning equipment, piping for diesel fuel generators and LP-gas cylinders for use in forklift trucks.

Item 4 allows cleaning establishments that utilize a closed system for all combustible liquid solvents with a flash point at or above 140°F (60°C) to be classified as something other than Group H. The reference to using equipment listed by an approved testing laboratory does not mean that the entire system needs to be approved, but rather the individual pieces of equipment. As with any mechanical equipment or appliance, it should bear the label of an approved agency and be installed in accordance with the manufacturer's installation instructions (see the IMC).

Item 5 covers cleaning establishments that use solvents that have very high flash points [at least 200°F (93°C)] and that are exceedingly difficult to ignite. Such liquids can be used openly, but with due care.

Item 6 exempts all retail liquor stores and liquor distribution facilities from the high-hazard occupancy classification, even though most of the contents are considered combustible liquids. The item takes into account that alcoholic beverages are packaged in individual containers of limited size.

Item 7 refers to refrigeration systems that utilize refrigerants that may be flammable or toxic. Refrigeration systems do not alter the occupancy classification of the building, provided that they are installed in accordance with the IMC. The IMC has specific limitations on the quantity and type of refrigerants that can be used, depending on the occupancy classification of the building.

Item 8 addresses materials that are used for agricultural purposes, such as fertilizers, pesticides and fungicides. Agricultural materials stored for direct or immediate use are not usually of large enough quantity that would constitute a large fuel load or an exceptionally hazardous condition. A Group H classification is not appropriate for these situations.

Item 9 exempts storage battery systems from the Group H classification provided that they are installed in accordance with the code. The installation provisions are found in Section 1206. This exemption also assumes that rooms containing stationary storage battery systems are in compliance with Section 1206.2 of this code and the enclosure requirements of Table 509 of the IBC.

Without Item 10, certain products that technically are corrosive could cause grocery stores and other mercantile occupancies to be inappropriately classified as Group H-4. This item allows the MAQ in Table 5003.1.1(2) [IBC Table 307.1(2)] for corrosives to be exceeded in the retail display area. This would include such things as bleaches, detergents and other household cleaning supplies in normal-size containers.

Item 11 exempts the storage or manufacture of commonly used building materials, such as Portland cement, from being inappropriately classified as Group H.

Item 12 exempts from a Group H classification those buildings and structures used for the storage of aerosol products, provided that they are protected in accordance with the provisions of NFPA 30B. The aerosol storage requirements of the code referred to in this item are based on the provisions of NFPA 30B. Compliance with this item exempts buildings from complying with the code provisions for Group H, provided that the storage of aerosol products complies with the applicable separation, storage limitations and sprinkler design requirements specified in the code and NFPA 30B.

Item 13 permits certain products found in mercantile and storage occupancies, which may be composed of hazardous materials, to exceed the MAQ of Tables 5003.1.1(1) and 5003.1.1(2) [IBC Tables 307.1(1) and 307.1(2)]. The products, however, must be composed of nonflammable solids or liquids that are nonflammable or noncombustible. Materials could include swimming pool chemicals, which are typically Class 2 or 3 oxidizers or industrial corrosive cleaning agents (see commentaries, Sections 5003.8.3.5 and 5003.8.3.5.1).

Item 14 permits the base maximum allowable quantity per control area of black powder, smokeless propellant and small arms primers in Group M and R-3 occupancies to be exceeded, provided that the material is stored in accordance with Chapter 56. The requirements are based on the provisions in NFPA 495. Similarly, special industrial explosive devices are found in a number of occupancies other than Group H (Groups B, F, M and S). Storage of these devices in accordance with the code is not required to have a high-hazard occupancy classification. Power drivers are commonly used in the construction industry, and there are stocks of these materials maintained for sale and use by the trade. The automotive airbag industry has evolved with the use of these devices, and they are located in automotive dealerships and personal use vehicles throughout society. The code currently exempts up to 50 pounds (23 kg) of these materials from regulation under Chapter 56.

Item 15 exempts fuel cell power systems, which generate energy through the conversion of the chemical energy of a fuel and oxidant via an electrochemical process. Where the system complies with Section 1205, it need not be classified as Group H.

Item 16 exempts capacitor energy storage systems, which are just one of an array of energy storage systems. Installation provisions are found in Section 1206.3. Where installed and operated in accordance with the provisions of this code, such systems are not Group H.

Item 17 exempts higher education laboratories, which are frequently used in universities and colleges for both educational and research purposes. Chapter 38 of this code and Section 428 of the IBC establish construction and operational requirements that allow such laboratories to be Group B rather than Group H.

High-hazard Group H-1. Buildings and structures containing materials that pose a *detonation* hazard shall be classified as Group H-1. Such materials shall include, but not be limited to, the following:

Detonable pyrophoric materials

Explosives:

Division 1.1
Division 1.2
Division 1.3
Division 1.4
Division 1.5
Division 1.6

Organic peroxides, unclassified detonable
Oxidizers, Class 4
Unstable (reactive) materials, Class 3 detonable, and Class 4

❖ The contents of occupancies in Group H-1 present a detonation hazard. Examples of materials that create this hazard are listed in the definition. The definitions for Group H-1 materials are listed in Section 5602 and defined in Chapter 2. Because of the explosion hazard potential associated with Group H-1 materials, occupancies in Group H-1, which exceed the MAQ indicated in Table 5003.1.1(1) [IBC Table 307.1(1)], are required to be located in detached one-story buildings without basements (see commentary to Section 5003.8.2 and IBC Sections 415.6.2, 415.7 and 508.3). Group H-1 occupancies cannot be located in a mixed occupancy building.

Occupancies containing explosives not classified as H-1. The following occupancies containing explosive materials shall be classified as follows:

1. Division 1.3 explosive materials that are used and maintained in a form where either confinement or configuration will not elevate the hazard from a mass fire hazard to mass explosion hazard shall be allowed in Group H-2 occupancies.
2. Articles, including articles packaged for shipment, that are not regulated as a Division 1.4 explosive under Bureau of Alcohol, Tobacco, Firearms and Explosives regulations, or unpackaged articles used in process operations that do not propagate a *detonation* or deflagration between articles shall be allowed in H-3 occupancies.

❖ There are certain explosive materials that pose a hazard level less than that anticipated for a Group H-1 occupancy. A Group H-2 classification is permitted for Division 1.3 explosive materials used or maintained under conditions where the hazard level will not rise from that of a mass fire hazard to a mass explosion hazard. A Group H-3 occupancy classification is permitted for packaged and unpackaged articles not regulated as Division 1.4 explosives by the Bureau of Alcohol, Tobacco, Firearms and Explosives (ATF), as well as unpackaged articles used in process operations, provided that there is no concern regarding the propagation of a detonation or deflagration between the articles during process operations.

High-hazard Group H-2. Buildings and structures containing materials that pose a *deflagration* hazard or a hazard from accelerated burning shall be classified as Group H-2. Such materials shall include, but not be limited to, the following:

Class I, II or IIIA flammable or *combustible liquids* that are used or stored in normally open containers or systems, or in closed containers or systems pressurized at more than 15 pounds per square inch gauge (103.4 kPa)
Combustible dusts where manufactured, generated or used in such a manner that the concentration and conditions create a fire or explosion hazard based on information prepared in accordance with Section 414.1.3 of the *International Building Code*
Cryogenic fluids, flammable
Flammable gases
Organic peroxides, Class I

Oxidizers, Class 3, that are used or stored in normally open containers or systems, or in closed containers or systems pressurized at more than 15 pounds per square inch gauge (103.4 kPa)
Pyrophoric liquids, solids and gases, nondetonable
Unstable (reactive) materials, Class 3, nondetonable
Water-reactive materials, Class 3

❖ The contents of occupancies in Group H-2 present a deflagration or accelerated burning hazard. Examples of materials that create this hazard are listed. The definitions for Group H-2 materials are contained in Chapter 2 also. Because of the severe fire or reactivity hazard associated with these types of materials, proper classification is essential in determining the applicable requirements with regard to the mitigation of these hazards.

High-hazard Group H-3. Buildings and structures containing materials that readily support combustion or that pose a *physical hazard* shall be classified as Group H-3. Such materials shall include, but not be limited to, the following:

Class I, II or IIIA flammable or *combustible liquids* that are used or stored in normally closed containers or systems pressurized at 15 pounds per square inch gauge (103.4 kPa) or less.
Combustible fibers, other than densely packed baled cotton, where manufactured, generated or used in such a manner that the concentration and conditions create a fire or explosion hazard based on information prepared in accordance with Section 414.1.3 of the *International Building Code*
Consumer fireworks, 1.4G (Class C, Common)
Cryogenic fluids, oxidizing
Flammable solids
Organic peroxides, Class II and III
Oxidizers, Class 2
Oxidizers, Class 3, that are used or stored in normally closed containers or systems pressurized at 15 pounds per square inch gauge (103 kPa) or less
Oxidizing gases
Unstable (reactive) materials, Class 2
Water-reactive materials, Class 2

❖ The contents of occupancies in Group H-3 present a hazard inasmuch as they contain materials that readily support combustion or that present a physical hazard. Examples of materials that create this hazard are listed in the definition. The definitions for Group H-3 materials are contained in Chapter 2 also. While Group H-3 materials are generally less of a fire or reactivity hazard than Group H-2 materials, they still present a greater physical hazard than materials not currently regulated as high hazard.

High-hazard Group H-4. Buildings and structures containing materials that are *health hazards* shall be classified as Group H-4. Such materials shall include, but not be limited to, the following:

Corrosives
Highly toxic materials
Toxic materials

❖ The contents of occupancies in Group H-4 present a hazard inasmuch as they contain materials that are health hazards. Examples of these hazards are listed in this definition. The definitions for Group H-4 materials are contained in Chapter 2 also. While reference is made to chemicals that cause these hazards, the SDS for these chemicals, which are furnished by the applicant, will need considerable subjective evaluation.

Some materials falling into the category of health hazard may also present a physical hazard and would, therefore, require the structure to be designed for multiple hazards in accordance with Section 5001.1 of the code and Section 307.8 of the IBC.

High-hazard Group H-5. Semiconductor fabrication facilities and comparable research and development areas in which hazardous production materials (HPM) are used and the aggregate quantity of materials is in excess of those listed in Tables 5003.1.1(1) and 5003.1.1(2) shall be classified as Group H-5. Such facilities and areas shall be designed and constructed in accordance with Section 415.11 of the *International Building Code.*

❖ HPM includes flammable liquids and gases, corrosives, oxidizers and, in many instances, highly toxic materials (see the definition for "Hazardous production material"). In determining the applicable requirements of other sections of the code, HPM facilities are considered to be Group H-5 occupancies. It is intended that the quantities of materials permitted in Table 2704.2.2.1 will take precedence over Tables 5003.1.1(1) and 5003.1.1(2).

[BG] Institutional Group I. Institutional Group I occupancy includes, among others, the use of a building or structure, or a portion thereof, in which care or supervision is provided to persons who are or are not capable of self-preservation without physical assistance or in which persons are detained for penal or correctional purposes or in which the liberty of the occupants is restricted. Institutional occupancies shall be classified as Group I-1, I-2, I-3 or I-4.

❖ There are, essentially, two types of institutional occupancies. The first type includes Groups I-1, I-2 and I-4 and consists of facilities that provide personal care, custodial care or medical care for people who, due to age, physical limitations, diseases, mental disabilities or other infirmities, need a supervised environment (see the commentaries for the definitions of "Custodial care," "Medical care" and "Personal care service"). This includes persons who are ambulatory and are capable of self-preservation as well as those who are restricted in their mobility or are totally immobile to the extent that they are incapable of self-preservation and therefore may need assistance to evacuate during an emergency situation, such as a fire. The code also addresses the idea of a defend-in-place protection option for hospitals and nursing homes (see the commentary for the definition of "Incapable of self-preservation" and Sections 403 and 404). The second type, Group I-3, relates primarily to detention and correctional facilities. Since security is the major operational consideration in these kinds of facilities, the occupants (inmates) are under some form of supervision and restraint and may be rendered incapable of self-preservation without direct intervention from staff in emergency situations due to locked cells and exits.

The degree of hazards in each type of institutional facility identified in this section varies respective to each kind of occupancy. The code addresses each occupancy separately and the regulatory provisions throughout the code provide the proper means of protection so as to produce an acceptable level of safety to life and property.

Groups I-1, I-2 and I-3 are further divided into "conditions" relative to unique aspects of the respective occupancies. Groups I-1 and R-4 are closely related and are primarily distinguished by the number of persons residing in the facility (see Section 308.2 of the IBC).

Another of the distinguishing characteristics between the different Group I occupancies and other occupancies is where care is provided for a length of time exceeding 24 hours. The intent is that this criteria is not specific to the hours of operation of the facility, but the length of time that care is provided for the patients, residents or those in day care. For example, an outpatient clinic that is open 24 hours a day is a Group B occupancy provided that care recipients are treated as outpatients and there are no patients that would stay at the facility 24 hours or longer. Another example would be a "day care" facility that is open 24 hours to serve workers who work any shift and need to have children in "day care" while they work. Provided that individual children receive care for less than 24 hours, the occupancy would be classified as a Group I-4 or possibly a Group E.

Each individual facility will have unique characteristics or a combination of characteristics that should be considered when classifying it to one occupancy and condition or another. For example, some of the newer care facilities are offering a combination of care levels to allow for persons to age-in-place within the same complex. A facility could easily have a mix of occupancies such as one wing providing full-time nursing care (Group I-2, Condition 1); a second wing providing assisted living care for residents with dementia, who may need direct physical contact from staff to react to an emergency (Group I-1, Condition 2); and yet a third wing providing custodial care where residents are capable of responding to an emergency on their own (Group I-2, Condition 1). Health care and custodial care facilities are subject to many state and some local regulations. Such regulations may be a determining factor in deciding which IBC occupancy classification is appropriate.

[BG] Institutional Group I-1. Institutional Group I-1 occupancy shall include buildings, structures or portions thereof for more than 16 persons, excluding staff, who reside on a 24-hour basis in a supervised environment and receive custodial care. Buildings of Group I-1 shall be classified as one of the occupancy conditions indicated below. This group shall include, but not be limited to, the following:

Alcohol and drug centers
Assisted living facilities
Congregate care facilities
Group homes
Halfway houses
Residential board and care facilities
Residential board and custodial care facilities
Social rehabilitation facilities

❖ Group I-4 and R-4 occupancies are similar facilities that differ only by the number of residents receiving care. Group I-1 and R-4 occupancies are based on four characterizations described in the occupancy classification: both are facilities where custodial care is provided, there is 24-hour-a-day supervision and the occupancy is either Condition 1 or Condition 2. The difference between I-1 and R-4 is the number of persons receiving care and residing in such facilities: Group I-1 has greater than 16 residents; Group R-4 has six to 16 persons. Note that Group I-1 and R-4 occupancies are limited facilities where custodial care is provided and not where medical care is provided (see the commentaries to "Custodial care" and "Medical care"). Both Group I-1 and R-4 occupancies list the same eight generic uses as example uses falling under the Group I-1/R-4 umbrella. Of these eight, only "Group home" is defined (see commentary to this definition). Some of these terms may be used in state and local regulations of care facilities. Caution should be taken before assuming that a state-defined "assisted living" facility should be classified under the IBC as a Group I-1 and R-4 occupancy.

Both Groups I-1 and R-4 include "conditions" to cover the variety of acuity and ability levels of custodial care recipients. Group I-1, Condition 1 and Group R-4, Condition 1 occupancies match requirements for previous editions of the code for Groups I-1 and R-4, before conditions were included. The conditions are intended to address the concerns that some residents may require limited assistance or verbal direction to evacuate. The building protection offered for Group I-1 and R-4 occupancies in previous editions of the code is maintained in Condition 1. Some additional requirements were added for Condition 2. Note that this is custodial care. Where nursing care is provided, the facility is a Group I-2, Condition 1. The Condition 1 care recipients may be slower during evacuation but all are capable of emergency evacuation without any physical assistance from others; they require no more than minor verbal cues from others during emergencies, as might be expected in the general population. Condition 2 custodial care recipients are also slower to evacuate and include any care recipients who may require limited assistance during evacuation. Group I-1, Condition 2 and Group R-4, Condition 2 integrate additional protection features, such as smoke barriers to subdivide the building and increased automatic sprinkler requirements.

In Group I-1, Condition 2 and Group R-4, Condition 2 facilities, assistance with evacuation can occur because of care recipients' physical or mental limitations, or both. The Condition 2 assistance with evacuation includes help getting out of bed into a wheelchair or walker, or help initiating ambulation. It includes continued physical assistance getting out of the building from a sleeping room, apartment or other rooms during an emergency. Assistance with evacuation includes assisting persons who may have resistance or confusion in response to an alarm, or require help with instructions. It can also include help for persons with short periods of impaired intermittent consciousness due to medications or illness. Custodial care Group I-1, Condition 2 and Group R-4, Condition 2 evacuation assistance is limited and does not include moving occupants in beds or stretchers during emergencies, as is allowed in Group I-2 medical care.

How individual state licensing agencies name, classify and regulate many of the uses listed in Groups I-1 and R-4 vary significantly from state to state and may not line up with the IBC classifications. It is for this reason that Group I-1 and R-4 lists of uses are included under the general occupancy classification and not under each "condition." The building permit applicant should confirm how the specific state licensing regulations correlate to the code's care type, occupancy, condition, evacuation capability and number of persons receiving care. The permit application drawings should identify the five criteria, while specifically noting that the state licensing regulations limit occupants to only include Condition 1 criteria or allow Condition 2 criteria. Most assisted living facilities and many residential board and care facilities will be classified as Group I-1, Condition 1 or R-4, Condition 1. Generally, almost all specially designated Alzheimer's/memory care facilities providing custodial care will be classified as Group I-1, Condition 2 or Group R-4, Condition 2, due to the inability of some residents to recognize how to respond to an emergency situation. Note that nursing facilities with specialized dementia wings that provide medical care would be classified as Group I-2, Condition 1. Also, it is important to keep in mind that facilities that may be classified initially as Group I-1, Condition 1 (capable of self-preservation) or R-4, Condition 1 can very easily need to be reclassified as a Group I-1/R-4, Condition 2 or as a Group I-2, Condition 1 if the abilities of the persons receiving care change over time. Therefore, it is essential for the proponents of a new facility to present to the building official information regarding the full range of patients and residents expected at a facility both initially and over time.

The occupant load for occupancy classification purposes refers to the number of care recipients only. The number of guests or staff is not included. Note, however, that the number of guests and staff is included for means of egress purposes.

For clarification purposes, a dormitory or apartment complex that houses only elderly people and has a nonmedically trained live-in manager is not classified as an institutional occupancy but, rather, as a residential occupancy (see the Group R definitions). A critical phrase in the code to consider when evaluating this type of facility is "reside on a 24-hour basis in a supervised residential environment." Such dormitories or apartment complexes may contain features, such as special emergency call switches, that are located in each dwelling unit, and that are monitored by health center staff. These emergency call switches are a convenience and do not necessarily indicate infirmity of the care recipients.

[BG] Condition 1. This occupancy condition shall include buildings in which all persons receiving custodial care who, without any assistance, are capable of responding to an emergency situation to complete building evacuation.

❖ See the general commentary to Group I-1 occupancies.

[BG] Condition 2. This occupancy condition shall include buildings in which there are any persons receiving custodial care who require limited verbal or physical assistance while responding to an emergency situation to complete building evacuation.

❖ See the general commentary to Group I-1 occupancies.

[BG] Six to 16 persons receiving custodial care. A facility housing not fewer than six and not more than 16 persons receiving custodial care shall be classified as Group R-4.

❖ Any building that has the characteristics of a Group I-1 occupancy but that has more than five and not more than 16 persons receiving custodial care is classified as Group R-4 (see Section 310.5 of the IBC). Ninety-eight percent of households in the US have fewer than 16 occupants; thus the limit of 16 is considered appropriate for a residential occupancy. Similar to Group I-1, Group R-4 is also divided into Conditions 1 and 2.

[BG] Five or fewer persons receiving custodial care. A facility with five or fewer persons receiving custodial care shall be classified as Group R-3 or shall comply with the *International Residential Code* provided an *automatic sprinkler system* is installed in accordance with Section 903.3.1.3 or with Section P2904 of the *International Residential Code.*

❖ Any building that has the characteristics of a Group I-1 occupancy (either Condition 1 or 2, or both) but has five or fewer persons receiving custodial care is classified as Group R-3 (see Section 310.4 of the IBC) or may be constructed in accordance with the IRC (see IBC Section 310.4.1). When the code allows compliance in accordance with the IRC, the only requirements that would apply would be those of the IRC, including the installation of automatic sprinkler protection. The intent is to allow persons to be cared for in a residential or home environment, often under the care of family members. Please note similar provisions for Group E occupancies as well as Groups I-2 and I-4.

[BG] Institutional Group I-2. Institutional Group I-2 occupancy shall include buildings and structures used for medical care on a 24-hour basis for more than five persons who are not capable of self-preservation. This group shall include, but not be limited to, the following:

Foster care facilities
Detoxification facilities
Hospitals
Nursing homes
Psychiatric hospitals

❖ An occupancy classified in Group I-2 is characterized by three conditions: it is a health care facility where the level of care offered is medical care, there is 24-hour-a-day medical supervision for the individuals receiving care and patients/residents require physical assistance by staff or others to reach safety in an emergency situation (see the definitions for "24-hour basis," "Custodial care" and "Medical care," and the five facility examples listed). Where a facility offers medical care instead of custodial care, it is assumed that residents may not be capable of self-preservation. This assessment of the level of care provided needs to be taken with caution and reliance on other state and federal guidelines and associated regulations may be necessary. Also, it is important to keep in mind that facilities that may be classified initially as Group I-1, Condition 1 (capable of self-preservation) or R-4, Condition 1 can very easily need to be reclassified as a Group I-1/R-4, Condition 2 or as a Group I-2, Condition 1 if the abilities of the persons receiving care change over time. Therefore, it is essential for the proponents of a new facility to present information to the building official regarding the full range of patients and residents expected at a facility both initially and over time.

Due to the diversification of how medical care is provided in the five characteristic occupancies currently specified in the IBC for Group I-2 occupancies, the Group I-2 occupancy has been split into two basic conditions: Condition 1, long-term care (nursing homes), and Condition 2, short-term care (hospitals). Although both of these subsets are based on medical treatment and are occupancies within which the occupants are protected with a defend-in-place method of safety, changes in the delivery of care in the two different conditions has changed in the past 10-20 years. Some examples of these changes include:

- Within hospitals, there has been a general increase in the floor area per patient due to the increase in diagnostic equipment and the movement toward single-occupant patient rooms.

- Within nursing homes, there has been a trend to provide more residential-type accommodations, such as group/suite living, gathering areas and cooking facilities in residential areas.

The most common examples of facilities classified in Group I-2 are hospitals (Condition 2) and nursing homes (Condition 1). Other facilities included are detoxification facilities, foster care facilities and psychiatric hospitals. How individual state licensing agencies name, classify and regulate many of the uses listed in Groups I-2 varies significantly from state to state and may not line up with the IBC classifications. It is for this reason that the Group I-2 list of uses is included under the general occupancy classification and not under each "condition."

The benefit to the "condition" concept is that a majority of code requirements will still apply to all Group I-2 occupancies such as mechanical systems, property maintenance and rehabilitation, but will provide for the opportunity for specific code requirements that apply to the different levels of care and acuity that are found in different facility types; thus allowing for the establishment of specific code requirements that are based on the operation of the facility.

It is not uncommon to find dining rooms (Group A-2), staff offices (Group B), gift shops (Group M), laundries (Group F) and other nonmedically related areas in buildings otherwise classified as Group I-2. Where such other occupancies occur, the building is considered as a mixed occupancy and subject to the provisions of Section 508. In addition to the general requirements contained in this section, Section 407 contains specific requirements for Group I-2.

[BG] Occupancy Conditions. Buildings of Group I-2 shall be classified as one of the following occupancy conditions:

❖ A distinction is made between Condition 1 and Condition 2 for Group I-2 occupancies. Section 407 of the IBC provides many requirements that apply to both conditions under the Group I-2 occupancy.

[BG] Condition 1. This occupancy condition shall include facilities that provide nursing and medical care but do not provide emergency care, surgery, obstetrics, or in-patient stabilization units for psychiatric or detoxification, including, but not limited to, nursing homes and foster care facilities.

❖ The principal use in this category is nursing homes. Typically, facilities in this category provide long-term medical care but not the types of care typically found in hospitals. Foster care facilities, by Chapter 2 definition are those where children up to $2^1/_2$ years old receive care. Foster care for more than five infants and toddlers would also be classified as Group I-2, Condition 1. Foster care facilities that provide care for five or more children older than $2^1/_2$ would typically be Group I-1/R-4, Condition 1, based on supervised living and capability of the residents.

[BG] Condition 2. This occupancy condition shall include facilities that provide nursing and medical care and could provide emergency care, surgery, obstetrics, or inpatient stabilization units for psychiatric or detoxification, including, but not limited to, hospitals.

❖ Hospitals and psychiatric hospitals are included in the Condition 2 category of the I-2 occupancy. Treatment is usually for periods longer than 24 hours and medical care not typically available in long-term nursing care facilities is provided.

[BG] Five or fewer persons receiving medical care. A facility with five or fewer persons receiving medical care shall be classified as Group R-3 or shall comply with the *International Residential Code* provided an *automatic sprinkler system* is installed in accordance with Section 903.3.1.3 or with Section P2904 of the *International Residential Code*.

❖ Any facility that has the characteristics of a Group I-2 occupancy but does not have more than five persons receiving care at any one time is to be classified as a Group R-3 occupancy. As an option, the facility may be designed and constructed under the provisions of the IRC, provided that the building has a sprinkler system. The intent is to allow persons to be cared for in a residential, or home, environment, often under the care of family members. The persons receiving the care do not need to be capable of self-preservation. The sprinkler system is to comply with the requirements for an NFPA 13D system or those of Section P2904 of the IRC. Please note similar provisions for Group E occupancies as well as Groups I-1 (see Section 308.2.4 of the IBC) and I-4 (See Section 308.5.4 of the IBC).

[BG] Institutional Group I-3. Institutional Group I-3 occupancy shall include buildings and structures which are inhabited by more than five persons who are under restraint or security. A Group I-3 facility is occupied by persons who are generally incapable of self-preservation due to security measures not under the occupants' control. This group shall include, but not be limited to, the following:

Correctional centers
Detention centers
Jails
Prerelease centers
Prisons
Reformatories

Buildings of Group I-3 shall be classified as one of the following occupancy conditions:

❖ An occupancy classified in Group I-3 is characterized by three conditions: it is a location where persons are under restraint or where security is closely supervised, there are more than five such persons and they are not capable of self-preservation because the conditions of confinement are not under their control (i.e., they require assistance by the facilities' staff to reach safety in an emergency situation). For occupancy classification purposes, the provision refers only to the number of persons being secured or restrained. The number of guests or staff is not included. Please note, however, that the number of guests and staff is included for means of egress purposes.

Buildings that have these characteristics but that contain not more than five persons who are being secured or restrained are to be classified based on the function to which they are associated. For example, the small holding cell in a Group B police station having only the one cell would simply be classified as a portion of the Group B occupancy. Regardless of the occupancy classification, the means of egress provisions for places of restraint are still applicable (see Chapter 10).

It is recognized that not all Group I-3 occupancies have the same level of restraint; thus, to distinguish these different levels, the code defines five different conditions of occupancy based on the degree of access to the exit discharge.

[BG] Condition 1. This occupancy condition shall include buildings in which free movement is allowed from sleeping areas and other spaces where access or occupancy is permitted to the exterior via *means of egress* without restraint. A Condition 1 facility is permitted to be constructed as Group R.

❖ Condition 1 areas are those where the occupants have unrestrained access to the exterior of the building. As such, a key or remote-control release device is not needed for any occupant to reach the exterior of the building (exit discharge) at any time. These types of buildings are referred to as "low-security facilities." A work-release center is a typical Condition 1 facility. Because of the lack of restraint associated with a Condition 1 building, it resembles a residential use more than a detention facility and, therefore, is permitted to be classified in Group R (see the definitions for "Group R" in this chapter).

[BG] Condition 2. This occupancy condition shall include buildings in which free movement is allowed from sleeping areas and any other occupied smoke compartment to one or more other smoke compartments. Egress to the exterior is impeded by locked *exits*.

❖ Condition 2 areas are those in which the movement of occupants is not controlled within the exterior walls of the building (i.e., the occupants have unrestrained access within the building). As such, there is free movement by the occupants between smoke compartments (as created by smoke barriers); however, the occupants must rely on someone else to allow them to exit the building to the area of discharge.

[BG] Condition 3. This occupancy condition shall include buildings in which free movement is allowed within individual smoke compartments, such as within a residential unit comprised of individual *sleeping units* and group activity spaces, where egress is impeded by remote-controlled release of *means of egress* from such smoke compartment to another smoke compartment.

❖ Condition 3 areas are those in which free movement by the occupants is permitted within an individual smoke compartment; however, movement of occupants from one smoke compartment (as created by smoke barriers) to another smoke compartment and from within the building to the exterior (exit discharge) is controlled by remote-release locking devices. As such, the occupants in the facility are dependent on the staff for their release from each smoke compartment or to the exterior (exit discharge).

[BG] Condition 4. This occupancy condition shall include buildings in which free movement is restricted from an occupied space. Remote-controlled release is provided to permit movement from *sleeping units*, activity spaces and other occupied areas within the smoke compartment to other smoke compartments.

❖ Condition 4 areas are those in which the movement of restrained persons from any room or space within a smoke compartment (as created by smoke barriers) to another smoke compartment or to the exterior (exit discharge) is controlled by remote-release locking devices. Any movement within the facility requires activation of a remote-control lock system to release the designated area. The persons being restrained or secured within a Condition 4 area must rely on an activation system in the event of an emergency in order to evacuate the area.

Condition 4 facilities most often are penal facilities where the restrained persons are considered relatively safe to handle in large groups. As such, many persons can be released simultaneously from their individual sleeping areas when they need to travel to dining areas or move to another area.

[BG] Condition 5. This occupancy condition shall include buildings in which free movement is restricted from an occupied space. Staff-controlled manual release is provided to permit movement from *sleeping units*, activity spaces and other occupied areas within the smoke compartment to other smoke compartments.

❖ Condition 5 areas are those in which the persons being secured or restrained are not allowed free movement to any other room or space within a smoke compartment (as created by smoke barriers) to another smoke compartment or to the exterior (exit discharge) unless the locking device controlling their area of confinement is manually released by a staff member. Once released from an individual space, a staff member is responsible for unlocking all doors from that location to the next smoke compartment. This is the most restrictive occupancy condition, as each secured person must be released on an individual basis and escorted to other areas.

Condition 5 facilities are most often used for maximum security or solitary confinement areas where the persons are considered to be dangerous to others, including staff members, and cannot safely be handled in large groups.

[BG] Institutional Group I-4, day care facilities. Institutional Group I-4 shall include buildings and structures occupied by more than five persons of any age who receive custodial care for less than 24 hours by persons other than parents or guardians, relatives by blood, marriage, or adoption, and in a place other than the home of the person cared for. This group shall include, but not be limited to, the following:

Adult day care
Child day care

❖ Facilities that contain provisions for the custodial care of more than five persons of any age are classified as Group I-4 (see definitions of "Custodial care" and "Personal care service"). Group I-4 facilities are less restrictive in some of the requirements (e.g., height and area) than the other Group I occupancies. Group I-4 facilities are intended to be used to provide care for less than 24 hours. Day care facilities are not intended to be a full-time residence for the people receiving care. The staff members are assumed not to be related to the individuals in the day care facilities. The premise of the provisions is that the numbers receiving care are exclusive of staff. The care recipients in a Group I-4 occupancy are not expected to respond to an emergency without physical assistance from others. Group I-4 occupancies include both adult day care and child day care.

Adult care facilities are assumed to be for people other than children who require some type of custodial care (i.e., nonmedical). A facility where adults gather for social activities such as a community center or a YMCA is not an adult care facility (Group I) and would be regulated under other provisions of the code (Group A-3 or B). The classification of Group I-4 for an adult day care facility does not apply to facilities that provide personal care services for adults who are capable of responding to an emergency unassisted. In that case, the facility is simply classified into the occupancy group it most resembles. A facility providing a similar degree of custodial care for infants and toddlers on less than a 24-hour-per-day basis would be considered as a Group I-4 day care facility.

[BG] Classification as Group E. A child day care facility that provides care for more than five but not more than 100 children $2^1/_2$ years or less of age, where the rooms in which the children are cared for are located on a *level of exit discharge* serving such rooms and each of these child care rooms has an *exit* door directly to the exterior, shall be classified as Group E.

❖ Children $2^1/_2$ years of age or less (i.e., infants and toddlers) typically are not capable of independently responding to an emergency and must be led or carried to safety. Under such circumstances, the infants and toddlers are considered nonambulatory. Therefore, a Group I-4 classification is given to those facilities where six or more infants and toddlers receive custodial care for less than 24 hours per day. A similar condition is found in foster care facilities (Group I-2, Condition 1) where infants and toddlers stay for extended periods of time. The distinguishing factor between the two occupancies is the amount of time the facility provides care for each individual. Group I-2 facilities provide care on a 24-hour basis, while in Group I-4 facilities individual care must be less than 24 hours. It is also assumed that medical care is not present in Group I-4 facilities.

A child care facility in which the number of infants and toddlers is greater than five but not more than 100 is permitted to be classified as Group E, provided that the infants and toddlers are all located in rooms on the level of exit discharge that serves such rooms and all of the rooms have exit doors directly to the exterior. This exception is only applicable to rooms and spaces used for child care and is not intended to apply to accessory spaces such as restrooms, offices and kitchens. Many day care facilities primarily catering to those under primary school age tend to divide the children into three general categories based on state laws and regulations. These include infant, toddler and preschool.

Some variations do occur in that larger day care facilities will have transition rooms for mobile infants or pre-K oriented rooms for those entering kindergarten. But, basically, there is a mixture of children $2^1/_2$ years or younger and older children. The older children can automatically be in a facility classified as a Group E occupancy, but for the younger children, the exception as discussed above would need to be applied to classify the entire occupancy as Group E. The total number of children can exceed 100 and the Group E classification is retained, provided that the number of children $2^1/_2$ years or younger is limited to 100 or fewer. The infant and toddler rooms would need to have exits directly to the outside on the level of exit discharge. If the exception is not applied, the entire facility would need to be classified as Group I-4 or a mixed occupancy classification would be necessary.

By permitting the facility to be classified as Group E, the building would not be required to be sprinklered unless the fire area was greater than 12,000 square feet (115 m^2). A Group I-4 facility would be required to be sprinklered regardless of the area. But as a Group E occupancy, panic hardware would be required in rooms and spaces exceeding 50 occupants.

[BG] Within a place of religious worship. Rooms and spaces within places of religious worship providing such care during religious functions shall be classified as part of the primary occupancy.

❖ The Group I-4 provisions do not apply to places of religious worship simply providing care services during worship and related religious functions. If the space is used at other times simply as a day care facility, then it would be classified as Group I-4 or E, as applicable.

[BG] Five or fewer occupants receiving care. A facility having five or fewer persons receiving custodial care shall be classified as part of the primary occupancy.

❖ Where five or fewer persons receive custodial care in a facility other than a dwelling unit, the classification of the care area is to be consistent with that of the primary occupancy. The limited number of care recipients reduces the hazard level to the point that classification as a Group I-4 occupancy is not warranted.

[BG] Five or fewer occupants receiving care in a dwelling unit. A facility such as the above within a *dwelling unit* and having five or fewer persons receiving custodial care shall be classified as a Group R-3 occupancy or shall comply with the *International Residential Code.*

❖ Buildings that have five or fewer persons receiving custodial care within a dwelling unit are to be classified as Group R-3, or shall be constructed in accordance with the IRC. The assumption is that this type of activity is possible in a residential environment where one or more family members require the high level of care required by Group I-4. Please note similar provisions for Group E occupancies, as well as Groups I-1 and I-2.

[BG] Mercantile Group M. Mercantile Group M occupancy includes, among others, the use of a building or structure or a portion thereof, for the display and sale of merchandise, and involves stocks of goods, wares or merchandise incidental to such purposes and accessible to the public. Mercantile occupancies shall include, but not be limited to, the following:

Department stores
Drug stores
Greenhouses with public access that maintain plants for display and sale
Markets
Motor fuel-dispensing facilities
Retail or wholesale stores
Sales rooms

❖ Group M (mercantile) occupancies normally involve the display and sale of large quantities of combustible merchandise, and the fuel load in such facilities can be relatively high, potentially exposing the occupants (customers and sales personnel) to a high degree of fire hazard. Mercantile operations often attract large crowds (particularly in large department stores and covered malls and especially during weekends and holidays). There are two factors that alleviate the risks to life safety: the occupant load normally has a low-to-moderate density and the occupants are alert, mobile and able to respond in an emergency situation. The degree of openness and the organization of the retail displays found in most mercantile occupancies is generally orderly and does not present an unusual difficulty for occupant evacuation.

Contained in the definition are general descriptions of the kinds of occupancies that are classified in Group M. Mercantile buildings most often have both a moderate occupant load and a high fuel load, which is in the form of furnishings and the goods being displayed, stored and sold.

The key characteristics that differentiate occupancies classified in Group M from those in Group B are the larger quantity of goods or merchandise available for sale and the lack of familiarity of the occupants with the building, particularly its means of egress. To be classified in Group M, the goods that are on display must be accessible to the public. If a patron sees an item for sale, then that item is generally available for purchase at that time (i.e., there is a large stock of goods). If a store allows people to see the merchandise but it is not available on the premises, such as an automobile showroom, then the occupancy classification of business (Group B) should be considered. A mercantile building is accessible to the public, many of whom may not be regular visitors. A business building, however, is primarily occupied by regular employees who are familiar with the building arrangement and, most importantly, the exits. This awareness of the building and the exits can be an important factor in a fire emergency.

Section 309.1 of the IBC does not specifically list storage as part of the mercantile occupancy. Mercantile business will usually operate either with most of their merchandise (stock) in open display readily available for the public to see and access; or the operation could follow a model of display of a representative sample with quantities of the merchandise in back stockrooms only open to staff. Section 311.1.1 of the IBC allows accessory storage to be classified as part of the principal occupancy. This would allow most typical retail stores to be of one classification, Group M, and therefore not classifying the storage of merchandise as a Group S occupancy. The mixed-use occupancy approach is still an option and may offer benefits in determining allowed building height and area or other requirements such as sprinkler protection. It should be noted that Table 508.4 does not require a fire-resistance rating on the separation between Groups M and S-1.

Automotive, fleet-vehicle, marine and self-service motor fuel-dispensing facilities, also defined in this chapter of the code, are classified in the mercantile occupancy group, as are the convenience stores often associated with such occupancies. Quick-lube, tuneup, muffler and tire shops are not included in this classification. Those facilities that typically conduct automotive service and repair work are treated as a repair garage (Group S-1), also defined in this chapter of the code.

A building containing a mercantile-type occupancy and having a dense occupant load does not qualify as an assembly occupancy unless the activity includes an assembly-type area where purchasing of goods is a group activity versus individual shoppers independently considering and purchasing merchandise. For example, a building in which auction sales occur may have a highly concentrated occupant load where the sales occur but the definition describes mercantile occupancies as "the use of a building or structure or portion thereof for the display and sale of merchandise and involves stocks of goods, wares or merchandise incidental to such purposes and accessible to the public." However, in an auction, the activity is dominated by an assembly use of the space as people gather to conduct and participate in the auction. As such, auction spaces must be assigned a Group A-3 occupancy (IBC Committee Interpretation No. 38-03). The presence of highly concentrated occupant loads does not in itself mandate an assembly use classification unless the activity is assembly in nature versus large numbers of people pursuing individual activities of acquisition.

[BG] Residential Group R. Residential Group R includes, among others, the use of a building or structure, or a portion thereof, for sleeping purposes when not classified as an Institutional Group I or when not regulated by the *International Residential Code* in accordance with Section 101.2 of the *International Building Code*.

❖ Residential occupancies represent some of the highest fire safety risks of any of the occupancies listed in Chapter 3 of the IBC. There are several reasons for this condition:

- Structures in the residential occupancy house the widest range of occupant types (i.e., from infants to the aged) for the longest periods of time. As such, residential occupancies are more susceptible to the frequency of careless acts of the occupants; therefore, the consequences of exposure to the effects of fire are the most serious.
- Most residential occupants are asleep approximately one-third of every 24-hour period. When sleeping, they are not likely to become immediately aware of a developing fire. Also, if awakened from sleep by the presence of fire, the residents often may not immediately react in a rational manner, which could delay their evacuation.
- The fuel load in residential occupancies is often quite high, both in quantity and variety. Also, in the construction of residential buildings, it is common to use extensive amounts of combustible materials.
- Another portion of the fire problem in residential occupancies relates to the occupants' lack of vigilance in the prevention of fire hazards. In their own domicile or residence, people tend to relax and are often prone to allow fire hazards to go unabated; thus, in residential occupancies, fire hazards tend to accrue over an extended period of time and go unnoticed or are ignored.

Most of the nation's fire problems occur in Group R buildings and, in particular, one- and two-family dwellings, which account for more than 80 percent of all deaths from fire in residential occupancies and about two-thirds of all fire fatalities in all occupancies. One- and two-family dwellings also account for more than 80 percent of residential property losses from fire and more than one-half of all property losses from fire.

Because of the relatively high fire risk and potential for loss of life in buildings classified in Groups R-1 (hotels and motels) and R-2 (apartments and dormitories), the code has stringent provisions for the protection of life in these occupancies. Group R-3 occupancies, however, are not generally considered to be in the same domain and, thus, are not subject to the same level of regulatory control as is provided in other occupancies. Group R-3 facilities are one- or two-family dwellings where the occupants are generally more familiar with their surroundings, and, because they are single units or duplexes, tend to pose a lower risk of injury or death.

Because of the growing trend to care for people in a residential environment, residential care/assisted living facilities are also classified as Group R. Specifically, these facilities are classified as Group R-4. "Mainstreaming" people who are recovering from alcohol or drug addiction and people who are developmentally disabled is reported to have therapeutic and social benefits. A residential environment often fosters this mainstreaming.

Buildings in Group R are described herein. A building or part of a building is considered to be a residential occupancy if it is intended to be used for sleeping accommodations (including residential care/assisted living facilities) and is not an institutional occupancy. Institutional occupancies are similar to residential occupancies in many ways; however, they differ from each other in that institutional occupants are in a supervised environment and, in the case of Group I-2 and I-3 occupancies, are under some form of restraint or physical limitation that makes them incapable of complete self-preservation. The number of these occupants who are under supervision or are incapable of self-preservation is the distinguishing factor for being classified as an institutional or residential occupancy.

The term "Group R" refers collectively to the four individual residential occupancy classifications: Groups R-1, R-2, R-3 and R-4. These classifications are differentiated in the code based on the following criteria: whether the occupants are transient or nontransient in nature, the type and number of dwellings contained in a single building, and the number of occupants in the facility.

[BG] Residential Group R-1. Residential Group R-1 occupancies containing *sleeping units* where the occupants are primarily transient in nature, including:

Boarding houses (transient) with more than 10 occupants

Congregate living facilities (transient) with more than 10 occupants

Hotels (transient)
Motels (transient)

❖ The key characteristic of Group R-1 that differentiates it from other Group R occupancies is the number of transient occupants (i.e., those whose length of stay is not more than 30 days).

The most common building types classified in Group R-1 are hotels and motels. Facilities classified as Group R-1 occupancies may include dwelling units, sleeping units, or a combination of both. A standard guestroom, with its associated bathroom is considered a sleeping unit. Some hotels offer a style of rooms that can include spaces similar to a living room and kitchenette. When a unit is not equipped with a kitchen with full cooking facilities (i.e., range), it does not meet the definition of a "dwelling unit" in Section 202. Where this occurs, such units are treated as sleeping units for the application of code provisions. Sleeping units are required to be separated from each other by fire partitions and horizontal assemblies (see IBC Sections 420, 708 and 711). A recent trend in development is the construction of "extended-stay hotels." While these units may have all of the characteristics of a typical dwelling unit (i.e., cooking, living, sleeping, eating, sanitation), the length of stay is still typically not more than 30 days. As such, these buildings would still be classified as Group R-1. If the length of stay is more than 30 days, these buildings would be classified as Group R-2. If a hotel offers its rooms for short-term housing (i.e., more than 30 days), the facility must comply with the provision for both Group R-1 and R-2.

Other occupancies are often found in buildings classified in Group R-1. These occupancies include nightclubs (Group A-2), restaurants (Group A-2), gift shops (Group M), health clubs (Group A-3) and storage facilities (Group S-1). When this occurs, the building is a mixed occupancy and is subject to the provisions of Section 508 of the IBC.

Transient congregate living facilities and boarding houses with 10 or fewer occupants can be constructed to the standards of Group R-3 occupancies rather than the general category of Group R-1. The primary intent of this provision is to permit bed-and-breakfast-type facilities to be established in existing single-family (one-family) structures. In comparison to the provision under Group R-2, which permits congregate living facilities with fewer than 16 nontransient occupants to be built as a Group R-3, the Group R-3 "transient" facility is limited to 10 or fewer occupants to reflect the lack of familiarity guests have with the building and its evacuation routes.

See Section 310.4.2 of the IBC for lodging houses with five or fewer rooms to rent. While these are transient, these types of bed-and-breakfast type facilities are specifically listed under Group R-3.

[BG] Residential Group R-2. Residential Group R-2 occupancies containing *sleeping units* or more than two *dwelling units* where the occupants are primarily permanent in nature, including:

Apartment houses
Congregate living facilities (nontransient) with more than 16 occupants
Boarding houses (nontransient)
Convents
Dormitories
Fraternities and sororities
Monasteries
Hotels (nontransient)
Live/work units
Motels (nontransient)
Vacation timeshare properties

❖ The length of the occupants' stay plus the arrangement of the facilities provided are the basic factors that differentiate occupancies classified in Group R-2 from other occupancies in Group R. The occupants of facilities or areas classified in Group R-2 are primarily nontransient, capable of self-preservation and share their means of egress in whole or in part with other occupants outside of their sleeping unit or dwelling unit. Building types ordinarily classified in Group R-2 include apartments, boarding houses (when the occupants are not transient) and nontransient congregate living facilities, such as dormitories, where there are more than 16 occupants.

Individual dwelling units in Group R-2 are either rented by tenants or owned by the occupants. The code does not make a distinction between either type of tenancy. Residential condominiums are treated in the code the same as Group R-2 apartments. Such condominiums are based on shared ownership of a building and related facilities. While an individual owner will have exclusive rights to a certain unit, the building, the lot the building sits upon, parking, common recreational facilities and similar features are owned in common by all the owners of individual dwelling units. In most cases condominiums do not establish separate lots and the walls between units are not setting on lot lines. Another type of shared ownership is referred to as a "co-op," short for cooperative. Occasionally a condominium will establish actual lots and lot lines distinguishing individual ownership. When the dwelling unit is located on a separate parcel of land, lot lines defining the parcel exist and the requirements for fire separation must be met.

A dwelling unit is defined in Section 202, and includes independent facilities of cooking, sleeping, eating and sanitation. Examples of sleeping units in Group R-2 occupancy could be a bedroom in a congregate living, boarding house, fraternity or sorority. The bedrooms provide independent provisions for sleeping, but the living, kitchen and sanitation facilities are shared. The new style of dormitory in colleges consists of two, three or four bedrooms with one or two single-occupant bathrooms and a shared living space. These facilities are considered a sleeping unit. Only where there are full cooking and eating facilities (i.e., a kitchen with a range) within the unit, is the unit considered a dwelling unit. The two-, three- or four-bedroom units operate similar to an apartment. Considering this group of rooms a sleeping unit clarifies that the provisions in Chapter 7 to separate dwelling or sleeping units allows for this group of rooms to be separated from adjacent groups and the corridors, but does not require the bedrooms to be separated from the associated living room or bathrooms. This also clarifies that only the main corridors have fire alarms, and smoke detectors can be within the unit. Prior to changes made for 2018, the definition of "Sleeping unit" was unclear as to whether the living and sanitation were considered part of the unit or an extension of the main corridor. Due to how universities administer dormitory assignments, the accessibility provisions in Section 1107 specify that bedrooms within sleeping units are counted separately for purposed the number of Accessible bedrooms required.

When college classes are not in session, the sleeping units in dormitories are sometimes rented out for periods of less than 30 days to convention attendees and other visitors. When dormitories undergo this type of transient use, they more closely resemble Group R-1 and must comply with both Group R-1 and R-2 requirements.

Buildings containing dormitories often contain other occupancies, such as cafeterias or dining rooms (Group A-2), recreation rooms (Group A-3), offices (Group B) and meeting rooms (Group A-3). Where this occurs, the building is considered a mixed occupancy and is subject to the provisions of Section 508 of the IBC.

Included in the listing of Group R-2 are live/work units. A live/work unit is a dwelling unit in which a significant portion of the space includes a nonresidential use operated by the tenant. Reflecting a growing trend in urban neighborhoods and the reuse of existing buildings, live/work units must comply with the provisions of Section 419 of the IBC.

The congregate living facility reference is intended to better define when a congregate living facility is operating as a single-family home. Blended families are now commonplace and not necessarily defined strictly by blood or marriage. Small boarding houses, convents, dormitories, fraternities, sororities and monasteries may be small enough to operate as a single-family unit and would be permitted to be constructed as Group R-3 occupancies as intended by the code. The threshold of 16 persons is consistent with the results of the most recent census, which showed that 98 percent of households in the US that identified themselves as a single family have fewer than 16 occupants. The 16-occupant limit is also consistent with the limits of an NFPA 13D sprinkler system.

[BG] Residential Group R-3. Residential Group R-3 occupancies where the occupants are primarily permanent in nature and not classified as Group R-1, R-2, R-4 or I, including:

Buildings that do not contain more than two *dwelling units*

Care facilities that provide accommodations for five or fewer persons receiving care

Congregate living facilities (nontransient) with 16 or fewer occupants

Boarding houses (nontransient)
Convents
Dormitories
Fraternities and sororities
Monasteries

Congregate living facilities (*transient*) with 10 or fewer occupants

Boarding houses (*transient*)

Lodging houses (*transient*) with five or fewer *guestrooms* and 10 or fewer occupants

❖ Group R-3 facilities include all detached one- and two-family dwellings and multiple (three or more) single-family dwellings (townhouses) more than three stories in height. Those buildings three or less stories in height are not classified as Group R-3 and are regulated by the IRC. Each pair of dwelling units in multiple single-family dwellings greater than three stories in height must be separated by fire walls (see Section 706 of the IBC) or by two exterior walls (see Table 602 of the IBC) in order to be classified as Group R-3. (Duplexes, buildings with two dwelling units, must be detached from other structures in order to be regulated by the IRC). A duplex attached to another duplex would be required to comply with the code and be classified as Group R-2 or R-3, depending on the presence of fire walls.

Buildings that are classified as Group R-3, while limited in height, are not limited in the allowable area per floor as indicated in Table 506.2.

One- and two-family dwellings and multiple single-family dwellings less than three stories in height that contain another occupancy (e.g., Groups B, M, I-4) must be regulated as a mixed occupancy in accordance with the code and are not permitted to be regulated by the provisions of the IRC. However, some mixed use dwelling units may qualify as live/work units under Section 419 and be classified as a Group R-2 occupancy.

In addition, congregate living facilities with not more than 16 nontransient occupants or not more than 10 transient occupants are to be classified as Group R-3.

Group R-3 occupancies include small care facilities where care is provided to five or fewer persons. The intent is to allow persons to be cared for, often by family members, in a residential, or home, environment that is typical within a single-family-type home. Allowances for the Group R-3 classification of smaller care facilities are established in Group E, Group I-1, Group I-2 and Group I-4. Because the intent is to accommodate persons who might otherwise be in other group occupancies, including Group I-2, the Group R-3 care facility is not limited to only persons who are capable of self-preservation. The only limit is the number receiving care, not the total number of occupants in the dwelling unit. If two people are receiving care, and the rest of the family includes four others, totaling six occupants in the dwelling does classify the dwelling as a Group R-3 occupancy.

Lodging houses with five or fewer guest rooms and 10 or fewer total occupants can be classified as a Group R-3 occupancy or, under Section 310.4.2 of the IBC, can be constructed under the provisions of the IRC. The definition of "Lodging house" allows the rental of guest rooms to transients, provided that there are one or more occupants who are permanent in nature. While Section 310.4.2 requires owner occupancy of the dwelling unit in order for it to be built in compliance with the IRC, there is no owner occupancy requirement for lodging houses that comply with Group R-3 requirements. The broad intent of the lodging house provisions is to allow bed-and-breakfast and similar facilities under the Group R-3 category, even though transient housing generally falls under the Group R-1 classification. There is a double limit of both the number of guest rooms and the number of occupants.

Under Section 310.4.2, which requires the owner to be in occupancy, the owner and the owner's family in residence will count toward the total number of occupants. Under the R-3 occupancy, owner occupancy is not required, but by definition at least one occupant must be permanent in nature. Again, any permanent residents will count toward the total allowed occupant limit.

[BG] Care facilities within a dwelling. Care facilities for five or fewer persons receiving care that are within a single-family dwelling are permitted to comply with the *International Residential Code* provided an *automatic sprinkler system* is installed in accordance with Section 903.3.1.3 or Section P2904 of the *International Residential Code*.

❖ The Group R-3 definition already states that care facilities that accommodate five or fewer persons receiving care can be classified as a Group R-3 occupancy. The definitions of Group E, Group I-1, Group I-2 and Group I-4 each state the option of providing the care of five or fewer persons within a structure regulated under the IRC. The intent is to allow persons to be cared for, often by family members, in a residential, or home, environment that is typical within a single-family-type home. As stated for those care facilities allowed within the Group R-3 occupancy, the persons receiving care in a building designed according to the IRC are not limited to those who are capable of self-preservation. Similar to those for Groups I-1 and I-2, this definition specifies that such an IRC-regulated facility must be provided with an automatic sprinkler system.

[BG] Lodging houses. Owner-occupied *lodging houses* with five or fewer guestrooms and 10 or fewer total occupants shall be permitted to be constructed in accordance with the *International Residential Code*.

❖ This section allows bed-and-breakfast type hotels that are both owner occupied and have five or fewer rooms to rent to be constructed under the IRC. In addition, there is also a maximum of 10 occupants permitted. See the commentary to Section 310.4.

[BG] Residential Group R-4. Residential Group R-4 shall include buildings, structures or portions thereof for more than five but not more than 16 persons, excluding staff, who reside on a 24-hour basis in a supervised residential environment and receive custodial care. Buildings of Group R-4 shall be classified as one of the occupancy conditions indicated below. This group shall include, but not be limited to, the following:

Alcohol and drug centers
Assisted living facilities
Congregate care facilities
Group homes
Halfway houses
Residential board and care facilities
Social rehabilitation facilities

Group R-4 occupancies shall meet the requirements for construction as defined for Group R-3, except as otherwise provided for in the *International Building Code*.

❖ Where five to 16 residents live in a supervised environment and receive custodial care, such a facility is classified as Group R-4. Ninety-eight percent of the households in the US that identified themselves as single family have fewer than 16 occupants. The 16-occupant limit is also consistent with the limits of an NFPA 13D sprinkler system. Thus, limiting the number of residents to 16 was deemed appropriate considering that this facility will operate similar to a single-family home. Under federal housing laws regarding nondiscrimination, families cannot be determined by blood or marriage. If a Group R-4 occupancy is expanded or allowed to have more than 16 care recipients, the facility needs to be reclassified as a Group I-1 occupancy. The number of persons used in the determination includes those who receive care and is not intended to include staff.

Similar to Group I-1, a Group R-4 occupancy is also one of two conditions. In a Condition 1 facility, care recipients may be slower during evacuation but are capable of self-preservation. In a Condition 2 facility, care recipients may require limited assistance with evacuation during emergency situations. See also the commentary in Section 308.2 of the IBC for Group I-1 for a further detailed explanation of both Group I-1 and R-4 custodial care occupancies (also see the definition of "Custodial care").

Group R-4 facilities must satisfy the construction requirements of Group R-3. Facilities with five or fewer persons receiving care will be either a Group R-3 occupancy (see Section 310.4 of the IBC), or can be built under the IRC (see Section 310.4.1 of the IBC).

[BG] Condition 1. This occupancy condition shall include buildings in which all persons receiving custodial care, without any assistance, are capable of responding to an emergency situation to complete building evacuation.

❖ See the commentary to the definition of "Group R-4 occupancies."

[BG] Condition 2. This occupancy condition shall include buildings in which there are any persons receiving custodial care who require limited verbal or physical assistance while responding to an emergency situation to complete building evacuation.

❖ See the commentary to the definition of "Group R-4 occupancies."

[BG] Storage Group S. Storage Group S occupancy includes, among others, the use of a building or structure, or a portion thereof, for storage that is not classified as a hazardous occupancy.

❖ This definition requires that all structures (or parts thereof) designed or occupied for the storage of moderate- and low-hazard materials are to be classified in either Group S-1 (moderate hazard) or S-2 (low hazard). Small storage areas are inherent in almost any activity or occupancy.

The life safety problems in structures used for storage of moderate- and low-hazard materials are minimal because the number of people involved in a storage operation is usually small and normal work patterns require the occupants to be dispersed throughout the facility. The problems of fire safety, particularly as they relate to the protection of stored contents, are directly associated with the amount and combustibility of the materials (including packaging) that are housed on the premises.

Storage facilities typically contain significant amounts of combustible or noncombustible materials that are kept in a common area. Because of the combustion, flammability or explosive characteristics of certain materials, a structure (or portion thereof) that is used to store high-hazard materials that exceed the MAQs, or that does not meet one of the exceptions identified in Section 307.1 of the IBC, cannot be classified as Group S; must be classified as Group H, high-hazard uses; and is to comply with Section 307 of the IBC.

Storage occupancies consist of two basic types: Groups S-1 and S-2, which are based on the properties of the materials being stored. The distinction between Groups S-1 and S-2 is similar to that between Groups F-1 and F-2, as outlined in those definitions.

[BG] Accessory storage spaces. A room or space used for storage purposes that is accessory to another occupancy shall be classified as part of that occupancy.

❖ This provision allows accessory storage areas to be classified in the same occupancy group as the primary occupancy of a space. There are no longer limits on the size of such spaces, nor how much of the floor area such accessory storage can occupy. These storage spaces could occur in any other occupancy, such as a Group B office building, a Group E classroom or a Group M retail store. If the storage isn't accessory to a primary use, then the storage would be classified in Group S; if it then is in with a mix of other occupancies, Section 508 would be applicable. Table 509 for incidental uses would require storage rooms in Group I-2 and ambulatory care facilities with an area over 100 square feet (9.3 m^2) to be separated by fire barrier or horizontal assemblies with a fire-resistance rating of at least 1 hour.

[BG] Moderate-hazard storage, Group S-1. Storage Group S-1 occupancies are buildings occupied for storage uses that are not classified as Group S-2, including, but not limited to, storage of the following:

Aerosols, Levels 2 and 3
Aircraft hangar (storage and repair)
Bags: cloth, burlap and paper
Bamboos and rattan
Baskets
Belting: canvas and leather
Books and paper in rolls or packs
Boots and shoes
Buttons, including cloth covered, pearl or bone
Cardboard and cardboard boxes
Clothing, woolen wearing apparel
Cordage
Dry boat storage (indoor)
Furniture
Furs
Glues, mucilage, pastes and size
Grains
Horns and combs, other than celluloid
Leather
Linoleum
Lumber
Motor vehicle repair garages complying with the maximum allowable quantities of hazardous materials listed in Table 5003.1.1(1) (see Section 406.8 of the *International Building Code*)
Photo engravings
Resilient flooring
Self-service storage facility (mini-storage)
Silks
Soaps
Sugar
Tires, bulk storage of

Tobacco, cigars, cigarettes and snuff
Upholstery and mattresses
Wax candles

❖ Buildings in which combustible materials are stored and that burn with ease are classified in Group S-1, moderate-hazard storage occupancies. Examples of the kinds of materials that, when stored, are representative of occupancies classified in Group S-1 are listed in the definition.

As defined by the code, a repair garage is any structure used for servicing or repairing motor vehicles. Therefore, regardless of the extent of work done (e.g., quick-lube, tune-up, muffler and tire shops, painting, body work, engine overhaul), repair garages are classified as Group S-1 and must be in compliance with Section 406.8 of the IBC. In addition, to avoid a Group H classification, the amounts of hazardous materials in the garage must be less than the MAQ indicated in Tables 5003.1.1(1) and 5003.1.1(2) [IBC Tables 307.1(1) and 307.1(2)] of the code.

Aircraft hangars for storage, repair or both would be classified as Group S-1. This classification correlates with the actual use of such hangars, which very frequently would include some level of repair work, and also works with the requirements of NFPA 409. Aircraft hangers accessory to one- and two-family structures are classified as Group U occupancies. Detailed provisions applicable to aircraft hangers can be found in Section 412.3 of the IBC. Residential hangers are addressed in Section 412.4 of the IBC.

[BG] Low-hazard storage, Group S-2. Storage Group S-2 occupancies include, among others, buildings used for the storage of noncombustible materials such as products on wood pallets or in paper cartons with or without single thickness divisions; or in paper wrappings. Such products are permitted to have a negligible amount of plastic trim, such as knobs, handles or film wrapping. Storage uses shall include, but not be limited to, storage of the following:

Asbestos
Beverages up to and including 16-percent alcohol in metal, glass or ceramic containers
Cement in bags
Chalk and crayons
Dairy products in nonwaxed coated paper containers
Dry cell batteries
Electrical coils
Electrical motors
Empty cans
Food products
Foods in noncombustible containers
Fresh fruits and vegetables in nonplastic trays or containers
Frozen foods
Glass
Glass bottles, empty or filled with noncombustible liquids
Gypsum board
Inert pigments
Ivory
Meats
Metal cabinets
Metal desks with plastic tops and trim
Metal parts
Metals
Mirrors
Oil-filled and other types of distribution transformers
Parking garages, open or enclosed
Porcelain and pottery
Stoves
Talc and soapstones
Washers and dryers

❖ Buildings in which noncombustible materials are stored are classified as Group S-2, low-hazard storage occupancies. It is acceptable for stored noncombustible products to be packaged in combustible materials as long as the quantity of packaging is kept to an insignificant level.

As seen in Group F-1 and F-2 classifications, it is important to be able to distinguish when the presence of combustible packaging constitutes a significant fuel load. As such, a fuel load might require the building to be classified in Group S-1, moderate-hazard storage. A simple guideline to follow is the "single-thickness" rule, which is when a noncombustible product is put in one layer of packaging material.

Examples of materials qualified for storage in Group S-2 storage facilities are as follows:

- Vehicle engines placed on wood pallets for transportation after assembly.
- Washing machines in corrugated cardboard boxes.
- Soft-drink glass bottles packaged in pressed paper boxes.

Structures used to store noncombustible materials packaged in more than one layer of combustible packaging material are to be classified in Group S-1.

Examples of materials that, because of packaging, do not qualify for classification in Group S-2 are:

- Chinaware wrapped in corrugated paper and placed in cardboard boxes.
- Glassware set in expanded foam forms and placed in a cardboard box.
- Fuel filters individually packed in pressed paper boxes, placed by the gross in a cardboard box and then stacked on a wood pallet for transportation.

An area often related to Group S occupancies is Chapter 32, which regulates high-piled combustible storage [storage over 12 feet (3658 mm) in height or 6 feet (1829 mm) if the material is considered high hazard]. Chapter 32 of the IFC is focused on not only the type of materials being stored but also the height and configuration of such storage. It is important to note that not all Group S occupancies will contain high-piled storage and that high-piled storage is not limited to Group S occupancies. High-piled storage can be found in occupancies such as Group H or F.

Open and enclosed parking garages are classified as Group S-2 occupancies as long as no repair activities occur in such buildings. Detailed provisions for parking garages can be found in Section 406 of the IBC. A garage in a fire station, for example, that undertakes maintenance and repairs limited to cleaning, hose change, water fill, fire equipment upgrades or wheel removal for off-premises repair would not constitute the same hazard associated with repair garages and would be appropriately classified as Group S-2.

[BG] Miscellaneous Group U. Buildings and structures of an accessory character and miscellaneous structures not classified in any specific occupancy shall be constructed, equipped and maintained to conform to the requirements of this code commensurate with the fire and life hazard incidental to their occupancy. Group U shall include, but not be limited to, the following:

Agricultural buildings
Aircraft hangar, accessory to a one- or two-family residence (see Section 412.4 of the *International Building Code*)
Barns
Carports
Communication equipment structures with a gross floor area of less than 1,500 square feet (139 m^3)
Fences more than 6 feet (1829 mm) high
Grain silos, accessory to a residential occupancy
Livestock shelters
Private garages
Retaining walls
Sheds
Stables
Tanks
Towers

❖ This definition identifies the characteristics of occupancies classified in Group U. Structures that are classified in Group U are typically accessory to another building or structure and are not more appropriately classified in another occupancy. Miscellaneous storage buildings accessory to detached one- and two-family dwellings and multiple single-family dwellings (townhouses) not more than three stories in height, however, are intended to be designed and built in accordance with the IRC.

Structures classified as Group U, such as fences, equipment, foundations, retaining walls, etc., are somewhat outside the primary scope of the code (i.e., means of egress, fire resistance). They are not usually considered to be habitable or occupiable. Nevertheless, many code provisions do apply and need to be enforced (e.g., structural design and material performance).

Structures housing accessory equipment that is part of a utility or communications system are often classified as Group U occupancies when there is no intent that these structures be occupied except for servicing and maintaining the equipment within the structure. A pumphouse for a water or sewage system or an equipment building at the base of a telecommunications tower are examples of such buildings.

Group U occupancies are subject to the same structural loadings as other occupancies, such as snow loads. The structural design requirements for roofs are the minimum deemed necessary to withstand such elements. Allowing construction of a building with an accessory occupancy that could reasonably be expected to collapse under the snow loads known to prevail in certain area is not in the best interest of public safety.

[BG] Greenhouses. Greenhouses not classified as another occupancy shall be classified as Use Group U.

❖ Greenhouses are uses in the Group U classification but only where a different classification doesn't make sense. A greenhouse is defined as a structure or thermally isolated part of a building in which a sunlit environment is maintained for cultivation, protection or maintenance of plants. Greenhouses are also listed in Group A-3, which might be a public arboretum building and Group M for the display and sale of plants. A greenhouse could be part of a school or university for educational purposes, or simply a growing facility.

[BG] OCCUPANT LOAD. The number of persons for which the *means of egress* of a building or portion thereof is designed.

❖ In addition to the limitation on the maximum occupant load for a space, the code also requires the determination of the occupant load that is to be utilized for the design of the means of egress system. The number for the floor area per occupant (occupant load factor) in Table 1004.1.2 reflects common and traditional occupant densities based on the empirical data for the density of similar spaces. This occupant load is also utilized to determine the required number of plumbing fixtures (see Chapter 29 of the IBC) and when automatic sprinkler systems or fire alarm and detection systems are required (see Chapter 9).

OPEN BURNING. The burning of materials wherein products of combustion are emitted directly into the ambient air without passing through a stack or chimney from an enclosed chamber. Open burning does not include road flares, smudgepots and similar devices associated with safety or occupational uses typically considered open flames, *recreational fires* or use of portable outdoor fireplaces. For the purpose of this definition, a chamber shall be regarded as enclosed when, during the time combustion occurs, only apertures, ducts, stacks, flues or chimneys necessary to provide combustion air and permit the escape of exhaust gas are open.

❖ Open burning is any burning that takes place in an unenclosed space. Examples include burning of leaves or grass clippings, burning construction debris and fires built on the ground for warmth in cold weather. The burning of wood scraps in a steel drum or in a piece of culvert over which a supply of construction sand can be dumped and kept thawed is common practice on construction sites in cold climates and could be evaluated by the fire code official as being an allowable "occupational use" as mentioned in the definition. The definition has also been revised to clarify that the use of portable outdoor fireplaces (also known as patio fireplaces) is specifically excluded, thus eliminating the confusion that previously existed as to how to treat those devices. See also the definition of "Recreational fire."

OPEN MALL. See "Covered mall building."

OPEN MALL BUILDING. See "Covered mall building."

[BG] OPEN PARKING GARAGE. A structure or portion of a structure with the openings as described in Section 406.5.2 of the *International Building Code* on two or more sides that is used for the parking or storage of private motor vehicles as described in Section 406.5 of the *International Building Code*.

❖ Open parking garages are defined as having uniformly distributed openings on not less than two sides totaling not less than 40 percent of the building perimeter. The aggregate area of the openings is to be a minimum of 20 percent of the total wall area of all perimeter walls (see the commentary to Section 406.5.2 of the IBC).

OPEN SYSTEM. The use of a solid or liquid hazardous material involving a vessel or system that is continuously open to the atmosphere during normal operations and where vapors are liberated, or the product is exposed to the atmosphere during normal operations. Examples of open systems for solids and liquids include dispensing from or into open beakers or containers, dip tank and plating tank operations.

❖ This definition is related primarily to hazardous materials use. Generally, an open system is one that will normally be open to the atmosphere; for example, a dip tank or dispensing or mixing of hazardous materials. Open systems are inherently more hazardous than closed systems. When evaluating the MAQs of hazardous materials and the associated requirements, open systems are more heavily regulated.

OPEN-AIR ASSEMBLY SEATING. Seating served by *means of egress* that is not subject to smoke accumulation within or under a structure and is open to the atmosphere.

❖ An example of open-air assembly seating is an open outdoor grandstand. The intent is to separate this from smoke-protected seating such as an indoor arena with a smoke control system. The code has less-stringent requirements for certain aspects of open-air or smoke-protected assembly seating than for seating that is not smoke protected, since occupants are subject to less hazard from the accumulation of smoke and fumes during a fire event. For example, an assembly dead-end aisle is permitted to be longer for an open-air assembly area.

[BE] OPEN-ENDED CORRIDOR. An interior *corridor* that is open on each end and connects to an exterior *stairway* or *ramp* at each end with no intervening doors or separation from the *corridor*.

❖ Breezeway configurations are common in hotels and apartment buildings, especially in areas where being open to the outside air is considered an amenity. By essentially being open to the outside, the intent and level of safety is similar to an exterior egress balcony (see Section 1027.6, Exception 3 for requirements)

[BF] OPENING PROTECTIVE. A *fire door assembly*, fire shutter assembly, fire window assembly or glass-block assembly in a *fire-resistance-rated* wall or partition.

❖ This definition is intended to provide clarity as to what is considered an opening protective and what is not. This assists in the enforcement of the maintenance requirements found in Chapter 7. This would not include openings in a smoke partition but would include a smoke barrier as such walls are fire-resistance rated. The term is used extensively in this code and the IBC.

OPERATING BUILDING. A building occupied in conjunction with the manufacture, transportation or use of *explosive materials*. Operating buildings are separated from one another with the use of intraplant or intraline distances.

❖ Magazines are used for storage of explosive materials. Manufacturing or operating buildings are not magazines and are not intended to be used for storage, although at times there may be storage incidental to the manufacturing function. This definition is included here to clarify this difference.

OPERATING LINE. A group of buildings, facilities or workstations so arranged as to permit performance of the steps in the manufacture of an *explosive* or in the loading, assembly, modification and maintenance of ammunition or devices containing *explosive materials*.

❖ This term is used by those engaged in the storage and manufacture of explosive materials, as well as with the regulators of these materials, including the DOD. The term is also consistent with terminology used by the DOD and the Institute of Makers of Explosives (IME). The term "operating line" is defined in relationship to operating buildings that may be grouped in such a manner so as to create a manufacturing process.

OPERATING PRESSURE. The pressure at which a system operates.

❖ This term is self-explanatory and is used in Chapters 9, 31, 55 and 60 of the code.

ORGANIC COATING. A liquid mixture of binders such as alkyd, nitrocellulose, acrylic or oil, and flammable and combustible solvents such as hydrocarbon, ester, ketone or alcohol, which, when spread in a thin film, convert to a durable protective and decorative finish.

❖ "Organic coatings" are defined as flammable and combustible paints and other protective or decorative coatings.

ORGANIC PEROXIDE. An organic compound that contains the bivalent -O-O- structure and which may be considered to be a structural derivative of hydrogen peroxide where one or both of the hydrogen atoms have been replaced by an organic radical. Organic peroxides can present an explosion hazard (*detonation* or *deflagration*) or they can be shock sensitive. They can also decompose into various unstable compounds over an extended period of time.

Class I. Describes those formulations that are capable of *deflagration* but not *detonation*.

Class II. Describes those formulations that burn very rapidly and that pose a moderate reactivity hazard.

Class III. Describes those formulations that burn rapidly and that pose a moderate reactivity hazard.

Class IV. Describes those formulations that burn in the same manner as ordinary combustibles and that pose a minimal reactivity hazard.

Class V. Describes those formulations that burn with less intensity than ordinary combustibles or do not sustain combustion and that pose no reactivity hazard.

Unclassified detonable. Organic peroxides that are capable of *detonation*. These peroxides pose an extremely high-explosion hazard through rapid explosive decomposition.

❖ The chemical structure of organic peroxides differs from that of hydrogen peroxide (an oxidizer) in that an organic radical replaces the hydrogen atoms. Commentary Figure 202-O6 shows an example of this chemical structure in which a benzoyl radical (C_6H_5CO) in the widely used Class I organic peroxide benzoyl peroxide replaces the hydrogen atoms in hydrogen peroxide (H_2O_2). Organic chemicals are all carbon based. As a result, organic peroxides pose varying degrees of fire or explosion hazards in addition to their oxidizing properties.

The classification system in this chapter (see Commentary Figure 202-O7) is derived from a system developed by the Society of the Plastics Industry (Bulletin 19A).

OUTDOOR ASSEMBLY EVENT. An outdoor gathering of persons for any purpose.

❖ This definition is somewhat broad but was placed in the code in support of Section 3106, which addresses requirements for such events where there are more than 1,000 persons in attendance. These events may or may not involve tents but do involve many people. With large gatherings there are many risks from various aspects, such as weather and fire hazards. Fire hazards at these events are typically related to cooking, smoking, electrical or use of flammable gases. Due to the size of the events, crowd managers may be required. Any temporary structures, such as tents used at such events, would need to comply with Chapter 31 as well.

OUTDOOR CONTROL AREA. An outdoor area that contains hazardous materials in amounts not exceeding the maximum allowable quantities of Table 5003.1.1(3) or Table 5003.1.1(4).

❖ This term refers to a storage area that is exposed to the elements (wind, rain, snow, etc.) and cannot

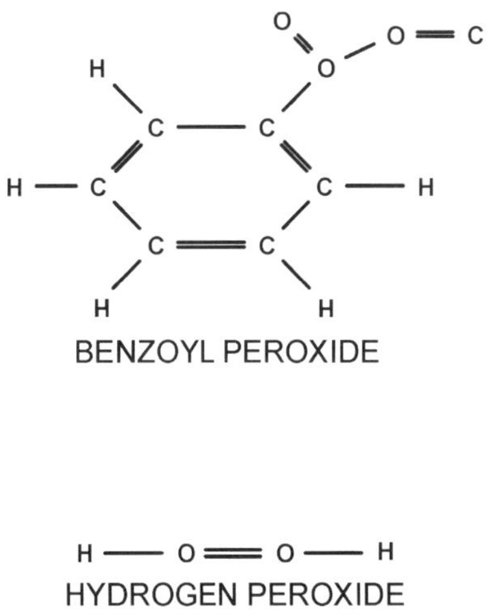

Commentary Figure 202-O6
COMPARISON OF HYDROGEN PEROXIDE STRUCTURE WITH BENZOYL PEROXIDE

IFC	DOTn 49 CFR, PART 173.128(b)	HAZARD DESCRIPTION
Unclassified detonatable	Type A	Detonation hazard when confined
Class I	Type B	Deflagration hazard when confined
Class II	Type C and Type D	Mass fire hazard similar to flammable liquid[a]
Class III	Type E	Fire hazard similar to combustible liquid
Class IV	Type F	Little or no fire or reactivity hazard
Class V	Type G	No fire or reactivity hazard

a. Moderate detonation or deflagration hazard when heated under confinement.

Commentary Figure 202-O7
COMPARISON OF ORGANIC PEROXIDE CLASSIFICATION SYSTEMS

exceed the MAQ listed in the code and the IBC. See Tables 5003.1.1(3), 5003.1.1(4) and Sections 5001 and 5003 of the code, and Section 414.6 in the IBC.

OUTPATIENT CLINIC. See "Clinic, outpatient."

OVERCROWDING. A condition that exists when either there are more people in a building, structure or portion thereof than have been authorized or posted by the *fire code official*, or when the *fire code official* determines that a threat exists to the safety of the occupants due to persons sitting and/or standing in locations that may obstruct or impede the use of *aisles*, passages, *corridors*, *stairways*, *exits* or other components of the *means of egress*.

❖ This definition notes that an unsafe condition exists when the actual number of people present in a building or a building space exceeds the maximum allowable occupant load of that building or space as determined and posted on the premises by the fire code official. Section 1004 of the code would allow a maximum occupant load of one person per every 5 square feet (0.5 m^2) of building area, as long as the egress components provide sufficient capacity for such a load. When that egress capacity is exceeded, then overcrowding exists. The definition also recognizes that, even though the number of occupants in a building or space may not be excessive, the inability of occupants to use the egress elements due to blockage by patrons is also a life safety hazard.

[A] OWNER. Any person, agent, operator, entity, firm or corporation having any legal or equitable interest in the property; or recorded in the official records of the state, county or municipality as holding an interest or title to the property; or otherwise having possession or control of the property, including the guardian of the estate of any such person, and the executor or administrator of the estate of such person if ordered to take possession of real property by a court.

❖ This term defines the person or other legal entity who is responsible for a building and its compliance with code requirements.

OXIDIZER. A material that readily yields oxygen or other oxidizing gas, or that readily reacts to promote or initiate combustion of combustible materials and, if heated or contaminated, can result in vigorous self-sustained decomposition.

Class 4. An oxidizer that can undergo an explosive reaction due to contamination or exposure to thermal or physical shock and that causes a severe increase in the burning rate of combustible materials with which it comes into contact. Additionally, the oxidizer causes a severe increase in the burning rate and can cause spontaneous ignition of combustibles.

Class 3. An oxidizer that causes a severe increase in the burning rate of combustible materials with which it comes in contact.

Class 2. An oxidizer that will cause a moderate increase in the burning rate of combustible materials with which it comes in contact.

Class 1. An oxidizer that does not moderately increase the burning rate of combustible materials.

❖ The classification of oxidizers had its origins in the provisions of NFPA 430 and is consistent with Department of Transportation (DOT) hazardous materials regulations. Oxidizers, whether a solid, liquid or gas, yield oxygen or another oxidizing gas during a chemical reaction or readily react to oxidize combustibles and increase their burning rate. This characteristic is a result of the enrichment of the air to more than 21-percent oxygen content.

This enrichment is a hazard because an ordinary combustible material that will burn freely at the atmospheric oxygen level of 21 percent will burn more rapidly at higher concentrations of oxygen. The rate of reaction varies with the class of oxidizer. Specific classification of oxidizers is important because of the varying degree of hazard. Examples of oxidizers include liquid hydrogen peroxide, nitric acid, sulfuric acid and solids, such as sodium chlorite, chromic acid and calcium hypochlorite. Many commercially available swimming pool chemicals are examples of Class 2 or 3 oxidizers.

OXIDIZING CRYOGENIC FLUID. An oxidizing gas in the cryogenic state.

❖ This definition is provided to correlate with the title of Chapter 63 and Section 6304.2.1.1, which is consistent with code-style improvement of providing hazard-specific requirements in material-specific chapters in addition to the general material chapters, in this case Chapter 55. The primary focus of the oxidizing cryogenic fluid provisions in this chapter is liquid oxygen.

OXIDIZING GAS. A gas that can support and accelerate combustion of other materials more than air does.

❖ Oxidizing gases present essentially the same hazard characteristics as solids and liquids. Examples of oxidizing gases are oxygen, ozone and the oxides of nitrogen, fluorine and chlorine.

OZONE-GAS GENERATOR. Equipment which causes the production of ozone.

❖ Ozone is considered a highly toxic gas. Ozone generators are addressed separately in Section 6005 because the code has traditionally dealt with the storage and use of hazardous materials, but not the generation.

[BE] PANIC HARDWARE. A door-latching assembly incorporating a device that releases the latch upon the application of a force in the direction of egress travel. See also "Fire exit hardware."

❖ Panic hardware is commonly used in educational and assembly-type spaces where the number of occupants who would use a doorway during a short time frame in an emergency is high in relation to an occupancy with a less dense occupant load, such as an office building. The hardware is required so that the door can be easily opened during an emergency where pressure on a door from a crush of people could tender normal hardware inoperable. Not all types of panic hardware are permitted on doors required to be fire-protection rated (see the definition for "Fire exit hardware" and Section 1010.1.10).

PASS-THROUGH. An enclosure installed in a wall with a door on each side that allows chemicals, HPM, equipment, and parts to be transferred from one side of the wall to the other.

❖ A pass-through is similar to a sally port and is used to store and receive HPM for the fabrication area. The pass-through must be separated from the exit access corridor by fire-resistance-rated construction, including a fire-resistance-rated, self-closing fire door on each side, and be sprinklered.

[BG] PENTHOUSE. An enclosed, unoccupied rooftop structure used for sheltering mechanical and electrical equipment, tanks, elevators and related machinery, and vertical shaft openings.

❖ Any enclosed structure that is located above the surrounding roof surfaces can be considered a penthouse as long as it meets the criteria within Section 1510.2 of the IBC. By complying with these requirements, the penthouse is considered to not contribute to the height of the building, either in number of stories or feet above grade plane. If the proposed penthouse does not meet these requirements, it must be considered as an additional story of the building or structure.

PERMISSIBLE EXPOSURE LIMIT (PEL). The maximum permitted 8-hour time-weighted-average concentration of an airborne contaminant. The exposure limits to be utilized are those published in DOL 29 CFR Part 1910.1000. The Recommended Exposure Limit (REL) concentrations published by the U.S. National Institute for Occupational Safety and Health (NIOSH), Threshold Limit Value-Time Weighted Average (TLV-TWA) concentrations published by the American Conference of Governmental Industrial Hygienists (ACGIH), Workplace Environmental Exposure Level (WEEL) Guides published by the American Industrial Hygiene Association (AIHA), and other *approved*, consistent measures are allowed as surrogates for hazardous substances not *listed* in DOL 29 CFR Part 1910.1000.

❖ The PEL is a maximum time-weighted concentration at which 95 percent of exposed, healthy adults suffer no adverse effects over a 40-hour workweek. The lower the PEL, the more toxic the substance.

[A] PERMIT. An official document or certificate issued by the *fire code official* that authorizes performance of a specified activity.

❖ The permit constitutes a license issued by the fire code official to proceed with a specific activity, such as construction of a building or conducting a certain type of business, in accordance with all applicable laws.

For the IBC and IRC, the "building official" is identified as the person responsible for issuing the permit. For the IFC, the "fire code official" is identified as the person responsible. For other I-Codes, the "code official" is identified as the person responsible.

[A] PERSON. An individual, heirs, executors, administrators or assigns, and also includes a firm, partnership or corporation, its or their successors or assigns, or the agent of any of the aforesaid.

❖ Corporations and other organizations listed in the definition are treated as persons under the law. Also, where the code provides for a penalty (see Section 110.4), the definition makes it clear that the individuals responsible for administering the activities of these various organizations are subject to these penalties.

[BG] PERSONAL CARE SERVICE. The care of persons who do not require medical care. Personal care involves responsibility for the safety of the persons while inside the building.

❖ Persons who need personal care may need supervision, but they are capable of self-preservation. See the commentary to Occupancy Group E day care.

Care facilities encompass a full spectrum of occupant acuity and support services and span a wide range of occupancy types including Groups E, I and R. There are three types of care defined in the codes: personal, custodial and medical. On the lower end of the care spectrum (i.e., personal care) is where occupants are supervised but do not need custodial or medical care. Where occupants may be elderly or impaired (i.e., custodial care), they may need occasional daily living assistance, such as cooking and cleaning. While occupants may take longer to evacuate than average, they are capable of self-preservation. On the opposite end of the care spectrum, persons receiving care may be completely bedridden and dependent on medical gases and emergency power to maintain life (i.e., medical care). The level of care provided is based on the condition and capabilities of an occupant, which, in turn, indicate appropriate standards for protection systems and building. See also the definitions for "24-hour basis," "Custodial care," "Detoxification facilities," "Foster care facilities," "Group home," "Hospitals and psychiatric hospitals," "Incapable of self-preservation," "Medical care" and "Nursing home."

PESTICIDE. A substance or mixture of substances, including fungicides, intended for preventing, destroying, repelling or mitigating pests and substances or a mixture of substances intended for use as a plant regulator, defoliant or desiccant. Products defined as drugs in the Federal Food, Drug and Cosmetic Act are not pesticides.

❖ Typically, pesticides are ranked in the toxic category of health hazards. They are primarily used to control a variety of pests.

[BE] PHOTOLUMINESCENT. Having the property of emitting light that continues for a length of time after excitation by visible or invisible light has been removed.

❖ Examples of photoluminescent material are paint and tape that are charged by exposure to light. When the lights are turned off, the product will "glow" in the dark. Products utilized to meet the requirements for luminous egress path markings in high-rise buildings (see Section 403.5.5 of the IBC and Section 1025) or exit signs (see Section 1013.5) may be photoluminescent or self-luminous. A variety of materials can comply with the referenced standards for egress path markings [UL 1994, *Standard for Safety of Low Level Path Marking and Lighting Systems* and ASTM E 2072, *Standard Specification for Photoluminescent (Phosphorescent) Safety Markings*] *and* for signs (UL 924, *Standard for Safety Emergency Lighting and Power Equipment*).

PHYSICAL HAZARD. A chemical for which there is evidence that it is a *combustible liquid*, *cryogenic fluid*, *explosive*, flammable (solid, liquid or gas), organic peroxide (solid or liquid), oxidizer (solid or liquid), oxidizing gas, pyrophoric (solid, liquid or gas), unstable (reactive) material (solid, liquid or gas) or water-reactive material (solid or liquid).

❖ Materials posing a detonation or deflagration hazard, or materials that readily support combustion, are considered physical hazards. Structures containing materials posing a physical hazard exceeding maximum allowable quantities are classified in Group H-1, H-2 or H-3. Materials posing a physical hazard may also present a health hazard.

PHYSIOLOGICAL WARNING THRESHOLD. A concentration of airborne contaminants, normally expressed in parts per million (ppm) or milligrams per cubic meter (mg/m^3), that represents the concentration at which persons can sense the presence of the contaminant due to odor, irritation or other quick-acting physiological responses. When used in conjunction with the permissible exposure limit (PEL), the physiological warning threshold levels are those consistent with the classification system used to establish the PEL. See the definition of "Permissible exposure limit (PEL)."

❖ The term "physiological warning properties" is not defined. From a practical standpoint, the physiological warning properties are represented by a concentration of a contaminant that allows the average individual to sense its presence by sensory stimuli such as odor, throat irritation, coughing, eye irritation, running nose and similar signals.

There may be a wide variability reported for some of the more common threshold levels including that of olfactory perception. Variations that may be encountered are due to a number of factors including the methods used in their determination, the population exposed and others. The requirements for gas detection established in the code are tied to the permissible exposure limit (PEL), and there are several methods for determining the PEL inherent in the definition of that term. This definition is intended to link the determination of the physiological warning threshold level to the data used to determine the PEL.

For example, the PEL as established by 29 CFR is primarily based on data developed by the American Conference of Governmental Industrial Hygienists (ACGIH) called threshold limit values (TLVs), as referenced in the definition of "Permissible exposure limit (PEL)." To substantiate the TLVs (PELs), the ACGIH publishes *Documentation of the Threshold Limit Values and Biological Exposure Indices* where the user is provided with data used in establishing those limits. The significant commercially available toxic and highly toxic gases with published TLVs are listed by ACGIH, and perception thresholds are provided. These warning properties are considered, as evidenced by the documentation where the TLV and hence the PEL is established. It is appropriate that the data used in the base documents be used as the basis for determining the threshold level where such data is available. The use of data from other sources may be used in the absence of data within the system used for the establishment of the PEL, but where such data has been considered in determining the PEL such data should take precedent.

By providing a definition for "Physiological warning threshold level" and guidance as to how it is to be applied, the code user is given guidance that carries out the intent of the provisions for gas detection that have been established in the code. See the commentary to Section 6004.2.2.10 for further discussion of gas detection.

PIER. A structure built over the water, supported by pillars or piles, and used as a landing place, pleasure pavilion or similar purpose.

❖ A pier extends from land over the water to facilitate the loading and unloading of marine vessels with both people and cargo. Many piers also have commercial operations located on them. Piers are typically longer than they are wide and may be constructed of concrete, wood or other combustible materials. When wood materials are used, they are usually heavily coated or pressure treated with preservatives. Exposure to weather will cause the wood materials to dry out and be susceptible to ignition. Wood piers, being elevated structures, will burn freely due to the configuration and amount of exposed material available to burn.

PLACE OF RELIGIOUS WORSHIP. See "Religious worship, place of."

[M] PLENUM. An enclosed portion of the building structure, other than an occupiable space being conditioned, that is designed to allow air movement and thereby serve as part of an air distribution system.

❖ A plenum is part of an air distribution system and is usually concealed within the building construction. Plenums can be used for supply, return, exhaust, relief and ventilation air. They can occur in ceiling, attic or under-floor spaces, in mechanical equipment rooms (air handler rooms) and in stud and joist cavities. The definition clarifies that plenums are uninhabitable, unoccupiable cavities and interstitial spaces only; an unoccupiable room or space is not a plenum (see the commentary to Section 602 of the IMC for restrictions on the use of plenums).

PLOSOPHORIC MATERIAL. Two or more unmixed, commercially manufactured, prepackaged chemical substances including oxidizers, flammable liquids or solids, or similar substances that are not independently classified as *explosives* but which, when mixed or combined, form an *explosive* that is intended for blasting.

❖ Plosophoric materials, or plosophors, also are known as two-component or binary explosives. When plosophoric materials are mixed or combined at the point of use, the procedures recommended by the manufacturer should be strictly enforced. Mixed or combined plosophoric materials must be transported, stored and used in the same manner as explosives.

PLYWOOD AND VENEER MILLS. Facilities where raw wood products are processed into finished wood products, including waferboard, oriented strandboard, fiberboard, composite wood panels and plywood.

❖ Veneer mills are unique because the milling is done with knives rather than saws. Veneer logs are often air dried for an extended period of time before processing.

PORTABLE OUTDOOR FIREPLACE. A portable, outdoor, solid-fuel-burning fireplace that may be constructed of steel, concrete, clay or other noncombustible material. A portable outdoor fireplace may be open in design, or may be equipped with a small hearth opening and a short chimney or chimney opening in the top.

❖ This definition describes a fairly recent innovation that has often been treated as open burning. These devices function similar to a masonry or factory-built indoor fireplace except that they are portable, solid fuel-burning fireplaces designed to provide ambience and warmth in outdoor settings. They come in many styles and designs, both open and enclosed. Some designs are constructed of steel with screening around the firebox while others are made of concrete or clay with a small hearth opening and are equipped with a short chimney or simply a chimney opening. Still others function as a fire pit on legs. The design will typically include a stand or legs to elevate the firebox above the surface upon which it is placed to provide clearance to combustible materials. Sections 307.4.3 and 307.5 of the code contain specific clearance and attendance requirements for these devices. See also the definitions of "Open burning" and "Recreational fire."

[BE] POWER-ASSISTED DOOR. Swinging door that opens by reduced pushing or pulling force on the door-operating hardware. The door closes automatically after the pushing or pulling force is released, and functions with decreased forces. See also "Low energy power-operated door" and "Power-operated door."

❖ There are basically three different types of doors that provide some type of power assistance for entry: low energy power-operated doors, power-assisted doors and power-operated doors. The power-assisted door is typically a side-swinging door that has the additional feature of powered assistance to move the door to the open position. Where a door has power assistance, the force or effort it takes to open the door while it is being pushed or pulled is reduced as long as a user maintains pressure on the hardware. Where the hardware is released, the door will move to the closed position. Power-assisted doors are typically used when a door is an unusual size or weight. The low-energy power-assisted door and power-assisted door both are operated by the user touching something; therefore, they both must comply with BMHA156.19.

POWERED INDUSTRIAL TRUCK. A forklift, tractor, platform lift truck or motorized hand truck powered by an electrical motor or internal combustion engine. Powered industrial trucks do not include farm vehicles or automotive vehicles for highway use.

❖ This kind of vehicle includes forklift trucks and other similar vehicles used to move stock in warehouses, industrial buildings, large retail spaces, storage yards and loading docks. These vehicles are not licensed for highway travel and do not include farm machinery.

[BE] POWER-OPERATED DOOR. Swinging, sliding, or folding door that opens automatically when approached by a pedestrian or opens automatically upon an action by a pedestrian. The door closes automatically and includes provisions such as presence sensors to prevent entrapment. See also "Low energy power-operated door" and "Power-assisted door."

❖ There are basically three different types of doors that provide some type of power assistance for entry: low energy power-operated doors, power-assisted doors and power-operated doors. The power-operated door can be a sliding, hinged or side-swinging door that operates automatically by either a motion sensor or sensor mat when someone approaches the door. Power-operated doors are most commonly installed at the busy entrances of commercial buildings. As a door with hands-free operation, the power-operated door must comply with BMHA156.10.

PRESSURE VESSEL. A closed vessel designed to operate at pressures above 15 psig (103 kPa).

❖ A pressure vessel used to contain hazardous materials must comply with the ASME *Boiler and Pressure Vessel Code* (BPVC), in accordance with Section 5003.2.1. Pressure vessels are constructed as cylindrical or spherical structures because such a design is safer, more economical, and it is easier to construct a vessel in these shapes to control axial and circumferential stresses. Pressure vessels can be constructed for either a horizontal (see Commentary Figure 202-P1) or vertical orientation (see Commentary Figure 202-P2). The design, construction and examination requirements for pressure vessels that are used for hazardous materials are contained in Section VIII, Division 1, of the BPVC, which sets forth requirements for unfired pressure vessels with design pressures up to 3,000 pounds per square inch gauge (psig) (20 685 kPa). For pressures over 3,000 psig (20 685 kPa), the alternative design rules in Division 2 or 3 of BPVC Section VIII must be applied. Pressure vessels are not listed by nationally recognized testing laboratories. Instead, when a pressure vessel is fabricated in accordance with the BPVC, the fabricator will employ an authorized inspector to perform examinations of the vessel to ensure it is constructed in accordance with the BPVC and the approved design drawings. The authorized inspector also verifies the proper materials of construction are selected, that welders have the appropriate certifications based on the welding methods used and that welds are performed in accordance with the approved welding procedures. The BPVC requires that all pressure vessels be equipped with a nameplate welded at a conspicuous location directly onto the shell of the vessel (or onto a welded bracket if the pressure vessel will be insulated) that demonstrates the vessel was constructed in accordance with the requirements of ASME. In addition to the pressure vessel's nameplate, ASME also requires that a Manufacturer's Data Report for Pressure Vessels (ASME Form U-1) be prepared by the manufacturer to document the construction of the vessel and its compliance with the applicable edition of the BPVC. It is quite common in the establishment of new construction processes to purchase and install used pressure vessels. Given the safety factors required by the BPVC, properly selected and maintained pressure vessels can easily perform for decades provided that they are operated within their design temperature and pressures, and are properly designed for external loads. Fire code officials should utilize the nameplate in conjunction with ASME Form U-1 to confirm that the installed vessel is constructed to the BPVC and use this documentation to demonstrate compliance with Section 5003.2.1. Pressure vessels that are not equipped with a nameplate should not be approved unless they are evaluated by a qualified engineer. In such instances, a technical report and opinion should be obtained in accordance with Section 104.7.2.

PRIMARY CONTAINMENT. The first level of containment, consisting of the inside portion of that container which comes into immediate contact on its inner surface with the material being contained.

❖ In most cases, this definition pertains to those components of tanks, portable tanks and containers that are the main mechanism for the containment of liquid (the basic walls of the tank, portable tank or container). The term "secondary containment" refers to the containment provided when the primary containment fails.

[BG] PRIVATE GARAGE. A building or portion of a building in which motor vehicles used by the owner or tenants of the building or buildings on the premises are stored or kept, without provisions for repairing or servicing such vehicles for profit.

❖ In Section 406 of the IBC, the code regulates two types of garages: private and public. Public garages are further separated into open or enclosed garages.

Commentary Figure 202-P1
INSULATED HORIZONTAL PRESSURE VESSEL

Commentary Figure 202-P2
VERTICAL PRESSURE VESSEL

Private garages are limited in size by Section 406.3 of the IBC and can be accessory to either residential or nonresidential uses. The definition is intended to help distinguish private garages from public garages. Carports are also addressed in Section 406.3 of the IBC.

PROCESS TRANSFER. The transfer of flammable or *combustible liquids* between tank vehicles or tank cars and process operations. Process operations may include containers, tanks, piping and equipment.

❖ The transfer of flammable or combustible liquids during any process operation may include the introduction of the flammable or combustible liquids into or within the process operation.

PROPELLANT. The liquefied or *compressed gas* in an aerosol container that expels the contents from an aerosol container when the valve is actuated. A propellant is considered flammable if it forms a flammable mixture with air, or if a flame is self-propagating in a mixture with air.

❖ The amount of flammable propellant content is important in properly classifying aerosol products, since it affects the overall chemical heat of combustion value. Common flammable propellants are hydrocarbons, such as butane, propane, isobutane or a combination of these.

PROXIMATE AUDIENCE. An audience closer to pyrotechnic devices than allowed by NFPA 1123.

❖ The separation distance of the pyrotechnic devices and the audience permitted by NFPA 1123 is in relationship to the shell size of the mortar. NFPA 1126 addresses the requirements for proximate audiences.

[B] PSYCHIATRIC HOSPITALS. See "Hospitals."

PUBLIC TRAFFIC ROUTE (PTR). Any public street, road, highway, navigable stream or passenger railroad that is used for through traffic by the general public.

❖ See the commentary to the definition of "Quantity-Distance (Q-D)."

[A] PUBLIC WAY. A street, alley or other parcel of land open to the outside air leading to a street, that has been deeded, dedicated or otherwise permanently appropriated to the public for public use and which has a clear width and height of not less than 10 feet (3048 mm).

❖ Public ways serve a variety of purposes in the code, including the determination of the allowable area of a building (see Section 506.2 of the IBC); the use as an open space for unlimited area buildings (see Section 507 of the IBC); the measurement of fire separation distance; as well as many provisions for the means of egress (Chapter 10).

[BE] PUBLIC-USE AREAS. Interior or exterior rooms or spaces that are made available to the general public.

❖ This term is utilized to describe all interior and exterior spaces or rooms that may be occupied by the general public for any amount of time. Spaces that are utilized by the general public may be located in facilities that are publicly or privately owned. Examples include the lobby in an office building, a high-school gymnasium with assembly seating, an open-air stadium, a multipurpose room, an exposition hall, a restaurant dining room, a health club, etc. (see also the commentaries to the definitions of "Common use" and "Employee work area").

PYROPHORIC. A chemical with an autoignition temperature in air, at or below a temperature of 130°F (54°C).

❖ The definition is derived from DOL 29 CFR Part 1910.1200. Pyrophoric materials, whether in a gas, liquid or solid form, are capable of spontaneous ignition at low temperatures. Pyrophoric materials, regardless of their physical state, may spontaneously ignite when exposed to air at normal or slightly elevated temperatures, even in small quantities. Many pyrophoric materials are also highly reactive with water. While even moist air may increase the possibility of ignition, the application of water may cause an explosive reaction (see commentary, Chapter 67).

PYROTECHNIC ARTICLE. A pyrotechnic device for use in the entertainment industry, which is not classified as fireworks.

❖ This definition refers to articles containing substances or a mixture of substances designed to produce heat, light, sound or smoke or a combination of such effects for theatrical purposes.

PYROTECHNIC COMPOSITION. A chemical mixture that produces visible light displays or sounds through a self-propagating, heat-releasing chemical reaction which is initiated by ignition.

❖ Pyrotechnic composition consists of those chemical components, including oxidizers, that cause fireworks to make noise or display light when ignited. The definition is derived from NFPA 1124, which is referenced in Section 5605.1. The amount of pyrotechnic composition is the determining factor in whether the storage area for consumer fireworks is classified as Group H-3. The pyrotechnic content of consumer fireworks is contained within a significant amount of packaging and nonexplosive materials used in their manufacture, which constitute the bulk of the weight of the fireworks devices. The term is used in the definitions of "Fireworks, 1.3G" and "Fireworks, 1.4G," and is the basis for establishing the allowable amounts in Table 5604.3.

PYROTECHNIC SPECIAL EFFECT. A visible or audible effect for entertainment created through the use of pyrotechnic materials and devices.

❖ Pyrotechnic special effects are widely used in motion-picture production to create all types of effects involving explosions, fires, light, smoke and sound concussions. The types of pyrotechnic materials used include flash powder, flash paper, gun cotton, black powder (gunpowder), smokeless powder, detonator explosives and many more. They are used in bullet hits (squibs), blank cartridges, flash pots, fuses, mortars, smoke pots, sparkle pots, etc.

The main problems of pyrotechnics include prematurely triggering the pyrotechnic effect; use of larger quantities or more dangerous materials than needed; causing a fire; lack of adequate fire-extinguishing capabilities; and, of course, inadequately trained and experienced pyrotechnic operators. As a result of these risks, all pyrotechnic special effects are regulated at the federal, state and local level.

PYROTECHNIC SPECIAL-EFFECT MATERIAL. A chemical mixture used in the entertainment industry to produce visible or audible effects by combustion, *deflagration* or *detonation*. Such a chemical mixture predominantly consists of solids capable of producing a controlled, self-sustaining and self-contained exothermic chemical reaction that results in heat, gas sound, light or a combination of these effects. The chemical reaction functions without external oxygen.

❖ Pyrotechnic special effects materials are Division 1.3 explosives. They will burn but not explode, unless confined. Examples are black powder and pellet powder, safety fuses, igniters, igniter cord, fuse lighters, Division 1.3 special fireworks and Division 1.3 composite solid propellants.

PYROTECHNICS. Controlled exothermic chemical reactions timed to create the effects of heat, hot gas, sound, dispersion of aerosols, emission of visible light or a combination of such effects to achieve the maximum effect from the least volume of pyrotechnic composition.

❖ This definition describes special devices that are used to create entertainment, exhibition, demonstration or simulation through the controlled use of flame, sounds, aerosols or other special effects before a proximate audience (see Section 5608 and NFPA 1126).

QUANTITY-DISTANCE (Q-D). The quantity of *explosive material* and separation distance relationships providing protection. These relationships are based on levels of risk considered acceptable for the stipulated exposures and are tabulated in the appropriate Q-D tables. The separation distances specified afford less than absolute safety:

Inhabited building distance (IBD). The minimum separation distance between an operating building or magazine containing *explosive materials* and an inhabited building or site boundary.

Intermagazine distance (IMD). The minimum separation distance between magazines.

Intraline distance (ILD) or Intraplant distance (IPD). The distance to be maintained between any two operating buildings on an *explosives* manufacturing site when at least one contains or is designed to contain *explosives*, or the distance between a magazine and an operating building.

❖ This definition (with subdefinitions) correlates with tables to be used for distance determination, and also with the terminology used by those engaged in the storage and manufacture of explosive materials as well as with the regulators of these materials, including the DOD. The term is also consistent with terminology used by the DOD and the IME. The terms will bring a consistent set of terminologies to the code.

The definition "Quantity-Distance (Q-D)" is the relationship between a quantity of explosive material and the minimum separation distances required. The use of Q-D relationships to establish building siting is fundamentally used in the planning and occupancy of buildings used to contain explosive materials. Section 5601.2.3 (permit restrictions) authorizes the fire code official to limit the quantity of explosives at any given location. The limitations on quantity are typically derived based on the location of the explosives. The distances required vary depending on the sensitivity of the receptor. Distances are generally greater where the public or those not engaged in the manufacturing process are involved.

The subelements of the definition include terms that typically appear on building and site plans used to confirm that the structure used to contain the explosive material (building or magazine) is properly located. Acronyms (e.g., IBD, ILD, IMD, etc.) are typically used to describe the distance used to separate the explosives from receptors such as inhabited buildings, public traffic or transportation routes (highways), other storage (magazines) and the like.

Notwithstanding the tabular distance established by the Q-D tables integral to the explosives industry, there are occasions where ancillary buildings that do not contain explosive materials must be constructed where such buildings will encroach on the building containing explosive materials. D_o is a fire separation distance, and not unlike that used by the IBC to determine the location of "detached buildings." As the buildings regulated by the Q-D tables are required to be detached, a minimum separation distance is established. This distance is noted in Tables 5601.8.1(1) through 5601.8.1(3), with 50 feet (15 240 mm) established as the minimum for buildings containing materials with mass fire and fire hazards, and 60 feet (18 288 mm) established as the minimum for buildings containing materials with mass explosion hazards. From a practical standpoint, the D_o distances will apply only to facilities where the explosive quantities are near the minimums as the distances are increased rapidly with increases in material content.

The term "intraline" is used in this chapter in the definition of "Operating, building," and in Note a to Table 5605.3. The term "intraline distance (ILD)" (intra = within the line) is used synonymously with intraplant distance (IPD), although there are differences applied on military sites for the purpose of separating different operating lines. For example, on military sites, it is common to separate one operating line from another by the inhabited building distance. On the other hand, on commercial sites, it is common to produce multiple product lines within an associated building group and to separate the various buildings within the group by IPD. By equating the terms "IPD" and "ILD," commercial uses are provided with a level of protection that is designed to address building safety that is not product specific, but is designed to address the explosive nature of materials involved.

The term "intraplant" is used in the title of Section 5605.3, Table 5605.3 and in the definition of "Operating building." It is a unique term, and as such requires the supporting definition included here.

RAILWAY. A steam, electric or other railroad or railway that carriers passengers for hire.

❖ The definition of "Railway" is intended to minimize the exposure of passengers to danger if an explosion occurs involving an explosives magazine.

[BE] RAMP. A walking surface that has a running slope steeper than one unit vertical in 20 units horizontal (5-percent slope).

❖ This definition is needed to determine the threshold at which the ramp requirements apply to a walking surface. Walking surfaces steeper than specified in the definition are subject to the ramp requirements in Sections 1012 and 1029.

RAMP, EXIT ACCESS. See "Exit access ramp."

RAMP, EXTERIOR EXIT. See "Exterior exit ramp."

RAMP, INTERIOR EXIT. See "Interior exit ramp."

RAW PRODUCT. A mixture of natural materials such as tree, brush trimmings, or waste logs and stumps.

❖ This term relates to Section 2808 in terms of the storage and processing of such materials as they are associated with yard waste, agro-industrial and recycling facilities versus similar products associated with lumber production facilities. Raw product can be a combination of materials as noted in the definition. The focus of Section 2808 is on managing the storage sites to reduce fire ignition and fire size and providing the necessary access to fire fighters to fight a fire. See the commentary to Section 2808.

[M] READY ACCESS (TO). That which enables a device, appliance or equipment to be directly reached, without requiring the removal or movement of any panel, door or similar obstruction [see "Access (to)"].

❖ Ready access can be described as the capability of being quickly reached or approached for the purpose of operation, inspection, observation or emergency action. Ready access means that nothing must be moved or removed (such as doors or panels), that there are no physical obstructions and that there is no change in elevation to reach the required location. This definition does not view an ingress/egress door as an obstruction.

READY BOX. A weather-resistant container with a self-closing or automatic-closing cover that protects fireworks shells from burning debris. Tarpaulins shall not be considered as ready boxes.

❖ After delivery and prior to the display, shells must be separated according to size and their designation as salutes. Any display fireworks that will be temporarily stored at the display site during the fireworks display must be stored in ready boxes separated according to size and their designation as salutes.

[A] RECORD DRAWINGS. Drawings ("as builts") that document the location of all devices, appliances, wiring, sequences, wiring methods and connections of the components of a fire alarm system as installed.

❖ To verify that the system has been installed to comply with the code and applicable referenced standards, complete as-built drawings of the fire alarm system must be available on site for review.

RECREATIONAL FIRE. An outdoor fire burning materials other than rubbish where the fuel being burned is not contained in an incinerator, outdoor fireplace, portable outdoor fireplace, barbeque grill or barbeque pit and has a total fuel area of 3 feet (914 mm) or less in diameter and 2 feet (610 mm) or less in height for pleasure, religious, ceremonial, cooking, warmth or similar purposes.

❖ This kind of fire includes ordinary campfires and other small fires used for the activities listed. The definition has also been revised to clarify that the use of portable outdoor fireplaces (also known as patio fireplaces) is specifically included thus eliminating the confusion that previously existed as to how to treat those devices. See also the definition of "Open burning."

REDUCED FLOW VALVE. A valve equipped with a restricted flow orifice and inserted into a *compressed gas* cylinder, portable tank or stationary tank that is designed to reduce the maximum flow from the valve under full-flow conditions. The maximum flow rate from the valve is determined with the valve allowed to flow to atmosphere with no other piping or fittings attached.

❖ This is a valve that allows the maximum flow rate from a container to be reduced. For the reduction to be accurate, the maximum flow rate of a container must be known. The maximum flow rate must be determined without any piping or fittings attached to the container. This ensures that the reduction valve can actually achieve what is intended.

REFINERY. A plant in which flammable or *combustible liquids* are produced on a commercial scale from crude petroleum, natural gasoline or other hydrocarbon sources.

❖ A refinery is the facility that produces flammable or combustible liquids from raw materials.

REFRIGERANT. The fluid used for heat transfer in a refrigeration system; the refrigerant absorbs heat and transfers it at a higher temperature and a higher pressure, usually with a change of state.

❖ The refrigerant is the working fluid in refrigeration and air-conditioning systems. In vapor refrigeration cycles, refrigerants absorb heat from the load side at the evaporator and reject heat at the condenser. Aside from having suitable thermodynamic properties, the selection of a refrigerant must also take into consideration chemical stability, flammability, toxicity and environmental compatibility. Refrigeration is a result of the physical laws of vaporization (evaporation) of liquids. Basically, evaporation of liquid refrigerant is an endothermic process and condensing of vapors is an exothermic process.

[M] REFRIGERATING (REFRIGERATION) SYSTEM. A combination of interconnected refrigerant-containing parts constituting one closed refrigerant circuit in which a refrigerant is circulated for the purpose of extracting heat.

❖ Such systems include, at minimum, a pressure-imposing element or generator, an evaporator, a condenser and interconnecting piping. A single piece of equipment can contain multiple refrigeration systems (circuits).

[A] REGISTERED DESIGN PROFESSIONAL. An architect or engineer, registered or licensed to practice professional architecture or engineering, as defined by the statutory requirements of the professional registration laws of the state in which the project is to be constructed.

❖ This term is used throughout the code where a special level of expertise and knowledge is required. The definition clearly notes that each state defines its own professional registration laws. Legal qualifications for engineers and architects are established by the state having jurisdiction. Licensing and registration of engineers and architects are accomplished by written or oral examinations offered by states or by reciprocity (licensing in other states).

[BG] RELIGIOUS WORSHIP, PLACE OF. A building or portion thereof intended for the performance of religious services.

❖ This term has been added to the code for the purpose of making the code more broadly applicable to the worship facilities of all religions. Major religions for the world include Christianity, Islam, Hinduism, Buddhism and Judaism, which use different terms to describe the main space used for religious services. The intent in the code is for the same application for all similar types of religious facilities. The term also makes it clear that it defines the room or sanctuary for the performance of religious worship services and not retreat complexes, rectories, convents and classroom or office areas.

REMOTE EMERGENCY SHUTOFF DEVICE. The combination of an operator-carried signaling device and a mechanism on the tank vehicle. Activation of the remote emergency shutoff device sends a signal to the tanker-mounted mechanism and causes fuel flow to cease.

❖ This definition describes an important safety device used in the mobile fueling operation regulated by Section 5706.5.4.5 and describes a portable device that a tank vehicle driver may use to prevent an overfill spill during mobile fueling when the driver is out of immediate reach of the tanker shutoff controls (see commentary, Section 5706.5.4.5).

REMOTE SOLVENT RESERVOIR. A liquid solvent container enclosed against evaporative losses to the atmosphere during periods when the container is not being utilized, except for a solvent return opening not larger than 16 square inches (10 322 mm^2). Such return allows pump-cycled used solvent to drain back into the reservoir from a separate solvent sink or work area.

❖ A remote solvent reservoir is the storage of flammable or combustible liquid in a container that is not in the same control area as the machine using the flammable or combustible liquid. The remote solvent reservoir is connected to the machine by piping or tubing.

REMOTELY LOCATED, MANUALLY ACTIVATED SHUTDOWN CONTROL. A control system that is designed to initiate shutdown of the flow of gases or liquids that is manually activated from a point located some distance from the delivery system.

❖ See the commentaries to the definitions for "Emergency shutoff valves."

REPAIR GARAGE. A building, structure or portion thereof used for servicing or repairing motor vehicles.

❖ A repair garage may or may not be part of a motor fuel-dispensing facility. The fuel-dispensing area will comply with the motor fuel-dispensing facility sections of Chapter 23 and the repair garage area will comply with the repair garage section (see Section 2311). A marine pleasure craft dealership with a boat repair area will be classified as a repair garage. Motor vehicle repair garages are classified in occupancy Group S-1 by the IBC and are specifically addressed in Section 406.8 of the IBC.

RESIN APPLICATION AREA. An area where reinforced plastics are used to manufacture products by hand lay-up or spray-fabrication methods.

❖ Glass fiber is used for reinforcement of plastics or polymers, and the resulting products are typically called glass fiber reinforced plastics or polymers (GFRP). It is common to use the acronym FRP (fiber reinforced polymers), which is applicable to all fiber-reinforced plastics or polymers.

RESPONSIBLE PERSON. A person trained in the safety and fire safety considerations concerned with hot work. Responsible for reviewing the sites prior to issuing permits as part of the hot work permit program and following up as the job progresses.

❖ This is the person designated to administer the hot work program (see that term's definition in this section) in Section 3503. Without this definition, the term "responsible person" is a vague descriptor. The definition includes the scope of responsibilities for this person.

RETAIL DISPLAY AREA. The area of a Group M occupancy open for the purpose of viewing or purchasing merchandise offered for sale. Individuals in such establishments are free to circulate among the items offered for sale which are typically displayed on shelves, racks or the floor.

❖ Products containing aerosol propellants range from hair spray to paint to pesticides, lubricants and adhesives. Most often, products of this kind are grouped on shelves, but may also be set out in aisle displays of stacked cartons with the top carton being "display cut" to show the product. A display cut carton, according to Section 3.3.26.2 of NFPA 30B, is a type of packaging in which the top and portions of the sides and front of the carton are removed to expose the product to the consumer.

ROLL COATING. The process of coating, spreading and impregnating fabrics, paper or other materials as they are passed directly through a tank or trough containing flammable or *combustible liquids*, or over the surface of a roller revolving partially submerged in a flammable or *combustible liquid.*

❖ Roll-coating methods apply material to flat work pieces, usually paper, cardboard, cloth or thin metals, using liquid-coated cylinders or rollers. Coating material may be applied to the rollers by rotating them in an open trough or pan or applying liquid to the space between two rollers. Please note that for this term to apply anywhere in the code, the tank or trough must contain flammable or combustible liquids.

The requirements in this chapter are for protection against, and mitigation in case of, a fire. In this case, the flammable vapors are typically heavier than air and may travel and spread a long distance unnoticed before reaching a potential ignition source and causing a vapor explosion or fire. In case of a fire within the tank or trough, there are additional concerns. The liquids are typically not water miscible and may overflow when the sprinkler system is activated or during the manual fire-fighting stages. This could spread the fire and liquids even farther.

RUBBISH (TRASH). Combustible and noncombustible waste materials, including residue from the burning of coal, wood, coke or other combustible material, paper, rags, cartons, tin cans, metals, mineral matter, glass crockery, dust and discarded refrigerators, and heating, cooking or incinerator-type appliances.

❖ The term "rubbish" is normally associated with combustible waste. In this code the term is much broader and would include noncombustible waste, such as metals. Generally, the scope of this definition includes anything that has been discarded.

SAFETY CAN. An *approved* container of not more than 5-gallon (19 L) capacity having a spring-closing lid and spout cover so designed that it will relieve internal pressure when subjected to fire exposure.

❖ Safety cans are commonly used where limited quantities of flammable and combustible liquids are required for manufacturing or research. The basic purpose of a safety can is to provide a safe and convenient means of transporting, dispensing and storing up to 5 gallons (19 L) of flammable and combustible liquids. All listed safety cans, regardless of material of construction, are required to be constructed as leak-tight containers. They must automatically vent any vapor if subjected to fire exposure at a pressure of 3 to 5 psig (20 685 to 34 475 kPa gauge) to prevent the container from being subjected to a deflagration resulting from the increased vapor pressure of the liquid. Openings on safety cans must close automatically after being filled or dispensing a liquid. Finally, all listed safety cans must be designed so that a two-dimensional fire that could occur during dispensing cannot reach the pour opening and potentially extend into the safety can. This is commonly prevented by installing a flame arrestor in the container's inlet and outlet openings.

UL (Underwriters Laboratories) lists safety cans using UL 30 for metallic cans and UL 1313 for nonmetallic cans. Factory Mutual (FM) Global also issues listings and approvals for metallic and nonmetallic safety cans. UL and FM both limit the volume of metallic safety cans to 5 gallons (19 L) or less—nonmetallic safety cans are permitted to have a volume of 6.6 gallons (25 L). UL assigns a designation to safety cans based on the number of openings at the top of the container and container appurtenances. A Type I safety can, as shown in Commentary Figure 202-S1, is commonly a single-spout can designed for filling containers or tanks with large receiving openings. A Type II safety can, as shown in Commentary Figure 202-S2, has an integral flexible dispensing hose to control the transfer of the liquid. These safety cans have a second opening that serves as a pressure-vacuum vent, which is also used to fill the safety can with liquid. Also see the commentary to Table 5003.1.1(1) and Section 5003.9.10.

SAFETY DATA SHEET (SDS). Information concerning a hazardous material which is prepared in accordance with the provisions of DOL 29 CFR Part 1910.1200 or in accordance

Commentary Figure 202-S1
TYPE I SAFETY CAN
Photo courtesy of
Justrite Manufacturing Co., LLC, Des Plaines, IL

Commentary Figure 202-S2
TYPE II SAFETY CAN
Photo courtesy of
Justrite Manufacturing Co., LLC, Des Plaines, IL

with the provisions of a federally approved state OSHA plan. A document titled as a Material Safety Data Sheet (MSDS) is equivalent to an SDS for the purposes of this code.

❖ To comply with right-to-know legislation, building owners are required to provide or prepare an SDS for all hazardous materials that may be on the premises. The SDS is the single best source of information in dealing with the requirements of the IBC and the code. Note that Safety Data Sheets were previously known as Material Safety Data Sheets.

[BE] SCISSOR STAIRWAY. Two interlocking *stairways* providing two separate paths of egress located within one *exit* enclosure.

❖ A scissor or interlocking stairway is sometimes used in high-rise buildings or to increase exit capacity of a stairwell enclosure. In this configuration, two independent stairway paths are located within the same exit enclosure and may or may not be visually open to one another. Where interlocking stairways are separated from each other with compliant fire barriers and horizontal assemblies, they are not considered scissor stairways (see Section 1007.1.1 and Section 403.5.2 of the IBC.

SECONDARY CONTAINMENT. That level of containment that is external to and separate from primary containment.

❖ If a spill or leak from the primary means of containment occurs, an additional level of containment may be necessary to isolate the hazardous materials from adjoining areas or the environment.

SEED COTTON. See "Cotton."

SEGREGATED. Storage in the same room or inside area, but physically separated by distance from *incompatible materials*.

❖ The mixture of two or more chemicals can create a toxic or explosive chemical that is more dangerous than any of the individual chemicals. When chemicals are stored in the same room or storage area it is important to segregate them either by distance or by curbs that will prevent the chemicals from mixing in the case of a discharge.

[BF] SELF-CLOSING. As applied to a fire door or other opening, means equipped with an *approved* device that will ensure closing after having been opened.

❖ A self-closing opening protective refers to a fire or smoke door assembly equipped with a listed closer for doors that must be maintained in the normally closed position. When the door is opened and released, the self-closing feature returns the door to the closed position. It is important to distinguish between the terms "self-closing" and "automatic closing" because they are not interchangeable. "Automatic closing" refers to an opening protective that is normally in the open position (see Section 716.2.6.4 of the IBC). Opening protectives with automatic closers are often held open and then returned to the closed position upon activation of fire detectors or smoke detectors or loss of power, which automatically releases the hold-open device allowing the door to close.

[BE] SELF-LUMINOUS. Illuminated by a self-contained power source, other than batteries, and operated independently of external power sources.

❖ Self-luminous products do not need an outside light source to charge them like photoluminescent materials do. Products utilized to meet the requirements for luminous egress path markings in high-rise buildings (see Section 403.5.5 of the IBC and Section 1025) or exit signs (see Section 1013.5) may be photoluminescent or self-luminous. A variety of materials can comply with the referenced standards, for egress path markings—UL 1994 and ASTM E2072—and for signs—UL 924.

SELF-PRESERVATION, INCAPABLE OF. See "Incapable of self-preservation."

SELF-SERVICE MOTOR FUEL-DISPENSING FACILITY. That portion of motor fuel-dispensing facility where liquid motor fuels are dispensed from fixed *approved* dispensing equipment into the fuel tanks of motor vehicles by persons other than a motor fuel-dispensing facility attendant.

❖ A self-service motor fuel-dispensing facility may be attended or, with the approval of the fire code official, unattended. A self-service motor fuel-dispensing facility is a facility where the fuel is dispensed by someone other than an employee of the facility operator. Motor fuel-dispensing facilities are classified in occupancy Group M by the IBC.

SEMICONDUCTOR FABRICATION FACILITY. A building or a portion of a building in which electrical circuits or devices are created on solid crystalline substances having electrical conductivity greater than insulators but less than conductors. These circuits or devices are commonly known as semiconductors.

❖ A semiconductor fabrication facility is a building or a portion of a building where semiconductors are produced. See Commentary Figure 202-S3 for an example of a typical floor plan of a semiconductor fabrication facility.

SERVICE CORRIDOR. A fully enclosed passage used for transporting HPM and purposes other than required *means of egress.*

❖ Though HPM facility occupants may be exposed to limited HPM quantities during the course of their employment, their means of egress are protected from the HPM hazards by confining the HPM being transferred to its own passageway. A service corridor is required only where the HPM must be carried from a storage room or external area to a fabrication area through a passageway.

SHELF STORAGE. Storage on shelves less than 30 inches (762 mm) deep with the distance between shelves not exceeding 3 feet (914 mm) vertically. For other shelving arrangements, see the requirements for rack storage.

❖ To be considered shelf storage, the shelving must be not deeper than 30 inches (762 mm) and must be separated by not more than 3 feet (914 mm) vertically. Further, shelf storage units must be separated horizontally by aisles not less than 30 inches (762 mm) wide to reduce the transfer of fire from one shelf unit across the aisle to another. The aisles also allow convenient access for fire department personnel to combat a fire and for salvage and debris removal after an incident.

SINGLE-STATION SMOKE ALARM. An assembly incorporating the detector, the control equipment and the alarm-sounding device in one unit, operated from a power

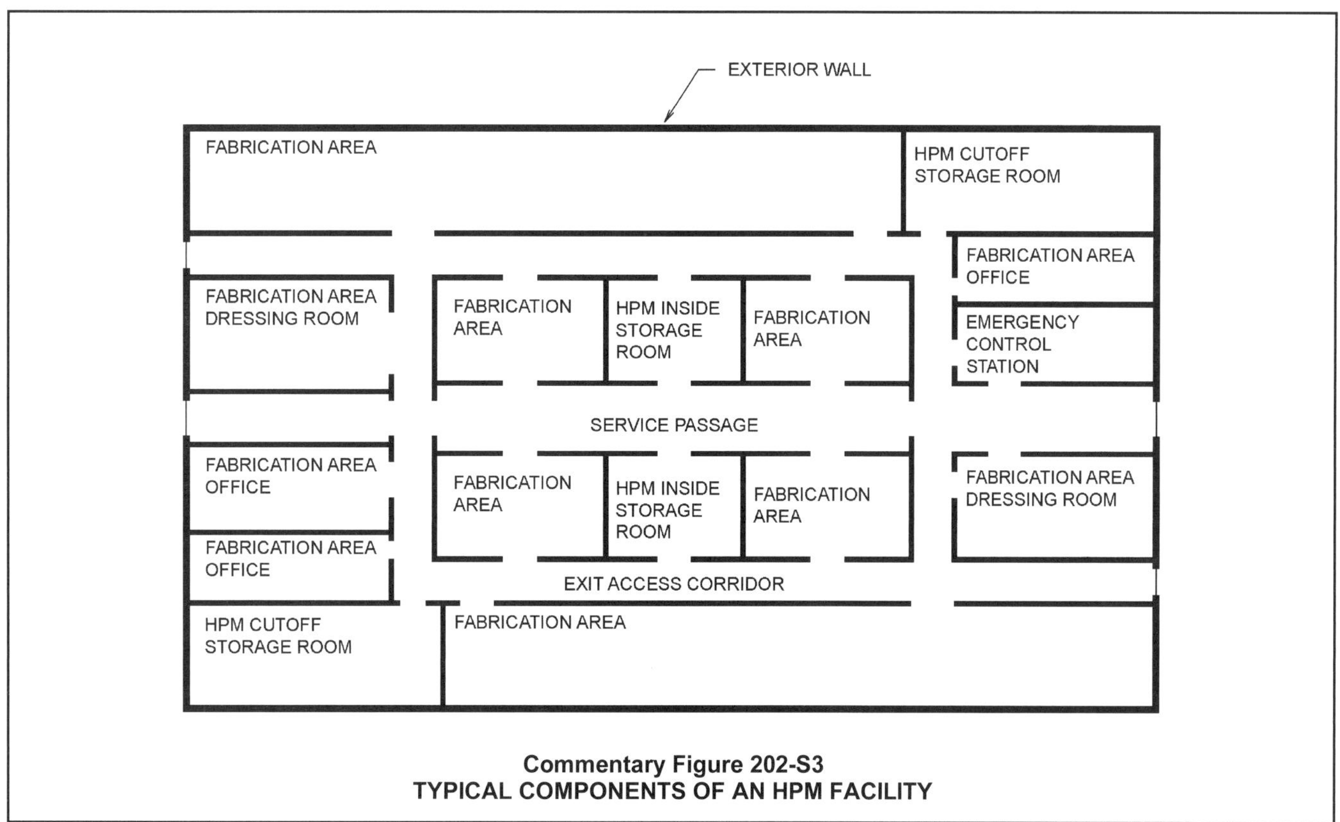

Commentary Figure 202-S3
TYPICAL COMPONENTS OF AN HPM FACILITY

supply either in the unit or obtained at the point of installation.

❖ A single-station smoke alarm is a self-contained alarm device that detects visible or invisible particles of combustion. Its function is to detect a fire in the immediate area of the detector location. Single-station smoke alarms are individual units with the capability to stand alone. Where the single-station smoke alarms are interconnected with other single-station devices they would be considered a multiple-station smoke alarm system. Single-station smoke alarms are not capable of notifying or controlling any other fire protection equipment or systems. They may be battery powered, directly connected to the building power supply or a combination of both. Single-station smoke alarms must be built to comply with UL 217 and are to be installed as required by Section 907.2.10.

[BG] SITE. A parcel of land bounded by a *lot line* or a designated portion of a public right-of-way.

❖ This definition establishes, for application of code requirements, the property within the boundaries of the site that is under the control of the owner. The owner can be held responsible for code compliance of the site and all facilities on it. Note that legal property lines do not always constitute site boundaries (i.e., malls, condominiums, townhouses). A site could contain multiple legal "lot" divisions.

[BG] SITE-FABRICATED STRETCH SYSTEM. A system, fabricated on site and intended for acoustical, tackable or aesthetic purposes, that is composed of three elements:

1. A frame constructed of plastic, wood, metal or other material used to hold fabric in place.
2. A core material (infill, with the correct properties for the application).
3. An outside layer, comprised of a textile, fabric or vinyl, that is stretched taut and held in place by tension or mechanical fasteners via the frame.

❖ Site-fabricated stretch systems are interior finish materials that are pulled taut across walls or ceilings with a frame that holds a fabric and core. These systems are now being used extensively because they can stretch to cover decorative walls and ceilings with unusual looks and shapes. The systems consist of three parts: a fabric (or vinyl), a frame and an infill core material. This type of product is not exclusive to any particular manufacturer. It is important to point out that these materials are not curtains or drapes because they are not free hanging like curtains. See the commentary to Section 803.10.

SKY LANTERN. An unmanned device with a fuel source that incorporates an open flame in order to make the device airborne.

❖ This definition coordinates with Section 308.1.6.3, which prohibits the use of sky lanterns. This definition simply clarifies what is considered a sky lantern. Sky lanterns have the potential to start structure fires and wildfires. The two aspects of sky lanterns that are cause for concern are the open flame and that they freely float in the air without the ability for control from the ground. Typically they are also made of combustible materials such as paper.

[BG] SLEEPING UNIT. A single unit providing rooms or spaces for one or more persons that includes permanent provisions for sleeping and can include provisions for living, eating and either sanitation or kitchen facilities but not both. Such rooms and spaces that are also part of a dwelling unit are not sleeping units.

❖ This definition is included to coordinate the Fair Housing Act Guidelines with the code. The definition for "Sleeping unit" clarifies the differences between sleeping units and dwelling units. In addition, using the term "sleeping unit" for spaces where people sleep will replace a multitude of other terms (i.e., patient room, cell, guest room) so that there is consistent application across occupancies. Some examples of sleeping units are hotel guestrooms; bedrooms in different types of congregate living facilities; patient sleeping rooms in hospitals, nursing homes or assisted living facilities; or housing cells in a jail. Another example would be a studio apartment with a kitchenette (i.e., countertop microwave, sink, refrigerator). Since the cooking arrangements are not the traditional permanent appliances (i.e., a range), this configuration would be considered a sleeping unit, and not a dwelling unit. As defined in the code, a dwelling unit must contain permanent facilities for living, sleeping, eating, cooking and sanitation.

The current trend in college dormitory configuration consists of two, three or four bedrooms with one or two single-occupant bathrooms and a shared living space. These facilities are considered a sleeping unit. Only where there are full cooking and eating facilities (i.e., kitchen with a range) within the unit, is the unit considered a dwelling unit. The two-, three- or four-bedroom units operate similarly to an apartment. Because this group of rooms meets the definition of "Sleeping unit," the bedrooms are not required to be separated by fire partitions from the associated living room or bathrooms. The provisions of Chapter 7 of the IBC, which detail the separation of dwelling or sleeping units, does allow for this group of rooms to be separated from adjacent groups and the corridors. This also clarifies that only the main corridors have fire alarms, and smoke alarms can be within the unit. Prior to the 2018 code, the definition was not clear as to whether the living and sanitation facilities were considered part of the unit or an extension of the main corridor. Due to how universities administer dormitory assignments, the accessibility provisions in Section 1107 of the IBC specify that bedrooms within sleeping units are counted separately for the purpose of determining the number of Accessible bedrooms required.

The current definition for "Sleeping unit" does not set a limit on the number of occupants in a sleeping unit. However, for consistency with the application of provisions in Groups I-1, I-2, R-1 and R-2, and where similar facilities are permitted to comply with R-3 provisions (i.e., 16 occupants for nontransient R-2, 10 occupants for transient R-1, 5 occupants for Groups I-1 and I-2), there is an implied transition on where these units are considered operating as a single unit rather than separate units with shared spaces.

Care suites, as addressed for Group I-2 in Section 407.4.4 of the IBC, would typically include several sleeping units. Care suites should not be confused with similar layouts in other parts of the hospital or within other occupancies that may be referred to as a "suite."

SMALL ARMS AMMUNITION. A shotgun, rifle or pistol cartridge and any cartridge for propellant-actuated devices. This definition does not include military ammunition containing bursting charges or incendiary, trace, spotting or pyrotechnic projectiles.

❖ Small arms ammunition consists of cylindrical casings containing a small amount of smokeless powder. These items are usually designed to propel a missile or bullet at a target, but they may also be used in explosive actuated devices, such as nail guns and riveters. Individual cartridges are typically packed in paperboard boxes shipped in cardboard cartons. In a fire, these articles pose no mass detonation hazard and only a moderate (low-velocity) projectile hazard. The ATF definition of "Ammunition" also includes percussion caps and $^{3}/_{32}$-inch (2.4 mm) and other external burning pyrotechnic hobby fuses. Black powder ammunition and black powder are not included in this definition.

SMALL ARMS PRIMERS. Small percussion-sensitive *explosive* charges, encased in a cap, used to ignite propellant powder.

❖ "Small arm primers" and "percussion caps" mean primers used for small arms ammunition.

SMOKE ALARM. A single- or multiple-station alarm responsive to smoke. See also "Single-station smoke alarm" and "Multiple-station smoke alarm."

❖ This is a general term that applies to both single- and multiple-station smoke alarms that are not part of an automatic fire detection system. It is the generic term for any device that both detects the products of combustion and initiates an alarm signal for occupant notification.

[BF] SMOKE BARRIER. A continuous membrane, either vertical or horizontal, such as a wall, floor, or ceiling assembly, that is designed and constructed to restrict the movement of smoke.

❖ A smoke barrier is a fire-resistance-rated assembly that is different from a fire partition, fire barrier or fire wall. Smoke barriers include walls and floor/ceiling assemblies that are constructed with a 1-hour fire-resistance rating and are one of the components in a smoke compartment. In Group I-2 and I-3 occupancies, smoke barriers are intended to create adjacent smoke compartments to which building occupants can be safely and promptly relocated during a fire, thus preventing the need to have complete and immediate egress from the building. For these occupancies, complete egress from the building would not be practical in most cases, due to restrictions on the mobility of the occupants. To maintain tenability in the adjacent smoke compartment, the smoke barrier is therefore intended to resist the spread of fire and hinder the movement of smoke. Smoke barriers are also used to compartment a building into separate smoke control zones where using the provisions of Section 909. The construction requirements for a smoke barrier provide resistance to the transmission of smoke.

[BG] SMOKE COMPARTMENT. A space within a building enclosed by *smoke barriers* on all sides, including the top and bottom.

❖ Smoke compartments create spaces that protect occupants from the products of combustion produced by a fire in an adjacent smoke compartment and to restrict smoke to the compartment of fire origin.

[BF] SMOKE DAMPER. A *listed* device installed in ducts and air transfer openings designed to resist the passage of smoke. The device is installed to operate automatically, controlled by a smoke detection system, and where required, is capable of being positioned from a *fire command center*.

❖ Similar to a fire damper, smoke dampers are intended to restrict the passage of smoke through ducts or openings in structural assemblies such as smoke barriers and corridor walls. They are also installed in smoke control systems. The smoke leakage rates of these devices are used to classify them in accordance with UL 555S. See also the commentaries to the definitions of "Damper" and "Fire damper."

SMOKE DETECTOR. A *listed* device that senses visible or invisible particles of combustion.

❖ These devices are considered early warning devices and have saved many people from smoke inhalation and burns. Smoke detectors have a wide range of uses, from sophisticated fire detection systems for industrial and commercial uses to residential. A smoke detector is a device, typically listed in accordance with UL 268, that activates a fire alarm system. These system smoke detectors contain only the components required to detect the products of combustion and activate a fire alarm system and are, therefore, different from single- and multiple-station smoke alarms.

Smoke detectors typically consist of two types: ionization and photoelectric. An ionization detector contains a small amount of radioactive material that ionizes the air in a sensing chamber and causes a current to flow through the air between two charged electrodes. When smoke enters the chamber, the particles cause a reduction in the current. When the level of conductance decreases to a preset level, the detector responds with an alarm.

A photoelectric smoke detector consists primarily of a light source, a light beam and a photosensitive device. When smoke particles enter the light beam, they reduce the light intensity in the photosensitive device. When obscuration reaches a preset level, the detector initiates an alarm.

SMOKE PARTITION. A wall assembly that extends from the top of the foundation or floor below to the underside of the floor or roof sheathing, deck or slab above or to the underside of the ceiling above where the ceiling membrane is constructed to limit the transfer of smoke.

❖ This term represents wall assemblies that are constructed in accordance with Section 710 of the IBC to resist the passage of smoke. Unless required elsewhere in the code, smoke partitions do not require a fire-resistance rating. An example of this would be where a smoke partition is also a corridor wall that requires a fire-resistance rating. In this case, the partition would need to meet all requirements applicable to smoke partitions and fire partitions.

[BG] SMOKE-DEVELOPED INDEX. A comparative measure, expressed as a dimensionless number, derived from measurements of smoke obscuration versus time for a material tested in accordance with ASTM E84.

❖ The ASTM E84 test method of measuring the density of smoke emitted from combustible materials determines the smoke-developed index. This value is only comparative and provides only a relative understanding of smoke generation potential. The smoke-developed index is sometimes abbreviated as SDI.

SMOKELESS PROPELLANTS. Solid propellants, commonly referred to as smokeless powders, used in small arms ammunition, cannons, rockets, propellant-actuated devices and similar articles.

❖ This term refers to a propellant explosive from which there is little or no smoke when fired, including smokeless powder for cannons and smokeless powder for small arms.

[BF] SMOKEPROOF ENCLOSURE. An *interior exit stairway* designed and constructed so that the movement of the products of combustion produced by a fire occurring in any part of the building into the enclosure is limited.

❖ A smokeproof enclosure is intended to provide an effective barrier to the entry of smoke into an exit stairway, thereby offering an additional level of protection for occupants of high-rise and underground structures.

[BE] SMOKE-PROTECTED ASSEMBLY SEATING. Seating served by means of egress that is not subject to smoke accumulation within or under a structure for a specified design time by means of passive design or by mechanical ventilation.

❖ An example of smoke-protected assembly seating is an indoor arena with a smoke control system. The intent is to separate this from open-air seating such as outdoor grandstands. The code has less stringent requirements for certain aspects of smoke-protected assembly seating and open-air seating than for seating that is not smoke protected, since occupants are subject to less hazard from the accumulation of smoke and fumes during a fire event. For example, an assembly dead-end aisle is permitted to be longer for a smoke-protected assembly area. For smoke control system requirements, see Section 909.

SOLID. A material that has a melting point and decomposes or sublimes at a temperature greater than 68°F (20°C).

❖ One of the three states of matter, solids must decompose (pyrolysis) before they can produce vapors that will support combustion. The surface area of a solid in relation to the heat source is a concern for fire fighters; the greater the surface being subjected to a heat source, the more rapid the pyrolysis.

SOLID BIOFUEL. Densified biomass made in the form of cubiform, polyhedral, polyhydric or cylindrical units, produced by compressing milled biomass.

❖ This definition coordinates with the definition of "Biomass" and the application of this term in Section 2809. Essentially, these materials need to be treated the same as materials such as finished lumber. The materials are compressed biomass materials. Section 2809.4 exempts the solid biofuel inside of buildings from the fencing requirements in the same way traditional lumber is exempted. Without these terms it makes it difficult to know how to regulate such materials.

SOLID BIOMASS FEEDSTOCK. The basic materials of which solid biofuel is composed, manufactured or made.

❖ This explains the types of materials that make up solid biofuel. This clarifies how the requirements of Section 2809 are to be applied. In addition, these materials need to be treated in accordance with Section 2808 prior to becoming a "solid biofuel." These materials are processed in agro-industrial facilities (see the definition for "Agro-industrial").

SOLID SHELVING. Shelving that is solid, slatted or of other construction located in racks and which obstructs sprinkler discharge down into the racks.

❖ Solid shelving generally consists of nominal wood (lumber), plywood, particleboard or metal shelves that span between the supports of the storage system to support the commodities. Solid shelving creates a condition where the rack storage system is effectively divided into areas by the shelving. The shelving can potentially act as a protective barrier for a fire and from fire service hose streams by preventing the penetration of water into the fire area. As a result, the sprinkler system design will require an in-rack sprinkler system, in addition to the ceiling sprinkler system for water distribution, to penetrate the shelving barriers.

SOLVENT DISTILLATION UNIT. An appliance that receives contaminated flammable or *combustible liquids* and which distills the contents to remove contaminants and recover the solvents.

❖ A solvent distillation unit recycles flammable and combustible liquids by the condensation and collection of the vapors that are produced as the mixture is heated. The solvent distillation unit processes waste solvents in a separate, stand-alone batch, on-line batch or continuous systems. The distillation units heat the waste solvent to its boiling point. This causes the solvent to evaporate and the solvent vapors are then condensed in a separate container. The basic components of a distillation unit are the process chamber or boiler, the encapsulated heaters, a water-cooled chamber and associated piping and instrumentation. Temperature sensors monitor the temperature and help maintain the required distillation temperature. Disposable vessel liners can be used for simple collection and disposal of still bottoms. Vacuum pumps that can distill high-boiling solvents at lower temperatures are also available. Solvent distillation units having a distillation chamber capacity of 60 gallons (227 L) or less are listed under UL 2208. Solvent distillation units having a distillation chamber capacity greater than 60 gallons (227 L) must comply with Section 5705.4.2.

SOLVENT OR LIQUID CLASSIFICATIONS. A method for classifying solvents or liquids according to the following classes:

Class I solvents. Liquids having a *flash point* below 100°F (38°C).

Class II solvents. Liquids having a *flash point* at or above 100°F (38°C) and below 140°F (60°C).

Class IIIA solvents. Liquids having a *flash point* at or above 140°F (60°C) and below 200°F (93°C).

Class IIIB solvents. Liquids having a *flash point* at or above 200°F (93°C).

Class IV solvents. Liquids classified as nonflammable.

❖ These dry cleaning solvent classifications parallel the flammable and combustible liquid classifications defined in Chapter 57, with a notable exception that, while flammable liquids (Class I) are divided into three subclasses (Class IA, IB and IC) based on flash point and boiling point, Class I solvents are not. Solvent classifications, on the other hand, include a classification (Class IV) for those solvents considered to be nonflammable, whereas the flammable and combustible liquid classifications have no comparable category.

SPECIAL AMUSEMENT BUILDING. A building that is temporary, permanent or mobile that contains a device or system that conveys passengers or provides a walkway along, around or over a course in any direction as a form of amusement arranged so that the egress path is not readily apparent due to visual or audio distractions or an intentionally confounded egress path, or is not readily available because of the mode of conveyance through the building or structure.

❖ Because of the nature of their use, these buildings contain special effects and other features that make it more difficult for occupants to determine when an emergency exists and where exits are located. The definition includes all such facilities, including portable and temporary structures. The hazard associated with such buildings is not related to the permanence or length of use; therefore, seasonal uses (such as "haunted houses" at Halloween) and portable uses (carnival attractions) are included if they meet the criteria in the definition. See also Section 411 of the IBC which regulates special amusement buildings.

[A] SPECIAL EXPERT. An individual who has demonstrated qualifications in a specific area, outside the practice of architecture or engineering, through education, training and experience.

❖ This term comes from the *International Code Council Performance Code*® (ICCPC®) and is focused on experts in fields such as hazardous materials, contents and process safety management, and fire protection design that is exempt in many jurisdictions from professional practice laws. These special experts may well be the most effective resource in these specialized areas, but since they are not officially recognized through licensing, they are not able to be part of projects where they have the most expertise. To impart some minimum discipline in the use of these experts, the code requires that such individuals or firms meet certain qualifications. The following is an excerpt from Appendix D of the ICCPC where the characteristics of a special expert are described.

Special experts are those individuals who possess the following qualifications:

1. Individual has credentials of education and experience in an area of practice that is needed to evaluate risks and safe operations associated with design, operations and special hazards.
2. Licensing or registration where required by a state or jurisdiction for the function to be performed. The use of this definition is specific to Chapter 38, Higher Education Laboratories.

SPECIAL INDUSTRIAL EXPLOSIVE DEVICE. An explosive power pack containing an *explosive* charge in the form of a cartridge or construction device. The term includes but is not limited to explosive rivets, explosive bolts, *explosive* charges for driving pins or studs, cartridges for *explosive*-actuated power tools and charges of *explosives* used in automotive air bag inflators, jet tapping of open hearth furnaces and jet perforation of oil well casings.

❖ Special industrial explosive devices are explosive-actuated power devices and propellant-actuated power devices. Examples of explosive-actuated power devices are jet tappers and jet perforators. "Propellant-actuated device" means a tool or special mechanized device or gas generator system that is actuated by a smokeless propellant or that releases and directs work through a smokeless propellant charge (also see commentary, Section 5601.1, Exception 6).

SPRAY BOOTH. A mechanically ventilated appliance of varying dimensions and construction provided to enclose or accommodate a spraying operation and to confine and limit the escape of spray vapor and residue and to exhaust it safely.

❖ Spray booths vary in construction, size and design. The definition is clear in that it can be a fully enclosed structure or it can be designed to contain the flammable or combustible vapors. An example of a fully enclosed structure is a spray booth where products are carried/carted into the booth for spraying operation and carted out once the operation is complete. This definition, however, also allows for what is typically described as "open-face booths," where the spray booth is enclosed on three sides and ventilated on the open side to confine the vapors to the spray booth area (see Commentary Figure 202-S4). An example of this is wood furniture finishing, where products such as wood tables are sprayed with stains and coating.

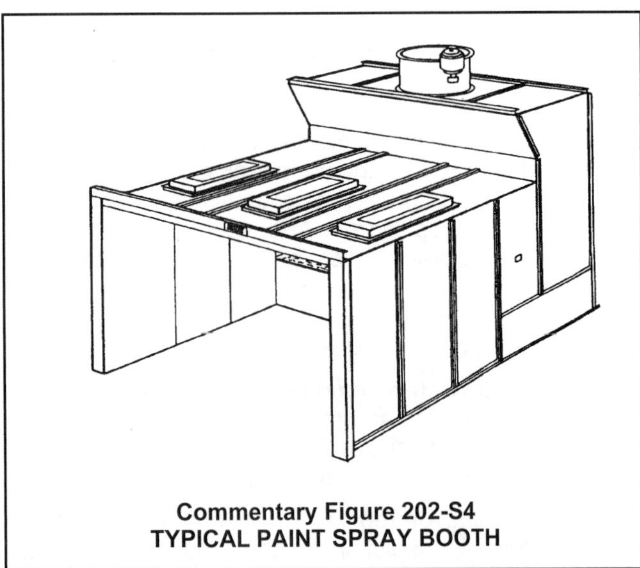

Commentary Figure 202-S4
TYPICAL PAINT SPRAY BOOTH

SPRAY ROOM. A room designed to accommodate spraying operations, constructed in accordance with the *International Building Code.*

❖ Where, because of size or for economic reasons, spray booths are insufficient, an entire room is dedicated to the spraying process. In many cases, the oversprayed flammable/combustible liquids are allowed to remain on the floor until cleaned. These rooms have specific ventilation requirements to prevent the accumulation of vapors at the floor. See the commentary to Section 2404.3.1 for further discussion of spray rooms.

SPRAYING SPACE. An area in which dangerous quantities of flammable vapors or combustible residues, dusts or deposits are present due to the operation of spraying processes. The *fire code official* is authorized to define the limits of the spraying space in any specific case.

❖ Spraying spaces generally occur in one or a combination of three forms. The least desirable form is open floor area spraying, where the spraying area consists of an entire floor of a building without isolating the spraying operation. A better form is the spray room, which isolates the spray operation by construction to less than an entire floor of the facility. The optimum form is a specially designed spray booth that isolates the operational hazards of spraying to an appropriately regulated space. Regardless of the form, all require special safeguards to address hazards, including adequate ventilation, fire suppression and management of overspray.

[BE] STAIR. A change in elevation, consisting of one or more risers.

❖ All steps, even a single step, are defined as a stair. This makes the stair requirements applicable to all steps unless specifically exempt in the code.

[BE] STAIRWAY. One or more *flights* of *stairs*, either exterior or interior, with the necessary landings and platforms connecting them, to form a continuous and uninterrupted passage from one level to another.

❖ It is important to note that this definition characterizes a stairway as connecting one level to another. The term "level" is not to be confused with "story." Steps that connect two levels, one of which is not considered a "story" of the structure, would be considered a stairway. For example, a set of steps between the basement level in an areaway and the outside ground level would be considered a stairway. A series of steps between the floor of a story and a mezzanine within that story would also be considered a stairway (see definitions for "Flight," "Interior exit stairway," "Stairway, exterior" and "Stairway, interior," and Sections 1011, 1019,1023 and 1027).

STAIRWAY, EXIT ACCESS. See "Exit access stairway."

STAIRWAY, EXTERIOR EXIT. See "Exterior exit stairway."

STAIRWAY, INTERIOR EXIT. See "Interior Exit Stairway."

STAIRWAY, SCISSOR. See "Scissor stairway."

[BE] STAIRWAY, SPIRAL. A *stairway* having a closed circular form in its plan view with uniform section-shaped treads attached to and radiating from a minimum-diameter supporting column.

❖ Spiral stairways are permitted as part of a means of egress in the limited circumstances given in Section 1011.10. Spiral staircases could be used for supplemental/convenience stairways in other locations. Spiral stairways are commonly used where a small number of occupants use the stairway and the floor space for the stair is very limited. Spiral stairways are typically supported by a center pole. Requirements are found with stairways in Section 1011.10.

STANDBY POWER SYSTEM. A source of automatic electric power of a required capacity and duration to operate required building, hazardous materials or ventilation systems in the event of a failure of the primary power. Standby power systems are required for electrical loads where interruption of the primary power could create hazards or hamper rescue or fire-fighting operations.

❖ This definition is intended to provide clarity for the fire code official as to exactly what systems are considered to be standby power systems and is consistent with definitions in NFPA 110 and NFPA 111. However, since the list of systems in the definition is not exhaustive, reference must be made to Section 1203 of the code, which provides the "where required" provisions. When the normal power supply to any of the indicated systems, or other systems designated by the code, fails, the standby power system is to provide a specified degree and duration of power to systems and equipment that are essential for life safety, such as elevators and platform lifts, emergency responder radio coverage and smoke control systems. See the commentary to Section 1203 for more detailed discussion on the difference between standby and emergency power.

STANDPIPE, TYPES OF. Standpipe types are as follows:

❖ A standpipe system is typically an arrangement of vertical piping located in exit stairways that allows fire-fighting personnel to connect hand-carried hoses at each level to manually extinguish fires. Section 905 and NFPA 14 recognize three different classes of standpipe systems. For a further discussion of standpipe classes and types, see the commentary to Section 905.3.1.

Automatic dry. A dry standpipe system, normally filled with pressurized air, that is arranged through the use of a device, such as a dry pipe valve, to admit water into the system piping automatically upon the opening of a hose valve. The water supply for an automatic dry standpipe system shall be capable of supplying the system demand.

❖ A typical automatic dry standpipe system has an automatic water supply retained by a dry pipe valve. The dry pipe valve clapper is kept in place by air placed in the standpipe system under pressure. Once a standpipe hose valve is opened, the air is released from the system, allowing water to fill the system through the dry pipe valve. This system is traditionally used in areas where the temperature falls below 40°F (4°C); where a wet system could freeze and possibly burst the pipe or simply not be available when needed.

Automatic wet. A wet standpipe system that has a water supply that is capable of supplying the system demand automatically.

❖ An automatic wet standpipe system is used in locations where the entire system would remain above 40°F (4°C). Because the system is pressurized with water, an immediate release of water occurs when a hose connection valve is opened. This is the most generally preferred type of standpipe but it is not necessarily the required type unless so stipulated.

Manual dry. A dry standpipe system that does not have a permanent water supply attached to the system. Manual dry standpipe systems require water from a fire department pumper to be pumped into the system through the fire department connection in order to supply the system demand.

❖ A manual dry standpipe system is filled with water only when the fire service is present. Typically, the fire service connects the discharge from a water source, such as a pumper truck, to the fire department connection of a manual dry standpipe system. When the fire service has suppressed the fire and is preparing to leave, the system is drained of the remaining water. Manual dry standpipe systems are commonly installed in open parking structures.

Manual wet. A wet standpipe system connected to a water supply for the purpose of maintaining water within the system but which does not have a water supply capable of delivering the system demand attached to the system. Manual wet standpipe systems require water from a fire department pumper (or the like) to be pumped into the system in order to supply the system demand.

❖ A manual wet standpipe system is connected to an automatic water supply, but the supply is not capable of providing the system demand. The manual wet system could be one that is connected with the sprinkler system such that it is capable of supplying the demand for the sprinkler system but not for the standpipe. The standpipe system demand is met when the fire service provides additional water through the fire department connection from the discharge of a water source, such as a pumper truck.

Semiautomatic dry. A dry standpipe system that is arranged through the use of a device, such as a deluge valve, to admit water into the system piping upon activation of a remote control device located at a hose connection. A remote control activation device shall be provided at each hose connection. The water supply for a semiautomatic dry standpipe system shall be capable of supplying the system demand.

❖ This type of dry standpipe is a special design that uses a solenoid-activated valve to retain the automatic water supply. Once the standpipe hose valve is opened, a signal is sent to the deluge valve retaining the automatic water supply to allow water to fill the system. This kind of system is used in areas where the temperature falls below 40°F (4°C), where a wet system would otherwise freeze. As such, there is no semiautomatic wet system type.

STANDPIPE SYSTEM, CLASSES OF. Standpipe system classes are as follows:

❖ A standpipe system is typically an arrangement of vertical piping located in exit stairways that allows fire-fighting personnel to connect hand-carried hoses at each level to manually extinguish fires. Section 905 and NFPA 14 recognize three different classes of standpipe systems. For a further discussion of standpipe classes and types, see the commentary to Section 905.3.1.

Class I system. A system providing $2^1/_2$-inch (64 mm) hose connections to supply water for use by fire departments and those trained in handling heavy fire streams.

❖ A Class I standpipe system is intended for use by trained fire service personnel as a readily available water source for manual fire-fighting operations. A Class I standpipe system is equipped with only $2^1/_2$-inch (64 mm) hose connections to allow the fire service to attach the appropriate hose and nozzles. A Class I standpipe system is not equipped with hose stations, which include a cabinet, hose and nozzle.

Class II system. A system providing $1^1/_2$-inch (38 mm) hose stations to supply water for use primarily by the building occupants or by the fire department during initial response.

❖ A Class II standpipe system is intended for use by building occupants or by the fire department for manual suppression. The hose stations defined in NFPA 14 as part of the Class II standpipe system include a hose rack, hose nozzle, hose and hose connection. The intent of providing the hose is for use by properly trained personnel. Occupant-use hose stations should only be provided where they can be used by people who have been properly trained in the use of the hose and nozzle.

Class III system. A system providing $1^1/_2$-inch (38 mm) hose stations to supply water for use by building occupants and $2^1/_2$-inch (64 mm) hose connections to supply a larger volume of water for use by fire departments and those trained in handling heavy fire streams.

❖ A Class III standpipe system is intended for use by building occupants as well as trained fire service personnel. The $1^1/_2$-inch (38 mm) hose station is for use by the building occupants or fire department for manual fire suppression and the $2^1/_2$-inch (64 mm) hose connection is intended for use primarily by fire service personnel or those who have received training in the use of the larger hoses. Class III systems allow the fire department to select the types of hose necessary based on the fire hazard present. Where a fire is effectively controlled by an automatic sprinkler system, the smaller hose size may be all that is necessary for fire department mop-up operations.

STATIC PILES. Piles in which processed wood product or solid biomass feedstock is mounded and is not being turned or moved.

❖ Static piles are long-term bulk storage piles that must be monitored for internal heat buildup. This term includes processed wood products but also addresses solid biomass feedstock. See the definition for "Solid biomass feedstock."

STATIONARY BATTERY ARRAY. An arrangement of individual stationary storage batteries in close proximity to each other, mounted on storage racks or in modules, battery cabinets or other enclosures.

❖ This definition clarifies the requirements in Section 1206.2 for stationary batteries. As a matter of controlling the risks, stationary batteries must be separated into arrays that do not exceed a certain capacity. The limit in Section 1206.2.8.3 is 50 kWh per array. This is seen as a reasonable number to reduce the risk of fire spread and fire size if the battery array should fail. Note that there are exceptions to the storage battery array size for lead acid or listed preengineering and prepackaged stationary batteries in Section 1206.2.

STEEL. Hot- or cold-rolled as defined by the *International Building Code*.

❖ This is a basic definition that clarifies that steel is either cold- or hot-rolled as defined by the IBC; however, the IBC does not specifically define cold- or hot-rolled steel but describes how it must be used.

STORAGE, HAZARDOUS MATERIALS. The keeping, retention or leaving of hazardous materials in closed containers, tanks, cylinders, or similar vessels; or vessels supplying operations through closed connections to the vessel.

❖ Storage of hazardous materials in a structure is governed either by the occupancy group that it is accessory to or by the hazard group that it is associated with. The determination of the occupancy class is based on the MAQs and the exceptions found in the IBC. This definition also clarifies what is considered storage and what is considered use. This may affect the occupancy classification as use creates more risk than storage and the MAQs tend to be more restrictive for use. See the definitions for "Open system" and "Closed system."

[BG] STORY. That portion of a building included between the upper surface of a floor and the upper surface of the floor or roof next above (see "Basement," "Building height," "Grade plane" and "Mezzanine"). A story is measured as the vertical distance from top to top of two successive tiers of beams or finished floor surfaces and, for the topmost story, from the top of the floor finish to the top of the ceiling joists or, where there is not a ceiling, to the top of the roof rafters.

❖ All levels in a building that conform to this description are stories, including basements. A mezzanine is considered part of the story in which it is located. See Chapter 5 of the IBC for code requirements regarding limitations on the number of stories in a building as a function of the type of construction.

[BG] STORY ABOVE GRADE PLANE. Any story having its finished floor surface entirely above grade plane, or in which the finished surface of the floor next above is:

1. More than 6 feet (1829 mm) above grade plane; or
2. More than 12 feet (3658 mm) above the finished ground level at any point.

❖ One determination of the allowed height of a building under Section 504 of the IBC is based on the number of stories above grade plane (see definitions of "Basement," "Building height" and "Grade plane"). The code establishes by this definition which stories of a building are those above grade plane. Clearly it includes those stories that are fully above grade plane. It also includes stories that may be partially below finished ground level, but the finished floor level is more than 6 feet (1829 mm) above grade plane. It also includes those floor levels that, due to an irregular terrain, have a finished floor level more than 12 feet (3658 mm) above finished ground level at any point surrounding the building. Any building level not qualifying as a story above grade plane is, by definition, a basement.

SUBORDINATE (FIRE PROTECTION AND LIFE SAFETY SYSTEM). A system that is activated by another fire protection or life safety system. For example, where a fire alarm system activates a smoke removal or elevator recall system, the smoke removal or elevator recall system is considered to be "subordinate" to the fire alarm system.

❖ This definition helps to describe what is being addressed in Section 901.6.2. Integrated testing is necessary where life safety systems need close coordination to work appropriately. Section 901.6.2 only requires this testing for high-rise buildings and smoke control systems. This particular definition describes a specific aspect of the life safety systems that are being inspected. This describes that it is not the initiation of the system that is considered subordinate but the system itself. In the case of a smoke control system, the smoke detector would be the initiating device and the system that actually removes the smoke would be considered the subordinate system. See also the commentary for the definition of "Integrated testing (fire protection and life safety system)."

SUPERVISING STATION. A facility that receives signals and at which personnel are in attendance at all times to respond to these signals.

❖ The supervising station is the location where all fire protection-system-related signals are sent and where trained personnel are present to respond to an emergency. The supervising station may be an approved central station, a remote supervising station, a proprietary supervising station or other constantly attended location approved by the fire code official. Each type of supervising station must comply with the applicable specific provisions described in NFPA 72.

SUPERVISORY SERVICE. The service required to monitor performance of guard tours and the operative condition of fixed suppression systems or other systems for the protection of life and property.

❖ The supervisory service is responsible for maintaining the integrity of the fire protection system by notifying the supervising station of a change in protection system status.

Guard tours are recognized as nonrequired (voluntary) systems. Where a guard tour is provided, the signals from that system can be transmitted through the supervisory service to the supervision station. Guard tours are not a required part of a fire alarm system.

SUPERVISORY SIGNAL. A signal indicating the need of action in connection with the supervision of guard tours, the fire suppression systems or equipment, or the maintenance features of related systems.

❖ Activation of a supervisory signal-initiating device transmits a signal indicating that a change in the status of the fire protection system has occurred and that action must be taken. These signals are the basis for the actions taken by the attendant at the supervising station. These signals do not indicate an emergency condition but indicate that a portion of the system is not functioning in the manner in which it should and that if the condition is not corrected it could impair the ability of the fire protection system to perform properly. A supervisory signal is also a part of the nonrequired guard tour system.

SUPERVISORY SIGNAL-INITIATING DEVICE. An initiating device such as a valve supervisory switch, water level indicator, or low-air pressure switch on a dry-pipe sprinkler system whose change of state signals an off-normal condition and its restoration to normal of a fire protection or life safety system; or a need for action in connection with guard tours, fire suppression systems or equipment, or maintenance features of related systems.

❖ The supervisory signal-initiating device detects a change in protection system status. Examples of a supervisory signal-initiating device include a flow switch to detect movement of water through the system and a tamper switch to detect when someone shuts off a water control valve.

SYSTEM. An assembly of equipment consisting of a tank, container or containers, appurtenances, pumps, compressors and connecting piping.

❖ As with tanks or containers, a system can be either open or closed. The difference between a closed system and an open system is whether the hazardous material involved in a process is exposed to the atmosphere. Materials in closed or open systems are assumed to be "in use" as opposed to "in storage."

Gases are always assumed to be in closed systems, since they would be immediately dispersed in an open system if exposed to the atmosphere without some means of containment.

TANK. A vessel containing more than 60 gallons (227 L).

❖ This definition establishes the distinction between containers and tanks for purposes of code application, with a container being defined as a vessel of 60 gallons (227 L) or less capacity (see the commentary to the definition of "Container").

TANK, ATMOSPHERIC. A storage tank designed to operate at pressures from atmospheric through 1.0 pound per square inch gauge (760 mm Hg through 812 mm Hg) measured at the top of the tank.

❖ This type of tank is not designed for an internal pressure that exceeds atmospheric pressure. Most require some type of emergency venting system to assist in the relief of pressure in a fire.

TANK, PORTABLE. A packaging of more than 60-gallon (227 L) capacity and designed primarily to be loaded into or on or temporarily attached to a transport vehicle or ship and equipped with skids, mountings or accessories to facilitate handling of the tank by mechanical means. It does not include any cylinder having less than a 1,000-pound (454 kg) water capacity, cargo tank, tank car tank or trailers carrying cylinders of more than 1,000-pound (454 kg) water capacity.

❖ A portable tank must be movable without having to detach permanently mounted electrical controls for the pumping or dispensing systems.

TANK, PRIMARY. A *listed* atmospheric tank used to store liquid. See "Primary containment."

❖ The primary tank is the principal storage vessel for flammable and combustible liquids. The tank may use a secondary containment system or be installed in a dike area to control leaks and spills.

TANK, PROTECTED ABOVE GROUND. A tank *listed* in accordance with UL 2085 consisting of a primary tank provided with protection from physical damage and fire-resistive protection from a high-intensity liquid pool fire exposure. The tank may provide protection elements as a unit or may be an assembly of components, or a combination thereof.

❖ A protected above-ground tank is a shop-fabricated above-ground storage tank that has been subjected to a fire test that replicates an exposure to a 2-hour flammable liquid pool fire. Such tanks are constructed with integral secondary containment and are evaluated for vehicle impact and bullet resistance. All openings on a protected above-ground tank are located at the top of the storage tank which further limits the potential for liquid leaks—openings below the liquid level in these tanks are prohibited by the code. These tanks are listed as meeting the requirements of UL 2085, *Standard for Protected Aboveground Tanks for Flammable and Combustible Liquids*. Section 5704.2.9.7 has a number of requirements for protected above-ground tanks, including overfill protection that limits the volume of fuel oil to 95 percent of the tank's capacity, an informational sign that explains how the tank is to be filled and that the tank volume must be verified before the tank is filled, and a minimum 5-gallon (19 L) spill container at the tank fill connection to capture any fuel trapped in the fuel delivery hose. If the liquid piping extends below the top of the tank, Section 5704.2.9.7.9 requires the installation of an antisiphon valve. An antisiphon valve is designed to prevent the siphoning of liquid from the tank in the event a pipe or fitting fails and leaks liquid.

TANK, STATIONARY. Packaging designed primarily for stationary installations not intended for loading, unloading or attachment to a transport vehicle as part of its normal operation in the process of use. It does not include cylinders having less than a 1,000-pound (454 kg) water capacity.

❖ This type of tank is placed in a permanent location and typically has electrically mounted controls attached to a permanent power source.

TANK VEHICLE. A vehicle other than a railroad tank car or boat, with a cargo tank mounted thereon or built as an integral part thereof, used for the transportation of flammable or *combustible liquids*, LP-gas or hazardous chemicals. Tank vehicles include self-propelled vehicles and full trailers and semitrailers, with or without motive power, and carrying part or all of the load.

❖ Tank vehicles used for storage and transportation of hazardous chemicals over public roadways are governed by the DOTn.

TEMPORARY SPECIAL EVENT STRUCTURE. Any temporary ground-supported structure, platform, stage, stage scaffolding or rigging, canopy, tower supporting audio or visual effects equipment or similar structures not regulated within the scope of the *International Building Code*.

❖ Prior to the 2018 code, this term was called "temporary stage canopy." It was revised as there are many structures at events that pose a threat to people that would not be seen as a stage canopy, such as tall speakers or lighting structures.

In terms of why this issue is addressed, there were four high-profile temporary special event structure collapses during the 2011 summer concert season: July 17 at the Cisco Ottawa Blues Festival in Ottawa, Canada; August 7 at the Brady District Block Party, Tulsa, Oklahoma; August 13 at the Indiana State Fair, which resulted in seven dead and 50 injured; and August 18 at Pukkelpop (music festival) in Kiewit, Belgium. In the summer of 2012, a life was lost at a Radiohead concert in Toronto. All resulted in tremendous property damage and two in multiple fatalities. The obvious concern is for the safety of the performers and audiences, stage-hands, lighting technicians, security personnel and every other individual in proximity to a temporary stage.

Temporary special event structures are very specialized and complex. The nature of the structures must accommodate a wide variety of changing components such as audio equipment, video walls and scenery. The entertainment industry is continually evolving with new ways to improve shows, creating larger and more complex spectacles.

Due to the unique design of temporary stage canopies, very specific requirements for these structures are necessary.

TENT. A structure, enclosure, umbrella structure or shelter, with or without sidewalls or drops, constructed of fabric or pliable material supported in any manner except by air or the contents it protects (see "Umbrella structure").

❖ Tents can be temporary or permanent structures. When permanent, they are regulated by Section 3104. When erected as temporary enclosures, they are regulated by Sections 3103 and 3104 (see also Chapter 31 of the IBC). Commentary Figure 202-T1 illustrates a tent. This definition also covers the concept of umbrella structures. See the commentary to "Umbrella structure."

THEFT RESISTANT. Construction designed to deter illegal entry into facilities for the storage of *explosive materials*.

❖ Theft-resistant designs are intended to provide security against illegal or unauthorized entry into magazines containing explosives. Security measures specified in this and subsequent sections require special tools, keys or excessive force to compromise the security measure.

[BF] THROUGH-PENETRATION FIRESTOP SYSTEM. An assemblage consisting of a *fire-resistance-rated* floor, floor-ceiling or wall assembly, one or more penetrating items passing through the breaches in both sides of the assembly and the materials or devices, or both, installed to resist the spread of fire through the assembly for a prescribed period of time.

❖ One method of protection for penetrations through fire walls, fire barriers, fire partitions and fire-resistance-rated floor/ceiling assemblies is to provide a through-penetration firestop system (see Sections 714.4.1.2 and 714.5.1.2 of the IBC). Through-penetration firestop systems maintain the required protection from the spread of fire, passage of hot gases and transfer of heat. The protection is often provided by an intumescent material. Upon exposure to high temperatures, this material expands as much as eight to 10 times its original volume, forming a high-strength char.

This is one of several types of through-penetration firestop systems available. This definition is based on information from three sources: ASTM E814, a compilation of definitions from ASTM International standards and the UL *Fire Resistance Directory.*

TIMBER AND LUMBER PRODUCTION FACILITIES. Facilities where raw wood products are processed into finished wood products.

❖ Wood is still our most used structural material. With the ever-increasing demand for wood products, growth of the forest products industry continues. Some woodworking facilities are a "one-man" shop while others employ as many as several thousand people.

TIRES, BULK STORAGE OF. Storage of tires where the area available for storage exceeds 20,000 cubic feet (566 m^3).

❖ This definition describes a storage space that is larger than what would be found in most typical mercantile and storage occupancies. Because of its size and the volume of combustible material it would house, it poses an extraordinary hazard for fire protection.

The volume is based on the legacy code definition, which was based on 10,000 passenger vehicle tires weighing an average of 25 pounds (11 kg) each rather than the volume of the stored tires. Assuming a 24-inch by 24-inch space (610 mm by 610 mm) for an average passenger vehicle tire and a 6-inch (152 mm) thickness, the result is 20,000 cubic feet (566 m^3):

$$10{,}000 \text{ tires} \times 2 \text{ ft} \times 2 \text{ ft} \times 0.5 \text{ ft} = 20{,}000 \text{ ft}^3$$

The 20,000 cubic feet (566 m^3) represents the actual volume of stored materials based on an equivalent height and area for passenger vehicle tires as

Commentary Figure 202-T1
EXAMPLE OF TENT STRUCTURE

shown in the preceding calculation and does not include circulation area or other portions of the building. Rather, it focuses on how much of the material is present. Although the definition uses the term "area" rather than "volume," it is the volume that becomes the threshold consideration. Still, the area where the tires are stored implies the footprint used for storage. It is not the intent to apply this to areas outside of those used for bulk tire storage.

Buildings used for the bulk storage of tires are classified as Group S-1 occupancies in accordance with Section 311.2 of the IBC. All Group S-1 occupancies, regardless of square footage, must be equipped with an NFPA 13 automatic sprinkler system where used for the bulk storage of tires as required by Section 903.2.9.2. Chapter 34 of the code also requires that bulk tire storage buildings be further designed to comply with NFPA 13, and Chapter 32 of the code includes additional requirements for high-piled rubber tire storage as a high-hazard commodity (see commentaries, Chapters 32 and 34).

TOOL. A device, storage container, workstation or process machine used in a fabrication area.

❖ A tool is basically any device or piece of equipment, including a workstation, in a fabrication area where hazardous materials are used, stored or handled.

TORCH-APPLIED ROOF SYSTEM. Bituminous roofing systems using membranes that are adhered by heating with a torch and melting asphalt back coating instead of mopping hot asphalt for adhesion.

❖ This is a very specific operation that relates to hot work that uses a torch to adhere the materials. It is not considered welding, but still falls within the definition of "Hot work" (see Commentary Figure 6104.3.1).

[A] TOWNHOUSE. A single-family *dwelling unit* constructed in a group of three or more attached units in which each unit extends from the foundation to roof and with open space on not less than two sides.

❖ This specific configuration of construction is called different things in different parts of the country, such as a rowhouse. A townhouse structure that meets the following four criteria is not regulated by this code but is regulated by the IRC. Those criteria are:

1. Each unit extends from foundation to roof with no vertical overlap of any parts of adjoining units.
2. Each unit must have open space on at least two sides (either two opposite or two adjoining sides).
3. Each unit must have a separate means of egress.
4. The building must not exceed three stories above grade plane.

If all of these criteria are met, then according to the exception to Section 101.2 of the IBC, the structure is within the scope of the IRC. (It should also be noted that townhouses within the IRC must be separated by a wall or walls meeting specific criteria.) Where a structure does not meet these four criteria, it will need to be regulated under the code and will either be classified as a Group R-2 or Group R-3 structure, depending on how the units are separated. A building containing three or more dwelling units is regulated as a Group R-2 occupancy. To be considered a Group R-3, the structure must have one or two dwelling units, or be subdivided by fire walls between every unit or every two units (see the definitions for "Area, building," "Dwelling" and "Dwelling unit"). Finally, the definition of "Townhouse" is not dependent on the presence of individual lots. A townhouse structure could be built with any number of attached units on the same lot, or it could be developed such that a property line lies at each common wall separating two units (see definition, "Lot").

TOXIC. A chemical falling within any of the following categories:

1. A chemical that has a median lethal dose (LD_{50}) of more than 50 milligrams per kilogram, but not more than 500 milligrams per kilogram of body weight when administered orally to albino rats weighing between 200 and 300 grams each.
2. A chemical that has a median lethal dose (LD_{50}) of more than 200 milligrams per kilogram but not more than 1,000 milligrams per kilogram of body weight when administered by continuous contact for 24 hours (or less if death occurs within 24 hours) with the bare skin of albino rabbits weighing between 2 and 3 kilograms each.
3. A chemical that has a median lethal concentration (LC_{50}) in air of more than 200 parts per million but not more than 2,000 parts per million by volume of gas or vapor, or more than 2 milligrams per liter but not more than 20 milligrams per liter of mist, fume or dust, when administered by continuous inhalation for 1 hour (or less if death occurs within 1 hour) to albino rats weighing between 200 and 300 grams each.

❖ The definition is derived from DOL 29 CFR Part 1910.1200. These materials are considered dangerous to humans when inhaled, absorbed or injected through the skin or orally ingested. Toxic materials differ from highly toxic materials with regard to the specified median lethal dose or concentration of a given chemical. Toxic materials present a health hazard and are subsequently listed as a Group H-4 material in Section 307.6 of the IBC. See also the commentary to the definition of "Highly toxic."

TRAFFIC CALMING DEVICES. Traffic calming devices are design elements of fire apparatus access roads such as street alignment, installation of barriers, and other physical measures intended to reduce traffic and cut-through volumes, and slow vehicle speeds.

❖ The definition for traffic calming is based on the definition provided by the Institute of Transportation Engineers. Many communities are facing increased traffic volumes. Both new and existing streets are experiencing higher vehicular volumes and speeds as drivers attempt to find "shortcuts" to ease their commutes. Designers, planning departments and traffic engineering departments are increasingly turning to traffic calming measures to preserve the quality and enjoyment of life for their citizens.

In many communities, a concern of homeowners is the use of residential streets as an alternative route to minor and major thoroughfares. There are concerns about pedestrian safety, vehicle speeds and the traffic volume on residential streets. On the other hand, property owners also want the lowest response time that is practical in the event of an emergency that requires a response by the fire or police department. In fact, response time is the primary measurement for quality of service used by the public. The installation of traffic calming devices competes with these two goals.

A number of studies have been conducted to evaluate the impact of traffic calming devices on the response time of fire and emergency medical services (EMS) apparatus. These studies found that traffic calming devices have no real impact on law enforcement vehicles because of their size; however, depending on the method of traffic calming used (e.g., "round-abouts," "speed bumps," "speed pillows," narrowing of streets, winding roads rather than straight roads, etc.) and the vehicle type, response times for fire and emergency services generally are increased by these devices by 2 to 10 seconds. Studies have also found that the vehicle frames of fire and EMS apparatus can be damaged and emergency services personnel have been injured while responding over certain traffic calming devices. See the commentary to Section 503.4.1 for further discussion of traffic calming devices. See also Commentary Figures 202-T2 and 202-T3 for illustrations of several typical traffic calming devices.

[BG] TRANSIENT. Occupancy of a dwelling unit or sleeping unit for not more than 30 days.

❖ This definition is intended to establish a time parameter to differentiate between transient and nontransient as listed under Groups R-1 and R-2. Real estate law dictates that a lease must be created after 30 days and time periods greater than 30 days are typically how extended-stay hotels and motels rent to people.

Such a time period enables the occupant to become familiar with the surroundings and, therefore, become more accustomed to any hazards of the built environment than an overnight guest or a guest who stays for just a few days would be. Since nontransient occupancies do not have the same level of protection in the code as transient occupancies, it is important to determine what makes an occupancy transient so as to provide consistency in enforcement.

[BG] TRANSIENT AIRCRAFT. Aircraft based at another location and that is at the transient location for not more than 90 days.

❖ In place of the undefined term "private aircraft" previously used in the code, a defined term, "transient aircraft," was added in the 2009 edition. Transient aircraft are those that are merely visiting an airport, as opposed to those that are based at that location. The definition is used in conjunction with Section 914.8.3 to establish the level of fire suppression needed in various aircraft hangars. Fixed-base operators, especially at larger airports, will have distinct hangars that are used for repair and maintenance of aircraft. The hangars used by transient aircraft are primarily a storage place for aircraft based at another location. This better identifies the intended use of this type of aircraft hangar. Most frequently, the owner

Commentary Figure 202-T2
SPEED PILLOW TRAFFIC CALMING DEVICE

that wants to develop an aircraft hangar that fits the Group II category, will do no "major maintenance" and will only "store" airplanes in their hangar (see commentary, Section 914.8.3).

TRANSVERSE FLUE SPACE. See "Flue space—Transverse."

TRASH. See "Rubbish."

TROUBLE SIGNAL. A signal initiated by the fire alarm system or device indicative of a fault in a monitored circuit or component.

❖ This type of signal indicates that there has been an abnormal change in the normal status of the fire detection system or devices and that a response is required to determine the nature of the fault condition. The trouble signal is only associated with electronic portions of a fire protection system. Physical conditions such as a closed valve are monitored electronically and would report as a supervisory signal rather than a trouble signal. A valve supervisory switch or "tamper switch," for example, would perform such a function.

TUBE TRAILER. A semitrailer on which a number of tubular gas cylinders have been mounted. A manifold is typically provided that connects the cylinder valves enabling gas to be discharged from one or more tubes or cylinders through a piping and control system.

❖ Tube trailers are a common method of supplying compressed gases to a variety of industrial processes, and it is not uncommon to have more than one tube trailer on a site. Depending on the cylinder's length and maximum allowable working pressure (MAWP), a trailer may have as few as six or as many as 18 to 24 cylinders varying in length from 20 feet (6096 mm) for small tube trailers to 38 feet (11 582 mm) on jumbo tube trailers. The vessels are generally designed for a MAWP from 2,800 to approximately 3,800 pounds per square inch (psi) (19 305 to 26 200 kPa), depending on the storage pressure. At such pressures, each cylinder can hold anywhere from 5,000 to 20,000 standard cubic feet (scf) (142 to 566 m^3), depending on the gas being stored. Tube trailers are subject to periodic inspections in accordance with US Department of Transportation (DOTn) regulations and each new or substantially modified tube is required to successfully pass a substantial hydrostatic pressure test.

The transport of compressed gases by these road trailers, which are regulated by the DOTn as a bulk compressed gas source, is an established distribution method used widely in the industrial gas industry for the transport over short distances of relatively small volumes of inert, flammable, oxidizer, corrosive or toxic compressed gases and gas mixtures, including hydrogen, methane, oxygen, nitrogen, argon, helium, many fluorocarbons, hydrogen sulfide and hydrogen chloride.

At one end of the trailer is a manifold to which each cylinder valve is connected so that one or more tubes can discharge gas into a piping and control system. The tube trailer is connected via the manifold to the building or process using the compressed gas (see Commentary Figure 202-T4 and commentary, Section 5303.7.11).

Commentary Figure 202-T3
ROUNDABOUT TRAFFIC CALMING DEVICE

Commentary Figure 202-T4
TUBE TRAILER

TWENTY-FOUR HOUR BASIS. See "24-hour basis" before the "A" entries.

UMBRELLA STRUCTURE. A structure, enclosure or shelter with or without sidewalls or drops, constructed of fabric or pliable material supported by a central pole or poles (see "Tent").

❖ This definition is provided to further explain the concept now included in the definition for "Tent." There are umbrellas that exceed 400 square feet in area. Even where individual umbrellas do not exceed 400 square feet, they are often designed to connect to other such umbrellas. These structures offer extended weather protection and include accessories such as rain gutters, side panels and additional electrical wiring for lights and heater attachment. These accessories allow the structure to mimic a tent with or without sides, be of substantial size and be used as protection over an assembly occupancy. Prior to being addressed within the definition of tent, however, the fabric did not require compliance with NFPA 701. Since these structures are now considered a tent by definition such umbrellas must meet the requirements of NFPA 701. See the commentary to Chapter 31. See Commentary Figure 202-U1.

UNAUTHORIZED DISCHARGE. A release or emission of materials in a manner which does not conform to the provisions of this code or applicable public health and safety regulations.

❖ Remember that hazardous chemicals pose a threat to life and property only when release is not authorized, controlled or properly protected.

UNSTABLE (REACTIVE) MATERIAL. A material, other than an *explosive*, which in the pure state or as commercially produced, will vigorously polymerize, decompose, condense or become self-reactive and undergo other violent chemical changes, including explosion, when exposed to heat, friction or shock, or in the absence of an inhibitor, or in the presence of contaminants, or in contact with *incompatible materials*. Unstable (reactive) materials are subdivided as follows:

Class 4. Materials that in themselves are readily capable of *detonation* or explosive decomposition or explosive reaction at *normal temperatures and pressures*. This class includes materials that are sensitive to mechanical or localized thermal shock at *normal temperatures and pressures*.

Class 3. Materials that in themselves are capable of *detonation* or of explosive decomposition or explosive reaction but which require a strong initiating source or which must be heated under confinement before initiation. This class includes materials that are sensitive to thermal or mechanical shock at elevated temperatures and pressures.

Commentary Figure 202-U1
Umbrella Structure

Class 2. Materials that in themselves are normally unstable and readily undergo violent chemical change but do not detonate. This class includes materials that can undergo chemical change with rapid release of energy at *normal temperatures and pressures*, and that can undergo violent chemical change at elevated temperatures and pressures.

Class 1. Materials that in themselves are normally stable but which can become unstable at elevated temperatures and pressure.

❖ The definition of an "Unstable (reactive) material" is based on NFPA 704. The different classes of unstable (reactive) material reflect the degree of susceptibility of the materials to release energy. Unstable (reactive) materials polymerize, decompose or become self-reactive when exposed to heat, air, moisture, pressure or shock. Separation from incompatible materials is essential to minimizing the hazards. Examples of unstable (reactive) materials include acetaldheyde, ammonium nitrate, ethylene oxide, hydrogen cyanide, nitromethane, perchloric acid, sodium perchlorate, vinyl acetate and acetic acid.

UNWANTED FIRE. A fire not used for cooking, heating or recreational purposes or one not incidental to the normal operations of the property.

❖ For the purposes of applying the code, a clarification is provided to note that certain fires present in buildings would be acceptable; for example, the normal operation of a water heater, a gas stove or a fireplace. The definition does not address whether a fire is intentional or unintentional (arson versus a welding accident, for example).

USE (MATERIAL). Placing a material into action, including solids, liquids and gases.

❖ This term refers to when a chemical or material is used in a process that forms another substance, whether it is hazardous or not, and when the chemical is used independently.

VAPOR PRESSURE. The pressure exerted by a volatile fluid as determined in accordance with ASTM D323.

❖ Vapor pressure is a characteristic property of liquids and varies with their temperature. As the temperature of the liquid increases, more and more of the liquid enters the vapor stage. This increased pressure can cause an emergency vent to release, or, if the conditions are serious enough, can result in a BLEVE.

[M] VENTILATION. The natural or mechanical process of supplying conditioned or unconditioned air to, or removing such air from, any space.

❖ Ventilation is the process of moving air to or from building spaces. Ventilation requirements are used in the code to establish minimum levels of air movement within a building for the purposes of providing a healthful interior environment. Ventilation would include both natural (openable exterior windows and doors for wind movement) and mechanical (forced air with mechanical equipment) methods.

VESSEL. A motorized watercraft, other than a seaplane on the water, used or capable of being used as a means of transportation. Nontransportation vessels, such as houseboats and boathouses, are included in this definition.

❖ Vessels, in this definition, are motorized watercraft, but by dictionary definition, a vessel is "...a watercraft or structure with its equipment, whether self-propelled or not, that is used or capable of being used as a means of transportation in navigation or commerce on water..." The definition could include small rowboats and sailboats. No minimum or maximum length is specified. Houseboats and boathouses that would be occupied, as dwelling or sleeping units are also included in the definition.

VISIBLE ALARM NOTIFICATION APPLIANCE. A notification appliance that alerts by the sense of sight.

❖ Visible alarm notification appliances are located anywhere an occupant notification system is required, in occupancies where occupants may be hearing impaired and in sleeping accommodations of Group I-1 and R-1 occupancies. These alarm notification devices must be located and oriented so that they will display alarm signals throughout the required space. Visible alarms, where provided, are typically installed in the public and common areas of buildings (see commentary, Section 907.5.2.3).

WATER MIST SYSTEM, AUTOMATIC. See "Automatic water mist system."

WATER-REACTIVE MATERIAL. A material that explodes; violently reacts; produces flammable, toxic or other hazardous gases; or evolves enough heat to cause autoignition or ignition of combustibles upon exposure to water or moisture. Water-reactive materials are subdivided as follows:

Class 3. Materials that react explosively with water without requiring heat or confinement.

Class 2. Materials that react violently with water or have the ability to boil water. Materials that produce flammable, toxic or other hazardous gases, or evolve enough heat to cause autoignition or ignition of combustibles upon exposure to water or moisture.

Class 1. Materials that react with water with some release of energy, but not violently.

❖ Class 2 and 3 water-reactive materials can liberate significant quantities of heat and hazardous gases when reacting with water. Combustible water-reactive materials are capable of self-ignition. Even noncombustible water-reactive materials pose a hazard because of the heat released during their reaction with water, which may be sufficient to ignite surrounding combustible materials. The description of each of the subdivisions is consistent with the approach used for the determination of water hazards in NFPA 704.

WET FUELING. See "Mobile fueling."

WET HOSING. See "Mobile fueling."

WET-CHEMICAL EXTINGUISHING AGENT. A solution of water and potassium-carbonate-based chemical, potassium-acetate-based chemical or a combination thereof, forming an extinguishing agent.

❖ This extinguishing agent is a suitable alternative to the use of a dry chemical, especially when protecting commercial kitchen range hoods. There is less cleanup time after system discharge. Wet chemical solutions are considered to be relatively harmless and normally have no lasting effect on the skin or respiratory system. These solutions may produce temporary irritation, which is usually mild and disappears when contact is eliminated. These systems must be preengineered and labeled. NFPA 17A applies to the design, installation, operation, testing and maintenance of wet-chemical extinguishing systems.

WHARF. A structure or bulkhead constructed of wood, stone, concrete or similar material built at the shore of a harbor, lake or river for vessels to lie alongside of, and to anchor piers or floats.

❖ A wharf is constructed along the shore and does not project significantly into the body of water as a pier would. Piers or floats may be attached to and project out from a wharf. Wharves may also have structures on them that support the use of the wharf.

WILDFIRE RISK AREA. Land that is covered with grass, grain, brush or forest, whether privately or publicly owned, which is so situated or is of such inaccessible location that a fire originating upon it would present an abnormally difficult job of suppression or would result in great or unusual damage through fire or such areas designated by the *fire code official*.

❖ This defined term, added to the code in 2009, provides clarification to Sections 105.6.23, 105.6.33, 308.1.6 and 308.1.6.1 where the undefined term "hazardous fire area" had been used in previous editions of the code, leaving the fire code official with little or no guidance as to the code's intent. The source for this definition was a definition for the term "hazardous fire area" in the legacy *Uniform Fire Code*. However, in order to avoid conflict and confusion with the already-defined term "fire area," the new term and the indicated section texts were changed to "wildfire risk area."

[BE] WINDER. A tread with nonparallel edges.

❖ Winders are used as components of stairways that change direction, just as "fliers" (rectangular treads) are components in straight stairways. A winder performs the same function as a tread, but its shape allows the additional function of a gradual turning of the stairway direction. The tread depth of a winder at the walkline and the minimum tread depth at the narrow end control the turn made by each winder. Winders are not landings. Winder treads are limited to curved or spiral stairways with all groups but are all stairways within dwelling units (see Section 1011.5.3).

WIRELESS PROTECTION SYSTEM. A system or a part of a system that can transmit and receive signals without the aid of wire.

❖ These systems use radio frequency transmitting devices that comply with the special requirements for supervision of low-power wireless systems in NFPA 72. Wireless devices have the advantage of flexibility in positioning. Consequently, portable wireless notification devices are frequently used in existing facilities where visual devices are not present throughout.

WORKSTATION. A defined space or an independent principal piece of equipment using HPM within a fabrication area where a specific function, laboratory procedure or research activity occurs. *Approved* or *listed* hazardous materials storage cabinets, flammable liquid storage cabinets or gas cabinets serving a workstation are included as part of the workstation. A workstation is allowed to contain ventilation equipment, fire protection devices, detection devices, electrical devices and other processing and scientific equipment.

❖ In HPM facilities, workstations further subdivide a fabrication area and provide relatively self-contained, specialized areas where HPM processes are conducted. Workstation controls limit the quantity of materials and impose limitations on the design of these processes to include, but not be limited to, protection by local exhaust; sprinklers; automatic and emergency shutoffs; construction materials and HPM compatibility. Excess materials are prohibited and must be contained in storage rooms designed to accommodate such hazards.

[BG] YARD. An open space, other than a *court*, unobstructed from the ground to the sky, except where specifically provided by the *International Building Code*, on the lot on which a building is situated.

❖ This definition is used, similar to the definition of "Court," to establish the applicability of code requirements where yards are utilized for natural light or natural ventilation purposes (see Section 1205.1 of the IBC). Whereas a court is bounded on three or more sides with the building or structure, a yard is bounded on two or fewer sides by the building or structure. See also the definition of "Egress court."

ZONE. A defined area within the protected premises. A zone can define an area from which a signal can be received, an area to which a signal can be sent or an area in which a form of control can be executed.

❖ Zoning a system is important to emergency personnel in locating a fire. When an alarm is designated to a specific zone, it allows the fire service to immediately respond to the area where the fire is in progress instead of searching the entire building for the origin of an alarm.

ZONE, NOTIFICATION. An area within a building or facility covered by notification appliances which are activated simultaneously.

❖ This definition is provided to clarify the code by making a distinction between fire alarm system initiation device zones required by Section 907.6.4 and the zones that may be designed into occupant notification device systems in a building. The term is used primarily in the exceptions for sprinkler systems found in the manual fire alarm system requirements in Section 907.2 and its subsections. Note that the code does not require audible and visible occupant notification device systems to be zoned; where such zones are provided, it is a matter of the system design engineer's judgment. Voice paging components in high-rise building emergency voice/alarm communication systems are, however, required to be zoned in accordance with Section 907.5.2.2.

Bibliography

The following resource materials were used in the preparation of the commentary for this chapter of the code:

2009 International Code Interpretations. Washington, DC: International Code Council, 2009.

Babrauskas, V., "Heat Release Rates," Volume 1 Chapter 26, SFPE *Handbook of Fire Protection Engineering*, 5th Edition. NYC: Springer Publications, 2016.

Bulletin 19A, *Suggested Relative Hazard Classification of Organic Peroxides*. Washington, DC: Society of the Plastics Industry, 1975.

Complete Revision History to the 2018 I-Codes: Successful Changes and Public Comments. Washington, DC: International Code Council, 2017.

Fire Protection Guide to Hazardous Materials, 13th Edition. Quincy, MA: National Fire Protection Association, 2001.

Gottuk, D., and White D., "Liquid Fuel Fires," Volume 3 Chapter 65, SFPE *Handbook of Fire Protection Engineering*, 5th Edition. NYC: Springer Publications, 2016.

Part II—General Safety Provisions

Chapter 3: General Requirements

General Comments

Fire is always a concern, whether a building is under construction, is occupied for normal use or is undergoing renovation, restoration, expansion or demolition. But careful planning combined with common sense can make buildings and premises much safer, regardless of the occupancy or other activities at the site.

The primary focus of the requirements in this chapter is making sure the three elements necessary for a fire—ignition source, fuel and oxygen—do not come in contact with one another. NFPA 550 describes in great detail the features of fire safety systems and includes a logic tree called "The Fire Safety Concepts Tree" to graphically show all the possible means of achieving user-defined fire safety objectives. A portion of that tree is reproduced here as Commentary Figure 3 to show how to avoid fire ignition. Activities on this diagram that follow a plus sign (+), also known as an "or" gate, may be undertaken independently of each other to arrive at the desired goal. Alternatives following a dot (•), also known as an "and" gate, must be combined to achieve the desired result.

Commentary Figure 3 shows that eliminating any one of the three elements required for a fire to occur will prevent a fire from happening. If there is no ignition source, a fuel load of any size should not catch fire. If there is no fuel load, there is nothing for an ignition source to ignite. If there is little or no air available to sustain combustion, any fire ignited in a fuel load will quickly die.

The requirements and precautions outlined in this chapter, when applied using good judgment and the common sense mentioned above, will help to foster safety for everyone.

Purpose

The requirements and precautions contained in this chapter are intended to improve premises safety for everyone, including construction workers, tenants, operations and maintenance personnel and emergency response personnel.

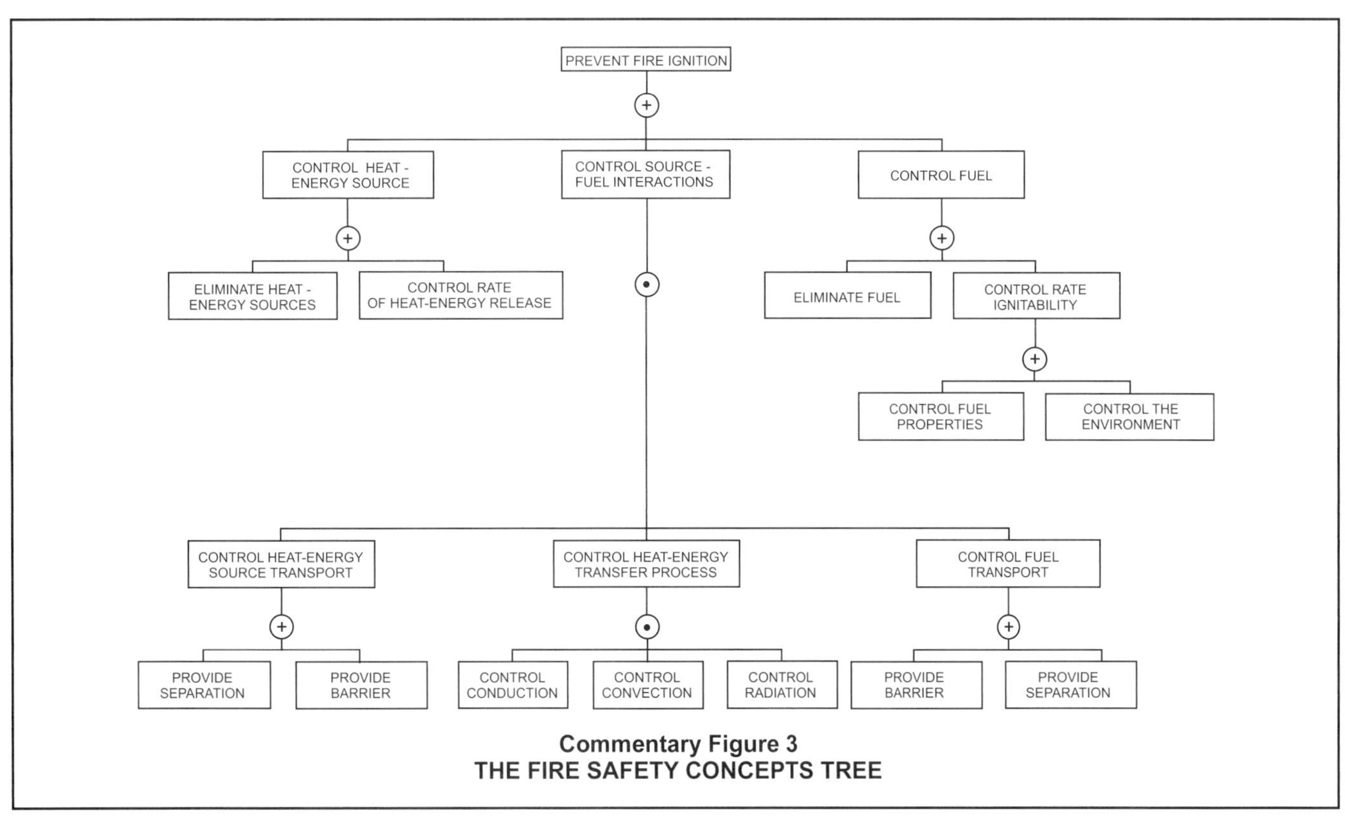

Commentary Figure 3
THE FIRE SAFETY CONCEPTS TREE

SECTION 301
GENERAL

301.1 Scope. The provisions of this chapter shall govern the occupancy and maintenance of all structures and premises for precautions against fire and the spread of fire and general requirements of fire safety.

❖ The requirements of Chapter 3 prescribe fire safety precautions for conditions that are likely to cause or contribute to the spread of fire in any building or structure or on any premises, regardless of occupancy.

301.2 Permits. Permits shall be required as set forth in Section 105.6 for the activities or uses regulated by Sections 306, 307, 308 and 315.

❖ Issuing permits gives the fire code official an opportunity to carefully evaluate and regulate hazardous operations. Applicants for permits should be required to demonstrate that their operations comply with the code before the permit is issued. See the commentary to Section 105.6 for a general discussion of operations requiring an operational permit.

SECTION 302
DEFINITIONS

302.1 Definitions. The following terms are defined in Chapter 2:

BONFIRE.

HI-BOY.

HIGH-VOLTAGE TRANSMISSION LINE.

OPEN BURNING.

PORTABLE OUTDOOR FIREPLACE.

POWERED INDUSTRIAL TRUCK.

RECREATIONAL FIRE.

SKY LANTERN.

❖ Definitions of terms can help in the understanding and application of the code requirements. This section directs the code user to Chapter 2 for the proper application of the indicated terms used in this chapter. Terms may be defined in Chapter 2 or in another International Code® (I-Code®) as indicated in Section 201.3, or the dictionary meaning may be all that is needed (see commentaries, Sections 201 through 201.4).

SECTION 303
ASPHALT KETTLES

303.1 Transporting. Asphalt (tar) kettles shall not be transported over any highway, road or street when the heat source for the kettle is operating.

> **Exception:** Asphalt (tar) kettles in the process of patching road surfaces.

❖ The hazards of hauling a fired kettle of molten asphalt over public ways are obvious. Most asphalt kettles for roofing, paving and similar uses are currently liquefied petroleum gas (LP-gas) fired. Contractors often wish to keep asphalt in a liquid state to save time between jobs and when work is interrupted. Once asphalt is transformed from a solid to a liquid by heating, it retains much of its heat for some time, and although it becomes increasingly viscous as it cools, it remains fluid for a considerable time. Maintaining a fire under a kettle during transport is usually unnecessary and, therefore, prohibited, since little additional heat is required to return the asphalt to a usable consistency. An accident, flat tire or anything else that could cause the kettle to overturn, spilling the molten asphalt in the presence of an open flame, could lead to a serious fire. Even hitting potholes or other bumps in the road could cause the molten asphalt to splash out of the kettle, causing injury to people nearby or damage to property.

The exception for asphalt being used for road repair is necessary for efficient operations for work crews sealing pavement joints and performing similar roadway repairs.

303.2 Location. Asphalt (tar) kettles shall not be located within 20 feet (6096 mm) of any combustible material, combustible building surface or any building opening and within a controlled area identified by the use of traffic cones, barriers or other *approved* means. Asphalt (tar) kettles and pots shall not be utilized inside or on the roof of a building or structure. Roofing kettles and operating asphalt (tar) kettles shall not block *means of egress*, gates, roadways or entrances.

❖ Asphalt kettles sometimes catch fire. Having one located inside a building would present a serious smoke problem, as well as the fire hazards of asphalt spills flowing to lower floors or the release of LP-gas inside the building. Having one located next to quantities of combustible materials would also represent a fire hazard, as well as the possibility that splashes and splatters could damage construction materials beyond use. Keeping egress pathways and other travel lanes free of obstructions provides a needed immediate exit from an area where an asphalt kettle-related incident might occur and enhances access to such areas for the fire department.

303.3 Location of fuel containers. Fuel containers shall be located not less than 10 feet (3048 mm) from the burner.

> **Exception:** Containers properly insulated from heat or flame are allowed to be within 2 feet (610 mm) of the burner.

❖ This section reduces the likelihood that any gas or vapors escaping from fuel containers would be ignited by the open flame of the kettle burner and that the heat of the burner would cause overheating of the fuel containers.

The exception acknowledges the greater safety of insulated containers.

303.4 Attendant. An operating kettle shall be attended by not less than one employee knowledgeable of the operations and hazards. The employee shall be within 100 feet (30 480 mm) of the kettle and have the kettle within sight. Ladders or similar obstacles shall not form a part of the route between the attendant and the kettle.

❖ Having a trained attendant watch the kettle helps to create a safe operation. The attendant is usually responsible for making sure the asphalt is at the proper temperature, the level of liquid in the kettle is maintained at the required level and the fuel supply for the kettle burner is adequate. The attendant should watch for any change in the kettle that would signal the potential for a safety hazard, and adjust the burner output or other factors to keep the kettle in safe operating condition. The attendant is also often responsible for keeping the area surrounding the kettle free of combustible materials and other construction debris that could become a safety hazard.

303.5 Fire extinguishers. There shall be a portable fire extinguisher complying with Section 906 and with a minimum 40-B:C rating within 25 feet (7620 mm) of each asphalt (tar) kettle during the period such kettle is being utilized. Additionally, there shall be one portable fire extinguisher with a minimum 3-A:40-B:C rating on the roof being covered.

❖ This section defines the type and size of extinguisher that must be available for use, both on the ground near the kettle and on the roof level to which the asphalt is being applied. In the event of a kettle fire, water should not be used as an extinguishing agent because it could cause the molten asphalt to froth and possibly overflow the kettle or spatter over anything or anyone in the surrounding area. See also the commentary to Section 3317.3 for roofing operations during construction.

303.6 Lids. Asphalt (tar) kettles shall be equipped with tight-fitting lids.

❖ A tight-fitting lid on a hot kettle limits the air supply available to feed a kettle fire. Any fire that might start in a closed kettle will quickly burn itself out because of the limited amount of air available for combustion. The lid also helps prevent splashes and splatters that could cause personal injury.

303.7 Hi-boys. Hi-boys shall be constructed of noncombustible materials. Hi-boys shall be limited to a capacity of 55 gallons (208 L). Fuel sources or heating elements shall not be allowed as part of a hi-boy.

❖ Hi-boys are used on the roof of a building to transport hot asphalt from a point of supply near the edge of the roof to the site of the roofing application. Due to the hazards of molten asphalt discussed in Section 303.1, hi-boys are limited in size to control the maximum amount of potential spills on the roof, which could ignite and pose a high-challenge fire-suppression operation for the fire department. A limited size also enhances the movability and stability of the hi-boy, thus reducing the potential for a tip over. As a further safeguard against a fire incident, hi-boys are prohibited from being fired or equipped with a fuel source for firing. Hi-boys must also be constructed of noncombustible materials to enhance their durability and prevent the container from contributing fuel to a fire. Hi-boys should be well-maintained, including the frame; steering mechanism; tires or wheels; faucets and fill connections (see commentary, Section 202 for the definition of "Hi-boy").

303.8 Roofing kettles. Roofing kettles shall be constructed of noncombustible materials.

❖ The requirement for noncombustible materials represents sound safety practice as well as good business practice. Portions of kettles constructed of combustible materials can be easily destroyed and could lead to larger fires. Replacement of destroyed kettles would be expensive. Paying for other fire damage would be even more costly.

Also note that roofing mops soaked in asphalt or pitch must never be left inside a building, near heating equipment or near combustible materials. These mops are subject to spontaneous heating no matter what material they are made of.

303.9 Fuel containers under air pressure. Fuel containers that operate under air pressure shall not exceed 20 gallons (76 L) in capacity and shall be *approved*.

❖ Limiting the size of pressurized fuel containers limits the probability of a container becoming a major fuel source in case of a kettle fire. Requiring the use of approved containers gives the fire code official more control over the type and suitability of the vessel to be used under pressure.

SECTION 304
COMBUSTIBLE WASTE MATERIAL

304.1 Waste accumulation prohibited. Combustible waste material creating a fire hazard shall not be allowed to accumulate in buildings or structures or upon premises.

❖ Accumulated waste, trash, construction debris and other natural materials, such as grass clippings, leaves and shrubbery cuttings, can become a serious fire hazard. The three subsections that follow this general statement address the most common situations.

304.1.1 Waste material. Accumulations of wastepaper, wood, hay, straw, weeds, litter or combustible or flammable waste or rubbish of any type shall not be permitted to remain on a roof or in any *court*, yard, vacant lot, alley, parking lot, open space, or beneath a grandstand, *bleacher*, pier, wharf, manufactured home, recreational vehicle or other similar structure.

❖ This section considers the kind of waste material that is most likely to accumulate during construction, renovation, additions or demolition and is often referred to as "the housekeeping section." It prohibits disorderly, unkempt storage or accumulation of trash, waste rags, wastepaper, scrub brush and weeds, litter and other combustible materials. Litter and trash represent a serious fire hazard because of their ease of ignition and rapid heat release once ignited. The importance of maintaining property and buildings in good order seems obvious, but sloppy housekeeping still occurs and can be the cause of serious fires. In one of the most serious fires in recent years, improper storage of linseed-oil-soaked rags used to refinish paneling in a high-rise office building caused a fire that destroyed eight floors of the building and killed three fire fighters.

304.1.2 Vegetation. Weeds, grass, vines or other growth that is capable of being ignited and endangering property, shall be cut down and removed by the *owner* or occupant of the premises. Vegetation clearance requirements in urban-wildland interface areas shall be in accordance with the *International Wildland-Urban Interface Code.*

❖ Accumulations of natural waste, such as grass clippings, weed growth and shrubbery cuttings, are not only unsightly, but also represent a serious fire hazard. All too often these accumulations occur at or near fence lines that are adjacent to streets or alleys. This makes accidental ignition by a cigarette butt tossed from a passing vehicle a good possibility. Common sense tells us that removal of this kind of waste is beneficial. The rules of nearly all jurisdictions make waste control and removal the responsibility of the building or property owner, his or her agent, the tenant or the contractor if work is being done on the site. Uncontrolled vegetation growth poses substantial risk to areas designated as wildland-urban interface areas. Accordingly, such areas must comply with the provisions of the *International Wildland-Urban Interface Code*® (IWUIC®).

304.1.3 Space underneath seats. Spaces underneath grandstand and bleacher seats shall be kept free from combustible and flammable materials. Except where enclosed in not less than 1-hour fire-resistance-rated construction in accordance with the *International Building Code.*

❖ Numerous fires in grandstands and stadiums have shown over the years that the accumulation of flammable or combustible materials under grandstand seating areas can lead to fire disasters. Except as noted in the *International Building Code*® (IBC®), areas under grandstand seating must be kept free of flammable materials, including accumulations of waste or trash. One of the best ways to prevent a fire is to make certain there is no fuel to feed one.

The IBC does allow space under the stands to be used for purposes other than means of egress if that space is separated from the seating area by construction having at least a 1-hour fire-resistance rating. The separation is intended to allow time for occupants in the seating to vacate if a fire should occur. The fire code official would usually have to approve plans for use of space under the stands for concession stands, sales areas or storage areas.

304.1.3.1 Spaces underneath grandstands and bleachers. Spaces underneath grandstands and bleachers shall not be occupied or utilized for purposes other than means of egress except where equipped with an automatic sprinkler system in accordance with Section 903.2.1.5.1, or separated with fire barriers and horizontal assemblies in accordance with Section 1029.1.1.1.

❖ This section provides specific clarification on the use of spaces under grandstands and bleachers and makes it clear that they are only to be used as a means of egress unless the space is provided with an automatic sprinkler system or is separated by fire barriers and horizontal assemblies. See the commentary to Section 304.1.3 for further information.

304.2 Storage. Storage of combustible rubbish shall not produce conditions that will create a nuisance or a hazard to the public health, safety or welfare.

❖ Storage of combustible rubbish either indoors or outdoors must be approved by the fire code official. Combustibles should be accumulated in noncombustible containers, such as metal trash cans with tight lids, steel barrels or steel dumpster bins, which should be removed from the site regularly. The use of plastic waste containers should be discouraged due to the extremely high fuel content of such materials, which can sometimes be several times the fuel content of the waste material they contain. Such containers could, under fire conditions, cause rapid fire spread and overtax sprinkler systems, where installed. This section mentions public health as well as safety and welfare, indicating concern over retention of decomposing organic waste as well as flammable and combustible materials.

304.3 Containers. Combustible rubbish, and waste material kept within or near a structure shall be stored in accordance with Sections 304.3.1 through 304.3.4.

❖ Proper containers must be used to improve the safety of indoor or outdoor storage (in close proximity to buildings) of trash and isolate readily combustible materials. This section introduces the more detailed requirements in Sections 304.3.1 through 304.3.4.

304.3.1 Spontaneous ignition. Materials susceptible to spontaneous ignition, such as oily rags, shall be stored in a *listed* disposal container. Contents of such containers shall be removed and disposed of daily.

❖ Disposal containers, often called "waste cans" or "oily rag cans," used for storage of materials that might auto-ignite as a result of the spontaneous combustion process must be tested and listed for that use by a recognized testing laboratory or agency and must bear a label showing that they have been tested, along with the name of the testing agency. Such containers are most commonly round and generally available in sizes ranging from 5 to 40 gallons (19 to 151 L). They are equipped with a manual or foot treadle-operated lid that opens to a maximum angle of 60 degrees (1.05 rad) and closes by gravity. These containers are designed to prevent continuing combustion of the contents if ignition occurs. Container design includes features that keep the can body containing waste from coming into contact with combustible surfaces of walls or floors (see commentary, Section 202, for the definition of "Listed"). Daily disposal of container contents reduces the amount of time that oily materials will lie dormant, generating internal heat that can lead to ignition. UL 32 provides further information on the construction, testing and listing of these containers.

304.3.2 Capacity exceeding 5.33 cubic feet. Containers with a capacity exceeding 5.33 cubic feet (40 gallons) (0.15 m^3) shall be provided with lids. Containers and lids shall be constructed of noncombustible materials or of combustible materials with a peak rate of heat release not exceeding 300 kW/m^2 where tested in accordance with ASTM E1354 at an incident heat flux of 50 kW/m^2 in the horizontal orientation.

Exception: Wastebaskets complying with Section 808.

❖ Requiring larger containers to meet stricter conditions is common sense. The larger the volume of waste each container holds, the larger the fire hazard. Isolating the containers from one another with lids helps reduce the possibility that a fire in one container will spread to nearby containers. The lid also helps to smother a fire within the container by limiting the oxygen available to feed it. Additionally, closed containers protect flammable and combustible materials from potential external ignition sources.

Combustible materials, used in such containers, must meet the performance criteria stated when tested in accordance with ASTM E1354. Most nonmetallic waste containers are manufactured from polyethylene, which has a fuel value of 20,050 Btu per pound (46 636 kJ/kg). In comparison, the fuel value of newsprint paper is 9,000 Btu per pound (20 934 kJ/kg). To contain combustible waste in another combustible material that has twice the fuel potential value makes little sense. This section will prohibit the use of larger, nonfire-retardant polyethylene trash containers within a structure. Several manufacturers have had the formulation for years to make a fire-retardant polyethylene.

The exception to this general provision points to more specific requirements for waste containers in Group I-3 facilities contained in Section 808.1.

304.3.3 Capacity exceeding 1.5 cubic yards. Dumpsters and containers with an individual capacity of 1.5 cubic yards [40.5 cubic feet (1.15 m^3)] or more shall not be stored in buildings or placed within 5 feet (1524 mm) of combustible walls, openings or combustible roof eave lines.

Exceptions:

1. Dumpsters or containers that are placed inside buildings in areas protected by an *approved automatic sprinkler system* installed throughout in accordance with Section 903.3.1.1, 903.3.1.2 or 903.3.1.3.
2. Storage in a structure shall not be prohibited where the structure is of Type I or IIA construction, located not less than 10 feet (3048 mm) from other buildings and used exclusively for dumpster or container storage.
3. Dumpsters or containers that are located adjacent to buildings where the exterior area is protected by an approved automatic sprinkler system.

❖ Although waste containers of this size are nearly always constructed of welded steel because of the weight of the waste load, the very fact that the waste load is large makes the containers a large fire hazard. Keeping these large containers in the open and away from combustible construction is the obvious way to keep the fire hazard low.

Exception 1 permits storage of these large containers indoors if the area is protected by an approved sprinkler system. It would be up to the fire code official to determine the maximum quantities that could be stored under these conditions.

Exception 2 applies only to buildings that are of fire-resistance-rated construction and are used exclusively for container storage. Such facilities might be found in scrap yards or at recycling centers, but rarely, if ever, in other occupancies.

Exception 3 permits storage of these large containers less than 5 feet from combustible walls, openings or combustible roof eave lines if the outside area is protected with an automatic sprinkler system.

304.3.4 Capacity of 1 cubic yard or more. Dumpsters with an individual capacity of 1.0 cubic yard [200 gallons (0.76 m^3)] or more shall not be stored in buildings or placed within 5 feet (1524 mm) of combustible walls, openings or combustible roof eave lines unless the dumpsters are constructed of noncombustible materials or of combustible materials with a peak rate of heat release not exceeding 300 kW/m^2 where tested in accordance with ASTM E1354 at an incident heat flux of 50 kW/m^2 in the horizontal orientation.

Exceptions:

1. Dumpsters in areas protected by an *approved automatic sprinkler system* installed throughout in accordance with Section 903.3.1.1, 903.3.1.2 or 903.3.1.3.
2. Storage in a structure shall not be prohibited where the structure is of Type I or IIA construction, located not less than 10 feet (3048 mm) from other buildings and used exclusively for dumpster or container storage.

❖ Medium-density polyethylene dumpsters up to 9 cubic yards [27 ft^3 (0.76 m^3)] in capacity and that have a fuel content of 20,020 Btu per pound (46 567 kJ/kg) [by comparison, municipal solid waste averages 4,500 Btu/lb (10 467 kJ/kg)] are now being distributed and used. Medium-density polyethylene is essentially equal to the fuel value for gasoline and becomes a burning liquid that spreads and flows when involved in a fire. As such, placing them 5 feet (1524 mm) away from a nearby structure will be of little value unless their flammability hazard is mitigated. This section does that by limiting container heat release rate and heat flux using the test parameters of ASTM E1354. The peak rate of heat release criterion is consistent with the one in Sections 304.3.2 and 808.1.

Exception 1 permits storage of these containers indoors if the area is protected by an approved sprinkler system. It would be up to the fire code official to determine the maximum quantities that could be stored under these conditions.

Exception 2 applies only to buildings that are of fire-resistance-rated construction and are used exclusively for waste container storage. Such facilities might be found in scrap yards or at recycling centers, but rarely, if ever, in other occupancies.

SECTION 305
IGNITION SOURCES

305.1 Clearance from ignition sources. Clearance between ignition sources, such as luminaires, heaters, flame-producing devices and combustible materials, shall be maintained in an *approved* manner.

❖ Establishing safe clearances will usually mean following the requirements of the IBC or other codes adopted by the jurisdiction as well as having the approval of the fire code official.

305.2 Hot ashes and spontaneous ignition sources. Hot ashes, cinders, smoldering coals or greasy or oily materials subject to spontaneous ignition shall not be deposited in a combustible receptacle, within 10 feet (3048 mm) of other combustible material including combustible walls and partitions or within 2 feet (610 mm) of openings to buildings.

> **Exception:** The minimum required separation distance to other combustible materials shall be 2 feet (610 mm) where the material is deposited in a covered, noncombustible receptacle placed on a noncombustible floor, ground surface or stand.

❖ This section covers two different, but equally serious, ignition source problems. First, hot ashes, embers and cinders from fireplaces, stoves or other fireboxes must never be placed in a combustible container. This point seems almost too obvious to be mentioned, but every year fires are started when someone carelessly scoops ashes containing glowing embers into paper bags or cardboard cartons. It is also not uncommon to see construction scrap being burned in steel drums on construction sites in cold weather. Care must be taken when emptying ashes from those containers to make sure no hot coals get dumped on paper waste or other combustible materials.

The second problem, greasy or oily materials subject to spontaneous combustion, is addressed by requiring such materials to be placed in listed containers (see commentary, Section 304.3.1).

In both cases, safe distances must be maintained from combustible construction and building openings for added protection.

The exception recognizes the added protection of tight-fitting covers on noncombustible trash containers as well as the reduced fire hazard when the containers are placed on a noncombustible surface.

305.3 Open-flame warning devices. Open-flame warning devices shall not be used along an excavation, road, or any place where the dislodgment of such device might permit the device to roll, fall or slide on to any area or land containing combustible material.

❖ Open-flame warning devices other than fusees used to mark road accidents or other short-term emergencies are rarely used today. The old-fashioned kerosene pots used to mark construction hazards in dark areas have been largely replaced by "sawhorse" barriers with battery-powered flashing lights. But, even though use may be limited, the warning in this section is nonetheless real. One fusee not firmly fixed in the ground or on another stable surface can fall into a roadside ditch filled with dry weeds and cause a roadside fire that could spread into dry woodland or cropland, causing enormous fire damage. Likewise, a burned-out hand-held fusee that is carelessly tossed aside while still hot could ignite dry refuse.

305.4 Deliberate or negligent burning. It shall be unlawful to deliberately or through negligence set fire to or cause the burning of combustible material in such a manner as to endanger the safety of persons or property.

❖ The deliberate setting of fires, whether in a structure or in a waste container located where it could endanger a structure or its occupants, is normally considered arson, which is a felony that is punishable by a lengthy prison sentence. Fortunately, arson is not that common. More likely, a fire would be caused by carelessness or by someone not considering the consequences of his or her actions.

Regardless of the circumstances, fires must be avoided. Following the requirements in the code as well as those in the IBC will help to maintain a safe, fire-free site. On construction or demolition sites, secure fencing around the site and its waste containers is good protection. Following good housekeeping practices, including routine disposal of combustible materials, is also an excellent first line of protection against fire. An ignition source cannot cause damage to property or endanger life unless there is a fuel load to be ignited.

305.5 Unwanted fire ignitions. Acts or processes that have caused repeated ignition of unwanted fires shall be modified to prevent future ignition.

❖ Many industrial processes have the potential to produce frequent nuisance fires that generate unwanted alarms necessitating emergency responses that risk the health and safety of fire fighters and citizens. This section empowers the fire code official to alter such processes to mitigate nuisance fires.

SECTION 306
MOTION PICTURE PROJECTION ROOMS AND FILM

306.1 Motion picture projection rooms. Electric arc, xenon or other light source projection equipment that develops hazardous gases, dust or radiation and the projection of ribbon-type cellulose nitrate film, regardless of the light source used in projection, shall be operated within a motion picture projection room complying with Section 409 of the *International Building Code*.

❖ The requirements in this section are specific to spaces housing equipment used to project cellulose acetate film, also called safety film, which is in common use today. This film has about the same fire hazard characteristics as paper of the same thickness and form. The equipment used to project the film, however, may also present fire or health hazards that can be minimized by proper construction of the room. Section 409 of the IBC covers these construction requirements in detail.

The older type of motion picture film was made of cellulose nitrate, which is also called pyroxylin, which presents a significantly greater fire hazard and, therefore, calls for stricter construction requirements, including sprinklers. These requirements are contained in Sections 903.2.5.3 and 6504. The greater hazard of cellulose nitrate film, which today is found mainly in museum collections and other archives or film preservation facilities, comes from the characteristic of the material to begin degrading at temperatures below its ignition temperature, causing a chemical reaction that can lead to spontaneous combustion. The combustion products of cellulose nitrate are both flammable and extremely toxic because they include oxides of nitrogen. Cellulose nitrate film burns at a rate that is as much as 15 times the rate of common combustibles.

306.2 Cellulose nitrate film storage. Storage of cellulose nitrate film shall be in accordance with NFPA 40.

❖ NFPA 40 contains minimum requirements for a reasonable level of protection for the storage and handling of cellulose nitrate film. The standard does not address the manufacture of the film because it has not been made in the United States since 1951.

SECTION 307
OPEN BURNING, RECREATIONAL FIRES AND PORTABLE OUTDOOR FIREPLACES

307.1 General. A person shall not kindle or maintain or authorize to be kindled or maintained any *open burning* unless conducted and *approved* in accordance with Sections 307.1.1 through 307.5.

❖ To control the hazards associated with it, open burning may not be authorized or undertaken without the approvals specified in Section 307. See the commentary to Section 202 for the definition of "Open burning" for a discussion of the types of burning intended to be regulated by this section.

307.1.1 Prohibited open burning. Open burning shall be prohibited when atmospheric conditions or local circumstances make such fires hazardous.

> **Exception:** Prescribed burning for the purpose of reducing the impact of wildland fire when authorized by the *fire code official*.

❖ This section is intended to protect the public from irresponsible burning when it endangers the safety, health or welfare of persons near the burn site. The terms "offensive" and "objectionable" in the previous code edition were undefined and unreasonably subjective, making the prohibition of open burning due to smoke emissions unenforceable. Also, there is not a referenced standard that provides a method for measuring or otherwise determining when smoke emissions are "offensive or objectionable." In the absence of such guidance, the legal requirements for consistency of enforcement were unattainable.

Fundamentally and historically, the code has regulated fire hazards and not poor air quality caused by smoke from fires. Experience strongly suggests that the previous wording encouraged citizens to request intervention by the fire code official to resolve neighborhood disputes regarding smoke emissions from many forms of outdoor fires that citizens correctly or incorrectly believed to be "open burning" (e.g., recreational fires, bonfires, charcoal burners, etc.); such situations should be civil matters rather than unlawful acts subject to the penalties prescribed in Section 109.

The revised wording empowers the fire code official to prohibit open burning when such fires would, in fact, be hazardous because of measurable environmental factors, such as weather (e.g., wind, temperature, relative humidity) or fuel characteristics (e.g., fuel moisture content).

The exception allows for prescribed burning that is conducted in an effort to minimize the fuel load in wildland and interface areas. Such prescribed burning is a common practice and is done with great planning and forethought and includes safeguards for proper fire control. Annually, several million wildland acres are subjected to prescribed burning in the U.S. to eliminate hazardous fuels, alter vegetation to promote the growth of fuels that produce less heat and burn slower, improve the habitat for wildlife and vegetation, control nuisance pests, and improve access for replanting and other recreational activities. The ability for a fire agency to utilize prescribed burning operations in a season when the fire can be more easily controlled reduces the personnel and resources needed to control a wildland fire when it occurs, and increases the likelihood that fewer structures and lives will be lost to wildland fire.

307.2 Permit required. A permit shall be obtained from the *fire code official* in accordance with Section 105.6 prior to kindling a fire for recognized silvicultural or range or wildlife management practices, prevention or control of disease or pests, or a bonfire. Application for such approval shall only be presented by and permits issued to the *owner* of the land on which the fire is to be kindled.

❖ This section defines a rather narrow range of purposes for which permits will be issued. Section 105.6.30 covers open-burning permits in general. This section restricts permissible fires to those used for silviculture (the cultivation of forests and shade trees); range or wildlife management; pest control; and bonfires as defined in the code. This section further restricts the permitting process to owners of the land on which the fire is to be kindled (see commentary, Section 301.2).

307.2.1 Authorization. Where required by state or local law or regulations, *open burning* shall only be permitted with prior approval from the state or local air and water quality management authority, provided that all conditions specified in the authorization are followed.

❖ This section requires permit applicants to comply with state and local regulations covering air and water quality as well as safety regulations established by the jurisdiction having authority.

307.3 Extinguishment authority. Where open burning creates or adds to a hazardous situation, or a required permit for open burning has not been obtained, the *fire code official* is authorized to order the extinguishment of the open burning operation.

❖ Where the fire code official finds that open burning creates a hazardous condition such as the potential for igniting exposures or is unsafe because of atmospheric conditions, this section establishes the authority of the fire code official to order that the open burning fire be extinguished. Note that the fire department is not included in the extinguishment scenario but, rather, the section relies on the provisions of Section 110.3.2, which establishes who must comply with the extinguishment order, i.e., "... the owner, the owner's authorized agent, operator, occupant or other person responsible for the condition or violation ..." This enhances public safety by not requiring the commitment of a piece of fire apparatus to extinguish an open-burning fire that is not an emergency (see commentary, Section 110.3.2).

307.4 Location. The location for *open burning* shall be not less than 50 feet (15 240 mm) from any structure, and provisions shall be made to prevent the fire from spreading to within 50 feet (15 240 mm) of any structure.

Exceptions:

1. Fires in *approved* containers that are not less than 15 feet (4572 mm) from a structure.
2. The minimum required distance from a structure shall be 25 feet (7620 mm) where the pile size is 3 feet (914 mm) or less in diameter and 2 feet (610 mm) or less in height.

❖ The 50-foot (15 240 mm) restriction applies to large fires in large open areas, such as those defined in Section 307.2. Exception 1 refers to fires that generally would be considerably smaller or would be controlled by the container in which they burn, presenting a reduced exposure risk to nearby buildings. Exception 2 allows a reduction in clearance from buildings based on the lesser hazard of fires that are limited in size.

307.4.1 Bonfires. A bonfire shall not be conducted within 50 feet (15 240 mm) of a structure or combustible material unless the fire is contained in a barbecue pit. Conditions that could cause a fire to spread within 50 feet (15 240 mm) of a structure shall be eliminated prior to ignition.

❖ Bonfires usually are large and associated with some kind of planned event (for example, a school pep rally, holiday celebration or camp celebration). This section restricts the location of these large fires to open areas in which sparks and burning embers would be unlikely to endanger structures and smoke would not be a significant hazard to public health. Allowing a bonfire in a barbeque pit automatically restricts the size of the fire to the fuel load that can be contained within the noncombustible fire pit.

307.4.2 Recreational fires. *Recreational fires* shall not be conducted within 25 feet (7620 mm) of a structure or combustible material. Conditions that could cause a fire to spread within 25 feet (7620 mm) of a structure shall be eliminated prior to ignition.

❖ Recreational fires are usually fairly small, but can still represent a significant fire hazard if the area in which they are kindled is not kept free of combustible trash and debris. Basic fire safety practices followed by campers make good guidelines. No fire should ever be kindled in a location where it would endanger structures or would be likely to ignite combustible materials close by.

307.4.3 Portable outdoor fireplaces. Portable outdoor fireplaces shall be used in accordance with the manufacturer's instructions and shall not be operated within 15 feet (3048 mm) of a structure or combustible material.

Exception: Portable outdoor fireplaces used at one- and two-family *dwellings*.

❖ Portable outdoor fireplaces (also known as patio fireplaces) designed to burn solid fuel are available at retailers ranging from big box stores to local groceries. Their widespread availability and use created considerable confusion for citizens and the fire service regarding if or how they were regulated by the code since Sections 307 and 308 were essentially silent on the use of this specific type of device. Fires in portable outdoor fireplaces could not be considered a "recreational fire" because critical to that definition is the concept that the fire is not contained in an incinerator, outdoor fireplace, barbeque grill or barbeque pit. It could then have been suggested that a portable outdoor fireplace is merely a type of "outdoor fireplace," but the code did not contain any references pertaining to where an outdoor fireplace could be located or operated. Since the use and hazards associated with operating such fireplaces are more consistent with the type of activities regulated in Section 307 than other types of open flames addressed in Section 308, specific regulations are now provided in Section 307.

This section makes it clear that the use of portable outdoor fireplaces is specifically regulated by the code. It prohibits the use of these devices within 15 feet (3048 mm) of any structure and is consistent with Section 307.4, Exception 1. Also, consistent with regulations for other appliances, this section relies on compliance with the manufacturer's instructions for additional safeguards.

The exception exempts one- and two-family dwellings from the requirements of this section. In those occupancies, the level of familiarity and control exercised by the building occupants is recognized as offsetting the hazards of using these devices. There are practical difficulties involved in enforcing such regulations in one- and two-family dwellings as well.

307.5 Attendance. *Open burning*, bonfires, *recreational fires* and use of portable outdoor fireplaces shall be constantly attended until the fire is extinguished. Not fewer than one portable fire extinguisher complying with Section 906 with a minimum 4-A rating or other *approved* on-site fire-extinguishing equipment, such as dirt, sand, water barrel, garden hose or water truck, shall be available for immediate utilization.

❖ This section reiterates basic common sense, but tends to be ignored quite often. Having one or more individuals responsible for keeping watch on a fire, even one of small size, is the first line of fire prevention. All too often news articles tell of wooden decks burning because hot embers from a charcoal grill fell unobserved onto the unprotected wooden surface, or of a huge brush or forest fire being caused by careless individuals who did not watch their campfires.

For practical purposes as well as for fire safety, some means of extinguishing a kindled fire should be kept close at hand. For small fires, a shovelful of dirt may be sufficient. For large fires, such as bonfires, large volumes of water may be necessary; however, no matter how much extinguishing equipment is available, it may prove useless unless someone is tending the fire and can sound an alarm.

SECTION 308
OPEN FLAMES

308.1 General. Open flame, fire and burning on all premises shall be in accordance with Sections 308.1.1 through 308.4.1 and with other applicable sections of this code.

❖ This section establishes the scope of the requirements of Section 308 as being applicable to both indoor and outdoor situations involving open flames.

308.1.1 Where prohibited. A person shall not take or utilize an open flame or light in a structure, vessel, boat or other place where highly flammable, combustible or explosive material is utilized or stored. Lighting appliances shall be well-secured in a glass globe and wire mesh cage or a similar *approved* device.

❖ This section is intended to maintain separation between ignitable combustible materials and ignition sources that involve an open flame in any vessel, structure or occupancy.

308.1.2 Throwing or placing sources of ignition. A person shall not throw or place, or cause to be thrown or placed, a lighted match, cigar, cigarette, matches, or other flaming or glowing substance or object on any surface or article where it can cause an unwanted fire.

❖ This section addresses the hazard caused by carelessness in disposing of smoking materials and other flaming or glowing objects. Smoking in bed or in situations where the smoker could forget about lighted smoking materials has caused large numbers of fires and fatalities over the years. Lack of attention to fireplaces and ash pits has caused great property loss as well. As one example, a three-story fraternity house at Iowa State University in Ames, Iowa, was completely destroyed by the fire that resulted from a burning log tumbling from an overflowing ash pit onto a combustible floor surface.

Lighted cigarettes discarded through the windows of moving vehicles each year cause grass, brush and forest fires that consume huge acreage in open country as well as dwellings and other structures.

308.1.3 Torches for removing paint. A person utilizing a torch or other flame-producing device for removing paint from a structure shall provide not less than one portable fire extinguisher complying with Section 906 and with a minimum 4-A rating, two portable fire extinguishers, each with a minimum 2-A rating, or a water hose connected to the water supply on the premises where such burning is done. The person doing the burning shall remain on the premises 1 hour after the torch or flame-producing device is utilized.

❖ Any time an open flame is used to soften old paint in preparation for removal, there is a risk of fire that must be covered by having approved fire extinguishers or a water source readily available. The requirement for a 1-hour fire watch after discontinuing the use of the open flame covers the possibility that paint fragments could still be hot enough to ignite flammable or combustible materials that might be lying around. It also considers the possibility that the flame used to remove paint from a combustible base material could heat that material to its ignition temperature and leave an almost undetectable smolder that might burst into flames later. Safe and effective means for removing paint at lower temperatures, such as warm-air heat devices capable of generating high-temperature convection air, are readily available for sale or rent and far less likely to result in an ignition of combustible materials.

308.1.4 Open-flame cooking devices. Charcoal burners and other open-flame cooking devices shall not be operated on combustible balconies or within 10 feet (3048 mm) of combustible construction.

Exceptions:

1. One- and two-family *dwellings*.
2. Where buildings, balconies and decks are protected by an *automatic sprinkler system*.
3. LP-gas cooking devices having LP-gas container with a water capacity not greater than $2^1/_2$ pounds [nominal 1 pound (0.454 kg) LP-gas capacity].

❖ This section contains a strict prohibition on the use of charcoal-burning grills and other open-flame cooking devices in the locations described. It is intended to mitigate the potential for hot embers to fall from the firebox of the cooking device and ignite a combustible surface, such as a wooden balcony or deck. The 10-foot (3048 mm) separation also reduces the likelihood that fire-starting or cooking flare-ups will come in contact with combustible wall construction that is easily ignited.

Since this section appears to regulate only the operation of the cooking devices, it is often asked if the devices can even be located or stored in the locations described. In the case of LP-gas-fired grills using containers larger than those described in Exception 3, the answer is generally no, based on Section 6.20.11.2 of NFPA 58, which does not allow larger containers to be transported through an occupied building. See Sections 6101.1 and 6104.1 of the code for references to NFPA 58.

In the case of locating non-LP-gas-fired cooking devices, the location would have to be approved by the fire code official. Note that the prohibition in this section would also apply to gas grills connected to the building's fuel gas piping system since they are still open-flame cooking devices. See also Section 603.4.2.1.1.

Exception 1 exempts one- and two-family dwellings from the requirements of this section and would allow the use of LP-gas barbeque grills of any size on balconies of such buildings. In those occupancies, the level of familiarity and control exercised by the building occupants is recognized as offsetting the hazards of using open-flame cooking devices. There are practical difficulties involved in enforcing such regulations in one- and two-family dwellings as well. Exception 2 recognizes the added protection provided by sprinklers. Exception 3 allows small LP-gas burning devices such as the tabletop grills or units that might be used in cooking within residential occupancies.

308.1.5 Location near combustibles. Open flames such as from candles, lanterns, kerosene heaters and gas-fired heaters shall not be located on or near decorative material or similar combustible materials.

❖ Each year in nearly every county and community in the country at least one house fire occurs that is caused by a gas-fired space heater igniting nearby combustibles. Accidents involving candles and lanterns used in both outdoor and indoor settings are not at all uncommon. In nearly all of these incidents, the exercise of common sense and the practice of keeping ignition sources and fuel packages well separated could have prevented property damage or loss of life.

308.1.6 Open-flame devices. Torches and other devices, machines or processes liable to start or cause fire shall not be operated or used in or on wildfire risk areas, except by a permit in accordance with Section 105.6 secured from the *fire code official*.

Exception: Use within inhabited premises or designated campsites that are not less than 30 feet (9144 mm) from grass-, grain-, brush- or forest-covered areas.

❖ This section establishes the fire code official's authority to control through the permitting process the use of open flames in areas susceptible to fires. The term "wildfire risk area" is defined in Chapter 2 of the code and is applied to land covered with grass, grain, brush, forest or similar vegetation that, if ignited, could pose a severe fire danger to surrounding areas. The exception recognizes open ground that is free of combustible materials as an acceptable barrier to fire spread (see the IWUIC for further information).

308.1.6.1 Signals and markers. Flame-employing devices, such as lanterns or kerosene road flares, shall not be operated or used as a signal or marker in or on wildfire risk areas.

Exception: The proper use of fusees at the scenes of emergencies or as required by standard railroad operating procedures.

❖ This section prohibits the use of flame-producing devices as signal or marker devices except for the use of fusees to mark the scene of an emergency or where routinely employed in railroad procedures, such as when a train is stopped across a roadway not protected by permanent signal lights.

308.1.6.2 Portable fueled open-flame devices. Portable open-flame devices fueled by flammable or combustible gases or liquids shall be enclosed or installed in such a manner as to prevent the flame from contacting combustible material.

Exceptions:

1. LP-gas-fueled devices used for sweating pipe joints or removing paint in accordance with Chapter 61.
2. Cutting and welding operations in accordance with Chapter 35.
3. Torches or flame-producing devices in accordance with Section 308.4.
4. Candles and open-flame decorative devices in accordance with Section 308.3.

❖ This section prohibits the use of portable devices in situations where they might be placed on unstable platforms or where they could be knocked over by human contact. The exceptions list the types of open-flame or heat-producing operations not regulated by this section but regulated elsewhere in the code.

308.1.6.3 Sky lanterns. A person shall not release or cause to be released an untethered sky lantern.

❖ Sky lanterns, variously known as Kongming lanterns, Chinese lanterns, fire balloons or fire parachutes, are typically made of paper and contain an open flame used to heat the air inside the device to make it airborne, similar to but on a much smaller scale than a hot air balloon. Once airborne, if these devices are untethered and their movement is thus unrestricted, they are subject to winds and other atmospheric conditions such that the location of the final landfall is completely unknown and uncontrolled by the user. Obviously, uncontrolled open flame devices descending out of the sky have a significant potential to start wildfires and structure fires.

308.1.7 Religious ceremonies. Where, in the opinion of the *fire code official*, adequate safeguards have been taken, participants in religious ceremonies are allowed to carry hand-held candles. Hand-held candles shall not be passed from one person to another while lighted.

❖ This section has a very narrow application. As stated, only religious ceremonies are covered and the judgment of the fire code official is required for final approval. Prohibiting the passing of lighted candles from person to person is intended to minimize the opportunities for the candles to be dropped where they could become an ignition source for flammable or combustible materials or come into contact with clothing or hair. Spiritual significance may be attached to the use of candles in places of worship; therefore, the local fire code official should work closely with religious groups when enforcing this section.

308.1.7.1 Aisles and exits. Candles shall be prohibited in areas where occupants stand, or in an *aisle* or *exit*.

❖ This prohibition is intended to prevent accidents caused by lighted candles being knocked from their holders onto combustible furniture, carpeting or decorative materials. Candles are commonly found at seasonal religious observances where attendance often exceeds the norm. In case of an emergency, people must be able to move through the aisles toward the exits without risking the ignition of clothing, hair or decorations.

308.1.8 Flaming food and beverage preparation. The preparation of flaming foods or beverages in places of assembly and drinking or dining establishments shall be in accordance with Sections 308.1.8.1 through 308.1.8.5.

❖ The regulations in this section of the code are necessary to give the fire code official guidance in allowing the preparation of flaming food and beverages to be conducted in restaurants in a safe manner. These types of foods, sometimes referred to as "flambé foods," are prepared by adding a small amount of flammable or combustible liquid in the form of alcoholic beverages to the food and igniting it. Many restaurants prepare popular selected dishes, such as cherries jubilee, brandied peaches and flaming bananas, in this manner, usually tableside within close proximity of the customers. The proximity plus the intentional ignition of flammable liquids in a Group A occupancy make regulation of this process appropriate. Note that the regulations in this section are not intended to address a fuel source, such as Sterno, used to keep food warm.

308.1.8.1 Dispensing. Flammable or *combustible liquids* used in the preparation of flaming foods or beverages shall be dispensed from one of the following:

1. A 1-ounce (29.6 ml) container.
2. A container not exceeding 1-quart (946.5 ml) capacity with a controlled pouring device that will limit the flow to a 1-ounce (29.6 ml) serving.

❖ These dispensing provisions limit the amount of flammable or combustible liquid being transported around the restaurant for use in flaming food or beverage preparation in order to minimize the fuel potential in a fire incident involving such operations. Item 1 could be referring to a typical shot glass. Item 2 could be referring to a "jigger-pourer," which is a device that fits into the neck of a bottle and is intended to limit the per-pour quantity to 1 ounce.

308.1.8.2 Containers not in use. Containers shall be secured to prevent spillage when not in use.

❖ Securing the containers used in flaming food or beverage preparation while not in use reduces the likelihood of an accidental spill.

308.1.8.3 Serving of flaming food. The serving of flaming foods or beverages shall be done in a safe manner and shall not create high flames. The pouring, ladling or spooning of liquids is restricted to a maximum height of 8 inches (203 mm) above the receiving receptacle.

❖ Limiting the height from which flammable or combustible liquids are poured reduces the likelihood of a spill or overpour that might miss the target dish and be ignited by a table candle, smoking materials or another ignition source.

308.1.8.4 Location. Flaming foods or beverages shall be prepared only in the immediate vicinity of the table being serviced. They shall not be transported or carried while burning.

❖ This section prohibits movement or transport of "flambé foods" while they are burning. This provision reduces the potential for incidents wherein the tray or dish might be dropped or tipped, causing a spill of burning liquid that could lead to a panic reaction by restaurant patrons or, if spilled on a patron, cause serious burn injuries.

308.1.8.5 Fire protection. The person preparing the flaming foods or beverages shall have a wet cloth towel immediately available for use in smothering the flames in the event of an emergency.

❖ Flaming-food preparation is a cooking hazard much the same as stovetop preparation. An efficient method for extinguishing a stovetop fire in a frying pan or similar utensil is to put the cover on the utensil to exclude oxygen. In flambé preparation, the food is prepared in a relatively small pan or in the dish in which it will be served, in either of which the flames can be easily smothered by a wet towel. Note that this precautionary measure is in addition to the portable fire extinguishers to be provided in accordance with Section 906.

308.2 Permits required. Permits shall be obtained from the *fire code official* in accordance with Section 105.6 prior to engaging in the following activities involving open flame, fire and burning:

1. Use of a torch or flame-producing device to remove paint from a structure.
2. Use of open flame, fire or burning in connection with Group A or E occupancies.
3. Use or operation of torches and other devices, machines or processes liable to start or cause fire in or on wildfire risk areas.

❖ This section establishes the authority of the fire code official to control the hazards of using open flames through the permitting process. The restrictions here do not prohibit the use of open-flame devices in the listed activities, but they do allow the fire code official to inspect plans and ongoing activities to make certain they are safe for the occupancy in which they are held. Permit applicants should be required to demonstrate that their regulated activities comply with the intent of the code before the permit is issued. See the commentary to Section 105.6 for a general discussion of operations requiring an operational permit and Sections 105.6.33 and 105.6.34 for a discussion of specific operational permits for the indicated regulated activities. The permit process also serves to notify the fire department of the increased hazard at particular locations.

308.3 Group A occupancies. Open-flame devices shall not be used in a Group A occupancy.

Exceptions:

1. Open-flame devices are allowed to be used in the following situations, provided that *approved* precautions are taken to prevent ignition of a combustible material or injury to occupants:
   - 1.1. Where necessary for ceremonial or religious purposes in accordance with Section 308.1.7.
   - 1.2. On stages and platforms as a necessary part of a performance in accordance with Section 308.3.2.
   - 1.3. Where candles on tables are securely supported on substantial noncombustible bases and the candle flames are protected.
2. Heat-producing equipment complying with Chapter 6 and the *International Mechanical Code*.
3. Gas lights are allowed to be used provided that adequate precautions satisfactory to the *fire code official* are taken to prevent ignition of combustible materials.

❖ The use of open-flame devices in Group A occupancies where large numbers of people gather for entertainment, instruction, food or drink consumption, deliberation, awaiting transportation or social or religious functions increases the likelihood of the occupants coming into contact with these devices and is, therefore, prohibited. Safe alternatives to open-flame devices should be used where practical, especially in restaurants and other assembly occupancies where the focus is on atmosphere rather than symbolism or religious significance.

Exception 1 refers to Sections 308.1.7 and 308.3.2 for use in religious and theatrical settings as well as permitting use on tabletops where properly secured and protected.

Exception 2 refers to building service heat-producing equipment that meets other code requirements.

Exception 3 covers gas lights installed with proper flame safeguards and with the approval of the fire code official. This kind of lighting is often a permanent installation that would be covered by additional code requirements.

308.3.1 Open-flame decorative devices. Open-flame decorative devices shall comply with all of the following restrictions:

1. Class I and Class II liquids and LP-gas shall not be used.
2. Liquid- or solid-fueled lighting devices containing more than 8 ounces (237 ml) of fuel must self-extinguish and not leak fuel at a rate of more than 0.25 teaspoon per minute (1.26 ml per minute) if tipped over.
3. The device or holder shall be constructed to prevent the spillage of liquid fuel or wax at the rate of more than 0.25 teaspoon per minute (1.26 ml per minute) when the device or holder is not in an upright position.
4. The device or holder shall be designed so that it will return to the upright position after being tilted to an angle of 45 degrees (0.79 rad) from vertical.

   Exception: Devices that self-extinguish if tipped over and do not spill fuel or wax at the rate of more than 0.25 teaspoon per minute (1.26 ml per minute) if tipped over.
5. The flame shall be enclosed except where openings on the side are not more than 0.375-inch (9.5 mm) diameter or where openings are on the top and the distance to the top is such that a piece of tissue paper placed on the top will not ignite in 10 seconds.
6. Chimneys shall be made of noncombustible materials and securely attached to the open-flame device.

   Exception: A chimney is not required to be attached to any open-flame device that will self-extinguish if the device is tipped over.
7. Fuel canisters shall be safely sealed for storage.

8. Storage and handling of *combustible liquids* shall be in accordance with Chapter 57.
9. Shades, where used, shall be made of noncombustible materials and securely attached to the open-flame device holder or chimney.
10. Candelabras with flame-lighted candles shall be securely fastened in place to prevent overturning, and shall be located away from occupants using the area and away from possible contact with drapes, curtains or other combustibles.

❖ This class of open-flame devices includes items such as wall-mounted candles or torch sconces; bug-repellant candles in glass jars or metal cans; tabletop candles and oil lamps; free-standing torch holders and candelabras. The criteria for the use of this kind of device are all intended to enhance safety.

308.3.2 Theatrical performances. Where *approved*, open-flame devices used in conjunction with theatrical performances are allowed to be used where adequate safety precautions have been taken in accordance with NFPA 160.

❖ Theatrical performances typically occur on stages and involve large quantities of combustible materials. Hazards associated with stages can include: combustible scenery and lighting suspended overhead; scenic elements, contents and acoustical treatment on the back and sides of the stage; workshops, scene docks and dressing rooms located around the stage perimeter, and storage areas and property rooms located underneath the stage. Because of the inherent dangers associated with the introduction of open flames into such a fuel-rich environment, the use of open-flame devices in theatrical performances requires review, evaluation and the approval of the fire code official on a case-by-case basis and must be safeguarded in accordance with the provisions of NFPA 160. For further discussion of the special hazard nature of stages, see the commentary for Section 410 of the IBC.

308.4 Group R occupancies. Open flame, fire and burning in Group R occupancies shall comply with the requirements of Sections 308.1 through 308.1.6.3 and Section 308.4.1.

❖ This section establishes the applicability of the indicated requirements of Section 308 to open flame activities in Group R occupancies.

308.4.1 Group R-2 dormitories. Candles, incense and similar open-flame-producing items shall not be allowed in sleeping units in Group R-2 dormitory occupancies.

❖ This section provides the fire code official with the needed authority to control the introduction of potential ignition sources into Group R-2 dormitory occupancies and help to stop dorm fires before lives are endangered and potentially lost. Fire represents a significant risk to life and property in dormitory occupancies, particularly at residential schools, colleges and universities. The large number of young people living in close proximity to one another creates the potential for a relatively small fire to have serious and possibly fatal consequences.

Candle and incense use presents a significant life safety risk in the close confines of a typical residence hall. According to NFPA fire loss data, there is an average of 4,100 fires each year in dormitories, causing $14 million in direct property damage. The data shows that only 7 percent of fires started in the bedroom, but these fires were responsible for 16 percent of injuries and 24 percent of direct property damage, which makes them the most costly type of fire in a residence hall. Prohibiting the use of candles, incense and similar open flame items reduces the potential ignition sources for a fire, providing for a safer living environment.

SECTION 309
POWERED INDUSTRIAL TRUCKS AND EQUIPMENT

309.1 General. Powered industrial trucks and similar equipment including, but not limited to, floor scrubbers and floor buffers, shall be operated and maintained in accordance with Section 309.2 through 309.7.

❖ This section establishes the fire safety requirements for control of the hazards associated with powered industrial trucks and industrial equipment. Because these trucks or equipment may have either battery-powered electric motors or internal combustion engines using liquid or gaseous fuel, Sections 309.2 through 309.6 cover the fire safety aspects of both.

309.2 Use in hazardous (classified) locations. Powered industrial trucks used in areas designated as hazardous (classified) locations in accordance with NFPA 70 shall be listed and labeled for use in the environment intended in accordance with NFPA 505.

❖ Powered industrial trucks used in hazardous locations as defined by NFPA 70 must meet the requirements of NFPA 505.

309.3 Battery chargers. Battery chargers shall be of an *approved* type. Combustible storage shall be kept not less than 3 feet (915 mm) from battery chargers. Battery charging shall not be conducted in areas open to the public.

❖ Battery chargers offer several safety challenges if they are not properly housed and operated. A battery that is connected to the charger with the poles reversed can explode when charging power is turned on, which could result in corrosive liquid being sprayed over the charger room and anyone who happens to be in it. Aside from the possibility of serious bodily injury from flying debris or corrosive spray, eye damage from the spray is a critical consideration. There is also the possibility of energized charging leads shorting, arcing or fusing and causing sparks to become an ignition source for combustibles if they are not kept out of the area.

When a charger is properly connected and energized, the charging process causes generation of hydrogen and oxygen gases as well as acid or alkali fumes. These gases must be vented to prevent them from reaching ignitable or detonable levels (see commentary, Section 309.3). A typical battery charger arrangement is illustrated in Commentary Figure 309.2. Note that these battery chargers are outside of the scope of Section 608 and thus not subject to its provisions.

Commentary Figure 309.2
BATTERY CHARGERS FOR
POWERED INDUSTRIAL TRUCKS

309.4 Ventilation. Ventilation shall be provided in an *approved* manner in battery-charging areas to prevent a dangerous accumulation of flammable gases.

❖ Charging lead-acid or nickel iron batteries is a process of electrolysis in which oxides created by operation of the battery are reduced to metal and redeposited on the electrode plates. The process results in the rejuvenation of the electrolyte in the battery and the emission of both oxygen and hydrogen gases as well as corrosive fumes. If these gases are allowed to accumulate in an enclosed space, they could eventually reach an ignitable or detonable level. Section 608.6 and the applicable provisions of the *International Mechanical Code*® (IMC®) describe one method of ventilation used to carry off and dilute the concentrations of hazardous gases. See the commentaries to Section 608.6 and its subsections.

309.5 Fire extinguishers. Battery-charging areas shall be provided with a fire extinguisher complying with Section 906 having a minimum 4-A:20-B:C rating within 20 feet (6096 mm) of the battery charger.

❖ Because of the electrical hazards associated with the battery-charging operation, the fuel load presented by the plastic battery cases and other area contents and the potential for the presence of gases in the room, an appropriately sized portable fire extinguisher must be located within the battery-charging area. The extinguisher must be accessible with minimum travel.

309.6 Refueling. Powered industrial trucks using liquid fuel, LP-gas or hydrogen shall be refueled outside of buildings or in areas specifically *approved* for that purpose. Fixed fuel-dispensing equipment and associated fueling operations shall be in accordance with Chapter 23. Other fuel-dispensing equipment and operations, including cylinder exchange for LP-gas-fueled vehicles, shall be in accordance with Chapter 57 for flammable and *combustible liquids* or Chapter 61 for LP-gas.

❖ Because of the hazards associated with liquid fuel spills and gaseous fuel discharges, this section requires that powered industrial trucks be refueled outside where the vapors or gas can be readily dissipated. This section also allows the alternative of fueling inside of buildings where safeguards mitigate the hazards of the operation and the location is specifically approved for the use by the fire code official. Where fueling with liquid or gaseous fuel is done from fixed equipment, compliance with Chapter 23 is required for both the fueling equipment and its operation because of the proven safeguards for such operations that are included in that chapter. Similarly, fueling equipment and operations for flammable or combustible liquids or LP-gas utilizing nonfixed equipment must be conducted in accordance with the applicable provisions of the appropriate material-specific chapter.

309.7 Repairs. Repairs to fuel systems, electrical systems and repairs utilizing open flame or welding shall be done in *approved* locations outside of buildings or in areas specifically *approved* for that purpose.

❖ Repairs that could create ignition sources or a fuel load for an ignition source must be done in indoor or outdoor locations that are designed specifically for vehicle repairs and that have been approved by the fire code official.

SECTION 310
SMOKING

310.1 General. The smoking or carrying of a lighted pipe, cigar, cigarette or any other type of smoking paraphernalia or material is prohibited in the areas indicated in Sections 310.2 through 310.8.

❖ This section states that smoking is prohibited in those areas designated in Sections 310.2 and 310.8. Before entering an area posted with "No Smoking" signs, anyone carrying a lighted smoking product or device must extinguish the smoking material and properly dispose of the ashes and other residue. Suitable ashtrays should be available at the entry to "No Smoking" areas for disposal of the prohibited smoking materials.

310.2 Prohibited areas. Smoking shall be prohibited where conditions are such as to make smoking a hazard, and in spaces where flammable or combustible materials are stored or handled.

❖ Smoking can be prohibited wherever it would be a hazard in the judgment of the fire code official.

310.3 "No Smoking" signs. The *fire code official* is authorized to order the posting of "No Smoking" signs in a conspicuous location in each structure or location in which smoking is prohibited. The content, lettering, size, color and location of required "No Smoking" signs shall be *approved.*

Exception: In Group I-2 occupancies where smoking is prohibited, "No Smoking" signs are not required in interior locations of the facility where signs are displayed at all major entrances into the facility.

❖ The fire code official is not only authorized to designate where signs are to be posted, but is also responsible for establishing the specification for all aspects of those signs. A typical sign design is shown in Commentary Figure 310.3.

The exception provides correlation with NFPA 101 on this topic. Since the majority of healthcare facilities already prohibit smoking, where signs are posted at the main entrances it is redundant and unnecessary to also require the signs to be posted throughout a facility that does not permit smoking, has a staff trained to monitor and policies in place to quickly stop or prevent the action (see Commentary Figure 310.3.)

Commentary Figure 310.3
NO SMOKING SIGN

310.4 Removal of signs prohibited. A posted "No Smoking" sign shall not be obscured, removed, defaced, mutilated or destroyed.

❖ Posted signs must remain in the locations designated by the fire code official and be readable at all times. Many, if not all, jurisdictions establish penalties for removing, obscuring, defacing or mutilating official signs.

310.5 Compliance with "No Smoking" signs. Smoking shall not be permitted nor shall a person smoke, throw or deposit any lighted or smoldering substance in any place where "No Smoking" signs are posted.

❖ Penalties are usually imposed for violating "no smoking" prohibitions. Smoking must be confined to approved areas, and discarded smoking materials must be deposited only in approved ashtrays or receptacles. Violation of this provision customarily constitutes a misdemeanor. Prosecution of misdemeanor offenses should be coordinated with the jurisdiction's legal counsel. Offense and penalty clauses, such as those included in Section 109, are required in order to prosecute infractions (see commentary, Section 109.3).

310.6 Ash trays. Where smoking is permitted, suitable noncombustible ash trays or match receivers shall be provided on each table and at other appropriate locations.

❖ Where smoking is permitted, smokers must have available a noncombustible ashtray or other receptacle where smoking materials can be safely deposited. These receptacles must be located on each table and other locations throughout the smoking area so that the smoker does not have to look for a place to discard used materials.

310.7 Burning objects. Lighted matches, cigarettes, cigars or other burning object shall not be discarded in such a manner that could cause ignition of other combustible material.

❖ Lighted matches, burning tobacco products and all other burning objects must be deposited in ashtrays or other approved noncombustible containers to separate these ignition sources from any potential fuel loads.

310.8 Hazardous environmental conditions. Where the *fire code official* determines that hazardous environmental conditions necessitate controlled use of smoking materials, the ignition or use of such materials in mountainous, brush-covered or forest-covered areas or other designated areas is prohibited except in *approved* designated smoking areas.

❖ This section gives the fire code official the authority to establish "no smoking" areas whenever and wherever environmental conditions are considered hazardous. This can include prohibiting burning dry grasses and leaves where lack of rain has rendered the environment dangerously dry or burning of specific materials where the smoke plume from the fire would endanger the health or welfare of a population. The possibilities for determination of hazardous conditions are too numerous to itemize. The judgment of the fire code official, with the advice of other officials being sought as needed, is the determining factor. The fire code official can also exercise the discretion of designating areas in which smoking is permitted.

SECTION 311
VACANT PREMISES

311.1 General. Temporarily unoccupied buildings, structures, premises or portions thereof, including tenant spaces, shall be safeguarded and maintained in accordance with Sections 311.1.1 through 311.6.

❖ Vacant buildings or portions of buildings that are open at doors or windows pose fire safety and criminal trespass hazards to a community and are correctly declared to be unsafe buildings in Section 110.1.1. Such premises are often called an "attractive nuisance" to neighborhood children who may enter them to play or to other persons who may enter seeking shelter from the elements or to engage in potential criminal activities.

311.1.1 Abandoned premises. Buildings, structures and premises for which an *owner* cannot be identified or located by dispatch of a certificate of mailing to the last known or registered address, which persistently or repeatedly become unprotected or unsecured, which have been occupied by unauthorized persons or for illegal purposes, or which present a danger of structural collapse or fire spread to adjacent properties shall be considered to be abandoned, declared unsafe and abated by demolition or rehabilitation in accordance with the *International Property Maintenance Code* and the *International Building Code*.

❖ This section establishes the authority to demolish or rehabilitate properties that pose a variety of public safety hazards when the owners of the property cannot be located by customary legal means. Because demolition and rehabilitation are regulated by the IBC, *International Property Maintenance Code®* (IPMC®) and applicable state laws, any action taken must be a carefully coordinated effort by all affected code officials in close relationship with the jurisdiction's legal counsel.

311.1.2 Tenant spaces. Storage and lease plans required by this code shall be revised and updated to reflect temporary or partial vacancies.

❖ This section is intended to keep storage and lease plans up to date so that the fire service will always have a complete picture of the kinds of hazards it might face in case of a fire, including vacant, unattended spaces.

311.2 Safeguarding vacant premises. Temporarily unoccupied buildings, structures, premises or portions thereof shall be secured and protected in accordance with **Sections** 311.2.1 through 311.2.3.

❖ This section lists a number of problems that commonly occur where buildings or portions of buildings remain vacant for long periods of time. It covers concerns for security, fire protection and fire separation in vacant spaces.

311.2.1 Security. Exterior and interior openings open to other tenants or unauthorized persons shall be boarded, locked, blocked or otherwise protected to prevent entry by unauthorized individuals. The *fire code official* is authorized to placard, post signs, erect barrier tape or take similar measures as necessary to secure public safety.

❖ Unauthorized or illegal activities in vacant buildings can lead to the presence of unanticipated fire loads susceptible to ready ignition and rapid fire spread, thus increasing the hazard to adjoining properties or spaces and fire department personnel (see commentary, Section 110.1.1). This section requires securing the openings of vacant buildings or spaces against unauthorized entry by any of the methods listed or by other equally effective means approved by the fire code official, and provides that appropriate signage or other readily visible warnings to the public may be posted. For a suggested standard for boarding windows and doors, see IPMC Appendix A.

311.2.2 Fire protection. Fire alarm, sprinkler and stand-pipe systems shall be maintained in an operable condition at all times.

Exceptions:

1. Where the premises have been cleared of all combustible materials and debris and, in the opinion of the *fire code official*, the type of construction, *fire separation distance* and security of the premises do not create a fire hazard.
2. Where *approved* by the *fire code official*, buildings that will not be heated and where *fire protection systems* will be exposed to freezing temperatures, fire alarm and sprinkler systems are permitted to be placed out of service and standpipes are permitted to be maintained as dry systems (without an automatic water supply), provided that the building does not have contents or storage, and windows, doors and other openings are secured to prohibit entry by unauthorized persons.
3. Where *approved* by the *fire code official*, fire alarm and sprinkler systems are permitted to be placed out of service in seasonally occupied buildings: that will not be heated; where fire protection systems will be exposed to freezing temperatures; where *fire areas* do not exceed 12,000 square feet (1115 m^2); and that do not store motor vehicles or hazardous materials.

❖ The basic requirement of this section is clearly stated. The on-site fire protection systems must be maintained whether the property is occupied or vacant. The systems would be subject to the same inspections in either case.

Exception 1 gives the fire code official the authority to determine whether vacant premises pose a significant hazard and lists criteria he or she can use in making that determination.

Exception 2 recognizes that systems located in unheated premises in cold climates could be rendered inoperable by freezing, and authorizes permission to disable those systems where the security of the premises and fire separation arrangements meet the requirements of Sections 311.2.1 and 311.2.3. Since an inoperative fire protection system has a direct effect on the tactical approaches and operations of the fire department, this exception is only applicable where the fire chief of the jurisdiction has approved the securing of the system.

Exception 3 permits a seasonally occupied building that would be subject to freezing temperatures to be treated like a storage occupancy rather than an occupancy having fire protection systems; mainly assembly occupancies. It incorporates the limitation of 12,000 square feet as the maximum fire area since this is the maximum size a Group S-1 fire area can be without sprinkler protection. Even though a Type VB construction building can only be 9,000 square feet as limited by IBC Table 506.2, allowing up to 12,000 square feet in line with the sprinkler requirements is considered to be more appropriate since these buildings generally have the access around them and the heating system is not operational. Further, the limitation of vehicles and hazardous materials is done to address areas where sprinkler protection would be required at a lower threshold. Even though the thresholds have been focused on sprinkler systems, the disabling of fire alarm systems and smoke alarms is less of an issue in seasonally occupied buildings since sprinkler thresholds are mainly based on the type and ability of occupants.

311.2.3 Fire separation. Fire-resistance-rated partitions, *fire barriers* and *fire walls* separating vacant tenant spaces from the remainder of the building shall be maintained. Openings, joints and penetrations in fire-resistance-rated assemblies shall be protected in accordance with Chapter 7.

❖ Fire-resistance-rated construction separating vacant spaces from the remainder of the building must be maintained to the satisfaction of the fire code official. The requirements for openings, joints and penetrations are covered in Chapter 7.

311.3 Removal of combustibles. Persons owning, or in charge or control of, a vacant building or portion thereof, shall remove therefrom all accumulations of combustible materials, flammable or combustible waste or rubbish and shall securely lock or otherwise secure doors, windows and other openings to prevent entry by unauthorized persons. The premises shall be maintained clear of waste or hazardous materials.

Exceptions:

1. Buildings or portions of buildings undergoing additions, *alterations*, repairs or change of occupancy in accordance with the *International Building Code*, where waste is controlled and removed as required by Section 304.
2. Seasonally occupied buildings.

❖ Property owners, their agents and persons leasing vacant spaces are responsible for preventing accumulations of flammable or combustible materials as well as for securing the vacant space against entry by unauthorized persons.

Exception 1 covers building situations in which larger amounts of flammable or combustible waste would reasonably be generated and cites code references to cover requirements in those situations.

Exception 2 allows reasonable accumulations of flammable or combustible materials in spaces that are occupied seasonally. For example, this exception would allow unattended off-season storage of stock for sale.

311.4 Removal of hazardous materials. Persons owning or having charge or control of a vacant building containing hazardous materials regulated by Chapter 50 shall comply with the facility closure requirements of Section 5001.6.

❖ This section gives the fire code official the authority to require property owners, their agents and their tenants to submit a facility closure plan, and make sure combustible and hazardous materials are removed from the premises. The requirements for the facility closure plan are given in Section 5001.6 (see Section 407.7).

311.5 Placards. Any vacant or abandoned buildings or structures determined to be unsafe pursuant to Section 110 of this code relating to structural or interior hazards shall be marked as required by Sections 311.5.1 through 311.5.5.

❖ Vacant or abandoned buildings are often of questionable structural integrity and have a very high probability of intentionally set fires. When fires occur in these buildings, they present a host of unusual hazards to fire fighters. Since the buildings are uninhabited, fires may develop for significant periods of time before they are detected and reported.

In December 1999, six professional fire fighters died after they became lost in a six-floor, maze-like, cold-storage and warehouse building while searching for two reportedly trapped people and fire extension. In the wake of this tragedy, the National Institute for Occupational Safety and Health (NIOSH) conducted a Fatality Assessment and Control Evaluation (FACE) as part of its Fire Fighter Fatality Investigation and Prevention Program and issued its findings in report FACE-99-F47 in September 2000. NIOSH investigators concluded that, to reduce the risk of similar occurrences, fire departments should, among other recommendations, implement a program to "identify dangerous vacant buildings by affixing warning placards to entrance doorways or other openings where fire fighters may enter."

In order to improve fire-fighter safety when responding to incidents in buildings that have structural safety issues and have been declared to be unsafe due to being vacant or abandoned, this section establishes an information placarding system that will assist incident commanders in making personnel and equipment deployment decisions.

311.5.1 Placard location. Placards shall be applied on the front of the structure and be visible from the street. Additional placards shall be applied to the side of each entrance to the structure and on penthouses.

❖ Prominent positioning of warning placards where they can be readily seen by first-in fire companies or other emergency responders will assist in the initial incident size-up and resource assignments.

311.5.2 Placard size and color. Placards shall be 24 inches by 24 inches (610 mm by 610 mm) minimum in size with a red background, white reflective stripes and a white reflective border. The stripes and border shall have a 2-inch (51 mm) minimum stroke.

❖ In order to be truly effective in conveying the critical information about a building's structural stability, placards must be fabricated so as to be in bold contrast to their mounting surface. The required reflectivity will enhance placard visibility under low ambient light conditions where flashlights, spotlights or emergency vehicle warning lights may be the only light-emitting source.

311.5.3 Placard date. Placards shall bear the date of their application to the building and the date of the most recent inspection.

❖ Including the date of placard posting and the most recent inspection information on the placard will assist the incident commander in verifying the validity and currency of the building's status.

311.5.4 Placard symbols. The design of the placards shall use the following symbols:

1. □ This symbol shall mean that the structure had normal structural conditions at the time of marking.
2. ⧅ This symbol shall mean that structural or interior hazards exist and interior fire-fighting or rescue operations should be conducted with extreme caution.
3. ⊠ This symbol shall mean that structural or interior hazards exist to a degree that consideration should be given to limit fire fighting to exterior operations only, with entry only occurring for known life hazards.
4. Vacant marker hazard identification symbols: The following symbols shall be used to designate known hazards on the vacant building marker. They shall be placed directly above the symbol.
   - 4.1. R/O—Roof open
   - 4.2. S/M—Stairs, steps and landing missing
   - 4.3. F/E—Avoid fire escapes
   - 4.4. H/F—Holes in floor

❖ The placard symbols required by this section are intended to provide clear information regarding the level of structural hazard facing personnel in the conduct of rescue and fire-fighting operations as of the inspection date on the placard. Upon considering the degree of hazards, incident commanders can restrict operations to strictly defensive or cautiously offensive.

311.5.5 Informational use. The use of these symbols shall be informational only and shall not in any way limit the discretion of the on-scene incident commander.

❖ This section simply states that the placards are but an operational tool and the scene incident commander is the final authority in applying the information provided by the placards to the situation at hand.

311.6 Unoccupied tenant spaces in mall buildings. Unoccupied tenant spaces in covered and open mall buildings shall be:

1. Kept free from the storage of any materials.
2. Separated from the remainder of the building by partitions of not less than 0.5-inch-thick (12.7 mm) gypsum board or an *approved* equivalent to the underside of the ceiling of the adjoining tenant spaces.
3. Without doors or other access openings other than one door that shall be kept key locked in the closed position except during that time when opened for inspection.
4. Kept free from combustible waste and be broomswept clean.

❖ This section (through the 2012 code, Section 408.11.3) is primarily concerned with the hazards posed by tenant spaces that are not in use or that are not under the supervision of employees. These spaces are more likely to be targets of vandalism and incendiary activity. Generally, a fire can grow unnoticed in such spaces as a result of the lack of supervision or activity in the space. To reduce these risks, this section contains several requirements that focus on reducing the fire ignition, growth and spread potential by limiting combustibles in the space, securing the space through the use of locks and installing fire separations constructed of $^1/_2$-inch-thick (12.7 mm) gypsum or similar materials. Note that mall buildings are required to be sprinklered throughout and that the systems in the tenant spaces must be independent of the mall area.

SECTION 312 VEHICLE IMPACT PROTECTION

312.1 General. Vehicle impact protection required by this code shall be provided by posts that comply with Section 312.2 or by other *approved* physical barriers that comply with Section 312.3.

❖ This section applies to those locations where a moving vehicle could strike a piece of equipment that contains fuel or is fuel fired. These applications include motor fuel-dispensing facilities, above-ground storage tanks and repair garages as well as other locations in which gas- or oil-fired equipment or appliances could be installed where they would be in harm's way. Additional requirements for equipment protection are contained in Chapter 3 of the IMC and

Section 305 of the *International Fuel Gas Code*® (IFGC®). Acceptable impact protection is dependent upon location and physical arrangement of the equipment requiring protection and is not limited to guard posts only. As indicated in Section 312.3, protection could consist of walls, barricades, guardrails or elevated locations that provide the requisite level of protection and are approved by the fire code official.

312.2 Posts. Guard posts shall comply with all of the following requirements:

1. Constructed of steel not less than 4 inches (102 mm) in diameter and concrete filled.
2. Spaced not more than 4 feet (1219 mm) between posts on center.
3. Set not less than 3 feet (914 mm) deep in a concrete footing of not less than a 15-inch (381 mm) diameter.
4. Set with the top of the posts not less than 3 feet (914 mm) above ground.
5. Located not less than 3 feet (914 mm) from the protected object.

❖ This section lists five requirements that guard posts must satisfy. Typical installations of posts in service stations and other locations are shown in Commentary Figures 312.2(1) and 312.2(2). These guard posts are designed to resist impact from vehicles moving at low speeds, as they would be when pulling up to a fuel pump at a motor fuel-dispensing facility or into a service area in an indoor service facility or repair garage.

312.3 Other barriers. Barriers, other than posts specified in Section 312.2, that are designed to resist, deflect or visually deter vehicular impact commensurate with an anticipated impact scenario shall be permitted where *approved*.

❖ This section provides a true performance option to Section 312.2. The text deliberately establishes a broad set of goals that must be achieved by the designer to fit a site-specific application, and the requirement places the onus on the designer to demonstrate selection of a satisfactory design scenario and a suitable solution to achieve approval of the fire code official. Although it could be argued that Section 312.3 could simply be deleted in favor of relying on Section 104.9 (alternate materials and methods), it made more sense to include the suggested guidance in Section 312.3 of the code. Previously, the 12,000-pound resistance “force” prescribed by this section was actually a static load (i.e., a load with no associated impact velocity or acceleration) rather than an impact load. Without knowing an intended impact velocity, the kinetic energy resistance for a barrier cannot be accurately calculated. It is more appropriate for a performance requirement to accommodate determination of a suitable vehicle weight and impact speed to provide protection from moving vehicles as a design basis. Barriers other than posts could include walls, barricades or elevated locations for equipment (see Commentary Figure 312.3).

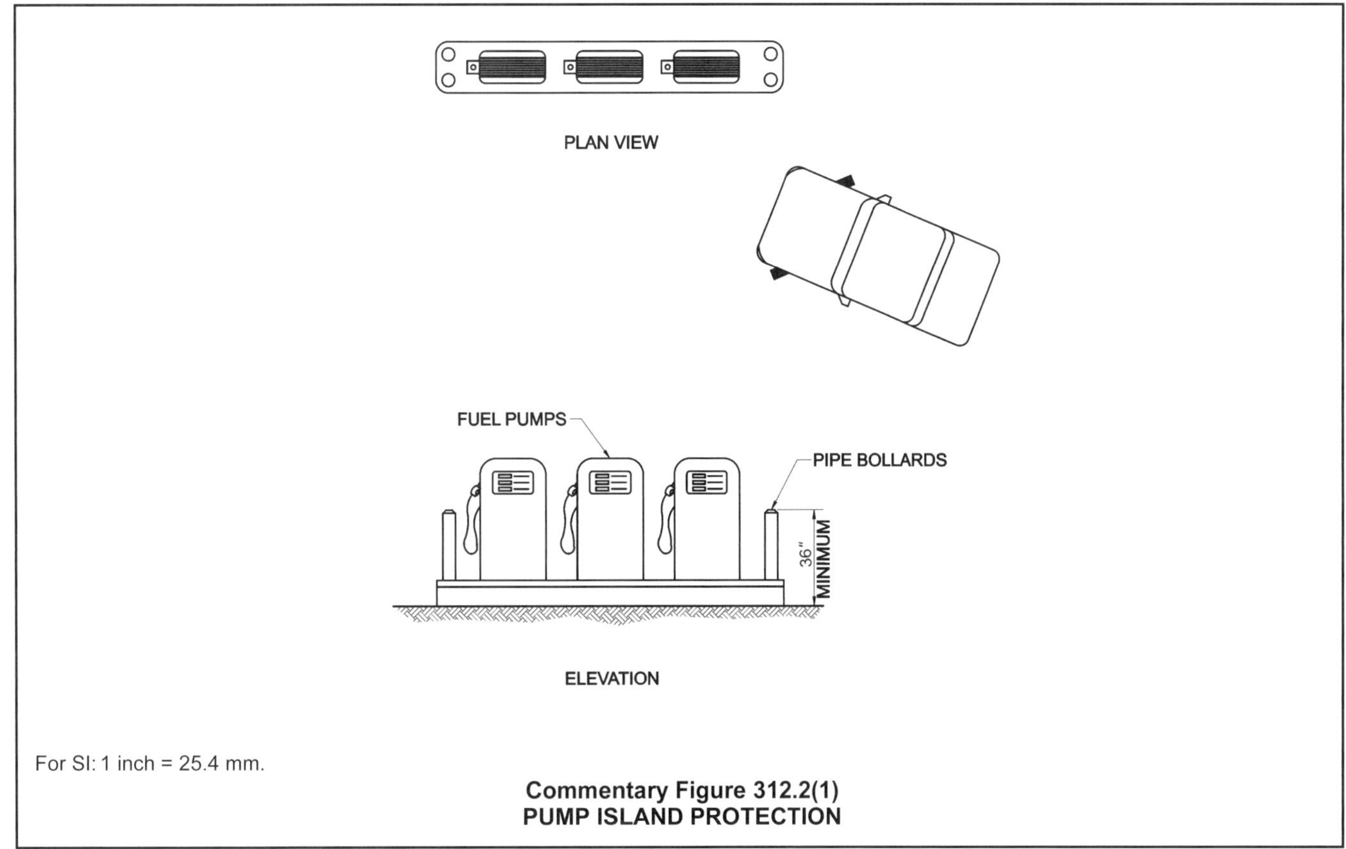

Commentary Figure 312.2(1)
PUMP ISLAND PROTECTION

SECTION 313
FUELED EQUIPMENT

313.1 General. Fueled equipment including, but not limited to, motorcycles, mopeds, lawn-care equipment, portable generators and portable cooking equipment, shall not be stored, operated or repaired within a building.

Exceptions:

1. Buildings or rooms constructed for such use in accordance with the *International Building Code*.
2. Where allowed by Section 314.
3. Storage of equipment utilized for maintenance purposes is allowed in *approved* locations where the aggregate fuel capacity of the stored equipment does not exceed 10 gallons (38 L) and the building is equipped throughout with an *automatic sprinkler system* installed in accordance with Section 903.3.1.1.

❖ The restrictions in this section are similar to those in Section 314.4, but this section also regulates the storage, operation or repair of portable liquid- or gas-fueled cooking equipment and generators, and certain vehicles (see commentary, Section 314.4). It has been documented that multiple fatalities occurred, related to natural disasters, as the result of the improper use and location of portable generators inside buildings. This section clarifies that portable generators are not allowed to be used inside buildings except when utilized in accordance with one of the exceptions.

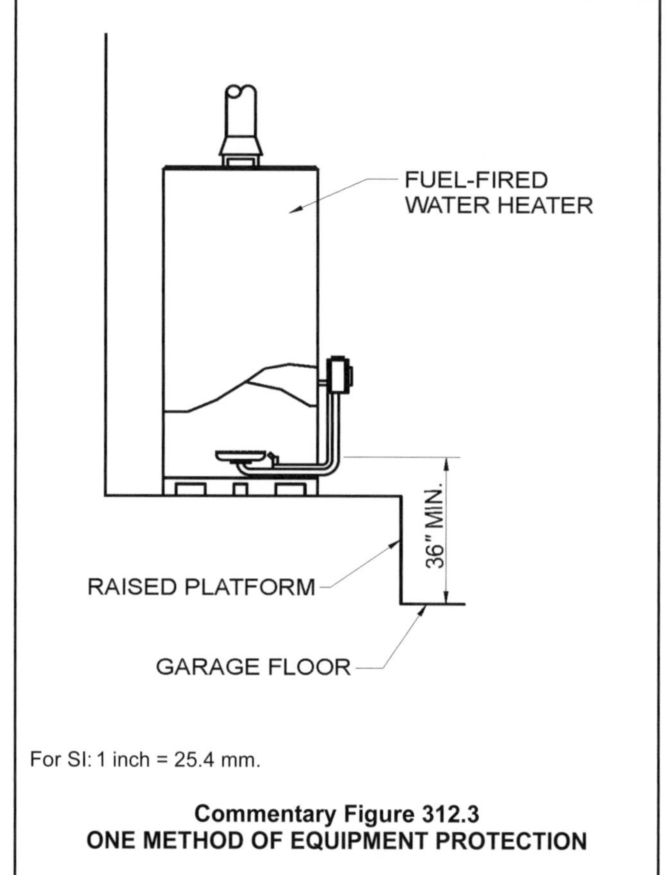

FUEL-FIRED
WATER HEATER
36" MIN.
RAISED PLATFORM
GARAGE FLOOR

For SI: 1 inch = 25.4 mm.

Commentary Figure 312.3
ONE METHOD OF EQUIPMENT PROTECTION

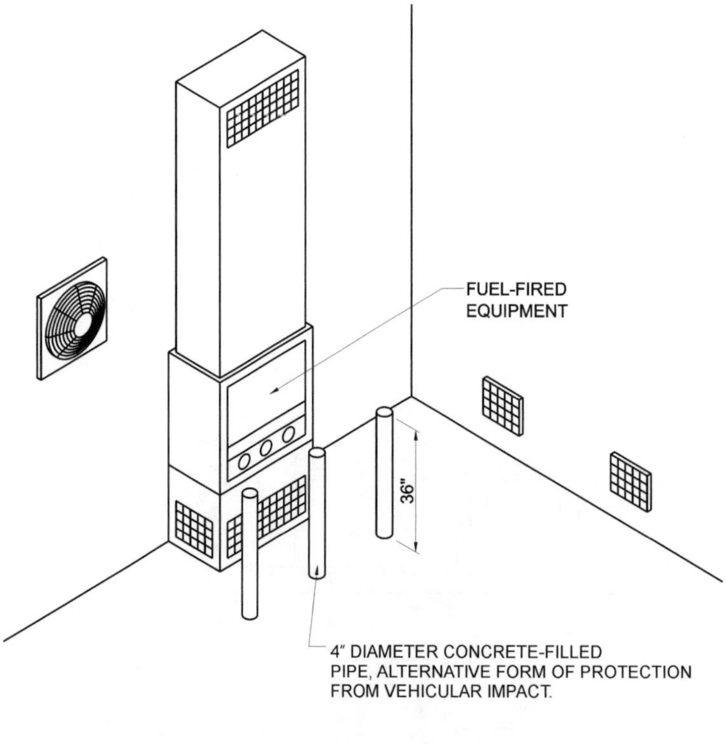

FUEL-FIRED
EQUIPMENT
36"
4" DIAMETER CONCRETE-FILLED
PIPE, ALTERNATIVE FORM OF PROTECTION
FROM VEHICULAR IMPACT.

For SI: 1 inch = 25.4 mm.

Commentary Figure 312.2(2)
GUARD POST INSTALLATION IN PUBLIC REPAIR GARAGE

Exception 1 recognizes the increased safety afforded when these uses are isolated from other parts of the building with fire-resistance-rated construction in accordance with the IBC. Exception 2 defers to the other section of the code that also regulates fueled equipment covered by this section. Exception 3 recognizes the enhanced level of protection provided by an approved automatic sprinkler system by allowing fueled equipment to be stored inside in a location approved by the fire code official, up to an aggregate quantity of 10 gallons (38 L) of fuel. This exception provides consistency with Section 5704.3.4.4 and, therefore, is applicable to flammable and combustible liquid fuels only; liquefied gas fuels are not included. Note also that the fuel quantities allowed by this exception are not to be counted when determining maximum allowable quantities in accordance with Table 5003.1.1(1), as indicated in Note p to that table.

313.1.1 Removal. The *fire code official* is authorized to require removal of fueled equipment from locations where the presence of such equipment is determined by the *fire code official* to be hazardous.

❖ This section gives the fire code official the authority to conduct inspections to determine whether vehicle operation, repair and storage in buildings comply with the requirements of this section and, if they do not, the authority to order the removal of fueled equipment from the building as a means of eliminating the hazard.

313.2 Group R occupancies. Vehicles powered by flammable liquids, Class II *combustible liquids* or compressed flammable gases shall not be stored within the living space of Group R buildings.

❖ Prohibiting storage of fuel-burning vehicles recognizes the hazards associated with having significant quantities of flammable or combustible liquids or compressed gases in inhabited spaces. Most vehicles that use liquid fuels have tanks that are not pressurized and are not vapor tight. Even a small leak over time can build to dangerous levels in enclosed spaces. For these reasons, this section prohibits the storage of gas- or liquid-fueled vehicles and equipment within the dwelling units or sleeping units of Group R buildings, including their associated balconies.

SECTION 314 INDOOR DISPLAYS

314.1 General. Indoor displays constructed within any occupancy shall comply with Sections 314.2 through 314.4.

❖ Indoor displays of merchandise and the display of all manner of vehicles inside of buildings can create a number of hazards to building occupants, including blocked egress and rapid fire buildup. This section describes reasonable measures to reduce the hazards associated with indoor displays without prohibiting them.

314.2 Fixtures and displays. Fixtures and displays of goods for sale to the public shall be arranged so as to maintain free, immediate and unobstructed access to exits as required by Chapter 10.

❖ The reason for maintaining free and unobstructed access to exits in public shopping spaces is, of course, personal safety in times of emergency. Chapter 10 contains the requirements, criteria and guidelines for this purpose.

314.3 Highly combustible goods. The display of highly combustible goods, including but not limited to fireworks, flammable or *combustible liquids*, liquefied flammable gases, oxidizing materials, pyroxylin plastics and agricultural goods, in main *exit access aisles*, *corridors*, covered and open malls, or within 5 feet (1524 mm) of entrances to *exits* and exterior exit doors is prohibited where a fire involving such goods would rapidly prevent or obstruct egress.

❖ As stated in Chapter 10, all elements of the means of egress of any occupancy open to the public must be kept clear of obstructions and other hazards that could prevent the occupants from exiting the premises quickly in an emergency. Displaying the hazardous materials itemized in this section where their involvement in a fire would block exit pathways is prohibited for this reason. The hazards associated with each of the materials mentioned in the section are discussed in the commentaries to Chapters 50 through 67.

314.4 Vehicles. Liquid-fueled or gaseous-fueled vehicles, boats or other motorcraft shall not be located indoors except as follows:

1. Batteries are disconnected except where the *fire code official* requires that the batteries remain connected to maintain safety features.
2. Fuel in fuel tanks does not exceed one-quarter tank or 5 gallons (19 L) (whichever is least).
3. Fuel tanks and fill openings are closed and sealed to prevent tampering.
4. Vehicles, boats or other motorcraft equipment are not fueled or defueled within the building.

❖ It has become commonplace for covered malls and larger retail stores to have various types of gas- or liquid-fueled vehicles on inside display, such as for promotional events or fire apparatus displays during Fire Prevention Week (see Commentary Figure 314.4). Because the hazards of such displays in a public building are similar to those in residential buildings, Section 314.4 parallels Section 313.1, Exception 2 (see commentary, Section 313.1).

Commentary Figure 314.4
INDOOR CAR DISPLAY

SECTION 315 GENERAL STORAGE

315.1 General. Storage shall be in accordance with Sections 315.2 through 315.6. Outdoor pallet storage shall be in accordance with Sections 315.2 and 315.7.

Exception: Wood and wood composite pallets stored outdoors at pallet manufacturing and recycling facilities and complying with Section 2810.

❖ This section addresses general safety precautions for the storage of materials, including those regulated elsewhere in the code. Where a material in storage is specifically regulated by another section of the code, that section would apply in addition to any applicable provisions in Section 315. For example, if the stored material were baled waste paper awaiting recycling, the material-specific provisions of Section 5205 would apply. However, Section 5205 does not specifically regulate the vertical clearance of the stored baled waste paper to the ceiling or sprinkler heads, nor does it regulate clearance from heaters or heating devices. Accordingly, the provisions of Sections 315.3 and 315.3.1 would apply. Also note that if the storage meets the definition of high-piled combustible storage in Section 202, the applicable provisions of Chapter 32 would apply. Control of combustible waste material is covered in Sections 304.2 and 304.3.

315.2 Permit required. A permit for miscellaneous combustible storage shall be required as set forth in Section 105.6.

❖ This section establishes the requirement that an operational permit for storage of certain combustible materials must be obtained from the fire code official. Permit fees, if any, must be paid prior to the issuance of the permit. See Section 105 for additional information on permits. Note that a permit is required only for storage of combustible materials. Even though Section 315.3 regulates storage of both combustible and noncombustible materials, a permit is required only for miscellaneous types of combustible materials and then only when the storage volume exceeds 2,500 cubic feet (70.79 m^3), as specified in the permit requirements in Section 105.6.30. The storage of such combustible materials can easily fall into disarray, present a fire load out of proportion to the surroundings and be susceptible to ready ignition and rapid, uncontrolled combustion. Conversely, the orderly storage of mercantile stocks and goods, business records, etc., in piles, on shelving or in casework cabinets, for example, while regulated by Section 315, is not considered to be a hazard requiring a permit.

315.3 Storage in buildings. Storage of materials in buildings shall be orderly and stacks shall be stable. Storage of combustible materials shall be separated from heaters or heating devices by distance or shielding so that ignition cannot occur.

❖ The first sentence of this section makes it clear that it applies to all storage and that the stacks of stored materials must be stable in order to prevent pile or stack collapse that could obstruct means of egress aisles and impede fire-fighter access. The second sentence applies only to storage of combustible materials and the need for them to be separated from ignition sources. Throughout the code, the use of fire-resistance-rated construction and spatial separation distances to minimize fire hazards and fire spread is stated as a requirement for a variety of materials. It is not necessary to separate noncombustible materials from ignition sources because there is no combustible material hazard.

315.3.1 Ceiling clearance. Storage shall be maintained 2 feet (610 mm) or more below the ceiling in nonsprinklered areas of buildings or not less than 18 inches (457 mm) below sprinkler head deflectors in sprinklered areas of buildings.

Exceptions:

1. The 2-foot (610 mm) ceiling clearance is not required for storage along walls in nonsprinklered areas of buildings.
2. The 18-inch (457 mm) ceiling clearance is not required for storage along walls in areas of buildings equipped with an *automatic sprinkler system* in accordance with Section 903.3.1.1, 903.3.1.2 or 903.3.1.3

❖ If the space is not equipped with sprinklers, the clearance between the stored materials and the ceiling must be 2 feet (610 mm) to allow manual hose streams to effectively reach the top of a burning pile as well as to project over and beyond adjacent piles to reach burning materials. Where sprinklers are installed, the 18-inch (457 mm) clearance permits timely activation of the sprinklers and allows unobstructed water distribution over the storage pile. Materials stored too close to sprinklers can not only prevent the heat of a fire from reaching the sprinkler fusible link but also inhibit water from reaching the seat of a fire once the sprinklers are activated.

In sprinklered areas of buildings, the question often arises as to whether storage on shelving can be installed on a wall not directly below sprinklers, with the storage extending above the level of a horizontal plane located 18 inches (457 mm) below the ceiling sprinkler deflector. Typically, storage on wall-mounted shelving functions the same as a wall with respect to its relationship to the automatic sprinklers installed at ceiling level and the relative obstruction it poses. As long as the storage is not directly below the sprinklers, the sprinkler clearance provisions of Section 315.2.1 would not apply. This is consistent with NFPA 13 annex notes on this topic.

Certain newer types of automatic sprinklers, because of their design or operating characteristics, may require greater clearance distances than the 18-inch (457 mm) minimum prescribed in this section. NFPA 13 and the sprinkler manufacturer's data should be consulted for specific information on the characteristics of the many different types of sprinklers that may be installed in a given building.

315.3.2 Means of egress. Combustible materials shall not be stored in *exits* or enclosures for *stairways* and *ramps*. Combustible materials in the means of egress during construction, demolition, remodeling or alterations shall comply with Section 3311.3.

❖ As was stated in Section 314.3, all elements of the means of egress must be kept free of obstructions that could block an exit pathway and, thus, jeopardize occupants of the affected space. Chapter 10 offers more guidance on means of egress.

315.3.3 Equipment rooms. Combustible material shall not be stored in boiler rooms, mechanical rooms, electrical equipment rooms or in *fire command centers* as specified in Section 508.1.5.

❖ This section is intended to keep ignition sources inherent in the use of certain indicated rooms (e.g., fuel-fired equipment, electrical panels) from coming into contact with combustible materials that might be stored in the rooms, whether the rooms are sprinklered or not. See also the commentary to Section 508.1.5 for storage prohibition in fire command centers and Section 605.3 for electrical equipment room clearance requirements and storage prohibition. Note that the IMC, Chapter 2, defines a "mechanical equipment/appliance room" as one in which nonfuel-fired mechanical equipment is located. Even though the ignition hazard is reduced in the absence of fuel-fired equipment in such rooms, they must be kept free of combustible storage to allow ready access for fire fighters and other authorized personnel to reach easily critical controls, such as power or equipment disconnects, in case of an emergency. Limited supplies of combustible materials related to mechanical room equipment (e.g., air distribution system filters) could be allowed but only in accordance with Section 315 of the code and with the specific approval of the fire code official. For additional discussion of requirements applicable to these and other specific occupancy rooms, see Section 509 of the IBC. Further discussion of the hazards of storage in boiler rooms can be found in Section 304 of the IMC.

315.3.4 Attic, under-floor and concealed spaces. Attic, under-floor and concealed spaces used for storage of combustible materials shall be protected on the storage side as required for 1-hour *fire-resistance-rated* construction. Openings shall be protected by assemblies that are self-closing and are of noncombustible construction or solid wood core not less than $1^3/_4$ inches (44.5 mm) in thickness. Storage shall not be placed on exposed joists.

Exceptions:

1. Areas protected by *approved automatic sprinkler systems*.
2. Group R-3 and Group U occupancies.

❖ This section recognizes the reality that attics, crawl spaces and similar unoccupied, concealed spaces in buildings are attractive to building occupants for storage of all kinds of combustible materials. Storage in such unattended and out-of-the-way spaces creates a hazardous condition by introducing a higher fire load to spaces that were neither designed nor intended for such a high-intensity use and in which a fire could rapidly develop unobserved until it had gained a considerable hold on the building. Placing stored combustibles on exposed joists also could hasten collapse of the joists in a fire, which could lead to flaming debris being dropped into the building space below the joists and possible collapse of all or part of the building structure.

The code provides alternatives to using such spaces for storage and, if they are used for storage, how they can be constructed to isolate the higher fire loads created. Since the intent is to protect against a fire in the storage area from endangering the other occupied areas of the building, the required 1-hour fire-resistance rating need only be achieved from the storage side. While any access openings in the 1-hour fire-resistant construction need not be rated, they must be self-closing and of either noncombustible construction or a minimum $1^3/_4$-inch (44 mm) thickness of solid wood core. Consistent with Section 102.4, any construction in connection with the concealed spaces regulated by this section must be in accordance with the IBC, especially Section 509.

Exception 1 recognizes the efficiency and reliability of automatic sprinklers as a trade-off for 1-hour fire-resistance-rated construction. This exception only requires the sprinkler system in the attic, under-floor or concealed space. Complete sprinkler protection throughout the building is not required in order to be in compliance with the exception.

Exception 2 exempts Group R-3 and U occupancies from the requirements of this section. In Group R-3, the level of familiarity and control exercised by the building occupants is recognized as offsetting the hazards of storage in concealed spaces. Because Group U occupancies are generally unoccupied, the hazards of miscellaneous storage are of little or no consequence to the few occupants that might be in such buildings. For further information on Group U occupancies, see Section 312 of the IBC and its commentary.

315.4 Outside storage. Outside storage of combustible materials shall not be located within 10 feet (3048 mm) of a *lot line*.

Exceptions:

1. The separation distance is allowed to be reduced to 3 feet (914 mm) for storage not exceeding 6 feet (1829 mm) in height.
2. The separation distance is allowed to be reduced where the *fire code official* determines that hazard to the adjoining property does not exist.

❖ Outside storage of combustible materials, such as raw materials for production, idle pallets, dunnage and packaging, must be neat and compact. The requirement for a 10-foot (3048 mm) separation is consistent with storage area aisle width requirements throughout the code, often expressed as "one-half the pile height or 10 feet (3048 mm), whichever is greater." The requirement of this section is consistent with that concept, as is Section 315.3.2, which limits pile height to 20 feet (6096 mm). This section is intended to provide fire suppression access on all sides of storage arrangements and reduce the likelihood of the spread of fire to adjacent properties in the event of a pile collapse. Pile collapses will generally not involve a full-height topple-over of a pile, but rather only a partial collapse. Accordingly, Exception 1 allows a reduction in separation distance where the pile height is substantially less than the separation requirement.

Exception 2 allows the fire code official to grant separation reductions when the combustibles are judged to be no threat to adjoining property. Examples of such conditions could include storage where the combustible materials are enclosed in noncombustible containers, the presence of an impervious property line barrier or the provision of fixed fire protection equipment, such as deluge monitors, especially designed for rapid fire suppression and exposure protection.

315.4.1 Storage beneath overhead projections from buildings. Where buildings are protected by an *automatic sprinkler system*, the outdoor storage, display and handling of combustible materials under eaves, canopies or other projections or overhangs are prohibited except where automatic sprinklers are installed under such eaves, canopies or other projections or overhangs.

❖ The storage or display of combustible materials beneath unsprinklered canopies or other building projections attached to an otherwise fully sprinklered building could lead to a rapidly developing fire in the stored material, which could gain sufficient headway beyond the capability of the building sprinkler system to suppress it, should it spread into the building's interior. This section reinforces the requirements of NFPA 13 concerning the use of areas beneath building projections, such as eaves or canopies, for the storage or display of combustible materials where those locations are exempt from sprinkler protection as allowed in Section 8.15 of NFPA 13. NFPA 13 mandates that the scope of required sprinkler protection includes canopies or roofed-over areas attached to sprinklered buildings, unless these projections are constructed of noncombustible materials and the areas are not used for the storage, handling or display of combustible materials. Because NFPA 13 is a design standard and cannot be enforced as a maintenance document, this section essentially restates the NFPA 13 design requirement exception conditions in enforceable terms. Also note that, in the event that Appendix B of the code is adopted by a jurisdiction, areas used for the storage of combustible materials beneath a building's horizontally projecting elements must be included in the building area for purposes of determining the required fire flow.

315.4.2 Height. Storage in the open shall not exceed 20 feet (6096 mm) in height.

❖ Storage pile height limitations are a means of controlling the size of potential fires and reducing tip-over potential, as well as a way to facilitate manual fire suppression by keeping the top of the pile within reach of conventional fire-fighting and overhaul tools, such as the ground ladders carried by an engine company or the long pike poles carried by ladder companies. The 20-foot (6096 mm) storage pile height limitation also correlates with Section 315.3 and helps reduce the likelihood that a fire would jeopardize adjacent properties in the event of a pile collapse.

315.5 Storage underneath high-voltage transmission lines. Storage located underneath high-voltage transmission lines shall be in accordance with Section 316.6.2.

❖ High-voltage transmission lines are a special hazard requiring specific regulations to prevent them from being exposed to fire conditions that could cause them to fail or fall to the ground. This general section directs the code user to the section containing more specific requirements for this topic.

315.6 Storage in plenums. Storage is prohibited in plenums. Abandoned material in plenums shall be deemed to be storage and shall be removed. Where located in plenums, the portion of abandoned cables that are able to be accessed without causing damage, or requiring demolition to the building shall be identified for future use with a tag or shall be deemed storage and shall be removed.

❖ This section introduces a concept that has long been in NFPA 70 and NFPA 90A—that plenums (see Chapter 2 commentary to the definition of "Plenum") are intended specifically to be a part of the air distribution system. Plenums are also legitimately used for stringing communications and data cables as well as utility pipes, sprinkler pipes and similar items. However, such items often are not removed from the plenum when they become obsolete. For example, when an updated data system is installed in a facility (which can occur every 18 to 24 months), it is not unusual for old wires to be cut out of the system but left in place with a new wiring system added on top of them (see Commentary Figure 315.6).

The suspended ceiling tile systems that often enclose plenums are not intended to support any significant weight and can, therefore, easily be overwhelmed by the added weight of storage or abandoned materials such as cables (see commentary to IBC, Section 808.1.1.1). Recently, a plenum space fuel load study showed how the safety of fire fighters is compromised by the weight of these abandoned cables. It pointed out that plenum space fuel loads and wiring issues are serious concerns for fire fighters during interior fire-fighting operations and its key recommendation was that abandoned wiring be removed.

Although the primary reason to require the removal of abandoned materials in plenums is the elimination of unnecessary weight, fire safety considerations should also be taken into account, as should the practical consideration that the HVAC design airflow through the plenum could be adversely affected. Such a requirement was long believed not to be enforceable primarily because fire code inspectors would rarely spend their time looking into plenums in existing buildings. However, the danger presented by the fire load of storage or abandoned materials is well-documented. Thus, there should be no significant difficulty in having inspectors identify the existence of abandoned products—especially abandoned cables—classify them as storage and require their removal. Note that only the "accessible portions" of abandoned cables must be removed because there is no intent to cause potential damage to the building or facility by attempting to remove cables or circuits that are strung through walls, floors or other building elements. Where some cables are left in place because they are intended to be reused at a future date, they must be clearly identified as such by affixing a tag. See also Section 605.12.

Commentary Figure 315.6
ABANDONED DATA CABLE IN A PLENUM

315.7 Outdoor pallet storage. Pallets stored outdoors shall comply with Sections 315.7 through 315.7.7. Pallets stored within a building shall be protected in accordance with Chapter 32.

❖ This section introduces the requirements for the outdoor storage of pallets. These requirements provide limitations and restrictions in order to address the high challenge fire protection issues involving large amounts of densely piled idle pallets. Note that this section is specific to pallets that are stored outdoors. The protection requirements for pallets that are stored indoors are provided in Chapter 32.

315.7.1 Storage beneath overhead projections from buildings. Where buildings are equipped throughout with an *automatic sprinkler system*, the outdoor storage of pallets under eaves, canopies or other projections or overhangs are prohibited except where automatic sprinklers are installed under such eaves, canopies or other projections or overhangs.

❖ This section makes it clear that if a building is protected with an indoor automatic sprinkler system, pallets are not allowed to be stored directly under eaves, canopies, projections or overhangs unless outside automatic sprinklers are provided under these construction elements.

315.7.2 Distance to lot line. Pallet storage shall not be located within 10 feet (3048 mm) of a *lot line*.

❖ This section requires that pallet storage areas be more than 10 feet from any lot lines in order to prevent fire spread to adjacent construction and to maintain sufficient separation distance from the hazard.

315.7.3 Storage height. Pallet storage shall not exceed 20 feet (6096 mm) in height.

❖ This section limits the pallet storage height to be 20 feet or less order to limit the total storage volume within an outdoor storage area. Note that in addition to this height limit, Section 315.7.4 also limits the area of any individual pallet pile to 400 square feet or less.

315.7.4 Pallet pile stability and size. Pallet stacks shall be arranged to form stable piles. Individual pallet piles shall cover an area not greater than 400 square feet (37 m^2).

❖ In addition to height limit of 20 feet or less provided in Section 315.7.3, this section limits the pallet storage area to be 400 square feet or less in order to limit the total storage volume within an individual outdoor storage pile area. In addition, this requirement allows for greater access to any stack within the storage area and minimizes the effect of tripping stacks on increasing the fire size.

315.7.5 Pallet types. Pallets shall be all wood, with slatted or solid top or bottom, with metal fasteners, or shall be plastic or composite pallets, listed and labeled in accordance with UL 2335 or FM 4996. Plastic pallets shall be both solid and gridded deck, independent of the pallet manufacturing process, type of resin used in fabrication or geometry of the pallet.

❖ This section limits the pallet types to be all wood, constructed as noted, or plastic or composite pallets, that are constructed as noted and are specifically listed and labeled in accordance with the referenced standards. These restrictions prohibit the outdoor storage of other, more hazardous types of pallets that have not been specifically fire tested in order to determine their performance and hazard level.

315.7.6 Pile separation distances. In addition to the other requirements of this section, pallet stacks and piles shall be separated in accordance with Sections 315.7.6.1 and 315.7.6.2.

❖ This section introduces the pile separation distance requirements that are listed in Tables 315.7.6(1) through 315.7.6(4).

315.7.6.1 Building separation. Pallet stacks and piles shall be separated from buildings in accordance with Table 315.7.6(1) for wood pallets and Table 315.7.6(2) for plastic pallets.

❖ This section provides direct reference to Tables 315.7.6(1) and 315.7.6(2). These tables list requirements based on building wall construction type, wall opening type and the number of total pallets that are stored. Table 315.7.6(1) is specific to wood pallets and Table 315.7.6(2) is specific to plastic pallets that meet the requirements of Section 315.7.5. These tables limit the pallet storage distances from any nearby building walls in order to prevent fire spread to adjacent construction on the same lot and to maintain sufficient separation distance from the hazard in order to maintain access.

315.7.6.2 Separation from other pallets and on-site storage. Pallets shall be separated from other pallet piles and other storage in accordance with Table 315.7.6(3) for wood pallets and Table 315.7.6(4) for plastic pallets.

❖ This section provides direct reference to Tables 315.7.6(2) and 315.7.6(4). These tables list requirements based on the distances between other pallet piles, as limited by Sections 315.7.3 and 315.7.4, other nonpallet storage areas and the number of total pallets that are stored in each individual pile. Table 315.7.6(3) is specific to wood pallets and Table 315.7.6(4) is specific to plastic pallets that meet the requirements of Section 315.7.5. These tables limit the pallet storage distances from other nearby pallet piles and nonpallet storage in order to prevent fire spread from any storage pile to an adjacent storage pile on the same lot and to maintain sufficient separation distance from the hazard in order to maintain access.

**TABLE 315.7.6(1)
SEPARATION DISTANCE BETWEEN WOOD PALLET STACKS AND BUILDINGS**

WALL CONSTRUCTION	OPENING TYPE	WOOD PALLET SEPARATION DISTANCE (feet)		
		≤ 50 Pallets	51 to 200 Pallets	>200 Pallets
Masonry	None	2	2	2
Masonry	Fire-rated glazing with open sprinklers	2	5	20
Masonry	Fire-rated glazing	10	5	20
Masonry	Plain glass with open sprinklers	10	5	20
Noncombustible	None	10	5	20
Wood with open sprinklers	—	10	5	20
Wood	None	15	30	90
Any	Plain glass	15	30	90

For SI: 1 foot = 304.8 mm.

**TABLE 315.7.6(2)
SEPARATION DISTANCE BETWEEN PLASTIC PALLET STACKS AND BUILDINGS**

WALL CONSTRUCTION	OPENING TYPE	PLASTIC PALLET SEPARATION DISTANCE (feet)		
		≤ 50 Pallets	51 to 200 Pallets	>200 Pallets
Masonry	None	2	2	2
Masonry	Fire-rated glazing with open sprinklers	10	20	50
Masonry	Fire-rated glazing	15	40	100
Masonry	Plain glass with open sprinklers	15	40	100
Noncombustible	None	15	40	100
Wood with open sprinklers	—	15	40	100
Wood	None	30	80	150
Any	Plain glass	30	80	150

For SI: 1 foot = 304.8 mm.

TABLE 315.7.6(3)
SEPARATION FROM OTHER PALLET PILES AND ON-SITE STORAGE (WOOD PALLETS)

	WOOD PALLET SEPARATION DISTANCE (feet)		
	≤ 50 Pallets	51 to 200 Pallets	>200 Pallets
Between pallet piles	7.5	15	45
Other on-site storage	7.5	15	45

For SI: 1 foot = 304.8 mm.

TABLE 315.7.6(4)
SEPARATION FROM OTHER PALLET PILES AND ON-SITE STORAGE (PLASTIC PALLETS)

	PLASTIC PALLET SEPARATION DISTANCE (feet)		
	≤ 50 Pallets	51 to 200 Pallets	>200 Pallets
Between pallet piles	15	40	75
Other on-site storage	15	40	75

For SI: 1 foot = 304.8 mm.

315.7.7 Prohibited locations. Pallets shall not be stored underneath high-voltage transmission lines, elevated roadways or elevated railways.

❖ This section prohibits the storage of pallets under the three listed, critical transmission and transportation structures due to the increased potential hazardous spread of fire and disruption of service as well the increased difficulty in accessing such a pallet storage area.

SECTION 316 HAZARDS TO FIRE FIGHTERS

316.1 Trapdoors to be closed. Trapdoors and scuttle covers, other than those that are within a *dwelling unit* or automatically operated, shall be kept closed at all times except when in use.

❖ Trapdoors and unguarded openings in floors and walkways must remain in the closed position or be designed to automatically close upon activation of the fire alarm system. Openings in floors or walkways can injure emergency responders, especially if vision is obscured.

316.2 Shaftway markings. Vertical shafts shall be identified as required by this section.

❖ This section was developed to prevent fire fighters from falling through shafts when entering buildings off ladders placed on the exterior of the building.

316.2.1 Exterior access to shaftways. Outside openings that can be reached by the fire department and that open directly on a hoistway or shaftway communicating between two or more floors in a building shall be plainly marked with the word SHAFTWAY in red letters not less than 6 inches (152 mm) high on a white background. Such warning signs shall be placed so as to be readily discernible from the outside of the building.

❖ Exterior wall openings that are accessible to fire fighters by way of ladders and aerial equipment and that open directly into shafts or hoistways communicating between two or more floors must be clearly marked (see Commentary Figure 316.2.1).

316.2.2 Interior access to shaftways. Door or window openings to a hoistway or shaftway from the interior of the building shall be plainly marked with the word SHAFTWAY in red letters not less than 6 inches (152 mm) high on a white background. Such warning signs shall be placed so as to be readily discernible.

Exception: Marking shall not be required on shaftway openings that are readily discernible as openings onto a shaftway by the construction or arrangement.

❖ Openings into shaftways from the interior of the building pose a threat to fire fighters when visibility is poor. Interior shaft openings must be marked so that they are plainly visible from the interior of the building.

If fire fighters can readily identify an opening into a shaft by the way the opening is constructed, the shaft opening need not be marked, keeping in mind that the fire fighter may be feeling his or her way in heavy smoke or darkness.

316.3 Pitfalls. The intentional design or *alteration* of buildings to disable, injure, maim or kill intruders is prohibited. A person shall not install and use firearms, sharp or pointed objects, razor wire, *explosives*, flammable or *combustible liquid* containers, or dispensers containing highly toxic, toxic, irritant or other hazardous materials in a manner that could passively or actively disable, injure, maim or kill a fire fighter who forcibly enters a building for the purpose of controlling or extinguishing a fire, rescuing trapped occupants or rendering other emergency assistance.

❖ This paragraph prohibits the use of “booby-traps” in buildings, for whatever reason, if they could injure or disable the emergency responder during the performance of his or her duties.

316.4 Obstructions on roofs. Wires, cables, ropes, antennas, or other suspended obstructions installed on the roof of a building having a roof slope of less than 30 degrees (0.52 rad) shall not create an obstruction that is less than 7 feet (2133 mm) high above the surface of the roof.

Exceptions:

1. Such obstruction shall be permitted where the wire, cable, rope, antenna or suspended obstruction is encased in a white, 2-inch (51 mm) minimum diameter plastic pipe or an approved equivalent.
2. Such obstruction shall be permitted where there is a solid obstruction below such that accidentally walking into the wire, cable, rope, antenna or suspended obstruction is not possible.

❖ Section 101.2 is intended, in part, to control conditions that can affect the safety of fire fighters and emergency responders during operations. These conditions include obstructions on the roofs of buildings. This section does not prohibit the installation of these items, but it requires that they be identified or protected. The primary concern is poorly identified or unidentified obstructions on building roofs that can become an entanglement hazard or, in the case of equipment such as cellular or wireless communication antennas, a potential pathway for stray current if the electrical ground is somehow compromised and an emergency responder comes into contact with it. These provisions will also help to protect maintenance workers as they are working on a rooftop.

This section addresses obstructions on building roofs and was developed to establish criteria for identifying such obstructions. It is applicable only to roofs with a slope of 30 degrees (0.52 rad) or less. This section requires that a means of identification, a barrier, or some other form of obstruction be provided when a guy wire, cable, or rope is less than 7 feet (2133 mm) above the roof level. The 7-foot (2133 mm) value is based on the potential of a firefighter in a smoke-obscured environment striking the cable or wire, especially in the head, neck or upper torso area. A common fire service slang term for this is "being clotheslined" and these events have resulted in serious injury from entanglement or falling from a roof, including permanent paralysis of fire fighters and other emergency responders.

Where the obstruction is located in the plane that is 7 feet (2133 mm) or less below the roof surface, Exception 1 allows the use of a protective collar such as a 2-inch (51 mm) diameter plastic pipe that is sleeved over the cable. Other options could include illuminating the cable, or providing reflective marking of the cable, wire or rope with a material similar to that used for marking of fire-fighter clothing and gear. Any method that offers equivalency to the prescribed pipe sleeve can be approved by the fire code official upon demonstration of equivalency.

Exception 2 recognizes that solid obstructions such as screen walls or fencing can provide a physical barrier so that walking under the wire is not possible and can eliminate the need for protecting the emergency responders from roof obstructions that are less than 7 feet (2133 mm) above the roof level.

316.5 Security device. Any security device or system that emits any medium that could obscure a *means of egress* in any building, structure or premise shall be prohibited.

❖ Security devices that, when activated, emit a medium such as smoke or other aerosols into a building could obscure exits or confuse occupants, thus creating an inherently dangerous situation for the public and responding emergency personnel. In cases of activation of these devices, armed criminal perpetrators could be trapped inside buildings. Law enforcement personnel arriving on the scene could easily believe that a building is on fire and responding fire fighters could enter and be confronted by the perpetrator. Another danger is that false fire alarms could be transmitted automatically or by passers-by because

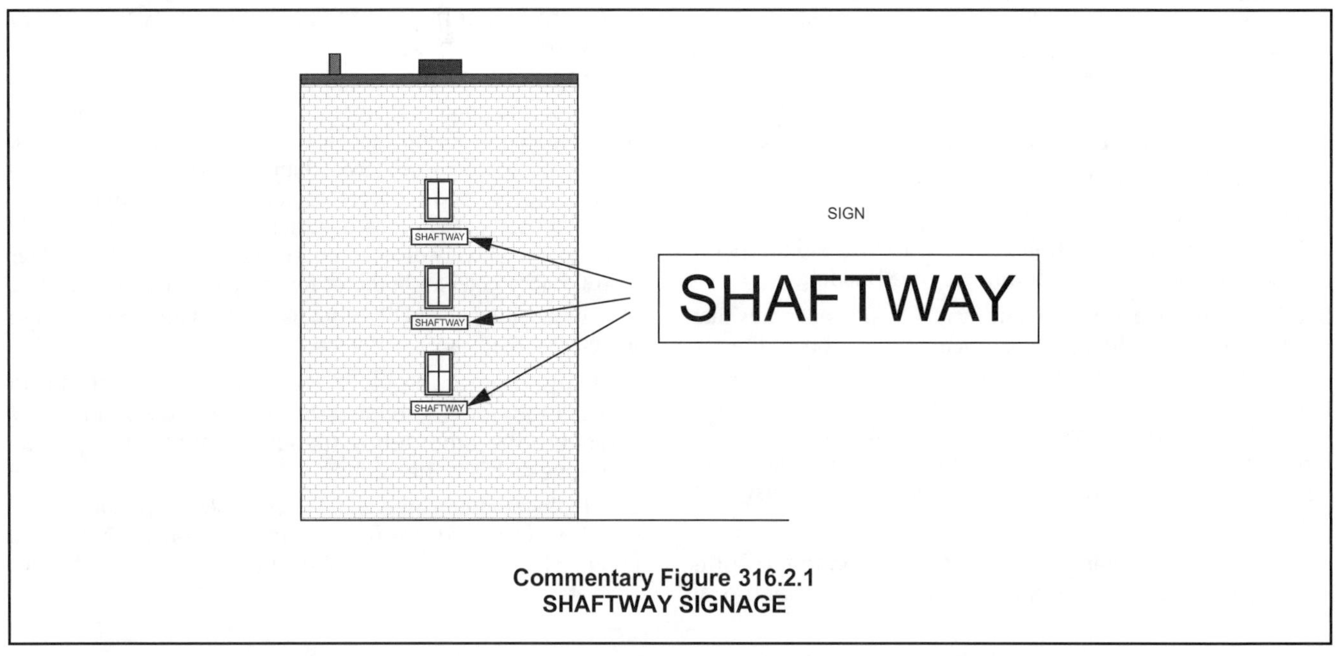

Commentary Figure 316.2.1
SHAFTWAY SIGNAGE

of the appearance of smoke in the building. See also the commentary to Section 1031.2 regarding the reliability of exits.

316.6 Structures and outdoor storage underneath high-voltage transmission lines. Structures and outdoor storage underneath high-voltage transmission lines shall comply with Sections 316.6.1 and 316.6.2, respectively.

❖ This section introduces code provisions that address requirements for structure construction and material storage beneath high-voltage transmission lines (see definition in Section 202). The importance of such regulations and their impact on fire-fighter safety cannot be overstated. Among the various hazards fire fighters face in the course of duty are electrical hazards during fire suppression or rescue activities. Performing fire-ground operations near power lines may expose fire fighters to electric shock hazards through the following means, among others:

- Energized electrical lines or equipment obscured by dense smoke.
- Smoke and hot gases from a large fire creating a conductive path for electricity. When a fire is burning under a high-voltage transmission line, electricity could arc from the conductor to the ground, endangering people and objects near the arc.
- Making accidental contact with power lines that are still energized.
- Overhead power lines falling on and energizing conductive equipment and materials located on the fire ground.
- Electrical currents flowing through the ground and extending several feet (ground gradient).
- Solid-stream water applications on or around energized or downed power lines or equipment.

The regulations in Sections 316.6.1 and 316.6.2 are intended to minimize the noted exposures by prohibiting buildings, structures and storage from being constructed or maintained beneath high-voltage transmission lines except under the strictest of conditions and only with the fire code official's approval.

316.6.1 Structures. Structures shall not be constructed within the utility easement beneath high-voltage transmission lines.

> **Exception:** Restrooms and unoccupied telecommunication structures of noncombustible construction less than 15 feet (4572 mm) in height.

❖ Structure fires underneath high-voltage transmission lines could cause arcing and shock hazard. Fire-fighting operations can involve the use of elevated platforms or aerial ladder apparatus and other emergency equipment, personnel above ground and hose streams that may come in close proximity to high-voltage transmission lines. According to nationally recognized utility companies, manual de-energization of lines may take 20 minutes or longer to accomplish.

The exception recognizes that certain ancillary structures, such as restroom buildings and telecommunications structures, do not generally present a significant exposure threat to overhead power lines.

316.6.2 Outdoor storage. Outdoor storage within the utility easement underneath high-voltage transmission lines shall be limited to noncombustible material. Storage of hazardous materials including, but not limited to, flammable and *combustible liquids* is prohibited.

> **Exception:** Combustible storage, including vehicles and fuel storage for backup power equipment serving public utility equipment, is allowed, provided that a plan indicating the storage configuration is submitted and *approved*.

❖ This section regulates the fire load that can be allowed to exist beneath overhead high-voltage transmission lines by restricting outdoor storage within the easement to only noncombustible materials. The exception recognizes that, in certain instances, combustible materials may need to be stored within the easement, such as for utility work on the power lines. Such materials storage must be strictly regulated through a plans submittal and review process and approval by the fire code official. This section also makes it clear that under no circumstances are hazardous materials allowed to be stored beneath the power lines.

SECTION 317
ROOFTOP GARDENS AND LANDSCAPED ROOFS

317.1 General. Rooftop gardens and landscaped roofs shall be installed and maintained in accordance with Sections 317.2 through 317.5 and Sections 1505 and 1507.16 of the *International Building Code.*

❖ Among the major elements of green building construction are energy conservation and preservation of natural resources such as water. Rooftop vegetation accomplishes both, in the form of gardens or using landscaping to cover part of a building roof. Roof gardens or landscaped roofs offer a number of savings to the building owner. For buildings constructed with a membrane-type roofing system, roof gardens or landscaping can increase the life of the roofing materials by almost 100 percent according to some studies. Depending on the design, roof area and local climate, research has found certain green roofs can reduce summer cooling loads by about 25 percent and in some cases have reduced heat gain by 95 percent. In addition to reduced energy costs, these reductions have the potential to reduce the size of HVAC equipment, which in turn lowers the capital costs for construction. These roofs and gardens can also reduce the sound pressure level inside of the building and are helpful in controlling storm water runoff.

Section 317 addresses rooftop gardens and landscaped roofs. The requirements in this section limit the area of roof gardens, require the use of roof assembles designed for severe fire exposures, and provide for the installation of a standpipe connection. It also sets forth requirements for establishing a maintenance plan for the vegetation installed on roof gardens or landscaped roofs. This section does not define what constitutes a roof garden or landscaped roof; however, it is intended to deal with the structural and fire safety concerns regarding construction that creates a green space on a building roof rather than the placement of a small roof garden.

This section references the requirements in Chapter 15 of the IBC for roof gardens and landscaped roofs. Section 1507.16 of the IBC requires compliance with the requirements of the code, Chapter 15 of the IBC and specific structural requirements in Chapter 16 of the IBC for special purpose roofs and landscaped roofs. The IBC requires roof gardens and landscaped roofs to be calculated at a minimum 20 pounds per square foot (0.958 kN/m^2) uniform live load and that the weight of landscaping materials be considered as dead loads and computed assuming the rooftop soil is saturated.

In addition to the IBC structural requirements, roof gardens and landscaped roofs can also require the installation of a Class A roof assembly. Section 317.1 of the code references the provisions in Section 1505 of the IBC, which sets forth the fire exposure ratings for roof assemblies. The IBC fire classification requirements for roof assemblies are based on the building's construction type, not on the classification of the building's occupancy. The minimum roof covering classification prescribed by the IBC is either a Class B or Class C roof assembly. Class A roof assemblies are specified where the jurisdiction has adopted Appendix D of the IBC and the building is located in a fire district or where required in the IWUIC. Section 1505.2 of the IBC requires Class A assemblies to be listed and identified as such by an approved testing agency, but because the IBC does not normally require the installation of Class A roof assemblies, the number of listed systems available to design professionals will be limited. Additional requirements on the design of green roofs are contained in the *International Green Construction Code*® (IgCC®). Another source of information on "green roofs" is contained in Property Loss Prevention Data Sheet 1-35, *Green Roof Systems*, published by FM Global.

317.2 Rooftop garden or landscaped roof size. Rooftop garden or landscaped roof areas shall not exceed 15,625 square feet (1450 m^2) in size for any single area with a maximum dimension of 125 feet (39 m) in length or width. A minimum 6-foot-wide (1.8 m) clearance consisting of a Class A-rated roof system complying with ASTM E108 or UL 790 shall be provided between adjacent rooftop gardens or landscaped roof areas.

❖ On large roofs, the code does not permit complete coverage of the roof with vegetation. This section limits the area of roof gardens or landscaping to an area not exceeding 15,625 square feet (1,450 m^2) and its maximum length or width dimension cannot exceed 125 feet (39 m). The 125-foot value is based on the typical amount of hose carried by fire departments for high-rise hose packs. If the area or dimension of a landscaped garden or roof exceeds the prescribed area or dimension limits, this section allows multiple landscaped areas where each is separated by a minimum 6-foot-wide (1.8 m) buffer space constructed as a Class A roof assembly. This buffer space will slow fire spread between multiple landscaped areas and will afford fire-fighter access to each separated segment and provide access to roof surface areas that may be used for fire department ventilation operations. Note that for buildings in which Section 905 requires the installation of a standpipe system, Section 905.3.8 will require the extension of a standpipe hose valve to the roof level serving the landscaped roof or roof garden.

317.3 Rooftop structure and equipment clearance. For all vegetated roofing systems abutting combustible vertical surfaces, a Class A-rated roof system complying with ASTM E108 or UL 790 shall be achieved for a minimum 6-foot-wide (1829 mm) continuous border placed around rooftop structures and all rooftop equipment including, but not limited to, mechanical and machine rooms, penthouses, skylights, roof vents, solar panels, antenna supports and building service equipment.

❖ Where a building utilizes combustible construction for the construction of penthouses, mechanical equipment or rooftop elevator machine rooms, this section requires a minimum 6-foot-wide (1.8 m) border constructed around the combustible construction. The buffer space is also constructed to the IBC requirements for a Class A roof assembly (see the commentary to Section 317.1). The buffer space is not required if the roof garden or landscaped roof is separated by more than 6 feet (1.8 m) from the combustible construction or when noncombustible construction is used. This buffer space will slow fire spread between landscaped areas and combustible construction and will afford fire-fighter access.

317.4 Vegetation. Vegetation shall be maintained in accordance with Sections 317.4.1 and 317.4.2.

❖ This section introduces requirements for the maintenance of rooftop gardens or landscaped roof areas to reduce the fire risk that could otherwise arise for buildings and exposure buildings because of the possible lack of maintenance. Basically, an unmaintained roof garden that catches fire could be likened to a brush fire being conducted on top of a building rather than on the ground, creating an increased exposure hazard since roof covering rating requirements are based on flying embers, not falling ones.

317.4.1 Irrigation. Supplemental irrigation shall be provided to maintain levels of hydration necessary to keep green roof plants alive and to keep dry foliage to a minimum.

❖ Care of rooftop vegetation by simple watering provides a basic line of defense against accumulation of dry biomass that can present a significant fire load if ignited. The frequency of watering is not specified due to the diverse moisture needs of the wide variety of planted materials possible on any given roof. The person responsible for the landscaped roof must determine the level of watering needed for this purpose and that information should be included in the maintenance plan authorized by Section 317.4.3.

317.4.2 Dead foliage. Excess biomass, such as overgrown vegetation, leaves and other dead and decaying material, shall be removed at regular intervals not less than two times per year.

❖ In order to manage the significant fuel load accumulation and fire hazard associated with dead or unkempt rooftop vegetation, this section sets a basic level of maintenance and regular removal of dead biomass, similar to that found in Section 304.1.2 for the maintenance of vegetation in and around a building (see commentary, Section 304.1.2).

317.4.3 Maintenance plan. The *fire code official* is authorized to require a maintenance plan for vegetation placed on roofs due to the size of a roof garden, materials used or where a fire hazard exists to the building or exposures due to the lack of maintenance.

❖ This section authorizes the fire code official to require a maintenance plan that may be used to guide maintenance personnel and inspectors in the care and upkeep of vegetation to reduce the hazard of having highly combustible dead plantings on the roof. This is beneficial to determine if the roof garden will be maintained or is just a bunch of vegetation placed on the roof as a "do-it-yourself" project. The maintenance plan is also beneficial to determine what happens to a building that goes vacant or where the building owner does not keep up with maintenance.

317.5 Maintenance equipment. Fueled equipment stored on roofs and used for the care and maintenance of vegetation on roofs shall be stored in accordance with Section 313.

❖ This section simply sends the code user to Section 313 for appropriate storage regulations for fueled equipment (see commentary, Section 313).

SECTION 318 LAUNDRY CARTS

318.1 Laundry carts with a capacity of 1 cubic yard or more. Laundry carts with an individual capacity of 1 cubic yard [200 gallons ($0.76\ m^3$)] or more, used in laundries within Group B, E, F-1, I, M and R-1 occupancies, shall be constructed of noncombustible materials or materials having a peak rate of heat release not exceeding 300 kW/m^2 at a flux of 50 kW/m^2 where tested in a horizontal orientation in accordance with ASTM E1354.

Exceptions:

1. Laundry carts in areas protected by an *approved automatic sprinkler system* installed throughout in accordance with Section 903.3.1.1.
2. Laundry carts in coin-operated laundries.

❖ The change from cooking with animal fat to vegetable oil has increased the number of spontaneous ignition fires. These fires occur frequently in laundry operations due to insufficient cool-down time in the laundry drying process and have been known to ignite in freshly folded linen, often contained in polyethylene laundry carts. Medium-density polyethylene laundry carts which have a fuel content of approximately 20,020 Btu per pound [27 ft^3 ($0.76\ m^3$)] are commonly used in industrial, commercial and institutional laundry operations. This material is essentially equal to the fuel value for gasoline and becomes a burning liquid that spreads and flows when involved in a fire. As such, the cart flammability hazard must be mitigated. This section does that by limiting combustible container heat release rate and heat flux using the test parameters of ASTM E1354. The peak rate of heat release criterion is consistent with the one in Sections 304.3.2, 304.3.4 and 808.1. The efficacy of using these lesser-hazard carts has been demonstrated in several commercial and institutional fire incidents wherein the burning commercial dryer contents were emptied into an ASTM E1354 container and taken outside and overhauled without evacuation of the building, loss to the structure or damage to the container.

Exception 1 permits the use and storage of ordinary laundry carts in areas protected by an approved sprinkler system. It would be up to the fire code official to determine the maximum number that could be stored under these conditions.

Exception 2 recognizes that the small carts used in neighborhood coin laundries do not present the same hazard as those used in commercial-type operations because the clothes and other laundered items do not remain in the cart for a significant length of time.

SECTION 319 MOBILE FOOD PREPARATION VEHICLES

319.1 General. Mobile food preparation vehicles that are equipped with appliances that produce smoke or grease-laden vapors shall comply with this section.

❖ This section introduces the requirements for mobile food preparation vehicles that have equipment that produces smoke or grease-laden vapors.

319.2 Permit required. Permits shall be required as set forth in Section 105.6.

❖ This section makes it clear that permits are required for this type of operation and provides direct reference to the requirement in Chapter 1. The specific section for mobile food preparation vehicles is Section 105.6.30.

319.3 Exhaust hood. Cooking equipment that produces grease-laden vapors shall be provided with a kitchen exhaust hood in accordance with Section 607.

❖ This section provides the direct section reference to the requirements for exhaust hoods that are used in these vehicles and makes it clear that those requirements apply in this specific use.

319.4 Fire protection. Fire protection shall be provided in accordance with Sections 319.4.1 and 319.4.2.

❖ This section introduces the requirements for the fire protection of mobile food preparation vehicles.

319.4.1 Fire protection for cooking equipment. Cooking equipment shall be protected by automatic fire extinguishing systems in accordance with Section 904.12.

❖ This section provides the direct section reference to fire protection requirements for these vehicles and makes it clear that the same requirements that apply to fixed indoor commercial cooking operations also apply in this specific mobile vehicle use.

319.4.2 Fire extinguisher. Portable fire extinguishers shall be provided in accordance with Section 906.4.

❖ This section provides the direct section reference to portable fire extinguisher requirements for these vehicles and makes it clear that the same requirements that apply to fixed indoor commercial cooking operations also apply in this specific mobile vehicle use.

319.5 Appliance connection to fuel supply piping. Gas cooking appliances shall be secured in place and connected to fuel-supply piping with an appliance connector complying with ANSI Z21.69/CSA 6.16. The connector installation shall be configured in accordance with the manufacturer's installation instructions. Movement of appliances shall be limited by restraining devices installed in accordance with the connector and appliance manufacturers' instructions.

❖ Similar to the requirements of Section 607.4, this section is intended to prohibit the practice of replacing listed flexible piping with residential flexible piping and using any connections that do not conform to the referenced standards. Residential flexible piping is more easily damaged when cooking equipment is moved for cleaning, and specifically in this case, movement due to vehicle motion, thus causing a fire/life safety problem with gas leaks and fires. In addition, it also limits the distance that the appliances can be moved for cleaning, further protecting the connection.

319.6 Cooking oil storage containers. Cooking oil storage containers within mobile food preparation vehicles shall have a maximum aggregate volume not more than 120 gallons (454 L), and shall be stored in such a way as to not be toppled or damaged during transport.

❖ This section provides the limit on the amount of cooking oil that can be stored in containers within the vehicles. The additional requirement for container restraint and protection is provided to ensure that the level of hazard is not increased in this specific use beyond what the code allows for a fixed container location.

319.7 Cooking oil storage tanks. Cooking oil storage tanks within mobile food preparation vehicles shall comply with Sections 319.7.1 through 319.7.5.2.

❖ This section introduces the requirements for cooking oil storage tanks within mobile food preparation vehicles.

319.7.1 Metallic storage tanks. Metallic cooking oil storage tanks shall be *listed* in accordance with UL 80 or UL 142, and shall be installed in accordance with the tank manufacturer's instructions.

❖ Similar to Section 608.2, this section provides the listing requirements for metallic storage tanks that are within mobile food preparation vehicles. Specifically, they are to be listed as complying with either UL 142 or UL 80. Both standards are limited to shop-fabricated, above-ground storage tanks (ASTs) designed to operate at atmospheric pressure. Both standards require tanks to be constructed of carbon steel meeting a certain specification and, before shipment, to be tested at the factory to confirm they are liquid tight. Tanks constructed to UL 80 have a maximum volume of 660 gallons (2271.25 L). UL 142 does not limit the volume of ASTs. Installations of metallic ASTs for cooking oil storage also must comply with the manufacturer's installation instructions

319.7.2 Nonmetallic storage tanks. Nonmetallic cooking oil storage tanks shall be installed in accordance with the tank manufacturer's instructions and shall comply with both of the following:

1. Tanks shall be *listed* for use with cooking oil, including maximum temperature to which the tank will be exposed during use.
2. Tank capacity shall not exceed 200 gallons (757 L) per tank.

❖ Similar to Section 608.3, this section provides the requirements for nonmetallic storage tanks that are within mobile food preparation vehicles. As discussed in the commentary for Section 608.1, cooking oil that has not been previously used must be stored in food grade tanks. Typically, nonmetallic tanks are more appropriate for nonused cooking oil. These provisions are not limited to fresh cooking oil and can be utilized for used, spent and inedible cooking oils. Section 608.3 references the appropriate standard for such tanks, which is UL 2152. Essentially, a listing for use with cooking oil is required, as is making sure that the maximum temperature limits associated with the tank match the application in which the tank is used.

The tanks are limited in size to 200 gallons. Metallic tanks have the potential for much larger capacities, as discussed in the commentary to Section 319.7.1.

319.7.3 Cooking oil storage system components. Metallic and nonmetallic cooking oil storage system components shall include, but are not limited to, piping, connections, fittings, valves, tubing, hose, pumps, vents and other related components used for the transfer of cooking oil.

❖ Similar to Section 608.4, this section lists what components make up a cooking oil storage system. Section 319.7.4 addresses the design and construction requirements for these components. This section also notes that these components are permitted to be either metallic or nonmetallic. The allowance for types of materials will depend on the requirements in Section 319.7.4.

319.7.4 Design criteria. The design, fabrication and assembly of system components shall be suitable for the working pressures, temperatures and structural stresses to be encountered by the components.

❖ Similar to Section 608.4.1, the performance-based language provided in this section requires that it be determined that the system's intended use is consistent with all the components of the system. In this situation, the addition of vehicle motion would add to the operational working conditions beyond that of Section 608.

319.7.5 Tank venting. Normal and emergency venting shall be provided for cooking oil storage tanks.

❖ Similar to Section 608.5, this section and the UL tank standards referenced in Section 319.7.2 require ASTs to be equipped with a normal vent and an emergency vent.

319.7.5.1 Normal vents. Normal vents shall be located above the maximum normal liquid line, and shall have a minimum effective area not smaller than the largest filling or withdrawal connection. Normal vents are not required to vent to the exterior.

❖ Similar to Section 608.5.1, tanks are vented to maintain the internal tank pressure within the design operating range. Low pressure can increase the generation of vapors while high pressure can damage the tank or piping system. Any pressure outside of the design pressure range (which could be caused if the vent line were not located above the highest level of liquid) can have an adverse effect on the operation of the system as well as the piping and equipment. This section is also consistent with Section 21.4.3 of NFPA 30.

While this section establishes the size of the normal vent line as being the same as the largest inflow or outflow connection, it should be noted that Section 21.4.3.3 of NFPA 30 also states that the minimum vent size must be $1^1/_4$ inches inside diameter.

Recognizing the reduced hazard of Class IIIB liquids, this section does not require the normal vent for a cooking oil AST installed in the vehicle to be terminated outside the vehicle. Note, however, that Section 5704.2.7.3.3 of the code allows this condition only where the tank is equipped with a normally closed pressure/vacuum vent.

319.7.5.2 Emergency vents. Emergency relief vents shall be located above the maximum normal liquid line, and shall be in the form of a device or devices that will relieve excessive internal pressure caused by an exposure fire. For nonmetallic tanks, the emergency relief vent shall be allowed to be in the form of construction. Emergency vents are not required to discharge to the exterior.

❖ Similar to Section 608.5.2, all ASTs for cooking oil storage require an emergency vent, meeting the requirements of Section 5704.2.7.4, that will relieve excessive internal pressure caused by exposure to fires; however, the emergency vents for ASTs storing Class IIIB liquids are generally permitted to discharge inside the building, in accordance with Exception 2 of that section.

319.8 LP-gas systems. Where LP-gas systems provide fuel for cooking appliances, such systems shall comply with Chapter 61 and Sections 319.8.1 through 319.8.5.

❖ This section introduces the requirements for LP-gas that is used as fuel for cooking appliances within mobile food preparation vehicles. Additionally, it makes it clear that the requirements of Chapter 61 also apply in this situation.

319.8.1 Maximum aggregate volume. The maximum aggregate capacity of LP-gas containers transported on the vehicle and used to fuel cooking appliances only shall not exceed 200 pounds (91 kg) propane capacity.

❖ This section provides the limit on the amount of LP-gas that can be stored in containers within the vehicles.

319.8.2 Protection of container. LP-gas containers installed on the vehicle shall be securely mounted and restrained to prevent movement.

❖ This section requires that containers be fully restrained to ensure that the level of hazard is not increased in this specific use beyond what the code allows for a fixed container location.

319.8.3 LP-gas container construction. LP-gas containers shall be manufactured in compliance with the requirements of NFPA 58.

❖ As required additionally by Chapter 61, LP-gas containers that are used on mobile vehicles are to be manufactured in accordance with NFPA 58.

319.8.4 Protection of system piping. LP-gas system piping, including valves and fittings, shall be adequately protected to prevent tampering, impact damage, and damage from vibration.

❖ Similar to Sections 6109.8 and 6109.13, this section requires that LP-gas system piping, valves and fittings be protected as stated. Valve assemblies must be protected from physical impact. Cylinders having propane capacities up to 60 pounds (27 kg) will usually have collars that extend above the height of the valves. Larger cylinders will have screw-on caps or domes that serve the same function.

Within the vehicles, tampering with LP-gas containers may be a problem. For that reason, locked metal cabinets can be used to provide not only tamper protection but also protection from impact. This section also adds the specific requirement that system piping be protected from the vibration that occurs due to vehicle motion and road conditions. This is to ensure that the level of hazard is not increased in this specific use beyond what the code allows for a fixed container location.

319.8.5 LP-gas alarms. A *listed* LP-gas alarm shall be installed within the vehicle in the vicinity of LP-gas system components, in accordance with the manufacturer's instructions.

❖ Specific to the use of LP-gas within mobile vehicles, a listed LP-gas alarm is required to be installed close to the system and as specified by the manufacturer's installation instructions. An applicable standard would be UL 2075.

319.9 CNG systems. Where CNG systems provide fuel for cooking appliances, such systems shall comply with Sections 319.9.1 through 319.9.4.

❖ This section introduces the requirements for CNG systems that are used a fuel for cooking appliances within mobile food preparation vehicles.

319.9.1 CNG containers supplying only cooking fuel. CNG containers installed solely to provide fuel for cooking purposes shall be in accordance with Sections 319.9.1.1 through 319.9.1.3

❖ This section introduces the requirements for vehicles that use CNG systems only as a fuel for cooking appliances and a different fuel for the vehicle itself.

319.9.1.1 Maximum aggregate volume. The maximum aggregate capacity of CNG containers transported on the vehicle shall not exceed 1,300 pounds (590 kg) water capacity.

❖ This section provides the limit of the total capacity of CNG containers allowed on the vehicle.

319.9.1.2 Protection of container. CNG containers shall be securely mounted and restrained to prevent movement. Containers shall not be installed in locations subject to a direct vehicle impact.

❖ This section adds the specific requirement that CNG containers be protected from the vibration that occurs due to vehicle motion and road conditions. This is to ensure that the level of hazard in this use is not increased beyond what the code allows for a fixed container location. In addition, it is not allowed to locate containers within areas of the vehicles that can sustain damage from collisions.

319.9.1.3 CNG container construction. CNG containers shall be an NGV-2 cylinder.

❖ This section lists the standard that CNG containers on mobile vehicles must conform to. NGV-2 contains requirements for the material, design, manufacture, and testing of serially produced, refillable containers intended only for the storage of compressed natural gas. These containers are to be permanently attached to the vehicle.

319.9.2 CNG containers supplying transportation and cooking fuel. Where CNG containers and systems are used to supply fuel for cooking purposes in addition to being used for transportation fuel, the installation shall be in accordance with NFPA 52.

❖ This section is specific to vehicles that use CNG systems as both a fuel for cooking appliances and the vehicle itself. As stated, all installations are to conform to NFPA 52.

319.9.3 Protection of system piping. CNG system piping, including valves and fittings, shall be adequately protected to prevent tampering, impact damage and damage from vibration.

❖ Similar to Section 319.8.4, this section requires that CNG system piping, valves and fittings be protected as stated. Valve assemblies must be protected from physical impact. This section also adds the specific requirement that system piping be protected from the vibration that occurs due to vehicle motion and road conditions. This is to ensure that the level of hazard in this use is not increased beyond what the code allows for a stationary system location.

319.9.4 Methane alarms. A listed methane gas alarm shall be installed within the vehicle in accordance with manufacturer's instructions.

❖ Specific to the use of CNG systems within mobile vehicles, a methane gas alarm is required to be installed close to the system and as specified by the manufacturer's installation instructions.

319.10 Maintenance. Maintenance of systems on mobile food preparation vehicles shall be in accordance with Sections 319.10.1 through 319.10.3.

❖ This section introduces the requirements for the maintenance of the systems in food preparation vehicles.

319.10.1 Exhaust system. The exhaust system, including hood, grease-removal devices, fans, ducts and other appurtenances, shall be inspected and cleaned in accordance with Section 607.3.

❖ This section provides direct reference to Section 607.3 for exhaust system maintenance requirements.

319.10.2 Fire protection systems and devices. Fire protection systems and devices shall be maintained in accordance with Section 901.6.

❖ This section provides direct reference to Section 901.6 for fire protection system maintenance requirements.

319.10.3 Fuel gas systems. LP-gas containers installed on the vehicle and fuel-gas piping systems shall be inspected annually by an *approved* inspection agency or a company that is registered with the U.S. Department of Transportation to requalify LP-gas cylinders, to ensure that system components are free from damage, suitable for the intended service and not subject to leaking. CNG containers shall be inspected every 3 years in a qualified service facility. CNG containers shall not be used past their expiration date as listed on the manufacturer's container label. Upon satisfactory inspection, the *approved* inspection agency shall affix a tag on the fuel gas system or within the vehicle indicating the name of the inspection agency and the date of satisfactory inspection.

❖ This section provides the inspection frequency requirement for LP-gas containers and fuel-gas piping systems on food preparation vehicles. As stated, the inspection of the LP-gas systems is to be performed by an entity that is registered with the US DOT. CNG containers are to be inspected every 3 years by a qualified facility and not used past the expiration date on the container. Completed satisfactory inspections are to be documented with a container tag being mounted on the fuel gas system or inside the vehicle with the name and date that it occurred.

Bibliography

The following resource materials were used in the preparation of the commentary for this chapter of the code:

Complete Revision History to the 2018 I-Codes: Successful Changes and Public Comments. Washington, DC: International Code Council, 2017.

FACE-99-F47, Six Career Fire Fighters Killed in Cold-storage and Warehouse Building Fire—Massachusetts. Washington, DC: National Institute for Occupational Safety and Health, September 2000.

NFPA 550-12, Fire Safety Concepts Tree. Quincy, MA: National Fire Protection Association, 2012.

Property Loss Prevention Data Sheet 1-35, Green Roof Systems. Johnston, RI: FM Global, 2011.

Chapter 4: Emergency Planning and Preparedness

General Comments

This chapter is an expansion of the provisions found in the legacy fire codes used to develop the code. The overall approach has been to place all similar requirements into general sections. Unique occupancy and use-specific requirements are provided in Section 403.

This chapter first provides general scope and requirements for reporting emergencies and preventing interference with fire department activities in Section 401.

Section 403 provides detailed requirements based on occupancy. These requirements include seating plans for Group A occupancies. This section also establishes requirements for general public safety regarding fire watch personnel, crowd managers and planning requirements for public assemblages.

Section 404 provides detailed requirements for fire safety plans, fire evacuation plans and lockdowns.

The frequency and required documentation related to evacuation drills are addressed in Section 405. The minimum criteria for the training of occupants for emergency situations are found in Section 406. Section 407 provides requirements that apply to occupancies that contain hazardous materials. Among of the key elements are Hazardous Materials Inventory Statements (HMIS) and Hazardous Materials Management Plans (HMMP).

Purpose

More so than other fire-related requirements, this chapter focuses on the actions of occupants during fires and other emergencies. These requirements are based on higher levels of care necessary related to the concentration of people, physical and mental capabilities of the occupants, lack of familiarity with a building, or the complexity and size of the building. These requirements are intended to improve the effectiveness of other measures required by this code and the *International Building Code*® (IBC®).

Basically, this chapter addresses human contributions to life safety in buildings when a fire or other emergency occurs. The requirements for continuous training and scheduled evacuation drills can be as important as the required periodic inspections and maintenance of built-in fire protection features. The level of preparation by the occupants also improves the emergency responders' abilities during an emergency.

The IBC focuses on built-in fire protection features, such as automatic sprinkler systems, fire-resistance-rated construction and properly designed egress systems. The human element is only indirectly addressed in the IBC, whereas this chapter fully addresses the human element. Traditionally, fire codes address the human element more directly in their role in the long-term maintenance of buildings and systems.

Chapters 3 and 6 through 10 of this code and Chapters 7 through 10 of the IBC set forth provisions for how and when buildings are to be properly equipped and maintained to prevent damage and loss of life in the event of a fire. These requirements are based on two complementary fire safety strategies: managing the fire and managing the occupants. These strategies are discussed in more detail in the commentary to Chapter 1.

Managing Fire

A fire can be either prevented or managed. This chapter of the code focuses on training and preparedness while also emphasizing prevention. In some cases, moving occupants to minimize their exposure to a hazard is difficult or impractical. In these situations, controlling or eliminating the hazard is preferable, especially while it is still manageable. In fact, this is the concept underlying all fire-suppression requirements. Successful fire control depends on building occupants recognizing the fire threat, deciding to respond, choosing how to respond and, in the case of choosing fire control, identifying, locating and using the correct method. All of these functions must promptly take place in that order. Failure to perform promptly may preclude alternative strategies; therefore, location and identification of fire extinguishers and occupant standpipe hose lines are provided so that incipient fire-fighting equipment is readily accessible to occupants. These appliances, however, are often difficult to operate, and regardless of experience, fighting fire is a difficult and dangerous task. This chapter prescribes training requirements that, if met, will better prepare occupants to respond to incipient fires.

Managing Occupants

The management of occupants is primarily moving them away from the hazard. Verifying that enough exits have ample capacity, are immediately accessible, adequately arranged, appropriately identified and suitably protected are only the first steps toward achieving functional life safety. Occupants must know not only where exits are, but also when and how to use them. For instance, studies have shown that people have a "learned irrelevance" to emergency exits. Learned irrelevance is a psychological phenomenon that occurs when a person is exposed to a stimulus but usually does not need to respond to it. Because of this phenomenon, most occupants are likely to exit the way they have entered, whether it is the correct way or not; therefore, beyond designing the building with an adequate number of exits, a method of encouraging the use of the best exits must be developed. Identifying dangerous conditions, deciding how to act and responding appropriately and promptly are essential. Various factors and situations can make evacuation not only difficult but potentially impractical. All of these factors involve the interaction between the building, its systems and features, occupants and the fire. This code concentrates on the last two factors while the IBC regulates the first two factors. Planning for life safety requires a response to these factors by defining the life safety strategies that must be implemented, as well as the means to achieve them. Life safety factors, such as buildings, fire and people, are important in managing exposed occupants.

This chapter concentrates on planning and practicing the desired actions of building occupants when a fire occurs. The remainder of the code focuses on the behaviors and procedures that must be practiced or observed to prevent or control a fire. The best way to create a safe building environment is through fire prevention. No system can ensure complete protection of building occupants.

Fires are not the only emergencies necessitating the implementation of life safety strategies; therefore, this chapter describes requirements for preparing and implementing life safety plans and programs in occupancies with special life safety problems. These include occupancies in which the number of occupants or the arrangement or complexity of the building may make evacuation or removal from hazardous conditions difficult or impractical.

A reality of the 21st century in the wake of terrorist attacks and school and business shootings is a need to establish so-called "lockdown" procedures in order to protect and defend building occupants. While the code does not mandate the implementation of lockdown plans and procedures, it does provide some minimum standards such plans must meet when they are prepared.

Not all occupants of each building are equally capable of performing tasks essential to their safety. A growing awareness, not only of people with physical disabilities, but also of what constitutes a disability, has focused life safety on everyone. Federal health care policies and funding criteria have spurred the deinstitutionalization of people who were formerly confined to nursing homes and other traditional health care institutions. This has created a new category of occupancies—board and care homes (institutional, residential care; I-1)—while the number of beds provided in nursing homes and hospitals continues to grow. Similarly, technological advances have promoted the creation of larger and more complex buildings, including high rises, open malls, domed stadiums, mixed-use complexes and convention centers. All of these situations create special life safety problems that physical features alone cannot remedy. Additionally, these situations require not only that adequate physical accommodations be provided, but also that building occupants be trained to respond to emergencies in these facilities.

Life Safety

Life safety strategies involve the development of an explicit statement of a desired life safety outcome. This statement, once designed to the capabilities of the building occupants and the physical arrangement of the exits, becomes a life safety strategy. Such approaches stress defining a specific strategy or strategies for protecting occupants. Protection may include moving them (assisting), causing them to move (directing), defending them in place or a combination of these measures. An effective strategy must consider the number and capabilities of building occupants; the type, location and arrangement of building exits; the fire; its effects on the people and building; and the number, training and capability of staff to direct or perform fire evacuation or incipient fire-fighting duties. Each strategy, combined with effective planning and practice, becomes the means for achieving the desired life safety outcome.

The life safety strategies for a health care facility, a high-rise office building and a multiplex theater could vary considerably based on the specific characteristics of the use. First, while the number of occupants will be significant in each case, the actual number occupying the building may be varied. Similarly, the occupant density and location of people in the building will vary, as well as the physical arrangement of the building, which in the first example that follows may be assumed as primarily horizontal and, in the second, as principally vertical. The most profound difference will be the capabilities of the occupants. In high rises and theaters, building occupants will be expected to perform life safety behaviors themselves, while patients in a health care facility may require substantial assistance or need to defend in place. High-rise and theater occupants will differ from each other in their levels of familiarity with the building design. Further, in a theater, lighting conditions may interfere with the occupants' ability to discern the path of egress travel.

In the first two examples, health care and high rise, removing all occupants from the building in the event of fire is impractical. In a high-rise building, occupants located above a fire are in greater danger than occupants located below the fire, since combustion products naturally rise. In a health care occupancy, the risk to most occupants is compounded by their weakened or disabled condition prior to the fire. In both of these examples, a life safety strategy should first address the needs of those at greatest risk by removing them from harm. Secondly, the life safety strategy should stress separating endangered occupants and their immediate neighbors from danger until the hazard can be controlled or confined. As seen in each example, life safety strategies should also incorporate both partial relocation and defend-in-place concepts. In the health care facility, however, occupants will be moved horizontally to achieve this objective, while in high-rise buildings, occupants will be expected to move downward or upward to separate themselves from danger. In the case of a multiplex theater, occupants will usually be directed to the nearest exit; however, its location may not be known to all or some of them. Further, because employees in assembly occupancies must be trained in the proper use of portable fire extinguishers, the life safety strategy should include instruction in using these appliances to minimize occupant exposure to fire effects. The resulting life safety strategies for these occupancies may resemble the following:

Example 1—Health Care Facility: Upon notice of fire, direct or assist evacuation and relocate occupants from the area of fire origin to an adjacent smoke compartment through horizontal exits. Remove the most critically ill patients and those with special needs to an area providing the most appropriate level of care.

Example 2—High-rise Building: Direct occupants in the area or floor of fire origin to the nearest exits. Occupants on the fire floor, the floor above and the floor below will relocate sequentially up or down at least two floors. Occupants located two floors above and two floors below the fire floor will be sequentially relocated following movement of fire floor occupants.

Example 3—Multiplex Theater: Announce exit locations and evacuation instructions prior to each movie. Over voice/alarm systems, direct occupants to nearest exit. Employees in the immediate vicinity of an incipient fire may attempt to control or extinguish it using a portable fire extinguisher after activating the fire alarm system.

Once the appropriate strategy has been defined, a plan can be expanded with little additional effort to form the backbone of a comprehensive life safety protocol. The following statements provide additional instructions for the aforementioned examples:

Example 1—Health Care Facility: Monitor or reinforce fire barriers and smoke barriers so that they provide adequate defense against fire until it is controlled and extinguished. Staff will report progress of the fire and relocation operation to the Private Branch Exchange (PBX) operator through the nurse call station in adjacent smoke compartments.

Example 2—High-rise Building: Building fire manager will meet fire department personnel at the central control station located off the main lobby.

Example 3—Multiplex Theater: Projectionist will stop films so that the alarm and evacuation instructions are heard and followed. Upon activation of the alarm, instructions are heard and followed while the on-duty manager telephones the fire department to confirm that the fire was reported. Ushers will follow occupants out of each auditorium as conditions permit, closing exit doors and preventing reentry. Upon completing assigned duties, all staff will report to the manager located in front of the lobby entrance.

These expanded statements certainly do not constitute a fully developed plan; however, with these elements of the life safety plan defined, details can be added to a plan that addresses everything from pre-incident preparation through post-incident follow-up. A well-developed plan should include all or most of the following elements:

- Assignment of roles and responsibilities.
- Description of fire protection systems, including operating instructions, if appropriate.
- Building floor plans and sections.
- Seating diagrams and occupant load.
- Number, location and path of travel to exits.
- Emergency notification lists and procedures.
- Post-incident follow-up procedures, including salvage and insurance information.
- Plan revision and evaluation procedures.

Once a plan is developed, reviewed and approved, it must be distributed, practiced and periodically revised.

SECTION 401
GENERAL

401.1 Scope. Reporting of emergencies, coordination with emergency response forces, emergency plans and procedures for managing or responding to emergencies shall comply with the provisions of this section.

Exception: Firms that have approved on-premises firefighting organizations and that are in compliance with approved procedures for fire reporting.

❖ This section describes the overall scope of Chapter 4, which notes that all procedures relating to reporting and managing fire and other emergencies be in accordance with this chapter. There is one exception recognizing organizations, such as large industrial sites, that have on-site fire brigades. The fire brigades and the associated reporting procedures must be approved by the fire code official.

401.2 Approval. Where required by this code, fire safety plans, emergency procedures and employee training programs shall be approved by the fire code official.

❖ To verify that emergency procedures, training and fire safety plans have taken all essential factors into account, the plans and procedures must be approved by the fire code official.

401.3 Emergency responder notification. Notification of emergency responders shall be in accordance with Sections 401.3.1 through 401.3.3.

❖ This section simply states that the notification of emergency forces must comply with Section 401.3 and all of its subsections.

401.3.1 Fire events. In the event an unwanted fire occurs on a property, the owner or occupant shall immediately report such condition to the fire department.

❖ This section requires prompt notification of the fire department in the event of a fire emergency. Employees or other occupants are prohibited from delaying in any way the notification of the fire department.

401.3.2 Alarm activations. Upon activation of a fire alarm signal, employees or staff shall immediately notify the fire department.

❖ This section specifically requires immediate notification of the fire department or other emergency response groups when an alarm signal is activated in order to bring emergency forces in the shortest amount of time.

401.3.3 Delayed notification. A person shall not, by verbal or written directive, require any delay in the reporting of a fire to the fire department.

❖ Emergency plans and procedures must not include a requirement that employees report an alarm to a supervisor or similar person before calling the fire department. There can be no substitute for immediate notification of emergency forces because a quick response is the key to efficient and effective rescue and firefighting.

401.4 Required plan implementation. In the event an unwanted fire is detected in a building or a fire alarm activates, the emergency plan shall be implemented.

❖ Sections 401.3.1 through 401.3.3 mandate the prompt notification of emergency responders whenever a fire alarm is activated or an actual fire or suspected fire occurs. Since the emergency plan is designed to safely and effectively deal with those circumstances and safeguard the occupants, it must be implemented simultaneously with emergency responder notification as required by this section.

401.5 Making false report. A person shall not give, signal or transmit a false alarm.

❖ Chapter 2 of the code defines a false alarm as an intentional activation of an alarm or notification of a fire or other emergency when no emergency exists. This would not include a malfunctioning alarm system. False alarms have the potential for causing confusion or panic among occupants of the affected premises, a situation that could lead to property damage, personal injury or death. False alarms also place fire fighters and other emergency personnel in potential danger during the unnecessary emergency response. This can jeopardize other lives and property in the community by committing emergency forces to a false situation when they might be needed at an actual emergency elsewhere.

401.6 Emergency evacuation drills. The sounding of a fire alarm signal and the carrying out of an emergency evacuation drill in accordance with the provisions of Section 405 shall be allowed.

❖ This section specifically allows fire alarm signals to be utilized as part of emergency evacuation drills.

401.7 Unplanned evacuation. Evacuations made necessary by the unplanned activation of a fire alarm system or by any other emergency shall not be substituted for a required evacuation drill.

❖ This section makes it clear that unplanned evacuations will not be applied toward fulfillment of the number of drills required. Evacuation drills are intended to provide for an assessment of the adequacy of an emergency action plan and the response of the building occupants. Occupants may or may not be forewarned of a pending drill depending on the circumstances. Responsible staff prepares for and conducts the drills, a key aspect of which is having monitors in place to assess individual and group performance. An unplanned evacuation does not allow for effective monitoring of performance and, therefore, must not be counted as a required drill.

401.8 Interference with fire department operations. It shall be unlawful to interfere with, attempt to interfere with, conspire to interfere with, obstruct or restrict the mobility of or block the path of travel of a fire department emergency vehicle in any way, or to interfere with, attempt to interfere with, conspire to interfere with, obstruct or hamper any fire department operation.

❖ A potential hazard when fire departments respond to an emergency is the inability to perform operations because of physical obstructions, restricted mobility or human interference. This section prohibits any type of interference with emergency response operations. The delay of even a few minutes can cause serious property damage, injuries or fatalities.

SECTION 402
DEFINITIONS

402.1 Definitions. The following terms are defined in Chapter 2:

EMERGENCY EVACUATION DRILL.

LOCKDOWN.

❖ Definitions of terms can help in the understanding and application of the code requirements. This section directs the code user to Chapter 2 for the proper application of the indicated terms used in this chapter. Terms may be defined in Chapter 2 or in another International Code® (I-Code®) as indicated in Section 201.3, or the dictionary meaning may be all that is needed (see commentaries, Sections 201 through 201.4).

SECTION 403 EMERGENCY PREPAREDNESS REQUIREMENTS

403.1 General. In addition to the requirements of Section 401, occupancies, uses and outdoor locations shall comply with the emergency preparedness requirements set forth in Sections 403.2 through 403.12.3.3. Where a fire safety and evacuation plan is required by Sections 403.2 through 403.11.5, evacuation drills shall be in accordance with Section 405 and employee training shall be in accordance with Section 406.

❖ Section 403 contains the occupancy-specific requirements for emergency preparedness. This section primarily notes where a fire safety and evacuation plan is required, but also provides specific requirements as necessary. For instance, seating plans must be provided for Group A occupancies or, in the case of Group I-2 occupancies, specific requirements are provided for staff training. Section 403 also has a section with special requirements to address the need for fire watches and planning for large gatherings (see Section 403.12).

The occupancies addressed by this section were chosen based on the density and location of occupants, the layout of the building or the limitations of the occupants during an emergency. The *Evacuation Planning Guide for Stadiums* published by the U.S. Department of Homeland Security (DHS) provides useful guidance for evacuation planning in large assembly structures. The principles used in that document could also be applied to the other occupancy groups listed in this section. Two additional resources to better understand the evacuation needs of specific types of structures such as tall buildings and airports are the SFPE *Engineering Guide: Fire Safety for Very Tall Buildings* and *Egress Design Solutions*.

403.2 Group A occupancies. An *approved* fire safety and evacuation plan in accordance with Section 404 shall be prepared and maintained for Group A *occupancies*, other than those occupancies used exclusively for purposes of religious worship with an occupant load less than 2,000, and for buildings containing both a Group A occupancy and an atrium. Group A occupancies shall comply with Sections 403.2.1 through 403.2.4.

❖ Group A occupancies are a special concern because of the high density and number of occupants. Additionally, occupants in Group A occupancies are generally not very familiar with the building. Due to lack of losses associated with those attending religious worship services, such occupancies are given an exception to the application of these requirements where the occupant load is less than 2,000 people.

403.2.1 Seating plan. In addition to the requirements of Section 404.2, the fire safety and evacuation plans for assembly occupancies shall include a detailed seating plan, *occupant load* and *occupant load* limit. Deviations from the *approved* plans shall be allowed provided that the *occupant load* limit for the occupancy is not exceeded and the *aisles* and exit accessways remain unobstructed.

❖ Proper planning for an assembly occupancy must consider the number, capacity and physical arrangement of exits. In turn, these factors will dictate how seating may be arranged to prevent obstruction of aisles and exits. The number of seats provided may not exceed what is permitted by the number, arrangement and capacity of exits. Floor area factors are only one element in determining whether the exit capacity is adequate. Additionally, the egress plan must be approved by the fire code official with a copy of the approved plan maintained on the premises for review by employees and inspectors. Many facilities have several approved plans to accommodate various situations and functions. The seating plan selected for any event should reflect the needs of the group and the requirement to keep aisles and exits clear. Deviations from an approved plan may be permitted only if they do not obstruct the complete egress path, including aisles and exits.

403.2.2 Announcements. In theaters, motion picture theaters, auditoriums and similar assembly occupancies in Group A used for noncontinuous programs, an audible announcement shall be made not more than 10 minutes prior to the start of each program to notify the occupants of the location of the exits to be used in the event of a fire or other emergency.

Exception: In motion picture theaters, the announcement is allowed to be projected on the screen in a manner approved by the fire code official.

❖ Announcements are intended to familiarize occupants with life safety system features potentially needed during a fire. Information is the most valuable commodity during fires and other emergencies; however, it is often difficult, if not impossible, to override the emotion and confusion caused by a fire or other emergency. Studies have generally shown, however, that occupants do not panic as once thought; therefore, it is imperative that occupants receive information necessary for them to make decisions before an emergency occurs. To convey information and motivate an adaptive response to fires or other emergencies, the message must stimulate interest and speak directly to the topic. Many movie theaters currently use “trailers” or “shorts” to market concession items, as well as fire safety. These messages can be especially effective if they are specific and adequately distinguished from other promotions. Any message should reflect the life safety strategy and must point out specific features of the occupancy. Occupants in most theaters and auditoriums are usually expected to leave the building immediately upon notification of a fire using the nearest available exit. This is largely a reflection on the building type and arrangement of exits. In these cases, the locations of all exits must be identified. Raising the house lights along the egress path or modulating aisle lighting at appropriate times during the message can reinforce the message.

This section specifically requires an audible announcement, but the exception for motion picture theaters would allow the message to be visually displayed on the screen as approved. A combination of both an audible and visual message would most likely be the most effective. This section also has a maximum time from the start of the show to provide such announcements. An announcement that comes too early will lose its effectiveness.

403.2.3 Fire watch personnel. Fire watch personnel shall be provided where required by Section 403.12.1.

❖ This section links to Section 403.12.1, which establishes the authority of the fire code official to require a fire watch as necessary.

403.2.4 Crowd managers. Crowd managers shall be provided where required by Section 403.12.3.

❖ Assembly occupancies contain many occupants potentially unfamiliar with the building. The larger the number of occupants in a single space, the more critical that crowd managers be available to direct people. Section 403.12.3 requires crowd managers when a gathering exceeds 500 people.

403.3 Ambulatory care facilities. Ambulatory care facilities shall comply with the requirements of Sections 401, 403.3.1 through 403.3.4 and 404 through 406.

❖ Ambulatory care facilities, similar to Group I-1, Condition 2 and Group I-2 occupancies, use a "defend-in-place" method of occupant protection. Defend-in-place is a widely used approach to protecting occupants who are bedridden, unconscious or otherwise unable to self-preserve in a fire event. The method relies on both active and passive fire protection systems as well as the actions of trained staff and responders. The heavy emphasis on staff action requires a comprehensive fire safety and evacuation plan. Any building containing an ambulatory healthcare occupancy will, by definition, contain occupants who may be incapable of self-preservation. Current IBC requirements for ambulatory care are intended to create a type of defend-in-place environment. Sections 403.3.1 through 403.3.4 provide requirements for ambulatory care that are more specific than those provided in Sections 404 and 405.

403.3.1 Fire evacuation plan. The fire safety and evacuation plan required by Section 404 shall include a description of special staff actions. This shall include procedures for stabilizing patients in a defend-in-place response, staged evacuation, or full evacuation in conjunction with the entire building if part of a multitenant facility.

❖ Fire safety and evacuation plans must be developed, reviewed and approved to support this strategy. The reference to "defend-in-place" was added in Section 404.2.2 to recognize the defend-in-place method. This is not a new concept. The IBC and legacy codes have been written to support this concept, and fire safety and evacuation plans must acknowledge this strategy. The term "Defend-in-place" is defined in the IBC. Fire safety plans should describe in the life safety strategy the method of notifying occupants, including the use of a private-mode alarm system as allowed by code. Procedures for dealing with occupants in a defend-in-place strategy should also be described so that it is clear what the staff will be trained on and what the first responders should expect to encounter. Fire evacuation plans are required to describe the special actions of staff, especially staff that must stabilize a patient prior to moving. This will be the basis of the staff education and training. This will also help the fire code official understand the expected performance of the building. It is imperative that the building and fire official know the size and location of the facility as well as the number of patients who are incapable of self-preservation. This information will help the building official determine the proper classification and mitigations required. It will also allow the fire official to preplan the response for a particular building. Any special characteristics of the means of egress, such as path to the adjacent smoke compartment and special locking arrangements, should also be described to aid in verifying code compliance. Practically, these documents will be the basis for staff training as well.

403.3.2 Fire safety plan. A copy of the plan shall be maintained at the facility at all times. The plan shall include all of the following in addition to the requirements of Section 404:

1. Locations of patients who are rendered incapable of self-preservation.
2. Maximum number of patients rendered incapable of self-preservation.
3. Area and extent of each ambulatory care facility.
4. Location of adjacent smoke compartments or refuge areas, where required.
5. Path of travel to adjacent smoke compartments.
6. Location of any special locking, delayed egress or access control arrangements.

❖ This section sets out information required for the fire safety plan specific to ambulatory care facilities. Fire safety plans are required to show the location where incapable patients are likely to be. They are required to show the location of smoke compartments, routes of travel, patient movement elevators and any locking constraints that might affect the horizontal evacuation of patients. All of these will be essential to robust staff training as well as operational planning for first responders.

403.3.3 Staff training. Employees shall be periodically instructed and kept informed of their duties and responsibilities under the plan. Records of instruction shall be maintained. Such instruction shall be reviewed by the staff not less than every two months. A copy of the plan shall be readily available at all times within the facility.

❖ In ambulatory care facilities, due to the condition of the occupants, the actions of the staff are critical to the success of the fire evacuation plan. Therefore, staff training on a regular basis is necessary. This section requires that the staff review the fire evacuation plan and fire safety plan regularly. These plans always need to be available for review.

403.3.4 Emergency evacuation drills. Emergency evacuation drills shall comply with Section 405.

Exception: The movement of patients to safe areas or to the exterior of the building is not required.

❖ This section requires not fewer than four evacuation drills each year. This requirement is more restrictive than what Table 405.2 would require. Therefore, although Table 405.2 requires only annual evacuation drills, they must be done four times a year. This is similar to what is required for Group I-2 occupancies. Such drills are limited to the employees. The exception emphasizes that patient participation is not required.

403.4 Group B occupancies. An *approved* fire safety and evacuation plan in accordance with Section 404 shall be prepared and maintained for buildings containing a Group B occupancy where the Group B occupancy has an *occupant load* of 500 or more persons or more than 100 persons above or below the lowest *level of exit discharge* and for buildings having an ambulatory care facility.

❖ This section requires a fire and evacuation plan where the number of occupants in a Group B occupancy becomes large. The increased risk where such occupants are not located on the level of exit discharge is also addressed. Generally, Group B occupancies are not used for sleeping and occupants are familiar with their surroundings. This section is for Group B occupancies that are not considered ambulatory care facilities. Ambulatory care facilities are also Group B occupancies but would be addressed more specifically by Section 403.3. Group F and M occupancies have the same occupant load and location trigger for fire safety and evacuation plans (see Sections 403.6 and 403.9).

403.5 Group E occupancies. An *approved* fire safety and evacuation plan in accordance with Section 404 shall be prepared and maintained for Group E occupancies and for buildings containing both a Group E occupancy and an atrium. Group E occupancies shall comply with Sections 403.5.1 through 403.5.3.

❖ Group E occupancies are among the primary occupancies requiring emergency evacuation drills. They are among the few occupancies that require all occupants to participate in evacuation drills. The effectiveness of pre-emergency planning in Group E occupancies has been significant, as evidenced by a remarkable decline in tragic fires in schools over the years. The evacuation skills learned by children in school are often carried with them into adulthood.

403.5.1 First emergency evacuation drill. The first emergency evacuation drill of each school year shall be conducted within 10 days of the beginning of classes.

❖ Group E occupants vary from year to year as children enter and leave grade levels. In addition, even though a child may be in the same school for a number of years, location within the building and leaders change. It is important, therefore, that the first evacuation drill occurs within the first 10 days of school. This provides students with nearly immediate training and the school and emergency responders with information about where problems exist. Additionally, in more recent years schools have been immersing students with disabilities into the general classroom. The location and number of these students vary each year. The ability to evacuate them must be assessed early in the school year.

403.5.2 Time of day. Emergency evacuation drills shall be conducted at different hours of the day or evening, during the changing of classes, when the school is at assembly, during the recess or gymnastic periods, or during other times to avoid distinction between drills and actual fires.

❖ If evacuation drills are done routinely, they will be easily distinguished as drills and not an actual fire. This is potentially dangerous because the behavior patterns will be different and actual preparedness for emergencies will be lessened. Time of day, therefore, should be varied, whether or not it is convenient. A fire will not differentiate between a convenient and an inconvenient time.

403.5.3 Assembly points. Outdoor assembly areas shall be designated and shall be located a safe distance from the building being evacuated so as to avoid interference with fire department operations. The assembly areas shall be arranged to keep each class separate to provide accountability of all individuals.

❖ A key element in safe evacuation is the exit discharge portion of the evacuation route. Once occupants are outside the building, they need to be located far enough away to avoid further hazards. Additionally, there is a potential for people at the assembly point to interfere with the emergency operations of the fire department, which may not be present during an evacuation drill. Locations, therefore, need to be designated such that they avoid hazards and keep the evacuated occupants away from probable paths of emergency response. Also, to simplify accounting for the occupants once outside, the code requires each class to remain together as a group and separate from other classes.

403.6 Group F occupancies. An *approved* fire safety and evacuation plan in accordance with Section 404 shall be prepared and maintained for buildings containing a Group F occupancy where any of the following conditions apply:

1. The Group F occupancy has an *occupant load* of 500 or more persons.
2. The Group F occupancy has an *occupant load* of more than 100 persons above or below the lowest *level of exit discharge*.
3. Group F pallet manufacturing and recycling facilities as required by Section 2810.

❖ Group F occupancies require a fire safety and evacuation plan under the same occupant load and location conditions as Group B and M occupancies. Essentially, where the occupant load reaches a certain number overall or increases on a level other than the level of exit discharge, such plans become more critical (see commentary, Section 403.4). Additionally, due to the hazards present at pallet manufacturing and recycling facilities, a fire safety and evacuation plan must be provided and maintained at such facilities.

403.7 Group H occupancies. An *approved* fire safety and evacuation plan in accordance with Section 404 shall be prepared and maintained for Group H occupancies.

❖ This section requires that all Group H occupancies have a fire safety and evacuation plan. These occupancies, regardless of size or type, tend to contain significant hazards that make the need for preplanning critical. Semiconductor facilities have more specific requirements found in Section 403.7.1.

403.7.1 Group H-5 occupancies. Group H-5 occupancies shall comply with Sections 403.7.1.1 through 403.7.1.4.

❖ Group H-5 occupancies are semiconductor fabrication facilities. These types of facilities are unique in that they have a very large allowable area and house a significant amount of hazardous materials. Essentially, the building is divided into fabrication areas, hazardous production materials (HPM) rooms (which are Group H occupancy storage rooms) and networks of service corridors and spaces. The area of the building needs to be large to incorporate all of the operations needed by the semiconductor industry. To facilitate these operations, a special package of requirements and occupancy classification was created. This package is found within the occupancy requirements in the IBC and Chapter 27 of the code. As part of the package, special emergency preparedness and preparation are also required. Sections 403.7.1.1 through 403.7.1.4 provide specific requirements for emergency preparedness and preparation. These requirements are in addition to others pertaining to hazardous materials found in Section 407.

403.7.1.1 Plans and diagrams. In addition to the requirements of Section 404 and Section 407.6, plans and diagrams shall be maintained in approved locations indicating the approximate plan for each area, the amount and type of HPM stored, handled and used, locations of shutoff valves for HPM supply piping, emergency telephone locations and locations of exits.

❖ The requirements for plans and diagrams are in addition to those required in Sections 404 and 407. More specifically, the additional details required include the approximate plan for each area of the building. This includes the amount of HPM stored, handled and used in both the fabrication areas and the HPM rooms. Additionally, since it is typical that such facilities tend to pipe HPM throughout the building for efficiency, all shutoff valves must be identified. Finally, exits must be clearly marked. This is specifically necessary because many service corridors for the transport of materials are not considered part of the means of egress. These details will assist both the occupants and the emergency responders.

403.7.1.2 Plan updating. The plans and diagrams required by Sections 404, 403.7.1.1 and 407.6 shall be maintained up to date and the *fire code official* and fire department shall be informed of major changes.

❖ Semiconductor facilities are constantly changing because of the needs of new technology; therefore, the types and amounts of materials and their application are constantly changing. These changes must be accounted for within the plans and diagrams required in Sections 403.7.1.1 and 407; otherwise, the critical information needed by the emergency responders may not be available.

403.7.1.3 Emergency response team. Responsible persons shall be designated as an on-site emergency response team and trained to be liaison personnel for the fire department. These persons shall aid the fire department in preplanning emergency responses, identifying locations where HPM is stored, handled and used, and be familiar with the chemical nature of such material. An adequate number of personnel for each work shift shall be designated.

❖ This section is similar to Section 407.4, but has some specific requirements unique to semiconductor facilities. More specifically, liaisons familiar with the location of HPM and hazards related to those materials must be on site. For example, semiconductor facilities make use of silane gas, which is a pyrophoric material—it will instantly ignite when exposed to atmospheric conditions. Knowing the characteristics of the material, where it is located and the quantity used is critical to the responding emergency personnel.

403.7.1.4 Emergency drills. Emergency drills of the on-site emergency response team shall be conducted on a regular basis but not less than once every three months. Records of drills conducted shall be maintained.

❖ This section requires employees to conduct drills every 3 months to practice specific emergency procedures for the facilities. Again, this requirement is specific to semiconductor facilities because of their unique layout and contents. The emergency responders rely heavily on the on-site actions of the employees because of their intimate knowledge of the site and the complexity of these buildings. Records must be maintained.

403.8 Group I occupancies. An *approved* fire safety and evacuation plan in accordance with Section 404 shall be prepared and maintained for Group I occupancies. Group I occupancies shall comply with Sections 403.8.1 through 403.8.3.4.

❖ Group I occupancies are those where occupants are often incapable of self-preservation due to their physical condition or they are physically able but under restraint. Therefore, fire safety and evacuation plans are critical and also have some specific needs unique from other occupancies.

403.8.1 Group I-1 occupancies. Group I-1 occupancies shall comply with Sections 403.8.1.1 through 403.8.1.7.

❖ A Group I-1 occupancy is one that houses more than 16 individuals who live in a supervised residential care facility on a 24-hour basis. This would include residential board and care homes, congregate care facilities, social rehabilitation facilities, alcohol and drug centers, assisted living facilities and convalescent facilities. Generally, occupants of these facilities are able to respond to an emergency with some assistance from staff. Note that there are two levels of Group I-1 occupancies (Condition 1 and Condition 2). These are further clarified in Section 202 but, essentially, those found in Condition 2 need additional protection due to an increased need for assistance.

403.8.1.1 Fire safety and evacuation plan. The fire safety and evacuation plan required by Section 404 shall include special employee actions, including fire protection procedures necessary for residents, and shall be amended or revised upon admission of any resident with unusual needs.

❖ This section is in addition to the general requirements found in Section 404. It specifies that requirements based on the particular needs of residents must be included as part of the plan. Thus, the plans must be reviewed each time a new occupant arrives and potentially altered to address any special needs. Group R-4 occupancies are being addressed in a similar manner (see Section 403.10.3.1).

403.8.1.1.1 Fire evacuation plan. The fire evacuation plan required by Section 404 shall include a description of special staff actions. In addition to the requirements of Section 404, plans in Group I-1, Condition 2 occupancies shall include procedures for evacuation through a refuge area in an adjacent smoke compartment and then to an exterior assembly point.

❖ Similar to ambulatory care facilities, the actions of the staff are critical and must be addressed beyond the requirements of Section 404. This is only applicable to Group I-1, Condition 2 occupancies where the residents depend more on the staff than they do in a Group I-1, Condition 1 occupancy. Group I-1, Condition 2 occupancies depend on the concept of smoke compartments similar to Group I-2 occupancies (see Section 420.6 of the IBC).

403.8.1.1.2 Fire safety plans. A copy of the fire safety plan shall be maintained at the facility at all times. Plans shall include the following in addition to the requirements of Section 404:

1. Location and number of resident sleeping rooms.
2. Location of special locking or egress control arrangements.

❖ This section requires that Group I-1 occupancies provide the location and number of residents sleeping and any special locking or egress control arrangements. This assists in search and rescue and understanding how the residents may be hampered in their evacuation. This information is critical for preplanning by both staff and the fire department. This applies to conditions of Group I-1 occupancies. The same requirement is provided for Group R-4 occupancies, which are essentially smaller Group I-1 occupancies.

403.8.1.2 Employee training. Employees shall be periodically instructed and kept informed of their duties and responsibilities under the plan. Such instruction shall be reviewed by employees at intervals not exceeding two months. A copy of the plan shall be readily available at all times within the facility.

❖ These types of facilities are normally occupied by people who have the ability to evacuate or relocate with a certain level of assistance from the staff; therefore, employee training is critical. Again, residents in Group I-1, Condition 2 occupancies will need more evacuation assistance than in Group I-1, Condition 1 occupancies. Group I-1, Condition 2 occupancies utilize the concept of smoke compartments. Additional training in this regard is necessary for employees. This section requires that training occur every 2 months because the needs of the occupants may change over time as certain physical or mental conditions progress or new occupants arrive.

403.8.1.3 Resident training. Residents capable of assisting in their own evacuation shall be trained in the proper actions to take in the event of a fire. In Group I-1, Condition 2 occupancies, training shall include evacuation through an adjacent smoke compartment and then to an exterior assembly point. The training shall include actions to take if the primary escape route is blocked. Where the resident is given rehabilitation or habilitation training, methods of fire prevention and actions to take in the event of a fire shall be a part of the rehabilitation training program. Residents shall be trained to assist each other in case of fire to the extent their physical and mental abilities permit them to do so without additional personal risk.

❖ As noted, Group I-1 occupants are capable of responding to an emergency but will most likely need direction from staff and perhaps physical assistance to ensure the appropriate response. This is more the case with Group I-1, Condition 2 occupancies. Unlike other Group I occupancies, I-1 occupancies rely on the abilities of residents to take some level of responsibility for their own evacuation or relocation; therefore, training residents in these occupancies is critical. One major element that must be communicated to residents is what to do when the main exit route is blocked.

If residents are receiving rehabilitation or habilitation, fire prevention and appropriate actions to take during a fire should be communicated as part of the sessions. This section also requires the occupants to assist one another as long as a physical or mental condition would not limit their ability to do so.

Since Group I-1, Condition 2 occupancies utilize the concept of smoke compartments, occupants must be trained to evacuate to the adjacent smoke compartment to the refuge area.

403.8.1.4 Drill frequency. In addition to the evacuation drills required in Section 405.2, employees shall participate in drills an additional two times a year on each shift. Twelve drills with all occupants shall be conducted in the first year of operation. Drills are not required to comply with the time requirements of Section 405.4.

❖ Occupants of Group I-1 facilities need to be reminded often of evacuation procedures given their sometimes limited abilities to recall procedures, changes in the residents' abilities over time and the introduction of new residents to the facility. Therefore, this section requires more frequent drills than Table 405.2. Employees on each shift are required to participate in additional drills. Each shift potentially has different staff and also different conditions due to the time of day. Another very specific difference from Table 405.2 is that such facilities are required to have, essentially, monthly drills for the first year. Over time, the occupants and staff will change, but this sets the tone for how the facility operates. This also increases staff awareness of procedures.

403.8.1.5 Drill times. Drill times are not required to comply with Section 405.4.

❖ This provides the flexibility to create an appropriate schedule that works with these facilities. The residents participate, making it slightly more difficult to follow Section 405.4.

403.8.1.6 Resident participation in drills. Emergency evacuation drills shall involve the actual evacuation of residents to a selected assembly point and shall provide residents with experience in exiting through all required exits. All required exits shall be used during emergency evacuation drills.

❖ This section clarifies that drills must include all occupants, not just staff. In other institutional occupancies where the occupants are not capable of evacuating or it is not desirable to evacuate them on their own, inclusion of the residents in drills is not necessary. Since dependence is placed on the residents to react in Group I-1 occupancies, their involvement is critical. This section is designed to promote resident familiarity with all the exits that are available in the building. This will help residents understand that, during emergencies, there are multiple paths to safety. Note that, in Group I-1, Condition 2 occupancies, smoke compartments are used and occupants will typically need to simply move to the adjoining smoke compartment to defend in place.

403.8.1.7 Emergency evacuation drill deferral. In severe climates, the *fire code official* shall have the authority to modify the emergency evacuation drill frequency specified in Section 405.2.

❖ It is not appropriate to send residents of Group I-1 occupancies outside during extreme weather conditions unnecessarily. Generally, the occupants of such facilities have failing health or are more susceptible to illness than the average population. This section provides the authority to the fire code official to make adjustments for these reasons.

403.8.2 Group I-2 occupancies. Group I-2 occupancies shall comply with Sections 401, 403.8.2.1 through 403.8.2.3 and 404 through 406.

❖ Group I-2 occupancies as well as ambulatory care facilities and Group I-1, Condition 2 occupancies use a "defend-in-place" method of occupant protection. Defend-in-place is a widely used approach to protect occupants who are bedridden, unconscious or otherwise unable to self-preserve in a fire event. The method relies on both active and passive fire protection systems as well as the actions of trained staff and responders. The heavy emphasis on staff action requires a comprehensive fire safety and evacuation plan. Any building containing an ambulatory healthcare occupancy will, by definition, contain occupants who may be incapable of self-preservation. Current IBC requirements for Group I-2 occupancies are intended to create a type of defend-in-place environment. Sections 403.8.2.1 through 403.8.2.3 provide requirements for Group I-2 occupancies that are more specific than what is provided in Sections 404 and 405.

403.8.2.1 Fire evacuation plans. The fire safety and evacuation plans required by Section 404 shall include a description of special staff *actions*. Plans shall include all of the following in addition to the requirements of Section 404.

1. Procedures for evacuation for patients with needs for containment or restraint and post-evacuation containment, where present.
2. A written plan for maintenance of the means of egress.
3. Procedure for a defend-in-place strategy.
4. Procedures for a full-floor or building evacuation, where necessary.

❖ Staff actions are critical to the success of a fire evacuation plan for Group I-2 occupancies; therefore, procedures need to be documented. In addition to the requirements of Section 404, this section provides four more-specific requirements for the fire evacuation plan. These requirements include how patients are to be evacuated and documentation of maintenance plans for means of egress in such facilities. Procedures for a defend-in-place strategy must be documented so that each shift is familiar with that strategy. Defend-in-place procedures depend on the use of refuge areas that need to be maintained. In some cases, the defend-in-place evacuation may need to escalate to full-floor or building evacuation. Such evacuations need to be documented, as well.

403.8.2.2 Fire safety plans. A copy of the plan shall be maintained at the facility at all times. Plans shall include all of the following in addition to the requirements of Section 404:

1. Location and number of patient sleeping rooms and operating rooms.
2. Location of adjacent smoke compartments or refuge areas.
3. Path of travel to adjacent smoke compartments.
4. Location of special locking, delayed egress or access control arrangements.
5. Location of elevators utilized for patient movement in accordance with the fire safety plan, where provided.

❖ Fire safety plans should describe the method of notifying occupants, including the use of a private-mode alarm system as allowed by code. Procedures for dealing with occupants in a defend-in-place strategy should also be described so that it is clear what the staff will be trained on and what the first responders should expect to encounter. It is imperative that the building and fire code officials know the size and location of the facility as well as the number of patients who are incapable of self-preservation. This information will help the building official determine the proper classification and mitigations required. It will also allow the fire official to preplan the response for a particular building. Any special characteristics of the means of egress, such as path to the adjacent smoke compartment and special locking arrangements, should also be described to aid in verifying code compliance. Practically, these documents will be the basis for staff training as well.

403.8.2.3 Emergency evacuation drills. Emergency evacuation drills shall comply with Section 405.

Exceptions:

1. The movement of patients to safe areas or to the exterior of the building is not required.
2. Where emergency evacuation drills are conducted after visiting hours or where patients or residents are expected to be asleep, a coded announcement shall be an acceptable alternative to audible alarms.

❖ Group I-2 occupancies are required to comply with the evacuation drill frequency established in Section 405. However, Group I-2 occupancies do not evacuate occupants from the building but instead utilize a defend-in-place strategy. This is related to the conditions of the patients found in such facilities. Therefore, Exception 1 clarifies that evacuation to the exterior is not required. Exception 2 allows the use of coded signals for staff evacuation drills. This avoids disturbing patients or alarming visitors. The drills in such facilities do not involve the patients.

403.8.3 Group I-3 occupancies. Group I-3 occupancies shall comply with Sections 403.8.3.1 through 403.8.3.4.

❖ Group I-3 occupancies are institutional occupancies where the occupants are under restraint. Typically, the occupants are physically able but are restrained from moving freely. Several levels of restraint in such occupancies are described in more detail in Chapter 2 under the definition of "Group I-3 occupancies." As in Group I-2 occupancies, the only participants in drills will be staff. These requirements are in addition to the requirements of Sections 404 and 405.

403.8.3.1 Employee training. Employees shall be instructed in the proper use of portable fire extinguishers and other manual fire suppression equipment. Training of new employees shall be provided promptly upon entrance to duty. Refresher training shall be provided not less than annually.

❖ Group I-3 facilities are more likely to have incendiary activity; therefore, staff must be trained in the use of various fire protection equipment, including fire extinguishers. Additionally, any new employees must be immediately trained in the use of this equipment. Because of difficulties presented by relocating or evacuating confinees, fires should be managed, when practical, to minimize the threat to occupants. Since combustibles are strictly limited in most of these occupancies, accidental fires generally remain small—at least long enough to be manageable. Incendiary fires often pose greater challenges and generally reflect a breakdown in security discipline. Notwithstanding this problem, fire extinguisher training, and even incipient fire brigades, may be especially effective elements of a fire safety plan in restrained-care occupancies. This training is required of new employees before they can begin their official duties. This training must then be refreshed once per year.

403.8.3.2 Employee staffing. Group I-3 occupancies shall be provided with 24-hour staffing. An employee shall be within three floors or 300 feet (91 440 mm) horizontal distance of the access door of each resident housing area. In Group I-3 Conditions 3, 4 and 5, as defined in Chapter 2, the arrangement shall be such that the employee involved can start release of locks necessary for emergency evacuation or rescue and initiate other necessary emergency actions within 2 minutes of an alarm.

Exception: An employee shall not be required to be within three floors or 300 feet (91 440 mm) horizontal distance of the access door of each resident housing area in areas in which all locks are unlocked remotely and automatically in accordance with Section 408.4 of the *International Building Code*.

❖ Group I-3 occupancies place a lot of importance on the actions of staff in emergencies. This section provides specific direction regarding the staff's locations and actions in an emergency. Staff members responsible for initiating the relocation or evacuation of confinees must be constantly alert to potential fire hazards and incipient fires. If a fire occurs, 2 minutes will seem like a long time to confined people. Where a remote-release locking system is neither required nor provided, the number of locks requiring manual unlocking should be limited with due regard to staff and confinee safety. This may require additional staff to accomplish the unlocking procedure in a timely manner. This section does have a specific exception for systems that utilize a remote locking and unlocking system.

403.8.3.3 Notification. Provisions shall be made for residents in Group I-3 Conditions 3, 4 and 5, as defined in Chapter 2, to readily notify an employee of an emergency.

❖ Group I-3 occupancies under Use Conditions 3, 4 and 5 where the occupants are very limited in their freedom would be considered moderate- and high-security facilities. Because the occupants are so limited and could be located remotely from guards or other staff members as a result of confinement within a compartment, a method is necessary for staff notification of a fire. In open cell blocks, staff members may be within earshot of occupants but generally this requirement necessitates monitors, intercoms or other communication appliances.

403.8.3.4 Keys. Keys necessary for unlocking doors installed in a means of egress shall be individually identifiable by both touch and sight.

❖ Keys must be distinctive from one another so they may be promptly and reliably identified under emergency conditions. Fumbling for the right key can cost valuable seconds, and possibly lives, in the event of a fire (see Commentary Figure 403.8.3.4).

Commentary Figure 403.8.3.4
TACTILE CODING OF INSTITUTIONAL KEYS

403.9 Group M occupancies. An *approved* fire safety and evacuation plan in accordance with Section 404 shall be prepared and maintained for buildings containing a Group M occupancy where the Group M occupancy has an *occupant load* of 500 or more persons or more than 100 persons above or below the lowest *level of exit discharge* and for buildings containing both a Group M occupancy and an atrium.

❖ This section requires a fire and evacuation plan where the number of occupants in a Group M occupancy exceeds a specified number, including where such occupants are not located on the level of exit discharge. This is the same requirement as that provided for Group B and F occupancies. However, Group M occupants may not be quite as familiar with their surroundings but the staff in such facilities are available to direct occupants during an emergency. Also, this is an occupancy where people do not sleep (see Sections 403.4 and 403.6).

403.10 Group R occupancies. Group R occupancies shall comply with Sections 403.10.1 through 403.10.3.6.

❖ This section provides fire safety and evacuation plans specific to Group R-1, R-2 and R-4 occupancies. These are occupancies where people sleep, thus the need for fire safety and evacuation plans is more critical.

403.10.1 Group R-1 occupancies. An approved fire safety and evacuation plan in accordance with Section 404 shall be prepared and maintained for Group R-1 occupancies. Group R-1 occupancies shall comply with Sections 403.10.1.1 through 403.10.1.3.

❖ Group R-1 occupancies are residential occupancies that include hotels and boarding houses. These occupancies contain residents that are temporary in nature; therefore, they are more unfamiliar with their surroundings than Group R-2 and R-3 occupants. Sections 403.10.1.1 through 403.10.1.3 provide specific requirements that take into account characteristics of Group R-1 occupancies.

403.10.1.1 Evacuation diagrams. A diagram depicting two evacuation routes shall be posted on or immediately adjacent to every required egress door from each hotel or motel sleeping unit.

❖ This section requires an evacuation plan diagram to be posted in each hotel or motel sleeping unit. Both the format of the diagram and its location must be approved by the fire code official. This diagram is to display both a primary and a secondary exit route in case a fire or other obstacle blocks the primary route. The plan should be prepared so that the orientation of rooms in relation to the exits is accurately portrayed and easily discernible to the occupant. Often, additional safety information is included on the plan diagram, such as fire alarm box and fire extinguisher locations; however, those added items should not clutter the diagram to the extent that they detract from the clarity of its primary purpose of showing exit routes and exit locations.

403.10.1.2 Emergency duties. Upon discovery of a fire or suspected fire, hotel and motel employees shall perform the following duties:

1. Activate the fire alarm system, where provided.
2. Notify the public fire department.
3. Take other action as previously instructed.

❖ This section contains specific actions employees are to take if a fire occurs. The requirement that they first activate the fire alarm and then call the fire department is intended to avoid a situation in which the employee first investigates or calls security. Immediate notification of the occupants facilitates evacuation or relocation as necessary. Notifying the fire department as early as possible will enable fire fighters to reach the building at an earlier stage in the fire.

403.10.1.3 Fire safety and evacuation instructions. Information shall be provided in the fire safety and evacuation plan required by Section 404 to allow guests to decide whether to evacuate to the outside, evacuate to an *area of refuge,* remain in place, or any combination of the three.

❖ The procedures for isolating occupants from a fire depend on the layout and overall fire protection design of a building. For example, a hotel in a high-rise building may be specifically designed to evacuate in phases; therefore, the occupants need to know the procedures to facilitate a smooth and organized reaction to a fire. The appropriate actions that are available should be communicated. Options may include occupants remaining in their rooms, evacuating or relocating.

403.10.2 Group R-2 occupancies. Group R-2 occupancies shall comply with Sections 403.10.2.1 through 403.10.2.3.

❖ Group R-2 occupancies are permanent residential occupancies that house multiple occupants in multiple dwelling units. Typically, this includes apartment buildings, dormitories and other related residential occupancies. Generally, the occupants tend to be familiar with their surroundings but may be sleeping when an emergency occurs. Sections 403.10.2.1 through 403.10.2.3 provide specific requirements in addition to the general requirements of Chapter 4. This section deals with Group R-2 occupancies generally and, more specifically, with Group R-2 college and university buildings.

403.10.2.1 College and university buildings. An *approved* fire safety and evacuation plan in accordance with Section 404 shall be prepared and maintained for Group R-2 college and university buildings. Group R-2 college and university buildings shall comply with Sections 403.10.2.1.1 and 403.10.2.1.2.

❖ This section establishes the applicability of certain provisions to college and university residence halls and dormitories classified in Group R-2. Fire represents a significant risk to life and property in dormitory occupancies, particularly at colleges and universities. The large number of young people living in close proximity to one another creates the potential for a relatively small fire to have serious and possibly fatal consequences. Applying these requirements in conjunction with the drills required by Table 405.2 will enhance the likelihood of occupants being familiar with exiting buildings under emergency conditions at varying times throughout the day.

403.10.2.1.1 First emergency evacuation drill. The first emergency evacuation drill of each school year shall be conducted within 10 days of the beginning of classes.

❖ The residents of Group R-2 college and dormitory occupancies typically change each year. It is important, therefore, that the first evacuation drill occurs within the first 10 days of school.

403.10.2.1.2 Time of day. Emergency evacuation drills shall be conducted at different hours of the day or evening, during the changing of classes, when school is at assembly, during recess or gymnastic periods or during other times to avoid distinction between drills and actual fires. One required drill shall be held during hours after sunset or before sunrise.

❖ If evacuation drills are done routinely, they will be easily distinguished as drills and not an actual fire. This is potentially dangerous because the behavior patterns will be different and actual preparedness for emergencies will be lessened. Time of day, therefore, should be varied whether or not it is convenient. A fire will not differentiate between a convenient and an inconvenient time. At least one of the drills required by Table 405.2 must be conducted between sunset and sunrise so that residents can experience nighttime evacuation.

403.10.2.2 Emergency guide. Fire emergency guides shall be provided for Group R-2 occupancies. Guide contents, maintenance and distribution shall comply with Sections 403.10.2.2.1 through 403.10.2.2.3.

❖ The next few sections lay out the requirements for emergency guides for Group R-2 occupancies. This includes what is to be in the guide, obtaining approval from the fire code official and distribution requirements. The guide in general will better inform the residents and provide preplanning tools for the fire department.

403.10.2.2.1 Guide contents. A fire emergency guide shall describe the location, function and use of fire protection equipment and appliances available for use by residents, including fire alarm systems, smoke alarms and portable fire extinguishers. Guides shall include an emergency evacuation plan for each *dwelling unit.*

❖ The guide must contain the intended evacuation plan for each unit and information about the various fire protection features provided to occupants. Providing this information to residents increases the likelihood of a proper response, which in turn increases resident safety and makes the fire department's job a little easier when responding to a scene.

403.10.2.2.2 Emergency guide maintenance. Emergency guides shall be reviewed and approved by the *fire code official.*

❖ This section makes it clear that the fire code official must sign off on the emergency guide contents. This will make fire department response consistent with the features of the building.

403.10.2.2.3 Emergency guide distribution. A copy of the emergency guide shall be given to each tenant prior to initial occupancy.

❖ This section requires that a guide illustrating the fire safety features of the building be provided to each dwelling unit. There is no purpose in having a guide to assist residents if there is no requirement that it be distributed. This must occur before they become occupants.

403.10.2.3 Evacuation diagrams for dormitories. A diagram depicting two evacuation routes shall be posted on or immediately adjacent to every required egress door from each dormitory *sleeping unit*. Evacuation diagrams shall be reviewed and updated as needed to maintain accuracy.

❖ The same concept is used for Group R-1 occupancies; this simply increases the information available to occupants. Group R-2 dormitory occupants are typically more transient than most occupants of Group R-2 occupancies (see commentary, Section 403.10.1.1).

403.10.3 Group R-4 occupancies. An *approved* fire safety and evacuation plan in accordance with Section 404 shall be prepared and maintained for Group R-4 occupancies. Group R-4 occupancies shall comply with Sections 403.10.3.1 through 403.10.3.6.

❖ A Group R-4 occupancy is a residential care/assisted living facility for more than five but not more than 16 residents. The occupants are similar to those found in a Group I-1 occupancy; therefore, they are capable of self-preservation but may have mental or physical conditions that could impede their reactions.

403.10.3.1 Fire safety and evacuation plan. The fire safety and evacuation plan required by Section 404 shall include special employee actions, including fire protection procedures necessary for residents, and shall be amended or revised upon admission of a resident with unusual needs.

❖ This section is in addition to the general requirements found in Section 404. It specifies that requirements based on the particular needs of residents must be included as part of the plan. These plans must be reviewed each time a new occupant arrives to assess any special features that need to be included in the plan to address those particular needs. This is the same requirement as provided for Group I-1 occupancies.

403.10.3.1.1 Fire safety plans. A copy of the plan shall be maintained at the facility at all times. Plans shall include the following in addition to the requirements of Section 404:

1. Location and number of resident sleeping rooms.
2. Location of special locking or egress control arrangements.

❖ This section requires that fire safety plans in Group R-4 occupancies provide the location and number of residents sleeping and any special locking or egress control arrangements. This assists in search and rescue and understanding how the residents may be hampered in their evacuation. This information is critical for preplanning by both staff and the fire department. This is the same requirement as provided for Group I-1 occupancies (see Section 403.8.1.1.2).

403.10.3.2 Employee training. Employees shall be periodically instructed and kept informed of their duties and responsibilities under the plan. Records of instruction shall be maintained. Such instruction shall be reviewed by employees at intervals not exceeding two months. A copy of the plan shall be readily available at all times within the facility.

❖ These types of facilities are normally occupied by people who have the ability to evacuate or relocate with a certain level of assistance from the staff; therefore, employee training is critical. Residents of Group R-4, Condition 2 occupancies will need more assistance in evacuation than in Group R-4, Condition 1. This section requires that training occur every 2 months because the needs of the occupants may change over time as certain physical or mental conditions progress or new occupants arrive.

403.10.3.3 Resident training. Residents capable of assisting in their own evacuation shall be trained in the proper actions to take in the event of a fire. The training shall include actions to take if the primary escape route is blocked. Where the resident is given rehabilitation or habilitation training, methods of fire prevention and actions to take in the event of a fire shall be a part of the rehabilitation training program. Residents shall be trained to assist each other in case of fire to the extent their physical and mental abilities permit them to do so without additional personal risk.

❖ As noted, Group R-4 occupants are capable of responding to an emergency, but most likely will need direction from staff and perhaps physical assistance. This is more the case with Group R-4, Condition 2 occupancies. Group R-4 occupancies, similar to Group I-1 occupancies, rely on the abilities of residents to take some level of responsibility for their own evacuation or relocation; therefore, training residents in these occupancies is critical. One major element that must be communicated to residents is what to do when the main exit route is blocked.

If residents are receiving rehabilitation or habilitation, fire prevention and appropriate actions to take during a fire should be communicated as part of the sessions. This section also requires the occupants to assist one another as long as a physical or mental condition would not limit their ability to do so.

Since Group R-4, Condition 2 occupancies utilize the concept of smoke compartments, occupants must be trained how to evacuate to the adjacent smoke compartment to the refuge area.

403.10.3.4 Drill frequency. In addition to the evacuation drills required in Section 405.2, employees shall participate in drills an additional two times a year on each shift. Twelve drills with all occupants shall be conducted in the first year of operation.

❖ Occupants of Group R-4 facilities need to be reminded often of evacuation procedures given their sometimes limited capabilities to recall procedures, changes in their abilities over time and the introduction of new residents to the facility. Therefore, this section requires more frequent drills than Table 405.2. Employees on each shift are required to participate in additional drills. Each shift potentially has different staff and also different conditions due to the time of day. Another very specific difference from Table 405.2 is that such facilities are required to have, essentially, monthly drills for the first year. Over time the occupants and staff will change, but this sets the tone for how the facility operates. This also increases staff awareness of procedures.

403.10.3.5 Drill times. Drill times are not required to comply with Section 405.4.

❖ This provides the flexibility to create an appropriate schedule that works with Group R-4 facilities. The residents participate, making it slightly more difficult to follow Section 405.4.

403.10.3.6 Resident participation in drills. Emergency evacuation drills shall involve the actual evacuation of residents to a selected assembly point and shall provide residents with experience in exiting through all required exits. All required exits shall be used during emergency evacuation drills.

> **Exception:** Actual exiting from emergency escape and rescue windows shall not be required. Opening the emergency escape and rescue window and signaling for help shall be an acceptable alternative.

❖ This section clarifies that drills must include all occupants, not just the staff. Since dependence is placed on the residents to react in Group R-4 occupancies, their involvement is critical. This section is designed to promote resident familiarity with all the exits that are available in the building. This will help residents understand that, during emergencies, there are multiple paths to safety.

403.11 Special uses. Special uses shall be in accordance with Sections 403.11.1 through 403.11.5.

❖ The next several sections are focused on special uses that require fire safety and evacuation plans, including:

- Malls and mall buildings (covered and open).
- High-rise buildings.
- Underground buildings.
- Occupant evacuation elevators.
- Buildings containing High piled combustible storage.

403.11.1 Covered and open mall buildings. Covered and open mall buildings shall comply with the requirements of Sections 403.11.1.1 through 403.11.1.6.

❖ A covered mall building is a special use as described in Section 402 of the IBC and as defined in Chapter 2 of the code. Generally, a covered mall building is a single building housing multiple occupancies including, but not limited to, retail, assembly, drinking, dining and entertainment in which two or more tenants have a main entrance into a mall area. A mall area is also defined in Chapter 2 of the IBC as "a roofed or covered mall building that serves as access for two or more tenants and does not exceed three levels that are open to each other"; therefore, it presents some unique issues concerning fire department response to an emergency.

An open mall is an uncovered common pedestrian walk that is open to the sky above and to tenant spaces within the open mall building, and typically connects to the anchor buildings. Unless noted otherwise, open malls must comply with all IBC provisions. The open mall building includes all of the buildings wherein two or more tenants have a main entrance into one or more open malls. Because open malls are characterized by there not being a roof connecting one side of the pedestrian mall to the other, the open mall "building" may actually be a collection of separate buildings that all rely on a shared pedestrian concourse for egress. Similar to the covered mall building, the open mall "building" does not include the anchor buildings. Unless noted otherwise, open mall buildings have to comply with all provisions for covered mall buildings.

The requirements of Sections 403.11.1.1 through 403.11.1.6 are related primarily to the complexity of the building and provide appropriate information to emergency responders so they can more effectively respond to a fire or other emergency.

403.11.1.1 Malls and mall buildings exceeding 50,000 square feet. An *approved* fire safety and evacuation plan in accordance with Section 404 shall be prepared and maintained for covered malls exceeding 50,000 square feet (4645 m^2) in aggregate floor area and for open mall buildings exceeding 50,000 square feet (4645 m^2) in aggregate area within the perimeter line.

❖ The requirement for fire safety and evacuation plans for both covered malls and open malls is only applicable when such malls become larger. Smaller malls simplify the evacuation process and detailed information such as a lease plan is not required.

403.11.1.2 Lease plan. In addition to the requirements of Section 404.2.2, a lease plan that includes the following information shall be prepared for each covered and open mall building:

1. Each occupancy, including identification of tenant.
2. Exits from each tenant space.

3. Fire protection features, including the following:
   3.1. Fire department connections.
   3.2. Fire command center.
   3.3. Smoke management system controls.
   3.4. Elevators, elevator machine rooms and controls.
   3.5. Hose valve outlets.
   3.6. Sprinkler and standpipe control valves.
   3.7. Automatic fire-extinguishing system areas.
   3.8. Automatic fire detector zones.
   3.9. Fire barriers.

❖ Item 1 assists the emergency responders by requiring detailed documentation regarding the identification of each tenant, location and occupancy. This will let them locate the highest density of occupants and the types of hazards that may be anticipated.

Item 2 is the identification of exits. This will assist emergency responders in the identification of necessary access routes and how they may interact with the exits.

Item 3 is a report of the available fire protection features. These features, such as identification of the fire detector zones, will help responders quickly assess where a fire is located. If the mall has a smoke control system, access to the controls may be necessary; therefore, the location of those controls is critical. This information gives the fire department a general feel for how the building is intended to perform during a fire. This information is valuable in the sense that they will have more information to promote effective use of the fire protection features installed. If little information is provided, the fire department could actually disrupt the essential activation of a system, such as smoke control.

403.11.1.3 Lease plan approval. The lease plan shall be submitted to the fire code official for approval, and shall be maintained on site for immediate reference by responding fire service personnel.

❖ The lease plan must be approved. This allows the fire department to determine whether all necessary information, from the perspective of the responders, is addressed. Also, this section requires that the lease plan is available on site for use by the emergency responders.

403.11.1.4 Lease plan revisions. The lease plans shall be revised annually or as often as necessary to keep them current. Modifications or changes in tenants or occupancies shall not be made without prior approval of the fire code official and building official.

❖ This section provides the authority to require a review of the lease plan at least once each year. In addition, the fire code official has the authority to ask for more frequent reviews of the plan.

If a change occurs in the building, the lease plan may no longer be valid; therefore, this section requires that no changes to any tenant space be made without approval and review by the fire code official. These changes would have to be documented in the lease plan.

403.11.1.5 Tenant identification. Tenant identification shall be provided for secondary *exits* from occupied tenant spaces that lead to an *exit corridor* or directly to the exterior of the building. Tenant identification shall be posted on the exterior side of the *exit* or exit access door and shall identify the business name and address using plainly legible letters and numbers that contrast with their background.

Exception: Tenant identification is not required for anchor stores.

❖ Identifying secondary exits from tenant spaces that enter into an exit passageway or lead directly outside is a critical need for emergency responders. This identification needs to contain the business name and address. Having multiple tenants within a building makes this identification necessary. Anchor stores do not need these labels, since they are fairly recognizable without them.

403.11.1.6 Unoccupied tenant spaces. The fire safety and evacuation plan shall provide for compliance with the requirements for unoccupied tenant spaces in Section 311.

❖ This section addresses the hazards posed by a tenant space that is not in use or that is not under the supervision of employees. These spaces are more likely to be targeted by vandalism and possibly incendiary activity. Generally, a fire can grow unnoticed in such spaces as a result of the lack of supervision or activity in the space. This section simply references Section 311.6, where requirements dealing with vacant premises are found. To reduce the risks in unsupervised tenant spaces, several requirements in Section 311.6 focus on reducing the fire ignition, growth and spread potential by limiting combustibles in the space, securing the space through the use of locks and installing fire separations constructed of $^1/_2$-inch-thick (12.7 mm) gypsum or similar materials. Note that mall buildings are required to be sprinklered throughout and that the systems in the tenant spaces must be independent of the mall area.

403.11.2 High-rise buildings. An *approved* fire safety and evacuation plan in accordance with Section 404 shall be prepared and maintained for high-rise buildings.

❖ High-rise buildings can involve many different uses, such as business, assembly and residential. The types of occupancies on their own may or may not have specific requirements for fire safety and evacuation plans, but due to the fact that the building is tall, evacuation and fire safety become more complex. Such buildings tend to use phased evacuation, but may have other unique evacuation requirements such as the need for full-building evacuation or assisting those who cannot use stairways. The types of evacuation strategies for high rises vary. More detailed discussion on these strategies can be found in the SFPE *Engineering Guide: Fire Safety for Very Tall Buildings* (ICC and SFPE 2013) and *Egress Design Solutions* (Tubbs and Meacham 2005).

403.11.3 Underground buildings. An *approved* fire safety and evacuation plan in accordance with Section 404 shall be prepared and maintained for underground buildings.

❖ Like high-rise buildings, underground buildings can contain a variety of uses. Those uses may not, on their own, require unique fire safety and evacuation plans, but since the building is located below grade, evacuation and fire fighting become more complex. Therefore, it is important that a fire safety and evacuation plan be required in accordance with Section 404. Note that Item 4 in Section 404.2.1 specifically addresses those unable to use the stairways.

403.11.4 Buildings using occupant evacuation elevators. In buildings using occupant evacuation elevators in accordance with Section 3008 of the *International Building Code*, the fire safety and evacuation plan and the training required by Sections 404 and 406, respectively, shall incorporate specific procedures for the occupants using such elevators.

❖ This is not a specific use but instead is an evacuation strategy that is very different than what the general public has been taught about the use of elevators during fires. The successful use of such elevators depends greatly on preplanning and training as to how they are to be used by building occupants. This section requires that where these elevators are used, specific procedures be worked into the fire safety and evacuation plans and into employee training. Note that Item 3 in Section 404.2.1 specifically requires these procedures to be included in the fire evacuation plans. It should be noted that this ties in with the requirements for high-rise buildings and how they are intended to be evacuated. As with high-rise buildings, a good resource for extensive discussion on occupant evacuation and evacuation using elevators can be found in the SFPE *Engineering Guide: Fire Safety for Very Tall Buildings* and *Egress Design Solutions* (Tubbs and Meacham 2005).

403.11.5 Buildings with high-piled storage. An approved fire safety and evacuation plan in accordance with Section 404 shall be prepared for buildings with *high-piled combustible storage* in any of the following situations:

1. The *high-piled storage area* exceeds 500,000 square feet (46 450 m^2) for Class I-IV commodities.
2. The *high-piled storage area* exceeds 300,000 square feet (27 870 m^2) for high-hazard commodities.
3. The *high-piled storage* is located in a Group H occupancy.
4. The *high-piled storage* is located in a Group F occupancy with an *occupant load* of 500 or more persons or more than 100 persons above or below the lowest *level of exit discharge*.
5. The *high-piled storage* is located in a Group M occupancy with an *occupant load* of 500 or more persons or more than than 100 persons above or below the lowest *level of exit discharge*.
6. Where required by the *fire code official* for other *high-piled storage areas*.

❖ This section correlates the requirement for a fire safety and evacuation plan for high-piled storage with the current requirements in Chapter 32. High-piled storage is a content-based use that has a large effect on the fire safety and evacuation aspects of a building. Chapter 32 requires that fire safety and evacuation plans be in compliance with this section. Prior to the 2018 code, those compliance details were addressed within Chapter 32. Placement in Chapter 4 is more consistent with other occupancies and uses being addressed in this chapter.

There are six thresholds as to when a fire safety and evacuation plan is required for high-piled combustible storage.

In Table 3206.2, high-piled storage areas of Class I-IV commodities over 500,000 square feet currently require additional fire protection measures. Therefore, the situation described in Item 1 is an appropriate time to request a fire safety and evacuation plan. Likewise, Item 2 addresses the fact that in Table 3206.2, high-piled storage areas of high-hazard commodities over 300,000 square feet currently require additional fire protection measures. Therefore, this situation is also an appropriate time to ask for a fire safety and evacuation plan.

Items 3–5 are consistent with Sections 403.6, 403.7 and 403.9.

Item 6 was previously the primary trigger for requiring a fire safety and evacuation plan specific to high-piled combustible storage. Now this is simply one of the criteria and retains that authority where it is felt necessary.

403.12 Special requirements for public safety. Special requirements for public safety shall be in accordance with Sections 403.12.1 through 403.12.3.3.

❖ The following requirements authorize a jurisdiction to require fire watches, address large public assemblies and provide specific requirements for crowd managers.

403.12.1 Fire watch personnel. Where, in the opinion of the *fire code official*, it is essential for public safety in a place of assembly or any other place where people congregate, because of the number of persons, or the nature of the performance, exhibition, display, contest or activity, the *owner*, agent or lessee shall provide one or more fire watch personnel, as required and *approved*. Fire watch personnel shall comply with Sections 403.12.1.1 and 403.12.1.2.

❖ Even though Chapter 31 requires standby personnel in tents and membrane structures because of the inherently higher life safety risks associated with such occupancies, this section gives the fire code official the authority to require fire watch personnel in indoor or outdoor venues where people congregate where the number of persons or the nature of the performance, exhibition, display, contest or activity is such that the presence of fire watch personnel are essential to public safety (see commentary, Section 202, definition of "Fire watch").

403.12.1.1 Duty times. Fire watch personnel shall remain on duty while places requiring a fire watch are open to the public, or when an activity requiring a fire watch is being conducted.

❖ This section establishes the key times a fire watch should be conducted. Once it is established that a fire watch is necessary, it is critical that it be conducted while the public is present. Also, it may be necessary for the fire watch to occur based on a specific hazard or activity even while not open to the public.

403.12.1.2 Duties. On-duty fire watch personnel shall have the following responsibilities:

1. Keep diligent watch for fires, obstructions to *means of egress* and other hazards.
2. Take prompt measures for remediation of hazards and extinguishment of fires that occur.
3. Take prompt measures to assist in the evacuation of the public from the structures.

❖ Fire watch personnel provide temporary fire safety where there are potential fire and life safety hazards that could affect large numbers of assembled people. Such personnel does not simply watch for a fire but is also present to prevent fire by identifying and controlling fire hazards; monitoring and maintaining the availability of the means of egress; and taking initial action to suppress a fire should one occur. Fire watch personnel also provide a method of notifying the fire department if a fire should occur.

403.12.2 Public safety plan for gatherings. Where the *fire code official* determines that an indoor or outdoor gathering of persons has an adverse impact on public safety through diminished access to buildings, structures, fire hydrants and fire apparatus access roads or where such gatherings adversely affect public safety services of any kind, the *fire code official* shall have the authority to order the development of or prescribe a public safety plan that provides an *approved* level of public safety and addresses the following items:

1. Emergency vehicle ingress and egress.
2. Fire protection.
3. Emergency egress or escape routes.
4. Emergency medical services.
5. Public assembly areas.
6. The directing of both attendees and vehicles, including the parking of vehicles.
7. Vendor and food concession distribution.
8. The need for the presence of law enforcement.
9. The need for fire and emergency medical services personnel.
10. The need for a weather monitoring person.

❖ This section is important because it grants the fire code official the authority to require the development of or to prescribe a specific plan for large gatherings. Such gatherings could include outdoor festivals, demonstrations or receptions. If such assemblies include the use of tents and canopies, Chapter 31 would also apply.

Again, the primary aim of this section is to address the fact that these large gatherings may hamper the ability of the fire department and other emergency responders to access and protect buildings and building occupants.

Further, this section provides some specific issues to be addressed, including: the direction of traffic; vendor and food concession distributors; and the need for law enforcement and medical services.

403.12.3 Crowd managers. Where facilities or events involve a gathering of more than 500 people, crowd managers shall be provided in accordance with Sections 403.12.3.1 through 403.12.3.3.

❖ This section is similar to the requirement for standby personnel for tents in Section 3107.17.2. Also note that Section 3106.4.3 addresses outdoor assembly events and requires crowd managers, meeting the requirements of this section where crowds exceed 1,000 people. There is an exception for outdoor gatherings less than 1,000 people in Section 403.12.3.1, which is consistent with Section 3106.4.3 and would not require compliance with this section. Large assemblies of people create the need for crowd management due to the increased potential for panic and fear in emergency situations. It is intended that crowd managers can be personnel already assigned and employed by the facility, provided that they are trained as crowd managers to fulfill this requirement. At the time of an emergency, the trained crowd managers would take on additional responsibilities to control and direct the audience or attendees in a safe manner.

403.12.3.1 Number of crowd managers. Not fewer than two trained crowd managers, and not fewer than one trained crowd manager for each 250 persons or portion thereof, shall be provided for the gathering.

Exceptions:

1. Outdoor events with fewer than 1,000 persons in attendance shall not require crowd managers.
2. Assembly occupancies used exclusively for religious worship with an occupant load not exceeding 1,000 shall not require crowd managers.
3. The number of crowd managers shall be reduced where, in the opinion of the *fire code official*, the fire protection provided by the facility and the nature of the event warrant a reduction.

❖ The minimum number of crowd managers would be two, based on the minimum requirements of Section 403.12.3. Additionally, this section would also require an additional crowd manager for any portion of 250 people after that. For instance, if you had an event with 530 people, you would need three crowd managers. Exception 1 addresses consistency with the requirements of Section 3106.4.3 for outdoor events that would not require crowd managers until the number of people in attendance exceeds 1,000. This is related to the fact that outdoor events eliminate many hazards since people can more freely leave such areas. Exception 2 is for assembly occupancies with 1,000 or fewer occupants where religious worship occurs, as such facilities have low risk of fire and life safety concerns. Because the fire and life safety profile of a facility is improved where an automatic sprinkler system is installed throughout, Exception 3 states that the fire code official is authorized to reduce the crowd manager-to-occupant ratio for events on a case-by-case basis (see commentary, Section 3107.17).

403.12.3.2 Training. Training for crowd managers shall be *approved*.

❖ Training is critical for crowd managers to be effective. This section provides the mechanism to ensure such training occurs. There are various crowd manager training courses available.

403.12.3.3 Duties. The duties of crowd managers shall include, but not be limited to:

1. Conduct an inspection of the area of responsibility and identify and address any egress barriers.
2. Conduct an inspection of the area of responsibility to identify and mitigate any fire hazards.
3. Verify compliance with all permit conditions, including those governing pyrotechnics and other special effects.
4. Direct and assist the event attendees in evacuation during an emergency.
5. Assist emergency response personnel where requested.
6. Other duties required by the *fire code official*.
7. Other duties as specified in the fire safety plan.

❖ The exact duties and responsibilities of individuals employed as crowd managers are not defined here other than the requirement that they be trained and present. They could serve as ushers, tour guides, service supervisors for table seating or in some other capacity related to making sure occupants are moved to or from assigned places in an orderly way. The key to the success of this section is that crowd managers must be trained in crowd management procedures appropriate to the activity being carried on in the facility and they must be present in the required numbers. Training of personnel and the duties assigned to them would have to be approved by the fire code official. See the commentary to Section 3107.17 for further information on crowd managers.

SECTION 404
FIRE SAFETY,
EVACUATION AND LOCKDOWN PLANS

404.1 General. Where required by Section 403, fire safety, evacuation and lockdown plans shall comply with Sections 404.2 through 404.4.1.

❖ This section simply states that all fire safety, evacuation and lockdown plans must comply with Section 404. Section 403 outlines, for many different occupancies and uses, when this section would apply. In addition, Section 403 provides specific requirements that are intended to be addressed along with the requirements in Section 404.

404.2 Contents. Fire safety, evacuation and lockdown plan contents shall be in accordance with Sections 404.2.1 through 404.2.3.2.

❖ The three primary plans addressed by Section 404.3 are a fire evacuation plan, a fire safety plan and a lockdown plan. The fire evacuation plan focuses primarily on the procedures for the evacuation of the occupants in an emergency. The fire safety plan focuses on the overall understanding of the fire protection package of the building as it pertains to the layout of the building, the contents of the building, the means of egress system, the fire hazards and the identification of key contacts during an emergency. Lockdown plans are permitted with approval by the fire code official and address security concerns while also maintaining the fire and life safety of the occupants.

404.2.1 Fire evacuation plans. Fire evacuation plans shall include the following:

1. Emergency egress or escape routes and whether evacuation of the building is to be complete by selected floors or areas only or with a defend-in-place response.
2. Procedures for employees who must remain to operate critical equipment before evacuating.
3. Procedures for the use of elevators to evacuate the building where occupant evacuation elevators complying with Section 3008 of the *International Building Code* are provided.
4. Procedures for assisted rescue for persons unable to use the general means of egress unassisted.
5. Procedures for accounting for employees and occupants after evacuation has been completed.
6. Identification and assignment of personnel responsible for rescue or emergency medical aid.
7. The preferred and any alternative means of notifying occupants of a fire or emergency.

8. The preferred and any alternative means of reporting fires and other emergencies to the fire department or designated emergency response organization.
9. Identification and assignment of personnel who can be contacted for further information or explanation of duties under the plan.
10. A description of the emergency voice/alarm communication system alert tone and preprogrammed voice messages, where provided.

❖ The primary focus of evacuation plans is to prepare for and define roles for evacuation and relocation of occupants during an emergency. The fire evacuation plan is important for both emergency responders and building or facility occupants. It focuses the occupants' activities on facilitating a smoother evacuation or relocation process and provides the fire department with critical information on the building and the location of the occupants. Keep in mind that these requirements apply to all occupancies listed in Section 404.2. The occupancy- and use-specific requirements are located within Section 403; therefore, the requirements listed here are general and will vary based on many factors, such as the occupants' mobility and familiarity with the building.

Item 1 requires that specific escape routes be defined. This is important because the building is generally designed to facilitate a particular pattern of evacuation or relocation in an emergency. For instance, as noted earlier, a high-rise building will most likely be evacuated in phases. If floors begin evacuating before intended, the evacuation of the occupants in the fire area may be delayed. Also, if everyone tries to use the same exits in a facility, such as a multiplex theater, evacuation of the building will be delayed. As stated earlier, studies have shown that people tend to exit the way they enter a building. Note that the code sometimes requires a certain level of redundancy to account for occupants using the same exits. For example, the IBC requires that the main exit of multiplex theaters be sized for at least half of the occupants even though plenty of egress width may be available elsewhere in the building. The more coordinated the plan, the more evenly the exits will be used.

Item 2 requires that specific procedures for evacuation be provided to those employees who must operate critical equipment before evacuation. These procedures are necessary to ensure a clear understanding to the occupant when evacuation is critical and the operation should be abandoned.

Item 3 requires that specific procedures be provided when occupant evacuation elevators are used. This is critical as each building may have unique aspects regarding the use of such elevators and the types of evacuations they may undertake.

Item 4 provides for the inclusion of procedures relative to those occupants unable to evacuate using the general egress features who, therefore, may need assisted rescue. It is important that there be adequate information and procedures established and available to staff and fire fighters so that assistance can be offered to anyone who needs help using the general means of egress as quickly as possible.

Item 5 simply states that a plan be developed to account for all occupants after evacuation or relocation. This is important not only to the occupants but also to the emergency responders to assess their actions when arriving at the scene.

Item 6 has two roles. First, it provides a designated person for occupants to look to for assistance in an emergency. This will reduce the stress of the situation. Second, when the emergency responders arrive they will have a specific contact to help them assess the situation. These contacts can also be beneficial to emergency responders when preplanning their response to that specific facility.

Item 7 requires that the notification to the occupants of the emergency be standardized. The approach will vary based on occupancy and use. For instance, all occupants in a multiplex theater would be notified, whereas in a correctional facility or hospital only staff will be notified. Also, if the method is standardized, it is easier to differentiate between emergency and nonemergency signals, which facilitates a smoother reaction when an emergency does occur.

Item 8 is focused on the notification of emergency responders. They are more likely to get the notification of an emergency if a standard protocol exists. This can vary from one occupancy or use to another, but as long as a straightforward, consistent method is used, it will facilitate a quicker response. Note that Section 401.3.2 requires direct contact with the fire department once the fire alarm signal is activated; therefore, no intermediate steps, such as an investigation, are allowed.

As with Item 6, Item 9 requires a specific contact that is familiar with the plan and how the building operates. This information is helpful for the emergency responders in their preplanning activities. Without a specific contact, the process of getting vital information can become much more difficult for the fire department. In a large building or facility, the safety officer or similar person is most appropriate for such a role.

Item 10 requires documentation of the voice/alarm communications system alert tone and preprogrammed voice messages. This provides emergency responders with a better understanding of the information provided to occupants to better assess the appropriate response. Additionally, if conditions in that building change, the plan can be evaluated to see whether this aspect of the notification system needs to be revised. For instance, if the procedures for evacuation have changed, the voice announcement may need to be revised.

404.2.2 Fire safety plans. Fire safety plans shall include the following:

1. The procedure for reporting a fire or other emergency.
2. The life safety strategy including the following:
    - 2.1. Procedures for notifying occupants, including areas with a private mode alarm system.
    - 2.2. Procedures for occupants under a defend-in-place response.
    - 2.3. Procedures for evacuating occupants, including those who need evacuation assistance.
3. Site plans indicating the following:
    - 3.1. The occupancy assembly point.
    - 3.2. The locations of fire hydrants.
    - 3.3. The normal routes of fire department vehicle access.
4. Floor plans identifying the locations of the following:
    - 4.1. Exits.
    - 4.2. Primary evacuation routes.
    - 4.3. Secondary evacuation routes.
    - 4.4. Accessible egress routes.
        - 4.4.1. Areas of refuge.
        - 4.4.2. Exterior areas for assisted rescue.
    - 4.5. Refuge areas associated with *smoke barriers* and *horizontal exits*.
    - 4.6. Manual fire alarm boxes.
    - 4.7. Portable fire extinguishers.
    - 4.8. Occupant-use hose stations.
    - 4.9. Fire alarm annunciators and controls.
5. A list of major fire hazards associated with the normal use and occupancy of the premises, including maintenance and housekeeping procedures.
6. Identification and assignment of personnel responsible for maintenance of systems and equipment installed to prevent or control fires.
7. Identification and assignment of personnel responsible for maintenance, housekeeping and controlling fuel hazard sources.

❖ This section requires an overall fire safety plan with emphasis on the building and building site layout and hazards. More specifically, information such as the evacuation and relocation aspects of the building layout must be clear, the list of specific hazards associated with normal use of the building must be noted and fire department access road locations must be provided.

This plan also includes identification of specific personnel charged with managing fire protection systems and equipment and with fire prevention duties, such as controlling combustibles on site. Having specific personnel assigned to perform this duty will work to increase the likelihood of these actions occurring.

The requirements of this plan provide the building owner and occupants a better understanding of how to react in an emergency and how to decrease the likelihood of an emergency occurring. Additionally, this report assists emergency responders during periodic inspections and evaluations of the plans and, more importantly, when responding to an emergency. Generally, buildings that have fairly rigid and well-maintained plans and procedures in place reduce not only the likelihood and magnitude of an incident within the jurisdiction but also the burden to emergency responders.

404.2.3 Lockdown plans. Lockdown plans shall only be permitted where such plans are approved by the *fire code official* and are in compliance with Sections 404.2.3.1 and 404.2.3.2.

❖ This section introduces the requirements for plans and procedures for lockdowns (see the commentary to the definition in Section 202). The section is clear that such plans are allowed only where approved by the fire code official. The code does not require a lockdown plan; however, if a lockdown plan is developed, it must be strictly supervised in order to maintain occupant safety at an acceptable level. Many facilities are adopting procedures that can significantly affect fire and life safety, such as using the fire alarm system to signal a security emergency, locking doors with devices that prevent egress in violation of the provisions of Chapter 10 of the code, and chaining exit discharge doors from the inside to prevent occupants from leaving the building. It is important that plans for security threats do not include procedures that result in violations of life safety and actually increase the hazard to the occupants. The sections that follow are intended to establish the conditions for lockdown plans so that they will not decrease the level of life safety in the event of fire.

404.2.3.1 Lockdown plan contents. Lockdown plans shall include the following:

1. Identification of individuals authorized to issue a lockdown order.
2. Security measures used during normal operations, when the building is occupied, that could adversely affect egress or fire department operations.
3. A description of identified emergency and security threats addressed by the plan, including specific lockdown procedures to be implemented for each threat condition.
4. Means and methods of initiating a lockdown plan for each threat, including:
    - 4.1. The means of notifying occupants of a lockdown event, which shall be distinct from the fire alarm signal.
    - 4.2. Identification of each door or other access point that will be secured.
    - 4.3. A description of the means or methods used to secure doors and other access points.

4.4. A description of how locking means and methods are in compliance with the requirements of this code for egress and accessibility.

5. Procedures for reporting to the fire department any lockdown condition affecting egress or fire department operations.
6. Procedures for determining and reporting the presence or absence of occupants to emergency response agencies during a lockdown.
7. Means for providing two-way communication between a central location and each area subject to being secured during a lockdown.
8. Identification of the prearranged signal for terminating the lockdown.
9. Identification of individuals authorized to issue a lockdown termination order.
10. Procedures for unlocking doors and verifying that the means of egress has been returned to normal operations upon termination of the lockdown.
11. Training procedures and frequency of lockdown plan drills.

❖ The items in this section are intended to more thoroughly address various security means and methods created and implemented in response to various incidents throughout the country. Several such means and methods, while solving security concerns, have unintended consequences regarding emergency egress and fire and life safety systems. Previous editions of this code did not provide the necessary amount of detail for such lockdown plans. It is important to ensure that the plan covers the topics pertinent to the fire code official thoroughly.

A key aspect of a lockdown plan is to identify the organizational structure in charge of making decisions during a lockdown. It is important to understand who is authorized to both initiate and lift a lockdown order. This section requires inclusion of lockdown procedures in the plan. There is often a need for different lockdown plans to address differing threats. The correct procedure during a chemical release incident might differ from the correct procedure during an active shooter incident. The correct procedure for an active shooter in the vicinity of a facility may differ from the procedure for an active shooter on the site of the facility.

A description of the normal status of security, a description of the various threat scenarios addressed by the lockdown plan, and the lockdown procedure for each such scenario are important items to include for review. Such details can impact fire department response and alert fire officials to the life safety implications of any given approach. This is especially true with the methods of locking included in the lockdown plan. There is concern about the proliferation of unlisted locking mechanisms and their potential detrimental impact on the means of egress. This section requires that all means and methods of locking for all access points be described, and that compliance with Chapter 10 requirements be demonstrated. This section also requires procedures as to how lockdown events are communicated with the fire department. In addition, the section requires that a central "command" location be preplanned and that a reliable means of two-way communication be provided in order to keep locked-down occupants apprised of the status of the situation, thus reducing their level of anxiety and the likelihood of panic. Finally, this section requires that the lockdown plan includes training procedures and a requirement as to how frequently drills are necessary.

404.2.3.2 Drills. Lockdown plan drills shall be conducted in accordance with the approved plan. Such drills shall not be substituted for fire and evacuation drills required by Section 405.2.

❖ To utilize lockdown training and the lessons learned from it to the best advantage, training should be conducted on a regular basis to familiarize staff and occupants with the lockdown plan. The training procedures and frequency of drills are established in Section 404.2.3.1. Training should be designed and practiced to reinforce lockdown procedures as adaptive planned responses to stressful and potentially dangerous situations. It is important to note that lockdown training and drills may not be counted toward the required number of fire and evacuation drills so as not to diminish the impact of either (see also commentary, Section 406.3.3).

404.3 Maintenance. Fire safety and evacuation plans shall be reviewed or updated annually or as necessitated by changes in staff assignments, occupancy or the physical arrangement of the building.

❖ In order to be of optimum value to a facility, plans must accurately reflect building conditions. Plans must be reviewed annually or when building changes affecting the instructions or procedures in the fire safety or emergency evacuation plan occur. Such a review should prompt an immediate revision and redistribution of the plan to all concerned parties, including emergency response personnel.

404.4 Availability. Fire safety and evacuation plans shall be available in the workplace for reference and review by employees, and copies shall be furnished to the fire code official for review on request.

❖ This essentially requires that these plans be easily accessible to building occupants and the fire code official. If the plans are difficult to access, they are less likely to be updated when necessary and are more likely to be lost or forgotten. This places a burden on the emergency responders when planning methods of response, and puts the occupants of the building at a higher risk during an emergency. Having the documents readily available makes review and use for training occupants more likely.

404.4.1 Distribution. The fire safety and evacuation plans shall be distributed to the tenants and building service employees by the owner or owner's agent. Tenants shall distribute to their employees applicable parts of the fire safety plan affecting the employees' actions in the event of a fire or other emergency.

❖ Fire safety and evacuation plans are only effective when all building occupants have been informed of the contents of the plan. In the case of a multiple-tenant building, the plan must address individual tenant spaces. Distribution to all affected occupants is important for a coordinated response to an emergency.

This section requires that the building owner or the owner's agent distribute the plan to all tenants and building service employees. Since the owner or agent of the owner usually does not have direct access to the tenants' employees, the individual tenants would then have the responsibility to distribute the applicable portion of the plan to their employees. This provides for a wider distribution of the responsibility to plan for emergencies and to follow the requirements of the plan.

SECTION 405 EMERGENCY EVACUATION DRILLS

405.1 General. Emergency evacuation drills complying with Sections 405.2 through 405.9 shall be conducted not less than annually where fire safety and evacuation plans are required by Section 403 or where required by the *fire code official*. Drills shall be designed in cooperation with the local authorities.

❖ The fire safety and evacuation plans required by Sections 403 and 404 are critical components of life safety strategies in high-density occupancies and extraordinary buildings, such as high-rise buildings. Many times such plans are developed with the best of intentions and available expertise, but fail to adequately consider certain site- or area-specific conditions. Just as emergency operations and hazardous material response plans require operational drills to verify their continued viability and effectiveness, so too do evacuation plans require periodic implementation to gauge effectiveness in achieving their objectives. Since not all of the occupancies that are required to prepare and maintain fire safety and evacuation plans by Section 403 are required to conduct drills by Table 405.2, this section requires at least an annual drill to exercise the required plan.

An additional benefit of an annual drill is the enhanced recognition by occupants. This is particularly beneficial in buildings such as high-rises that evacuate by selected floors. Given the generally heightened awareness following the events of September 11, 2001, building occupants understandably exhibit a greater reluctance to remain inside a building in the event of an emergency. A complete building evacuation may be unnecessary in a large number of cases and may actually work counter to effective fireground operations if uncontrolled. An annual drill in these instances would serve to reinforce the local jurisdiction's preferences regarding evacuation and provide a verification tool that the plan, as developed, is functional, while also providing opportunities for critique and improvement. The use of an annual drill could easily be incorporated with specific additional training to satisfy the requirements in Section 406 as well.

405.2 Frequency. Required emergency evacuation drills shall be held at the intervals specified in Table 405.2 or more frequently where necessary to familiarize all occupants with the drill procedure.

❖ To utilize fire drills and the lessons that they teach to the best of their advantage, drills should be conducted on a regular basis to familiarize both staff and residents with the evacuation plan. The element of surprise is not necessarily of significant benefit in those occupancies where residents may be prone to maladaptive behavior. Drills should be designed and practiced to reinforce relocation or evacuation behaviors as adaptive planned responses to stressful and potentially dangerous situations. Drills should be scheduled so that all staff members on all shifts have an opportunity to participate in them. Practice makes perfect, and when it comes to effective egress, there is no substitute for fire drills at regular intervals so that all occupants are familiar with the plan's details and their particular responsibilities in implementing them. Truly effective drills test the plan by varying conditions and forcing occupants to adapt. Many conditions can combine to affect available safe egress time, and drills should incorporate some allowance for unanticipated conditions, such as delayed detection, rapid fire growth, reduced staffing or poor weather conditions, as may be appropriate for the occupancy. Discovering deficiencies in the evacuation plan should be encouraged, and every opportunity should be taken to improve the plans.

TABLE 405.2. See page 4-24.

❖ Table 405.2 provides varying evacuation drill frequencies based on building occupancy. The table also prescribes who should be involved in these drills. The level of participation is based on the type of occupancy. In some cases, this is further qualified by the number or location of such occupants with respect to the lowest level of fire department vehicle access. It is unreasonable, for example, in a Group A occupancy such as a hospital or correctional facility to require the general public to participate in an evacuation drill. It is potentially dangerous to involve anyone but the employees in such drills.

The overall strategy for these occupancies is to provide a package of relevant information before an emergency and to have the employees facilitate and direct occupants during an emergency. The necessary participants in the drills are related to the overall emergency strategies for those buildings. Note that

Group B, E, I-1 assisted living, I-4, R-2 and R-4 occupancies require that everyone be involved. This is related to the fact that occupants are generally able to evacuate. In the case of educational occupancies, drills serve as a learning tool for children to carry through their lives. Schools have generally stressed these drills because of large losses in fires, such as in 1958 at Our Lady of Angels School in Chicago. In terms of Group I-1, I-4 and R-4 facilities, the occupants generally are able to evacuate with some assistance. In Group R-2 occupancies, the occupants are usually able-bodied and it is in their best interest to be familiar with the egress routes. More occupancy-specific discussion is provided in the commentary for Section 403.

TABLE 405.2
FIRE AND EVACUATION DRILL FREQUENCY AND PARTICIPATION

GROUP OR OCCUPANCY	FREQUENCY	PARTICIPATION
Group A	Quarterly	Employees
Group B[b]	Annually	All occupants
Group B[c] (Ambulatory care facilities)	Quarterly on each shift[a]	Employees
Group B[b] (Clinic, outpatient)	Annually	Employees
Group E	Monthly[a]	All occupants
Group F	Annually	Employees
Group I-1	Semiannually on each shift	All occupants
Group I-2	Quarterly on each shift[a]	Employees
Group I-3	Quarterly on each shift[a]	Employees
Group I-4	Monthly on each shift[a]	All occupants
Group R-1	Quarterly on each shift	Employees
Group R-2[d]	Four annually	All occupants
Group R-4	Semiannually on each shift[a]	All occupants

a. In severe climates, the fire code official shall have the authority to modify the emergency evacuation drill frequency.

b. Emergency evacuation drills are required in Group B buildings having an occupant load of 500 or more persons or more than 100 persons above or below the lowest level of exit discharge.

c. Emergency evacuation drills are required in ambulatory care facilities in accordance with Section 403.3.

d. Emergency evacuation drills in Group R-2 college and university buildings shall be in accordance with Section 403.10.2.1. Other Group R-2 occupancies shall be in accordance with Section 403.10.2.2.

405.3 Leadership. Responsibility for the planning and conduct of drills shall be assigned to competent persons designated to exercise leadership.

❖ This section requires a focal point in the planning and execution of evacuation drills. Having a single point of contact streamlines the process and provides a necessary leadership role.

405.4 Time. Drills shall be held at unexpected times and under varying conditions to simulate the unusual conditions that occur in case of fire.

❖ If fire and emergency drills are a routine planned occurrence, they will not simulate actual reaction to an emergency but will provide an inaccurate and most likely optimistic outcome; therefore, the drills need to occur at random.

405.5 Record keeping. Records shall be maintained of required emergency evacuation drills and include the following information:

1. Identity of the person conducting the drill.
2. Date and time of the drill.
3. Notification method used.
4. Employees on duty and participating.
5. Number of occupants evacuated.
6. Special conditions simulated.
7. Problems encountered.
8. Weather conditions when occupants were evacuated.
9. Time required to accomplish complete evacuation.

❖ Documenting the frequency and efficiency of emergency evacuation drills not only aids the fire code official in verifying that drills complying with these provisions have been performed but may also help administrators identify trends in emergency evacuation drill performance. Accurate records help life safety planners determine the adequacy of their plans. Identifying issues such as problems encountered and weather conditions helps to further determine which elements create the largest delays and why.

405.6 Notification. Where required by the fire code official, prior notification of emergency evacuation drills shall be given to the fire code official.

❖ In some cases, the fire code official will want prior notification of evacuation drills because he or she may need to prepare for such an event. This section provides the fire code official with the authority to require such notification.

405.7 Initiation. Where a fire alarm system is provided, emergency evacuation drills shall be initiated by activating the fire alarm system.

❖ To simulate conditions normally experienced during an emergency, the emergency notification procedures, which would include a fire alarm system in many cases, must be used.

405.8 Accountability. As building occupants arrive at the assembly point, efforts shall be made to determine if all occupants have been successfully evacuated or have been accounted for.

❖ This requirement is key to the success of evacuation plans. If a method is not available to account for the occupants once evacuation or relocation is complete, search and rescue activities will be more difficult for the emergency responders. Also, it would be difficult to measure the success of the plan.

405.9 Recall and reentry. An electrically or mechanically operated signal used to recall occupants after an evacuation shall be separate and distinct from the signal used to initiate the evacuation. The recall signal initiation means shall be manually operated and under the control of the person in charge of the premises or the official in charge of the incident. Persons shall not reenter the premises until authorized to do so by the official in charge.

❖ This section is primarily aimed at the concern that occupants will be confused if similar signals are used to notify them of an alarm and for reentry. This confusion has the consequences of slowing or even halting evacuation during an actual emergency. Additionally, to make sure that occupants do not go back into the building prematurely, any reentry signal must be operated manually to avoid a situation where it automatically sounds. Finally, this section specifically prohibits reentry until authorization is provided by the official in charge at the scene.

SECTION 406 EMPLOYEE TRAINING AND RESPONSE PROCEDURES

406.1 General. Where fire safety and evacuation plans are required by Section 403, employees shall be trained in fire emergency procedures based on plans prepared in accordance with Section 404.

❖ In most cases, the success of an evacuation and fire safety plan hinges on the appropriate reactions of the building occupants. The main activity that building occupants must undertake is removing themselves from the hazards. In some cases, fire safety and evacuation plans involve additional actions by the employees of the facility. For instance, in the case of hospitals, the nurses and other hospital staff must relocate care recipients; therefore, specific training is required for those activities.

Additionally, employees must be trained based on the specific fire safety and fire evacuation plans.

406.2 Frequency. Employees shall receive training in the contents of fire safety and evacuation plans and their duties as part of new employee orientation and not less than annually thereafter. Records of training shall be maintained.

❖ This section requires that employee training occur during new employee indoctrination and annually thereafter. A record of this training must be provided to the fire code official when requested. This section provides a minimum criterion for the training frequency for all occupancies addressed by Chapter 4. Section 403 may require more restrictive training frequencies.

406.3 Employee training program. Employees shall be trained in fire prevention, evacuation and fire safety in accordance with Sections 406.3.1 through 406.3.4.

❖ This is a general section that requires all employees to be trained in fire prevention, evacuation and fire safety in accordance with the subsections that follow. These provisions are primarily intended as a mechanism to ensure that training occurs, not as a requirement for establishing training criteria.

406.3.1 Fire prevention training. Employees shall be apprised of the fire hazards of the materials and processes to which they are exposed. Each employee shall be instructed in the proper procedures for preventing fires in the conduct of their assigned duties.

❖ If a fire can be prevented, evacuation and relocation of the occupants will be avoided. Employees must be made aware of the potential hazards related to their particular area of the facility and what can be done to avoid a hazardous situation. Having specific procedures increases the likelihood that proper fire prevention techniques will be followed. Generally, people tend to be unaware of many hazards unless they are alerted to them. An example is the use of space heaters.

406.3.2 Evacuation training. Employees shall be familiarized with the fire alarm and evacuation signals, their assigned duties in the event of an alarm or emergency, evacuation routes, areas of refuge, exterior assembly areas and procedures for evacuation.

❖ In the event that an emergency does occur, employees must be prepared to assist in the evacuation or relocation of occupants. This training will vary widely from one occupancy type to another. In a high-rise building only some of the occupants will be evacuated at a time, whereas a school will evacuate all occupants at once. This section requires that the training occurs.

406.3.3 Fire safety training. Employees assigned fire-fighting duties shall be trained to know the locations and proper use of portable fire extinguishers or other manual fire-fighting equipment and the protective clothing or equipment required for its safe and proper use.

❖ Any time employees are to take specific action during a fire event, proper training is required. This section holds the building owner or operator responsible for making sure the training occurs.

406.3.4 Emergency lockdown training. Where a facility has a lockdown plan, employees shall be trained on their assigned duties and procedures in the event of an emergency lockdown.

❖ If a facility has created a lockdown plan, the staff needs to be versed in the plan's contents. Training should be scheduled so that all staff members on all shifts or occupants, as applicable, have an opportunity to participate. Practice makes perfect, and when it comes to effective lockdowns, there is no substitute for training at regular intervals so that all staff and occupants are familiar with the plan's details and their particular responsibilities in implementing it. Drills should be scheduled to test the plan by varying conditions, forcing occupants to adapt and respond instinctively to emergencies without panicking and allowing the staff to identify weaknesses in the preparations.

Many conditions can conspire to affect lockdown success and drills should incorporate some allowance for unanticipated conditions as may be appropriate for the occupancy. Discovering deficiencies in the plan should be encouraged, and every opportunity should be taken to improve the plans (see also commentary, Section 404.2.3.2).

SECTION 407 HAZARD COMMUNICATION

407.1 General. The provisions of Sections 407.2 through 407.7 shall be applicable where hazardous materials subject to permits under Section 5001.5 are located on the premises or where required by the fire code official.

❖ This section is specific to buildings and facilities that contain hazardous materials over the permitted amounts listed in Section 105.6. Knowledge related to which hazardous materials are on site is critical for several reasons. First, it assists emergency responders in knowing what to expect when responding to a scene. Second, it provides emergency responders with an idea of incidents that may occur at a building or facility. Lastly, it provides a better understanding to the occupants of the potential hazards present and how to avoid emergencies.

Facilities that store, use or handle hazardous materials on a large scale generally depend heavily on the actions of the employees to prevent or minimize hazardous materials incidents. Therefore, the occupants play a strong role in the overall protection of the building. These types of requirements would, in the past, have been found only within the hazardous materials section of the code. These provisions have also been located within this chapter because of the nature of the information. These requirements are aimed at preparing both the occupants and the emergency responders. Hazardous materials present a wide range of problems because of the significant variation of properties and reactions; therefore, a reference to these requirements has been included in Chapter 4. These specific provisions are found in Section 5001.

This section states that when subject to permit requirements, hazardous materials must also be addressed. This section has requirements for the submittal of Safety Data Sheets (SDS), which were formerly called Material Safety Data sheets; the labeling or marking of hazardous materials through placarding and related identification; training; the compilation, where required, of both HMIS and HMMP; and finally, the submittal of a closure plan where a facility is being shut down.

407.2 Safety Data Sheets. Safety Data Sheets (SDS) for all hazardous materials shall be either readily available on the premises as a paper copy, or where approved, shall be permitted to be readily retrievable by electronic access.

❖ SDS provide critical information about individual chemicals and their related hazards. This section requires that these data sheets be readily available on the premises or, where equivalent access can be achieved, as approved by the fire code official, they may be retrievable by electronic means. This allows availability for review by both employees and emergency responders. An appropriate location may be the security room at a facility or perhaps the main office. These sheets can potentially play a role in the response to an emergency. For example, if a chemical is noted on the SDS as being water reactive, depending on the level of water reactivity, applying water to that spill may not be an appropriate response.

407.3 Identification. Individual containers of hazardous materials, cartons or packages shall be marked or labeled in accordance with applicable federal regulations. Buildings, rooms and spaces containing hazardous materials shall be identified by hazard warning signs in accordance with Section 5003.5.

❖ This section requires two activities related to the identification of hazardous materials. First, chemicals must be specifically labeled. Second, rooms or areas where the materials are located must be specifically labeled. In this case, the code essentially requires placarding as defined in Section 5003.5, which references NFPA 704.

407.4 Training. Persons responsible for the operation of areas in which hazardous materials are stored, dispensed, handled or used shall be familiar with the chemical nature of the materials and the appropriate mitigating actions necessary in the event of a fire, leak or spill. Responsible persons shall be designated and trained to be liaison personnel for the fire department. These persons shall aid the fire department in preplanning emergency responses and identification of where hazardous materials are located, and shall have access to Material Safety Data Sheets and be knowledgeable in the site emergency response procedures.

❖ This section requires training specific to the hazards of the materials located and used at a particular building or facility. As noted, the actions taken will vary based on the hazards associated with the materials. Additionally, this section requires specific persons to be designated as points of contact for the fire department. Having specific points of contact is critical because it eases planning and response procedures. These contacts also provide the fire department with specific persons who are more familiar with the hazards of the building or facility. The fire department is charged with responding to many different businesses within a community. Having specified contacts at facilities containing hazardous materials helps them prepare and respond.

407.5 Hazardous Materials Inventory Statement. Where required by the fire code official, each application for a permit shall include a Hazardous Materials Inventory Statement (HMIS) in accordance with Section 5001.5.2.

❖ An HMIS is further described in Chapter 50 but is essentially a document listing all the hazardous materials found on site. This documentation includes information such as the type and amount of specific hazards associated with the material and how it is used. All of this information can be very important for emergency planning and preparedness. An HMIS is necessary only if the fire code official specifically requires one. See Appendix H for further information on HMIS and HMMP preparation.

407.6 Hazardous Materials Management Plan. Where required by the fire code official, each application for a permit shall include a Hazardous Materials Management Plan (HMMP) in accordance with Section 5001.5.1. The fire code official is authorized to accept a similar plan required by other regulations.

❖ As with the HMIS, an HMMP is necessary only where the fire code official specifically requires one. This document is somewhat different from the HMIS in that it is geared to the layout of the building and the location and use of the hazardous materials. This document provides a better understanding of how the facility operates. This information in turn provides more detailed information to the emergency responders. This plan will also include such information as the location of aisles; the type and location of emergency equipment available; and location of specific shutoff valves and other operating equipment. The detailed requirements for HMMP are located in Chapter 50. See Appendix H for further information on HMIS and HMMP preparation.

407.7 Facility closure plans. The permit holder or applicant shall submit to the fire code official a facility closure plan in accordance with Section 5001.6.3 to terminate storage, dispensing, handling or use of hazardous materials.

❖ It is important for emergency responders to be made aware of the closure of a plant that uses or stores hazardous materials. First, closure means a readjustment in their planning. Second, the extent of the closure must be communicated so that the emergency responders are made aware of hazards that may still be present. Any hazards that are still present may potentially be more dangerous since the facility is now unattended; therefore, the building owner must develop a plan that is acceptable to the fire code official. In some cases, a facility will be only temporarily closed, which would mean maintaining a permit and continuing inspections.

Bibliography

The following resource materials were used in the preparation of the commentary for this chapter of the code:

Evacuation Planning Guide for Stadiums. Washington, DC: U.S. Department of Homeland Security, 2008.

SFPE *Engineering Guide: Fire Safety for Very Tall Buildings* (ICC and SFPE 2013).

Egress Design Solutions (Tubbs and Meacham 2005).

Part III—Building and Equipment Design Features

Chapter 5: Fire Service Features

General Comments

The requirements of this chapter apply to all occupancies and pertain to access roads; access to building openings and roofs; premises identification; key boxes; hazards to fire fighters; fire protection water supplies; fire command centers; fire department access to equipment; and emergency responder radio/communication system coverage.

Purpose

This chapter contains the requirements for fire service access to the property that is to be protected, including access roads, security devices and access through openings in the building.

The chapter also addresses fire fighter hazards, the requirements for a fire department command center and fire fighter access to equipment, such as fire suppression equipment, air-handling equipment, emergency power equipment and access to the roof. In addition, this chapter addresses the fire protection water supply.

Finally, this chapter addresses fire department emergency responder radio and communication system coverage so that emergency personnel can communicate during a fire or emergency.

SECTION 501 GENERAL

501.1 Scope. Fire service features for buildings, structures and premises shall comply with this chapter.

❖ This chapter contains requirements that will enable the fire service to respond to an emergency on the premises of a building or structure.

501.2 Permits. A permit shall be required as set forth in Sections 105.6 and 105.7.

❖ Permits must be obtained from the fire code official. Permit fees, if any, must be paid prior to the issuance of the permit. There are two types of permits: operational and construction. The operational permits required by this section are for the use or operation of fire protection valves and fire hydrants (see Section 105.6.15) or the use or removal from service of a private fire hydrant (see Section 105.6.39) The construction permit (see Section 105.7.19) allows the applicant to install or modify private fire hydrants. See Section 105 for additional information on permits.

501.3 Construction documents. *Construction documents* for proposed fire apparatus access, location of *fire lanes*, security gates across fire apparatus access roads and *construction documents* and hydraulic calculations for fire hydrant systems shall be submitted to the fire department for review and approval prior to construction.

❖ The integrity of the design of fire apparatus access roads and private fire hydrant systems is critical to successful fire department operations in protecting lives and property. Construction documents must be drawn to scale and clearly show the details of the indicated features in order for the fire department to properly evaluate fire service features and issue approvals. While this section is primarily for new installations, if a security gate was not on the original construction plans for fire apparatus access, this section reinforces that a security gate installed at a later time requires a construction plan to be submitted and approved prior to construction.

501.4 Timing of installation. Where fire apparatus access roads or a water supply for fire protection are required to be installed, such protection shall be installed and made serviceable prior to and during the time of construction except where *approved* alternative methods of protection are provided. Temporary street signs shall be installed at each street intersection where construction of new roadways allows passage by vehicles in accordance with Section 505.2.

❖ Buildings under construction are quite vulnerable to fire and other types of construction incidents, such as injuries from falling objects. Access roads and water for fire protection are essential for fire-fighting purposes. Temporary street signs are also valuable to emergency responders because the streets in new developments will most likely not be familiar to them or be on their maps.

Marked access roads and an emergency water supply should be in place before any large amount of combustible building materials is placed on site and before any construction is initiated.

SECTION 502 DEFINITIONS

502.1 Definitions. The following terms are defined in Chapter 2:

AGENCY.

FIRE APPARATUS ACCESS ROAD.

FIRE COMMAND CENTER.

FIRE DEPARTMENT MASTER KEY.

FIRE LANE.

KEY BOX.

TRAFFIC CALMING DEVICES.

❖ Definitions of terms can help in the understanding and application of code requirements. This section directs the code user to Chapter 2 for the proper application of the indicated terms used in this chapter. Terms may be defined in Chapter 2, or in another International Code® (I-Code®) as indicated in Section 201.3, or the dictionary meaning may be all that is needed (also see the commentaries to Sections 201 through 201.4).

SECTION 503 FIRE APPARATUS ACCESS ROADS

503.1 Where required. Fire apparatus access roads shall be provided and maintained in accordance with Sections 503.1.1 through 503.1.3.

❖ This section introduces the requirements for dedicated fire apparatus access roads serving new and relocated buildings in the jurisdiction. The requirements are to be established in coordination with the local fire service to accommodate the jurisdiction's fire apparatus and equipment. The requirements are intended to provide the fire department with sufficient access to buildings to enable efficient fire suppression and rescue operations.

503.1.1 Buildings and facilities. *Approved* fire apparatus access roads shall be provided for every facility, building or portion of a building hereafter constructed or moved into or within the jurisdiction. The fire apparatus access road shall comply with the requirements of this section and shall extend to within 150 feet (45 720 mm) of all portions of the facility and all portions of the *exterior walls* of the first story of the building as measured by an *approved* route around the exterior of the building or facility.

Exceptions:

1. The *fire code official* is authorized to increase the dimension of 150 feet (45 720 mm) where any of the following conditions occur:
   - 1.1. The building is equipped throughout with an *approved automatic sprinkler system* installed in accordance with Section 903.3.1.1, 903.3.1.2 or 903.3.1.3.
   - 1.2. Fire apparatus access roads cannot be installed because of location on property, topography, waterways, nonnegotiable grades or other similar conditions, and an *approved* alternative means of fire protection is provided.
   - 1.3. There are not more than two Group R-3 or Group U occupancies.
2. Where approved by the *fire code official*, fire apparatus access roads shall be permitted to be exempted or modified for solar photovoltaic power generation facilities.

❖ This section establishes a requirement for a fire apparatus access road and the maximum distance from buildings or facilities to fire apparatus access roads. The provisions are intended to limit the maximum length of hose needed to reach any point along the exterior of a building or facility from a fire department vehicle. Large-area buildings may require a fire apparatus access road on all four sides. An access road is required to extend to within 150 feet (45 720 mm) of all portions along the exterior wall of the grade level story of each new or relocated building [see Commentary Figure 503.1.1(1)]. The 150-foot (45 720 mm) distance is based on the standard length of preconnected hoses carried on fire apparatus and is not intended to be measured to any point within the building.

A long, narrow building may require fire department access roads on two sides only, if all portions of the exterior of the grade level story are within 150 feet (45 720 mm) of the access road [see Commentary Figure 503.1.1(2)].

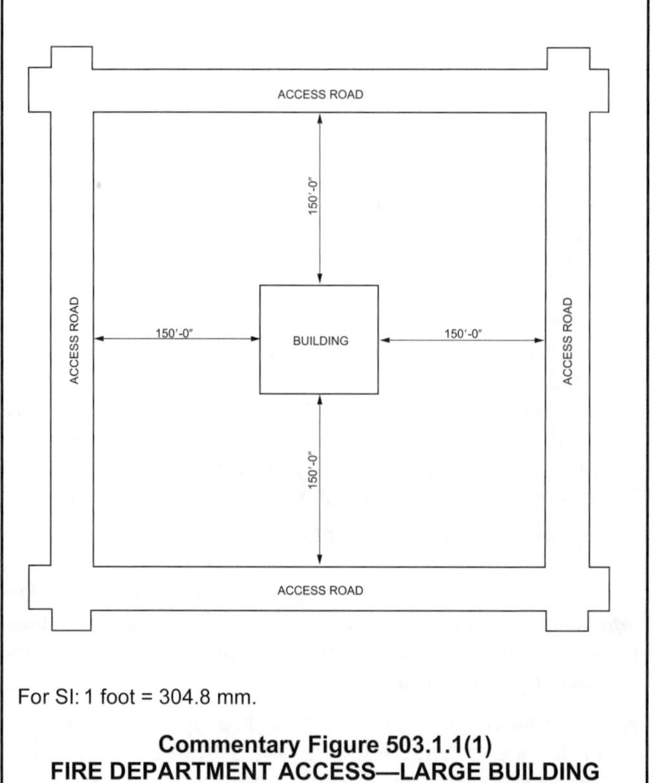

For SI: 1 foot = 304.8 mm.

Commentary Figure 503.1.1(1)
FIRE DEPARTMENT ACCESS—LARGE BUILDING

Small buildings may require an access road on one side only, if the access road is within 150 feet (45 720 mm) of all portions of the grade level floor [see Commentary Figure 503.1.1(3)].

In a case where new construction creates an addition ("... portion of a building hereafter constructed ...") to an existing building, the new building as completed should be evaluated as it relates to compliance with this section because the new addition increases the fuel load and potential fire-fighting complications. An addition to a building may require the construction of a new fire apparatus access road or the reconfiguration of an existing fire apparatus access road. This is consistent with the prescriptive compliance method provisions of Section 402.1 of the *International Existing Building Code*® (IEBC®), which require that the "... existing building or structure together with the addition are not less complying ... than the existing building or structure ... was prior to the addition." This is also consistent with Section 1101.2 of the IEBC, which states, "An *addition* shall not create or extend any nonconformity in the *existing building* to which the *addition* is being made with regard to accessibility, structural strength, fire safety, means of egress, or the capacity of mechanical, plumbing, or electrical systems." In other words, an existing, nonconforming condition should not be made more nonconforming by construction of the addition. Note also that, since an addition is an increase in the area or height of an existing building, where a new building is erected immediately adjacent to an existing building, and they are separated by a fire wall constructed in accordance with Section 706 of the *International Building Code*® (IBC®), they are considered a separate building, not an addition to the existing structure. In that scenario, only the new building would be subject to this section. In any event, each case must be evaluated independently, especially if site topography or other conditions can slow or limit the response.

Condition 1.1 of Exception 1 states that the 150-foot (45 720 mm) distance may be increased, with the approval of the fire code official, where the building is equipped throughout with an NFPA 13, 13R or 13D automatic sprinkler system, as applicable. The code does not give the fire code official guidance on how much of an increase over 150 feet (45 720 mm) is reasonable. The fire code official must make the determination based on the response capabilities of his or her emergency response units and the anticipated magnitude of the incident.

The "alternative means" in Condition 1.2 of Exception 1 may include standpipes, automatic sprinklers, remote fire department connections or additional fire hydrants.

The Group R-3 facilities noted in Condition 1.3 of Exception 1 include one- and two-family dwellings and townhouses not falling within the scope of the *International Residential Code*® (IRC®); care facilities that accommodate five or fewer people; and congregate living facilities (nontransient) with 16 or fewer persons or congregate living facilities (transient) with 10 or fewer persons, among others. Group U occupancies are utility and miscellaneous accessory buildings or structures. Note that, since Section 903.2.8.1 requires that Group R-3 buildings be equipped throughout with automatic sprinkler systems, this condition is redundant with Condition 1.1. Note also that there is no exception for nonsprinklered buildings built under the IRC. See "Occupancy Classification" for the definitions of "Residential Group R" and "Miscellaneous Group U" in Section 202; the IRC Commentary, Section R101.2; and the IBC Commentary, Section 310.1.

Exception 2 addresses photovoltaic panel system/array power generation facilities and provides guidance to jurisdictions in determining if a fire apparatus road is needed for hazard mitigation or if it can be exempted. Consideration must be given to the

ACCESS ROAD
150'
150'
BUILDING
150'
150'
ACCESS ROAD

For SI: 1 foot = 304.8 mm.

Commentary Figure 503.1.1(2)
FIRE DEPARTMENT ACCESS ON TWO SIDES

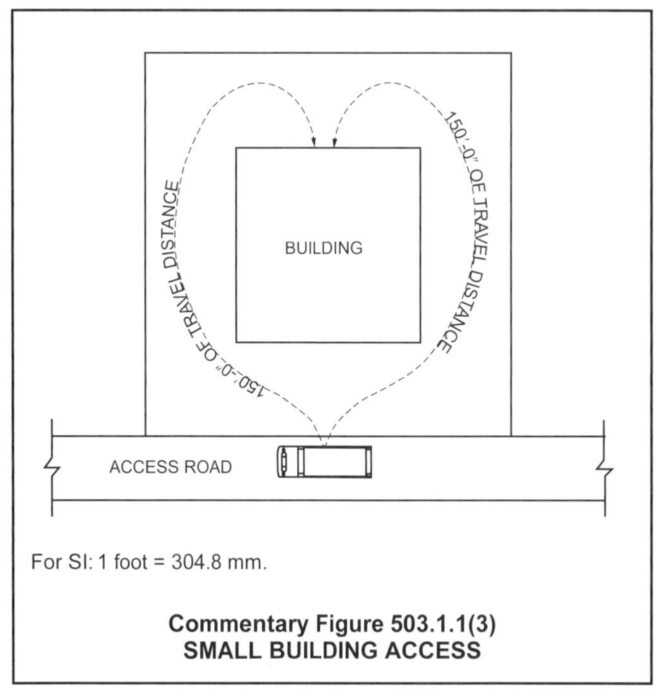

For SI: 1 foot = 304.8 mm.

Commentary Figure 503.1.1(3)
SMALL BUILDING ACCESS

purpose of fire apparatus access roads within these facilities and how the provisions would be applied. Several issues arise when applying Section 503 of the code to ground-mounted photovoltaic systems/ arrays. When considering the issues listed below, the fire code official should also consider other available code requirements that provide for appropriate hazard mitigation and risk reduction. Issues for consideration include:

1. Risk/hazard to be mitigated.
2. Risk/hazard to fire fighters or other emergency responders.
3. Interest of public safety and welfare.
4. Economics.
5. Intended access use.
6. Fuel load of the facility and adjacent areas that impact the facility.
7. Array configuration (tightly spaced, access aisles, height).
8. Actual hazard to public safety and welfare.

A question that often arises is whether code requirements pertaining to fire apparatus access roads are intended to be applicable to residential development sites upon which buildings are constructed under the provisions of the IRC. For information on this topic, see the commentary to Section 102.5.

Another question that arises is whether this section is intended to preclude locating a new building directly on a lot line, often referred to as a "zero lot line building." While it is true that some very large area buildings may require a fire apparatus access road on all four sides, this section does not specifically deal with exterior walls that may be located on the lot line in such buildings where the distance to a portion of that wall exceeds 150 feet (45 720 mm) from a fire apparatus access road. As such, the fire code official must determine the code's application in accordance with Section 102.9 and in consideration of the exception to this section.

In determining the application, however, it should be considered that, in order for the fire department access contemplated by this section to be effective, an exterior wall would need to have openings in it through which access to the interior of the building could be achieved by hose streams or personnel. In the case of an exterior wall constructed on a property line with a zero-foot fire separation distance, Table 602 of the IBC requires that such walls have a fire-resistance rating of between 1 and 3 hours (depending on the occupancy group assigned to the building), and IBC Section and Table 705.8 require that such walls be without any openings. As such, access to the first (or any) floor level of that exterior wall would appear to provide little or no tactical usefulness to the fire department, especially if code-complying access is provided to other sides of the building.

503.1.2 Additional access. The *fire code official* is authorized to require more than one fire apparatus access road based on the potential for impairment of a single road by vehicle congestion, condition of terrain, climatic conditions or other factors that could limit access.

❖ Additional access roads may be required by the fire code official based on his or her knowledge of traffic patterns, local weather conditions, terrain or the anticipated magnitude of a potential incident.

503.1.3 High-piled storage. Fire department vehicle access to buildings used for *high-piled combustible storage* shall comply with the applicable provisions of Chapter 32.

❖ Chapter 32 has special requirements for building access in occupancies with high-piled storage, but the requirements for fire apparatus access roads are the same as those required in this chapter.

503.2 Specifications. Fire apparatus access roads shall be installed and arranged in accordance with Sections 503.2.1 through 503.2.8.

❖ The dimensions of fire department access roads are based on the size, height and turning radius of emergency vehicles and the fact that emergency vehicles may be required to pass each other on the access road.

503.2.1 Dimensions. Fire apparatus access roads shall have an unobstructed width of not less than 20 feet (6096 mm), exclusive of shoulders, except for *approved* security gates in accordance with Section 503.6, and an unobstructed vertical clearance of not less than 13 feet 6 inches (4115 mm).

❖ The dimensions in this section are established to give fire apparatus continuous and unobstructed access to buildings and facilities.

This section requires that the unobstructed width of a fire apparatus access road must not be less than 20 feet (6096 mm). The intent of the minimum 20-foot (6096 mm) width is to provide space for fire apparatus to pass one another during fire-ground operations. The need to pass may occur when engines are parked for hydrant hook-up, laying hose or when trucks are performing aerial ladder operations. When an engine company is connected to a fire hydrant parallel to the curb using a front suction connection and using a side-discharge port on the pump, the horizontal distance that is needed to make a no-kink bend in the discharge fire hose can be considerable, especially when a large-diameter hose (LDH) is being used. The roadway width needed to accommodate such a common operational scenario would be the width of the apparatus plus the no-kink bending radius of the discharge hose, leaving minimal roadway width for other apparatus to squeeze by, if needed. Including adjacent road shoulders in the 20-foot (6096 mm) width measurement could yield substandard and inadequate driving surfaces for apparatus and, as such, shoulders are not to be included in the minimum width.

The minimum vertical clearance of 13 feet, 6 inches (4115 mm) is the standard clearance used for highway bridges and underpasses. The vertical clearance requirement would apply in cases where a building or portion of a building, such as a canopy or porte-cochere, projects over all or a portion of the required width of the fire apparatus access road. Conversely, if the full required width of the fire apparatus access road is provided outside of the footprint of the projecting building element, the vertical clearance requirement would not apply. It is not intended that all projecting elements be constructed with a 13-foot, 6-inch (4115 mm) vertical clearance, regardless of whether they encroach on the required width of a fire apparatus access road. Appendix D contains additional guidance on fire apparatus access road dimensions. It is important to note that the appendices are not considered part of the code unless specifically adopted.

503.2.2 Authority. The *fire code official* shall have the authority to require or permit modifications to the required access widths where they are inadequate for fire or rescue operations or where necessary to meet the public safety objectives of the jurisdiction.

❖ Fire departments respond to many types of emergency situations and the jurisdictions they serve may have traffic safety criteria that impact the design of access roadways used by emergency response vehicles. This section authorizes the fire code official to require greater, or to allow lesser, access-width dimensions based on the size and maneuverability of the anticipated emergency response apparatus, including mutual-aid apparatus from neighboring communities or agencies, among other considerations.

503.2.3 Surface. Fire apparatus access roads shall be designed and maintained to support the imposed loads of fire apparatus and shall be surfaced so as to provide all-weather driving capabilities.

❖ This provision does not specify a particular type of surface. It is written in performance language; therefore, the surface must carry the load of the anticipated emergency response vehicles and be driveable in all kinds of weather.

The term "all-weather driving capabilities" would typically require some type of paved or hard surface. Gravel would be prone to problems in areas subject to heavy rain or in snowy climates where plowing could reduce the gravel roadbed to mud very quickly. Alternatives to concrete or asphalt, such as interlocking pavers, may be used where approved by the fire code official. Jurisdictions may benefit from developing a local policy outlining specific design requirements for fire apparatus access roads to clarify local interpretations of the section. The policy should include local requirements for surfacing and include acceptable surfacing materials.

503.2.4 Turning radius. The required turning radius of a fire apparatus access road shall be determined by the *fire code official.*

❖ The turning radius of an access road should be based on the turning radius of the anticipated responding emergency vehicles and must be approved by the fire code official.

503.2.5 Dead ends. Dead-end fire apparatus access roads in excess of 150 feet (45 720 mm) in length shall be provided with an *approved* area for turning around fire apparatus.

❖ In consideration of the hazards inherent in attempting to back emergency vehicles, especially larger ones such as tower ladders, out of a long dead-end roadway, this section is intended to create a safer situation by requiring that dead-end access roads over 150 feet long (45 720 mm) be equipped with an approved turnaround designed for the largest anticipated emergency-response vehicles. Appendix D contains examples of dead-end turnaround configurations. It is important to note that the appendices are not considered part of the code unless specifically adopted.

503.2.6 Bridges and elevated surfaces. Where a bridge or an elevated surface is part of a fire apparatus access road, the bridge shall be constructed and maintained in accordance with AASHTO HB-17. Bridges and elevated surfaces shall be designed for a live load sufficient to carry the imposed loads of fire apparatus. Vehicle load limits shall be posted at both entrances to bridges where required by the *fire code official.* Where elevated surfaces designed for emergency vehicle use are adjacent to surfaces that are not designed for such use, *approved* barriers, *approved* signs or both shall be installed and maintained where required by the *fire code official.*

❖ Bridges and elevated surfaces must be capable of carrying the weight of emergency response apparatus and must be marked with signage posting the weight limit of the bridge or elevated surface. Evaluation of bridges should be done in cooperation with the appropriate local or state agency having jurisdiction over private or public roadway bridges.

503.2.7 Grade. The grade of the fire apparatus access road shall be within the limits established by the *fire code official* based on the fire department's apparatus.

❖ Generally, any grade exceeding 10 percent [e.g., greater than a 10-foot (3048 mm) rise in a 100-foot (30 480 mm) length] is required to have the approval of the fire code official. See Appendix D for additional guidance on fire apparatus access roads. Note that the appendices are not considered part of the code unless specifically adopted.

503.2.8 Angles of approach and departure. The angles of approach and departure for fire apparatus access roads shall be within the limits established by the *fire code official* based on the fire department's apparatus.

❖ The angle of approach is the angle between the ground and a line running from the bottom of the front tire to the lowest-hanging point directly in front of it, which is usually the front bumper of the apparatus. This angle gives an indication of how steep an incline the vehicle can clear when approaching that angle.

The angle of departure is the angle between the ground and a line running from the bottom of the rear tire to the lowest-hanging point directly behind it, which is usually the rear step/tailboard of the apparatus. Similar to the approach angle, this angle indicates how steep an incline the vehicle can clear when departing from that angle.

These design aspects of a fire apparatus access road are crucial to successful navigation by apparatus and must be tailored to accommodate each piece of fire apparatus of the jurisdiction. See Commentary Figure 503.2.8.

503.3 Marking. Where required by the *fire code official, approved* signs or other *approved* notices or markings that include the words NO PARKING—FIRE LANE shall be provided for fire apparatus access roads to identify such roads or prohibit the obstruction thereof. The means by which *fire lanes* are designated shall be maintained in a clean and legible condition at all times and be replaced or repaired when necessary to provide adequate visibility.

❖ Fire department access roads are normally designated on private property to provide fire service access; therefore, maintenance of the access roads, signage and any supplementary markings (pavement marking, curbs markings, etc.) are the responsibility of the owner of the property on which the fire apparatus road is located. Signage and supplemental markings should be in accordance with applicable local or state motor vehicle laws and should be enforced with the cooperation of the local police agency. Appendix D contains examples of signage. It is important to note that the appendices are not considered part of the code unless specifically adopted.

503.4 Obstruction of fire apparatus access roads. Fire apparatus access roads shall not be obstructed in any manner, including the parking of vehicles. The minimum widths and clearances established in Sections 503.2.1 and 503.2.2 shall be maintained at all times.

❖ To enforce "no parking" in fire apparatus access roads (fire lanes), the roads must be clearly marked. Some jurisdictions cite the building owner if the fire apparatus road is not properly marked and posted, and cite the vehicle for parking or blocking the access road if the access road is clearly marked. Other jurisdictions place the responsibility for marking the access roads, as well as the policing of "no parking" zones, on the building owner. In some states, motor vehicle laws may stipulate that fire apparatus access roads/fire lanes posted on private property may only be enforced by a traffic citation where an enforcement contract has been executed between the property owner and the local jurisdiction, that all markings be in accordance with the motor vehicle code and that the designated roadways be described in detail in the local "no parking" ordinances of the jurisdiction.

503.4.1 Traffic calming devices. Traffic calming devices shall be prohibited unless *approved* by the *fire code official.*

❖ This section prohibits the installation of traffic calming devices on fire apparatus access roads unless the devices are approved by the fire code official. What it doesn't do is detail how that approval is to be made within various jurisdictions. Each jurisdiction has its own traffic pattern emergency response challenges. The purpose of this requirement is to ensure that the fire department is part of this decision-making process. In most jurisdictions, the design and construction or review and approval of traffic calming devices is the responsibility of the municipal public works, transportation or engineering department. As a result, the fire code official and the appropriate engineering staff will need to work closely with one another to ensure that traffic calming devices, when approved, not only meet traffic engineering needs but also have the least impact on response time to emergencies. Traffic officials and fire code officials both have the responsibility to ensure that all public interests are properly considered in their decision-making process since both sets of officials have detailed regulations to provide for those interests. See the commentary to the Section 202 definition of "Traffic calming device" for further discussion.

503.5 Required gates or barricades. The *fire code official* is authorized to require the installation and maintenance of gates or other *approved* barricades across fire apparatus

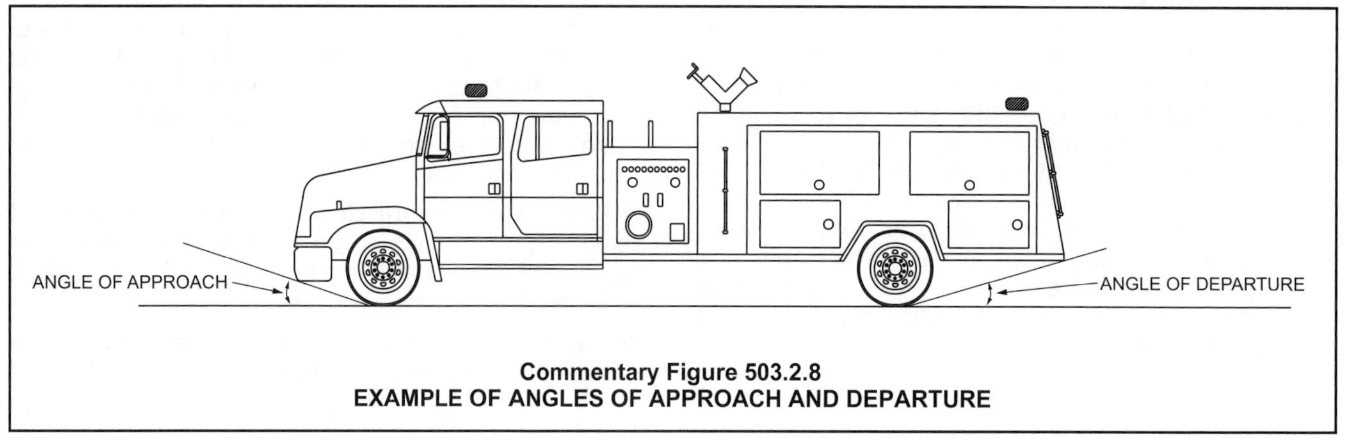

Commentary Figure 503.2.8
EXAMPLE OF ANGLES OF APPROACH AND DEPARTURE

access roads, trails or other accessways, not including public streets, alleys or highways. Electric gate operators, where provided, shall be *listed* in accordance with UL 325. Gates intended for automatic operation shall be designed, constructed and installed to comply with the requirements of ASTM F2200.

❖ The fire code official may require the installation and maintenance of gates or barricades across fire apparatus roads to prevent unauthorized vehicles from blocking or parking in the access road. The design and dimensions of the gates or barricades must be approved by the fire code official. Additionally, the gate or barricade must be operable or removable by the responding emergency units to provide them with quick access.

This section also addresses an important public safety issue regarding automatic operation of vehicular gates. Protection is needed from potential entrapment of individuals between an automatically moving gate and a stationary object or surface in close proximity to such gate. Gates intended for automation require specific design, construction and installation to accommodate entrapment protection to minimize or eliminate excessive gate gaps, openings and protrusions identified as contributing to the hazard of entrapments that have historically caused numerous serious injuries and deaths.

This section references two appropriate standards that deal with automatic gate safety: UL 325 and ASTM F2200. UL 325 is an ANSI-recognized safety standard containing provisions governing gate openers. Gate openers listed to the requirements of UL 325 provide an improved level of assurance that safety requirements have been met for such openers. ASTM F2200 is a consensus document containing provisions governing the construction of vehicular gates intended for automation, and has been harmonized with the applicable provisions of UL 325.

503.5.1 Secured gates and barricades. Where required, gates and barricades shall be secured in an *approved* manner. Roads, trails and other accessways that have been closed and obstructed in the manner prescribed by Section 503.5 shall not be trespassed on or used unless authorized by the *owner* and the *fire code official.*

Exception: The restriction on use shall not apply to public officers acting within the scope of duty.

❖ The owner may secure the fire apparatus access road and restrict its use to emergency vehicles only, if warranted. If there is a need to secure gates or barricades, jurisdictions may require a padlock or key switch (on electrically operated gates) designed for the same key as key boxes provided in accordance with Section 506. Occasionally, electronically operated gates are required to be provided with a backup mechanism or breakaway feature in case the primary operating means fails.

The exception makes it clear that the securing of fire apparatus access roads is not intended to impede the legitimate and necessary use of the road by duly authorized public officers, such as police officers or other municipal personnel.

503.6 Security gates. The installation of security gates across a fire apparatus access road shall be *approved* by the *fire code official.* Where security gates are installed, they shall have an *approved* means of emergency operation. The security gates and the emergency operation shall be maintained operational at all times. Electric gate operators, where provided, shall be *listed* in accordance with UL 325. Gates intended for automatic operation shall be designed, constructed and installed to comply with the requirements of ASTM F2200.

❖ This section does not require that security gates be installed, but since they can affect fire department operations, their installation must be approved by the fire chief. Where installed, security gates must be operable in an emergency by the emergency response units and the means of operation must be acceptable to the fire chief. Electrically operated gates should also include a manual method of operation (also see commentary, Section 503.5.1).

This section requires ongoing maintenance of security gates so that ready access to the roadway may be accomplished. If gates are not maintained in a manner that prevents appreciable delay of emergency response, the fire code official has the authority to have gates removed because they would be considered an obstruction of the required roadway width as regulated in Section 503.4.

This section also addresses an important public safety issue regarding automatic operation of vehicular gates. Protection is needed from potential entrapment of individuals between an automatically moving gate and a stationary object or surface in close proximity to such gate. Gates intended for automation require specific design, construction and installation to accommodate entrapment protection to minimize or eliminate excessive gate gaps, openings and protrusions identified as contributing to the hazard of entrapments that have historically caused numerous serious injuries and deaths.

This section references two appropriate standards that deal with automatic gate safety: UL 325 and ASTM F2200. UL 325 is an ANSI-recognized safety standard containing provisions governing gate openers. Gate openers listed to the requirements of UL 325 provide an improved level of assurance that safety requirements have been met for such openers. ASTM F2200 is a consensus document containing provisions governing the construction of vehicular gates intended for automation, and has been harmonized with the applicable provisions of UL 325.

SECTION 504 ACCESS TO BUILDING OPENINGS AND ROOFS

504.1 Required access. Exterior doors and openings required by this code or the *International Building Code* shall be maintained readily accessible for emergency access by the fire department. An *approved* access walkway leading from fire apparatus access roads to exterior openings shall be provided where required by the *fire code official.*

❖ The exterior openings referred to in this section are typically exit discharge doors, since such openings provide fire department access directly into the building or to a fire-resistance-rated enclosure from which to operate in multiple-story buildings. This section also includes access openings for rack or high-piled storage buildings required by Section 3206.7. Under certain circumstances, in order for emergency response personnel to get equipment from the emergency apparatus to the building, the fire code official is authorized to require approved walkways from the apparatus access road to the building openings on grade level.

504.2 Maintenance of exterior doors and openings. Exterior doors and their function shall not be eliminated without prior approval. Exterior doors that have been rendered nonfunctional and that retain a functional door exterior appearance shall have a sign affixed to the exterior side of the door with the words THIS DOOR BLOCKED. The sign shall consist of letters having a principal stroke of not less than $^{3}/_{4}$ inch (19.1 mm) wide and not less than 6 inches (152 mm) high on a contrasting background. Required fire department access doors shall not be obstructed or eliminated. Exit and *exit access* doors shall comply with Chapter 10. Access doors for *high-piled combustible storage* shall comply with Section 3206.7.

❖ This section pertains to emergency access openings and to all exterior doors that have a functional appearance from the outside but are not operable. Doors that are part of the required means of egress or that are required by Section 3206.7 must not be rendered unusable or blocked. Only doors not required by the code or the IBC for means of egress may be blocked or made unusable. Even then, they must be marked from the outside so that emergency personnel will not attempt to use them.

504.3 Stairway access to roof. New buildings four or more stories above grade plane, except those with a roof slope greater than four units vertical in 12 units horizontal (33.3-percent slope), shall be provided with a *stairway* to the roof. *Stairway* access to the roof shall be in accordance with Section 1011.12. Such *stairway* shall be marked at street and floor levels with a sign indicating that the *stairway* continues to the roof. Where roofs are used for roof gardens or for other purposes, *stairways* shall be provided as required for such occupancy classification.

❖ The stairway to the roof, required by this section, must comply with Sections 1011.12 through 1011.12.2. If the stairway to the roof serves as a means of egress from an occupied roof, then the stairway must be equipped with all the components of an exit stairway, such as the required riser and tread dimensions, handrails, etc. If the stairway to the roof is not required for roof egress, Section 1011.14 allows the stairway segment from the top floor to the roof to be an alternating tread device. The access to the roof is required for fire fighter use and not the general public; therefore, the door leading to the roof may be secured in a manner approved by the fire code official with due consideration given to whether the door is an egress element for the roof. These provisions apply only to new buildings four or more stories in height (see commentaries, Sections 1011.12 and 1023.9).

SECTION 505 PREMISES IDENTIFICATION

505.1 Address identification. New and existing buildings shall be provided with *approved* address identification. The address identification shall be legible and placed in a position that is visible from the street or road fronting the property. Address identification characters shall contrast with their background. Address numbers shall be Arabic numbers or alphabetical letters. Numbers shall not be spelled out. Each character shall be not less than 4 inches (102 mm) high with a minimum stroke width of $^{1}/_{2}$ inch (12.7 mm). Where required by the *fire code official*, address identification shall be provided in additional *approved* locations to facilitate emergency response. Where access is by means of a private road and the building cannot be viewed from the *public way*, a monument, pole or other sign or means shall be used to identify the structure. Address identification shall be maintained.

❖ Buildings must be provided and maintained with address identification that is easily identifiable by emergency responders from the emergency response vehicle. This should include the backs of buildings that face alleys or roads, since the emergency response unit may often be directed to the back entrance to a building, such as in a strip shopping center. The back door of each tenant space should have the numerical address and store name on or above the door.

This section also provides the fire code official with the authority to require additional address locations for facilities with unusual or problematic configurations, such as college or hospital campuses, strip malls, business parks, apartment complexes and other complex properties where identification of buildings is essential to emergency responders. The additional requirements proposed by the added language will assist various emergency responders in identifying specific addresses when an emergency response from locations other than the primary access point is required.

There are also situations where a building's setback from the street is so large that the building itself may not even be visible to emergency responders. In such circumstances, this section requires that the road or driveway giving access to the building be marked to assist emergency responders in promptly identifying their access. It is important that such remote markings be reviewed and approved by the fire code official prior to installation.

505.2 Street or road signs. Streets and roads shall be identified with *approved* signs. Temporary signs shall be installed at each street intersection when construction of new roadways allows passage by vehicles. Signs shall be of an *approved* size, weather resistant and be maintained until replaced by permanent signs.

❖ The names of streets in new developments may not be on maps, making them hard for emergency responders to find. Temporary street signs must be installed before construction begins and replaced later with permanent signs.

SECTION 506
KEY BOXES

506.1 Where required. Where access to or within a structure or an area is restricted because of secured openings or where immediate access is necessary for life-saving or fire-fighting purposes, the *fire code official* is authorized to require a key box to be installed in an *approved* location. The key box shall be of an *approved* type listed in accordance with UL 1037, and shall contain keys to gain necessary access as required by the *fire code official.*

❖ The fire code official has the authority to require special key vaults where, in his or her opinion, the need for rapid entry into facilities warrants it. The key boxes or vaults are located on the exterior of the building for ready access, and are openable with a special master key in the possession of the emergency responders. See Commentary Figures 506.1(1) and 506.1(2) and the commentaries to the definitions of "Key box" and "Fire department master key" in Section 202.

The section also specifies a level of security for key boxes. Where a rapid-entry key box is required, there is an obligation to make sure that the key box required or approved by the fire code official is secure to prevent the key box from becoming a security threat. This section addresses the issue of security by requiring an approved key box to be listed in accordance with UL 1037. The major key box manufacturers have their rapid entry devices listed under this standard.

Section 506.1 is a discretionary provision based on the jurisdiction's determination that the use of a key box is safer for fire fighters than performing manual forcible entry into a structure. If properly maintained in accordance with Section 506.2, a key box can also lower property losses because it expedites the entry of fire fighters into a structure without necessitating the damage associated with forcing entry. The decision for the use of key boxes rests solely with the fire code official.

506.1.1 Locks. An *approved* lock shall be installed on gates or similar barriers where required by the *fire code official.*

❖ The key box suppliers also have special padlocks and electronic key-operated switches that are controlled by the same fire department master key that opens the key vaults. These padlocks can be required by the fire code official for security gates (also see commentaries, Sections 503.5, 503.5.1 and 503.6). The key-activated electronic switches may also be required for the control of certain equipment in the building, such as smoke control equipment, or to shut down a dangerous process.

Commentary Figure 506.1(1)
SURFACE-MOUNTED KEY BOX
(Photo courtesy of Knox Company)

Commentary Figure 506.1(2)
RECESSED-MOUNTED KEY BOX
(Photo courtesy of Knox Company)

506.1.2 Key boxes for nonstandardized fire service elevator keys. Key boxes provided for nonstandardized fire service elevator keys shall comply with Section 506.1 and all of the following:

1. The key box shall be compatible with an existing rapid entry key box system in use in the jurisdiction and *approved* by the *fire code official*.
2. The front cover shall be permanently labeled with the words "Fire Department Use Only—Elevator Keys."
3. The key box shall be mounted at each elevator bank at the lobby nearest to the lowest level of fire department access.
4. The key box shall be mounted 5 feet 6 inches (1676 mm) above the finished floor to the right side of the elevator bank.
5. Contents of the key box are limited to fire service elevator keys. Additional elevator access tools, keys and information pertinent to emergency planning or elevator access shall be permitted where authorized by the *fire code official*.
6. In buildings with two or more elevator banks, a single key box shall be permitted to be used where such elevator banks are separated by not more than 30 feet (9144 mm). Additional key boxes shall be provided for each individual elevator or elevator bank separated by more than 30 feet (9144 mm).

Exception: A single key box shall be permitted to be located adjacent to a *fire command center* or the nonstandard fire service elevator key shall be permitted to be secured in a key box used for other purposes and located in accordance with Section 506.1.

❖ Many jurisdictions have elevators built prior to the introduction of a standardized elevator key and, as a result, each building with an elevator requires its own elevator key. The key is most likely to be based on the model of the elevator and the year it was manufactured. This section sets forth requirements to assist jurisdictions in managing the issue of having different elevator keys in different buildings. These provisions specify where the key box is to be located inside the building and require it to be compatible with the rapid-entry existing key boxes that may already be in use in the jurisdiction. The exception allows key box installation adjacent to a fire command center or in other locations where approved by the fire code official. See the commentaries to Sections 607.8 through 607.8.4 for a discussion of standardized fire service elevator keys.

506.2 Key box maintenance. The operator of the building shall immediately notify the *fire code official* and provide the new key where a lock is changed or rekeyed. The key to such lock shall be secured in the key box.

❖ In most cases, the owner of a building cannot open the key vault or box and must call the fire code official to have someone open it to replace keys that have been changed. The building owner is responsible for maintaining the key box, as well as keeping the keys inside the box current.

SECTION 507
FIRE PROTECTION WATER SUPPLIES

507.1 Required water supply. An *approved* water supply capable of supplying the required fire flow for fire protection shall be provided to premises on which facilities, buildings or portions of buildings are hereafter constructed or moved into or within the jurisdiction.

❖ This section requires that adequate fire protection water be provided to premises on which new buildings are constructed or onto which a building is moved, from either outside of the jurisdiction or another location within the jurisdiction. Note that this section states that the water supply must be capable of supplying the required fire flow to the premises; however, the means by which the fire flow is supplied is determined by the policies of the jurisdiction, such as a pumper taking suction from a hydrant, tanker or lake (also see Appendices B and C for further information on fire flows and fire hydrants). It is important to note that the appendices are not considered part of the code unless specifically adopted. The phrase "... hereafter constructed or moved ..." used in this section (and in Appendices B and C, if duly adopted) limits the application of water supply provisions to only newly erected or relocated buildings, as opposed to existing buildings or existing remodeled buildings.

A question that often arises is whether the code's regulations pertaining to fire protection water supply are intended to be applicable to one- and two-family residential development sites on which buildings are constructed under the provisions of the IRC. The IRC is intended to be a stand-alone code for the construction of detached one- and two-family dwellings and townhouses not more than three stories in height. As such, all of the provisions for the construction of buildings of those descriptions are to be regulated exclusively by the IRC and not by another I-Code. However, the IRC applies only to the construction of the structures of those buildings and not to the development of the site on which such structures are built. Accordingly, where this code is adopted, its fire protection water supply provisions (including specifically adopted related appendices) apply. This code's requirements address only land development requirements for providing fire protection water supply to residential sites on the same basis as to the rest of the community (also see commentaries, Sections 102.5 and 503.1.1).

507.2 Type of water supply. A water supply shall consist of reservoirs, pressure tanks, elevated tanks, water mains or other fixed systems capable of providing the required fire flow.

❖ A good water supply consists of an adequate source of water, distribution system and proper pressure for delivery. If the water source is not reliable, it should not be considered as an acceptable water supply.

507.2.1 Private fire service mains. Private fire service mains and appurtenances shall be installed in accordance with NFPA 24.

❖ Private fire service mains are often installed on private property where facilities are located well away from municipal water distribution systems. Private hydrants may not be installed on mains less than 6 inches (152 mm) in diameter (see Section 5.2.1 of NFPA 24). Where installed, private fire service mains, private hydrants, control valves, hose houses and related equipment must be installed and maintained in accordance with NFPA 24. Private (yard) hydrants may be tested, painted and marked in accordance with NFPA 291 where approved by the fire code official and the fire department.

507.2.2 Water tanks. Water tanks for private fire protection shall be installed in accordance with NFPA 22.

❖ Water tanks for private fire protection may be required where municipal water systems do not exist or are incapable of supplying sprinkler or standpipe demand, or where Section 403.3.3 of the IBC requires a secondary water supply for high-rise buildings in Seismic Design Category C, D, E or F. NFPA 22 and Section 1510.3 of the IBC govern the installation of water tanks on buildings. Pressure tanks must bear the label of an approved agency and be installed in accordance with the manufacturer's instructions.

507.3 Fire flow. Fire-flow requirements for buildings or portions of buildings and facilities shall be determined by an *approved* method.

❖ Appendix B of the code, which sets forth minimum fire flow requirements for one- and two-family dwellings and commercial buildings, offers one method for determining fire flow and its duration that could be approved by the fire code official. In areas that do not have a water supply, such as rural areas with no conventional water storage and distribution system, the jurisdiction may chose to utilize the methods contained in NFPA 1142, *Standard on Water Supplies for Suburban and Rural Fire Fighting,* the *International Wildland-Urban Interface Code®* (IWUIC®), or the ISO *Guide for Determination of Needed Fire Flow.* Appendix Table B105.1 bases fire flow on the type of construction and the square footage of the fire flow calculation area. All calculations in the table are based on a 20-pounds-per-square-inch (psi) (138 kPa) residual pressure. Note that the provisions of Section B103 provide for increases, reductions and specific alternative methods for determining flows. In addition to Section B103, Sections 104.8 and 104.9 also provide the fire code official with authority concerning modifications and alternative methods. See the commentary to Appendix B for discussion of the fire flow requirements. It is important to note that the appendices are not considered part of the code unless specifically adopted.

507.4 Water supply test. The *fire code official* shall be notified prior to the water supply test. Water supply tests shall be witnessed by the *fire code official* or *approved* documentation of the test shall be provided to the *fire code official* prior to final approval of the water supply system.

❖ Whatever type of water supply is proposed in order to comply with Section 507.1, it must be tested in a manner that will verify it is capable of providing the required fire flow. The water supply system must be tested and the contractor is required to notify the fire code official prior to performing the test on the system. The fire code official will make the final approval by either witnessing the test or accepting the certification documentation. NFPA 291 contains recommended test methodology.

If the water supply system includes private fire service mains, NFPA 24, referenced in Section 507.2.1, contains the testing requirements for private fire service mains, as well as a test certificate form. It should be noted that the test certificate form has signature blocks only for the building owner's representative and the installing contractor's representative. There is no place on the form for the fire code official's signature, nor should he or she expose him or herself to liability of any kind for the installation by signing the form.

507.5 Fire hydrant systems. Fire hydrant systems shall comply with Sections 507.5.1 through 507.5.6.

❖ Where fire hydrant systems are part of the approved water supply, the system must comply with this section.

507.5.1 Where required. Where a portion of the facility or building hereafter constructed or moved into or within the jurisdiction is more than 400 feet (122 m) from a hydrant on a fire apparatus access road, as measured by an *approved* route around the exterior of the facility or building, on-site fire hydrants and mains shall be provided where required by the *fire code official.*

Exceptions:

1. For Group R-3 and Group U occupancies, the distance requirement shall be 600 feet (183 m).
2. For buildings equipped throughout with an *approved automatic sprinkler system* installed in accordance with Section 903.3.1.1 or 903.3.1.2, the distance requirement shall be 600 feet (183 m).

❖ The intent is that not more than 400 feet (122 m) of hose will have to be laid out to reach all portions of the exterior grade level of the building. Each hydrant must be accessible to fire apparatus and the 400-foot (122 m) distance should be measured from the hydrant(s) to all portions of the exterior at ground level [see Commentary Figure 507.5.1(1)]. When on-site hydrants and mains are required to achieve compliance with the distance requirement, this section gives the fire code official the authority to determine and approve hydrant locations on the site.

This paragraph is not intended to prevent development in rural areas where fire hydrants are not available, as long as the fire code official has approved an alternative water supply. The alternative water supply could be a fire department water tanker or a static, all-weather water supply that is approved by the fire code official.

In recognition of the smaller relative size and fire hazard characteristics of one- and two-family dwellings and utility buildings, Exception 1 increases the 400-foot (122 m) distance to 600 feet (183 m) [see Commentary Figure 507.5.1(2)]. Note that the one- and two-family dwellings classified in Group R-3 are those that are not within the scope of the IRC. See Section 102.5.

In recognition of the proven efficiency of sprinklers in applying water directly on the seat of the fire for buildings equipped throughout with automatic sprinklers in accordance with NFPA 13 or NFPA 13R, as applicable, Exception 2 increases the 400-foot (122 m) distance to 600 feet (183 m) [see Commentary Figure 507.5.1(3)].

507.5.1.1 Hydrant for standpipe systems. Buildings equipped with a standpipe system installed in accordance with Section 905 shall have a fire hydrant within 100 feet (30 480 mm) of the fire department connections.

> **Exception:** The distance shall be permitted to exceed 100 feet (30 480 mm) where *approved* by the *fire code official.*

❖ This section provides correlation with NFPA 14, Section 6.4.5.4, which requires that standpipe fire department connections be placed within 100 feet (30 m) of a fire hydrant, unless otherwise approved by the authority having jurisdiction. However, that requirement is frequently missed where site work and approval has been based only on the fire apparatus access road and fire protection water supply requirements in this chapter. With the requirement now included in this section, the code user is directed to this requirement during the site design review stage and not as an afterthought as has often happened during the building permit site plan review. The exception provides design flexibility but protects operational needs of the fire department by requiring the fire code official to approve any increase in distance between the fire department connection (FDC) and the hydrant. Note that this requirement is not applicable to sprinkler connections since NFPA 13 does not have a distance requirement to a fire hydrant for connections serving only sprinkler systems.

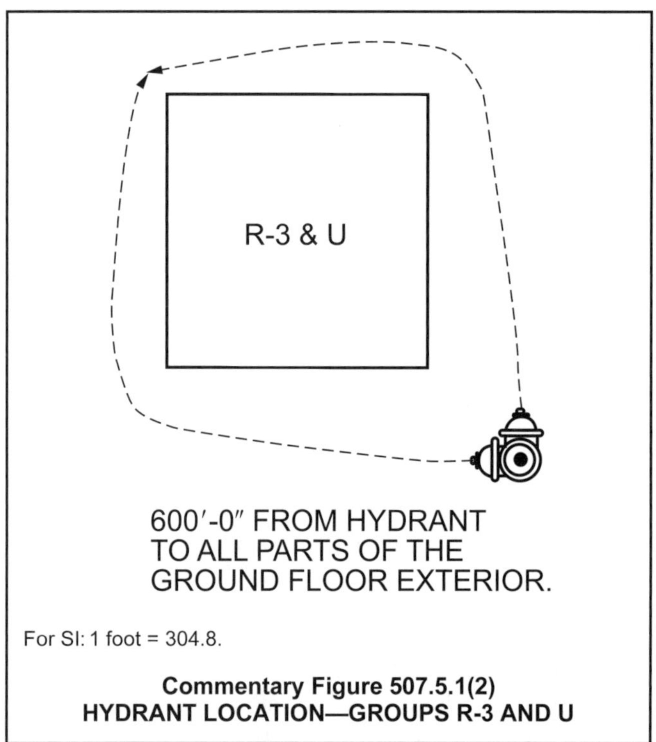

For SI: 1 foot = 304.8.

Commentary Figure 507.5.1(2)
HYDRANT LOCATION—GROUPS R-3 AND U

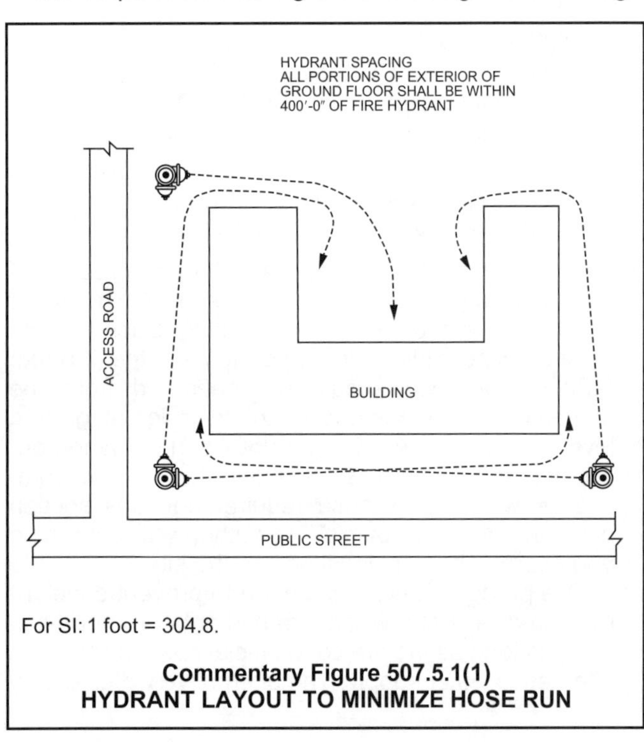

For SI: 1 foot = 304.8.

Commentary Figure 507.5.1(1)
HYDRANT LAYOUT TO MINIMIZE HOSE RUN

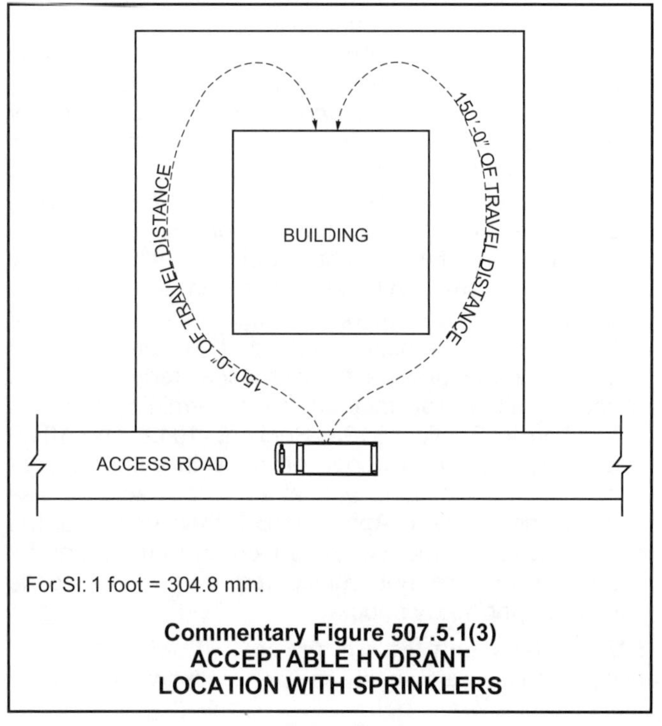

For SI: 1 foot = 304.8 mm.

Commentary Figure 507.5.1(3)
ACCEPTABLE HYDRANT LOCATION WITH SPRINKLERS

507.5.2 Inspection, testing and maintenance. Fire hydrant systems shall be subject to periodic tests as required by the *fire code official*. Fire hydrant systems shall be maintained in an operative condition at all times and shall be repaired where defective. Additions, repairs, *alterations* and servicing shall comply with *approved* standards. Records of tests and required maintenance shall be maintained.

❖ The fire code official has the authority to require periodic tests and to specify the frequency of such tests. The generally accepted procedure is to inspect hydrants annually for proper operation and drainage by opening and closing the hydrants and lubricating all threads. This section also requires that written inspection and maintenance records be kept. Such records should indicate the date and time and the name of the person conducting the inspection or maintenance. These records must be maintained by the owner and should be made available to the fire code official for review when requested. This requirement relieves the fire code official of the administrative burden of maintaining test records.

507.5.3 Private fire service mains and water tanks. Private fire service mains and water tanks shall be periodically inspected, tested and maintained in accordance with NFPA 25 at the following intervals:

1. Private fire hydrants of all types: Inspection annually and after each operation; flow test and maintenance annually.
2. Fire service main piping: Inspection of exposed, annually; flow test every 5 years.
3. Fire service main piping strainers: Inspection and maintenance after each use.

Records of inspections, testing and maintenance shall be maintained.

❖ NFPA 25 is the *Standard for the Inspection, Testing and Maintenance of Water-Based Fire Protection Systems*. Chapter 7 of that standard covers private fire service mains and Chapter 9 covers water storage tanks. This section also requires that written inspection and maintenance records be kept. Such records should indicate the date and time and the name of the person conducting the inspection or maintenance. These records must be maintained by the owner and should be made available to the fire code official for review when requested. This requirement relieves the fire code official of the administrative burden of maintaining test records.

507.5.4 Obstruction. Unobstructed access to fire hydrants shall be maintained at all times. The fire department shall not be deterred or hindered from gaining immediate access to fire protection equipment or fire hydrants.

❖ Nothing can be allowed to be placed near a fire hydrant, FDC or control valve that would prevent responding fire fighters from immediately recognizing the device and gaining access to it. Plants and shrubs on public or private property are probably the most common object that can make fire hydrants, FDCs or fire protection system valves virtually invisible to responding fire apparatus engineers. In residential areas especially, some homeowners do not like "that ugly piece of iron" (i.e., a fire hydrant) in their yard, so they plant all manner of vegetation around it in an effort to hide it—a clear violation of this section. On construction sites, fire hydrants or FDCs are often hidden from view and access by deliveries of construction materials randomly dumped at the most convenient spot on the site without regard for the need of the fire department to gain immediate access to hydrants or FDCs.

507.5.5 Clear space around hydrants. A 3-foot (914 mm) clear space shall be maintained around the circumference of fire hydrants, except as otherwise required or *approved*.

❖ Care must be taken so that fences, utility poles, barricades and other obstructions do not prevent access to and operation of fire hydrants. A clear space of 3 feet (914 mm) must be maintained around hydrants (see Commentary Figure 507.5.5) to allow easy hose connections to the hydrant and the efficient use of hydrant wrenches, spanner wrenches and other tools needed by the apparatus engineer. This section is not intended to allow any of the obstructions described in Section 507.5.4 to exist as long as they are kept 3 feet (914 mm) from the hydrant, FDC or valve.

Though not specifically mentioned in this section, it is also important that hydrants be installed with the center of the outlet cap nuts at least 18 inches (457 mm) above adjoining grade to accommodate the free turning of a hydrant wrench when removing the caps (see NFPA 24, Chapter 7, for further information).

507.5.6 Physical protection. Where fire hydrants are subject to impact by a motor vehicle, guard posts or other *approved* means shall comply with Section 312.

❖ Section 312 requires vehicle impact protection by placing steel posts filled with concrete around the

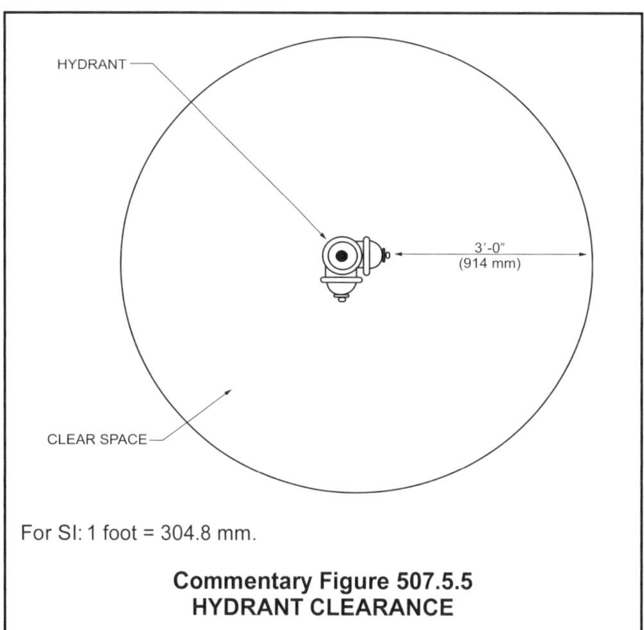

For SI: 1 foot = 304.8 mm.

Commentary Figure 507.5.5
HYDRANT CLEARANCE

hydrant (see Commentary Figure 507.5.6). Section 312 gives the specifications for the posts. Note that the provisions of Section 507.5.5 apply to the installation of posts or other protective features.

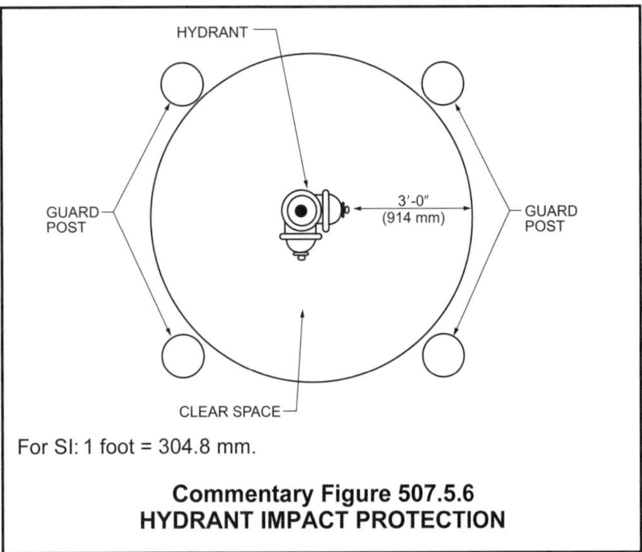

For SI: 1 foot = 304.8 mm.

Commentary Figure 507.5.6
HYDRANT IMPACT PROTECTION

SECTION 508
FIRE COMMAND CENTER

508.1 General. Where required by other sections of this code and in all buildings classified as high-rise buildings by the *International Building Code*, a *fire command center* for fire department operations shall be provided and shall comply with Sections 508.1.1 through 508.1.6.

❖ Fire-ground operations usually involve establishing an incident command post where the incident command officer can observe what is happening; control arriving personnel and equipment; and direct the resources and fire-fighting operations effectively. Because of the difficulties in controlling a fire in a high-rise building, an adequately sized, protected, readily accessible, separate room for this purpose within the building must be established to assist the incident command officer (see also the commentary to Section 202 for the definition of "Fire command center").

A fire command center is also required by Section 909.16 in buildings containing smoke-protected assembly seating to house the fire fighter's smoke control panel. Facilities with smoke-protected seating tend to be larger facilities that, at the very least, would already have a central security center that could also function as a fire command center where approved by the jurisdiction (see commentary, Section 909.16).

508.1.1 Location and access. The location and accessibility of the *fire command center* shall be *approved* by the *fire code official*.

❖ Because of its importance to fire suppression and rescue operations, the fire command center must be provided at a location that is acceptable to the fire department, usually near the front of the building near the main entrance, so that the first arriving command officer can access it quickly and undertake operations. Though this section references the fire code official, in many cases command officer and code official may be one and the same. In cases where they are not, it is expected that input from those who will fight fires and respond to emergencies will be accounted for in this decision.

508.1.2 Separation. The *fire command center* shall be separated from the remainder of the building by not less than a 1-hour *fire barrier* constructed in accordance with Section 707 of the *International Building Code* or *horizontal assembly* constructed in accordance with Section 711 of the *International Building Code*, or both.

❖ Because of its importance to fire suppression and rescue operations, the fire command center must be separated from the remainder of the building by 1-hour fire barriers and horizontal assemblies, including opening protectives, to protect the room, its contents and occupants from an incident in adjacent areas of the building, and to limit noise and distractions during command operations within the room.

508.1.3 Size. The *fire command center* shall be not less than 0.015 percent of the total building area of the facility served or 200 square feet (19 m^2) in area, whichever is greater, with a minimum dimension of 0.7 times the square root of the room area or 10 feet (3048 mm), whichever is greater.

❖ This section is intended to provide a minimum size and configuration of the fire command center that allows sufficient space for the necessary command personnel to effectively perform required tasks associated with a fire command center without interfering with each other. Fire command centers must be designed to accommodate several emergency response commanders wearing full protective equipment, provide space to review building emergency plans during incidents, collocate decision-makers within the incident command system (ICS), and interpret fire protection system and building system information generated by the features required by Section 508.1.6. This section also recognizes that larger buildings may need a larger fire command center. Therefore, criteria is provided to determine what size the fire command center must be. The fire command center must be a minimum of 200 square feet or .015 percent of the total building area, whichever is greater. This percentage is fairly low and would not amount to an increase of over 200 square feet until a building is over 1,333,333 square feet in building area. The following equation shows how the minimum building square footage is derived:

Total building area ×.015/100 = 200 square feet minimum

Total building area = 200 square feet × 100/.015

Total building area = 1,333,333 square feet

The criteria for a minimum width is also provided as .7 times the square root of the room area or 10 feet, whichever is greater. In most cases, the width would be 10 feet. The increase in width is necessary for rooms with the following area or greater. The following equation shows how the minimum square footage is calculated:

$$\sqrt{\text{Area of the fire command center}} \times .7 = 10 \text{ feet}$$

$$\sqrt{\text{Area of the fire command center}} = 10 \text{ feet}/.7$$

$$\text{Area of the fire command center} = \left(\frac{10 \text{ feet}}{.7}\right)^2$$

$$\text{Area of the fire command center} = 204 \text{ square feet}$$

Given the multiple uses of a fire command center, any smaller room would compromise the effectiveness of incident management.

❖ **508.1.4 Layout approval.** A layout of the *fire command center* and all features required by this section to be contained therein shall be submitted for approval prior to installation.

❖ The flow of critical tactical information into, within and out of a fire command center is, by its very nature, both high in volume and intense in nature, and has a direct bearing on the safety of building occupants and emergency response personnel at work at an incident. For that reason, the layout and arrangement of the fire command center must comport with the operational procedures of the local fire department to optimize the receipt, processing and dissemination of operational information and orders. Accordingly, the fire code official must review and approve the arrangement of the fire command center prior to the installation of any of the controls and features required by Section 508.1.6. Given the operational importance of the fire command center, the fire code official should work closely with the jurisdiction's fire chief to make sure that all operational needs are identified and met during the design stages.

508.1.5 Storage. Storage unrelated to operation of the *fire command center* shall be prohibited.

❖ Fire command centers are unique rooms in unique buildings and are strictly reserved for emergency management operations. As such, they must be neat and orderly at all times so as not to obstruct or limit access to all of the system controls they contain. This section supports that need by prohibiting the storage within a fire command center of anything not directly related to the function of fire command.

508.1.6 Required features. The *fire command center* shall comply with NFPA 72 and shall contain all of the following features:

1. The emergency voice/alarm communication system control unit.
2. The fire department communications system.
3. Fire detection and alarm system annunciator.
4. Annunciator unit visually indicating the location of the elevators and whether they are operational.
5. Status indicators and controls for air distribution systems.
6. The fire fighter's control panel required by Section 909.16 for smoke control systems installed in the building.
7. Controls for unlocking *interior exit stairway* doors simultaneously.
8. Sprinkler valve and waterflow detector display panels.
9. Emergency and standby power status indicators.
10. A telephone for fire department use with controlled access to the public telephone system.
11. Fire pump status indicators.
12. Schematic building plans indicating the typical floor plan and detailing the building core, *means of egress*, *fire protection systems*, fire-fighter air-replenishment systems, fire-fighting equipment and fire department access, and the location of *fire walls*, *fire barriers*, *fire partitions*, *smoke barriers* and smoke partitions.
13. An *approved* Building Information Card that includes, but is not limited to, all of the following information:
    - 13.1. General building information that includes: property name, address, the number of floors in the building above and below grade, use and occupancy classification (for mixed uses, identify the different types of occupancies on each floor) and the estimated building population during the day, night and weekend;
    - 13.2. Building emergency contact information that includes: a list of the building's emergency contacts including but not limited to building manager, building engineer and their respective work phone number, cell phone number and e-mail address;
    - 13.3. Building construction information that includes: the type of building construction including but not limited to floors, walls, columns and roof assembly;
    - 13.4. *Exit access stairway* and *exit stairway* information that includes: number of *exit access stairways* and *exit stairways* in building; each *exit access stairway* and *exit stairway* designation and floors served; location where each *exit access stairway* and *exit*

stairway discharges, *interior exit stairways* that are pressurized; *exit stairways* provided with emergency lighting; each *exit stairway* that allows reentry; *exit stairways* providing roof access; elevator information that includes: number of elevator banks, elevator bank designation, elevator car numbers and respective floors that they serve; location of elevator machine rooms, control rooms and control spaces; location of sky lobby; and location of freight elevator banks;

13.5. Building services and system information that includes: location of mechanical rooms, location of building management system, location and capacity of all fuel oil tanks, location of emergency generator and location of natural gas service;

13.6. *Fire protection system* information that includes: location of standpipes, location of fire pump room, location of fire department connections, floors protected by automatic sprinklers and location of different types of *automatic sprinkler systems* installed including but not limited to dry, wet and pre-action;

13.7. Hazardous material information that includes: location and quantity of hazardous material.

14. Work table.
15. Generator supervision devices, manual start and transfer features.
16. Public address system, where specifically required by other sections of this code.
17. Elevator fire recall switch in accordance with ASME A17.1/CSA B44.
18. Elevator emergency or standby power selector switch(es), where emergency or standby power is provided.

❖ The fire command center must contain all equipment necessary to enable the incident commander to monitor or control fire protection and other building service systems as listed in this section (also see commentary, Section 909.16). This room houses fire protection, smoke control and building system controls, as well as a work space for emergency responders. The room also contains schematic plans and a work table so that responders have the basic layout and geometry of the building and can identify locations of utility controls, standby or emergency power systems, and where hazardous materials are stored or used. Providing concise information in a uniform format is essential to fire fighters and emergency responders and improves their ability to utilize building systems to their advantage. This was confirmed during the National Institute of Science and Technology (NIST) investigations of the World Trade Center attacks on September 11, 2001. The Final Report on the collapse of the World Trade Center contained 30 key recommendations compiled by the NIST designed to address the building vulnerabilities learned in that tragedy. Three of those 30 recommendations embrace increasing situational awareness and emergency communications of first responders in large-scale emergencies. As a result of that investigation, this section includes an Item 13 that prescribes requirements for the Building Information Card (BIC).

The BIC is divided into multiple information areas and is intended to be formatted as a single form to provide a quick, concise source of information about the building. The code does not prescribe any particular format or layout for the BIC and does not have any limits on the level of information required to satisfy the requirements. It should be recognized that the BIC is intended to provide an easily understood and consistent tool to emergency responders who are taking control of systems in high-rise and smoke-protected assembly buildings. Jurisdictions should develop a policy to ensure that BICs are prepared in a standard, consistent format to avoid confusing the responders, and yet provide the minimum information required so they can correctly and efficiently utilize all of the building features. The number and types of features required by this section can create a large volume of data, thus reinforcing the need for an approved layout as required by Section 508.1.4.

SECTION 509
FIRE PROTECTION AND UTILITY EQUIPMENT IDENTIFICATION AND ACCESS

509.1 Identification. Fire protection equipment shall be identified in an *approved* manner. Rooms containing controls for air-conditioning systems, sprinkler risers and valves, or other fire detection, suppression or control elements shall be identified for the use of the fire department. *Approved* signs required to identify fire protection equipment and equipment location shall be constructed of durable materials, permanently installed and readily visible.

❖ In an emergency, it is vitally important that the fire department and other emergency responders be able to quickly locate and access critical controls for fire protection systems. Obstructed or poorly marked equipment can cause delays in fire-fighting operations while fire fighters locate other hose stations and stretch additional hose, for example. Valves and other controls are often located in rooms or other enclosures. Their location must be clearly identified with written or pictographic signs, which must be clearly visible and legible. Signs using the NFPA 170 symbols for fire protection equipment can provide standardized markings throughout a jurisdiction. White reflective symbols on a red reflective background are effective. For exterior signs, heavy-gage, sign-grade aluminum is recommended. Interior signs may be constructed of plastic, light-gage aluminum or other approved, durable, water-resistant material. As a general rule, fire protection piping, cabinets, enclosures, wiring, equipment and accessories are red or are identified by red or red/white markings. The manner of identification is subject to the approval of the fire code official.

509.1.1 Utility identification. Where required by the *fire code official*, gas shutoff valves, electric meters, service switches and other utility equipment shall be clearly and legibly marked to identify the unit or space that it serves. Identification shall be made in an *approved* manner, readily visible and shall be maintained.

❖ This section provides the fire code official with the authority to require utility identification for services serving multiple-unit or multiple-building properties, including facilities, campuses, strip malls, business parks, residential properties and similar locations where identification of utilities is considered essential to emergency responders. Note that this section does not prescribe any particular design requirements for utility identification markings. It should be recognized that the markings are intended to provide an easily understood and consistent tool to emergency responders who must secure utilities during emergency operations. Jurisdictions should develop a policy to ensure that utility identification markings are prepared in a standard, consistent format to avoid confusing the responders, and yet provide the minimum information required so they can correctly and efficiently utilize them. Note that the photovoltaic requirements in Section 1204.5 address signage to identify the rapid shutdown switches for these systems.

509.2 Equipment access. *Approved* access shall be provided and maintained for all fire protection equipment to permit immediate safe operation and maintenance of such equipment. Storage, trash and other materials or objects shall not be placed or kept in such a manner that would prevent such equipment from being readily accessible.

❖ This section requires immediate access to and working space around all fire suppression, protection, and detection system devices and control elements necessary for fire department use. It further prohibits obstruction of such equipment by materials or objects that may prevent such equipment from being immediately accessed by emergency responders.

SECTION 510 EMERGENCY RESPONDER RADIO COVERAGE

510.1 Emergency responder radio coverage in new buildings. New buildings shall have *approved* radio coverage for emergency responders within the building based on the existing coverage levels of the public safety communication systems utilized by the jurisdiction, measured at the exterior of the building. This section shall not require improvement of the existing public safety communication systems.

Exceptions:

1. Where *approved* by the building official and the *fire code official*, a wired communication system in accordance with Section 907.2.12.2 shall be permitted to be installed or maintained instead of an *approved* radio coverage system.
2. Where it is determined by the *fire code official* that the radio coverage system is not needed.
3. In facilities where emergency responder radio coverage is required and such systems, components or equipment required could have a negative impact on the normal operations of that facility, the *fire code official* shall have the authority to accept an automatically activated emergency responder radio coverage system.

❖ The provisions of Section 510 are concerned with the reliability of portable radios used by emergency responders inside buildings. This is in keeping with the philosophy inherent in the I-Codes that, when a facility grows too large or complex for effective fire response, fire protection features must be provided within the building. While modeling and other techniques may provide a good prediction as to whether a building will interfere with radio communications, the reality is that it is unknown if a building will need to install any type of radio system enhancements until after the building is constructed. Determining factors may include construction type, shadows of other buildings, size of the structure, and use of building products such as low-emission glass. Though this section does not offer specific types of buildings that should be targeted, discussions with public safety radio professionals found that, based on current radio technologies, these requirements should be applied in any building with one or more basements or below-grade building levels, underground buildings or buildings more than five stories in height.

Emergency responders use portable radios to communicate with other emergency responders, the incident commander and the public safety communications center. Building construction features and materials can absorb or block the radio frequency energy used to carry the signals inside or outside the building. Blockage or absorption of the radio frequency signal can prevent a critical message from an emergency responder from being received and acknowledged. Depending on the incident, this loss of information can place other emergency responders in greater danger, or may prevent an injured or disoriented emergency responder from communicating for assistance. The requirements apply to analog or digital radio systems and are applicable to all buildings.

This section requires that all buildings have approved radio coverage for emergency responders within the building. Approved radio coverage is based on the ability of the existing public safety communications system to transmit a signal inside and outside the building.

Where testing using the existing public safety communications system finds that the signal strengths are not satisfactory, Exception 1 allows for the alternative installation of a wired communication system in accordance with Section 907.2.12.2, which requires that such a system be designed in accordance with NFPA 72. When applying this exception, the concurrent approval of fire and building code officials is required.

Where testing using the existing public safety communications system finds that the signal strengths are satisfactory, Exception 2 allows the fire code official to waive the requirements when it is determined that emergency responder radio coverage is not needed. This exception does not give any criteria as to buildings that can be exempted. However, discussions with public safety radio professionals found that, based on current radio technologies, most wood frame or mixed construction Group R-1 and R-2 occupancies, single-family dwellings, townhomes and buildings with an area less than 50,000 square feet (4645 m^2) without basements, should engender little concern for loss of radio signal strength inside the building or an inability to transmit to an outdoor receiver.

Exception 3 provides a means for the fire code official to allow the installation of a manual or automatic switch that turns on the emergency responder radio coverage system (ERRCS) when it is needed. These systems allow emergency responders to operate their radios inside telephone central offices (COs) or similar occupancies without disrupting telephone network operations, including calls for service to a jurisdiction's public safety answering point via 9-1-1. Exception 3 also recognizes that operating public safety radio systems in certain buildings with electronic equipment sensitive to radio frequency (RF) energy can cause damage to the equipment, or worse, impact the operations of a local or regional computer network. One such occupancy is a telephone CO, which is where landline and cellular telephone signals are received and dispatched to the recipient caller. It is not uncommon for a telephone CO to be capable of receiving and processing more than 250,000 telephone calls within a 1-minute period. Telephone COs serve an important public safety function because they process emergency or information calls routed via 9-1-1 to a jurisdiction's public safety answering point.

Exception 3 was written to address testing sponsored by the major telecommunications companies and performed at UL. The purpose of the tests was to determine the impact of operating hand-held radios within a telephone CO. Telephone COs contain an array of digital and analog equipment that receives and routes telephone calls. Some of the equipment, such as digital switches that receive and route calls over landline and cellular circuits, is sensitive to the RF energy generated by hand-held radios. Testing by UL confirmed that portable radios programmed to operate in many of the public safety frequency ranges can cause severe service interruptions to equipment in telephone COs. The level of impact to the telephone CO equipment is dependent on the radio's wattage and its sphere of radiation at the antenna. Conversely, the impact of the telephone CO equipment and radio operation inside the building is also dependent on whether the equipment is electrically shielded or unshielded from stray RF energy.

510.2 Emergency responder radio coverage in existing buildings. Existing buildings shall be provided with *approved* radio coverage for emergency responders as required in Chapter 11.

❖ See the commentary to Section 1103.2.

510.3 Permit required. A construction permit for the installation of or modification to emergency responder radio coverage systems and related equipment is required as specified in Section 105.7.6. Maintenance performed in accordance with this code is not considered a modification and does not require a permit.

❖ A construction permit must be obtained in accordance with Section 105.7.6 prior to the installation of the ERRCS and for any modification or alteration to the system to ensure that the work is done correctly and any parts replacement will be compatible with the existing system components. Note that normal maintenance required for the system would not require a permit.

510.4 Technical requirements. Systems, components and equipment required to provide the emergency responder radio coverage system shall comply with Sections 510.4.1 through 510.4.2.8.

❖ This section simply introduces Sections 510.4.1 through 510.4.2.8, which are the technical requirements for the ERRCS.

510.4.1 Emergency responder communication enhancement system signal strength. The building shall be considered to have acceptable emergency responder communications enhancement system coverage when signal strength measurements in 95 percent of all areas on each floor of the building meet the signal strength requirements in Sections 510.4.1.1 through 510.4.1.3.

❖ This section introduces the minimum acceptable signal criteria that must be achieved and maintained throughout 95 percent of all areas on each floor of a building, as indicated in Sections 510.4.1.1 and 510.4.1.3.

510.4.1.1 Minimum signal strength into the building. The minimum inbound signal strength shall be sufficient to provide usable voice communications throughout the coverage area as specified by the *fire code official*. The inbound signal level shall be sufficient to provide not less than a Delivered Audio Quality (DAQ) of 3.0 or an equivalent Signal-to-Interference-Plus-Noise Ratio (SINR) applicable to the technology for either analog or digital signals.

❖ The focus of this section is the signal received within the building. Section 510.4.1.2 addresses the minimum signal to a radio on the outside of the building. The language provided for minimum signal strength into and out of the building in this section and Section 510.4.1.2 is performance based in that it simply requires that the signal strength be sufficient to provide ususable voice communication. A criteria is provided in the form of a minimum delivered audio quality of 3.0, or an equivalent signal to interference plus noise ratio (SINR). This approach aligns national standards with industry practices in delivering communications quality to the users of emergency responder systems. Utilizing a quality measure in dBm, as previous editions of this code have, only addresses signal strength, not interference of noise, and thus is an incomplete assessment of usable signal. Delivered Audio Quality (DAQ) refers to a range of usable voice parameters and is useful regardless of the modulation or system technology utilized. This allows a measure of how the signal will sound to the end user, which is critical to emergency operations. Again, this is the same criteria provided for minimum outbound signal.

510.4.1.2 Minimum signal strength out of the building. The minimum outbound signal strength shall be sufficient to provide usable voice communications throughout the coverage area as specified by the *fire code official*. The outbound signal level shall be sufficient to provide not less than a DAQ of 3.0 or an equivalent SINR applicable to the technology for either analog or digital signals.

❖ The criteria for outbound signal is the same as the inbound signal. See commentary for Section 510.4.1.1.

510.4.1.3 System performance. Signal strength shall be sufficient to meet the requirements of the applications being utilized by public safety for emergency operations through the coverage area as specified by the *fire code official* in Section 510.4.2.2.

❖ This section addresses data network performance for other emergency responder signals such as Long Term Evolution (LTE), which is part of the nationwide public safety responder network commonly known as FirstNet.

510.4.2 System design. The emergency responder radio coverage system shall be designed in accordance with Sections 510.4.2.1 through 510.4.2.8 and NFPA 1221.

❖ This section simply introduces Sections 510.4.2.1 through 510.4.2.8 as the system design criteria for the ERRCS. NFPA 1221 is the standard that addresses installation, maintenance and use of emergency services communication systems.

510.4.2.1 Amplification systems and components. Buildings and structures that cannot support the required level of radio coverage shall be equipped with systems and components to enhance the public safety radio signals and achieve the required level of radio coverage specified in Sections 510.4.1 through 510.4.1.3. Public safety communications enhancement systems utilizing radio-frequency-emitting devices and cabling shall be approved by the *fire code official*. Prior to installation, all RF-emitting devices shall have the certification of the radio licensing authority and be suitable for public safety use.

❖ In many cases, buildings cannot provide the necessary inbound and outbound performance levels without providing amplification within the building. This section stresses that additional amplification must be provided to achieve the necessary performance. There are several methods to provide the amplification needed by fire departments in structures identified as needing ERRCS. These enhancements need to be both approved by the fire code official and also through certification through the radio licensing authority. In the case of the US this would be the Federal Communications Commission (FCC). The wording is more performance based than previous editions to state more clearly that a variety of different methods can be used.

510.4.2.2 Technical criteria. The *fire code official* shall maintain a document providing the specific technical information and requirements for the emergency responder communications coverage system. This document shall contain, but not be limited to, the various frequencies required, the location of radio sites, the effective radiated power of radio sites, the maximum propagation delay in microseconds, the applications being used and other supporting technical information necessary for system design.

❖ In order to effectively install such systems, the fire code official must provide basic information such as the frequency range to be supported and maximum propagation delay. For example, a fire department may provide a requirement such as "The frequency ranges that must be supported shall be 806 MHz to 824 MHz and 851 MHz to 869 MHz." The fire code official will likely need to provide a reference to the local communications center or provide details on radio sites in the jurisdiction.

510.4.2.3 Standby power. Emergency responder radio coverage systems shall be provided with dedicated standby batteries or provided with 2-hour standby batteries and connected to the facility generator power system in accordance with Section 1203. The standby power supply shall be capable of operating the emergency responder radio coverage system at 100-percent system capacity for a duration of not less than 12 hours.

❖ This section requires secondary power to operate the equipment in cases where the primary building power must be shut down or is lost. There are two options provided: dedicated standby batteries or through a traditional generator-type source with 2-hour standby batteries. The standby power supply, regardless of how it is provided, must be capable of operating the in-building radio amplification system for a minimum 12-hour duration. The 12-hour value was selected to ensure the reliability of the signal boosters during long-term emergency operations such as response to natural disasters where utility-supplied electrical power is disabled. See Section 1203 for secondary power system specifics and standards. The 12-hour duration is consistent with NFPA 72 Section 24.5.2.5.5.2.

510.4.2.4 Signal booster requirements. If used, signal boosters shall meet the following requirements:

1. All signal booster components shall be contained in a National Electrical Manufacturer's Association (NEMA) 4-type waterproof cabinet.
2. Battery systems used for the emergency power source shall be contained in a NEMA 3R or higher-rated cabinet.
3. Equipment shall have FCC or other radio licensing authority certification and be suitable for public safety use prior to installation.
4. Where a donor antenna exists, isolation shall be maintained between the donor antenna and all inside antennas to not less than 20dB greater than the system gain under all operating conditions.
5. Bi-Directional Amplifiers (BDAs) used in emergency responder radio coverage systems shall have oscillation prevention circuitry.
6. The installation of amplification systems or systems that operate on or provide the means to cause interference on any emergency responder radio coverage networks shall be coordinated and approved by the *fire code official.*

❖ If a building is equipped with a signal booster, this section requires that the components of the signal booster be located in a National Electrical Manufacturers Association (NEMA) Type 4 cabinet. A NEMA Type 4 cabinet is designed to protect personnel having incidental contact with the equipment and to protect the equipment from falling dirt, rain, snow, windblown dust, and both splashing and hose-directed water. The standby power source is to be located in a NEMA Type 3R cabinet, which provides similar protection but with the ventilation necessary for most batteries. Type 3R does not require protection from splashing water and hose-directed water but is felt to provide an appropriate level of protection. The system is also required to be certified by the Federal Communications Commission (FCC) or other radio licensing authority. This document may be used outside the United States where the FCC is not applicable. Items 4, 5 and 6 provide requirements that limit the opportunity for interference and/or noise created by inadequate system components and their location and placement.

510.4.2.5 System monitoring. The emergency responder radio enhancement system shall be monitored by a listed *fire alarm control unit*, or where approved by the *fire code official*, shall sound an audible signal at a constantly attended on-site location. Automatic supervisory signals shall include the following:

1. Loss of normal AC power supply.
2. System battery charger(s) failure.
3. Malfunction of the donor antenna(s).
4. Failure of active RF-emitting device(s).
5. Low-battery capacity at 70-percent reduction of operating capacity.
6. Failure of critical system components.
7. The communications link between the *fire alarm system* and the emergency responder radio enhancement system.

❖ The system monitoring requirements were previously wrapped into the signal booster requirements. This location clarifies and provides detail as to what is required to be monitored. These requirements are those necessary to maintain integrity of the emergency responder communications enhancement system.

510.4.2.6 Additional frequencies and change of frequencies. The emergency responder radio coverage system shall be capable of modification or expansion in the event frequency changes are required by the FCC or other radio licensing authority, or additional frequencies are made available by the FCC or other radio licensing authority.

❖ Because of potential changes in public safety radio frequency bands, the code requires the capability for changing the frequency in the future. Note that since this code can be applied outside the United States, reference is made to the FCC or other radio licensing authority.

510.4.2.7 Design documents. The *fire code official* shall have the authority to require "as-built" design documents and specifications for emergency responder communications coverage systems. The documents shall be in a format acceptable to the *fire code official.*

❖ This information is readily available as documentation typically exists electronically where systems are designed and installed. Many jurisdictions utilize this type of information within their electronic records management systems and computer-aided dispatch systems. This section is consistent with other construction document requirements in Chapter 9.

510.4.2.8 Radio communication antenna density. Systems shall be engineered to minimize the near-far effect. Radio enhancement system designs shall include sufficient antenna density to address reduced gain conditions.

Exceptions:

1. Class A narrow band signal booster devices with independent AGC/ALC circuits per channel.
2. Systems where all portable devices within the same band use active power control features.

❖ The near-far effect occurs when too few indoor antennas are used to enhance coverage inside the building, creating an excessively wide dynamic range of operation. A portable device in close proximity to an indoor antenna, when keyed, can cause the talk-out amplifier's AGC/ALC circuit to reduce the gain, leaving other portables farther away at risk of not hitting the repeater site due to insufficient gain. If the near-far effect occurs, some public safety communications equipment will not function as required by the code and will leave responders at risk.

510.5 Installation requirements. The installation of the public safety radio coverage system shall be in accordance with NFPA 1221 and Sections 510.5.1 through 510.5.4.

❖ This section simply introduces the installation requirements for such systems. In addition, it also notes that such systems must also comply with NFPA 1221. NFPA 1221 is the standard that addresses installation, maintenance and use of emergency services communication systems.

510.5.1 Approval prior to installation. Amplification systems capable of operating on frequencies licensed to any public safety agency by the FCC or other radio licensing authority shall not be installed without prior coordination and approval of the *fire code official*.

❖ The installation of ERRCS in a building is similar to other building features where review of the plans and installation is required and covered under a permit. Part of the approval process for amplification systems operating on frequencies licensed to a public safety agency requires approval of the local fire code official.

510.5.2 Minimum qualifications of personnel. The minimum qualifications of the system designer and lead installation personnel shall include both of the following:

1. A valid FCC-issued general radio operators license.
2. Certification of in-building system training issued by an approved organization or approved school, or a certificate issued by the manufacturer of the equipment being installed.

These qualifications shall not be required where demonstration of adequate skills and experience satisfactory to the *fire code official* is provided.

❖ This section is to ensure that a qualified person designs and installs the ERRCS in the building. The qualification may be from a school program in communications or a manufacturer's training program. This section also allows the jurisdiction to accept a person or business upon adequate demonstration of skills and experience to the fire code official.

510.5.3 Acceptance test procedure. Where an emergency responder radio coverage system is required, and upon completion of installation, the building *owner* shall have the radio system tested to verify that two-way coverage on each floor of the building is not less than 95 percent. The test procedure shall be conducted as follows:

1. Each floor of the building shall be divided into a grid of 20 approximately equal test areas.
2. The test shall be conducted using a calibrated portable radio of the latest brand and model used by the agency talking through the agency's radio communications system or equipment approved by the fire code official.
3. Failure of more than one test area shall result in failure of the test.
4. In the event that two of the test areas fail the test, in order to be more statistically accurate, the floor shall be permitted to be divided into 40 equal test areas. Failure of not more than two nonadjacent test areas shall not result in failure of the test. If the system fails the 40-area test, the system shall be altered to meet the 95-percent coverage requirement.
5. A test location approximately in the center of each test area shall be selected for the test, with the radio enabled to verify two-way communications to and from the outside of the building through the public agency's radio communications system. Once the test location has been selected, that location shall represent the entire test area. Failure in the selected test location shall be considered to be a failure of that test area. Additional test locations shall not be permitted.
6. The gain values of all amplifiers shall be measured and the test measurement results shall be kept on file with the building *owner* so that the measurements can be verified during annual tests. In the event that the measurement results become lost, the building *owner* shall be required to rerun the acceptance test to reestablish the gain values.
7. As part of the installation, a spectrum analyzer or other suitable test equipment shall be utilized to ensure spurious oscillations are not being generated by the subject signal booster. This test shall be conducted at the time of installation and at subsequent annual inspections.
8. Systems incorporating Class B signal-booster devices or Class B broadband fiber remote devices shall be tested using two portable radios simultaneously conducting subjective voice quality checks. One portable radio shall be positioned not greater than 10 feet (3048 mm) from the indoor antenna. The second portable radio shall be positioned at a distance that represents the farthest distance from any indoor antenna. With both portable radios simultaneously keyed up on different frequencies within the same band, subjective audio testing shall be conducted and comply with DAQ levels as specified in Sections 510.4.1.1 and 510.4.1.2.

❖ This section provides a testing procedure to be followed upon completion of system installation and prior to acceptance of the system by the jurisdiction. The 95-percent coverage required is consistent with that required in Section 510.4.1. The building owner or agent is responsible for ensuring that the ERRCS is functioning properly prior to the building being occupied. Note that if there are problems as a result of the testing, the test area is to be altered to provide more specific data on the strength of the signal-boosting capability of the system. Testing results are to be kept on file by the building owner for annual testing verification. If the testing results are lost, a retest of the building shall be required to determine compliance levels. The testing identified in Item 8 will ensure that there is consistent, objective data for the fire code official to use to ensure quality and conformance and to maintain consistency with the DAQ requirements in Section 510.4.

510.5.4 FCC compliance. The emergency responder radio coverage system installation and components shall comply with all applicable federal regulations including, but not limited to, FCC 47 CFR Part 90.219.

❖ As with all radio systems, the ERRCS and its components must comply with all applicable FCC regulations.

510.6 Maintenance. The emergency responder radio coverage system shall be maintained operational at all times in accordance with Sections 510.6.1 through 510.6.4.

❖ This section simply introduces the maintenance requirements for the ERRCS for continued successful operation of the system.

510.6.1 Testing and proof of compliance. The owner of the building or owner's authorized agent shall have the emergency responder radio coverage system shall be inspected and tested annually or where structural changes occur including additions or remodels that could materially change the original field performance tests. Testing shall consist of the following:

1. In-building coverage test as described in Section 510.5.3.
2. Signal boosters shall be tested to verify that the gain is the same as it was upon initial installation and acceptance or set to optimize the performance of the system.
3. Backup batteries and power supplies shall be tested under load of a period of 1 hour to verify that they will properly operate during an actual power outage. If within the 1-hour test period the battery exhibits symptoms of failure, the test shall be extended for additional 1-hour periods until the integrity of the battery can be determined.
4. Other active components shall be checked to verify operation within the manufacturer's specifications.
5. At the conclusion of the testing, a report, which shall verify compliance with Section 510.5.3, shall be submitted to the *fire code official*.

❖ Signal boosters are tested to verify that the gain is equal to that produced during the initial acceptance. Testing must also include functional tests of the secondary power supply and an inspection of any other components connected to the in-building amplification system. The inspection report must be submitted to the fire code official and requires documentation that the amplification system complies with the requirements in Section 510.5.3. This section authorizes the fire code official to require additional tests when structural changes or modifications occur that could materially change the performance of the signal boosting system. This section also emphasizes that the responsibility to undertake this testing is that of the owner.

510.6.2 Additional frequencies. The building *owner* shall modify or expand the emergency responder radio coverage system at his or her expense in the event frequency changes are required by the FCC or other radio licensing authority, or additional frequencies are made available by the FCC or other radio licensing authority. Prior approval of a public safety radio coverage system on previous frequencies does not exempt this section.

❖ Where additional frequencies are needed to change or expand the coverage of the ERRCS, the building owner is the responsible person to ensure that the work is performed. Previous approvals of the system do not apply when changes are needed. Changes to the system are not exempt because of prior approval. If the change is needed, the work must be done.

510.6.3 Nonpublic safety system. Where other nonpublic safety amplification systems installed in buildings reduce the performance or cause interference with the emergency responder communications coverage system, the nonpublic safety amplification system shall be corrected or removed.

❖ With the public's reliance on cellular devices as a primary method of communications, many buildings are being equipped with cellular enhancement systems that provide improved coverage. If not properly designed, installed and maintained these nonpublic safety systems may cause interference and performance issues on the public safety radio enhancement system. This section provides the necessary tool for the fire code official to address interference of a required public safety system. Requiring correction or removal of the nonpublic safety system where it is causing interference or performance issues is vital to the public safety responders in the event of an incident.

510.6.4 Field testing. Agency personnel shall have the right to enter onto the property at any reasonable time to conduct field testing to verify the required level of radio coverage.

❖ Like all systems, ERRCS need to be tested to verify their continued sufficiency. Whether the test is an annual review of the system or an in-service familiarization test by an engine, truck or squad company, this section provides the ability of the personnel to enter the building at reasonable hours to test and operate the system. As with any inspection, the right of entry for testing the system is limited by constitutional constraints. See the commentary to Section 104.3 for further discussion on the right of entry.

Bibliography

The following resource materials were used in the preparation of the commentary for this chapter of the code:

2012 *International Code Interpretations*. Washington, DC: International Code Council, 2011.

Bunte, Leslie W., *Traffic Calming Programs and Emergency Response: A Competition of Two Public Goods*, unpublished thesis (M.P.A.), University of Texas at Austin, 2000.

Complete Revision History to the 2018 I-Codes: Successful Changes and Public Comments. Washington, DC: International Code Council, 2017.

Final Report of the National Construction Safety Team on the Collapses of the World Trade Center Towers. Washington, DC: National Institute of Standards & Technology, United States Government Printing Office, 2005.

US Fire Administration Voice Radio Communications Guide for the Fire Service—October 2008, FEMA.

Chapter 6:
Building Services and Systems

General Comments

This chapter focuses on building systems and services, potential related safety hazards and when and how they should be installed. In some cases, many of the provisions are located in other portions of the code. This chapter brings together all building system- and service-related issues for convenience and provides a more systematic view of buildings. The following building services and systems are addressed:

- Fuel-fired appliances (Section 603).
- Electrical equipment, wiring and hazards, including solar photovoltaic power systems (Section 604).
- Mechanical refrigeration (Section 605).
- Elevator recall and maintenance (Section 606).
- Commercial kitchen hoods (Section 607).
- Commercial kitchen cooking oil storage tank systems (Section 608).
- Hyperbaric facilities (Section 609)

Some of the sections specifically deal with installation while others deal with reducing the hazards from the use of the services or systems. For example, Section 604 notes that using too many extension cords on the building electrical system may present a fire hazard. On the other hand, the discussion of elevator recall and maintenance in Section 606 simply states when and how recall is required.

Purpose

As technology progresses and societal expectations increase, building systems and services become more complex and numerous. The use of computers has resulted in a more frequent use of uninterruptible power supplies and emergency power, which are often powered through the use of lead-acid battery systems. In the past, these provisions were scattered throughout the code. These various building services and system requirements have been brought together in this chapter to simplify the code requirements and increase the likelihood that these elements are properly addressed. Note that previous to the 2018 *International Fire Code*® (IFC®), standby and emergency power, photovoltaic installations and battery storage systems were addressed in this chapter as a building system. These provisions have been moved to Chapter 12. Chapter 12 addresses energy systems in general. Such systems are becoming more prevalent and evolving rapidly. Chapter 12 also addresses stationary fuel cell energy systems and capacitor energy storage systems.

SECTION 601 GENERAL

601.1 Scope. The provisions of this chapter shall apply to the installation, operation and maintenance of fuel-fired appliances and heating systems, electrical systems and equipment, mechanical refrigeration systems, elevator recall and commercial kitchen equipment.

❖ This section establishes the applicability of the chapter to a variety of building systems and services when they are being installed, during their operation and for long-term maintenance. Note that the provisions related to energy, including standby and emergency power, photovoltaic installations and battery systems, have been moved to Chapter 12, which is a new chapter dedicated to energy systems.

601.2 Permits. Permits shall be obtained for refrigeration systems as set forth in Sections 105.6 and 105.7.

❖ Only one system discussed in Chapter 6 requires permits: the operation of refrigeration systems. The permit for operation of refrigeration systems is intended to warn emergency responders that a potential hazard exists. This information will better equip them to respond to such a call (see commentary, Section 105).

SECTION 602 DEFINITIONS

602.1 Definitions. The following terms are defined in Chapter 2:

COMMERCIAL COOKING APPLIANCES.

CRITICAL CIRCUIT.

HOOD.

Type I.

Type II.

REFRIGERANT.

REFRIGERATING (REFRIGERATION) SYSTEM.

❖ Definitions of terms can help in the understanding and application of the code requirements. This section directs the code user to Chapter 2 for the proper application of the indicated terms used in this chapter. Terms may be defined in Chapter 2, in another International Code® (I-Code®) as indicated in Section 201.3, or the dictionary meaning may be all that is needed (see also commentaries, Sections 201 through 201.4).

SECTION 603 FUEL-FIRED APPLIANCES

603.1 Installation. The installation of nonportable gas-fired appliances and systems shall comply with the *International Fuel Gas Code*. The installation of nonportable liquid fuel-fired appliances and systems shall comply with this section and the *International Mechanical Code*. The installation of all other fuel-fired appliances, other than portable internal combustion engines, oil lamps and other portable devices such as blow torches, melting pots and weed burners, shall comply with this section and the *International Mechanical Code*.

❖ The code regulates the installation of portable gas-fired appliances and portable appliances fueled by liquids and methods other than gaseous fuels. The *International Mechanical Code®* (IMC®) and the *International Fuel Gas Code®* (IFGC®) do not cover portable appliances. The code also has provisions that apply to appliances that are not portable and use fuels other than gas.

603.1.1 Manufacturer's instructions. The installation shall be made in accordance with the manufacturer's instructions and applicable federal, state and local rules and regulations. Where it becomes necessary to change, modify or alter a manufacturer's instructions in any way, written approval shall first be obtained from the manufacturer.

❖ Compliance with the appliance manufacturer's installation instructions is a fundamental requirement of all I-Codes and those instructions are an enforceable extension of the code. Federal, state, county or municipal laws might supersede part of the installation instructions or could be applied in addition to the requirements in the instructions.

603.1.2 Approval. The design, construction and installation of fuel-fired appliances shall be in accordance with the *International Fuel Gas Code* and the *International Mechanical Code*.

❖ The code relies on the IMC and the IFGC for the coverage of appliance installations and contains only a limited number of requirements that apply in addition to those of the IMC and IFGC.

603.1.3 Electrical wiring and equipment. Electrical wiring and equipment used in connection with oil-burning equipment shall be installed and maintained in accordance with Section 604 and NFPA 70.

❖ Section 604 contains provisions intended to mitigate fire hazards and shock hazards associated with the use of existing appliances. NFPA 70 covers the installation of electrical appliances.

603.1.4 Fuel oil. The grade of fuel oil used in a burner shall be that for which the burner is *approved* and as stipulated by the burner manufacturer. Oil containing gasoline shall not be used. Waste crankcase oil shall be an acceptable fuel in Group F, M and S occupancies where utilized in equipment *listed* for use with waste oil and where such equipment is installed in accordance with the manufacturer's instructions and the terms of its listing.

❖ Different grades of fuel oil have different viscosities and chemical makeup. A burner and fuel mismatch could result in poor combustion, sooting and burner component failure. Oil burners are not designed to burn oil contaminated with chemicals of higher volatility. Appliances that consume used engine oil are allowed only in occupancies of low-occupant density (those without sleeping rooms) and where such appliances will likely be monitored and maintained by facility personnel. Used engine oil appliances use a specialized type of atomizing oil burner designed to burn dirty waste oil collected from internal combustion engine maintenance operations.

603.1.5 Access. The installation shall be provided with access to equipment for cleaning hot surfaces; removing burners; replacing motors, controls, air filters, chimney connectors, draft regulators and other working parts; and for adjusting, cleaning and lubricating parts.

❖ The IMC and the IFGC require access for the initial installation as well as for the life of the appliance. Safe operation depends on observation and maintenance, which depend on adequate access to the appliances. In order for the installation to be considered as providing appropriate access, personnel should be able to reach it without having to remove building elements or obstacles of any kind, or use climbing aids.

603.1.6 Testing, diagrams and instructions. After installation of the oil-burning equipment, operation and combustion performance tests shall be conducted to determine that the burner is in proper operating condition and that all accessory equipment, controls, and safety devices function properly.

❖ Testing of an appliance after installation is also required by the IMC and the appliance manufacturer's installation instructions.

603.1.6.1 Diagrams. Contractors installing industrial oil-burning systems shall furnish not less than two copies of diagrams showing the main oil lines and controlling valves, one copy of which shall be posted at the oil-burning equipment and another at an *approved* location that will be available in case of emergency.

❖ For large systems, the piping and control valve layout may be complicated and extensive. In the event of an emergency, facility personnel or fire fighters might need to be able to access control valves to protect piping and to limit the fire hazard.

603.1.6.2 Instructions. After completing the installation, the installer shall instruct the *owner* or operator in the proper operation of the equipment. The installer shall furnish the *owner* or operator with the name and telephone number of persons to contact for technical information or assistance and routine or emergency services.

❖ Appliances are more likely to be properly (safely) operated and maintained if the owner or operator is instructed in the operation of the equipment and given the necessary means to obtain technical and emergency services.

603.1.7 Clearances. Working clearances between oil-fired appliances and electrical panelboards and equipment shall be in accordance with NFPA 70. Clearances between oil-fired equipment and oil supply tanks shall be in accordance with NFPA 31.

❖ NFPA 70 requires working clearances around electrical equipment for protection of personnel. NFPA 31 requires clearances between appliances and oil-supply tanks to protect the oil tank from excessive heat and to lessen the fire hazard from any oil leakage.

603.2 Chimneys. Masonry chimneys shall be constructed in accordance with the *International Building Code*. Factory-built chimneys shall be installed in accordance with the *International Mechanical Code*. Metal chimneys shall be constructed and installed in accordance with NFPA 211.

❖ The *International Building Code*® (IBC®) regulates masonry chimney construction in Chapter 21. Factory-built chimneys are regulated by Section 805 of the IMC. Metal chimneys are distinct from factory-built chimneys, are industrial occupancy related (e.g., smokestacks) and are regulated by NFPA 211 (see IMC commentary, Section 806.1).

603.3 Fuel oil storage systems. Fuel oil storage systems shall be installed in accordance with this code. Fuel-oil piping systems shall be installed in accordance with the *International Mechanical Code*.

❖ This code regulates the storage of fuel oil. The IMC regulates installation of the fuel oil distribution piping system.

603.3.1 Fuel oil storage in outside, above-ground tanks. Where connected to a fuel-oil piping system, the maximum amount of fuel oil storage allowed outside above ground without additional protection shall be 660 gallons (2498 L). The storage of fuel oil above ground in quantities exceeding 660 gallons (2498 L) shall comply with NFPA 31.

❖ To limit the potential fire hazard resulting from oil spillage, the code sets a quantity limitation on unprotected storage. NFPA 31 requires protection, such as spill containment, for storage in excess of 660 gallons (2498 L). The storage of 660 gallons (2498 L) is allowed to be in any configuration of containers that does not exceed a total of 660 gallons (2498 L).

603.3.2 Fuel oil storage inside buildings. Fuel oil storage inside buildings shall comply with Sections 603.3.2.1 through 603.3.2.7 or Chapter 57.

❖ This section introduces Sections 603.3.2.1 through 603.3.2.7, which contain requirements for controlling the hazards associated with the storage of fuel oil inside of buildings. Fuel oil is defined in the IMC as "Kerosene or any hydrocarbon oil having a flash point not less than 100°F (38°C)." This would include Number 2 diesel fuel, which is classified as either a Class II or IIIA combustible liquid, depending on the refiner and the region where the fuel will be used. Number 2 diesel fuel is commonly used as a fuel source for diesel-driven electric generators.

The indicated sections have been revised to allow larger amounts of fuel oil in storage inside of buildings in response to increased fuel oil storage requirements for switch and data centers and similar telecommunications facilities. Such facilities are constructed to house large numbers of computers to serve as remote data centers for the protection of computer data or data switches for internet providers. To increase the likelihood that the data is always available, design professionals place a great deal of emphasis on the building's electrical power supply. These types of uses consume large amounts of electrical power. Accordingly, large generators are installed to ensure that service is not disrupted. These generators have fairly demanding fuel requirements. Consider, for example, that a single 2-megawatt (2 million watt) generator can have a fuel consumption rate of 3-4 gallons/minute under full electrical load conditions. As a result, these facilities require a large volume of fuel. The fuel storage is commonly located inside of a building because many of these facilities are located in commercial or other densely populated areas of a community.

603.3.2.1 Quantity limits. One or more fuel oil storage tanks containing Class II or III *combustible liquid* shall be permitted in a building. The aggregate capacity of all tanks shall not exceed the following:

1. 660 gallons (2498 L) in unsprinklered buildings, where stored in a tank complying with UL 80, UL 142 or UL 2085.
2. 1,320 gallons (4996 L) in buildings equipped with an *automatic sprinkler* system in accordance with Section 903.3.1.1, where stored in a tank complying with UL 142.
3. 3,000 gallons (11 356 L) where stored in protected above-ground tanks complying with UL 2085 and Section 5704.2.9.7 and the room is protected by an *automatic sprinkler system* in accordance with Section 903.3.1.1.

❖ This section correlates with Table 5003.1.1(1), Note i and Section 5701.2, Item 4 of this code and Table 307.1(1), Note i of the IBC. This section essentially provides flexibility to allow more combustible fuel in buildings beyond that allowed by MAQs for other code applications. These amounts are essentially exceptions to the maximum allowance quantities of 120 gallons for Class II liquids and 330 Gallons for Class IIIA liquids in Table 5003.1.1(1) and IBC Table 307.1(1). Note that these amounts would be allowed to be doubled where the building is provided with a sprinkler system throughout, in accordance with Note e. In order to apply this section, such fuel supplies are required to be connected to a closed fuel oil piping system. This would apply to most oil-fired stationary equipment in industrial, commercial and residential occupancies. Note that this provision applies only to the aggregate storage of fuel oil and does not include the capacity of the piping system.

Where the need for an aggregate indoor storage quantity of fuel oil connected to a closed fuel oil piping system exceeds the MAQs in Table 5001.1(1) and IBC Table 307.1(1), the allowances of this section may be applied. The first allowance is applicable to buildings that are not equipped with a sprinkler system throughout. Such buildings are allowed 660 gallons, which relates to previous editions. However, in the past, the limit was to both buildings with or without sprinkler systems. The second allowance provides credit to fuel storage amounts in buildings equipped throughout with sprinklers. Essentially, this is a 100-percent increase for an automatic sprinkler system, similar to what Table 5003.1.1(1) and IBC Table 307.1(1) provide. Both Items 1 and 2 list tank standards UL 80 and UL 142. However, Item 1 also references UL 2085, which is the protected above-ground standard. Item 3 addresses the allowance for using protected above-ground tanks where sprinklers are also provided. Sprinklered buildings or rooms containing such tanks are allowed increases based on the safety feature being provided. Item 3 allows 3,000 gallons where a UL 2085-protected, above-ground tank is used and sprinklers are provided throughout either the building or room. These tanks have extensive regulations in Chapter 57, and the listing requirements further document their safety. Included in the design requirements for these tanks are the ability to survive a 2-hour pool fire test conducted in accordance with the UL 1709 fire exposure protocol; a limitation that all penetrations must be made through the top of the tank (to avoid the risk of a gravity-fed leak that might be associated with a connection below liquid level); and that piping connected to the tank must be provided with anti-siphon controls where needed to prevent a siphon risk, among others. The safety level, which allows increased storage, is further enhanced by requiring the room in which the tank is installed to be equipped with an automatic sprinkler system. See the commentary to the Section 202 definition of "Tank, protected above ground" and Section 5704.2.9.7.

603.3.2.2 Restricted use and connection. Tanks installed in accordance with Section 603.3.2 shall be used only to supply fuel oil to fuel-burning equipment, generators or fire pumps installed in accordance with Section 603.3.2.4. Connections between tanks and equipment supplied by such tanks shall be made using closed piping systems.

❖ This section makes it clear that the fuel oil storage quantity limits in Section 603.3.2 are applicable only to fuel oil supplies for oil-burning equipment, generators and fire pumps and then only when connected to a fuel oil piping system supplying such equipment. Fuel oil piping systems are regulated by Chapter 13 of the IMC.

603.3.2.3 Applicability of maximum allowable quantity and control area requirements. The quantity of *combustible liquid* stored in tanks complying with Section 603.3.2 shall not be counted towards the maximum allowable quantity set forth in Table 5003.1.1(1), and such tanks shall not be required to be located in a *control area*.

❖ This section clearly states that the fuel oil quantities in Section 603.3.2, sometimes referred to as a "special quantity," are outside the scope of the maximum allowable quantity (MAQ) per control area provisions of Chapter 50, including any requirement to install the tank in a control area in accordance with Section 5003.8.3. Table 5003.1.1(1), Note i is also correlated with these provisions and indicates that the MAQ provisions of the table do not apply to fuel oil storage complying with Section 603.3.2.

The "special quantity" concept originated in an ad-hoc hazardous materials committee constituted by one of the legacy model code groups. As the committee developed updated regulations pertaining to flammable and combustible liquids, it concluded that a closed fuel oil storage and piping system feeding oil-fired building service equipment should not be penalized for providing sufficient fuel oil on site for long-term operation of such systems. Accordingly, the ad-hoc committee, using NFPA 31 as a guide, created the original provisions of Section 603.3 and its subsections to provide that relief.

603.3.2.4 Installation. Tanks and piping systems shall be installed in accordance with Section 915 and Chapter 13, both of the *International Mechanical Code*, as applicable.

❖ Section 915 of the IMC addresses liquid-fueled internal combustion engines, turbines and permanently installed equipment and appliances powered by internal combustion engines and turbines. Engine-driven electrical generators for private use are becoming more popular, as are engine-driven cooling appliances and heat pumps. Such equipment is also used to power fire pumps, generators, water pumps, refrigeration machines and other stationary equipment. Section 915 of the IMC also references NFPA 37, which addresses the fire safety of this kind of equipment including requirements for enclosures, controls, fuel supplies, exhaust systems, cooling systems and combustion air.

Chapter 13 of the IMC complements this code's fuel oil storage provisions and regulates the design and installation of fuel oil piping systems. The regulations reference construction standards for above-ground and underground storage tanks, material standards for piping systems (both above ground and underground) and extensive requirements for the proper assembly of system piping and components.

603.3.2.5 Separation. Rooms containing fuel oil tanks for internal combustion engines shall be separated from the remainder of the building by *fire barriers*, *horizontal assemblies*, or both, with a minimum 1-hour fire-resistance rating with 1-hour fire-protection-rated *opening protectives* constructed in accordance with the *International Building Code.*

Exception: Rooms containing protected above-ground tanks complying with Section 5704.2.9.7 shall not be required to be separated from surrounding areas.

❖ This section addresses the separation of the tank from the remainder of the building. The requirement for 1-hour separation is not a new requirement. The requirement for separation is located in Section 4.1.2.1.1 and Section 6.3.5.2 of NFPA 37, both of which require 1-hour construction to separate internal combustion engines and associated fuel tanks up to 1,320 gallons from the remainder of the building in which they are located. Section 4.1.2.1.5 of NFPA 37 specifies that openings are protected with 1-hour opening protectives. This section eliminates the additional navigation to NFPA 37 through the reference to IMC Section 915 within Section 603.3.2.4.

The exception here, as in Section 603.3.2.1, recognizes the increased safety provided by protected above-ground tanks. See the commentary to Section 603.3.2.1 for a discussion of those tanks and their enhanced safety.

603.3.2.6 Spill containment. Tanks exceeding 55-gallon (208 L) capacity or an aggregate capacity of 1,000 gallons (3785 L) that are not provided with integral secondary containment shall be provided with spill containment sized to contain a release from the largest tank.

❖ Section 603.3.2 states that the installation must comply with Section 603 or IFC Chapter 57. The designer has an option to select either design method. However, spill containment is found in Chapter 57, which the designer may or may not comply with. Therefore, this section specifies that spill containment is required where a single tank exceeds 55 gallons, or the aggregate exceeds 1,000 gallons. These thresholds are identical to the thresholds in Section 5004.2.1 for spill containment of liquids.

The secondary containment is sized to contain the largest spill. Even for tanks located inside a sprinklered building, only the tank contents must be contained. This is consistent with the requirements found in Section 6.3.5.3 of NFPA 37. This section provides a more direct path to comply with NFPA 37.

603.3.2.7 Tanks in basements. Tanks in *basements* shall be located not more than two stories below grade plane.

❖ This section prohibits tank installations more than two stories below grade because the further an incident is below grade, the greater challenge for the fire department to mitigate it. This is consistent with the control area approach in Table 5003.8.3.2, which also limits control areas to two levels below grade.

603.3.3 Underground storage of fuel oil. The storage of fuel oil in underground storage tanks shall comply with NFPA 31.

❖ Section 603.3 does not require that fuel oil tanks be installed underground; however, there may be circumstances under which such an installation is either desirable or advisable. The code user is directed to NFPA 31 for specific requirements applicable to the installation of underground combustible liquid storage tanks.

603.4 Portable unvented heaters. Portable unvented fuel-fired heating equipment shall be prohibited in occupancies in Groups A, E, I, R-1, R-2, R-3 and R-4 and ambulatory care facilities.

Exceptions:

1. In one- and two-family *dwellings* portable unvented fuel-fired heaters, where approved and *listed* in accordance with UL 647.
2. Portable outdoor gas-fired heating appliances in accordance with Section 603.4.2.

❖ Portable unvented fuel-fired heating equipment refers to portable space heaters, such as LP-gas fired or kerosene-fueled appliances. This section would also apply to movable gas-fired appliances that connect to gas convenience outlets with gas hose connectors. This section does not apply to permanently installed appliances. Portable space-heating appliances are moved around at will by the occupants and might be placed too close to combustibles or where they are susceptible to being hit, tipped over, etc. Because of potential misuse, such appliances are considered an unacceptable risk in the listed, higher life hazard occupancies. Exception 1 is based on the assumption that, in one- and two-family dwellings, the occupants will take greater care in the use of such appliances. Exception 2 is based on the provisions of Section 603.4.2 and its subsections, which provide strict regulation of portable outdoor gas-fired heating appliances in all occupancies.

603.4.1 Prohibited locations. Unvented fuel-fired heating equipment shall not be located in, or obtain combustion air from, any of the following rooms or spaces: sleeping rooms, bathrooms, toilet rooms or storage closets.

❖ This section is intended to prevent fuel-fired appliances from being installed in rooms and spaces where the combustion process could pose a threat to occupants. Potential threats include depleted oxygen levels; elevated levels of carbon dioxide, nitrous oxides, carbon monoxide, and other combustion gases; ignition of combustibles; and elevated levels of flammable gases.

In small rooms, such as bedrooms and bathrooms, the doors are typically closed when the room is occupied, which could allow combustion gases to build up to life-threatening levels. In bedrooms, sleeping occupants would not be alert to or aware of impending danger. This section is parallel in intent with Section 303.3 of both the IMC and the IFGC. Note that, as a subsection of Section 603.4, this section is addressing portable appliances in Groups A, E, I and R (see also IFGC commentary, Section 303.3).

603.4.2 Portable outdoor gas-fired heating appliances. Portable gas-fired heating appliances located outdoors shall be in accordance with Sections 603.4.2.1 through 603.4.2.3.4.

❖ This section introduces Sections 603.4.2.1 through 603.4.2.3.4, which contain requirements for controlling the hazards associated with portable gas-fired heating appliances located outdoors. In many jurisdictions, LP-gas-fired portable heaters, also called patio heaters, are being utilized in outdoor areas of restaurants, sidewalk cafes, hotel dining areas, outdoor smoking areas and retail sites in increasing numbers. These heaters are also readily available to consumers at local home and building supply locations. These sections provide regulations to allow for the conditional use of outdoor patio heaters and establish general safety requirements for the storage and use of such heaters (see Commentary Figure 603.4.2).

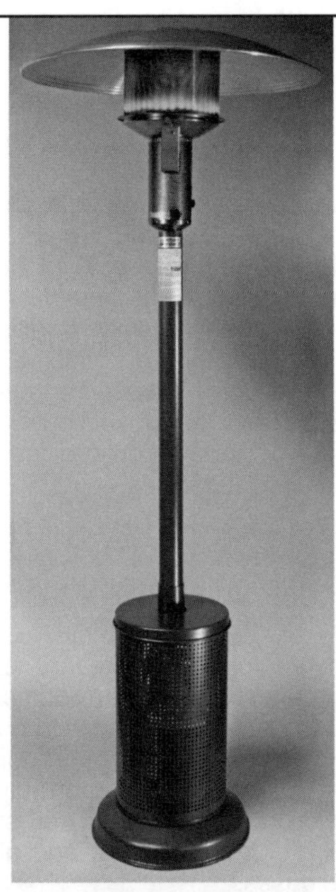

Commentary Figure 603.4.2
PORTABLE OUTDOOR GAS-FIRED HEATING APPLIANCE/PATIO HEATER
(Photo courtesy of Infrared Dynamics, Yorba Linda, CA)

603.4.2.1 Location. Portable outdoor gas-fired heating appliances shall be located in accordance with Sections 603.4.2.1.1 through 603.4.2.1.4.

❖ This section introduces Sections 603.4.2.1.1 through 603.4.2.1.4, which contain requirements for controlling the location hazards associated with portable outdoor gas-fired heating appliances, sometimes called "patio heaters."

603.4.2.1.1 Prohibited locations. The storage or use of portable outdoor gas-fired heating appliances is prohibited in any of the following locations:

1. Inside of any occupancy where connected to the fuel gas container.
2. Inside of tents, canopies and membrane structures.
3. On exterior balconies.

Exception: As allowed in Section 6.22 of NFPA 58.

❖ These "patio heaters" are not designed or listed for indoor use because they are unvented appliances. The potential fire and life safety hazard of LP-gas warrants their prohibition inside of occupied buildings and structures, making this section consistent with the prohibitions of containers inside of buildings in NFPA 58.

603.4.2.1.2 Clearance to buildings. Portable outdoor gas-fired heating appliances shall be located not less than 5 feet (1524 mm) from buildings.

❖ The 5-foot (1524 mm) separation reduces the likelihood that operating portable outdoor gas-fired heating appliances will come in contact with heat-damageable building surfaces or material that is easily ignited.

603.4.2.1.3 Clearance to combustible materials. Portable outdoor gas-fired heating appliances shall not be located beneath, or closer than 5 feet (1524 mm) to combustible decorations and combustible overhangs, awnings, sunshades or similar combustible attachments to buildings.

❖ The 5-foot (1524 mm) separation reduces the likelihood that operating portable outdoor gas-fired heating appliances will come in contact with combustible construction or material that is easily ignited.

603.4.2.1.4 Proximity to exits. Portable outdoor gas-fired heating appliances shall not be located within 5 feet (1524 mm) of *exits* or *exit discharges*.

❖ In order to not compromise the means of egress in a potential fire or other emergency evacuation scenario and to prevent LP-gas from entering the building and finding an ignition source in case of a leak, portable outdoor gas-fired heating appliances must be kept a minimum of 5 feet (1524 mm) from any exit or exit discharge.

603.4.2.2 Installation and operation. Portable outdoor gas-fired heating appliances shall be installed and operated in accordance with Sections 603.4.2.2.1 through 603.4.2.2.4.

❖ This section introduces Sections 603.4.2.2.1 through 603.4.2.2.4, which contain requirements for controlling the installation and operation hazards associated with portable outdoor gas-fired heating appliances.

603.4.2.2.1 Listing and approval. Only *listed* and *approved* portable outdoor gas-fired heating appliances utilizing a fuel gas container that is integral to the appliance shall be used.

❖ Even though portable outdoor gas-fired heating appliances can be listed under the standard ANSI Z83.26/CSA 2.37 for natural gas or LP-gas (propane) use, this section makes it clear that only appliances employing an integral LP-gas container can be used. The safety feature here is that the gas hoses used to connect natural gas-fired appliances to an external fuel source are eliminated, thus eliminating the hazard of wear-and-tear effects on the hose and the possibility of persons tripping over the hoses, the latter reducing the risk of personal injury or heaters tipping over. Another safety feature required by the ANSI standard is the connection between the LP-gas cylinder and the hose supplying the appliance's burner. The standard requires the hose connected to the appliance to be equipped with a Compressed Gas Association (CGA) 790 fitting as described in CGA V-1. A CGA 790 fitting provides three separate safety features. First, the fitting has a thermal link that is designed to activate at temperatures of 200°F to 250°F (93°C–121°C), thus stopping the flow of LP-gas in the event of a fire. Second, the fitting requires a positive connection to the cylinder before LP-gas can flow into the appliance. Finally, the fitting is equipped with an internal excess flow control valve, which is designed to stop the flow of a gas or liquid in the event of hose or pipe rupture.

603.4.2.2.2 Installation and maintenance. Portable outdoor gas-fired heating appliances shall be installed and maintained in accordance with the manufacturer's instructions.

❖ Compliance with the appliance manufacturer's installation and maintenance instructions is a fundamental requirement of all I-Codes and those instructions are an enforceable extension of the code because they are typically an integral part of the appliances' listing, as required by Section 603.4.2.2.1. Federal, state, county or municipal laws might supercede part of the installation instructions or could be applied in addition to the requirements in the instructions.

603.4.2.2.3 Tip-over switch. Portable outdoor gas-fired heating appliances shall be equipped with a tilt or tip-over switch that automatically shuts off the flow of gas if the appliance is tilted more than 15 degrees (0.26 rad) from the vertical.

❖ For safety, listed commercial heaters feature a safety switch that immediately shuts the unit off if it senses that the heater is tilted more than 15 degrees (0.26 rad) from vertical. This is especially important given these heaters can be more than 7 feet (2137 mm) tall and weigh more than 80 pounds (36 kg). This safety feature reduces the likelihood of personal injury and the heating element coming into contact with combustible material.

603.4.2.2.4 Guard against contact. The heating element or combustion chamber of portable outdoor gas-fired heating appliances shall be permanently guarded so as to prevent accidental contact by persons or material.

❖ This safety feature reduces the likelihood of personal injury and the heating element coming into direct contact with combustible material.

603.4.2.3 Gas containers. Fuel gas containers for portable outdoor gas-fired heating appliances shall comply with Sections 603.4.2.3.1 through 603.4.2.3.4.

❖ This section introduces Sections 603.4.2.3.1 through 603.4.2.3.4, which contain requirements for controlling the hazards associated with fuel gas containers for portable outdoor gas-fired heating appliances.

603.4.2.3.1 Approved containers. Only *approved* DOTn or ASME gas containers shall be used.

❖ This section is consistent with Chapter 61 and the provisions of NFPA 58, which is the LP-gas referenced standard in that chapter of the code. Using only DOTn and ASME containers increases the likelihood of the appliance being safe because the containers are built to exacting standards.

603.4.2.3.2 Container replacement. Replacement of fuel gas containers in portable outdoor gas-fired heating appliances shall not be conducted while the public is present.

❖ In order to avoid exposing the public to the potential for a gas leak during cylinder replacement, the portable outdoor gas-fired heating appliance being serviced must either be removed to a nonpublic area or the area in which it is being used must be cleared of patrons while the container exchange is in progress.

603.4.2.3.3 Container capacity. The maximum individual capacity of gas containers used in connection with portable outdoor gas-fired heating appliances shall not exceed 20 pounds (9 kg).

❖ The maximum size of the gas container to be used in portable outdoor gas-fired heating appliances is the same as those typically used in gas grills and is dictated by the listing standard.

603.4.2.3.4 Indoor storage prohibited. Gas containers shall not be stored inside of buildings except in accordance with Section 6109.9.

❖ Requirements for the storage of idle replacement containers of LP-gas are specified in this section. Indoor storage of 20-pound (9 kg) LP-gas cylinders in a building that is accessible to the public is a violation of Section 6109.9. Both ANSI Z83.26/CSA 2.37 and Section 603.4.2.3.3 limit the volume of the LP-gas containers to 20 pounds (9 kg). Containers must also be qualified to be filled in accordance with the requirements in NFPA 58. Section 6109 provides regulations for the storage of containers awaiting use, which is applicable to replacement containers for portable outdoor gas-fired heating appliances.

603.5 Heating appliances. Heating appliances shall be *listed* and shall comply with Sections 603.5.1 and 603.5.2.

❖ The IMC and the IFGC require that all space-heating appliances be listed and labeled.

603.5.1 Guard against contact. The heating element or combustion chamber shall be permanently guarded so as to prevent accidental contact by persons or material.

❖ The injury and ignition protection feature required by this section is typically designed into the appliance.

603.5.2 Heating appliance installation and maintenance. Heating appliances shall be installed and maintained in accordance with the manufacturer's instructions, the *International Building Code*, the *International Mechanical Code*, the *International Fuel Gas Code* and NFPA 70.

❖ Depending on the type of fuel utilized, appliance installation and maintenance can be subject to the requirements of multiple codes, including the IBC, the IMC, the IFGC, and NFPA 70 in addition to the appliance manufacturer's instructions.

603.6 Chimneys and appliances. Chimneys, incinerators, smokestacks or similar devices for conveying smoke or hot gases to the outer air and the stoves, furnaces, fireboxes or boilers to which such devices are connected, shall be maintained so as not to create a fire hazard.

❖ A primary function of the code is to reduce or eliminate fire hazards through proper maintenance of appliances and systems that are potential fire and life safety hazards.

603.6.1 Masonry chimneys. Masonry chimneys that, upon inspection, are found to be without a flue liner and that have open mortar joints which will permit smoke or gases to be discharged into the building, or which are cracked as to be dangerous, shall be repaired or relined with a *listed* chimney liner system installed in accordance with the manufacturer's instructions or a flue lining system installed in accordance with the requirements of the *International Building Code* and appropriate for the intended class of chimney service.

❖ See Section 2113 of the IBC, Section 801.16 of the IMC and Sections 501.12, 501.13 and 503.5 of the IFGC for information on masonry chimney liners and masonry chimneys.

603.6.2 Metal chimneys. Metal chimneys that are corroded or improperly supported shall be repaired or replaced.

❖ See the commentary to Section 603.2.

603.6.3 Decorative shrouds. Decorative shrouds installed at the termination of factory-built chimneys shall be removed except where such shrouds are *listed* and *labeled* for use with the specific factory-built chimney system and are installed in accordance with the chimney manufacturer's instructions.

❖ This section is retroactive in that it requires removal of a previously installed trim item. Section 805.6 of the IMC and Section 503.5.4 of the IFGC prohibit the installation of decorative shrouds not meeting the listing criteria. The code addresses those noncomplying shrouds that were illegally installed (see IMC commentary, Section 805.6, and IFGC commentary, Section 503.5.4).

603.6.4 Factory-built chimneys. Existing factory-built chimneys that are damaged, corroded or improperly supported shall be repaired or replaced.

❖ Defective or inadequately supported chimneys could leak flue gas and could fail structurally, resulting in separation, collapse, a fire hazard and a life safety hazard. This section is consistent with the maintenance focus of the code.

603.6.5 Connectors. Existing chimney and vent connectors that are damaged, corroded or improperly supported shall be repaired or replaced.

❖ See the commentary to Section 603.6.4.

603.7 Discontinuing operation of unsafe heating appliances. The *fire code official* is authorized to order that measures be taken to prevent the operation of any existing stove, oven, furnace, incinerator, boiler or any other heat-producing device or appliance found to be defective or in violation of code requirements for existing appliances after giving notice to this effect to any person, *owner*, firm or agent or operator in charge of the same. The *fire code official* is authorized to take measures to prevent the operation of any device or appliance without notice when inspection shows the existence of an immediate fire hazard or when imperiling human life. The defective device shall remain withdrawn from service until all necessary repairs or *alterations* have been made.

❖ When a heat-producing appliance or system is determined to be unsafe, the fire code official is required to notify the owner or agent of the building as the first step in correcting the difficulty. This notice may describe the repairs and improvements necessary to correct the deficiency and keep the system in operation or require the unsafe equipment or system to be removed or replaced. The notice must specify a time frame in which the corrective actions must occur. Additionally, the notice should require the immediate response of the owner or agent.

If the owner or agent is not available, public notice of the declaration would be enough to comply with this section. The fire code official may also determine that the system must be disconnected to correct an unsafe condition and must give written notice to that effect; however, an immediate disconnection can be ordered if it is essential for protection of public health and safety.

603.7.1 Unauthorized operation. It shall be a violation of this code for any person, user, firm or agent to continue the utilization of any device or appliance (the operation of which has been discontinued or ordered discontinued in accordance with Section 603.7) unless written authority to resume operation is given by the *fire code official*. Removing or breaking the means by which operation of the device is prevented shall be a violation of this code.

❖ Appliances or systems removed from service in accordance with Section 603.7 may be sealed or otherwise secured in a manner approved by the fire code official and may only be returned to service upon written authorization of the fire code official.

603.8 Incinerators. Commercial, industrial and residential-type incinerators and chimneys shall be constructed in accordance with the *International Building Code*, the *International Fuel Gas Code* and the *International Mechanical Code*.

❖ See the commentaries to Section 907.1 of the IMC, Section 606.1 of the IFGC and Section 2113 of the IBC.

603.8.1 Residential incinerators. Residential incinerators shall be of an *approved* type.

❖ Residential incinerators have gone out of use today but may still be found in older homes and in rural areas.

603.8.2 Spark arrestor. Incinerators shall be equipped with an effective means for arresting sparks.

❖ Spark arrestor chimney caps are designed with a screened outlet that prevents the escape of burning embers and particles.

603.8.3 Restrictions. Where the *fire code official* determines that burning in incinerators located within 500 feet (152 m) of mountainous, brush or grass-covered areas will create an undue fire hazard because of atmospheric conditions, such burning shall be prohibited.

❖ The fire code official must determine whether incinerator use would present an unacceptable risk of wild fires in timber, brush and grass-covered areas. For wildland-urban interface areas, see the *International Wildland-Urban Interface Code*® (IWUIC®). The local air-quality agency may also have restrictions.

603.8.4 Time of burning. Burning shall take place only during *approved* hours.

❖ The jurisdiction must determine the periods that would be safe for burning and those that would be unsafe. Consideration must be given to daylight, prevailing winds, ambient temperatures, impact on air quality, moisture levels and presence of observers and supervisory personnel.

603.8.5 Discontinuance. The *fire code official* is authorized to require incinerator use to be discontinued immediately if the *fire code official* determines that smoke emissions are offensive to occupants of surrounding property or if the use of incinerators is determined by the *fire code official* to constitute a hazardous condition.

❖ The fire code official can prohibit incinerator use if it would be a nuisance or a health or fire hazard. Coordination with the local air-quality agency may also be necessary.

603.8.6 Flue-fed incinerators in Group I-2. In Group I-2 occupancies, the continued use of existing flue-fed incinerators is prohibited.

❖ This type of incinerator is hazardous and would not comply with current code requirements. This section is simply making sure that such incinerators are no longer used.

603.8.7 Incinerator inspections in Group I-2. Incinerators in Group I-2 occupancies shall be inspected not less than annually in accordance with the manufacturer's instructions. Inspection records shall be maintained on the premises and made available to the *fire code official* upon request.

❖ Incinerators pose a hazard to the building and its occupants if not properly maintained. This is more of a concern in Group I-2 occupancies where the residents are at particular risk from such hazards.

603.9 Gas meters. Above-ground gas meters, regulators and piping subject to damage shall be protected by a barrier complying with Section 312 or otherwise protected in an *approved* manner.

❖ Vehicle impact protection is necessary to prevent gas leakage resulting from impact damage to gas service equipment. Protection can be accomplished by location alone or by the construction of barriers as prescribed by Section 312. Barriers are required only where gas service equipment is located where vehicle impact is likely to occur.

SECTION 604 ELECTRICAL EQUIPMENT, WIRING AND HAZARDS

604.1 Abatement of electrical hazards. Identified electrical hazards shall be abated. Identified hazardous electrical conditions in permanent wiring shall be brought to the attention of the responsible code official. Electrical wiring, devices, appliances and other equipment that is modified or damaged and constitutes an electrical shock or fire hazard shall not be used.

❖ Maintenance of electrical systems and services to achieve compliance with the requirements of NFPA 70 is required. The leading causes of electrical fires include inadequate or improper maintenance; nonconforming modifications to existing installations; failure to maintain clearances around electrical equipment and devices; and improper use of electrical equipment and devices. A detailed analysis of the causes of residential electrical fires by the U.S. Consumer Products Safety Commission suggests that misuse and improper modifications to conforming electrical systems are the leading causes of these fires.

604.2 Illumination. Illumination shall be provided for service equipment areas, motor control centers and electrical panelboards.

❖ Adequate lighting in electrical service distribution equipment areas is required to facilitate the location of the electrical service shutoff during a fire or other emergency and to minimize potential hazards during maintenance or repair work. Although not required, this lighting should be connected to an emergency or standby power source to permit continued illumination when power to service equipment is interrupted during maintenance repair activities or emergencies.

604.3 Working space and clearance. A working space of not less than 30 inches (762 mm) in width, 36 inches (914 mm) in depth and 78 inches (1981 mm) in height shall be provided in front of electrical service equipment. Where the electrical service equipment is wider than 30 inches (762 mm), the working space shall be not less than the width of the equipment. Storage of materials shall not be located within the designated working space.

Exceptions:

1. Where other dimensions are required or allowed by NFPA 70.
2. Access openings into attics or under-floor areas that provide a minimum clear opening of 22 inches (559 mm) by 30 inches (762 mm).

❖ Adequate clearance serves two important purposes: physical separation of combustibles from heat-producing electrical devices and equipment to minimize the possibility of ignition, and providing adequate work space to perform maintenance and repair work safely (see Commentary Figure 604.3). The exceptions note that NFPA 70 may allow different dimensions than those prescribed in this section. Additionally, the lack of space in areas such as attics and underfloor areas is recognized by also allowing a smaller opening width.

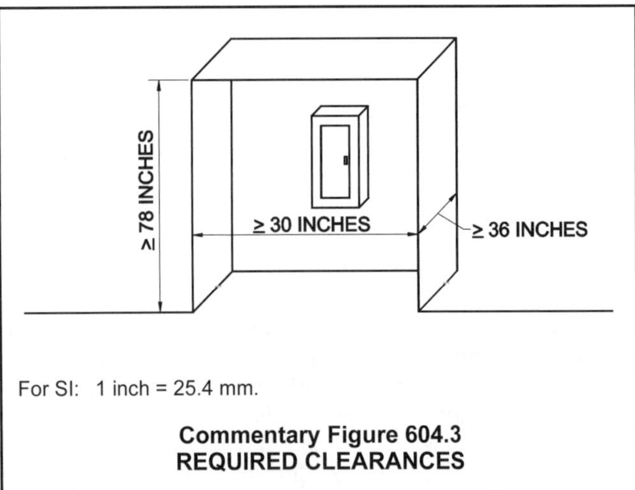

For SI: 1 inch = 25.4 mm.

Commentary Figure 604.3
REQUIRED CLEARANCES

604.3.1 Labeling. Doors into electrical control panel rooms shall be marked with a plainly visible and legible sign stating ELECTRICAL ROOM or similar approved wording. The disconnecting means for each service, feeder or branch circuit originating on a switchboard or panelboard shall be legibly and durably marked to indicate its purpose unless such purpose is clearly evident. Where buildings or structures are supplied by more than one power source, markings shall be provided at each service equipment location and at all interconnected electric power production sources identifying all electric power sources at the premises in accordance with NFPA 70.

❖ In addition to the illumination required in Section 604.2, additional labeling is required for the electrical equipment to assist emergency responders in identifying and shutting down electrical service controls during a fire or other emergency. The last sentence recognizes the fact that multiple power sources may be available and in use in a building. This is becoming a more common hazard to first responders. It is important to know where the building or structure is supplied by alternate energy sources. Without this marking, simply turning off the main disconnect there may be an assumption that the building or structure has been fully de-energized. However there may still be energized systems that pose a serious hazard to first responders.

604.4 Multiplug adapters. Multiplug adapters, such as cube adapters, unfused plug strips or any other device not complying with NFPA 70 shall be prohibited.

❖ This section is intended to prohibit conditions that could lead to the overloading of building electrical circuits that, in turn, could result in a fire. The device intended to be regulated by this section is referred to as a "multiplug adapter" but is more correctly identified as a "current tap." UL, in its Guide Information for the listing category EMDV, defines "current tap" as follows: "A male and female contact device that, when connected to an outlet receptacle or cord set, provides multiple outlets or outlet configurations. An outlet configuration may consist of a slot configuration, or provision for the connection of flexible cord." An adapter, on the other hand, is defined there as "a device that adapts one blade or slot configuration to another (including a grounding adapter for a non-grounding receptacle)." The term "cube adapter" (more correctly "cube tap") refers to the shape of the device, i.e., cube-shaped. They can also be known as "octopus taps."

Overcurrent protection interrupts power to an outlet only when connected loads exceed the current rating of the overcurrent device for a specified amount of time. When multiplug adaptors are used for several appliances, such devices may produce enough heat to ignite nearby combustibles in the time it takes to trip the overcurrent protection device. Simultaneous operation of many small loads may cause dangerous localized resistance heating without tripping the overcurrent protection device. Additionally, these devices may result in loose electrical connections because of the weight of the cords pulling on them.

The use of these devices may also indicate that the building's electrical wiring is inadequate for the connected loads or occupancy demands. These devices are intended for temporary use only, not at a fixed location or in place of wiring complying with NFPA 70.

The code does allow for the use of listed, relocatable power taps complying with specific criteria mentioned in Sections 604.4.1 through 604.4.3. Commentary Figure 604.4 shows the difference between a multiplug adapter and a power tap.

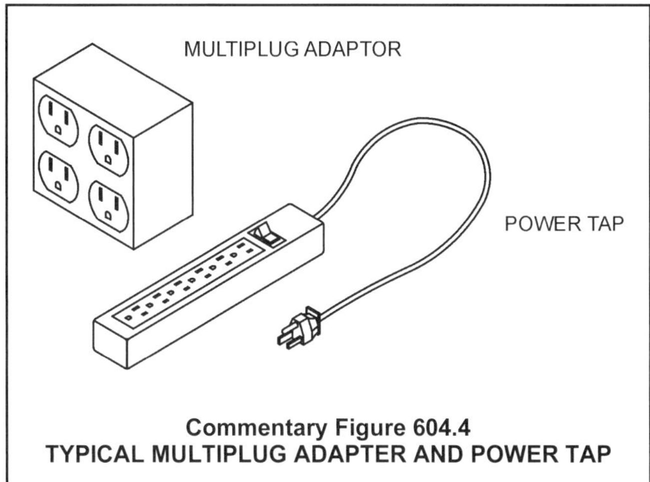

Commentary Figure 604.4
TYPICAL MULTIPLUG ADAPTER AND POWER TAP

604.4.1 Power tap design. Relocatable power taps shall be of the polarized or grounded type, equipped with overcurrent protection, and shall be *listed* in accordance with UL 1363.

❖ This section sets out the basic requirements for relocatable power taps (RPTs). The testing requirements of UL 1363 are applied to relocatable, cord-connected power taps rated at 250 volts AC or less and 20 amps or less. These devices are intended only for indoor use as a temporary extension of a branch circuit for general use to supply home workshop tools, computers, audio and video equipment, etc. They consist of an attachment plug and a length of flexible cord terminating in an enclosure containing one or more receptacles and may also be provided with fuses or other supplemental overcurrent protection, switches, line surge suppressors or indicator lights. The flexible cord length is dependent on the listing of the particular device, but power taps have been listed for lengths up to 25 feet (7620 mm). The scope of UL 1363 indicates that RPTs are neither intended to be connected in series nor used with medical equipment.

604.4.2 Power supply. Relocatable power taps shall be directly connected to a permanently installed receptacle.

❖ The restrictions on power taps are similar to those on extension cords. Power taps should not be used as a substitute for building wiring. Relocatable power taps are intended to be plugged directly into a permanently installed receptacle and are not intended to be connected in series or connected to other power taps or extension cords. They are also not intended for use outdoors, at construction sites and similar hard-use locations.

604.4.3 Installation. Relocatable power tap cords shall not extend through walls, ceilings, floors, under doors or floor coverings, or be subject to environmental or physical damage.

❖ To prevent use as a substitute for permanent wiring, power taps cannot be placed in locations such as within or through walls, under doors or on building surfaces, furnishings, cabinets or similar structures where they would be subject to physical damage. This section would prohibit relocatable power taps from being plugged into a receptacle in one room to power a device in another room.

604.5 Extension cords. Extension cords and flexible cords shall not be a substitute for permanent wiring and shall be listed and labeled in accordance with UL 817. Extension cords and flexible cords shall not be affixed to structures, extended through walls, ceilings or floors, or under doors or floor coverings, nor shall such cords be subject to environmental damage or physical impact. Extension cords shall be used only with portable appliances. Extension cords marked for indoor use shall not be used outdoors.

❖ Frequent or improper use of extension cords in place of permanent fixed wiring is another indication of inadequate electrical wiring capacity or incompatible demands (see Commentary Figure 604.5). Physical damage to extension cords caused by concealment or inadequate maintenance may result in localized resistance heating, shorts or ground faults.

Extension cords must also meet the listing and labeling requirements of UL 817. This enables a fire code official to remove inappropriate or nonlisted extension cords. This provides more specific guidance to inspectors and will decrease fire risk.

The amount of electrical current that any extension cord can safely conduct is limited by the size of its conductor, its insulation type and its environment. This principle is often not understood by the general public. As a result, extension cords are commonly overloaded by connecting appliances and other loads in excess of the cord's capacity.

Overloading of extension cords causes an increase in the conductor's temperature. This increase in temperature can exceed the temperature rating of the conductor insulation, causing it to melt, decompose or burn. The burning insulation can ignite other combustible materials. The resulting loss of conductor insulation can also cause a short circuit or ground fault that can act as a source of ignition. The buildup of heat in an extension cord is often made worse by excessive cord length and by the insulating effect of rugs that often cover extension cords. Extension cords are much more susceptible to physical damage than permanent wiring. Damage to extension cords increases the likelihood of shorts and poor connections, both of which can cause a fire.

In addition to the fire hazard, extension cords pose a tripping hazard to occupants and, when damaged, can pose an electrical shock hazard. Securing flexible cords to a wall baseboard, door jambs, etc., with nails, staples or other fasteners to eliminate tripping hazards can create another dangerous condition by pinching or piercing the cord and causing shorts or faults that could lead to ignition.

Also, as a way of limiting the use of extension cords, their use is restricted to portable appliances. The reference to "portable" primarily denotes smaller, often-relocated appliances, such as a fan or a power tool. Extension cords must not be used with major appliances or equipment, such as refrigerators, which are obviously not portable. See the definitions for "Portable equipment" and "Portable appliance" in NFPA 70 Sections 520.2 and 550.2, respectively.

The last sentence addresses the fire and shock hazard associated with the use of indoor use extension cords in outdoor environments.

604.5.1 Power supply. Extension cords shall be plugged directly into an *approved* receptacle, power tap or multiplug adapter and, except for *approved* multiplug extension cords, shall serve only one portable appliance.

❖ This restriction means that multiple extension cords must not be connected to one another. Additionally, extension cords are limited to one appliance unless they are specifically approved multiplug extension cords.

604.5.2 Ampacity. The ampacity of the extension cords shall be not less than the rated capacity of the portable appliance supplied by the cord.

❖ Although most building occupants may have difficulty understanding ampacity, which is the amount of electrical current that a particular conductor is capable of handling without exceeding its temperature limits, it is extremely important. If an appliance demands a higher electrical current than the extension cord is intended to handle, the extension cord will be overloaded, causing overheating and a potential fire. Familiarity with the types of extension cords available for sale and the general relationships to common appliances will help with the enforcement of this section.

604.5.3 Maintenance. Extension cords shall be maintained in good condition without splices, deterioration or damage.

❖ When extension cords are damaged, they become potential shock hazards and a source of ignition.

604.5.4 Grounding. Extension cords shall be grounded where serving grounded portable appliances.

❖ If an extension cord serves an appliance that requires a grounding conductor to avoid potential shock, that cord must provide a grounding conductor.

604.6 Unapproved conditions. Open junction boxes and open-wiring splices shall be prohibited. *Approved* covers shall be provided for all switch and electrical outlet boxes.

❖ Without covers, connections made in junction boxes may be subject to physical damage. Such damage may loosen electrical connections, resulting in high-resistance arcing. Switches and outlet boxes are subject to arcing from loose connections and reduced clearances between contacts as they age. Accumulation of dirt and debris in open electrical boxes creates an ignitable fuel concentration. Fires in open electrical boxes may spread to wire or cable insulation or other fuels in electrical and mechanical concealed spaces. Furthermore, unprotected electrical connections are electrical shock hazards to personnel working in concealed spaces.

604.7 Equipment and fixtures. Electrical equipment and fixtures shall be tested and *listed* by an *approved* agency and installed and maintained in accordance with all instructions included as part of such listing.

❖ The fire code official should look for the listing mark of an approved testing or inspection agency on equipment and fixtures. In some cases the fire code official may need to request the agency's published report showing the listing to verify that the equipment and fixtures meet an applicable standard for electrical safety. Fire code officials experiencing difficulties interpreting the marking or listing of an agency, as in the case of a laboratory not located within the United States, should consult representatives of the agency or the U.S. Consumer Products Safety Commission (CPSC) for assistance.

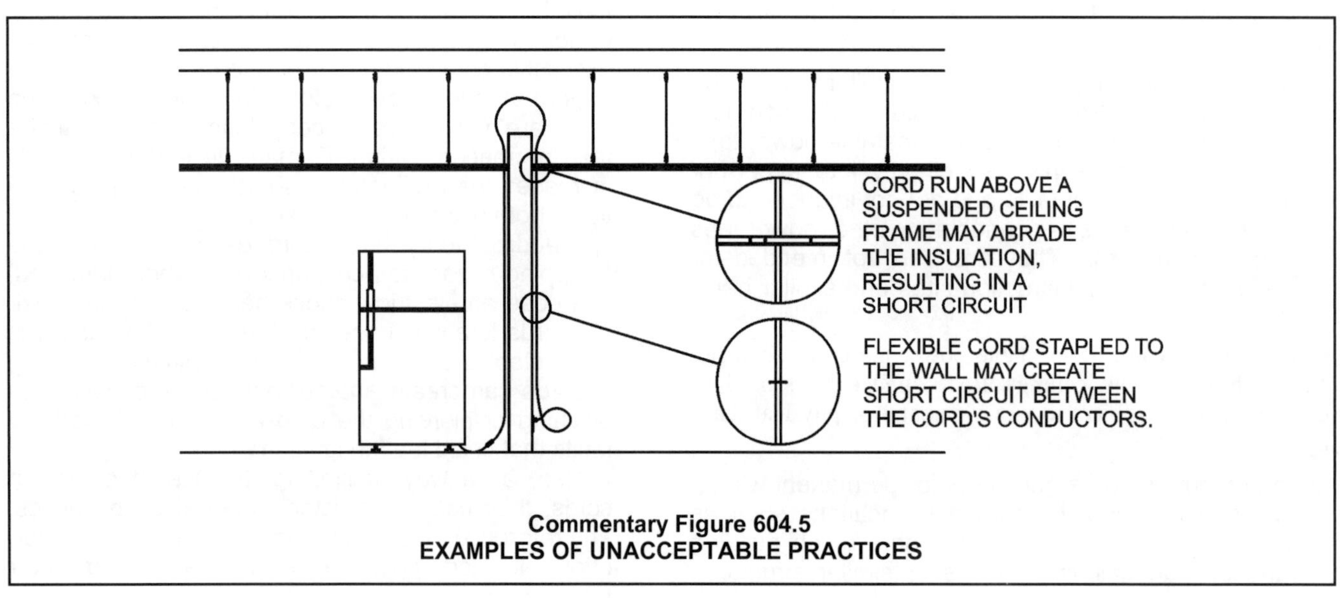

Commentary Figure 604.5
EXAMPLES OF UNACCEPTABLE PRACTICES

604.8 Electrical motors. Electrical motors shall be maintained free from excessive accumulations of oil, dirt, waste and debris.

❖ Internal heating is commonly associated with the operation of electrical motors. Excessive accumulations of dust, oil, grease, dirt or other debris may be easily ignited by the internal frictional heating of electrical motor components.

604.9 Temporary wiring. Temporary wiring for electrical power and lighting installations is allowed for a period not to exceed 90 days. Temporary wiring methods shall meet the applicable provisions of NFPA 70.

> **Exception:** Temporary wiring for electrical power and lighting installations is allowed during periods of construction, remodeling, repair or demolition of buildings, structures, equipment or similar activities.

❖ In some cases, because of a specific need and the temporary nature of the need, temporary wiring is allowed for a period of not more than 90 days. This allowance is primarily aimed at needs such as for holiday lighting. The exception allows temporary wiring to exceed 90 days for certain activities, such as remodeling or general construction of a building. Section 590 of NFPA 70 contains specific requirements for temporary wiring.

The term "temporary wiring" is not referring here to the use of power taps or extension cords (see commentaries, Sections 604.4 and 604.5). The requirements for temporary wiring are less restrictive than those for permanent wiring but are much more rigorous than the requirements for the use of power taps and extension cords.

604.9.1 Attachment to structures. Temporary wiring attached to a structure shall be attached in an *approved* manner.

❖ When wiring is specifically attached to a structure, care must be taken to make sure that the attachment will not damage the wiring in a way that would cause resistance heating in localized areas of the wiring (see commentary, Section 604.5).

604.10 Portable, electric space heaters. Where not prohibited by other sections of this code, portable, electric space heaters shall be permitted to be used in all occupancies in accordance with Sections 604.10.1 through 604.10.5.

❖ Portable, electric space heaters are a readily available, commonly used source of supplementary heat for homes or workplaces, but should not be relied on to replace a building's fixed heating system. Because a portable, electric space heater's heating element operates at high temperatures, improper use of the heater creates a fire risk. This section provides minimum safety requirements for the use of portable, electric space heaters that have historically been carelessly or incorrectly installed or used.

604.10.1 Listed and labeled. Only *listed* and *labeled* portable, electric space heaters shall be used.

❖ Using only tested, listed and labeled portable, electric space heaters provides both the consumer and the fire code official with an increased level of confidence that the heater has been thoroughly and carefully examined by an independent agency concerned with public safety. An important part of the product listing is the manufacturer's use and care booklet that should be read and carefully followed before using a portable, electric space heater for the first time and periodically thereafter. An appropriate standard that could be used to examine and list these heaters would be UL 1278.

604.10.2 Power supply. Portable, electric space heaters shall be plugged directly into an *approved* receptacle.

❖ Because of the amount of current required for an electric space heater, its listing will limit the length of the power supply cord provided with the unit to prevent overheating of the conductors. Using an extension cord or other temporary wiring device defeats the purpose of the limited-length cord and can lead to conductor overheating or damage to the heater itself. The heater's power supply cord should be kept away from high traffic areas to prevent the cord from being damaged or tripped over. Power supply cords should also not be run under rugs or furniture where they could be walked on or have heavy objects set on them. This could cause a damaged cord to overheat and cause a fire.

604.10.3 Extension cords. Portable, electric space heaters shall not be plugged into extension cords.

❖ See the commentaries to Sections 604.5 and 604.10.2.

604.10.4 Prohibited areas. Portable, electric space heaters shall not be operated within 3 feet (914 mm) of any combustible materials. Portable, electric space heaters shall be operated only in locations for which they are *listed*.

❖ Because portable electric space heaters have hot and arcing or sparking parts inside of them, adequate clearance from combustible materials must be maintained to avoid ignition of the combustibles. Likewise, flammable liquid vapors could be liberated during liquid transfer or in the event of a spill during travel to the heater where the arcing or sparking components could cause ignition.

604.10.5 Group I-2 occupancies and ambulatory care facilities. Where used in Group I-2 and ambulatory care facilities, portable, electric space heaters shall be limited to those having a heating element that cannot exceed a temperature of 212°F (100°C), and such heaters shall only be used in nonsleeping staff and employee areas.

❖ Group I-2 occupancies have a higher life hazard that results in a longer evacuation time. The use of these devices in such occupancies is prohibited except where it is recognized that there is a reduced life hazard. In areas of Group I-2 occupancies designated for nonsleeping staff and employees, portable heaters with certain temperature limiting requirements are allowed to be used. Limiting portable heater placement and temperature will reduce the incidence of fire from these devices. These provisions correlate the code with federal regulations for these facilities.

604.11 Abandoned wiring in plenums. Abandoned cables in plenums that are able to be accessed without causing damage, or requiring demolition to the building, shall be tagged for future use or shall be removed.

❖ This section introduces a concept that has long been in NFPA 70 and NFPA 90A—that plenums (see Chapter 2 commentary to the definition of "Plenum") are intended specifically to be a part of the air distribution system. Plenums are also used legitimately for stringing communications and data cables as well as utility pipes, sprinkler pipes and similar items. However, such items often are not removed from the plenum when they become obsolete. For example, when an updated data system is installed in a facility (which can occur every 18 to 24 months), it is not unusual for old wires to be cut out of the system but left in place with a new wiring system added on top of them (see Commentary Figure 604.11).

The suspended ceiling tile systems that often enclose plenums are not intended to support any significant weight and can, therefore, easily be overwhelmed by the added weight of storage or abandoned materials such as cables (see commentary to IBC Section 808.1.1.1). Recently, a plenum space fuel load study showed how the safety of fire fighters is compromised by the weight of these abandoned cables. It pointed out that plenum space fuel loads and wiring issues are serious concerns for fire fighters during interior fire-fighting operations and its key recommendation was that abandoned wiring be removed.

Although the primary reason to require the removal of abandoned materials in plenums is the elimination of unnecessary weight, fire safety considerations should also be taken into account, as should the practical consideration that the HVAC design airflow through the plenum could be adversely affected. Such a requirement was long believed not to be enforceable primarily because fire code inspectors would rarely spend their time looking into plenums in existing buildings. However, the danger presented by the fire load of storage or abandoned materials is well-documented. Thus, there should be no significant difficulty in having inspectors identify the existence of abandoned products—especially abandoned cables—classify them as storage and require their removal. Note that only abandoned cable that can be "accessed without causing damage or requiring demolition" must be removed because there is no intent to cause potential damage to the building or facility by attempting to remove cables or circuits that are strung through walls, floors or other building elements. Where some cables are left in place because they are intended to be reused at a future date, they must be clearly identified as such by affixing a tag. See also Section 315.6.

SECTION 605
MECHANICAL REFRIGERATION

[M] 605.1 Scope. Refrigeration systems shall be installed in accordance with the *International Mechanical Code*.

❖ Chapter 11 of the IMC, in conjunction with ASHRAE 15 and IIAR 2, provides complete coverage for the design, installation and maintenance of refrigeration systems.

605.1.1 Refrigerants other than ammonia. Where a refrigerant other than ammonia is used, refrigeration systems and the buildings in which such systems are installed shall be in accordance with ASHRAE 15.

❖ This section is simply making sure that all refrigeration systems other than ammonia and the buildings that they are located in comply with ASHRAE 15 in addition to the requirements of Section 605.

Commentary Figure 604.11
ABANDONED WIRING IN PLENUM

605.1.2 Ammonia refrigeration. Refrigeration systems using ammonia refrigerant and the buildings in which such systems are installed shall comply with ANSI/IIAR-2 for system design and installation and ANSI/IIAR-7 for operating procedures. Decommissioning of ammonia refrigeration systems shall comply with ANSI/IIAR-8.

❖ This section is specific to ammonia, whereas Section 605.1.1 deals with all other refrigerant types. The references in this section provide standards for ammonia refrigeration system design and installation, operating procedures and decommissioning. These standards are considered essential for facilities with ammonia refrigeration systems as a basis of providing for the safety of these facilities, as well as surrounding communities.

[M] 605.2 Refrigerants. The use and purity of new, recovered and reclaimed refrigerants shall be in accordance with the *International Mechanical Code*.

❖ Refrigeration equipment is designed to operate with a specific type or types of refrigerant. Using the wrong refrigerant or a contaminated refrigerant could cause equipment damage or loss of operating efficiency. Refrigerant types differ in how they react with system lubricants, seals, gaskets and other components.

Existing equipment may have to be converted to a different type of refrigerant or charged with refrigerant recovered from it or another system; however, it would be an unnecessary risk to charge new equipment with any refrigerant other than that specified by the equipment manufacturer. See the commentary to Section 1102.2 of the IMC.

[M] 605.3 Refrigerant classification. Refrigerants shall be classified in accordance with the *International Mechanical Code*.

❖ The classification of refrigerants is based on ASHRAE 34, which numbers and classifies refrigerants in accordance with their potential hazards. In the IMC, refrigerants are identified by their number, which is preceded by the letter "R" (for example, R-22). Trademark names of manufacturers, such as "Freon," are not used. The refrigerant number, name and chemical formula can be found in IMC Table 1103.1.

Each refrigerant is classified into a safety group that is based on two factors: flammability and toxicity. The safety group in which an individual refrigerant is classified relates to the potential hazard to building occupants and fire fighters and is one of the factors used to determine the maximum quantities of refrigerants allowed by the IMC. See the commentary to Section 1103.1 of the IMC.

[M] 605.4 Change in refrigerant type. A change in the type of refrigerant in a refrigeration system shall be in accordance with the *International Mechanical Code*.

❖ This section is intended to keep the local fire code official up-to-date on the status of large refrigeration systems and systems containing toxic and/or flammable refrigerants. See the commentary to Section 1101.8 of the IMC.

605.5 Access. Access to refrigeration systems having a refrigerant circuit containing more than 220 pounds (100 kg) of Group A1 or 30 pounds (14 kg) of any other group refrigerant shall be provided for the fire department at all times as required by the *fire code official*.

❖ Where any one or more refrigeration circuits contain more than the specified quantity limits, the room or building housing the system or systems must be constructed with fire department access for emergency response, inspection and hazard assessment. Refrigerants of other than Group A1 tend to be more flammable or toxic. This section could require that the fire department be given keys to refrigeration machinery rooms and buildings.

605.6 Testing of equipment. Refrigeration equipment and systems having a refrigerant circuit containing more than 220 pounds (100 kg) of Group A1 or 30 pounds (14 kg) of any other group refrigerant shall be subject to periodic testing in accordance with Section 605.6.1. Records of tests shall be maintained. Tests of emergency devices or systems required by this chapter shall be conducted by persons trained and qualified in refrigeration systems.

❖ This section sets forth which refrigeration systems are subject to periodic testing and states that records of such testing must be maintained. Minimum qualifications are also required for testing personnel.

As a result of a review of Recommendation 2(c) of the NIST Charleston, South Carolina Sofa Superstore Fire Report, changes were made to Sections 108.2 and 108.3, along with 49 other sections (including this section), to comprehensively address recordkeeping requirements. Section 108.3 provides standardized recordkeeping requirements for periodic inspection, testing, servicing and other operational and maintenance requirements of the code and makes it clear that records must be maintained on the premises or another approved location and that copies of records must be provided to the fire code official upon request. Section 108.3 also makes it clear that records must be maintained for a period of not less than 3 years unless a different time interval is specified in the code or a referenced standard, and that the fire code official is authorized to prescribe the form and format of such records. See the commentaries to Sections 108.2, 108.3, 108.4 and 605.6.1.

605.6.1 Periodic testing. The following emergency devices or systems shall be periodically tested in accordance with the manufacturer's instructions and as required by the *fire code official*.

1. Treatment and flaring systems.
2. Valves and appurtenances necessary to the operation of emergency refrigeration control boxes.

3. Fans and associated equipment intended to operate emergency ventilation systems.

4. Detection and alarm systems.

❖ The devices and systems listed in this section are critical life safety and fire protection elements; therefore, it is imperative that they be tested periodically to assess their condition and dependability. Failure of the safety systems could lead to deadly consequences for building occupants and fire personnel entering the building in an emergency situation. See also the commentary to Section 1109.1 of the IMC.

605.7 Emergency signs. Refrigeration units or systems having a refrigerant circuit containing more than 220 pounds (100 kg) of Group A1 or 30 pounds (14 kg) of any other group refrigerant shall be provided with *approved* emergency signs, charts and labels in accordance with NFPA 704. Hazard signs shall be in accordance with the *International Mechanical Code* for the classification of refrigerants listed therein.

❖ Signs, charts and labels are necessary to assist emergency response personnel in carrying out their duties to protect building occupants and protect themselves from the hazards associated with refrigerant chemicals (see IMC Table 1103.1).

605.8 Refrigerant detection. Machinery rooms shall be provided with a refrigerant detector with an audible and visible alarm. Where ammonia is used as the refrigerant, detection shall comply with ANSI/IIAR 2. For refrigerants other than ammonia, refrigerant detection shall comply with Section 605.8.1.

❖ This section triggers the requirement for refrigerant detection and alarms. This section noted that ammonia is specifically dealt with in the standard IIAR2; all other refrigerants are required to comply with Section 605.8.1. Previously, the provisions of Section 605.8.1 were applied to all refrigerants including ammonia.

605.8.1 Refrigerants other than ammonia. A detector, or a sampling tube that draws air to a detector, shall be provided at an approved location where refrigerant from a leak is expected to accumulate. The system shall be designed to initiate audible and visible alarms inside of and outside each entrance to the refrigerating machinery room and transmit a signal to an approved location where the concentration of refrigerant detected exceeds the lesser of the following:

1. The corresponding TLV-TWA values shown in the *International Mechanical Code* for the refrigerant classification.

2. Twenty-five percent of the lower flammable limit (LFL).

Detection of a refrigerant concentration exceeding the upper detection limit or 25 percent of the lower flammable limit (LFL), whichever is lower, shall stop refrigerant equipment in the machinery room in accordance with Section 605.9.1.

❖ Section 1105.3 of the IMC refers to this code for refrigerant detector requirements. Refrigerant detectors provide early warning of refrigerant leakage. Such leakage could result in a significant fire or health hazard if not discovered and stopped or if occupants are not evacuated from the building. Machinery rooms are required by the IMC where refrigerant quantities exceed specified limits.

Detector location is critical to early leakage warning and should comply with the detector manufacturer's instructions. The required detectors must be designed for application with the refrigerant or refrigerants used in the machinery room. Because machinery rooms are unattended most of the time, once the refrigerant gas is detected at the levels noted in this section (the lesser of the TLV-TWA values in the IMC or 25 percent of the LFL), a local alarm must be initiated and a signal must be transmitted to an approved location remote from the machinery room. Such locations typically include a security room or fire command center. A signal may also be transmitted to an on-duty, on-site technician via pager or cell phone. The alarm is intended to alert those both inside the area of detection and in the immediate vicinity to prevent harm to those outside the area of refrigerant gas release. The notification to an approved location provides timely information to those who must take a role in emergency response, whereas the local alarm is a warning for those in the vicinity of the release. As a first step in the mitigation of the hazards of fugitive refrigerant gas, the required detectors have the additional important role of activating the emergency ventilation/exhaust systems in the machinery rooms required by Sections 1105.6.3 of the IMC (see the definition of "Machinery room" and Table 1103.1, both in the IMC). This section also requires that the system be shut down in accordance with Section 605.9.1.

605.9 Remote controls. Where flammable refrigerants are used and compliance with Section 1106 of the *International Mechanical Code* is required, remote control of the mechanical equipment and appliances located in the machinery room as required by Sections 605.9.1 and 605.9.2 shall be provided at an approved location immediately outside the machinery room and adjacent to its principal entrance.

❖ Emergency controls located outside of the machinery room enclosure will allow shutdown of the compressors and related equipment without requiring someone to enter the room and risk being exposed to refrigerant or fire. This arrangement would also permit equipment shutdown by fire-fighting personnel without the risk of fire spreading into or out of the fire-resistance-rated enclosure. The controls must be located near the entrance to the machinery room so that their location is conspicuous. The controls should be labeled and color coded so that their purpose is obvious. Such controls are customarily painted red to make them readily identifiable as emergency devices.

605.9.1 Refrigeration system emergency shutoff. A clearly identified switch of the break-glass type or with an *approved* tamper-resistant cover shall provide off-only control of refrigerant compressors, refrigerant pumps and normally closed automatic refrigerant valves located in the machinery room. Additionally, this equipment shall be automatically shut off when the refrigerant vapor concentration in the machinery room exceeds the vapor detector's upper detection limit or 25 percent of the LEL, whichever is lower.

❖ This section of the code is intended to provide a safe environment for emergency response personnel when responding to an incident in a refrigeration room. Shutting down compressors and related refrigeration equipment could be necessary to prevent a hazardous condition from worsening and to allow the room to be safely entered. The emergency "kill" switch must be a tamper-resistant type (similar to manual fire alarm boxes) that requires more than one action to actuate it. To prevent an accidental startup, the switch must be capable of only stopping the controlled machinery, not restarting it. The switch must not affect the operation of life safety systems, such as detectors and exhaust equipment, and must not affect room and egress lighting. In addition to the manual switch, the required refrigerant room detector must also shut down the same equipment when the vapor concentration exceeds the lesser of the detector's upper detection limit or 25 percent of the refrigerant's lower explosive limit (LEL).

605.9.2 Ventilation system. A clearly identified switch of the break-glass type or with an approved tamper-resistant cover shall provide on-only control of the machinery room ventilation fans.

❖ For the same reasoning stated in the commentary to Section 605.9.1, a remote switch is required that is not connected to the exhaust system. Although not specifically stated, the intent is for the remote control to activate the emergency mode of operation (see IMC commentary, Section 1106.6.2). To maximize the dependability of the exhaust systems, ASHRAE 15 requires that they be powered from independent dedicated electrical branch circuits.

605.10 Emergency pressure control system. Permanently installed refrigeration systems containing more than 6.6 pounds (3 kg) of flammable, toxic or highly toxic refrigerant or ammonia shall be provided with an emergency pressure control system in accordance with Sections 605.10.1 and 605.10.2.

❖ Technological advances in refrigeration system control equipment now make it possible to provide an automatic emergency control system to replace key functions of the traditional emergency control box. The automatic controls required by Sections 605.10.1 through 605.10.2.2 provide a means of mitigating an overpressure condition prior to operation of emergency pressure-relief vents and, most likely, prior to the arrival of emergency responders. The automatic valves also eliminate the need for emergency responders to decipher the condition of a system in an attempt to determine whether operation of manual crossover valves in an emergency control box would be of benefit in mitigating a system malfunction. The 6.6-pound (3 kg) threshold parallels existing provisions in Section 605.11. This section parallels Section 1105.9 of the IMC to increase the likelihood that designers don't miss this design requirement in the code. Note that these provisions are intended for permanently installed systems versus portable systems such as agricultural cooling trailers used in fields and at processing facilities. This is specifically clarified by the term "permanently installed."

Overall, these provisions add a requirement for a fully redundant safety control system in lieu of a manual system that has proven itself to be rarely, if ever, utilized by the fire service. This favorably resolves long-standing concerns regarding the potential for harm caused by an untrained person operating valves in an emergency control box. There is no condition where removal of refrigerant from a refrigeration system by the fire service is considered advisable. In contrast, automatic transfer of excess pressure to another zone of the system in conjunction with stopping the pressure source (i.e., the compressors) can safely mitigate an overpressure condition.

605.10.1 Automatic crossover valves. Each high- and intermediate-pressure zone in a refrigeration system shall be provided with a single automatic valve providing a crossover connection to a lower pressure zone. Automatic crossover valves shall comply with Sections 605.10.1.1 through 605.10.1.3.

❖ The requirement for a single crossover valve between systems is based on the traditional industry practice of providing a single manual crossover valve in the emergency control box. In the unlikely event that a fire causes an overpressure condition, allowing system zones to automatically interconnect creates a much larger heat sink to limit pressure buildup while safely containing refrigerant. If the exposure fire continues to grow, emergency relief vents can protect the refrigeration system and automatic reseating valves can automatically limit the release of refrigerant to the amount necessary to maintain the system within design limits. In contrast, most emergency responders would not possess the expertise to properly cycle a manual valve in an emergency control box to limit the release of refrigerant to the minimum amount necessary for safety.

605.10.1.1 Overpressure limit set point. Automatic crossover valves shall be arranged to automatically relieve excess system pressure to a lower pressure zone if the pressure in a high- or intermediate-pressure zone rises to within 90 percent of the set point for emergency pressure relief devices.

❖ This section provides a safety buffer between activation of the emergency pressure control system (EPCS) and operation of a relief valve. Because of variances in operational tolerances among relief valves and because some relief valves may begin to seep at 90 percent of their rated operating pressure, it is appropriate to have the EPCS shut down a system if system pressure rises to 90 percent of the relief valve set pressure. This further reduces the potential for any release from a system that has malfunctioned and overpressurized.

605.10.1.2 Manual operation. Where required by the *fire code official*, automatic crossover valves shall be capable of manual operation.

❖ This section authorizes the local fire code official to require manual control capabilities for the crossover valve. Although this provision is not regarded as necessary by the industry, it is recognized that some fire departments will prefer to have the manual control capability for backup.

605.10.1.3 System design pressure. Refrigeration system zones that are connected to a higher pressure zone by an automatic crossover valve shall be designed to safely contain the maximum pressure that can be achieved by interconnection of the two zones.

❖ This provision requires lower pressure zones to be capable of handling additional pressure added by a crossover condition without overpressurizing or operating the emergency relief vents on the lower zone. The legacy codes did not address this concern, given the assumption that someone operating a manual bypass valve in the emergency control box would be knowledgeable with regard to system limitations; however, this may or may not be true. Nevertheless, the legacy codes never required the low pressure side of the system to handle the high-side pressure, and as a result, some systems with emergency control boxes present the potential for an emergency responder to overpressurize a system zone by fully opening a manual crossover valve too quickly. The resulting overpressure condition could cause operation of a relief vent or even a failure in the piping system.

605.10.2 Automatic emergency stop. An automatic emergency stop feature shall be provided in accordance with Sections 605.10.2.1 and 605.10.2.2.

❖ This establishes applicability of the requirements for the additional safety feature of an emergency stop feature in refrigeration systems.

605.10.2.1 Operation of an automatic crossover valve. Operation of an automatic crossover valve shall cause all compressors on the affected system to immediately stop. Dedicated pressure-sensing devices located immediately adjacent to crossover valves shall be permitted as a means for determining operation of a valve. To ensure that the automatic crossover valve system provides a redundant means of stopping compressors in an overpressure condition, high-pressure cutout sensors associated with compressors shall not be used as a basis for determining operation of a crossover valve.

❖ This section is intended to ensure the automatic crossover system has a fully redundant means of stopping compressors. Compressors are ordinarily provided with automatic high-pressure cutout controls, but this section requires that these controls not be used to satisfy the requirement. An additional set of controls can be required to serve as a backup means of preventing a severe overpressure condition that could cause operation of an emergency relief vent.

605.10.2.2 Overpressure in low-pressure zone. The lowest pressure zone in a refrigeration system shall be provided with a dedicated means of determining a rise in system pressure to within 90 percent of the set point for emergency pressure relief devices. Activation of the overpressure sensing device shall cause all compressors on the affected system to immediately stop.

❖ The lowest pressure zone of a system cannot be arranged to bleed pressure to another system zone since crossing the lowest pressure zone to a higher pressure zone would most likely result in reverse flow. However, by providing a redundant emergency stop control, which would disengage the compressor, an overpressure condition should be automatically mitigated. Overpressure on a low-pressure zone would most likely result from a defrost line from the high side that is stuck in the open position, and stopping the compressor will disengage the pressure source for the defrost system. Note that compressors will only cut out if an overpressure condition occurs. If the emergency condition involves a leak on the low side, compressors will continue to operate, which is beneficial in pumping down the low side for this type of event.

605.11 Storage, use and handling. Flammable and combustible materials shall not be stored in machinery rooms for refrigeration systems having a refrigerant circuit containing more than 220 pounds (100 kg) of Group A1 or 30 pounds (14 kg) of any other group refrigerant. Storage, use or handling of extra refrigerant or refrigerant oils shall be as required by Chapters 50, 53, 55 and 57.

Exception: This provision shall not apply to spare parts, tools and incidental materials necessary for the safe and proper operation and maintenance of the system.

❖ Storage of materials could introduce additional hazards in rooms already considered to be hazardous because of large quantities of refrigerants in the system circuits and machines.

605.12 Discharge and termination of pressure relief and purge systems. Pressure relief devices, fusible plugs and purge systems discharging to the atmosphere from refrigeration systems containing flammable, toxic or highly toxic refrigerants or ammonia shall comply with Sections 605.12.2 through 605.12.4.

❖ Discharge systems are intended to treat, incinerate or absorb flammable or toxic refrigerants that would otherwise be released unaltered into the atmosphere. Release would result from the operation of pressure relief devices or intentional dumping of refrigerant in an emergency. Specific requirements are found in the subsections for each type of refrigeration system.

605.12.1 Fusible plugs and rupture members. Discharge piping and devices connected to the discharge side of a fusible plug or rupture member shall have provisions to prevent plugging the pipe in the event the fusible plug or rupture member functions.

❖ This section is intended to ensure that, through the use of discharge piping and devices, the emergency pressure relief system will not become obstructed in the event that a fusible plug or rupture member operates and causes debris to be ejected into the relief system.

605.12.2 Flammable refrigerants. Systems containing more than 6.6 pounds (3 kg) of flammable refrigerants having a density equal to or greater than the density of air shall discharge vapor to the atmosphere only through an *approved* treatment system in accordance with Section 605.12.5 or a flaring system in accordance with Section 605.12.6. Systems containing more than 6.6 pounds (3 kg) of flammable refrigerants having a density less than the density of air shall be permitted to discharge vapor to the atmosphere provided that the point of discharge is located outside of the structure at not less than 15 feet (4572 mm) above the adjoining grade level and not less than 20 feet (6096 mm) from any window, ventilation opening or *exit*.

❖ Where they have a density greater than air (i.e., are heavier than air) and pose the hazard of collecting in low points, which could bring them into contact with ignition sources, flammable refrigerants (A2, B2, A3, B3) must be incinerated in a flaring system (see Section 6004.2.2.7.1). The second sentence of the provision is derived from ANSI/ASHRAE 15 and recognizes the reduced hazard of lighter-than-air flammable refrigerants by allowing them to discharge to the atmosphere without incineration or treatment since they would either dissipate into the air or flare at the point of discharge. Because of their flammability hazard, however, the point of discharge must be located out of reach from grade and well away from building openings. Note that these provisions apply only to systems that contain more than 6.6 pounds (3 kg) of refrigerant because systems containing smaller quantities are considered "small systems" and their relative hazard is considered insignificant.

605.12.3 Toxic and highly toxic refrigerants. Systems containing more than 6.6 pounds (3 kg) of toxic or highly toxic refrigerants shall discharge vapor to the atmosphere only through an *approved* treatment system in accordance with Section 605.12.5 or a flaring system in accordance with Section 605.12.6.

❖ Toxic refrigerants, like flammable refrigerants, must be treated to reduce their toxicity or be destroyed by incineration (see Section 6004.2.2.7.1).

605.12.4 Ammonia refrigerant. Systems containing more than 6.6 pounds (3 kg) of ammonia refrigerant shall discharge vapor to the atmosphere in accordance with one of the following methods:

1. Directly to atmosphere where the *fire code official* determines, on review of an engineering analysis prepared in accordance with Section 104.7.2, that a fire, health or environmental hazard would not result from atmospheric discharge of ammonia.
2. Through an *approved* treatment system in accordance with Section 605.12.5.
3. Through a flaring system in accordance with Section 605.12.6.
4. Through an *approved* ammonia diffusion system in accordance with Section 605.12.7.
5. By other *approved* means.

Exception: Ammonia/water absorption systems containing less than 22 pounds (10 kg) of ammonia and for which the ammonia circuit is located entirely outdoors.

❖ This section is more restrictive than ASHRAE 15 in that it requires the discharge to be treated in one of the listed methods. Item 1 recognizes that there are some cases, such as at remote facilities, where atmospheric discharge of ammonia would pose no danger to people or property. Further, it provides a basis in the code for permitting relief lines on ammonia refrigeration systems to discharge to the atmosphere where an appropriate analysis, accepted by the fire code official, has shown that such discharge can be accomplished safely. In such cases, a flaring or water diffusion system would serve no beneficial purpose, since ammonia is naturally biodegradable. Items 2 through 4 allow the use of one of three methods, including treatment systems, flaring system or an ammonia diffusion system.

Item 5 recognizes that engineered designs can be used to activate an alarm and automatically stop the leak rather than relying on manual means to stop the leak and a water tank to treat whatever release may occur before manual intervention can be accomplished.

The exception recognizes the reduced hazard in smaller systems where the ammonia circuit is completely outdoors.

605.12.5 Treatment systems. Treatment systems shall be designed to reduce the allowable discharge concentration of the refrigerant gas to not more than 50 percent of the IDLH at the point of exhaust. Treatment systems shall be in accordance with Chapter 60.

❖ See the commentary to Section 6004.2.2.7. "Immediately Dangerous to Life and Health (IDLH)" is defined in Section 202.

605.12.6 Flaring systems. Flaring systems for incineration of flammable refrigerants shall be designed to incinerate the entire discharge. The products of refrigerant incineration shall not pose health or environmental hazards. Incineration shall be automatic upon initiation of discharge, shall be designed to prevent blowback and shall not expose structures or materials to threat of fire. Standby fuel, such as LP-gas, and standby power shall have the capacity to operate for one and one-half the required time for complete incineration of refrigerant in the system. Standby electrical power, where required to complete the incineration process, shall be in accordance with Section 1203.

❖ Destruction of refrigerant by incineration is supposed to render the discharge harmless, so obviously the flames and the combustion byproducts do not pose a hazard themselves. Because most refrigerants would not support combustion unaided, a fuel source is necessary to sustain incineration.

605.12.7 Ammonia diffusion systems. Ammonia diffusion systems shall include a tank containing 1 gallon of water for each pound of ammonia (8.3 L of water for each 1 kg of ammonia) that will be released in 1 hour from the largest relief device connected to the discharge pipe. The water shall be prevented from freezing. The discharge pipe from the pressure relief device shall distribute ammonia in the bottom of the tank, but not lower than 33 feet (10 058 mm) below the maximum liquid level. The tank shall contain the volume of water and ammonia without overflowing.

❖ Ammonia is readily absorbed by water; therefore, an ammonia discharge into a water tank would be chemically held in the tank. The water tank may have to be heated to prevent it from freezing, which would block the discharge pipe and make the water useless for absorbing ammonia. The deeper the discharge pipe extends below the water surface, the greater the pressure the discharge would have to overcome to escape from the pipe. A 33-foot (10 058 mm) depth of water would exert a pressure approximately equal to sea level atmospheric pressure [14.7 psi (101 kPa)].

605.13 Mechanical ventilation exhaust. Exhaust from mechanical ventilation systems serving refrigeration machinery rooms containing flammable, toxic or highly toxic refrigerants, other than ammonia, capable of exceeding 25 percent of the LFL or 50 percent of the IDLH shall be equipped with *approved* treatment systems to reduce the discharge concentrations to those values or lower.

Exception: Refrigeration systems containing Group A2L complying with Section 605.17.

❖ Prior to the 2009 edition of the code, this section required the discharge of mechanical ventilation systems serving refrigeration machinery rooms utilizing anhydrous ammonia to be directed to a treatment system to reduce the toxicity to 50 percent of its IDLH value, the same as the more hazardous refrigerants. This section now permits the mechanical ventilation system to exhaust directly to the atmosphere when anhydrous ammonia is the refrigerant. Anhydrous ammonia is classified by Table 1103.1 of the IMC as a corrosive liquefied compressed gas. It is not a toxic or highly toxic gas, as defined in Section 202 of the code, nor does it meet the definition of a flammable gas. It has a vapor density of 0.597, making it lighter than air, and is extremely hygroscopic (a Latin word literally meaning "water seeking"), thus it aggressively absorbs water. Anhydrous ammonia's water-absorbing abilities can be of benefit to fire fighters, who can use hose or master streams to control anhydrous ammonia if it is leaking.

Exclusion of anhydrous ammonia from the requirement of this section also provides correlation with Section 1105.8 of the IMC, which addresses pressure relief systems for refrigeration systems. The IMC requires pressure relief devices be terminated in accordance with the requirements of American Society of Refrigeration and Air Conditioning Engineers (ASHRAE) Standard 15, Safety Standard for Refrigeration Systems. ASHRAE 15 requires pressure relief devices serving ammonia refrigeration equipment to be terminated outside of buildings and permits these devices to discharge to the atmosphere.

The exception to this section recognizes the reduced risk of the lower flammability rating of A2L refrigerants when they comply with Section 605.17. Essentially, Section 605.17 provides detection and ventilation, which removes the need to provide a treatment system as the flammability concentration is much lower.

605.14 Notification of refrigerant discharges. The *fire code official* shall be notified immediately when a discharge becomes reportable under state, federal or local regulations in accordance with Section 5003.3.1.

❖ Emergency personnel must be informed of a discharge so that they can respond appropriately. The refrigerant discharge notification requirements of this section parallel those required for all hazardous materials in Section 5003.3.1. There is no reason for different requirements for refrigerants than for other hazardous materials.

605.15 Records. A record of refrigerant quantities brought into and removed from the premises shall be maintained.

❖ Emergency personnel must be able to maintain accurate assessments of the dangers they may face and the hazards the public may face in and around buildings housing refrigeration systems.

As a result of a review of Recommendation 2(c) of the NIST Charleston, South Carolina Sofa Superstore Fire Report, changes were made to Sections 108.2 and 108.3, along with 49 other sections (including this section), to comprehensively address record-keeping requirements. Section 107.3 provides standardized record-keeping requirements for periodic inspection, testing, servicing and other operational and maintenance requirements of the code and makes it clear that records must be maintained on the premises or another approved location and that copies of records must be provided to the fire code official upon request. Section 107.3 also makes it clear that records must be maintained for a period of not less than 3 years unless a different time interval is specified in the code or a referenced standard, and that the fire code official is authorized to prescribe the form and format of such records. See the commentaries to Sections 108.2 and 108.3.

[M] 605.16 Electrical equipment. Where *refrigerant* of Groups A2, A3, B2 and B3, as defined in the *International Mechanical Code*, are used, refrigeration machinery rooms shall conform to the Class I, Division 2 hazardous location classification requirements of NFPA 70.

Exceptions:

1. Ammonia machinery rooms that are provided with ventilation in accordance with Section 1106.3 of the *International Mechanical Code*.
2. Machinery rooms for systems containing Group A2L *refrigerants* that are provided with ventilation in accordance with Section 605.17.

❖ This section mirrors the text of Section 1106.4 of the IMC and is included in the code because, in some jurisdictions, the fire code official is designated to inspect classified electrical equipment. A reference to classified electrical requirements here is consistent with the approach taken in Chapters 50 and 57 for other hazardous materials and flammable liquids, and it provides the fire code official with the provisions that are to be enforced.

The first exception for ammonia refrigerant is consistent with requirements of NFPA 70 and is included here to avoid possible confusion regarding the need for classified electrical equipment in ammonia machinery rooms. Because ammonia can combust within a limited range of concentrations in the air, the fire code official might be led to believe that classified electrical equipment should be provided in ammonia storage and use areas; however, when such areas are ventilated to maintain ammonia vapor in a concentration that is outside of the flammable range, there is no need for classified electrical equipment.

The second exception recognizes the lower hazard associated with A2L refrigerants and does not require electrical classification where ventilation in accordance with 605.17.2 is provided. Note that the hazards associated with A2L are similar to that of ammonia. The ventilation rates in Table 605.17.2 are founded in published research.

[M] 605.17 Special requirements for Group A2L refrigerant machinery rooms. Machinery rooms with systems containing Group A2L refrigerants shall comply with Sections 605.17.1 through 605.17.3.

Exception: Machinery rooms conforming to the Class 1, Division 2 hazardous location classification requirements of NFPA 70.

❖ This section addresses a class of refrigerants with very low flammability characteristics in refrigerant machinery rooms. Exception 2 of Section 605.16 allows A2L refrigerants in refrigeration machinery rooms to comply with the current code requirements for Group 1, Division 2 Electrical systems, or the installation of detection and ventilation systems to mitigate the hazard. This is similar to the mitigation scheme for many other hazardous operations, including repair garages (Section 2311.4.3), hazardous materials (dozens of examples), compressed gases, corrosives, etc. This is a common and accepted mitigation scheme within the IFC and other codes.

Federal agencies have begun limiting the use of refrigerants that have high global warming potential (GWP) properties. Industry has responded by developing a number of replacement refrigerants. One of the characteristics of most of these products is that they are minimally flammable. Proven protection schemes are available to mitigate the reduced risk posed by these products.

The codes (IMC, IFC, ASHRAE) have historically classified the flammability of refrigerants as Group 1 (nonflammable), Group 2 (moderately flammable), and Group 3 (highly flammable). Because the newly developed environmentally preferred refrigerants present a significantly lower hazard than Class 2 refrigerants, a new classification was established for them. The new flammability classification is 2L. In addition to flammability, the codes classify refrigerants as either nontoxic (A) or toxic (B), The new refrigerants are primarily classified as A2L—nontoxic, mildly flammable. Table 1103.1 in the IMC recognizes 2L refrigerants as a subclass of Group 2.

The 2L refrigerants have a burning velocity of less than 10 cm/sec. The energy required for ignition is very high, and the pressure rise is much less than refrigerants with a higher flammability, resulting in a far safer product than current Group 2 refrigerants. Historically, ammonia was the only widely used refrigerant with these burning characteristics. The IFC and other codes recognize this, and have made a number of exceptions for ammonia. These exceptions are based on the fact that its burning characteristics reduce the risk of ignition, and the risk of damage should ignition occur is greatly reduced. These risks are further reduced by code requirements for detection and ventilation. The fire history for ammonia is excellent where these mitigation measures have been in place. The mitigation measures are working to minimize the fire risks associated with the product.

This section provides similar mitigation measures for products with similar burning characteristics. The ventilation rates are based on research that clearly shows that the rates will maintain a safe environment in more than 90 percent of the leaks. This level of protection is more than adequate. Utilizing the same protection scheme for other 2L refrigerants provides the same level of safety as that for ammonia, and adheres to the philosophy of maintaining a level playing field for industry.

The provisions of Section 606.17 focus on requirements for machinery rooms that contain systems with A2L refrigerants. This section simply states that the provisions of Sections 605.17.1 through 605.17.3 apply where A2L refrigerants are used. The exception recognizes that these provisions are not required if the room is classified as a Class 1, Division 2 hazardous location. If so, no additional detection or ventilation would be required.

605.17.1 Refrigerant detection system. The machinery room shall be provided with a refrigerant detection system. The refrigerant detection system shall be in accordance with Section 605.8 and all of the following:

1. The detectors shall activate at or below a refrigerant concentration of 25 percent of the LFL.
2. Upon activation, the detection system shall activate the emergency ventilation system in Section 605.17.3.
3. The detection, signaling and control circuits shall be supervised.

❖ This section specifies the detection criteria for machinery rooms where A2L refrigerants are used. First reference to Section 605.8 is provided as the base for how the detection should operate. Item 1 is consistent with Section 605.8.1 and requires detector activation at 25 percent of the LFL. Item 2 requires the activation of the ventilation system. Item 3 requires supervision of all circuits so that any problems with the system will be addressed.

[M] 605.17.2 Emergency ventilation system. An emergency ventilation system shall be provided at the minimum exhaust rate specified in ASHRAE 15 or Table 605.17.2. Shut down of the emergency ventilation system shall be by manual means.

❖ This section provides the specific ventilation rates through compliance with either ASHRAE 15 or Table 605.17.2. The ventilation shutdown is also addressed and required to be manual.

TABLE [M] 605.17.2
MINIMUM EXHAUST RATE

REFRIGERANT	Q (m^3/sec)	Q (cfm)
R32	15.4	32,600
R143a	13.6	28,700
R444A	6.46	13,700
R444B	10.6	22,400
R445A	7.83	16,600
R446A	23.9	50,700
R447A	23.8	50,400
R451A	7.04	15,000
R451B	7.05	15,000
R1234yf	7.80	16,600
R1234ze(E)	5.92	12,600

❖ These criteria, including the table, are founded in research conducted by UTC/Carrier. This is widely accepted as the best research on the subject currently available. The ventilation rates in the table are based upon the following formula:

$$Q \geq \frac{m}{LFL \cdot S} \quad \text{(Equation-1)}$$

$$m = c_d \cdot \rho \cdot v \cdot A \quad \text{(Equation-2)}$$

Where variables are defined as:

c_d		coefficient of discharge (c_d = 1.00)
ρ	lb/ft^3 [kg/m^3]	refrigerant density per Equation 2
v	ft/s [m/s]	refrigerant velocity assuming choke vapor flow conditions, equal to the refrigerant acoustic velocity (speed of sound) per Equation 2
A	ft^2 [m^2]	cross-section flow area of refrigerant leak assuming 0.50 in. [12.7 mm] circular opening (A = 0.001364 ft^2 = 0.0001267 m^2)
m	lb/s [kg/s]	refrigerant leak mass flow rate
LFL	lb/ft^3 [g/m^3]	Lower Flammability Limit, or $ETFL_{60}$ if no LFL exists, published value per ASHRAE Standard 34
S		Factor to achieve desired safety factor (currently 0.5, for a safety factor of 2)
Q	ft^3/s [m^3/s]	required air flow rate, conversion to other units of measure is permitted

[M] 605.17.3 Emergency ventilation system discharge. The point of discharge to the atmosphere shall be located outside of the structure at not less than 15 feet (4572 mm) above the adjoining grade level and not less than 20 feet (6096 mm) from any window, ventilation opening or exit.

❖This section addresses where the emergency ventilation should discharge. Technically, the discharge may contain some flammable concentrations so, as a precaution, the prescribed distances from the building and openings are necessary. These distances are consistent with Section 605.12.2 for flammable refrigerants being discharged from treatment systems.

SECTION 606
ELEVATOR OPERATION, MAINTENANCE AND FIRE SERVICE KEYS

606.1 Emergency operation. Existing elevators with a travel distance of 25 feet (7620 mm) or more shall comply with the requirements in Chapter 11. New elevators shall be provided with Phase I emergency recall operation and Phase II emergency in-car operation in accordance with ASME A17.1/CSA B44.

❖ Elevators are often used as a tool by emergency personnel when responding to fires and other emergencies. Due to these needs, the elevators must be capable of providing certain functions such as recall and emergency operation.

This section establishes requirements for both new and existing elevators. Existing elevators that travel 25 feet (635 mm) or more above or below the main level must, as a minimum, be equipped with emergency operation capabilities that comply with ASME A17.3 as required by Section 1103.3.2. New elevator installations are held to more restrictive guidelines for increased cost effectiveness and must have both emergency recall (Phase I) and emergency in-car operation (Phase II) to comply with ASME A17.1 for any amount of travel distance. The ASME standards are safety codes for elevators and escalators: ASME A17.3 is for existing elevators and ASME A17.1 for new elevator installations.

606.2 Standby power. In buildings and structures where standby power is required or furnished to operate an elevator, standby power shall be provided in accordance with Section 1203. Operation of the system shall be in accordance with Sections 606.2.1 through 606.2.4.

❖ This section states how standby power is to be supplied to elevators when required by other sections, such as Sections 1009.4.1 and 1009.5. The requirements from this section are the same as those located in Chapter 30 of the IBC. Section 1203 addresses the overall requirements for emergency and standby power including the relevant standards and other performance criteria.

606.2.1 Manual transfer. Standby power shall be manually transferable to all elevators in each bank.

❖ This section requires that all elevators in each bank of elevators must be equipped for manual transfer to standby power. All elevators, however, would not need to operate on standby power at the same time; they would have to have manual transfer capability.

606.2.2 One elevator. Where only one elevator is installed, the elevator shall automatically transfer to standby power within 60 seconds after failure of normal power.

❖ Where a building has a single elevator, it must be automatically transferred to standby power within 60 seconds. The 60 seconds is a reflection of the NFPA 70 requirements for standby power.

606.2.3 Two or more elevators. Where two or more elevators are controlled by a common operating system, all elevators shall automatically transfer to standby power within 60 seconds after failure of normal power where the standby power source is of sufficient capacity to operate all elevators at the same time. Where the standby power source is not of sufficient capacity to operate all elevators at the same time, all elevators shall transfer to standby power in sequence, return to the designated landing and disconnect from the standby power source. After all elevators have been returned to the designated level, not less than one elevator shall remain operable from the standby power source.

❖ Where there is more than one elevator operating off a common system, the elevators must all be transferred to standby power within 60 seconds. Where only one elevator needs to be available during a loss of power, all elevators must still have the ability to run on standby power. Specifically, all elevators must initially connect to the standby power system and then, in sequence, return to the designated floor where all but one would be disconnected from the standby power.

606.2.4 Machine room ventilation. Where standby power is connected to elevators, the machine room ventilation or air conditioning shall be connected to the standby power source.

❖ This section reduces the likelihood that the equipment running the elevators will overheat during a loss of power because standby power is also required to power the ventilation or air conditioning for those areas. Note that this would also address machine spaces, control rooms and control spaces.

[BE] 606.3 Emergency signs. An *approved* pictorial sign of a standardized design shall be posted adjacent to each elevator call station on all floors instructing occupants to use the exit stairways and not to use the elevators in case of fire. The sign shall read: IN FIRE EMERGENCY, DO NOT USE ELEVATOR. USE EXIT STAIRS.

Exceptions:

1. The emergency sign shall not be required for elevators that are part of an accessible *means of egress* complying with Section 1009.4.
2. The emergency sign shall not be required for elevators that are used for occupant self-evacuation in accordance with Section 3008 of the *International Building Code*.

❖ Because of the needs of fire fighters and the possible risks posed by the use of elevators during a fire, signage is required that prohibits the use of elevators by building occupants during a fire emergency. The need to evacuate all occupants regardless of their physical abilities is becoming a more important issue and, in some cases, elevators are specifically used for such purposes. Elevators used as part of the means of egress must comply with Section 1009.4.

606.4 Fire service access elevator lobbies. Where fire service access elevators are required by Section 3007 of the *International Building Code*, fire service access elevator lobbies shall be maintained free of storage and furniture.

❖ The fire service access elevator in high-rise buildings over 120 feet (3657 mm) in height above fire department vehicle access, as required by Section 403.6.1 of the IBC, is a tool which enhances fire fighters' abilities to gain access to the fire floor and undertake necessary operational staging activities in a protected area. This section complements the provisions of the fire service access elevator provisions contained in Section 3007 of the IBC by requiring that fire service access elevator lobbies always be fully and immediately accessible by the fire service without impediment by storage or furniture and the fire load that some items might present. It is not unusual, especially in Group R-1 occupancies, to see tables, chairs, sofas or the like placed in areas opposite elevator entrances for aesthetic purposes in what may now be a required fire service access elevator lobby. This section would prohibit that practice. It should also be noted that the provisions of this section apply to noncombustible storage and furnishings, as well as combustible (see commentaries, IBC Sections 403.6.1 and 3007).

606.5 Occupant evacuation elevator lobbies. Where occupant evacuation elevators are provided in accordance with Section 3008 of the *International Building Code*, occupant evacuation elevator lobbies shall be maintained free of storage and furniture.

❖ This section is similar in intent to Section 606.4 for fire service access elevators except that the focus is providing adequate space for those awaiting evacuation via the elevators. If storage or furnishings are allowed, it takes away from that space and also will cause more people to wait outside the protected lobby. Placing combustibles within the lobby also creates potential fire hazards.

606.6 Water protection of hoistway enclosures. Methods to prevent water from infiltrating into a hoistway enclosure required by Section 3007.3 and Section 3008.3 of the *International Building Code* shall be maintained.

❖ Sections 3007.3 and 3008.3 of the IBC require that hoistway openings be protected from water originating from sprinklers activated outside of the elevator lobby. This is critical to extend the use of elevators during a fire. The methods used are not prescribed in the IBC but often will require some level of maintenance to make sure they will be available during a fire. This section creates the maintenance mechanism.

606.7 Elevator key location. Keys for the elevator car doors and fire-fighter service keys shall be kept in an *approved* location for immediate use by the fire department.

❖ The fire service often responds to elevator emergencies and other emergencies that require the use or operation of the elevators and associated components. Most elevators will have at least five or six key-switched functions, including those for standby power transfer, Phase I emergency elevator recall (hall switch located in the elevator lobby at the designated level), Phase II in-cab emergency operation, inspection function, normal lighting and fan operation. Ready access to elevator keys is an important factor in the timely and efficient response to emergency situations. Because experience has shown that this important safety element is often overlooked, this section requires that elevator keys be kept in a location approved by the fire code official to ensure immediate access. Many elevator installers will provide, as part of their package, an elevator key box (see Commentary Figure 606.7), which will accommodate all of the required operating keys, plus an appropriate hoistway access key or tool for fire department use in accessing the hoistway in case of an elevator emergency. Elevator inspection reports should note the presence and locations of the keys. Inspectors may verify the availability of the keys during periodic fire safety inspections and prefire planning surveys.

606.8 Standardized fire service elevator keys. Buildings with elevators equipped with Phase I emergency recall, Phase II emergency in-car operation, or a fire service access elevator shall be equipped to operate with a standardized fire service elevator key approved by the *fire code official.*

Exception: The owner shall be permitted to place the building's nonstandardized fire service elevator keys in a key box installed in accordance with Section 506.1.2.

❖ When fire departments and other emergency response agencies respond to emergencies, their ability to quickly access the location of the emergency can be the deciding factor of a successful response. Elevators are increasingly being relied on for emergency operations and their importance has been highlighted by adding Section 3007 to the IBC, requiring the installation of fire service access elevators and providing requirements for the installation of occupant evacuation elevators. One of the difficulties the fire service and other emergency response agencies have when accessing facilities and attempting to use elevators is the number of nonstandardized keys that may not be available at the time of response. Even when emergency responders are provided the necessary keys in case of response, the correct key may have to be identified from a large collection of keys for any one building. In larger jurisdictions, the sheer number of keys makes possession of them unwieldy for the emergency responders. An elevator key is an important tool to fire fighters. The key allows fire fighters to access the interior of the shaft housing an elevator cabin to initiate rescue in case of a malfunction or the loss of building power. More often, an elevator key is used to capture and control an elevator in emergencies. This section establishes requirements for elevator keys used by the fire service that will only apply to those buildings that have elevators with Phase I or Phase II emergency service or to

Commentary Figure 606.7
TYPICAL ELEVATOR KEY BOX

those buildings equipped with a fire service access elevator. Note that this section is aimed at providing consistency within a jurisdiction to facilitate successful emergency responses.

The exception recognizes that many jurisdictions have elevators built prior to the introduction of a standard elevator key and, as a result, each building with an elevator requires its own elevator key, and authorizes the jurisdiction to require the installation of a key box to house nonstandardized elevator keys (see commentary, Section 506.1.2).

606.8.1 Requirements for standardized fire service elevator keys. Standardized fire service elevator keys shall comply with all of the following:

1. All fire service elevator keys within the jurisdiction shall be uniform and specific for the jurisdiction.Keys shall be cut to a uniform key code.
2. Fire service elevator keys shall be of a patent-protected design to prevent unauthorized duplication.
3. Fire service elevator keys shall be factory restricted by the manufacturer to prevent the unauthorized distribution of key blanks. Uncut key blanks shall not be permitted to leave the factory.
4. Fire service elevator keys subject to these rules shall be engraved with the words "DO NOT DUPLICATE."

❖ This section requires that keys for any new elevators installed in the jurisdiction use a unique but standard format, regardless of elevator manufacturer or model. Standardizing the type of elevator key creates a consistent arrangement for fire fighters who utilize the elevators for EMS incidents or for the deployment of personnel and equipment in a multiple-story fire fighting operation. The keys must be manufactured to prevent unauthorized duplication. Consistency between jurisdictions may be important where there are mutual aid agreements.

606.8.2 Access to standardized fire service keys. Access to standardized fire service elevator keys shall be restricted to the following:

1. Elevator owners or their authorized agents.
2. Elevator contractors.
3. Elevator inspectors of the jurisdiction.
4. *Fire code officials* of the jurisdiction.
5. The fire department and other emergency response agencies designated by the *fire code official*.

❖ Access to or possession of a key that can take control of an elevator in a building is an area of vulnerability for buildings that was not previously addressed with simple key designs being utilized. In addition to the limitations placed on the unauthorized duplication and distribution of standardized elevator keys in Section 606.8.3, this section specifies exactly to whom the keys will be accessible. This list includes only those persons who have a vested interest in the building, the elevator equipment or the protection of the building.

606.8.3 Duplication or distribution of keys. A person shall not duplicate a standardized fire service elevator key or issue, give, or sell a duplicated key unless in accordance with this code.

❖ This section provides for a level of security for the standardized key by prohibiting its unauthorized duplication and distribution. Note that Section 606.8.1 requires that keys be stamped or embossed with a duplication prohibition warning.

606.8.4 Responsibility to provide keys. The building owner shall provide up to three standardized fire service elevator keys where required by the *fire code official*, upon installation of a standardized fire service key switch or switches in the building.

❖ This section establishes the responsibility of the building owner to provide at least three keys of the same standard design where an elevator is equipped with Phase I and II fire-fighter service or is a fire service access elevator. Multiple keys allow fire companies to use multiple elevators to carry personnel and equipment to the fire floor or swiftly remove multiple injured or otherwise incapacitated persons from upper or lower floors.

SECTION 607 COMMERCIAL KITCHEN HOODS

[M] 607.1 General. Commercial kitchen exhaust hoods shall comply with the requirements of the *International Mechanical Code.*

❖ Rather than including detailed commercial hood requirements here, the code simply references the IMC for hood design (see IMC commentary, Section 507).

[M] 607.2 Where required. A Type I hood shall be installed at or above all commercial cooking appliances and domestic cooking appliances used for commercial purposes that produce grease vapors.

Exceptions:

1. Factory-built commercial exhaust hoods that are listed and labeled in accordance with UL 710, and installed in accordance with Section 304.1 of the *International Mechanical Code*, shall not be required to comply with Sections 507.1.5, 507.2.3, 507.2.5, 507.2.8, 507.3.1, 507.3.3, 507.4 and 507.5 of the *International Mechanical Code*.
2. Factory-built commercial cooking recirculating systems that are listed and labeled in accordance with UL 710B, and installed in accordance with Section 304.1 of the *International Mechanical Code*, shall not be required to comply with Sections 507.1.5, 507.2.3, 507.2.5, 507.2.8, 507.3.1, 507.3.3, 507.4 and 507.5 of the *International Mechanical Code*. Spaces in which such systems are located shall be considered to be kitchens and shall be ventilated in accordance with Table 403.3.1.1 of the *International Mechanical Code*. For the purpose of determining

the floor area required to be ventilated, each individual appliance shall be considered as occupying not less than 100 square feet (9.3 m^2).

3. Where cooking appliances are equipped with integral down-draft exhaust systems and such appliances and exhaust systems are listed and labeled for the application in accordance with NFPA 96, a hood shall not be required at or above them.

4. A Type I hood shall not be required for an electric cooking appliance where an approved testing agency provides documentation that the appliance effluent contains 5 mg/m^3 or less of grease when tested at an exhaust flow rate of 500 cfm (0.236 m^3/s) in accordance with UL 710B.

❖ A Type I hood (see definition of "Hood, Type I" in Section 202) is required for all appliances used for commercial cooking as defined in Section 202. In addition to the specific cooking appliances identified in the definition, further examples of commercial cooking appliances that require a commercial kitchen exhaust system are griddles (flat or grooved); tilting skillets or woks; braising and frying pans; roasters; pastry ovens; pizza ovens; charbroilers; salamanders and upright broilers; infrared broilers and open-burner stoves; ranges; and barbecue equipment. Further, the definition of "Commercial cooking appliances" defines a food service establishment as "...any building or portion thereof used for the preparation and serving of food."

The term "grease" refers to animal and vegetable fats and oils that are used to cook foods or that are a byproduct of cooking foods. Cooking appliances are primarily used for the preparation of food for compensation, trade or services rendered. Where the nature of the cooking produces grease or smoke, a Type I hood is required. The intent is not to require a Type I hood where there is a possibility of food being burned and producing smoke. For example, smoke that is produced when toast is burned does not mean that a Type I hood is required over a toaster.

Section 607 does not require exhaust hoods for cooking equipment or appliances installed outdoors where the grease-laden vapors, etc., discharge directly to the outside atmosphere, nor is this chapter intended to regulate cooking appliances installed in vehicles or towed trailers (see definition of "Commercial cooking appliances"). Note that cooking appliances installed outdoors but located under a roof should be evaluated for installation under a Type I hood just as if they were located inside a building having enclosing walls.

Exception 1 states the requirements for factory-built commercial exhaust hoods and specifies which code provisions are not applicable to factory-built hoods. Shop-built and field-constructed hoods are subject to all of the design and fabrication requirements of Section 507.2 of the IMC.

A factory-built commercial exhaust hood that has been tested in accordance with UL 710 and listed and labeled by an approved agency must be installed in accordance with the manufacturer's instructions. The importance of installing the system in strict compliance with the manufacturer's instructions cannot be overemphasized. These instructions contain specific installation requirements that are critical to the proper and efficient operation of the hood.

Note that hoods listed and labeled in accordance with UL 710 are not exempt from Section 507.2.6 of the IMC; therefore, the 18-inch (457 mm) clearance requirement applies regardless of what is stated on the hood labels. The following is a list of some of the information that must be contained within the manufacturer's installation instructions or on the label:

- Minimum and maximum spacing between the front lower edge of the hood and the cooking surface.
- Minimum exhaust airflow quantity.
- Maximum supply airflow if the supply air is directed into the hood.
- Minimum overhangs of the exhaust hood over the cooking surface.
- Maximum allowable surface temperature of the cooking appliance.
- The specific type of cooking appliance an exhaust hood is intended to serve.

It is also important to determine that all parts and subassemblies of an exhaust hood are components of the listed and labeled exhaust hood, or that the parts and subassemblies have been evaluated under the same conditions of fire severity as the exhaust hood. Furthermore, the exhaust hood must be compatible with and intended for the type of cooking appliance it will serve. The label of a factory-built hood tested in accordance with UL 710 will indicate the duty classification (i.e., extra-, heavy-, medium- and light-duty) of the appliances the hood is intended to serve. This will make it easy for the inspector in the field to determine whether the hood that is installed is suited for the appliances that are being installed under the hood.

This section is not intended to require labeling of exhaust hoods. Unlabeled factory-built hoods and shop/field-constructed hoods are permitted.

A factory-built or field-constructed commercial exhaust hood that has not been listed and labeled in accordance with UL 710 is permitted if it is designed, constructed and installed in accordance with Section 507 of the IMC and all other applicable requirements of Chapter 5 of the IMC. This section addresses hood material requirements, hood construction, hood dimensions, exhaust quantities and makeup air requirements. Kitchen exhaust systems must discharge all effluent to the outdoors to comply with Sections 501.2, 506.3.13 and 506.4 of the IMC.

Exception 2 allows installation of factory-built commercial cooking recirculating systems if they have been listed and labeled in accordance with UL 710B. It is important that recirculating systems be installed in accordance with the manufacturer's installation instructions so that the listing requirements are met. An improper installation could result in hazardous vapors being discharged back into the kitchen.

Factory-built commercial cooking recirculating systems consist of an electric cooking appliance and an integral or matched packaged hood. The hood assembly consists of a fan, collection hood, grease filter, fire damper, fire-extinguishing system and air filter such as an electrostatic precipitator. These systems are tested for fire safety and emissions. The grease vapor (condensable particulate matter) in the effluent at the system discharge is not allowed to exceed a concentration of 5.0 mg/m^3. Recirculating systems are not used with fuel-fired appliances because the filtering systems do not remove products of combustion. This exception states that listed and labeled hoods have demonstrated compliance with the construction and design requirements of Sections 507.1.5, 507.2.3, 507.2.5, 507.2.8, 507.3.1, 507.3.3, 507.4 and 507.5 of the IMC.

Recirculating systems are becoming more and more popular, especially in smaller businesses that serve food—for example, a sandwich shop that wants to expand its menu without becoming a full kitchen. A possible concern with using such a system is that they are tested to prevent particulate matter from being redistributed into the space, but they do not completely remove all contaminants and odors. For this reason, a space where one of these appliances is installed must be considered as a kitchen for the purpose of applying Table 403.3.1.1 of the IMC. A space not considered to be a traditional kitchen and containing recirculating systems with no exhaust to the outdoors, would not be ventilated if not for this provision in the code. The ventilation rate for kitchens is 0.7 cfm/ft^2 of exhaust, so to apply this rate, each individual recirculating appliance is considered as occupying 100 square feet. The purpose of this requirement is to provide a minimal amount of exhaust in the area where one or more of these appliances is installed. If a recirculating appliance is installed in a typical commercial kitchen where the kitchen ventilation rate is being applied to the whole space, then the area of the kitchen would be used to determine the ventilation rate without adding the additional 100 square feet for each recirculating appliance. Note however, if the kitchen is small and the number of recirculating appliances multiplied by 100 square feet is greater than the area of the kitchen, the exhaust rate for the kitchen must be based on the area calculated in accordance with this section.

All hoods, listed and unlisted, must capture and confine cooking vapors within the hood to prevent spillage into the room.

Exception 3 recognizes the hoodless griddle-type of cooking appliance that is becoming very popular in restaurants. These types of cooking appliances are often referred to as hibachi tables, where food is prepared for customers at the table where they are seated. These cooking tables have a built-in integral down-draft exhaust system that is designed to capture the cooking vapors by drawing the air across the table into exhaust inlets located at the edge of the cooking surface. The cooking vapors are routed to grease filters located under the cooking surface and then to the grease duct that is under the floor. The grease duct must be installed in accordance with Section 506.3.10 of the IMC. These hoods must be listed and labeled for this application. Chapter 15 of NFPA 96 contains specific requirements for integral down-draft exhaust systems.

Exception 4 recognizes the growing use of small electrical appliances used for cooking, such as in small sandwich shops and convenience stores, where little or no grease is produced. The installation of a Type I hood in these small establishments would create the expense of the hood and the energy costs of running the fan and tempering the makeup air where grease emissions are minimal or nonexistent. The grease emission threshold requirement is consistent with NFPA 96 and the testing procedure is done in accordance with Section 17 of UL 710B. In order for an appliance to qualify for use without a Type I hood it must be tested by an approved agency and shown that the effluent contains 5 mg/m3 or less of grease when tested at an exhaust flow rate of 500 cfm. See also the IMC definitions of "Light-," "Medium-," "Heavy-" and "Extra-heavy duty cooking appliances" as well as IMC Section 507.2.

607.3 Operations and maintenance. Commercial cooking systems shall be operated and maintained in accordance with Sections 607.3.1 through 607.3.4.

❖ The provisions of this section introduce Sections 607.3.1 through 607.3.4, which contain requirements for controlling the hazards associated with the operation and maintenance of commercial cooking systems.

607.3.1 Ventilation system. The ventilation system in connection with hoods shall be operated at the required rate of air movement, and grease filters listed and labeled in accordance with UL 1046 shall be in place where equipment under a kitchen grease hood is used.

❖ The hood must be designed to adequately collect and exhaust fumes, smoke and vapors from the area over which it is installed. To accomplish this, the hood must cause an airflow pattern that will sweep and direct the fumes, smoke and vapors from the cooking surfaces into the hood inlet.

The IMC specifies the minimum quantity of exhaust air necessary for effective removal of cooking vapors and the approximate amount of makeup air necessary for proper operation. The quantity of required exhaust is as much a function of the operational characteristics of the cooking equipment as it is a function of the size of the cooking surface or the exhaust hood opening area and the presence of walls and side panels. Manufacturer recommendations must be followed where applicable.

Grease filters prevent large amounts of grease from collecting in the hood, in exhaust ducts, on fan blades and at the exhaust system termination. The accumulation of grease can cause blockage in ducts, cause equipment failure and create a fire hazard. It therefore makes sense to have grease filters in place whenever commercial cooking equipment is used. This section requires the grease filters to be listed and labeled in accordance with UL 1046. This is consistent with the requirements of the IMC.

607.3.2 Grease extractors. Where grease extractors are installed, they shall be operated when the commercial-type cooking equipment is used.

❖ As noted in the commentary for Section 607.3.1, it is imperative that grease removal devices operate where commercial cooking equipment is used. Grease extractors and similar grease removal devices range from simple designs, such as a configuration of baffles, to elaborate hot water scrubbers and electrostatic precipitators. The devices must be installed to comply with the IMC and the manufacturer's installation instructions.

607.3.3 Cleaning. Hoods, grease-removal devices, fans, ducts and other appurtenances shall be cleaned at intervals as required by Sections 607.3.3.1 through 607.3.3.3.

❖ The provisions of this section introduce Sections 607.3.3.1 through 607.3.3.3, which contain requirements for controlling the hazards associated with grease accumulation in commercial cooking systems. This includes appliances that produce grease-laden vapors, the hood, any grease extractors, the exhaust duct and the exhaust fan. The date of the cleaning and the extent of the work performed must be documented and be maintained on the premises.

607.3.3.1 Inspection. Hoods, grease-removal devices, fans, ducts and other appurtenances shall be inspected at intervals specified in Table 607.3.3.1 or as *approved* by the *fire code official.* Inspections shall be completed by qualified individuals.

❖ A regular inspection schedule must be maintained to prevent the accumulation of grease residue within the exhaust system. The hood, grease removal devices, ducts, fans, fire suppression system discharge nozzles and other components of the system must be cleaned regularly to prevent excessive accumulation of grease. The frequency of such cleaning can vary, depending on the amount and type of usage; however, at a minimum, the equipment must be inspected at the intervals indicated in Table 607.3.3.1. Commercial cooking equipment exhaust systems may be viewed in some respects as a combustible material conveying system inasmuch as the grease carried within the duct is very combustible under the right conditions. As such, the inspection of the system should be entrusted only to persons trained and qualified in system inspection practices. While there are no identified nationally recognized criteria for gauging if an individual is or is not qualified to perform this work, several companies have developed their own certification programs for establishing requirements for individuals who supervise the cleaning of commercial cooking operations. In any case, the fire code official will make the final determination, in accordance with Section 102.8.

TABLE 607.3.3.1
COMMERCIAL COOKING SYSTEM INSPECTION FREQUENCY

TYPE OF COOKING OPERATIONS	FREQUENCY OF INSPECTION
High-volume cooking operations such as 24-hour cooking, charbroiling or wok cooking	3 months
Low-volume cooking operations such as places of religious worship, seasonal businesses and senior centers	12 months
Cooking operations utilizing solid fuel-burning cooking appliances	1 month
All other cooking operations	6 months

❖ Inspection frequencies are established in this table, which is based on the volume of cooking being performed, the type of cooking operation and the type of fuel used. The most restrictive requirement is for cooking operations using solid fuels, such as barbeque pits and meat smokers. When these or similar appliances use a solid fuel such as wood or charcoal, a minimum monthly inspection frequency is required. Cooking operations that use charbroilers or woks require a minimum 3-month inspection frequency, as do high volume cooking operations such as are found in 24-hour restaurants. The frequency of inspection is reduced to 12 months for lower intensity cooking activities including, but not limited to, seasonal businesses, places of worship and facilities for the care of senior citizens. All other cooking operations are subject to a 6-month inspection frequency. Depending on the nature of the commercial cooking activities, a single kitchen could have activities that require different inspection frequencies. For example, a restaurant that serves smoked meats would require that the appliance used for the preparation of the meat be inspected monthly, while other equipment would require inspection every 3 or 6 months, depending on the volume of cooking being performed.

607.3.3.2 Grease accumulation. If during the inspection it is found that hoods, grease-removal devices, fans, ducts or other appurtenances have an accumulation of grease, such components shall be cleaned in accordance with ANSI/IKECA C10.

❖ Frequent cleaning of exhaust systems is essential to the fire safety of cooking establishments to eliminate the potentially flammable and highly dangerous collection of grease within the exhaust system. The most common cleaning method is hand scraping, which requires that a person remove the hood filters and the access doors in the exhaust ductwork and physically scrape the accumulated grease from the interior surfaces of the exhaust system. Done properly, this method is effective but far from perfect. Regular inspection and diligence by the owner and the fire code official are needed to achieve the desired level of cleanliness of the exhaust system.

A frequently asked question about grease accumulation is, “How much of an accumulation is enough to warrant a cleaning?” Grease buildup in a commercial cooking exhaust system and the frequency with which the system must be cleaned depend on several factors, including but not limited to: the types of appliances under the hood, the type of grease-removal devices in use, exhaust velocity within the system, number of joints in the ductwork, changes in direction of the duct run, temperature of the grease-laden air being exhausted, efficiency of the exhaust fan and whether the duct is insulated or exposed to the outdoors. Just as the frequency of inspection in Table 609.3.3.1 varies based on the intensity of the cooking operation, so does the rate of grease accumulation. The referenced standard, ANSI/IKECA C-10, provides requirements to determine the frequency and necessity for commercial kitchen exhaust system cleaning through inspection procedures. In addition, the standard defines acceptable methods for cleaning exhaust systems and components and sets standards for acceptable cleanliness.

607.3.3.3 Records. Records for inspections shall state the individual and company performing the inspection, a description of the inspection and when the inspection took place. Records for cleanings shall state the individual and company performing the cleaning and when the cleaning took place. Such records shall be completed after each inspection or cleaning and maintained.

❖ Adequate records of inspections and cleanings not only provide documentation of the required inspections and the resulting cleanings but are also essential in establishing a workable cleaning schedule. A record of all cleaning must be maintained by the person or party responsible for the system. The records must indicate the method of cleaning and the time between cleanings as well as what components were cleaned.

As a result of a review of Recommendation 2(c) of the NIST Charleston, South Carolina Sofa Superstore Fire Report, changes were made to Sections 108.2 and 108.3, along with 49 other sections (including this section), to comprehensively address record-keeping requirements. Section 108.3 provides standardized record-keeping requirements for periodic inspection, testing, servicing and other operational and maintenance requirements of the code and makes it clear that records must be maintained on the premises or another approved location and that copies of records must be provided to the fire code official upon request. Section 107.3 also makes it clear that records must be maintained for a period of not less than 3 years unless a different time interval is specified in the code or a referenced standard, and that the fire code official is authorized to prescribe the form and format of such records. See the commentaries to Sections 108.2 and 108.3.

607.3.3.3.1 Tags. When a commercial kitchen hood or duct system is inspected, a tag containing the service provider name, address, telephone number and date of service shall be provided in a conspicuous location. Prior tags shall be covered or removed.

❖ This section details the markings required to visually confirm serviceability of commercial kitchen hood and duct systems. The text is consistent with the requirements set forth in ANSI/IKECA C-10, as referenced in Section 607.3.3.2.

607.3.4 Extinguishing system service. Automatic fire-extinguishing systems protecting commercial cooking systems shall be serviced as required in Section 904.12.5.

❖ See the commentary to Section 904.12.5.

607.4 Appliance connection to building piping. Gas-fired commercial cooking appliances installed on casters and appliances that are moved for cleaning and sanitation purposes shall be connected to the piping system with an appliance connector listed as complying with ANSI Z21.69. The commercial cooking appliance connector installation shall be configured in accordance with the manufacturer’s installation instructions. Movement of appliances with casters shall be limited by a restraining device installed in accordance with the connector and appliance manufacturer’s instructions.

❖ This requirement is intended to end the practice of replacing listed flexible piping with residential flexible piping. Residential flexible piping is more easily damaged when the cooking equipment is moved for cleaning, thus causing a fire/life safety problem with gas leaks and fires. This section is also intended to limit the distance the appliances can be moved for cleaning to further protect the connection.

SECTION 608
COMMERCIAL KITCHEN COOKING OIL STORAGE

608.1 General. Storage of cooking oil (grease) in commercial cooking operations utilizing above-ground tanks with a capacity greater than 60 gal (227 L) installed within a building shall comply with Sections 608.2 through 608.7 and NFPA 30. For purposes of this section, cooking oil shall be classified as a Class IIIB liquid unless otherwise determined by testing.

❖ In these times of increasing interest in alternative fuels, used cooking oil has benefits in that it can be recycled for commercial cooking operations. It can also be chemically modified into biodiesel and used as fuel for mobile or stationary equipment. Because it can be recycled and reused, many restaurants and similar businesses that perform commercial cooking operations have found that capturing used cooking oil reduces waste disposal costs. As a result, the food service industry is seeking options for the safe storage of waste cooking oils in buildings and, as such, there has arisen a large market for collecting and recycling used cooking oil (grease) from commercial cooking operations. This is sometimes done using a system designed to store the used cooking oil on-site in an above-ground tank. These systems typically include wheeled recovery carts and hoses (see Commentary Figure 608.2) to assist in transferring the grease from the cooking appliance to the storage tank, and from the storage tank to a recovery truck. Some systems include heating elements that assist in keeping the grease in a form that is easily pumped to the recovery truck. This arrangement could create a problem if the system is not properly designed and installed. Without the requirements of Section 608 addressing the storage of cooking oils, many installations may not be installed with the safety features needed to protect employees and the public.

It should be noted that this section also addresses fresh cooking oil versus used, spent or inedible cooking oil. These oils need to be stored in tanks and related components that are food grade. That is why there are specific requirements for nonmetallic tanks. Most metallic tanks, as required by this section, could not meet these specifications.

This section also specifies that, for the application of these requirements, cooking oils are classified as Class IIIB liquids in accordance with the definition of "Combustible liquids" in Chapter 2 of the code. These liquids have a closed-cup-flash-point temperature greater than 200°F (93.33°C). Flash point and ignition temperatures for common cooking oils are shown in Commentary Figure 608.1 and the data confirms that this classification is correct.

Note that installation of the cooking oil storage tank and its piping will require a construction permit in accordance with Section 105.7.9.

608.2 Metallic storage tanks. Metallic cooking oil storage tanks shall be listed in accordance with UL 142 or UL 80, and shall be installed in accordance with the tank manufacturer's instructions.

❖ This section requires storage tanks for cooking oil storage to be listed as complying with either UL 142 or UL 80. Both standards are limited to shop-fabricated above-ground storage tanks (ASTs) designed to operate at atmospheric pressure. Both standards require tanks to be constructed of carbon steel meeting a certain specification and, before shipment, to be tested at the factory to confirm they are liquid tight. Tanks constructed to UL 80 have a maximum volume of 660 gallons (2271.25 L) versus UL 142, which does not limit the volume of ASTs. Installations of metallic ASTs for cooking oil storage also must comply with the manufacturer's installation instructions (see Commentary Figure 608.2).

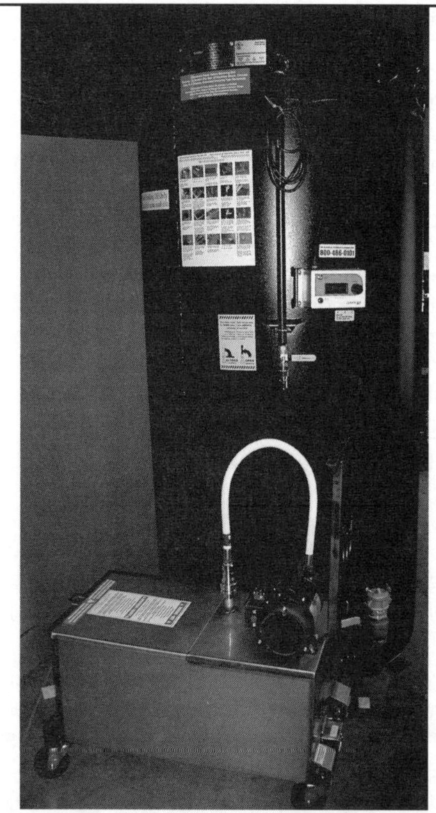

Commentary Figure 608.2
COOKING OIL STORAGE TANK AND RECOVERY CART
(Photo courtesy of Darling International Inc., Irving, TX)

COOKING OIL TYPE	FLASH POINT TEMPERATURE (°F)	IGNITION TEMPERATURE (°F)
Canola oil	450	626
Corn oil	490	740
Cotton seed oil	486	650
Palm oil	323	600
Peanut oil	540	833
Soybean oil	549	833
Sunflower seed oil	550	Undetermined

For SI: °C = (°F - 32)/1.8.

Commentary Figure 608.1
COOKING OIL FLASH POINT AND IGNITION TEMPERATURES

608.3 Nonmetallic storage tanks. Nonmetallic cooking oil storage tanks shall be listed in accordance with UL 2152 and shall be installed in accordance with the tank manufacturer's instructions. Tank capacity shall not exceed 200 gallons (757 L) per tank.

❖ As discussed in Section 608.1, cooking oil that has not been previously used must be stored in food grade tanks. Typically, nonmetallic tanks are more appropriate for nonused cooking oil. These provisions are not limited to fresh cooking oil and can be utilized for used, spent and inedible cooking oils. This section references the appropriate standard, UL 2152, for such tanks. Essentially, a listing for use with cooking oil is required, as is making sure that the maximum temperature limits associated with the tank match the application in which the tank is used.

The tanks are limited in size to 200 gallons. Metallic tanks have the potential for much larger capacities, as discussed in the commentary for Section 608.2

608.4 Cooking oil storage system components. Cooking oil storage system components shall include but are not limited to piping, connections, fittings, valves, tubing, hose, pumps, vents and other related components used for the transfer of cooking oil, and are permitted to be of either metallic or nonmetallic construction.

❖ This section simply describes what components make up a cooking oil storage system. Section 608.4.1 addresses the design and construction requirements for these components. This section also notes that these components are permitted to be either metallic or nonmetallic. The allowance for types of materials will depend on the requirements in Section 608.4.1.

608.4.1 Design standards. The design, fabrication and assembly of system components shall be suitable for the working pressures, temperatures and structural stresses to be encountered by the components.

❖ The performance-based language provided in this section requires that it be determined that the system's intended use is consistent with all the components of the system.

608.4.2 Components in contact with heated oil. System components that come in contact with heated cooking oil shall be rated for the maximum operating temperatures expected in the system.

❖ Cooking oil storage system components may be exposed to elevated temperatures, such as when draining spent oil from deep fat fryers. Manufacturers must document that components can withstand the highest temperature to be expected during normal operations to avoid component deterioration or failure from heat exposure.

608.5 Tank venting. Normal and emergency venting shall be provided for cooking oil storage tanks.

❖ This section and the UL tank standards referenced in Section 608.2 require ASTs to be equipped with a normal vent and an emergency vent.

608.5.1 Normal vents. Normal vents shall be located above the maximum normal liquid line, and shall have a minimum effective area not smaller than the largest filling or withdrawal connection. Normal vents shall be permitted to vent inside the building.

❖ Tanks are vented to maintain the internal tank pressure within the design operating range. Low pressure can increase the generation of vapors while high pressure can damage the tank or piping system. Any pressure outside of the design pressure range (which could be caused if the vent line were not located above the highest level of liquid) can have an adverse effect on the operation of the system as well as the piping and equipment. This section is also consistent with Section 21.4.3 of NFPA 30.

While this section establishes the size of the normal vent line as being the same as the largest inflow or outflow connection, it should be noted that Section 21.4.3.3 of NFPA 30 also states that the minimum vent size must be $1^1/_4$ inches inside diameter.

Recognizing the reduced hazard of Class IIIB liquids, this section does not require the normal vent for a cooking oil AST installed indoors to be terminated outside the building. Note, however, that Section 5704.2.7.3.3 of the code allows this condition only where the tank is equipped with a normally closed pressure/vacuum vent.

608.5.2 Emergency vents. Emergency relief vents shall be located above the maximum normal liquid line, and shall be in the form of a device or devices that will relieve excessive internal pressure caused by an exposure fire. For nonmetallic tanks, the emergency relief vent shall be allowed to be in the form of construction. Emergency vents shall be permitted to vent inside the building.

❖ All ASTs for cooking oil storage require an emergency vent that will relieve excessive internal pressure caused by exposure to fires in accordance with Section 5704.2.7.4 of the code; however, the emergency vents for ASTs storing Class IIIB liquids are generally permitted to discharge inside the building in accordance with that section.

608.6 Heating of cooking oil. Electrical equipment used for heating cooking oil in cooking oil storage systems shall be listed to UL 499 and shall comply with NFPA 70. Use of electrical immersion heaters shall be prohibited in nonmetallic tanks.

❖ Many cooking oil storage tank systems contain internal heaters to keep the oil above its melting temperature so that it can be efficiently removed by a recovery vacuum truck. This section requires that the electrical equipment associated with the heating of cooking oil be listed and its design and installation comply with NFPA 70. Note that this section does not require any temperature controls to ensure the cooking oil is not heated above its flash point temperature. See the commentary to Section 5701.5 for a discussion of the impact of heating combustible liquids above their flash point.

608.7 Electrical equipment. Electrical equipment used for the operation of cooking oil storage systems shall comply with NFPA 70.

❖ The phrase "cooking oil storage system" as used in this section could lead to the incorrect assumption that it is listed as a complete assembly of components. Fire code officials will need to evaluate the electrical equipment separately for compliance with the code and NFPA 70.

SECTION 609
HYPERBARIC FACILITIES

609.1 General. Hyperbaric facilities shall be inspected, tested and maintained in accordance with NFPA 99.

❖ Section 425 of the IBC requires that hyperbaric facilities, regardless of occupancy, comply with NFPA 99 for installation. This section provides the maintenance requirements so that such facilities continue to operate safely. The standard provides detailed responsibilities for testing and inspecting these facilities, such as requirements for an on-site hyperbaric safety director and for training.

609.2 Records. Records shall be maintained of all testing and repair conducted on the hyperbaric chamber and associated devices and equipment. Records shall be available to the *fire code official*.

❖ This section requires that records be kept to document compliance with the maintenance and testing requirements of NFPA 99 for the benefit of the facility owner and the fire code official.

As a result of a review of Recommendation 2(c) of the NIST Charleston, South Carolina Sofa Superstore Fire Report, changes were made to Sections 108.2 and 108.3, along with 49 other sections, to comprehensively address recordkeeping requirements. Section 107.3 provides standardized recordkeeping requirements for periodic inspection, testing, servicing and other operational and maintenance requirements of the code and makes it clear that records must be maintained on the premises or another approved location and that copies of records must be provided to the fire code official upon request. Section 108.3 also makes it clear that records must be maintained for a period of not less than 3 years unless a different time interval is specified in the code or a referenced standard, and that the fire code official is authorized to prescribe the form and format of such records. See the commentaries to Sections 108.2 and 108.3.

Bibliography

The following resource materials were used in the preparation of the commentary for this chapter of the code:

CGA V-1, *Standard Compressed Gas Cylinder Valve Outlet and Inlet Connections*. Chantilly, VA: Compressed Gas Association, 2005.

Complete Revision History to the 2018 I-Codes: Successful Changes and Public Comments. Washington, DC: International Code Council, 2017.

Commercial Kitchen Hood—Application Guide. Washington, DC: International Code Council, 2010.

National Institute of Standards and Technology (NIST) Charleston, South Carolina, Sofa Super Store Fire Report, June 18, 2007. NIST-SP 1118 Volume I, March 2011.

Chapter 7: Fire and Smoke Protection Features

General Comments

This chapter provides the requirements for the inspection and maintenance of existing passive fire protection features in existing buildings and structures. In general, these requirements are intended to maintain the required fire-resistance ratings and limit the spread of fire and smoke.

Chapter 7 is divided into seven sections. Section 701 lists the general administrative provisions that require fire-resistance-rated construction, smoke barriers, and smoke partitions to be maintained. Section 702 provides a list of the definitions that are used in the chapter. The remainder of the chapter describes the required specific maintenance of Penetrations (703), Joints and Voids (704), Door and Window Openings (705), Ducts and Air Transfer Openings (706) and Concealed Spaces (707). These sections use the same terminology that is used in the *International Building Code*® (IBC®). As stated in Section 701.1, the requirements for the installation of passive fire protection features in new buildings are located in Chapter 7 of the IBC.

Purpose

The maintenance of assemblies required to be fire-resistance rated is a key component in a passive fire protection philosophy. This chapter reinforces this component and further regulates specific protection elements that, when properly maintained, prevent fire spread and smoke migration through buildings.

SECTION 701 GENERAL

701.1 Scope. The provisions of this chapter shall govern the inspection and maintenance of the materials, systems and assemblies used for structural *fire resistance*, *fire-resistance-rated* construction separation of adjacent spaces and construction installed to resist the passage of smoke to safeguard against the spread of fire and smoke within a building and the spread of fire to or from buildings. New buildings shall comply with the *International Building Code*.

❖This section establishes the scope of Chapter 7, introduces the requirements for maintaining the integrity of fire-resistance-rated assemblies (see Section 703) and prescribes the types of floor opening protection required in existing buildings (see Section 704). The provisions of Chapter 7 apply to the ongoing maintenance of the materials, assemblies and systems used to protect against the passage of fire and smoke within and between buildings. The assemblies outlined herein provide various degrees of protection. The required fire-resistance rating varies with the potential fire hazard associated with type of construction, occupancy, height and area of the building and degree of protection for different elements of the means of egress. The potential fire hazard associated with various occupancies is reflected in the IBC. Chapter 7 of the IBC provides the details and the extent of the protection (horizontal and vertical continuity); however, the actual fire-resistance-rated construction is mandated by provisions in Chapters 4, 5, 6, 7 and 10 of the IBC.

701.2 Fire-resistance-rated construction. The *fire-resistance rating* of the following *fire-resistance-rated* construction shall be maintained:

1. Structural members.
2. *Exterior walls.*
3. *Fire walls, fire barriers, fire partitions.*
4. *Horizontal assemblies.*
5. Shaft enclosures.

❖Fire walls, fire barriers and fire partitions are key components in a passive fire- and life-safety design. Fire walls constructed in accordance with Section 706 of the IBC serve to create separate buildings (see the commentary to the definition of "Area, building" in Chapter 2 of the code); therefore, all applicable provisions of the code are applied individually to the building on each side of the fire wall. As such, the fire wall must also provide the same protection afforded by exterior walls, namely: structural integrity, structural independence and adequate fire resistance for exposure protection.

Fire barriers constructed in accordance with Section 707 of the IBC provide a higher degree of protection than fire partitions, but lack the inherent structural integrity of fire walls and, unlike fire partitions, there are no circumstances under which a fire barrier wall is permitted to terminate at a ceiling. Fire barriers are used to separate a variety of areas, including: exits and certain areas of refuge; mixed occupancies and incidental use areas; shafts; floor opening enclosures; hazardous materials control areas; and fire areas. It is important to note that, since fire barriers are intended to provide a reliable subdivision of areas, the construction that structurally supports the assembly is required to provide and maintain at least the same hourly fire-resistance rating as the fire barrier being supported.

Fire partitions constructed in accordance with Section 708 of the IBC are wall assemblies that enclose exit access corridors; separate tenant spaces in covered malls, dwelling units and sleeping units; and separate elevator lobbies from the balance of a floor. Openings in fire partitions must be properly protected, but the total area of openings in a fire partition is not limited. Unlike the continuity requirements for fire walls and fire barriers, fire partition continuity must only be continuous from floor slab to the floor slab or roof deck above or to the ceiling of a fire-resistance-rated floor/ceiling or roof/ceiling assembly. Although fire partitions must normally be supported by construction having a comparable fire-resistance rating in buildings of Types IIB, IIIB and VB construction, as defined in the IBC, Section 708.4 of that code does not require such supportive construction for sleeping units and tenant separations and exit access corridor walls.

The IBC includes requirements for fire-resistance rating, continuity and opening and penetration protection in these types of assemblies. Because these assemblies and their opening protectives are critical life safety components of a building, they must be maintained throughout the life of the building. Opening protective maintenance provisions for these types of assemblies are contained in NFPA 80. For further information on fire walls, fire barriers and fire partitions, see the commentaries to Sections 706, 707 and 708 of the IBC, respectively.

Vertical openings that are not properly protected can act as a chimney for smoke, hot gases and products of combustion. Unprotected floor openings have been a major contributing factor in many large loss-of-life fires. Unless indicated otherwise, Chapter 11 retroactively requires the enclosure of vertical openings between floors with approved fire barriers (see commentaries, Sections 1103.4 through 1103.4.10).

701.2.1 Hanging displays. The hanging and displaying of salable goods and other decorative materials from acoustical ceiling systems that are part of a fire-resistance-rated horizontal assembly shall be prohibited.

❖This section is only applicable to acoustical ceiling systems that are a component of an approved fire-resistance-rated floor/ceiling or roof/ceiling assembly required to be rated by the type of construction of the building. Fire-resistance-rated floor/ceiling and roof/ceiling assemblies must be tested using the methods in ASTM E119 to demonstrate a fire-resistance rating. Locating a substantial fuel load and additional weight directly beneath an acoustical ceiling, however, may expose the ceiling to a direct fire source and weight overload not contemplated in the ASTM E119 testing. That could breech the ceiling, which is an integral part of the tested assembly. Depending on the contribution of the ceiling to the overall fire-resistance rating, this may result in the assembly not functioning as intended or failing completely.

New acoustical ceiling systems, whether or not they are a component of an approved fire-resistance-rated assembly, are required to comply with Section 808 of the IBC. Section 808.1.1 of the IBC requires that acoustical ceiling systems comply with the manufacturer's installation instructions. Section 808.1.1.1 of the IBC further requires compliance with several ASTM standards that govern the installation of such systems. Those standards do not contemplate the addition of loads to the metal support framework of the system beyond the load of the system itself plus light fixtures, or other components that might be part of the approved design. Adding any weight to the system beyond that for which it was designed or approved by the building official could lead to failure of the system and should only be done after a review of the structural components by a registered design professional.

701.3 Smoke barriers. The *fire-resistance rating* and smoke-resistant characteristics of *smoke barriers* shall be maintained.

❖Smoke barriers divide areas of a building into separate smoke compartments to create an area of safety for occupants. A smoke barrier is designed and installed in accordance with IBC Section 709 to resist fire and smoke spread so that occupants can be evacuated or relocated to adjacent smoke compartments (see the commentaries to the definitions of "Smoke barrier" and "Smoke compartment" in Chapter 2). This concept has proven effective in Group I-2 and I-3 occupancies, and Sections 407.5 and 408.6 of the IBC identify where smoke barriers are required in those occupancies. Smoke barriers may also be utilized in other applications, such as part of a smoke control system (see Section 909.5 of this code), separation of accessible areas of refuge in accessible means of egress (see Section 1009.6.4 of this code), compartmentation of underground buildings (see Section 405.4.2 of the IBC) and elevator lobbies in underground buildings (see Section 405.4.3 of the IBC), Fire Service Access Elevator lobbies (IBC Section 3007.6.2) and occupant evacuation elevator lobbies (IBC Section 3008.6.2) among others. Other than the wall itself, all of the elements in the smoke barrier that can potentially allow smoke travel through the smoke barrier are required to have a quantified resistance to leakage. This includes doors, joints, through penetrations and dampers. The maximum leakage limits are as established in the individual code sections referenced above for each element. A smoke barrier is not intended or expected to be exposed to fire for extended periods and is, therefore, not required to have a fire-resistance rating exceeding 1 hour. Also, the occupancies in which smoke barriers are required are generally required to be sprinklered by Section 903 of this code. Smoke barriers are to be continuous from outside wall to outside wall and from the top of the foundation or floor/ceiling assembly below to the underside of the floor or roof sheathing, deck or slab. The provisions require the barrier to be continuous through all concealed and interstitial spaces, including suspended ceilings and the space between the ceiling and the floor or roof sheathing, deck or slab above. Smoke barriers are not required to extend through interstitial spaces if the space is designed and constructed such that fire and smoke will not spread from one smoke compartment to another; therefore, the construction assembly forming the bottom of the interstitial space must provide the required fire-resistance rating and be capable of resisting the passage of smoke from the spaces below.

701.4 Smoke partitions. The smoke-resistant characteristics of smoke partitions shall be maintained.

❖Smoke partitions are nonrated walls that serve to resist the spread of fire and the unmitigated movement of smoke for an unspecified period of time. Their primary purpose is to prevent the ready and quick passage of smoke into corridors in Group I-2 occupancies or for elevator lobby protection in a sprinklered building. Unlike 1-hour fire-resistance-rated smoke barriers, unless required by the IBC, smoke partitions are not required to have a fire-resistance rating. Smoke partitions are intended to provide less protection than a smoke barrier, and therefore are not required to be continuous through the concealed spaces and through the ceiling. The construction of a smoke partition is prescribed in Section 710 of the IBC; however, the level of performance or a method of testing them is not provided.

Because these assemblies and their opening protectives are critical life safety components of a building, they must be maintained throughout the life of the building. Opening protective maintenance provisions for these types of assemblies are contained in NFPA 105. For further information on incidental uses, smoke barriers and smoke partitions, see the commentaries to Sections 509, 709 and 710 of the IBC, respectively.

701.5 Maintaining protection. Materials, systems and devices used to repair or protect breaches and openings in fire-resistance-rated construction and construction installed to resist the passage of smoke shall be maintained in accordance with Sections 703 through 707.

❖This section provides a general reference to the sections of this chapter that provide requirements that are used to maintain, repair or protect breaches and openings in fire-resistance-rated construction and the construction installed to resist the passage of smoke.

701.6 Owner's responsibility. The owner shall maintain an inventory of all required *fire-resistance-rated* construction, construction installed to resist the passage of smoke and the construction included in Sections 703 through 707. Such construction shall be visually inspected by the *owner* annually and properly repaired, restored or replaced where damaged, altered, breached or penetrated. Records of inspections and repairs shall be maintained. Where concealed, such elements shall not be required to be visually inspected by the *owner* unless the concealed space is accessible by the removal or movement of a panel, access door, ceiling tile or similar movable entry to the space.

❖Maintaining an inventory is critical to the owner, the fire code official, and anyone who may be providing the inspection service. This inventory record is necessary for these individuals to perform a complete inspection of the existing protection elements and allow for the continuing documentation that they are still in place and able to perform their required function.

701.7 Unsafe conditions. Where any components in this chapter are not maintained and do not function as intended or do not have the *fire resistance* or the resistance to the passage of smoke required by the code under which the building was constructed, remodeled or altered, such component(s) or portion thereof shall be deemed an unsafe condition, in accordance with Section 111.1.1. Components or portions thereof determined to be unsafe shall be repaired or replaced to conform to that code under which the building was constructed, remodeled, altered or this chapter, as deemed appropriate by the *fire code official*.

Where the condition of components is such that any building, structure or portion thereof presents an imminent danger to the occupants of the building, structure or portion thereof, the *fire code official* shall act in accordance with Section 111.2.

❖This section is intended to clarify to code officials, designers, contractors and property owners that a building's fire-resistance-rated construction must be maintained at the original level of safety required by the codes that were applicable when the building was constructed or last remodeled. Failure to maintain fire-resistant components to that level of safety will result in the component being declared unsafe in accordance with Section 110.1.1 and repair or restoration being required.

Code provisions, which require maintenance to a level of safety required by an often-unknown code or an unknown edition of a known code, are sometimes viewed as problematic and unenforceable. However, communities should have some record of when a building was constructed, and knowing the year of construction should make it relatively easy to determine an edition of the code that was published close to or prior to that year. In many communities, local historical societies can also be helpful in doing research to determine the year of construction. These types of methods for determining the originally applicable code, if any, could be viewed as haphazard and arbitrary, but they can be considered better than trying to make a building constructed 30, 50 or 100 years ago comply with today's requirements. In the event that no information of any kind can be found to shed light on an original construction date, this chapter provides for an acceptable level of safety and can be retroactively required where deemed appropriate by the fire code official.

This section also provides that where component conditions are so bad due to lack of maintenance as to constitute a clear and present threat to the safety of the occupants, the fire code official must take the steps required by Section 110.2.

SECTION 702 DEFINITIONS

702.1 Definitions. The following terms are defined in Chapter 2:

DRAFTSTOP.

FIREBLOCKING.

FIRE-RESISTANT JOINT SYSTEM.

MEMBRANE-PENETRATION FIRESTOP SYSTEM.

OPENING PROTECTIVE.

SMOKE BARRIER.

SMOKE PARTITION.

THROUGH-PENETRATION FIRESTOP SYSTEM.

❖Definitions of terms can help in the understanding and application of the code requirements. This section directs the code user to Chapter 2 for the proper application of the indicated terms used in this chapter. Terms may be defined in Chapter 2 or in another International Code® (I-Code®) as indicated in Section 201.3, or the dictionary meaning may be all that is needed (see also commentaries, Sections 201 through 201.4).

SECTION 703 PENETRATIONS

703.1 Maintaining protection. Materials and firestop systems used to protect membrane and through penetrations in *fire-resistance-rated* construction and construction installed to resist the passage of smoke shall be maintained. The materials and firestop systems shall be securely attached to or bonded to the construction being penetrated with no openings visible through or into the cavity of the construction. Where the system design number is known, the system shall be inspected to the listing criteria and manufacturer's installation instructions.

❖The code mandates that all equipment, systems, devices and safeguards required by the current and previously adopted codes be maintained in good working order (see Section 102.1). This section reiterates that requirement specifically for fire-resistance-rated assemblies in existing buildings.

Once a building is occupied, its component parts are often damaged, altered or penetrated for installation of new piping, wiring and the like. These actions may reduce the effectiveness of assemblies that must be fire-resistance rated. This section requires the building owner, annually, to visually inspect nonconcealed elements and that any damage to a fire-resistance-rated assembly be repaired in a manner that restores the original required performance characteristics. Concealed elements must be visually inspected if they may be accessed by a door, removable ceiling tile, access panel or the like. Similarly, if a fire-resistance-rated assembly is altered or penetrated, the alteration or penetration must comply with the applicable requirements of the IBC for the particular type of alteration or penetration.

This section also requires that written records of maintenance and repairs to rated assemblies must be kept and should indicate the date, time and the name of the person conducting the inspection or repair for each rated assembly. These records must be maintained by the owner and made available to the fire code official for review when requested. This requirement relieves the fire code official of the administrative burden of maintaining test records. Note that, if the owner does not have the design number, the base inspection criteria would still apply, inspecting to make sure the system is properly secured and inspecting for visible openings through the system or into the cavity.

SECTION 704 JOINTS AND VOIDS

704.1 Maintaining protection. Where required when the building was originally constructed, materials and systems used to protect joints and voids in the following locations shall be maintained. The materials and systems shall be securely attached to or bonded to the adjacent construction, without openings visible through the construction.

1. Joints in or between *fire-resistance-rated* walls, floors or floor/ceiling assemblies and roof or roof/ceiling assemblies.
2. Joints in *smoke barriers*.
3. Voids at the intersection of a horizontal floor assembly and an exterior curtain wall.
4. Voids at the intersection of a horizontal smoke barrier and an exterior curtain wall.
5. Voids at the intersection of a nonfire-resistance-rated floor assembly and an exterior curtain wall.
6. Voids at the intersection of a vertical *fire barrier* and an exterior curtain wall.
7. Voids at the intersection of a vertical *fire barrier* and a nonfire-resistance-rated roof assembly.

Unprotected joints and voids do not need to be protected where such joints and voids were not required to be protected when the building was originally constructed.

❖This section lists the specific locations where fire and smoke protection joints and voids need to be maintained. In general these occur where two individual building protection elements come together and those elements need to be continually connected at their intersecting junction. There should be no visible openings or any way for fire and smoke to pass through. Note that this section is not intended to be retroactive in the addition of protection elements. As stated, joints and voids that were not required to be protected when the building was originally built are not required to have protection added as part of the building maintenance.

704.2 Opening protectives. Where openings are required to be protected, opening protectives shall be maintained self-closing or automatic-closing by smoke detection. Existing fusible-link-type automatic door-closing devices are permitted if the fusible link rating does not exceed 135°F (57°C).

❖This section requires that fire door assemblies provided for protection of openings in vertical enclosures be self-closing or automatic-closing in order to maintain the integrity of the vertical opening enclosure. This section also recognizes that some opening protectives in existing buildings may already be equipped with heat-actuated closing devices rather than the smoke-detector-actuated devices otherwise required by the section. Such devices are allowed to continue in service, provided that the temperature rating of their fusible element is as low as is available [i.e., 135°F (57°C)] to provide the fastest possible operation in the event of a fire. In the event that an existing fusible link on an opening protective is rated higher than the maximum 135°F (57°C) allowed by this section, it would need to be removed and the door maintained as self-closing or be replaced with a smoke-detector-actuated closer in accordance with this section and Section 907.3. New opening protectives must comply with Section 716 of the IBC. See the commentary to that section for further information.

SECTION 705 DOOR AND WINDOW OPENINGS

705.1 General. Where required when the building was originally constructed, opening protectives installed in *fire-resistance-rated* assemblies, *smoke barriers* and *smoke partitions* shall be inspected and maintained in accordance with this section.

❖This section provides a general reference to ensuing sections that list specific requirements for the maintenance of existing opening protectives that were required and installed as part of fire and smoke protection construction when the building was originally built.

705.2 Inspection and maintenance. Opening protectives in *fire-resistance-rated* assemblies shall be inspected and maintained in accordance with NFPA 80. *Opening protectives* in *smoke barriers* shall be inspected and maintained in accordance with NFPA 80 and NFPA 105. Openings in smoke partitions shall be inspected and maintained in accordance with NFPA 105. Fire doors and smoke and draft control doors shall not be blocked, obstructed, or otherwise made inoperable. Fusible links shall be replaced promptly whenever fused or damaged. *Opening protectives* and smoke and draft control doors shall not be modified.

❖Openings in fire-resistance-rated assemblies must be protected to prevent the passage of fire in accordance with Section 716 of the IBC. After opening protectives are installed and approved, they may become damaged, corroded or otherwise less effective than required. This section specifically requires that all opening protectives required by the IBC be maintained in compliance with NFPA 80 so that they can perform their intended function, which is to prevent the passage of smoke, fire or combustion products through openings in fire-resistance-rated walls, ceilings and shafts during a fire emergency. Sections 705.2.3 and 705.2.4 of the code indicate specific points of inspection and enforcement regarding these doors. Prohibited modifications to fire door assemblies include the attachment of materials, cutting, boring holes or other alterations that could affect the performance of the door as a fire protection-rated assembly.

Proper maintenance necessitates that the manufacturer's installation instructions and the listing organization's instructions are followed in order to maintain the listing and proper operation of the assemblies and devices as required by the code, the manufacturer and the listing organization.

705.2.1 Labeling requirements. Where approved by the *fire code official*, the application of field-applied labels associated with the maintenance of *opening protectives* shall follow the requirements of the *approved* third-party certification organization accredited for *listing* the opening protective.

❖This section addresses the very real issue of maintaining labeled opening protectives by requiring field-applied labels to follow the requirements of the third-party certification organization, which is accredited for listing the specific opening protective. The relabeling of existing fire doors is a common practice and, due to the importance of the rating requirements, a level of monitoring by a third party to ensure the labeling matches the rating of the door assembly is necessary.

In the listing documentation, there are specific criteria for field application of labels. One of the criteria is whether the local fire code official allows this practice, and this section provides guidance in this area to the fire code official. IBC Section 716.2.9.1 requires that new fire doors or new fire door assemblies must be labeled at the factory (see the definition of "Labeled" in Chapter 2 of this code). However, it is not uncommon for an existing fire door to have either a damaged or missing label, or a label that has been painted over or otherwise obscured. The fire code official needs to make a determination as to whether field application of the label is acceptable or not. If field application is allowed, then the certification organization can follow the proper criteria for labeling the opening protective.

705.2.2 Signs. Where required by the *fire code official*, a sign shall be permanently displayed on or near each *fire door* in letters not less than 1 inch (25 mm) high to read as follows:

1. For doors designed to be kept normally open: FIRE DOOR—DO NOT BLOCK.
2. For doors designed to be kept normally closed: FIRE DOOR—KEEP CLOSED.

❖Any door in a fire-resistance-rated wall assembly represents a potential "weak link" in maintaining the degree of compartmentation intended. That is the reason for requiring a rated assembly. The IBC calls for adequate opening protection in the form of a door with a specified fire protection rating. This section allows the fire code official to require signage on or near the rated doors to make the occupants aware of the importance of the door as a fire- and life-safety feature. Also, see the commentary to Section 705.2.3 for a discussion on door closing and the improper use of props to hold doors open.

705.2.3 Hold-open devices and closers. Hold-open devices and automatic door closers, where provided, shall be maintained. During the period that such device is out of service for repairs, the door it operates shall remain in the closed position.

❖The only devices acceptable for holding fire doors open are fire-detector-activated, automatic-closing devices that automatically close the doors (or allow the doors to swing closed using self-closing devices) in the event of a fire. Numerous devices, such as electromagnetic hold-opens, pneumatic systems and systems of pulleys and weights connected to a fusible link, are available.

The detection method for the closing device must be consistent with the purpose of the opening protective; that is, doors in smoke barriers must be activated by smoke detectors. Heat detectors or fusible links are adequate where maintenance of the fire-resistance rating alone is required.

Where smoke-detector-activated automatic door closers are used and the detectors are interconnected with a required fire alarm system, the devices and wiring methods must be checked for compatibility with the fire alarm system control panel before installation. Some fire alarm control equipment is compatible only with the manufacturer's automatic smoke detectors. Fire detectors used for automatic door release service in buildings that are not equipped with a fire alarm system must comply with Section 907.3.

A common violation of fundamental safety principles, as well as this section of the code, is having wooden or rubber wedges, or kick-down-type door hold-opens prop open fire doors or smoke barrier doors. This renders them totally ineffective as opening protectives. Building maintenance personnel who do not understand the purpose of these doors often do this to aid movement of people, equipment or air in a hallway or other area without realizing the potential hazard to life safety if a fire were to occur. This violation is especially problematic as it pertains to means of egress stairwells or horizontal exit doors as well. For further information on door closing requirements for fire doors, see Section 716.2.6 of the IBC.

705.2.4 Door operation. Swinging *fire doors* shall close from the full-open position and latch automatically.

❖Fire doors must be closed to be effective. Swinging fire doors should be frequently checked to make sure they close and latch on their own power from any position.

705.2.5 Smoke- and heat-activated doors. Smoke-activated doors shall be maintained to self-close or automatically close upon detection of smoke. Existing fusible-link-type automatic door-closing devices are permitted if the fusible link rating does not exceed 135°F (57°C).

❖This section requires that fire door assemblies provided for protection of openings in vertical enclosures be self-closing or automatic-closing in order to maintain the integrity of the vertical opening enclosure. This section also recognizes that some opening protectives in existing buildings may already be equipped with heat-actuated closing devices rather than the smoke-detector-actuated devices otherwise required by the section. Such devices are allowed to continue in service, provided that the temperature rating of their fusible element is as low as is available [i.e., 135°F (57°C)] to provide the fastest possible operation in the event of a fire. In the event that an existing fusible link on an opening protective is rated higher than the maximum 135°F (57°C) allowed by this section, it would need to be removed and the door maintained as self-closing or be replaced with a smoke-detector-actuated closer in accordance with this section and Section 907.3. New opening protectives must comply with Section 716 of the IBC. See the commentary to that section for further information.

705.2.6 Testing. Horizontal and vertical sliding and rolling *fire doors* shall be inspected and tested annually to confirm proper operation and full closure. Records of inspections and testing shall be maintained.

❖Annual tests are intended to determine that required fire doors operate freely and close completely. Where fusible links are used as the releasing mechanism, the link may be temporarily removed rather than activated during testing. Fusible links in poor condition must be replaced as part of the maintenance of fire-resistance components. Smoke detectors and heat detectors other than fusible links must be tested as required by the manufacturer's instructions (see NFPA 72 for recommended testing procedures for various fire detectors).

This section also requires that written records of inspection and testing of opening protectives must be kept and should indicate the date, the time and the name of the person conducting the inspection or repair for each rated assembly. These records must be maintained by the owner and should be made available to the fire code official for review when requested. This requirement relieves the fire code official of the administrative burden of maintaining test records.

SECTION 706
DUCT AND AIR TRANSFER OPENINGS

706.1 Maintaining protection. Dampers protecting ducts and air transfer openings shall be inspected and maintained in accordance with NFPA 80 and NFPA 105. Other products or materials used to protect the openings for ducts and air transfer openings shall be securely attached to or bonded to the construction containing the duct or air transfer opening, without visible openings through or into the cavity of the construction. Any damaged products or materials protecting duct and air transfer openings shall be repaired, restored or replaced.

❖This section addresses the maintenance of dampers in ducts and air transfer openings. The referenced NFPA standards provide the details of the required inspections. NFPA 80 is specific to fire doors and NFPA 105 is specific to smoke doors. Furthermore, any other products or materials that are installed to protect openings in ducts or air transfer openings are to be inspected to ensure that they continue to be firmly attached. There should be no visible openings or any way for fire and smoke to pass through. If the inspection discovers any components that are damaged or otherwise not performing their intended function, they are to be repaired or replaced as necessary.

706.2 Unprotected openings. Unprotected duct and air transfer openings in *fire-resistance-rated* construction and construction installed to resist the passage of smoke shall be protected so as to comply with requirements that were in effect when the building was constructed.

❖This section makes it clear that unprotected duct and air transfer openings in fire and smoke protected construction are only required to be protected with the requirements that were in effect when the building was originally built.

SECTION 707
CONCEALED SPACES

707.1 Fireblocking and draftstopping. Required *fireblocking* and draftstopping in combustible concealed spaces shall be maintained to provide continuity and integrity of the construction.

❖Fireblocking and draftstopping (see the Chapter 2 commentaries for the definitions "Fireblocking" and "Draftstop") slow the spread of fire and the products of combustion through concealed spaces within a building. To fulfill their intended function, fireblocking and draftstopping must be properly maintained. Most frequently, damage or repairs to other building components, such as mechanical piping, results in fireblocking or draftstopping being removed and not properly replaced. This section specifically requires that where fireblocking and draftstopping required by the IBC are damaged, removed or otherwise altered, they must be replaced or restored.

Chapter 8: Interior Finish, Decorative Materials and Furnishings

General Comments

This chapter is consistent with the *International Building Code*® (IBC®), which regulates the interior finishes of buildings through the regulation of their flame spread potential. The code goes beyond interior finishes, also regulating furnishings and vegetation in buildings in certain occupancies. Additionally, the code addresses interior finishes and decorative materials in existing buildings.

This chapter is related to fire growth and spread potential in terms of the immediate effect on building occupants. The flame spread characteristics of certain materials will affect the potential fire scenarios within a building. Fire-resistance-rated construction, which is dealt with in Chapter 7 of both the IBC and this code, is more concerned with the spread of fire throughout the structure once the fire has reached a substantial size, with an emphasis on structural failure during a fire.

The regulation of flame spread can be traced back to large life-loss events, such as the Cocoanut Grove night-club fire that killed 492 people in 1942. This fire was thought to have started when a light bulb in a basement cocktail lounge came in contact with the cotton cloth that had been applied to the ceiling for decorative purposes. Post-fire testing of the cotton cloth indicated that it had a flame spread rating of 2,500, more than 33 times the maximum allowable flame spread in today's codes. This factor, in addition to a series of problems with the egress system, led to one of the worst fire disasters in history. The need for these regulations was further emphasized after The Station nightclub fire in West Warwick, Rhode Island, where 100 people died in February 2003. The soundproofing material in the nightclub was not approved for such use and was a major factor in the fire growth.

In addition to flame spread ratings of surface materials, certain furnishing types and vegetation, such as Christmas trees, pose a significant fire hazard because of their potential fire size and intensity. The materials used in furnishings have changed dramatically from past materials and many more plastics are now used for both decoration and furnishings. Plastics not only burn more vigorously than materials like cotton and wood, but also produce more toxic fire effluents.

Purpose

The overall purpose of Chapter 8 is to regulate interior finishes, furnishings and vegetation so they do not significantly add to or create fire hazards in buildings. The provisions tend to aim at occupancies with specific risk characteristics, such as vulnerability of occupants, density of occupants, lack of familiarity with the building and societal expectations of importance. Since this is a fire code, it includes both new and existing buildings.

SECTION 801 GENERAL

801.1 Scope. The provisions of this chapter shall govern interior finish, interior trim, furniture, furnishings, decorative materials and decorative vegetation in buildings. Existing buildings shall comply with Sections 803 through 808. New buildings shall comply with Sections 804 through 808, and Section 803 of the *International Building Code*.

❖This chapter reflects the same scope of issues as Chapter 8 of the IBC but has a slightly different emphasis. Fire codes are intended to address fire hazards of buildings and facilities over their life span; therefore, there is greater emphasis on the furnishings and contents of buildings and on the maintenance of flame spread indexes over time. Section 803 requires the same flame spread indexes as the IBC. Generally, regulating the combustibility of contents is a fairly difficult task once the building is occupied and is considered existing. Because of this difficulty, only some combustible contents and decorative materials are regulated in a limited number of occupancies. More specifically, the use of combustible furnishings, contents and decorative materials in Group A occupancies is addressed because of the high occupant load and the lack of familiarity of most occupants with the building. The type of furniture allowed in Group I occupancies is limited because of the vulnerability of the occupants and the likely fire scenarios that may occur where a building is nonsprinklered.

SECTION 802
DEFINITIONS

802.1 Definitions. The following terms are defined in Chapter 2:

FLAME SPREAD.

FLAME SPREAD INDEX.

INTERIOR FLOOR-WALL BASE.

SITE-FABRICATED STRETCH SYSTEM.

SMOKE-DEVELOPED INDEX.

❖Definitions of terms can help in the understanding and application of the code requirements. This section directs the code user to Chapter 2 for the proper application of the indicated terms used in this chapter. Terms may be defined in Chapter 2 or in another International Code® (I-Code®) as indicated in Section 201.3, or the dictionary meaning may be all that is needed (see commentary, Sections 201 through 201.4).

SECTION 803
INTERIOR WALL AND CEILING FINISH IN EXISTING BUILDINGS

803.1 General. The provisions of this section shall limit the allowable fire performance and smoke development of interior wall and ceiling finishes in existing buildings based on location and occupancy classification. Interior wall and ceiling finishes shall be classified in accordance with Section 803 of the *International Building Code*. Such materials shall be classified in accordance with NFPA 286, as indicated in Section 803.1.1, or in accordance with ASTM E84 or UL 723, as indicated in Section 803.1.2.

Materials tested in accordance with Section 803.1.1 shall not be required to be tested in accordance with Section 803.1.2.

❖ This section specifically addresses existing buildings, whereas Sections 804 through 808 address both new and existing buildings. This section provides two methods for compliance with interior wall and ceiling finish fire performance requirements. Both are fire test methods that address the potential for flame to spread.

The first test is NFPA 286, which is called a "room corner test." The second test method is ASTM E84, also known as the "Steiner tunnel" or the "tunnel test." These two tests are discussed further in the commentary for Sections 803.1.1 and 803.1.2, respectively. Requirements for interior wall and ceiling finishes and interior wall and ceiling trim within existing buildings are based on occupancy. Section 803.3 and Table 803.3 address these occupancy limitations in more detail.

There are two specific exemptions to the requirements of this section listed in Sections 803.14 and 803.15. Section 803.14 exempts materials with a thickness less than 0.036 inches that are applied directly to the surface of walls and ceilings and Section 803.15 exempts the exposed portions of heavy timber construction elements that meet the requirements of the IBC for Class IV Construction.

Note that Section 803 also addresses the following:

- Textiles and expanded vinyl used as a wall or ceiling finish.
- Limitations on the use of foam.
- Polyethylene and polypropylene used as interior finish.
- Site-fabricated stretch systems.
- Facings or wood veneers intended to be applied on site over a wood substrate.
- Laminated products factory produced with an attached wood substrate.

803.1.1 Interior wall and ceiling finish materials tested in accordance with NFPA 286. Interior wall and ceiling finish materials shall be classified in accordance with NFPA 286 and tested in accordance with Section 803.1.1.1. Materials complying with Section 803.1.1.1 shall be considered to comply with the requirements of Class A specified in Section 803.1.2.

❖The NFPA test method for determining compliance for interior wall and ceiling finish and trim other than textiles is found in standard 286. This test is known as a "room corner" fire test and is similar to that referenced for textile wall coverings in Section 803.5 (see NFPA 265) [see Commentary Figures 803.1.1(1) and 803.1.1(2)]. In this test, materials are mounted covering three walls of the compartment (excluding the wall containing the door) and the ceiling. In the case where testing is only for ceiling finish properties, the sample only needs to be mounted on the ceiling. Then a fire source consisting of a gas burner is placed in one corner, flush against both walls (furthest from the doorway) of the compartment with the following exposure conditions:

- 40 kilowatts (kW) for 5 minutes; then
- 160 kW for 10 minutes.

The test then measures heat release and smoke release through the collection of the fire effluents and measurement of oxygen concentrations in the exhaust duct. Heat release is calculated by the oxygen consumption principle, which has shown that heat release is a function of the decrease in oxygen concentration in the fire effluents. Thus, exhaust duct measurements include temperatures, pressures and smoke values for use in the calculations. Temperatures and heat fluxes are also measured in the room. This generally provides a more realistic understanding of the fire hazard associated with the materials (see also Section 803.5.1 for more details on the room corner test concept).

The NFPA 286 test method does not contain pass/fail criteria; however, the code provides such criteria in Section 803.1.1.1.

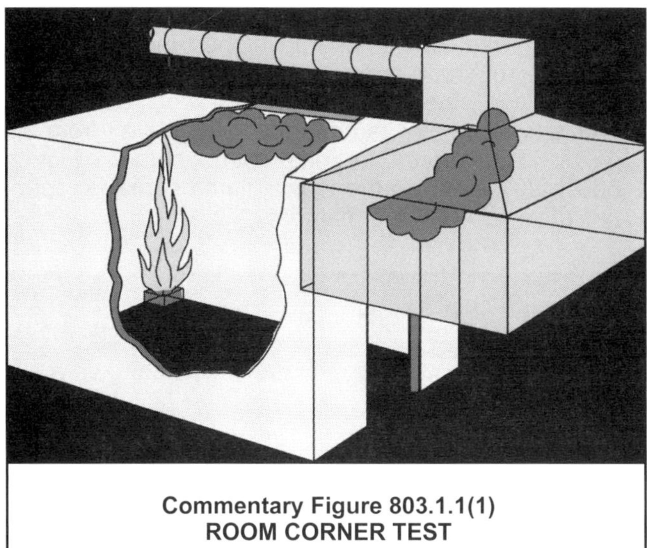

Commentary Figure 803.1.1(1)
ROOM CORNER TEST

Commentary Figure 803.1.1(2)
FLAME IN ROOM CORNER TEST

803.1.1.1 Acceptance criteria for NFPA 286. The interior finish shall comply with the following:

1. During the 40 kW exposure, flames shall not spread to the ceiling.
2. The flame shall not spread to the outer extremity of the sample on any wall or ceiling.
3. Flashover, as defined in NFPA 286, shall not occur.
4. The peak heat release rate throughout the test shall not exceed 800 kW.
5. The total smoke released throughout the test shall not exceed 1,000 m^2.

❖As noted in Section 803.1.1, there are two levels of exposure during an NFPA 286 fire test in order to better represent a growing fire: 40 kW fire size for 5 minutes and 160 kW for 10 minutes. The 40 kW exposure represents the beginning of a fire where the initial spread is critical; therefore, the stated criteria is that the fire cannot spread to the ceiling. The 160 kW exposure is obviously a more intense fire situation and the criteria relates to preventing flashover (as defined by NFPA 286) and the extent of flame spread throughout the entire test assembly. There is also a total smoke production criterion of 1,000 m^2. It should be noted that the criteria used in NFPA 286 and NFPA 265 to determine if flashover has occurred would include any two of the following:

- Heat release exceeds 1 mega watt (MW).
- Heat flux at the floor exceeds 20 kW/m^2.
- Average upper layer temperature exceeds 1112°F (600°C).
- Flames exit the doorway.
- Autoignition of paper target on the floor occurs.

Furthermore, it should be noted that there is an additional criteria when applying NFPA 286 for new buildings, which is a maximum peak heat release rate of 800 kW. The reasoning for this criterion relates to the fact that some poorer-performing materials can achieve compliance with the flashover criteria but could have a higher peak heat release rate.

803.1.2 Interior wall and ceiling finish materials tested in accordance with ASTM E84 or UL 723. Interior wall and ceiling finishes shall be classified in accordance with ASTM E84 or UL 723. Such interior finish materials shall be grouped in the following classes in accordance with their flame spread and smoke-developed indices.

Class A: Flame spread index 0–25; smoke-developed index 0–450.

Class B: Flame spread index 26–75; smoke-developed index 0–450.

Class C: Flame spread index 76–200; smoke-developed index 0–450.

Exception: Materials tested in accordance with Section 803.1.1 and as indicated in Sections 803.1.3 through 803.15.

❖Wall and ceiling interior finish and trim materials are required to have limits on flame spread and smoke-developed indexes as prescribed in Section 803.3, based on occupancy. ASTM E84 is one of the tests available to demonstrate compliance with the requirements of Section 803. This test method has been around since 1944 [see Commentary Figure 803.1.2(1)]. It is the primary method used but, as noted earlier, NFPA 286 is an alternative test, which is discussed in the commentary for Section 803.1.1.

ASTM E84 is intended to determine the relative burning behavior of materials on exposed surfaces, such as ceilings and walls, by visually observing the flame spread along the test specimen [see Commentary Figure 803.1.2(2)]. Flame spread and smoke density indexes are then reported. The test method is not appropriate for materials that are not capable of supporting themselves, or of being supported in the test tunnel. There may also be concerns with materials that drip, melt or delaminate and that are very thin. A distinction is made, therefore, for textile wall or ceiling coverings, expanded vinyl wall or ceiling coverings, wood veneers applied on site, foam plastic insulation materials, high density polyethene and polypropylene and site-fabricated stretch systems (see Sections 803.5 through 803.10).

ASTM E84 establishes a flame spread index based on the area under a curve when the actual flame spread distance is plotted as a function of time. The code has divided the acceptable range of flame spread indexes (0–200) into three classes: Class A (0–25), Class B (26–75) and Class C (76–200). For all three classes, the code has established a common acceptable range of smoke-developed index of 0–450. An indication of relative fire performance is as follows: an inorganic reinforced-cement board has a flame spread and smoke-developed index of zero, while select grade red oak wood flooring has a flame spread and smoke-developed index of 100. Not to preclude more detailed information resulting from an ASTM E84 test report, Commentary Figure 803.1.2(3) identifies the typical flame spread properties of certain building materials.

Commentary Figure 803.1.2(1)
ASTM E84 TUNNEL TEST

Commentary Figure 803.1.2(2)
FLAME IN TUNNEL TEST

Material	Flame spread
Glass-fiber sound-absorbing blanks	15 to 30
Mineral-fiber sound-absorbing panels	10 to 25
Shredded wood fiberboard (treated)	20 to 25
Sprayed cellulose fibers (treated)	20
Aluminum (with baked enamel finish on one side)	5 to 10
Asbestos-cement board	0
Brick or concrete block	0
Cork	175
Gypsum board (with paper surface on both sides)	10 to 25
Northern pine (treated)	20
Southern pine (untreated)	130 to 190
Plywood paneling (untreated)	75 to 275
Plywood paneling (treated)	100
Carpeting	10 to 600
Concrete	0

Commentary Figure 803.1.2(3)
TYPICAL FLAME SPREAD OF COMMON MATERIALS

803.1.3 Interior wall and ceiling finish materials with specific requirements. The materials indicated in Sections 803.4 through 803.15 shall be tested as indicated in the corresponding sections.

❖This section states that the purpose of Sections 803.4 through 803.15 is to provide specific testing requirements for the interior wall and ceiling finish materials that are listed in each individual section. The materials that are included are: fire-retardant coatings, textile wall and ceiling coverings, expanded vinyl wall and ceiling coverings, high-density polyethylene (HDPE) and polypropylene (PP), site-fabricated stretch systems, foam plastic materials, facings or wood veneers intended to be applied on site over a wood substrate, and laminated products factory produced with an attached wood substrate. There are also testing exemptions for thin materials and exposed portions of heavy timber construction.

803.2 Stability. Interior finish materials regulated by this chapter shall be applied or otherwise fastened in such a manner that such materials will not readily become detached where subjected to room temperatures of 200°F (93°C) for not less than 30 minutes.

❖Interior finishes are not to become detached for a minimum of 30 minutes under exposure to elevated temperatures [200°F (93°C)]. No standard test method has yet been developed to evaluate this requirement. Some sections of the IBC, however, do offer some additional guidance. For example, the performance of the method of attachment of finish materials during a fire-resistance test will usually be an adequate indication of performance. The stability criterion is necessary because, if these materials were to fall off of walls or the ceiling during a fire, they may contribute to the fire and increase the hazard beyond what is typically expected.

803.3 Interior finish requirements based on occupancy. Interior wall and ceiling finish shall have a flame spread index not greater than that specified in Table 803.3 for the group and location designated. Interior wall and ceiling finish materials tested in accordance with NFPA 286, and meeting the acceptance criteria of Section 803.1.1.1, shall be used where a Class A classification in accordance with ASTM E84 or UL 723 is required.

❖The requirements for flame spread indexes for interior finish materials applied to walls and ceilings are contained in Table 803.3. The referenced test for determining flame spread indexes is ASTM E84, which establishes a relative measurement of flame spread across the surface of the material. The classifications used in Table 803.3 are defined in Section 803.1.2 (see the commentary to Section 803.1.2 for additional information on the uses and limitations of the test procedure). Again, NFPA 286 can be used as an alternative to ASTM E84. Passing NFPA 286 means that the material would be considered to be equivalent to a Class A material.

TABLE 803.3. See page 8-6.

❖This table prescribes the minimum requirements for interior finishes applied to walls and ceilings; therefore, the use of a Class A material in an area that requires a minimum Class B material is always allowed. Likewise, when the table requires Class C materials, Classes A and B can be used. The requirements are based on the use of the space. To determine the applicable criteria, first determine whether the space is an exit passageway, interior exit stairway or interior exit ramp; a corridor; or a room or enclosed space. Interior finishes in spaces that are not separated from a corridor (for example, waiting areas in business or health care facilities) must comply with the requirements for a corridor space. As shown in the table, the code places a higher emphasis on the allowable flame spread index for exits than for enclosed rooms because of the critical nature and relative importance of maintaining exit integrity to aid in building evacuation. Numerous notes amend the basic requirements of Table 803.3. Notes a through l apply only where specifically referenced in the table.

Note a

A limited amount of combustible wainscotting or other paneling material does not appreciably reduce the level of safety of an exit element; therefore, up to 1,000 square feet (93 m^2) of Class C wainscotting or paneling is permitted by Note a in a grade-level lobby used as an exit element when applied in accordance with Section 803.3 of the IBC.

Note b

This note allows the reduction of flame spread indexes in exit enclosures in buildings less than three stories high, not including Group I-3 occupancies. The time required to exit a building less than three stories is much shorter than that for taller buildings and enough time usually exists to use other exit enclosures.

Note c

Because the intended use of certain rooms in buildings is sometimes more hazardous than the group classification for the overall building, the finish classification must be determined by the group and occupancy classification for the room or area. Additionally, rooms or enclosed spaces not properly separated from one another must be looked at as a single space for the purposes of applying flame spread index requirements.

Note d

This note allows lobbies in Group A-1, A-2 and A-3 occupancies to be Class B instead of Class A. This is likely a result of the low fire load in such areas.

Note e

Note e recognizes that with a relatively small number of occupants, egress is accomplished more quickly and the activities tend to be more structured and manageable than with a large number of occupants.

When the design occupant load is 300 or less in rooms or spaces of Group A-1 and A-2 occupancies, the interior finish materials may be Class C instead of Class B for rooms and enclosed spaces.

Note f

This note correlates with the allowance in Section 807.5.1.3 for places of religious worship.

Note g

The time required for exiting increases with the number of stories of the structure. Interior finish materials can play a major role in fire spread within a structure. Because of the materials stored and used within a Group H occupancy, interior wall and ceiling finish materials with high heat release (or flame spread) potential can have a significant impact on the way a fire spreads throughout the building. To abate the hazard of rapid fire growth, Note g places a further restriction of a minimum of a Class B classification on interior finishes of enclosed spaces within sprinklered buildings when the building exceeds two stories.

Note h

Spaces that are used as offices in Group I-2 and I-4 occupancies have a low occupant load, the activity in those spaces is generally not very hazardous and the occupants are not as vulnerable as the general population of those facilities, partially because of their knowledge of the exits; therefore, Class C materials are allowed in administrative spaces.

Note i

Rooms in Group I-2 and I-4 occupancies with low occupant loads (four or less) pose a low risk and are quickly evacuated; therefore, Class C finish materials are appropriate.

Note j

In Group I-3 occupancy corridors, Note j allows interior finish materials, such as wainscotting, that are a maximum height of 48 inches (1219 mm) above the floor to be Class B. This reduction from Class A is based on full-scale fire research demonstrating that Class B wall finish used on the lower 4 feet (1219 mm) of a corridor wall is not likely to spread fire

TABLE 803.3
INTERIOR WALL AND CEILING FINISH REQUIREMENTS BY OCCUPANCY[k]

GROUP	SPRINKLERED[l]			NONSPRINKLERED		
	Interior exit stairways and ramps and exit passageways[a, b]	Corridors and enclosure for exit access stairways and ramps	Rooms and enclosed spaces[c]	Interior exit stairways and ramps and exit passageways[a, b]	Corridors and enclosure for exit access stairways and ramps	Rooms and enclosed spaces[c]
A-1 and A-2	B	B	C	A	A[d]	B[e]
A-3[f], A-4, A-5	B	B	C	A	A[d]	C
B, E, M, R-1, R-4	B	C[m]	C	A	B[m]	C
F	C	C	C	B	C	C
H	B	B	C[g]	A	A	B
I-1	B	C	C	A	B	B
I-2	B	B	B[h, i]	A	A	B
I-3	A	A[j]	C	A	A	B
I-4	B	B	B[h, i]	A	A	B
R-2	C	C	C	B	B	C
R-3	C	C	C	C	C	C
S	C	C	C	B	B	C
U	No Restrictions			No Restrictions		

For SI: 1 inch = 25.4 mm, 1 square foot = 0.0929 m^2.

a. Class C interior finish materials shall be allowed for wainscoting or paneling of not more than 1,000 square feet of applied surface area in the grade lobby where applied directly to a noncombustible base or over furring strips applied to a noncombustible base and fireblocked as required by Section 803.11 of the *International Building Code*.

b. In exit enclosures of buildings less than three stories in height of other than Group I-3, Class B interior finish for nonsprinklered buildings and Class C for sprinklered buildings shall be permitted.

c. Requirements for rooms and enclosed spaces shall be based on spaces enclosed by partitions. Where a fire-resistance rating is required for structural elements, the enclosing partitions shall extend from the floor to the ceiling. Partitions that do not comply with this shall be considered as enclosing spaces and the rooms or spaces on both sides shall be considered as one. In determining the applicable requirements for rooms and enclosed spaces, the specific occupancy thereof shall be the governing factor regardless of the group classification of the building or structure.

d. Lobby areas in Group A-1, A-2 and A-3 occupancies shall be not less than Class B materials.

e. Class C interior finish materials shall be allowed in Group A occupancies with an occupant load of 300 persons or less.

f. In places of religious worship, wood used for ornamental purposes, trusses, paneling or chancel furnishing shall be allowed.

g. Class B material is required where the building exceeds two stories.

h. Class C interior finish materials shall be allowed in administrative spaces.

i. Class C interior finish materials shall be allowed in rooms with a capacity of four persons or less.

j. Class B materials shall be allowed as wainscoting extending not more than 48 inches above the finished floor in corridors.

k. Finish materials as provided for in other sections of this code.

l. Applies where the vertical exits, exit passageways, corridors or rooms and spaces are protected by an approved automatic sprinkler system installed in accordance with Section 903.3.1.1 or 903.3.1.2.

m. Corridors in ambulatory care facilities shall have a Class B or better interior finish material.

because fire primarily spreads on ceilings and upper walls before affecting the lower portions of walls.

Note k

This note is referenced in the title of Table 803.3 and refers to other sections of the code that may have further restrictions or allowances for material classification for specific uses.

Note l

Sprinklered facilities provide more protection to occupants than nonsprinklered facilities. In many instances, materials with lower restrictions on fire performance may be used, as shown in Table 803.3. The footnote clarifies what areas of the building need to be sprinklered in order to qualify for these reductions in interior finish classifications.

Note m

The Class B requirement for corridors in ambulatory facilities is consistent with federal regulations for buildings that are provided with an automatic sprinkler system. It is also shown in the column for the buildings without an automatic sprinkler system to prevent confusion between the two types.

803.4 Fire-retardant coatings. The required flame spread or smoke-developed index of surfaces in existing buildings shall be allowed to be achieved by application of *approved* fire-retardant coatings, paints or solutions to surfaces having a flame spread index exceeding that allowed. Such applications shall comply with NFPA 703 and the required fire-retardant properties shall be maintained or renewed in accordance with the manufacturer's instructions. The fire-retardant paint, coating or solution shall have been assessed by testing over the same substrate to be used in the application.

❖Many times, fire retardants can be used to reduce the flame spread index of a material that, without treatment, has an index higher than permissible. It should be recognized that the most desirable situation is to have a material that has a specific flame spread rating or has been tested and passed in accordance with NFPA 286. It is also recognized that in existing buildings there are often situations where such an approach is not possible and the application of fire retardants is the only solution. Flame retardants may either be factory or field applied. A wide variety of proprietary flame retardants for field application are on the market. Both factory- and field-applied products may require reapplication to sustain the flame retardancy of a particular article. When reviewing an installation, the fire code official should require the owner or other responsible person to submit a manufacturer's or contractor's certificate documenting a given treatment. This documentation should specify if a particular treatment must be repeated and, if so, at what intervals. If no retreatment interval is specified, the manufacturer's or contractor's warranty should be recognized as the retreatment interval because it is the longest period for which that individual accepts responsibility for the product's performance. Fire code officials evaluating flame-retardant treatments should carefully evaluate the performance conditions of these preparations. Many of them are not intended to be exposed to direct sunlight, high humidity or weather. Flame-retardant treatment must be used or applied in a manner consistent with the manufacturer's instructions.

There are several methods of increasing the flame resistance of materials. The strategy is either to slow the ignition process or control combustion itself. Commentary Figure 803.4 lists various methods and whether they can be achieved in the field.

It should also be noted that in more recent times there has been growing concern over the use of polybrominated diphenyl ethers (PBDE) to achieve flame resistance due to the possible health effects. Some states, including California, have passed legislation to ban the use of such products. Several manufacturers have also begun a voluntary phase-out of such chemicals.

803.5 Textile wall coverings. Where used as interior wall finish materials, textile wall coverings, including materials having a woven, nonwoven, napped, tufted, looped or similar surface, shall be tested in the manner intended for use, using the product mounting system, including adhesive, and shall comply with the requirements of Section 803.1.1, 803.5.1 or 803.5.2.

❖This section is primarily intended to apply to carpet and carpet-like wall coverings that include textile materials having woven or nonwoven, napped, tufted, looped or similar surfaces. If not addressed, these easily ignitable materials can contribute extensively to a fire. There are three testing options for these coverings as given in Section 803.1.1, 803.5.1 or 803.5.2. In each case, it shall be tested in the manner intended for use, using the product mounting system, including adhesive.

803.5.1 Room corner test for textile wall coverings and expanded vinyl wall coverings. Textile wall coverings and expanded vinyl wall coverings shall meet the criteria of Section 803.5.1.1 when tested in the manner intended for use in accordance with the Method B protocol of NFPA 265 using the product mounting system, including adhesive. Test specimen preparation and mounting shall be in accordance with ASTM E2404.

❖As an alternative to a Class A flame spread index and sprinklers, testing in accordance with NFPA 265 may be used for textile wall coverings. Just as discussed for NFPA 286, NFPA 265 is known as a full-scale room corner fire test. This test helps to determine the contribution of textile wall coverings to overall fire growth and spread in a compartment fire. Past research conducted with this kind of configuration has shown that flame spread indexes produced by ASTM E84 or UL 723 may not reliably predict the fire behavior of textile wall coverings in realistic fire scenarios. Thus, NFPA 265 is based on a more reliable test procedure, developed at the University of California. The research findings are described in a report from the University of California Fire Research Laboratory titled, "Room Fire Experiments of Textile Wall Coverings." The NFPA 265 test is only slightly different from NFPA 286. NFPA 286 is more severe in three ways:

1. The gas diffusion burner used to expose the material on the wall in the room fire test starts with a heat release rate exposure of 40 kW for the first 5 minutes in both tests, but it is then followed by 150 kW for 10 minutes in NFPA 265 and 160 kW for 10 minutes in NFPA 286.
2. The gas burner is placed 2 inches (51 mm) from each of the walls in NFPA 265, whereas it is placed flush against both walls in NFPA 286.
3. The test sample is mounted on the walls only in NFPA 265, whereas it is mounted on both the walls and ceiling in NFPA 286.

A key result of the difference in intensity and location of the gas burner is that the burner flame does not reach the ceiling during the 150 kW exposure (while it does reach the ceiling during the 160 kW exposure in NFPA 286). Therefore, NFPA 265 is not considered suitable for testing ceiling coverings.

It should be noted that the code does not require measurement of smoke release from materials tested to NFPA 265 unless the material is newly introduced, but does have a smoke pass/fail criterion for NFPA 286. NFPA 265 has two test methods, but the code only allows the use of Method B. In the Method A test protocol, 2-foot-wide (610 mm) strips of the material are mounted on the two walls closest to the corner with the burner, whereas in the Method B test protocol the sample is mounted completely covering three walls (except for the wall containing the door). Therefore, Method B is more severe. This test method does not contain pass/fail criteria, just as NFPA 286 does not. The code therefore provides such criteria, based on the use of only the Method B test protocol from NFPA 265, in Section 803.5.1.1. It should be noted that the IBC also only allows the use of Method B from NFPA 265. The code applies to existing buildings and the IBC would only apply to new buildings with regard to this particular test.

803.5.1.1 Acceptance criteria for NFPA 265 Method B test protocol. Where testing to NFPA 265, the interior finish shall comply with the following:

1. During the 40-kW exposure, flames shall not spread to the ceiling.
2. The flame shall not spread to the outer extremities of the samples on the 8-foot by 12-foot (203 by 305 mm) walls.
3. Flashover, as defined in NFPA 265, shall not occur.
4. For newly introduced wall coverings, the total smoke released throughout the test shall not exceed 1,000 m^2.

❖The criteria are very similar to those used in NFPA 286. The pass/fail criteria in the code are as follows:

The flame cannot spread to the ceiling when the textile is exposed to the burner at 40 kW. With the burner at 150 kW, the following criteria must be met:

- The fire cannot reach the outer areas of the 8-foot by 12-foot (2438 mm by 8657 mm) wall.
- Flashover, as defined by NFPA 265, must not occur.
- Newly introduced wall coverings are limited to a total smoke release of 1,000 m^2.

METHOD OF ACHIEVING FLAME RESISTANCE	APPROPRIATE USE	APPLICATION	OTHER INFORMATION
Chemical	Synthetics; Plastics	Chemical added during manufacturing process Example: Polymers	Actual chemical change occurs Changes the behavior of materials
Impregnation	Absorbent or porous materials; not wood (too dense)	In the field by spray or immersion	Sometimes done at wet pulp stage (Paper, acoustical tile and building panels)
Coating	Nonabsorbant materials Example: Wood paneling, ceiling tiles, etc.	In the field by spray, brush or roller application	Actively inhibits flame spread or simply provides a noncombustible surface Needs periodic renewal per manufacturer
Pressure Impregnation	Dense, nonabsorbent materials such as wood	Only during manufacturing	Replaces air pockets with fire-retardant solution Chemical deposits while drying Vacuum-pressure methods are used to impregnate materials Far more effective than impregnation alone

Commentary Figure 803.4
APPLIED FLAME-RETARDANT COATINGS

803.5.2 Acceptance criteria for wall and ceiling coverings. Textile wall and ceiling coverings shall have a Class A flame spread index in accordance with ASTM E84 or UL 723, and be protected by an automatic sprinkler system installed in accordance with Section 903.3.1.1 or 903.3.1.2. Test specimen preparation and mounting shall be in accordance with ASTM E2404.

❖This section requires that textile materials on walls or ceilings have a Class A flame spread index and be located in a sprinklered area in accordance with NFPA 13 or 13R. As an alternative to a Class A flame spread index and sprinklers, testing in accordance with NFPA 265 may be used for textile wall coverings. Just as discussed for NFPA 286, NFPA 265 is known as a full-scale room corner fire test. This test helps to determine the contribution of textile wall coverings to overall fire growth and spread in a compartment fire. Past research conducted with this kind of configuration has shown that flame spread indexes produced by ASTM E84 or UL 723 may not reliably predict the fire behavior of textile wall coverings in realistic fire scenarios. Thus, NFPA 265 is based on a more reliable test procedure, developed at the University of California. The research findings are described in a report from the University of California Fire Research Laboratory titled, "Room Fire Experiments of Textile Wall Coverings." The NFPA 265 test is only slightly different from NFPA 286. NFPA 286 is more severe in three ways:

1. The gas diffusion burner used to expose the material on the wall in the room fire test starts with a heat release rate exposure of 40 kW for the first 5 minutes in both tests, but it is then followed by 150 kW for 10 minutes in NFPA 265 and 160 kW for 10 minutes in NFPA 286.
2. The gas burner is placed 2 inches (51 mm) from each of the walls in NFPA 265, whereas it is placed flush against both walls in NFPA 286.
3. The test sample is mounted on the walls only in NFPA 265, whereas it is mounted on both the walls and ceiling in NFPA 286.

A key result of the difference in intensity and location of the gas burner is that the burner flame does not reach the ceiling during the 150 kW exposure (while it does reach the ceiling during the 160 kW exposure in NFPA 286). Therefore, NFPA 265 is not considered suitable for testing ceiling coverings.

It should be noted that the code does not require measurement of smoke release from materials tested to NFPA 265 unless the material is newly introduced, but does have a smoke pass/fail criterion for NFPA 286. NFPA 265 has two test methods, but the code only allows the use of Method B. In the Method A test protocol, 2-foot-wide (610 mm) strips of the material are mounted on the two walls closest to the corner with the burner, whereas in the Method B test protocol the sample is mounted completely covering three walls (except for the wall containing the door). Therefore, Method B is more severe. This test method does not contain pass/fail criteria, just as NFPA 286 does not. The code therefore provides such criteria, based on the use of only the Method B test protocol from NFPA 265, in Section 803.5.1.1. It should be noted that the IBC also only allows the use of Method B from NFPA 265. The code applies to existing buildings and the IBC would only apply to new buildings with regard to this particular test.

803.6 Textile ceiling coverings. Where used as interior ceiling finish materials, textile ceiling coverings, including materials having a woven, nonwoven, napped, tufted, looped or similar surface and carpet or similar textile materials, shall be tested in the manner intended for use, using the product mounting system, including adhesive, and shall comply with the requirements of Section 803.1.1 or 803.5.2.

❖This section is basically the same as Section 803.5.1 with one exception focused on preparing test specimens for the tunnel test (ASTM E84). The reason for this difference is that existing materials would possibly be out of compliance since they were tested prior to the development of ASTM E2404, which has specific mounting requirements for materials during the test. It was felt reasonable in existing buildings to hold new textile wall and ceiling coverings to this higher standard. The correct specimen preparation and mounting method for textile, paper and vinyl wall and ceiling coverings tested in accordance with the ASTM E84 (Steiner tunnel) test is ASTM E2404. The ASTM E05 Committee on Fire Standards developed a standard practice for test specimen preparation and mounting, ASTM E2404, for textile, paper or vinyl wall or ceiling coverings specifically to provide a mandatory, standardized way of preparing test specimens and mounting them in the tunnel. This replaced optional guidance on mounting methods found in the appendix of ASTM E84 and ensures testing consistency.

This section also allows the use of NFPA 265 and NFPA 286 with the same criteria as cited in Section 803.5.1. Note that NFPA 265 is not applicable for the testing of ceiling materials due to the limitations of that test (see commentary, Section 803.5.1).

803.7 Expanded vinyl wall coverings. Where used as interior wall finish materials, expanded vinyl wall coverings shall be tested in the manner intended for use, using the product mounting system, including adhesive, and shall comply with the requirements of Section 803.1.1, 803.5.1 or 803.5.2.

❖This section is specific to the use of expanded vinyl as wall coverings. It requires compliance with one of three testing methods. These methods are: NFPA 286 as listed in Section 803.1.1, NFPA 265 Method B as listed in Section 803.5.1 or ASTM E84 as listed in Section 803.5.2. The coverings are required to be tested as they are intended to be used, including mounting systems and adhesives.

This section does not limit the requirements to newly introduced materials but instead applies to any expanded vinyl wall coverings. See also the commentaries to Sections 803.5.2 and 803.5.1.

803.8 Expanded vinyl ceiling coverings. Where used as interior ceiling finish materials, expanded vinyl ceiling coverings shall be tested in the manner intended for use, using the product mounting system, including adhesive, and shall comply with the requirements of Section 803.1.1 or 803.5.2.

❖This section is specific to the use of expanded vinyl as ceiling coverings. It requires compliance with one of two testing methods. These methods are: NFPA 286, as listed in Section 803.1.1 or ASTM E84, as listed in Section 803.5.2. It is required that the specific testing of the coverings be performed in the exact manner that the product is intended for use, using the actual mounting system, and includes the adhesive.

This section does not limit the requirements to newly introduced materials but instead applies to any expanded vinyl ceiling coverings. See also the commentary to Section 803.5.2.

[BF] 803.9 High-density polyethylene (HDPE) and polypropylene (PP). Where high-density polyethylene or polypropylene is used as an interior finish, it shall comply with Section 803.1.1.

❖High-density polyethylene (HDPE) and polypropylene (PP) are thermoplastics that give off considerable energy and produce a pooling flammable liquid fire when they burn. Recent full-scale room-corner tests of HDPE using NFPA 286 have demonstrated a significant hazard. These tests had to be terminated prior to the standard 15-minute duration due to flashover occurring while there was still much of the product left to burn. Extensive flammable liquid pool fires occurred during the tests, yet this same material, when tested in accordance with the tunnel test, ASTM E84, is often given a flame spread index of 25 or less. However, the resulting test is so intense some labs will not test HDPE partitions due to the damage such tests can do to the tunnel. This section ensures that when using HDPE partitions they will be formulated in such a manner as to reduce the hazard that they present by specifically requiring compliance with NFPA 286. The following are some of the data gleaned from one of the NFPA 286 tests: Peak Heat Release Rate 1733 kW; Total Heat Released 121 MJ; Peak Heat Flux to the Floor 35.2 kW/m^2; Peak Average Ceiling Temperature 805°C, 1481°F. Polypropylene is very similar in material and fire performance.

[BF] 803.10 Site-fabricated stretch systems. Where used as newly installed interior wall or interior ceiling finish materials, site-fabricated stretch systems containing all three components described in the definition in Chapter 2 shall be tested in the manner intended for use, and shall comply with the requirements of Section 803.1.1 or 803.1.2. If the materials are tested in accordance with ASTM E84 or UL 723, specimen preparation and mounting shall be in accordance with ASTM E2573.

❖Site-fabricated stretch systems are interior finish materials that are stretched taut across walls or ceilings with a frame that holds a fabric and core. These systems are now being used extensively because they can stretch to cover decorative walls and ceilings with unusual looks and shapes. The systems consist of three parts: a fabric (or vinyl), a frame and an infill core material. Therefore, they must be fire tested like all other interior wall and ceiling materials, using either ASTM E84 (the Steiner tunnel test) or NFPA 286 (the room-corner test). The ASTM Committee on Fire Standards (ASTM E05) has issued ASTM E2573, a standard practice for specimen preparation and mounting of site-fabricated stretch systems. It is not a test method but rather a mounting method that was developed specifically for use when testing these materials in the ASTM E84 Steiner tunnel test. Before it was issued, there was no correct mandatory way to test these systems. The testing has often been done of each component separately instead of testing the composite system. That is an inappropriate way to test and not the safe way to conduct the testing. Now that a consensus standard method of testing exists, the code recognizes it.

It is important to note that these materials are not curtains or drapes because they are not free hanging like curtains. Therefore, it would be inappropriate for them to be tested using NFPA 701, a test for vertically hanging fabrics, or any other test that was developed for free-hanging materials.

As previously stated, it is important to test all components together. If the system in question does not contain all three components of site-fabricated stretch systems, then such systems should be tested in a manner appropriate to their use. In particular, systems that contain a stretch membrane only and no core material have been shown to behave very differently in a fire situation than site-fabricated stretch systems. It is important that the correct mounting method be used for each system.

803.11 Foam plastic materials. Foam plastic materials shall not be used as interior wall and ceiling finish unless specifically allowed by Section 803.11.1 or 803.11.2. Foam plastic materials shall not be used as interior trim unless specifically allowed by Section 804.2.

❖This section allows foam plastic interior wall and ceiling finish materials to be used in accordance with Section 803.11.1 or 803.11.2. The ASTM E84 test has the potential to produce misleading fire test results when used to test foam plastic interior wall and ceiling finish materials. In particular, if the foam plastics have low density, the amount of material may be insufficient for the ASTM E84 Steiner tunnel test to properly evaluate the plastics' flame spread characteristics. Moreover, if the foams are thermoplastic, they are likely to melt and fall away from the flame front when exposed in the test and provide artificially low flame spread information on the surface of the test sample, and thus give an inaccurate indication of the fire hazard. It was thus generally agreed, in the early 1970s, that foam insulation products should be assessed for combustibility with a test that represents more realistically the way the materials behave in actual applications, and tests, such as UL 1715, UL 1040, FM 4880 and NFPA 286, were developed for such purposes to be used instead of ASTM E84.

803.11.1 Foam plastic combustibility characteristics. Foam plastic materials shall be allowed on the basis of fire tests that substantiate their combustibility characteristics for the use intended under actual fire conditions, as indicated in Section 2603.9 of the *International Building Code*. This section shall apply both to exposed foam plastics and to foam plastics used in conjunction with a textile or vinyl facing or cover.

❖This section requires that where foam plastics are used as interior wall or ceiling finish, they must meet the requirements of Section 2603.9 of the IBC. The IBC states that foam plastic is not permitted to be used exposed as interior finish unless it has been tested under actual fire conditions. The IBC requires foam plastic insulation to be tested in accordance with a standard such as FM 4880, UL 1040, NFPA 286 or UL 1715, all of which are large-scale fire tests measuring heat release. NFPA 286 does not have pass/fail criteria; those criteria are contained in Section 803.1.1 of the code. This section also clarifies that covering the foam plastic with a vinyl or textile cover (as is often done in high school gymnasiums) will not change the requirements, so the same tests should be applied to the covered foam.

803.11.2 Thermal barrier for foam plastics. Foam plastic material shall be allowed if it is separated from the interior of the building by a thermal barrier in accordance with Section 2603.4 of the *International Building Code*.

❖Another option the code allows is to use foam plastic where it is separated from the room interior by means of a thermal barrier, so that the foam plastic is not exposed and is not actually used as interior finish. This section refers the user to Section 2603.4 of the IBC to address how this is to be accomplished. Section 2603.4 of the IBC requires a $^{1}/_{2}$-inch (12.7 mm) gypsum wallboard or equivalent thermal barrier. Section 2603.4 of the IBC also provides criteria for testing equivalent thermal barriers.

803.12 Facings or wood veneers intended to be applied on site over a wood substrate. Facings or veneers intended to be applied on site over a wood substrate shall comply with one of the following:

1. The facing or veneer shall meet the criteria of Section 803.1.1 when tested in accordance with NFPA 286 using the product mounting system, including adhesive, described in Section 5.8.9 of NFPA 286.
2. The facing or veneer shall have a Class A, B or C flame spread index and smoke-developed index based on the requirements of Table 803.3, in accordance with ASTM E84 or UL 723. Test specimen preparation and mounting shall be in accordance with ASTM E2404.

❖This section details the proper way to test facings or wood veneers intended to be applied over a wood substrate. They are to be treated the same way as any other wall or ceiling covering applied "on site" to a wood substrate, but differently from panels where the facing or veneer is applied in the factory over the wood substrate and the entire panel is installed. The following section addresses this situation. This section allows the use of either NFPA 286 or ASTM E84. As noted, the ASTM E2404 mounting method must be applied if the ASTM E84 test method is chosen.

803.13 Laminated products factory produced with an attached wood substrate. Laminated products factory produced with an attached wood substrate shall comply with one of the following:

1. The laminated product shall meet the criteria of Section 803.1.1 when tested in accordance with NFPA 286 using the product mounting system, including adhesive, of actual use.
2. The laminated product shall have a Class A, B or C flame spread index and smoke-developed index based on the requirements of Table 803.3, in accordance with ASTM E84 or UL 723. Test specimen preparation and mounting shall be in accordance with ASTM E2579.

❖This section provides the product testing requirements for the use of laminated products with an attached wood substrate as interior wall or ceiling finishes. This section allows the use of either NFPA 286 or ASTM E84. As noted, the ASTM E2579 mounting method must be applied if the ASTM E84 test method is chosen.

803.14 Thickness exemption. Materials having a thickness less than 0.036 inch (0.9 mm) applied directly to the surface of walls or ceilings shall not be required to be tested.

❖This section provides a specific testing exemption for thin materials that are directly applied to the surfaces of walls or ceilings. It is not necessary for these thin materials to be tested due to the negligible effect they have on the overall wall or ceiling construction fire performance.

803.15 Heavy timber exemption. Exposed portions of building elements complying with the requirements of Type IV construction in accordance with the *International Building Code* shall not be subject to interior finish requirements.

❖This section provides a specific application interior finish requirement exemption for the use of heavy timber exposed construction building elements that meet the IBC requirements for Type IV construction. Thus, it is not necessary to meet the interior finish requirements of this section if the requirements for Type IV construction in the IBC are met.

SECTION 804 INTERIOR WALL AND CEILING TRIM AND INTERIOR FLOOR FINISH IN NEW AND EXISTING BUILDINGS

804.1 Interior trim. Combustible trim in new and existing buildings, excluding handrails and guards, shall not exceed 10 percent of the specific wall or ceiling areas to which it is attached. Other than foam plastic, material used as interior trim shall comply with Section 804.1.1 or 804.1.2. Foam plastic used as interior trim shall comply with Section 804.2.

❖In accordance with Section 801.1, Section 804.1 addresses both new and existing buildings whereas Section 803 is applicable only to existing buildings. In occupancies of any group, unless otherwise noted in the code, all combustible material used as interior trim, with the exception of foam plastic, is to meet the testing requirements of either Section 804.1.1 or 804.12. Only one testing method is required.

804.1.1 Testing in accordance with NFPA 286. Interior trim material shall be tested in accordance with NFPA 286 and comply with the acceptance criteria in Section 803.1.1.1. Where the interior trim material has been tested as an interior finish in accordance with NFPA 286 and complies with the acceptance criteria in Section 803.1.1.1, it shall not be required to be tested for flame spread index and smoke-developed index in accordance with ASTM E84 or UL 723.

❖This section lists the first testing option for combustible material used as interior trim as NFPA 286 and provides the section reference for the acceptance criteria. Chapter 8 of the IBC and Section 803.1.1 of this code already make it clear that any material that meets the criteria of Section 803.1.1.1 is permitted to be used for interior finish. If the material is allowed to be used to cover the entire wall or ceiling, it is also allowed to be used to cover 10 percent of it.

804.1.2 Testing in accordance with ASTM E84 or UL 723. Material, other than foam plastic, used as interior trim shall have minimum Class C flame spread and smoke-developed indices, when tested in accordance with ASTM E84 or UL 723, as described in Section 803.1.2.

❖This section lists the second testing option for combustible material used as interior trim as ASTM E84 or UL 723, with the result that the minimum classification of all trim must be at least Class C. The criteria for interior trim (whether a foam plastic or not) are basically just less severe and apply to smaller areas only. If the material is allowed to be used to cover the entire wall or ceiling, it is also allowed to be used to cover 10 percent of it. Although a Class C flame spread index may be lower than the flame spread inex required for a particular building or facility, this quantity of combustible material will not significantly increase the fuel load.

804.2 Foam plastic interior trim. Foam plastic used as interior trim shall comply with Sections 804.2.1 through 804.2.4.

❖As noted in Section 803.8.3, foam plastic is allowed as interior trim under certain conditions. This section introduces Sections 804.2.1 through 804.2.4, which establish that some dense foam plastic materials may be used as interior trim if the thickness, width and area of coverage is specifically limited.

804.2.1 Density. The minimum density of the interior trim shall be 20 pounds per cubic foot (320 kg/m^3).

❖This section establishes a minimum density of 20 pounds per cubic foot (pcf) (320 kg/m^3) for foam interior trim. A minimum instead of a maximum density is specified because the denser the foam plastic material, the less likely it is that it will generate misleading ASTM E84 test results due to having insufficient material for fire testing of the foam.

804.2.2 Thickness. The maximum thickness of the interior trim shall be $^1/_2$ inch (12.7 mm) and the maximum width shall be 8 inches (203 mm).

❖Even though other trim materials are not limited in dimension, the maximum thickness and width of foam plastic trim is limited to $^1/_2$ inch (12.7 mm) and 8 inches (203 mm), respectively. These dimensions were selected because they were typical of the maximums being produced at the time this provision was included in the code (see Commentary Figure 804.2.2).

804.2.3 Area limitation. The interior trim shall not constitute more than 10 percent of the specific wall or ceiling area to which it is attached.

❖Trim cannot constitute more than 10 percent of the individual area of the wall and ceiling of a room. This limitation is simply a restatement of the general requirement for all combustible trim, which appears in Section 804.1 (see Commentary Figure 804.2.3).

804.2.4 Flame spread. The flame spread index shall not exceed 75 where tested in accordance with ASTM E84 or UL 723. The smoke-developed index shall not be limited.

> **Exception:** Where the interior trim material has been tested as an interior finish in accordance with NFPA 286 and complies with the acceptance criteria in Section 803.1.1.1, it is not required to be tested for flame spread index in accordance with ASTM E84 or UL 723.

❖This section specifically calls out a numerical flame spread index limitation of 75 for foam plastic used as trim, which is a Class B flame spread index. The value of 75 was selected to be consistent with the requirement for foam plastic insulation, even though other materials used as trim are permitted to have flame spread indexes of up to 200 in many locations. No thermal barrier is required for the use of foam plastic as trim and the smoke-developed index is not limited. It should be noted that Section 2604 of the IBC, which regulates the use of foam plastic as trim for new construction, has essentially identical requirements to those found in this section. Neither this section nor Section 2603.4.1.11 of the IBC requires a thermal barrier for interior trim. The exception recognizes the stringency of testing in accordance with NFPA 286 as being equivalent to this section.

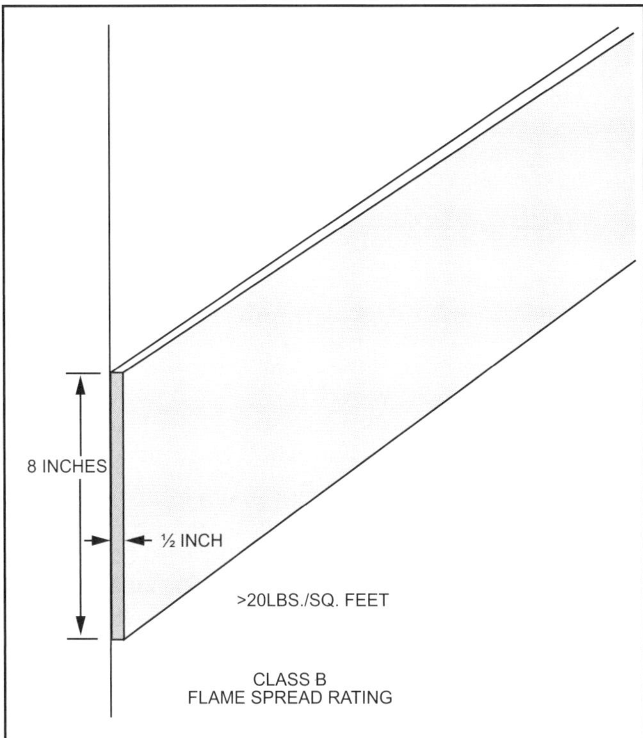

For SI: 1 foot = 304.8 mm, 1 pound per square foot = 4.882 kg/m^2.

Commentary Figure 804.2.2
MAXIMUM DIMENSIONS—FOAM PLASTIC TRIM

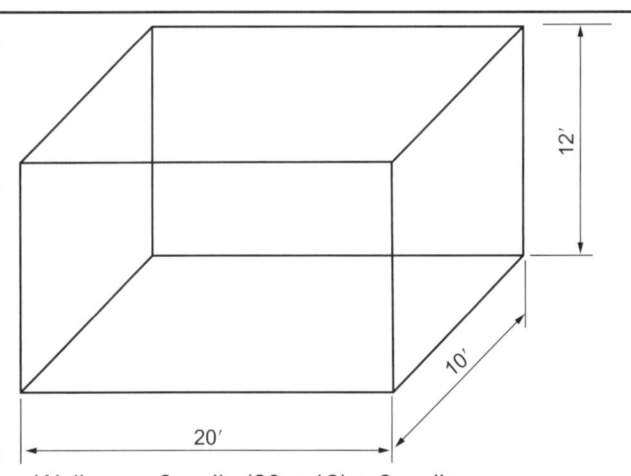

Wall area: 2 walls (20 × 12) + 2 walls (10 × 12) = 720 ft^2

10% of walls = 720 × 0.10 = 72 ft^2

Decorative trim coverage = 72 ft^2

Ceiling 20 × 10 = 200 ft^2

10% of ceiling = 200 × 0.10 = 20

Decorative trim coverage = 20 ft^2

For SI: 1 foot = 304.8 mm, 1 square foot = 0.0929 m^2.

Commentary Figure 804.2.3
FOAM PLASTIC DECORATIVE TRIM COVERAGE AREA

804.3 New interior floor finish. New interior floor finish and floor covering materials in new and existing buildings shall comply with Sections 804.3.1 through 804.3.3.2.

Exception: Floor finishes and coverings of a traditional type, such as wood, vinyl, linoleum or terrazzo, and resilient floor covering materials that are not composed of fibers.

❖This section regulates the design and installation of floor finish and floor covering materials and is identical to Section 804 of the IBC. Since Section 804.3 is located within a section that could apply to both existing and new buildings, it is specifically clarified that these requirements are only applicable to new flooring. Traditional floor coverings, such as wood, vinyl, terrazzo and other resilient floor covering material, must be exempt from this section since they generally contribute minimally to a fire. The focus is on textile floor coverings such as carpets.

804.3.1 Classification. Interior floor finish and floor covering materials required by Section 804.3.3.2 to be of Class I or II materials shall be classified in accordance with ASTM E648 or NFPA 253. The classification referred to herein corresponds to the classifications determined by ASTM E648 or NFPA 253 as follows: Class I, 0.45 watts/cm^2 or greater; Class II, 0.22 watts/cm^2 or greater.

❖The use of a classification system eliminates the need to state the actual critical radiant flux value for a product to meet the identification requirements of Section 804.3. Over the years, a classification system has been found to be much easier for the industry to follow and still provides the building official with the information required to verify compliance. The test required to measure the combustibility of floor coverings can be either ASTM E648 or NFPA 253. This standard is a radiant floor panel test, which basically simulates materials subjected to heat from a fire above. The primary concern with flooring is related to the spread of a fire that has already been ignited within a space or room to a different room. Commentary Figure 804.3.1 shows the test apparatus. The critical heat flux indicates the threshold value above which flame spread occurs in the testing environment.

804.3.2 Testing and identification. Interior floor finish and floor covering materials shall be tested by an *approved* agency in accordance with ASTM E648 or NFPA 253 and identified by a hang tag or other suitable method so as to identify the manufacturer or supplier and style, and shall indicate the interior floor finish or floor covering classification in accordance with Section 804.3.1. Carpet-type floor coverings shall be tested as proposed for use, including underlayment. Test reports confirming the information provided in the manufacturer's product identification shall be furnished to the *fire code official* upon request.

❖The only method to ascertain that a floor meets the criteria of this section is to request a copy of the test report for the specific material being installed; therefore, it is critical that the carpeting be properly identified in order to verify that acceptable materials are being provided in the appropriate locations. The identification is to be provided on the material itself since a manufacturer's designation is required.

804.3.3 Interior floor finish requirements. New interior floor coverings materials shall comply with Sections 804.3.3.1 and 804.3.3.2, and interior floor finish materials shall comply with Section 804.3.1.

❖Sections 804.3.3.1 and 804.3.3.2 prescribe where the pill test for floor covering material is applicable and which occupancies and locations require a Class I or Class II classification in accordance with NFPA 253. Section 804.3.1 specifies the criteria for Classes I and II. More information about the specific test is discussed in Section 804.3.1. Generally the focus is on more critical areas, such as exit passage-ways, interior exit stairways and exit access corridors.

804.3.3.1 Pill test. In all occupancies, new floor covering materials shall comply with the requirements of the DOC FF-1 "pill test" (CPSC 16 CFR Part 1630) or of ASTM D2859.

❖DOC FF-1, also referred to as the "Methenamine Pill Test," was developed as a means of preventing the distribution of highly flammable soft floor coverings within the United States. The test essentially evaluates the performance of the floor covering when subject to a cigarette-type ignition by using a small methenamine tablet. All carpeting greater than 24 square feet (2.2 m^2) in area sold in the United States is required by federal law to pass this test procedure as a minimum.

Commentary Figure 804.3.1
RADIANT FLOOR PANEL TEST (NFPA 253)

804.3.3.2 Minimum critical radiant flux. In all occupancies, new interior floor finish and floor covering materials in enclosures for *stairways* and *ramps*, *exit passageways*, *corridors* and rooms or spaces not separated from *corridors* by full-height partitions extending from the floor to the underside of the ceiling shall withstand a minimum critical radiant flux. The minimum critical radiant flux shall be not less than Class I in Groups I-1, I-2 and I-3 and not less than Class II in Groups A, B, E, H, I-4, M, R-1, R-2 and S.

> **Exception:** Where a building is equipped throughout with an *automatic sprinkler system* in accordance with Section 903.3.1.1 or 903.3.1.2, Class II materials shall be permitted in any area where Class I materials are required and materials complying with DOC FF-1 "pill test" (CPSC 16 CFR Part 1630) or with ASTM D2859 shall be permitted in any area where Class II materials are required.

❖This section prescribes the minimum requirements for interior floor finish materials that are used in interior exit stairways, exit passageways and exit access corridors. The criteria are based on the occupancy classification and the relationship of the space to the egress system. Similar to Table 803.3, the occupancy classification designation is meant to apply to the actual occupancy of the space and not necessarily the overall building classification.

Classifications I and II as used in this section are defined in Section 804.3.1 and are based on the results of the NFPA 253 test procedure.

Recognizing the ability of automatic sprinkler systems to control a fire and the minimal contribution of interior floor finishes to the early stages of fire growth, the exception allows the required interior floor finish ratings to be reduced where an automatic sprinkler system is provided throughout the building. The reference to Section 903.3.1.1 or 903.3.1.2 clarifies that the system is to be installed in accordance with NFPA 13 or 13R. In cases where Class II materials are required and an automatic sprinkler system is provided, the minimum requirement is that the material simply meet the DOC FF-1 test criteria.

804.4 Interior floor-wall base. Interior floor-wall base that is 6 inches (152 mm) or less in height shall be tested in accordance with ASTM E648 or NFPA 253 and shall be not less than Class II. Where a Class I floor finish is required, the floor-wall base shall be Class I. The classification referred to herein corresponds to the classifications determined by ASTM E648 or NFPA 253 as follows: Class I, 0.45 watt/cm^2 or greater; Class II, 0.22 watts/cm^2 or greater.

> **Exception:** Interior trim materials that comply with Section 804.1.

❖In trimming out the interior of a building, rather than install separate baseboards or materials, in many cases the floor covering material is simply seamlessly turned up for a few inches or used at the intersection of the floor and the wall, thus becoming the floor-wall base trim. Previously, these materials could have been considered as interior trim in accordance with Section 804.1 and would have been required to be tested in accordance with ASTM E84 even though the floor covering may be required to be tested in accordance with ASTM E648 or NFPA 253. Based on the small amount of material used, it is very difficult to test these materials in a reliable manner, upside down in the ASTM E84 test method. This section addresses the issue of testing and regulation of wall base interior floor finish trim materials and eliminates that difficulty.

Because of their location at the floor line, wall base materials are not likely to be involved in a fire until the floor covering is also involved, usually at room flashover. Thus, it is reasonable that wall base materials meet the same criteria as floor coverings. This is true since in some applications, for sanitary reasons, the floor covering is seamlessly turned up on the wall to form a wall base. Thus, this section specifies that the wall base be tested in accordance with ASTM E648 or NFPA 253 as required for floor coverings and has requirements for its use. This section also limits the height of the wall base such that its application is controlled in a similar manner as the 10-percent limitation for interior trim. The exception recognizes that some materials used as interior finish trim that meet the flammability requirements of Section 804.1 can be used in this specific application without the need for additional testing.

SECTION 805 UPHOLSTERED FURNITURE AND MATTRESSES IN NEW AND EXISTING BUILDINGS

❖Furnishings and contents are subjects that codes have not addressed very strongly in the past. Ultimately, the fire hazard potential within a building depends heavily on what is in the building and where it is placed. First, the burning characteristics of the materials will vary and the location of the material will change the characteristics of a fire. For instance, a couch within a small compartment will create a much different fire event than the same couch burning in a large open atrium (see Commentary Figure 805.1). The compartment may be limited by the amount of oxygen available, while the atrium fire will be limited only by the amount of combustibles to burn because oxygen will be plentiful; therefore, the compartment is likely to reach flashover while the atrium will not. Generally, upholstered furniture and mattresses are the largest fire hazards in most residential buildings because mattresses or upholstered furniture are the only products typically present where people live that can cause room flashover on their own.

805.1 Group I-1, Condition 2. The requirements in Sections 805.1.1 through 805.1.2 shall apply to facilities in Group I-1, Condition 2.

❖This section introduces Sections 805.1.1 through 805.1.2.3, which contain requirements for controlling the hazards associated with upholstered furniture and mattresses in new and existing Group I-1, Condition 2 occupancies. Group I-1, Condition 2 occupancies contain, in a supervised setting, more than 16 persons on a 24-hour basis because of age, mental disability or other reasons. It should be noted that Group I-1, Condition 2 occupancies have occupants who need limited assistance both verbally and physically to evacuate whereas occupants of Group I-1, Condition 1 do not need such assistance. The provisions throughout the I-Codes differentiate between these two types of occupancy classifications. In general, these occupants are considered more vulnerable than the general population and have had a history of starting fires in beds or upholstered furniture. There is also more of a concern than with a Group I-2 occupancy over occupants having the ability to purposely start a fire. This is less likely in an assisted living setting but more likely in a halfway house setting; therefore, limitations on combustibility of upholstered furniture and mattresses are also required. Reducing ignitability and combustibility will significantly reduce the level of fire hazard. The requirements are slightly different than for Group I-2 occupancies in that different tests and performance criteria are required because of the nature of the hazards.

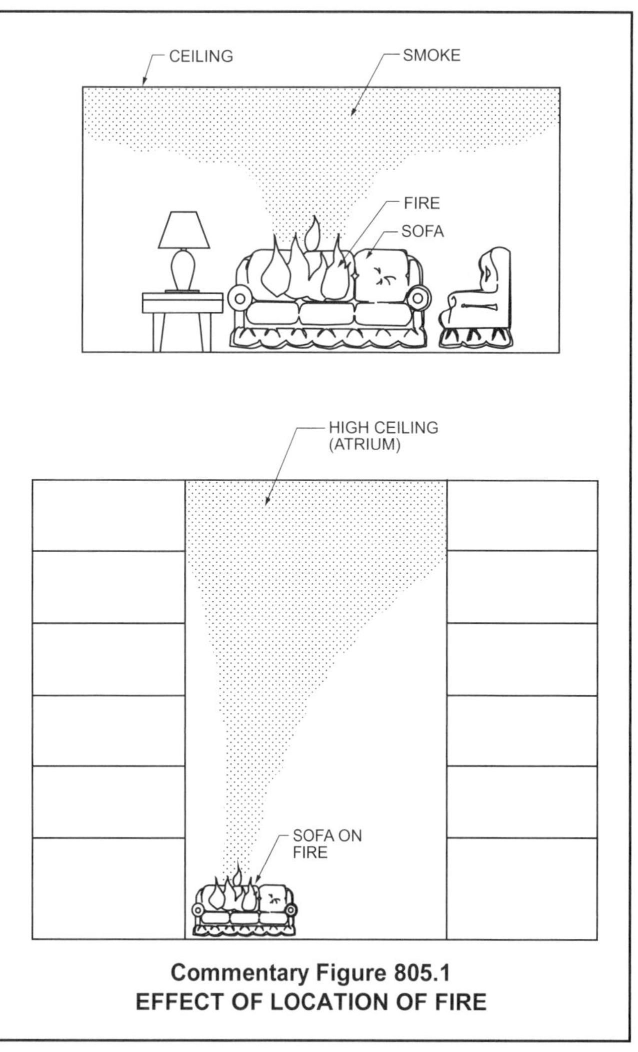

Commentary Figure 805.1 EFFECT OF LOCATION OF FIRE

805.1.1 Upholstered furniture. Newly introduced upholstered furniture shall meet the requirements of Sections 805.1.1.1 through 805.1.1.3.

❖This section informs the user that two aspects of upholstered furniture are regulated: the ignitability by cigarettes and the maximum allowable heat release in accordance with ASTM E1537.

805.1.1.1 Ignition by cigarettes. Newly introduced upholstered furniture shall be shown to resist ignition by cigarettes as determined by tests conducted in accordance with one of the following:

1. Mocked-up composites of the upholstered furniture shall have a char length not exceeding 1.5 inches (38 mm) when tested in accordance with NFPA 261.
2. The components of the upholstered furniture shall meet the requirements for Class I when tested in accordance with NFPA 260.

❖This section focuses on the ignitability of furniture when exposed to lighted cigarettes and is consistent with Section 805.2.1.1 for Group I-2 occupancies and Section 805.3.1.1 for Group I-3 detention and correctional facilities. It offers an alternative test (NFPA 261) for approval of cigarette ignition resistance of newly introduced upholstered furniture in Group I-1 occupancies (board and care facilities). The same test method is already permitted for use in Group I-2 and I-3 occupancies. The difference between NFPA 260 and NFPA 261 is that NFPA 260 uses an overall classification system that looks at the cigarette ignition behavior of the individual components that may be found in upholstered furniture while NFPA 261 specifically looks at ignitability of a mock-up of upholstered furniture. It presents a method for study of the ignitability of the furniture mock-up and a technique to measure the char length, and limits the maximum char length to 1.5 inches (38.1 mm). In fact, results from NFPA 261 are more likely to be predictive of real fire behavior.

The previously existing exception to this section for upholstered furniture in rooms or spaces protected by an approved NFPA 13 automatic sprinkler system has been deleted because: a. Sprinklers have no effect on controlling smoldering ignition (ignition by cigarettes), since they require an increase in room temperature to act and there will be no increase in room temperature until well after the upholstered furniture which fails the cigarette test has erupted into flames; and b. Newly introduced upholstered furniture is very likely to meet smoldering ignition requirements. The trade association for manufacturers of residential upholstered furniture, the Upholstered Furniture Action Council (UFAC), its sister organization, the American Home Furnishings Alliance (AHFA) and the trade association for manufacturers of institutional and contract upholstered furniture, the Business and Institutional Furniture Manufacturers Association (BIFMA), require that their members comply with the smoldering resistance test. UFAC requires NFPA 260 (equivalent to ASTM E1353 and the UFAC test) and BIFMA requires NFPA 261 (equivalent to ASTM E1352). Note that this section does not affect existing upholstered furniture.

805.1.1.2 Heat release rate. Newly introduced upholstered furniture shall have limited rates of heat release when tested in accordance with ASTM E1537 or California Technical Bulletin 133, as follows:

1. The peak rate of heat release for the single upholstered furniture item shall not exceed 80 kW.

   Exception: Upholstered furniture in rooms or spaces protected by an *approved automatic sprinkler system* installed in accordance with Section 903.3.1.1.

2. The total heat released by the single upholstered furniture item during the first 10 minutes of the test shall not exceed 25 megajoules (MJ).

   Exception: Upholstered furniture in rooms or spaces protected by an *approved automatic sprinkler system* installed in accordance with Section 903.3.1.1.

❖The two tests specified in this section measure the overall combustibility of furniture. Where a building is sprinklered in accordance with NFPA 13, this section does not apply. Upholstered furniture must be tested to either ASTM E1537 or California Technical Bulletin 133 (which are basically the same test, but ASTM E1537 has no pass/fail criteria). This test uses a full-scale calorimeter, with the furniture item either in a standard room or under a hood. A full-scale calorimeter allows a representative piece of furniture to be burned and the products of combustion to be collected and analyzed in the exhaust duct by measuring gases (principally oxygen) in order to measure heat release. The test also measures weight loss during the test [see Commentary Figure 805.1.1.2(1) for a representation of the test]. The acceptance criteria set by the code are as follows:

- Peak heat release is limited to 80 kW.
- Total energy (or heat) release within the first 10 minutes cannot exceed 25 mega joules (MJ).

Limitations are placed on the maximum intensity and fire effluents produced by restricting the peak heat release rate and the amount of combustibles actually burned. The total energy release of 25 MJ could be translated to a steady fire as follows, where:

X = Steady fire heat release rate expressed in kW

X × 10 minutes = 25 MJ
(10 minutes = 600 sec and 25 MJ = 25,000 kJ)

X × 600 sec = 25,000 kJ

X = 25,000 kJ/600 sec = 41.66 kJ/sec

X = 41.66 kJ/sec = 41.66 kW ~ 42 kW heat release rate

A steady fire of 42 kW (133 kJ/sec) for 10 minutes will result in a total energy release of 25 MJ.

Because fires in more realistic conditions do not burn steadily and vary in their characteristics, the criterion is given in the form of a peak heat release rate and total energy release. To provide a better understanding, if the fire were burning at the maximum peak heat release rate of 80 kW for the first 10 minutes, the total energy output would be 75 MJ [80 kW (kJ/sec) H 10 minutes (600 sec) = 48,000 kJ = 48 MJ], which is well over the criterion of 25 MJ. A fire burning at a steady rate from start to finish is not realistic because fires must go through an initial growth stage before a peak heat release rate will be reached, followed by a decay phase; therefore, because a realistic fire will not burn at the peak heat release rate from the start of the fire, it is possible for a piece of furniture to have a peak heat release rate of 80 kW and still stay within the 25 MJ limitation. Commentary Figure 805.1.1.2(2) demonstrates the difference between a steady fire and a more realistic unsteady fire. As stated in the exceptions, the heat release rates will not apply to buildings sprinklered in accordance with NFPA 13. Sections 805.2.1.2 and 805.3.1.2 address the heat release rate limitations for upholstered furniture in the same manner. It should be noted that Section 805.3.1.2 does not reference California Technical Bulletin 133.

See also the commentary for mattresses in Section 805.1.2.

805.1.1.3 Identification. Upholstered furniture shall bear the label of an *approved* agency, confirming compliance with the requirements of Sections 805.1.1.1 and 805.1.1.2.

❖In order to achieve verifiable compliance, labeling by an approved agency is required. Otherwise, this information would be extremely difficult to verify in the field. See the commentary for the definition of "Labeled" in Section 202.

805.1.2 Mattresses. Newly introduced mattresses shall meet the requirements of Sections 805.1.2.1 through 805.1.2.3.

❖Sections 805.1.2.1 and 805.1.2.2 deal with the combustibility of mattresses. Section 805.1.2.1 focuses on initial ignition and the ability of a mattress to sustain a fire; Section 805.1.2.2 is focused primarily on the burning characteristics of mattresses.

805.1.2.1 Ignition by cigarettes. Newly introduced mattresses shall be shown to resist ignition by cigarettes as determined by tests conducted in accordance with DOC 16 CFR Part 1632 and shall have a char length not exceeding 2 inches (51 mm).

❖This section sets a maximum char length of 2 inches (51 mm) when the mattress is tested under DOC 16 CFR, Part 1632. This test is a mandatory regulation for all mattresses sold in the United States. More specifically, it is part of the regulations governed by the Consumer Products Safety Commission (CPSC) under the Department of Commerce (DOC). Sections 805.2.2.1 and 805.3.2.1 have the same reference and requirements for Group I-2 and I-3 occupancies. Thus, mattresses that fail to meet the 16 CFR 1632 test will be those sold either before the CPSC regulation went into effect (in 1972) or outside of the United States.

805.1.2.2 Heat release rate. Newly introduced mattresses shall have limited rates of heat release when tested in accordance with ASTM E1590 or California Technical Bulletin 129, as follows:

1. The peak rate of heat release for the single mattress shall not exceed 100 kW.

   Exception: Mattresses in rooms or spaces protected by an *approved automatic sprinkler system* installed in accordance with Section 903.3.1.1.

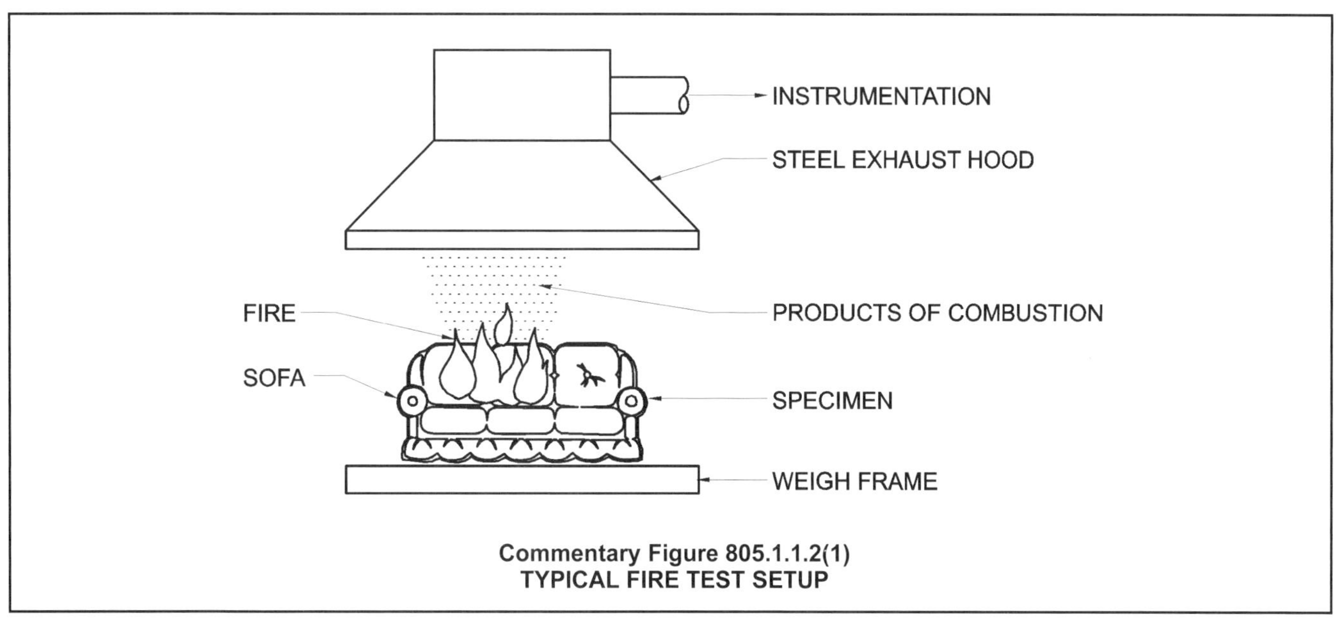

Commentary Figure 805.1.1.2(1)
TYPICAL FIRE TEST SETUP

2. The total heat released by the single mattress during the first 10 minutes of the test shall not exceed 25 MJ.

   Exception: Mattresses in rooms or spaces protected by an *approved automatic sprinkler system* installed in accordance with Section 903.3.1.1.

❖As noted, an occupant smoking in bed and initiating a mattress fire is a major fire hazard in Group I-1, Condition 2 occupancies. This section, like Section 805.1.1.2, limits combustibility by restricting the peak heat release rate and on the total energy output in the first 10 minutes of burning. These limitations vary slightly from those for upholstered furniture. Each mattress is allowed a maximum heat release rate of 100 kW, whereas each upholstered furniture item is limited to 80 kW. The total energy (or heat) release limitation is the same as for upholstered furniture items, which is 25 MJ in the first 10 minutes. As with upholstered furniture, these restrictions are not applicable in buildings sprinklered in accordance with NFPA 13. The tests that determine the peak heat release rate and total heat release are specific to mattresses. These tests are detailed in ASTM E1590 and California Technical Bulletin 129 (which are the same test, except that ASTM E1590 does not have pass/fail criteria). These tests, like that referenced in Section 805.1.1.2, make use of a full scale calorimeter to measure the products of combustion. There are two differences between ASTM E1537 and ASTM E1590: the object being tested (see commentary, Section 805.1.1.2) and the ignition source. Both tests use a gas burner, but they are different in geometry, gas flow rate, duration of gas flow and position of flame application. Section 805.2.2.2 contains the same restrictions and testing requirements on combustibility for mattresses in Group I-2 occupancies, Section 805.3.2.2 for Group I-3 detention and correctional facilities and Section 805.4.2.2 for Group R-2 dormitories.

805.1.2.3 Identification. Mattresses shall bear the label of an *approved* agency, confirming compliance with the requirements of Sections 805.2.2.1 and 805.2.2.2.

❖This section provides the fire code official with a valuable tool in evaluating and approving mattresses in Group I-2 occupancies. In order to achieve verifiable compliance, labeling by an approved agency is required. Otherwise, this information would be extremely difficult to verify in the field. See the commentary for the definition of "Labeled" in Section 202.

805.2 Group I-2 and Group B ambulatory care facilities. The requirements in Sections 805.2.1 through 805.2.2 shall apply to Group I-2 occupancies and Group B ambulatory care facilities.

❖This section introduces Sections 805.2.1 through 805.2.2.3, which contain requirements for controlling the hazards associated with upholstered furniture and mattresses in new and existing Group I-2 occupancies and Group B ambulatory care facilities. Occupants of nursing homes (Group I-2, Condition 1), hospitals (Group I-2, Condition 2) and ambulatory care facilities (Group B) are considered more vulnerable than the general population. Many of the patients of these occupancies are confined because of respirators, IVs and other medical equipment, and may not be capable of self-preservation. Hospital employees may have to make several trips into the fire area to assist in evacuating patients; therefore, it is imperative that every effort be made to preserve the integrity of the corridors and minimize the fuel loading caused by furnishings and contents, such as upholstered furniture and mattresses.

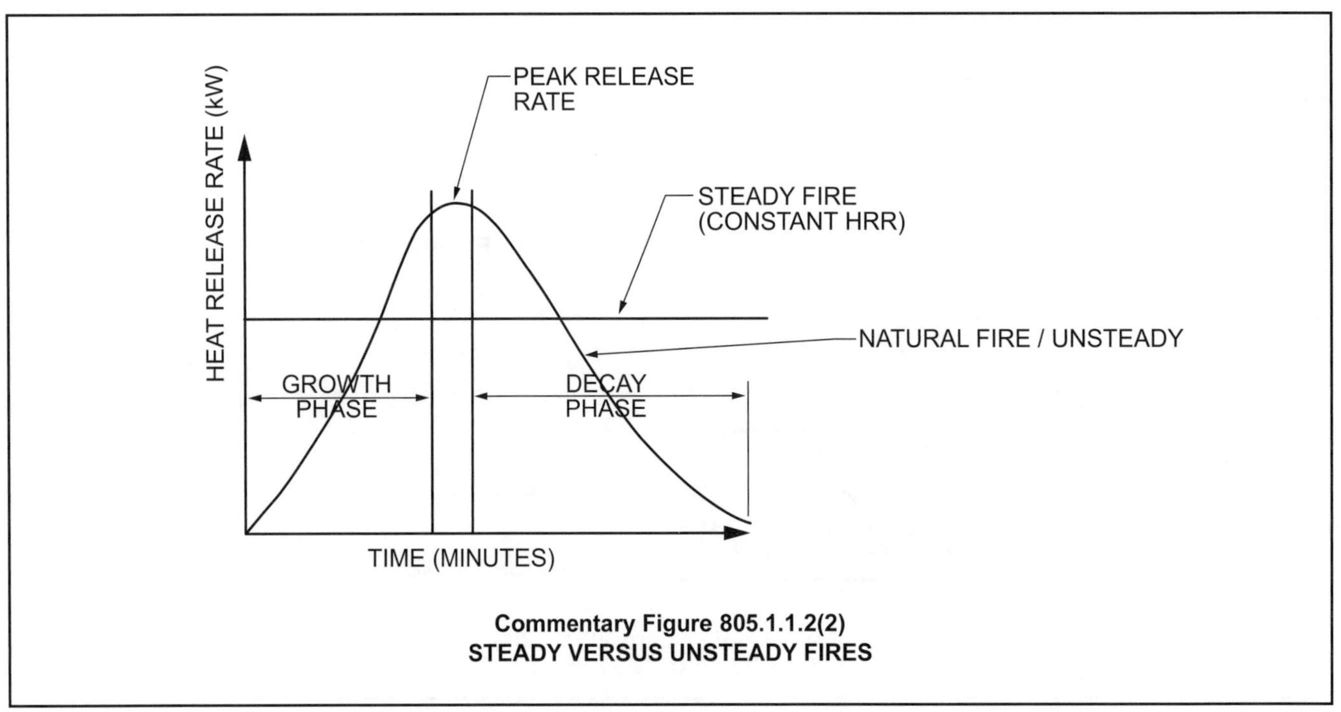

Commentary Figure 805.1.1.2(2)
STEADY VERSUS UNSTEADY FIRES

Historically, fires have been ignited through the use of cigarettes in bed or falling asleep while smoking in a chair. In addition to these hazards, such occupancies usually have additional medical oxygen sources within their rooms. This section, therefore, states several ignitability and combustibility limitations for upholstered furniture and mattresses that might be introduced into such occupancies.

805.2.1 Upholstered furniture. Newly introduced upholstered furniture shall meet the requirements of Sections 805.2.1.1 through 805.2.1.3.

❖This section informs the user that two aspects of upholstered furniture are regulated: the ignitability by cigarettes and the maximum allowable heat release in accordance with ASTM E1537.

805.2.1.1 Ignition by cigarettes. Newly introduced upholstered furniture shall be shown to resist ignition by cigarettes as determined by tests conducted in accordance with one of the following: (a) mocked-up composites of the upholstered furniture shall have a char length not exceeding 1.5 inches (38 mm) when tested in accordance with NFPA 261 or (b) the components of the upholstered furniture shall meet the requirements for Class I when tested in accordance with NFPA 260.

Exception: Upholstered furniture belonging to the patients in sleeping rooms of Group I-2, Condition 1 occupancies provided that a smoke detector is installed in such rooms. Battery-powered, single-station smoke alarms shall be allowed.

❖The exception allows nursing home patients to bring their furniture with them into their rooms without having to comply with the test requirements, provided that the basic protection of a system smoke detector (in buildings equipped with a fire alarm system) or a battery-operated smoke alarm is present in the room (see commentary, Section 805.1.1.1). Note that all new Group I-2, Condition 1 occupancies are required to be equipped throughout with an automatic sprinkler system. Additionally, Section 1105.8 requires an automatic sprinkler system in existing Group I-2 occupancies. This requirement is retroactive, which means it applies regardless of whether work is being done to the building.

805.2.1.2 Heat release rate. Newly introduced upholstered furniture shall have limited rates of heat release when tested in accordance with ASTM E1537 or California Technical Bulletin 133, as follows:

1. The peak rate of heat release for the single upholstered furniture item shall not exceed 80 kW.

   Exception: Upholstered furniture in rooms or spaces protected by an *approved automatic sprinkler system* installed in accordance with Section 903.3.1.1.

2. The total heat released by the single upholstered furniture item during the first 10 minutes of the test shall not exceed 25 MJ.

   Exception: Upholstered furniture in rooms or spaces protected by an *approved automatic sprinkler system* installed in accordance with Section 903.3.1.1.

❖This section is identical to Section 805.1.1.2 and focuses on the potential heat release rate of upholstered furniture if a fire occurs (see commentary, Section 805.1.1.2).

805.2.1.3 Identification. Upholstered furniture shall bear the label of an *approved* agency, confirming compliance with the requirements of Sections 805.2.1.1 and 805.2.1.2.

❖In order to achieve verifiable compliance, labeling by an approved agency is required. Otherwise, this information would be extremely difficult to verify in the field. See the commentary to the definition of "Labeled" in Section 202.

805.2.2 Mattresses. Newly introduced mattresses shall meet the requirements of Sections 805.2.2.1 through 805.2.2.3.

❖Sections 805.2.2.1 and 805.2.2.2 deal with the combustibility of mattresses. Section 805.2.2.1 focuses on initial ignition and the ability of a mattress to sustain a fire; Section 805.2.2.2 is focused primarily on the burning characteristics of mattresses.

805.2.2.1 Ignition by cigarettes. Newly introduced mattresses shall be shown to resist ignition by cigarettes as determined by tests conducted in accordance with DOC 16 CFR Part 1632 and shall have a char length not exceeding 2 inches (51 mm).

❖This section is the same as Sections 805.1.2.1 and 805.3.2.1 and requires compliance with DOC 16 CFR Part 1632 (see commentary, Section 805.1.2.1).

805.2.2.2 Heat release rate. Newly introduced mattresses shall have limited rates of heat release when tested in accordance with ASTM E1590 or California Technical Bulletin 129, as follows:

1. The peak rate of heat release for the single mattress shall not exceed 100 kW.

   Exception: Mattresses in rooms or spaces protected by an *approved automatic sprinkler system* installed in accordance with Section 903.3.1.1.

2. The total heat released by the single mattress during the first 10 minutes of the test shall not exceed 25 MJ.

   Exception: Mattresses in rooms or spaces protected by an *approved automatic sprinkler system* installed in accordance with Section 903.3.1.1.

❖This section is the same as Section 805.1.2.2 in limiting the maximum heat release rate and the total heat release (see commentary, Section 805.1.2.2).

805.2.2.3 Identification. Mattresses shall bear the label of an *approved* agency, confirming compliance with the requirements of Sections 805.2.2.1 and 805.2.2.2.

❖In order to achieve verifiable compliance, labeling by an approved agency is required. Otherwise, this information would be extremely difficult to verify in the field. See the commentary to the definition of "Labeled" in Section 202.

805.3 Group I-3, detention and correction facilities. The requirements in Sections 805.3.1 through 805.3.2 shall apply to detention and correction facilities classified in Group I-3.

❖This section introduces Sections 805.3.1 through 805.3.2.3, which contain requirements for controlling the hazards associated with upholstered furniture and mattresses in new and existing Group I-3 detention and correctional occupancies. These facilities have a higher likelihood of incendiary activities, and because of the restrictions on movement, the occupants are placed in a more vulnerable position than the general public; therefore, combustibility limitations are placed on furniture and mattresses.

805.3.1 Upholstered furniture. Newly introduced upholstered furniture shall meet the requirements of Sections 805.3.1.1 through 805.3.1.3.

❖This section informs the user that two aspects of upholstered furniture are regulated: the ignitability by cigarettes and the maximum allowable heat release in accordance with ASTM E1537.

805.3.1.1 Ignition by cigarettes. Newly introduced upholstered furniture shall be shown to resist ignition by cigarettes as determined by tests conducted in accordance with one of the following:

1. Mocked-up composites of the upholstered furniture shall have a char length not exceeding 1.5 inches (38 mm) when tested in accordance with NFPA 261.
2. The components of the upholstered furniture shall meet the requirements for Class I when tested in accordance with NFPA 260.

❖These requirements are the same as those found in Sections 805.1.1.1 and 805.2.1.1 (see commentary, Section 805.1.1.1).

805.3.1.2 Heat release rate. Newly introduced upholstered furniture shall have limited rates of heat release when tested in accordance with ASTM E1537, as follows:

1. The peak rate of heat release for the single upholstered furniture item shall not exceed 80 kW.
2. The total heat released by the single upholstered furniture item during the first 10 minutes of the test shall not exceed 25 MJ.

❖See the commentary to Section 805.1.1.2.

805.3.1.3 Identification. Upholstered furniture shall bear the label of an *approved* agency, confirming compliance with the requirements of Sections 805.3.1.1 and 805.3.1.2.

❖In order to achieve verifiable compliance, labeling by an approved agency is required. Otherwise, this information would be extremely difficult to verify in the field. See the commentary to the definition of "Labeled" in Section 202.

805.3.2 Mattresses. Newly introduced mattresses shall meet the requirements of Sections 805.3.2.1 through 805.3.2.3.

❖Sections 805.3.2.1 and 805.3.2.2 deal with the combustibility of mattresses. Section 805.3.2.1 focuses on initial ignition and the ability of a mattress to sustain a fire; Section 805.3.2.2 focuses primarily on the burning characteristics of mattresses.

805.3.2.1 Ignition by cigarettes. Newly introduced mattresses shall be shown to resist ignition by cigarettes as determined by tests conducted in accordance with DOC 16 CFR Part 1632 and shall have a char length not exceeding 2 inches (51 mm).

❖This section is the same as Sections 805.1.2.1 and 805.3.2.1 and requires compliance with DOC 16 CFR Part 1632 (see commentary, Section 805.1.2.1).

805.3.2.2 Fire performance tests. Newly introduced mattresses shall be tested in accordance with Section 805.3.2.2.1 or 805.3.2.2.2.

❖This section provides two options for fire tests: ASTM E1590, which is a cone calorimeter test, and Annex A3 of ASTM F1085, which provides a simple burn test to determine how much mass the mattress will lose with this exposure.

805.3.2.2.1 Heat release rate. Newly introduced mattresses shall have limited rates of heat release when tested in accordance with ASTM E1590 or California Technical Bulletin 129, as follows:

1. The peak rate of heat release for the single mattress shall not exceed 100 kW.
2. The total heat released by the single mattress during the first 10 minutes of the test shall not exceed 25 MJ.

❖This section is the same as Section 805.1.2.2 in limiting the maximum heat release rate and the total energy heat release (see commentary, Section 805.1.2.2).

805.3.2.2.2 Mass loss test. Newly introduced mattresses shall have a mass loss not exceeding 15 percent of the initial mass of the mattress where tested in accordance with the test in Annex A3 of ASTM F1085.

❖The test in Annex A3 of ASTM F1085 was developed originally for use in detention and correctional occupancies and is a very severe test that is a reasonable (and less expensive) alternative to ASTM E1590.

This test is very simple, can be conducted at any facility and does not require the use of an instrumented fire test lab. The test can be described in a few words: it involves rolling up a mattress, placing it at an angle (for example by holding it with a brick), introducing newspaper into the volume surrounding the rolled up mattress and igniting the newspaper with a match.

If mattress materials melt away from the flame with flaming drips they may "pass" the ASTM E1590 test; however, melting would result in a failure of the ASTM F1085 Annex A test. In this test, the material that flames on the floor will keep burning the mattress itself.

Commentary Figure 805.3.2.2.2 provides a table that shows the results using the ASTM F1085 Annex A3 test for a number of mattresses in two studies (one in 1980 and one in 2003) and it also shows whether the mattresses meet the ASTM E1590 requirements in the code. It is clear from the table that mattresses will either burn up almost completely or lose very little mass. The ASTM F1085 test will not pass mattresses that fail ASTM E1590.

The test from Annex A3 of ASTM F1085 is also described in Section 10.2 of ASTM F1870 (*Standard Guide for Selection of Fire Test Methods for the Assessment of Upholstered Furnishings in Detention and Correctional Facilities*) as a test method "Designed for Detention and Correction Facilities."

805.3.2.3 Identification. Mattresses shall bear the label of an *approved* agency, confirming compliance with the requirements of Sections 805.3.2.1 and 805.3.2.2.

❖In order to achieve verifiable compliance, labeling by an approved agency is required. Otherwise, this information would be extremely difficult to verify in the field. See the commentary to the definition of "Labeled" in Section 202.

805.4 Group R-2 college and university dormitories. The requirements of Sections 805.4.1 through 805.4.2.3 shall apply to college and university dormitories classified in Group R-2, including decks, porches and balconies.

❖This section introduces Sections 805.4.1 through 805.4.2.3, which contain requirements for controlling the hazards associated with upholstered furniture and mattresses in new and existing Group R-2 college and university dormitories. Fire represents a significant risk to life and property in dormitory occupancies, particularly at residential schools, colleges and universities. The large number of young people living in close proximity to one another creates the potential for a relatively small fire to have serious and possibly fatal consequences. According to NFPA fire loss data, there are an average of 1,425 fires each year in dormitories causing $6.3 million in direct property damage. For these reasons, upholstered furniture and mattresses in dormitories must comply with the same requirements for fire performance as those in Group I-1, I-2 and I-3 occupancies. The test methods and criteria are identical to those in Sections 805.1, 805.2 and 805.3. Section 805.3.2.2.2 provides an option for a mass loss test for mattresses.

Note that this section also includes upholstered furniture and mattresses on porches, decks and balconies, which, for this particular occupancy, can be frequently found in such locations. Since the decks, porches or balconies are likely not sprinklered, this would severely limit or eliminate the allowance of such items in these areas. Many jurisdictions have specifically banned furniture such as couches from these areas. These provisions are not as strict but will limit the potential for fires to spread to the structure.

Section 805.4 provides the fire code official and college and university campus housing authorities with the needed authority to limit the combustibility of student-owned furnishings. Those furnishings can

MATTRESS	ASTM F1085 MASS LOSS %	ASTM E1590 PER SECTION 805.3.2.2.1 PASS OR FAIL
1 (2003)	1.22	Pass
2 (2003)	9.47	Pass
3 (2003)	3.30	Pass
4 (2003)	100	Fail
5 (2003)	100	Fail
1 (1980)	100	Fail
2 (1980)	100	Fail
3 (1980)	98.5	Fail
4 (1980)	91.1	Fail
5 (1980)	91	Fail
6 (1980)	83.1	Fail
7 (1980)	44.7	Fail
8 (1980)	3.0	Pass

Commentary Figure 805.3.2.2.2
ANNEX A3 ASTM F1085 TEST RESULTS

include both upholstered furniture and mattresses, which are the high-fuel items in Group R-2 dormitory occupancies. Strictly enforced, these provisions, coupled with the limitations on the use of open flames in Group R-2 dormitories found in Section 308.4.1, should provide a much-improved level of fire safety in these occupancies.

805.4.1 Upholstered furniture. Newly introduced upholstered furniture shall meet the requirements of Sections 805.4.1.1 through 805.4.1.3.

❖This section informs the user that two aspects of upholstered furniture are regulated: the ignitability by cigarettes and the maximum allowable heat release in accordance with recognized standards.

805.4.1.1 Ignition by cigarettes. Newly introduced upholstered furniture shall be shown to resist ignition by cigarettes as determined by tests conducted in accordance with one of the following:

1. Mocked-up composites of the upholstered furniture shall have a char length not exceeding $1^1/_2$ inches (38 mm) when tested in accordance with NFPA 261.
2. The components of the upholstered furniture shall meet the requirements for Class I when tested in accordance with NFPA 260.

❖These requirements are the same as those found in Sections 805.1.1.1, 805.2.1.1 and 805.3.1.1 (see commentary, Section 805.1.1.1).

805.4.1.2 Heat release rate. Newly introduced upholstered furniture shall have limited rates of heat release when tested in accordance with ASTM E1537 or California Technical Bulletin 133, as follows:

1. The peak rate of heat release for the single upholstered furniture item shall not exceed 80 kW.

   Exception: Upholstered furniture in rooms or spaces protected by an *approved automatic sprinkler system* installed in accordance with Section 903.3.1.1.

2. The total heat released by the single upholstered furniture item during the first 10 minutes of the test shall not exceed 25 MJ.

   Exception: Upholstered furniture in rooms or spaces protected by an *approved automatic sprinkler system* installed in accordance with Section 903.3.1.1.

❖This section is identical to Sections 805.1.1.2 and 805.2.1.2 and focuses on the potential heat release rate of upholstered furniture if a fire occurs (see commentary, Section 805.1.1.2).

805.4.1.3 Identification. Upholstered furniture shall bear the label of an *approved* agency, confirming compliance with the requirements of Sections 805.4.1.1 and 805.4.1.2.

❖In order to achieve verifiable compliance, labeling by an approved agency is required. Otherwise, this information would be extremely difficult to verify in the field. See the commentary for the definition of "Labeled" in Section 202.

805.4.2 Mattresses. Newly introduced mattresses shall meet the requirements of Sections 805.4.2.1 through 805.4.2.3.

❖Sections 805.4.2.1 and 805.4.2.2 deal with the combustibility of mattresses. Section 805.4.2.1 focuses on initial ignition and the ability of a mattress to sustain a fire; Section 805.4.2.2 focuses primarily on the burning characteristics of mattresses.

805.4.2.1 Ignition by cigarettes. Newly introduced mattresses shall be shown to resist ignition by cigarettes as determined by tests conducted in accordance with DOC 16 CFR Part 1632 and shall have a char length not exceeding 2 inches (51 mm).

❖This section is the same as Sections 805.1.2.1, 805.2.2.1 and 805.3.2.1 and requires compliance with DOC 16 CFR Part 1632 (see commentary, Section 805.1.2.1).

805.4.2.2 Heat release rate. Newly introduced mattresses shall have limited rates of heat release when tested in accordance with ASTM E1590 or California Technical Bulletin 129, as follows:

1. The peak rate of heat release for the single mattress shall not exceed 100 kW.

   Exception: Mattresses in rooms or spaces protected by an *approved automatic sprinkler system* installed in accordance with Section 903.3.1.1.

2. The total heat released by the single mattress during the first 10 minutes of the test shall not exceed 25 MJ.

   Exception: Mattresses in rooms or spaces protected by an *approved automatic sprinkler system* installed in accordance with Section 903.3.1.1.

❖This section is the same as Sections 805.1.2.2, 805.2.2.2 and 805.3.2.2.1 in limiting the maximum heat release rate and the total heat release (see commentary, Section 805.1.2.2).

805.4.2.3 Identification. Mattresses shall bear the label of an *approved* agency, confirming compliance with the requirements of Sections 805.4.2.1 and 805.4.2.2.

❖In order to achieve verifiable compliance, labeling by an approved agency is required. Otherwise, this information would be extremely difficult to verify in the field. See the commentary to the definition of "Labeled" in Section 202.

SECTION 806 NATURAL DECORATIVE VEGETATION IN NEW AND EXISTING BUILDINGS

806.1 Natural cut trees. Natural cut trees, where allowed by this section, shall have the trunk bottoms cut off not less than 0.5 inch (12.7 mm) above the original cut and shall be placed in a support device complying with Section 806.1.2.

❖This section focuses on the fire hazards posed by vegetation within a building. The majority of this section deals specifically with fresh Christmas trees. Natural cut trees, such as Christmas trees, within buildings pose a significant fire threat to occupants if they are not properly cared for. Because of the symmetric way in which these trees are normally groomed, the large surface area of the foliage and the amount of airspace throughout the branches, fires have the potential to burn very efficiently and vigorously if the tree is dry. The National Fire Protection Association (NFPA) reports that there are an estimated annual average of 200 home structure fires that begin with Christmas trees. Based on data from 2011 through 2015, these fires caused an average of 6 civilian deaths, 16 civilian injuries, and $14.8 million in direct property damage per year. The NFPA analysis also shows that although the number of Christmas tree fires is low, these fires represent a higher level of hazard. On average, one of every 32 Christmas tree fires resulted in a fatality compared to an average of one death per 143 nonconfined home structure fires overall. Further, 69 percent of Christmas tree fires spread beyond the room of origin. The fires that spread beyond the room of origin caused all of the associated fatalities. The percentage of trees involved in structure fires represents an extremely small portion of the total number of natural Christmas trees sold in the United States each year, which is estimated at 20 to 30 million. The moisture content of each tree can play a dominant role in determining the fire hazard it represents. Properly maintaining a cut Christmas tree is important to retaining a high moisture content in the needles of the tree to limit accidental ignition and prevent rapid flame spread. A tree that has dry needles can readily ignite with a flaming source and generate heat release rates that are capable of causing flashover in residential scale rooms. The above statistics addressed home structure fires and natural Christmas trees, which are required by the IFC to be kept moist and fresh at all times.

In tests performed at NIST in 1999 to better understand the severity of Christmas tree fires, eight Scotch pine Christmas trees were placed in a room at 73°F (23°C) at approximately 50-percent relative humidity for approximately three weeks. Seven of the eight trees were given no additional moisture; the eighth tree was watered according to local rules for trees within business occupancies. This required the tree to be cut in a certain manner and placed in a stand with at least a 2-gallon (7.6 L) capacity. The seven dry trees were ignited and burned intensely; however, the tree that had been watered continuously throughout the three weeks could not be ignited. The peak heat releases from the dry trees ranged from approximately 1,600 kW to 5,000 kW within about 50 to 80 seconds of ignition [see Commentary Figure 806.1(1) for a summary of results and Commentary Figure 806.1(2) for a graphical representation of Test No. 3]. These test results demonstrate that the proper care for trees (i.e., making sure that the tree remains humid or wet) makes a significant difference on the fire hazard presented. This section requires at least $^{1}/_{2}$ inch (12.7 mm) of tree trunk to be removed above the original cut to optimize the tree's ability to absorb water to maintain a minimum level of moisture. This section also requires a support device (tree stand or equivalent) that meets the criteria of Section 806.1.2. Such devices are intended to bring the correct amount of moisture into contact with the tree. The specifics of this section cannot realistically be monitored in all buildings within a jurisdiction. The focus must be on occupancies such as assembly or mercantile. All occupancies benefit, however, because there is now a method that a fire department could use to educate the general public on the treatment of Christmas trees. This tool can be helpful in fire prevention within a jurisdiction.

806.1.1 Restricted occupancies. Natural cut trees shall be prohibited within ambulatory care facilities and Group A, E, I-1, I-2, I-3, I-4, M, R-1, R-2 and R-4 occupancies.

Exceptions:

1. Trees located in areas protected by an *approved automatic sprinkler system* installed in accordance with Section 903.3.1.1 or 903.3.1.2 shall not be prohibited in Groups A, E, M, R-1 and R-2.
2. Trees shall be allowed within *dwelling units* in Group R-2 occupancies.

❖Although trees that have been properly watered and handled are less hazardous, there is still a concern that they should not be located in certain occupancies and specific uses. The occupancies listed in this section are those where the occupant load is high, occupants are vulnerable or the potential hazards that exist if the tree is not properly handled are too great. These occupancies and specific uses include ambulatory care facilities and Group A, E, I-1, I-2, I-3, I-4, M, R-1 and R-2 occupancies. There are exceptions for Group A, E, M, R-1 and R-2 occupancies when the trees are located in areas that are sprinklered in accordance with NFPA 13 or 13R, as applicable, and for trees within individual dwelling units in Group R-2. Essentially, the only occupancies that would be completely prohibited from having cut trees are institutional occupancies because of the vulnerability of the occupants and, in some cases, concerns for incendiary tendencies of some occupants.

806.1.2 Support devices. The support device that holds the tree in an upright position shall be of a type that is stable and that meets all of the following criteria:

1. The device shall hold the tree securely and be of adequate size to avoid tipping over of the tree.
2. The device shall be capable of containing a minimum two-day supply of water.

3. The water level, when full, shall cover the tree stem not less than 2 inches (51 mm). The water level shall be maintained above the fresh cut and checked not less than once daily.

❖This section is intended to prevent the tree from tipping over, potentially into an ignition source, and ensure that the support device is designed and used to keep the water supply to the tree at a useful level. More specifically, Item 1 requires the device to prevent the tree from tipping; Item 2 states that the device must be capable of holding a two-day water supply; and Item 3 requires a minimum coverage of water to 2 inches (51 mm) above the bottom of the stem. The water level must be checked at least once daily to verify that an adequate supply remains. The restrictions in Section 806.1.1 are in place because the provisions in Section 806.1.2 are generally difficult for a fire department to monitor. Having a sprinkler system or generally prohibiting natural cut trees in higher risk occupancies provides a redundancy to deal with the potential hazards.

806.1.3 Dryness. The tree shall be removed from the building whenever the needles or leaves fall off readily when a tree branch is shaken or if the needles are brittle and break when

TEST NO.	WEIGHT (kg)		HEIGHT (m)	WIDTH[a] (m)	MOISTURE CONTENT (%)
	Before Test	After Test			
1	17.2	6.8	2.6	1.7	30
2	15.9	8.2	2.7	1.3	27
3	20.0	6.8	2.3	1.7	30
4	9.5	5.0	2.5	1.2	30
5	19.1	8.6	2.5	1.7	28
6	12.7	7.7	2.5	1.1	32
7	18.6	7.7	3.1	1.5	25
8	28.1	28.1	2.7	1.4	36

(From NIST Report FR 4010)

a. The width is measured at the widest point of the tree.

Commentary Figure 806.1(1)
SUMMARY OF TREE PARAMETERS

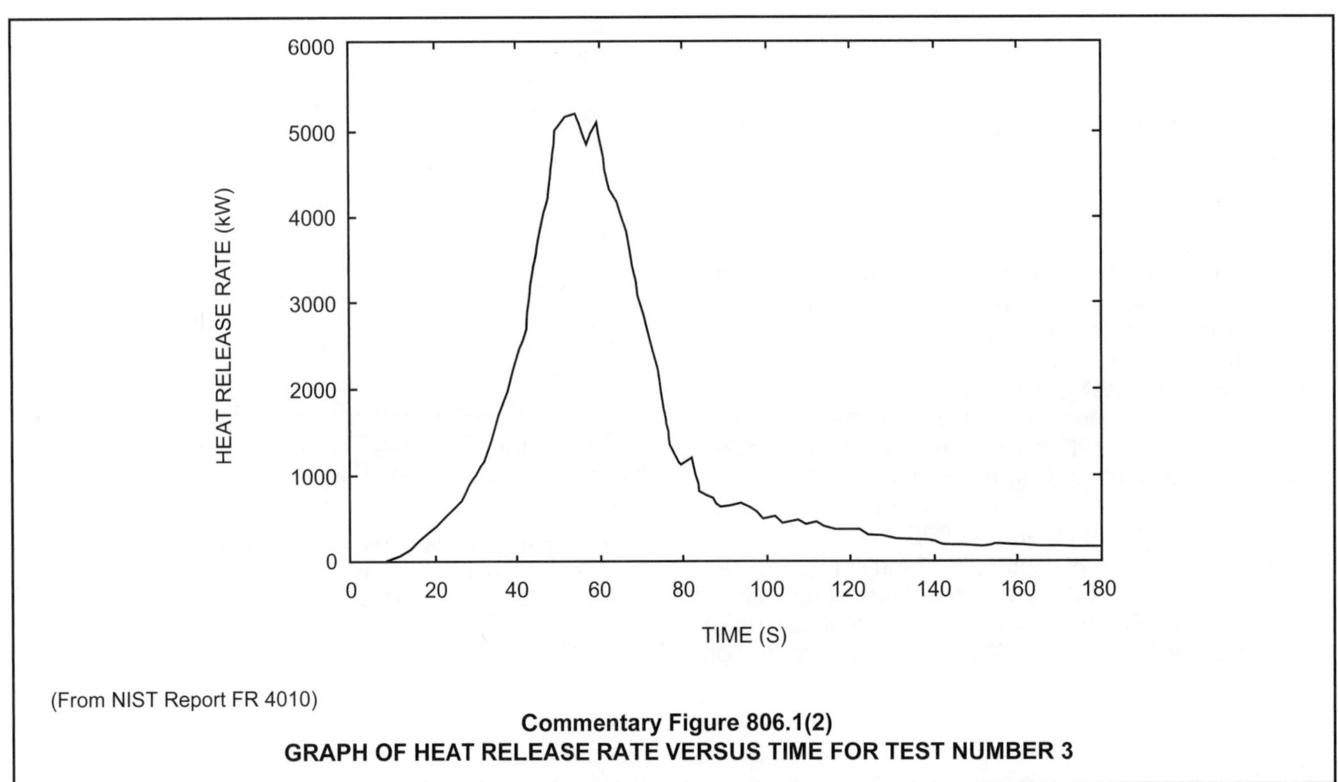

(From NIST Report FR 4010)

Commentary Figure 806.1(2)
GRAPH OF HEAT RELEASE RATE VERSUS TIME FOR TEST NUMBER 3

bent between the thumb and index finger. The tree shall be checked daily for dryness.

❖ Lack of moisture is the primary problem with natural cut trees within buildings. This section describes a daily test to assist in evaluating whether the tree is considered too dry to remain in the building.

806.2 Obstruction of means of egress. The required width of any portion of a *means of egress* shall not be obstructed by decorative vegetation. Natural cut trees shall not be located within an exit, corridor, or a lobby or vestibule.

❖Decorative vegetation is often placed in a location that does not normally accommodate combustibles. This section restricts locations so that the vegetation does not block the egress width and increase the fire hazard in such areas. For example, this would likely prohibit trees in main lobby areas of a movie theater.

806.3 Open flame. Candles and open flames shall not be used on or near decorative vegetation. Natural cut trees shall be kept a distance from heat vents and any open flame or heat-producing devices not less than the height of the tree.

❖This section addresses the primary ignition hazards associated with decorative vegetation. More specifically, candles should never be placed on or near Christmas trees. Also, heat sources such as vents may pose an ignition hazard in addition to being a source of airflow that could dry out a tree, making it more susceptible to ignition.

806.4 Electrical fixtures and wiring. The use of unlisted electrical wiring and lighting on natural vegetation, including natural cut trees, shall be prohibited.

❖Decorations are quite often used year after year on Christmas trees. Some of this decor consists of lights that are not specifically listed and can fail and become very hot, potentially posing an ignition source. Additionally, this wiring may arc and create an ignition source. In fact, it has been found that many Christmas tree fires have actually been started by decorative lights on the tree. Therefore, this section simply prohibits the use of unlisted wiring or lighting (such lights and ornaments are listed in accordance with UL 588).

SECTION 807 DECORATIVE MATERIALS AND ARTIFICIAL DECORATIVE VEGETATION IN NEW AND EXISTING BUILDINGS

807.1 General. The following requirements shall apply to all occupancies:

1. Furnishings or decorative materials of an explosive or highly flammable character shall not be used.
2. Fire-retardant coatings in existing buildings shall be maintained so as to retain the effectiveness of the treatment under service conditions encountered in actual use.
3. Furnishings or other objects shall not be placed to obstruct exits, access thereto, egress therefrom or visibility thereof.
4. The permissible amount of noncombustible decorative materials shall not be limited.

❖The requirements in this section apply to decorative materials and artificial decorative vegetation in new and existing buildings. The bulk of the requirements in this section are applicable to all occupancy groups. Section 807.2 is applicable to the occupancy groups listed. In the specific case of Group I-3, combustible decorative materials are prohibited (See Section 807.5.4). Decorative materials must be noncombustible or meet the flame propagation performance criteria of Section 806.4 and NFPA 701. Note that Section 807.5 is occupancy based and addresses combustible decorative materials that may not comply with Section 807.3, such as artwork in classrooms. Instead, specific limitations on amounts and types of materials are provided. The occupancies addressed include Group A, E, I and R-2 dormitories.

This section addresses some basic hazards with certain finishes and materials associated with decorative materials. These are discussed below.

1. This is a general statement prohibiting furnishings and contents or decorative materials that pose an extreme fire potential. These materials tend to have a significant impact on fire size in a building.
2. In many cases, the IBC and this code allow use of certain combustible or flammable materials based on the application of a fire-retardant coating (see commentary, Section 803.4).
3. Similar to Section 806.3, this section prohibits any decorations or other objects from obstructing the means of egress, including visibility.
4. It is clarified that noncombustible decorative materials are not limited, as they pose no fire hazard. It is important that they comply with Item 3 in terms of obstruction of the means of egress.

807.2 Combustible decorative materials. In Groups A, B, E, I, M and R-1 and in dormitories in Group R-2, curtains, draperies, fabric hangings and other similar combustible decorative materials suspended from walls or ceilings shall comply with Section 807.3 and shall not exceed 10 percent of the specific wall or ceiling area to which such materials are attached.

Fixed or movable walls and partitions, paneling, wall pads and crash pads applied structurally or for decoration, acoustical correction, surface insulation or other purposes shall be considered to be *interior finish*, shall comply with Section 803 and shall not be considered *decorative materials* or furnishings.

Exceptions:

1. In auditoriums in Group A, the permissible amount of curtains, draperies, fabric hangings and similar combustible decorative material suspended from

walls or ceilings shall not exceed 75 percent of the aggregate wall area where the building is equipped throughout with an *approved automatic sprinkler system* in accordance with Section 903.3.1.1, and where the material is installed in accordance with Section 803.15 of the *International Building Code*.

2. In Group R-2 dormitories, within sleeping units and dwelling units, the permissible amount of curtains, draperies, fabric hangings and similar decorative materials suspended from walls or ceilings shall not exceed 50 percent of the aggregate wall areas where the building is equipped throughout with an *approved automatic sprinkler system* installed in accordance with Section 903.3.1.
3. In Group B and M occupancies, the amount of combustible fabric partitions suspended from the ceiling and not supported by the floor shall comply with Section 807.3 and shall not be limited.
4. The 10-percent limit shall not apply to curtains, draperies, fabric hangings and similar combustible decorative materials used as window coverings.

❖Meeting the flame propagation performance criteria of NFPA 701, which is required by Section 807.4, does not mean that materials will not burn, only that they are going to spread flame relatively slowly. These materials are, therefore, limited to a maximum of 10 percent of the total wall or ceiling area of the space under consideration. Unlike incidental trim, decorative materials are not necessarily distributed evenly throughout the room. Additionally, consideration of the long-term maintenance of the materials, including possible periodic retreatment, should be taken into account.

In any occupancy classification, when a movable wall, partition, paneling, wall pads or crash pads cover larger areas, they need to be dealt with as interior finishes instead of as decorative materials.

The first two exceptions relate to the 10-percent limitation in Section 807.3. Exception 1 is for Group A auditoriums that would allow 75-percent coverage of the walls and ceilings (instead of the limit of 10 percent) if the space is sprinklered in accordance with NFPA 13 and the material is applied in accordance with Section 803.11 of the IBC.

Exception 2 allows an increased amount of decorative materials in Group R-2 dormitories. An allowance of up to 50 percent is provided as long as the building is equipped throughout with an automatic sprinkler system. The reference to Section 903.3.1 allows the use of a NFPA 13 or 13R system as applicable. This allowance is likely provided as it is more realistic to what is typically found in dormitories and is more easily managed from an enforcement standpoint. The sprinklers provide the necessary protection to allow such an increase.

Exception 3 clarifies that, in Group B and M occupancies, fabric partitions suspended from the ceiling but not physically contacting the floor should be treated as decorative materials similar to curtains or draperies and comply with the flame propagation performance heat release criteria of Section 807.4. These partitions are also permitted to be unlimited. This is with or without the use of sprinklers within a building.

Exception 4 provides specific clarification that the 10-percent limit does not apply to combustible materials that are used specifically as window coverings.

807.3 Acceptance criteria and reports. Where required to exhibit improved fire performance, curtains, draperies, fabric hangings and other similar combustible decorative materials suspended from walls or ceilings shall be tested by an *approved* agency and meet the flame propagation performance criteria of Test Method 1 or Test Method 2, as appropriate, of NFPA 701 or exhibit a maximum rate of heat release of 100 kW when tested in accordance with NFPA 289, using the 20 kW ignition source. Reports of test results shall be prepared in accordance with the test method used and furnished to the *fire code official* upon request.

❖One of the standard test methods used to evaluate the ability of a material to propagate flame is NFPA 701, which contains two test methods. Test 1 is less severe than Test 2 and uses smaller specimens. Test 1 is intended for lighter weight materials and single-layer fabrics. The limit is a linear density of 700 g/m^2 (21 oz/yd^2). Test 2 is intended for higher density materials and multilayered fabrics. It also applies to vinyl-coated fabric blackout linings and lined draperies using any density, because they have been shown to give misleading results using Test 1. NFPA 701 sets out the types of materials, including fabrics that should be tested using each method.

Essentially, NFPA 701 provides a mechanism to distinguish between materials that allow flames to spread quickly and those that do not when using a small fire exposure.

Materials tested only to NFPA 701 are not permitted for use as interior finish materials, but instead are generally used as shades, swags, curtains and other similar materials. These tests are used to determine whether materials propagate flame beyond the area exposed to the ignition source. They are not intended to indicate whether the material tested will resist the propagation of flame under fire exposures more extreme than the test conditions.

It should be noted that the historic "small-scale test" is no longer accepted. The other standard test method that can be used is NFPA 289. This test method quantifies the contribution of materials to heat and smoke release when subjected to different ignition sources. This test method also determines the potential for growth of a fire and the fire-spread of a given material when exposed to an ignition source in a controlled environment. See the commentary to Section 807.5.1.1 for a more detailed discussion of this test method.

807.4 Artificial decorative vegetation. Artificial decorative vegetation shall comply with this section and the requirements of Sections 806.2 and 806.3. Natural decorative vegetation shall comply with Section 806.

Exception: Testing of artificial vegetation is not required in Group I-1; Group I-2, Condition 1; Group R-2; Group R-3; or Group R-4 occupancies equipped throughout with an *approved automatic sprinkler system* installed in accordance with Section 903.3.1, where such artificial vegetation complies with the following:

1. Wreaths and other decorative items on doors shall not obstruct the door operation and shall not exceed 50 percent of the surface area of the door.
2. Decorative artificial vegetation shall be limited to not more than 30 percent of the wall area to which it is attached.
3. Decorative artificial vegetation not on doors or walls shall not exceed 3 feet (914 mm) in any dimension.

❖This section addresses artificial decorative vegetation, which generally contains a high concentration of plastic material in the form of plastic artificial leaves. The goal, therefore, is to reduce initial ignitability by treating artificial vegetation with flame retardants to improve fire performance or to use materials that have inherently better fire performance. The exception for the specific occupancies listed provides the limited conditions where it can be used without having to meet the testing requirements in buildings that are fully protected with an automatic sprinkler system.

807.4.1 Flammability. Artificial decorative vegetation shall meet the flame propagation performance criteria of Test Method 1 or Test Method 2, as appropriate, of NFPA 701. Meeting such criteria shall be documented and certified by the manufacturer in an *approved* manner. Alternatively, the artificial decorative vegetation shall be tested in accordance with NFPA 289, using the 20 kW ignition source, and shall have a maximum heat release rate of 100 kW.

❖Artificial decorative vegetation is required by this section to be tested either to the flame propagation performance criteria of NFPA 701 or in accordance with NFPA 289 using the 20 kW ignition source and with a maximum allowed heat release rate of 100 kW.

NFPA 289 is a furniture calorimeter heat release fire test specifically developed for these types of products. NFPA 289 uses a propane gas burner as the ignition source. The 20 kW gas burner ignition source in NFPA 289 was specifically designed with the intent of being a substitute for UL 1975 and would be suitable as an ignition source for Christmas trees.

As discussed extensively in Section 806.1, there are substantial fire safety requirements for natural Christmas trees; however, testing in accordance with NFPA 701 was the only option until this requirement was added.

807.4.2 Electrical fixtures and wiring on artificial vegetation. The use of unlisted electrical wiring and lighting on artificial decorative vegetation shall be prohibited. The use of electrical wiring and lighting on artificial trees constructed entirely of metal shall be prohibited.

❖Decorations are quite often used year after year on Christmas trees. Some of this decor consists of lights that are not specifically listed and can fail and become very hot, potentially posing an ignition source. Additionally, this wiring may arc and create an ignition source. In fact, it has been found that many Christmas tree fires have actually been started by decorative lights on the tree. Therefore, this section simply prohibits the use of unlisted wiring or lighting (such lights and ornaments are listed in accordance with UL 588). Due to the shock and ignition potential resulting from a short or direct contact of part of the tree with one of the light sockets, electrical wiring and lighting is not allowed on metal trees.

807.5 Occupancy-based requirements. Occupancies shall comply with Sections 807.5.1 through 807.5.6.

❖The provisions of Sections 807.5.1 through 807.5.6 address the vulnerability of occupants by addressing hazards likely found in certain occupancies. Group A occupancies are generally densely populated with occupants being unfamiliar with their surroundings. Such occupancies are also more likely to contain a large amount of decorative materials, such as stage scenery or exhibit booths utilizing foam plastics. Group E, I and R-2 dormitories have the potential to deal with a large amount of decorative materials and storage. Occupants in Group E, I and R-2 dormitories are also considered more vulnerable than other occupancies, such as Group B or M, because of occupant age or infirmity and occupancies such as dormitories where the occupants sometimes place themselves at increased risks. Group I-3, as will be discussed, should not have any combustible decorative materials. It is important to stress that this section specifically addresses materials that do not meet the requirements of NFPA 701, as is required in Section 807.3.

807.5.1 Group A. In Group A occupancies, the requirements in Sections 807.5.1.1 through 807.5.1.4 shall apply.

❖The requirements in Sections 803.5.1.1 through 803.5.1.4 are specific to Group A occupancies. These particular requirements are fairly specific to activities and uses that occur in Group A occupancies, such as trade shows and movie theaters. Generally, fire hazards are moderate in Group A occupancies. The concerns are more closely related to the high occupant density and the occupants' lack of familiarity with the building.

807.5.1.1 Foam plastics. Exposed foam plastic materials and unprotected materials containing foam plastic used for decorative purposes or stage scenery or exhibit booths shall have a maximum heat release rate of 100 kW when tested in accordance with UL 1975, or when tested in accordance with NFPA 289 using the 20 kW ignition source.

Exceptions:

1. Individual foam plastic items or items containing foam plastic where the foam plastic does not exceed 1 pound (0.45 kg) in weight.
2. Cellular or foam plastic shall be allowed for trim in accordance with Section 804.2.

❖As discussed in Section 803.8, foam plastics can produce misleading results when tested to ASTM E84. In some instances, they can burn vigorously and at high rates of heat release. Group A occupancies tend to contain materials for stages, movie theaters and exhibit halls. These uses will likely have combustible scenery or exhibit booths that contain foam plastics. Therefore, because the occupants are unlikely to be familiar with the premises, and the hazards presented by these combustibles can be high, a heat release rate limit of 100 kW, when tested in accordance with UL 1975 or NFPA 289, is placed on foam plastic materials used in Group A occupancies.

In the past, restrictions on the combustibility of materials were based on the heat content of the materials instead of the rate at which the heat content is released. The problem with using heat content (which can be equated to "potential energy" of the material) as the limitation criterion is that it does not provide a good understanding of the rate at which the "potential energy" is released. The rate at which heat is released is a more important characteristic of fire and is a measure of the intensity of the fire. UL 1975 and NFPA 289 are furniture calorimeter types of tests that assess the actual heat release rate based on the exposure of the foam plastics to a specific heat input (340-gram wood crib for UL 1975 and 20kW propane gas burner ignition source for NFPA 289).

Some alternatives to testing are provided in the exceptions, which primarily focus on limiting the amount of combustibles. The exceptions give two prescriptive approaches with no direct relationship to the actual combustibility of the foam plastic except to limit the amount used. Exception 1 is related to plastic display items, such as a small statue. Exception 2 relates specifically to decorative trim and directs the code user to the requirements for that material found in Section 804.2 (see commentary, Section 804.2).

807.5.1.2 Motion picture screens. The screens on which motion pictures are projected in new and existing buildings of Group A shall either meet the flame propagation performance criteria of Test Method 1 or Test Method 2, as appropriate, of NFPA 701 or shall comply with the requirements for a Class B interior finish in accordance with Section 803 of the *International Building Code*.

❖Movie screens are not considered interior finish and, therefore, would not be addressed by Chapter 8 of the IBC. These screens consist of a fabric base covered with a thin coating impregnated with reflective glass beads. Movie screens are generally fairly large and typically take up most of the front wall of a movie theater; therefore, the flame spread characteristics must be addressed. Because movie theaters tend to be densely occupied, a material with a high rate of flame spread can pose a significant hazard. Screens can comply in one of two ways. The screen must meet the applicable flame propagation performance criteria set out in NFPA 701 Test Method 1 or 2 (which focus on combustibles such as curtains, shades and window treatments, but are not appropriate for wall coverings), or qualify as a Class B interior finish material in accordance with ASTM E84. NFPA 286, which is also found in Section 803, would be a viable alternative for testing. It should be noted that the historic "small-scale test" in NFPA 701 is no longer accepted.

807.5.1.3 Wood use in places of religious worship. In places of religious worship, wood used for ornamental purposes, trusses, paneling or chancel furnishing shall not be limited.

❖Places of religious worship are generally open spaces. The occupants, because of the nature of the activities in these assemblies, tend to be orderly. For this reason, wood, which is a combustible material, is allowed extensively as a finish material without restriction.

807.5.1.4 Pyroxylin plastic. Imitation leather or other material consisting of or coated with a pyroxylin or similarly hazardous base shall not be used.

❖Use of pyroxylin plastics, also known as cellulose nitrate plastics, in Group A occupancies as imitation leather or other materials is strictly prohibited because of the normally high occupant loads of such occupancies. This type of material is very hazardous because it will begin decomposition at temperatures starting at 300°F (149°C), and has the potential to develop explosive atmospheres with high heat emission once it ignites. Because cellulose nitrate tends to become somewhat unstable and is easily ignitable, its use has generally declined. Specifically, use of cellulose nitrate for motion picture film was discontinued in 1951.

807.5.2 Group E. Group E occupancies shall comply with Sections 807.5.2.1 through 807.5.2.3.

❖Group E occupancies are occupancies used by six or more persons for educational purposes through the 12th grade or buildings and structures used for educational, supervision or personal care services for more than five children over the age of $2^1/_2$ years. This section regulates the amount of combustibles within corridors, lobbies and classrooms by regulating clothing, personal effects and artwork.

807.5.2.1 Storage in corridors and lobbies. Clothing and personal effects shall not be stored in *corridors* and lobbies.

Exceptions:

1. *Corridors* protected by an *approved automatic sprinkler system* installed in accordance with Section 903.3.1.1.
2. *Corridors* protected by an *approved* fire alarm system installed in accordance with Section 907.
3. Storage in metal lockers, provided the minimum required egress width is maintained.

❖Materials, such as clothing, other personal effects and artwork, have the potential for creating a fire hazard within the main path of egress travel. This section allows the storage of clothing and other personal effects within these areas only if corridors and lobbies contain one of the following features:

- A sprinkler system.
- A fire alarm system.
- Metal lockers for storage.

The sprinkler system must meet the requirements of NFPA 13. The fire alarm system must be approved by the fire code official. The fire alarm system is intended to specifically focus on the contents of the corridors, would typically be a smoke detection system and is not intended to be required throughout.

807.5.2.2 Artwork in corridors. Artwork and teaching materials shall be limited on the walls of *corridors* to not more than 20 percent of the wall area.

❖Educational occupancies tend to display various artwork and related educational materials on the walls of classrooms and corridors. This section limits the potential combustibility levels of artwork in critical areas of the means of egress system; therefore, decorations or artwork can cover no more than 20 percent of the corridor walls. See Commentary Figure 807.5.2.2 for representation of the 20-percent coverage area.

807.5.2.3 Artwork in classrooms. Artwork and teaching materials shall be limited on walls of classrooms to not more than 50 percent of the specific wall area to which they are attached.

❖This is consistent with requirements for restrictions on artwork in the corridors. The limit is less restrictive at 50 percent versus the 20 percent that is permitted for corridors. This relates to the fact that the corridors make up the more critical portion of the exit access for the building.

807.5.3 Groups I-1 and I-2. In Group I-1 and I-2 occupancies, combustible *decorative materials* shall comply with Sections 807.5.3.1 through 807.5.3.4.

❖Sections 807.5.3.1 through 807.5.3.4 provide a series of requirements for care facilities where the occupants are at increased level of risk due to their physical and cognitive limitations. In Group I-1 and I-2 occupancies, the occupants are present 24 hours a day with varying levels of care depending on the type of occupancy. Section 407.2.1 of the IBC allows waiting or similar areas to be open to corridors. These types of spaces typically have magazines, bulletin boards with paper notices tacked to them, and other combustible items not treated with flame retardants or tested to NFPA 701. Allowing a specified percentage of untreated, combustible decorative materials in Group I-1 and I-2 buildings equipped throughout with an automatic sprinkler system will not exceed the "ordinary occupancy" classification outlined in NFPA 13, nor does it increase the fire loading above what is currently permitted. These requirements offer consistent language to aid enforcement and a guide to providers to determine compliance within their facilities. The intent of these requirements is to eliminate the haphazard and inconsistent application of these provisions in facilities nationwide.

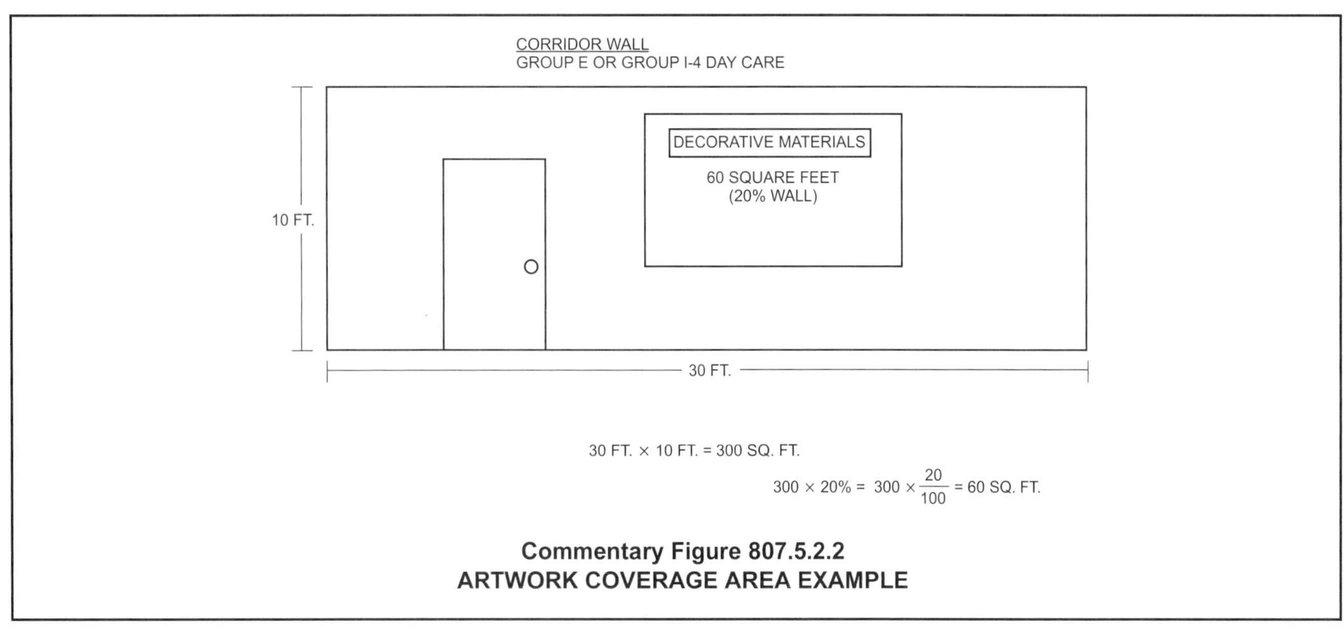

Commentary Figure 807.5.2.2
ARTWORK COVERAGE AREA EXAMPLE

807.5.3.1 Group I-1 and I-2 Condition 1 within units. In Group I-1 and Group I-2 Condition 1 occupancies, equipped throughout with an *approved automatic sprinkler system* installed in accordance with Section 903.3.1.1, within sleeping units and dwelling units, combustible decorative materials placed on walls shall be limited to not more than 50 percent of the wall area to which they are attached.

❖This section is focused on the sleeping units and dwelling units within Group I-1, which are typically assisted living and similar occupancies, and Group I-2, Condition 1, which are nursing homes. Since the requirements are focused within the sleeping and dwelling unit, the requirements are more lenient than those associated with the main exit access. Similar to the artwork restrictions for classrooms, such spaces are permitted to have 50 percent of the wall area occupied by combustible decorative materials. It should be noted that Group I-2 occupancies require the retroactive installation of sprinklers in accordance with Section 1105.8. All new Group I occupancies require the installation of an automatic sprinkler system.

807.5.3.2 In Group I-1 and I-2, Condition 1 for areas other than within units. In Group I-1 and Group I-2, Condition 1 occupancies, equipped throughout with an *approved automatic sprinkler system* installed in accordance with Section 903.3.1.1, combustible decorative materials placed on walls in areas other than within dwelling and sleeping units shall be limited to not more than 30 percent of the wall area to which they are attached.

❖This section focuses on the same occupancies as Section 807.5.3.1, but on areas outside the sleeping and dwelling units. The allowance in sprinklered buildings is 30 percent versus the 50 percent in Section 807.5.3.1. These areas tend to expose a greater percentage of the building occupants to the hazards of combustible decorative materials. It should be noted that Group I-2 occupancies require the retroactive installation of sprinklers in accordance with Section 1105.8. All new Group I occupancies require the installation of an automatic sprinkler system.

807.5.3.3 In Group I-2, Condition 2. In Group I-2, Condition 2 occupancies, equipped throughout with an *approved automatic sprinkler system* installed in accordance with Section 903.3.1.1, combustible decorative materials placed on walls shall be limited to not more than 30 percent of the wall area to which they are attached.

❖This section is the same as Section 807.5.3.2, except that it is focused on hospitals—specifically, areas of the hospital where more occupants are exposed to combustible decorative materials. As noted in Sections 807.5.3.1 and 807.5.3.2, all Group I-2 occupancies require the retroactive installation of an automatic sprinkler system. Note that Section 1105.8 only requires sprinkler installation from the story containing the Group I-2 occupancy to the level of exit discharge.

807.5.3.4 Other areas in Groups I-1 and I-2. In Group I-1 and I-2 occupancies, in areas not equipped throughout with an *approved automatic sprinkler system*, combustible decorative materials shall be of such limited quantities that a hazard of fire development or spread is not present.

❖This section addresses Group I-1 and I-2 occupancies. The focus is on areas of such buildings where an automatic sprinkler system does not provide coverage. As noted, Group I-2 occupancies require the retroactive installation of an automatic sprinkler system but Group I-1 occupancies do not. Although Group I-2 occupancies should be provided with sprinklers, there may be transitional periods where this is not the case. This requirement in general is nonspecific and generally gives authority to the fire code official to address situations that appear hazardous.

807.5.4 Group I-3. In Group I-3, combustible *decorative materials* are prohibited.

❖Due to the nature of such occupancies, where occupants have a tendency to start fires, combustible decorative materials are prohibited.

807.5.5 Group I-4. Group I-4 occupancies shall comply with the requirements in Sections 807.5.5.1 through 807.5.5.3.

❖A Group I-4 day care facility is an occupancy that cares for people of any age for less than 24 hours per day. Most often, these facilities are for small children not yet able to attend school, but also included are adult day care facilities. These occupancies will have features similar to those of Group E occupancies; therefore, the same restrictions on combustibles in corridors, lobbies and classrooms exist. The key issue here is that the occupants of Group I-4 facilities are often not capable of self-preservation without some level of assistance; therefore, combustibles must be kept to a minimum, especially in critical portions of the means of egress system.

807.5.5.1 Storage in corridors and lobbies. Clothing and personal effects shall not be stored in *corridors* and lobbies.

Exceptions:

1. *Corridors* protected by an *approved automatic sprinkler system* installed in accordance with Section 903.3.1.1.
2. *Corridors* protected by an *approved fire alarm system* installed in accordance with Section 907.
3. Storage in metal lockers, provided the minimum required egress width is maintained.

❖See the commentary to Section 807.5.2.1.

807.5.5.2 Artwork in corridors. Artwork and teaching materials shall be limited on walls of corridors to not more than 20 percent of the wall area.

❖See the commentary to Section 807.5.2.2.

807.5.5.3 Artwork in classrooms. Artwork and teaching materials shall be limited on walls of classrooms to not more than 50 percent of the specific wall area to which they are attached.

❖See the commentary to Section 807.5.2.3.

807.5.6 Dormitories in Group R-2. In Group R-2 dormitories, within sleeping units and dwelling units, the combustible decorative materials shall be of limited quantities such that a hazard of fire development or spread is not present.

❖This section is consistent with the needs of facilities where occupants often take unnecessary risks. This provides a mechanism for the fire code official to limit the potential hazards in such sleeping units and dwelling units. Note that Section 807.3, Exception 2 allows up to 50 percent of the aggregate wall areas to contain decorative materials if an automatic sprinkler system is provided.

SECTION 808 FURNISHINGS OTHER THAN UPHOLSTERED FURNITURE AND MATTRESSES OR DECORATIVE MATERIALS IN NEW AND EXISTING BUILDINGS

808.1 Wastebaskets and linen containers in Group I-1, I-2 and I-3 occupancies and Group B ambulatory care facilities. Wastebaskets, linen containers and other waste containers, including their lids, located in Group I-1, I-2 and I-3 occupancies and Group B ambulatory care facilities shall be constructed of noncombustible materials or of materials that meet a peak rate of heat release not exceeding 300 kW/m^2 when tested in accordance with ASTM E1354 at an incident heat flux of 50 kW/m^2 in the horizontal orientation. Metal wastebaskets and other metal waste containers with a capacity of 20 gallons (75.7 L) or more shall be *listed* in accordance with UL 1315 and shall be provided with a noncombustible lid. Portable containers exceeding 32 gallons (121 L) shall be stored in an area classified as a waste and linen collection room and constructed in accordance with Table 509 of the *International Building Code.*

Exception: Recycling containers complying with Section 808.1.2 are not required to be stored in waste and linen collection rooms.

❖Although residents of these occupancies are generally closely monitored, there is an increased life safety risk in these facilities since in each type, the occupants have limited or no self-evacuation ability. Plastic containers can add a tremendous fuel load to a fire in a trash or linen container; many plastic containers will more than triple the fuel load in a fire situation. This section will control the fuel load for these containers that are used routinely throughout the facilities and will correlate the code with federal regulations for these facilities. Steps can be taken to reduce the impact of a fire once it has been ignited by limiting wastebaskets to those that can meet certain combustibility criteria in accordance with ASTM E1354. ASTM E1354 is a small-scale calorimeter test that measures heat flux output based on a given heat source. This concept is similar to that required in full-scale tests for upholstered furniture and mattresses in Section 805. It should be noted that this section is not focused on ignition prevention but instead assumes that ignition has occurred. The focus is reducing the contribution of the trash container to a fire.

Compliance with this test allows any material that can pass the test to be used. This may allow the use of fire-retardant plastics or other materials that will meet the criteria of the test. Generally, in larger areas of the facility, if a fire can be contained to a wastebasket, it will not spread but will simply burn out.

Since a larger wastebasket means a larger fire, this section also addresses larger metal wastebaskets by requiring compliance with UL 1315 and that they be equipped with a noncombustible lid. This increases the likelihood that the fire will stay contained to the wastebasket and possibly reduce the fire size by restricting the combustion process. The general performance of wastebaskets meeting the requirements of UL 1315 is as follows:

- Limit the external surface temperatures of the container bottom should their contents become ignited.
- Extinguish the fire.
- Contain the contents without contributing fuel to the fire.

See also the commentaries to Sections 304.3.2, 304.3.4 and 318.1.

808.1.1 Capacity density. The average capacity density of containers located in an individual room or space, other than waste and linen collection rooms, shall not be greater than 0.5 gal/ft^2 (20.4 L/m^2).

❖This section provides a limit on the density of the contents of the containers when they are located in a room or space that is not a waste and linen collection room. The purpose of the limit is to prevent the concentration of these materials so as not to create a hazard that goes beyond the active and passive fire containment systems that are in place within the room or space that the container is located.

808.1.2 Recycling clean waste containers. Recycling clean waste containers, including their lids, shall not exceed an individual capacity of 96 gallons (363 L).

❖This section provides a limit on the size of individual recycling clean waste containers. Similar to the limit on the container density, the purpose is to limit the amount of these recyclables in an individual container so as not to create a hazard that goes beyond the active and passive fire containment systems that are in place within the room or space that the container is located.

808.2 Waste containers with a capacity of 20 gallons or more in Group R-2 college and university dormitories. Waste containers, including their lids, located in Group R-2 college and university dormitories, and with a capacity of 20 gallons (75.7 L) or more, shall be constructed of noncombustible materials or of materials that meet a peak rate of heat release not exceeding 300 kW/m^2 when tested in accordance with ASTM E1354 at an incident heat flux of 50 kW/m^2 in the horizontal orientation. Metal wastebaskets and other metal waste containers with a capacity of 20 gallons (75.7 L) or more shall be *listed* in accordance with UL 1315 and shall be provided with a noncombustible lid. Portable containers exceeding 32 gallons (121 L) shall be stored in an area classified as a waste and linen collection room constructed in accordance with Table 509 of the *International Building Code*.

❖This section is similar to Section 808.1, but is applicable to larger capacity containers (exceeding 20 gallons) and is focused on Group R-2 college and university dormitories. The large waste containers in college and university dormitories should comply with the same requirements as any waste container in Group I-2 and I-3 occupancies. Most nonmetallic waste containers are manufactured from polyethylene, which has a fuel value more than double that of newsprint and can generate a high heat release rate fire. These waste containers hold combustible waste (much of which is paper) while having very combustible walls. See the commentary to Section 808.1 for more information on the test methods prescribed.

808.3 Signs. Foam plastic signs that are not affixed to interior building surfaces shall have a maximum heat release rate of 150 kW when tested in accordance with UL 1975, or when tested in accordance with NFPA 289 using the 20-kW ignition source.

Exception: Where the aggregate area of foam plastic signs is less than 10 percent of the floor area or wall area of the room or space in which the signs are located, whichever is less, subject to the approval of the *fire code official*.

❖This section correlates with Section 402.6.4.4 of the IBC, which requires a limit on the combustibility of signs in covered mall buildings, though it should be noted that the requirements of this code are not specific to such buildings. The requirement of this section is that, when a foam plastic sign is tested in accordance with UL 1975 or NFPA 289 (see commentary, Section 807.5.1.1), a maximum heat release rate of 150 kW is allowed.

Note that smoke development is not part of the acceptance criteria.

The exception recognizes that a relatively small aggregate surface coverage of a room or space by these signs (i.e., when the aggregate area of foam plastic signs constitutes the lesser of 10 percent of the floor or wall area of the room or space in which the signs are located) does not present a sufficient enough hazard to require compliance with the section. However, specific approval by the fire code official is required.

808.4 Combustible lockers. Where lockers constructed of combustible materials are used, the lockers shall be considered to be interior finish and shall comply with Section 803.

Exception: Lockers constructed entirely of wood and noncombustible materials shall be permitted to be used wherever interior finish materials are required to meet a Class C classification in accordance with Section 803.1.2.

❖Traditionally, lockers in schools (high schools, middle schools, universities), clubs, swimming pools and gymnasiums were constructed of steel. In recent years, the use of lockers constructed of combustible materials has become prevalent. These lockers typically line an entire wall (for example, a corridor in a school) and are not regulated by the code. Lockers are not usually considered interior finish. The only other materials regulated by the code at present are interior trim, upholstered furniture, decorations, decorative vegetation, wastebaskets, linen containers and signs. Lockers do not fall into any of those categories.

Combustible lockers can present a significant fire load and, if ignited, are likely to spread fire the same way that interior finish materials spread fire. They are considered interior finish materials and regulated like all other interior finish materials for any occupancy. Plastic lockers have the benefit of being more immune to the effects of water from wet clothing and are generally very durable—but, with these benefits comes a fire hazard. The lockers by one manufacturer are constructed of $^3/_8$-inch-thick (9.52 mm) solid plastic bodies and heavy duty $^1/_2$-inch-thick (12.7 mm) doors. Typically the "solid plastic" used is either high-density polyethylene or polypropylene. Polypropylene, as discussed in the commentary to Section 803.9, is a thermoplastic that gives off considerable energy and produces a pooling flammable liquid fire when it burns.

Bibliography

The following resource material was originally used in the preparation of the commentary for this chapter of the code:

DeLauter, L., J. Lee, G. Roadarmel and D.W. Stroup,. *Scotch Pine Christmas Tree Fire Tests*. FR4010. Gaithersburg, MD: National Institute of Standards and Technology, US Department of Commerce, 1999.

Chapter 9: Fire Protection and Life Safety Systems

General Comments

The provisions required by Chapter 9 are just part of the overall fire protection system of a building or structure. All fire protection requirements contained in the code must be considered as a package or overall system. Noncompliance with any part of the overall system may cause other parts of the system to fail. Failure to install the systems in accordance with code provisions may result in an increased loss of life and property due to a reduction in the level of protection provided.

Every effort must be made to verify the proper design and installation of a given fire protection system, especially those that result in construction alternatives and other code trade-offs.

The title of Chapter 9 has been expanded to include life safety systems. This reflects that the chapter has been expanded over the years to include emergency alarm systems, smoke control systems, explosion control and carbon monoxide detection, which are not fire protection systems. The requirements in Chapter 9 are active fire safety provisions. They are directed at containing and extinguishing a fire once it has erupted. This chapter parallels and duplicates much of Chapter 9 in the *International Building Code*® (IBC®). The code, however, contains additional specific provisions that are applicable only to existing buildings. It also contains periodic testing criteria that are not duplicated in the IBC. Proper testing, inspection and maintenance of the various systems are critical to establishing the reliability of the system. Additionally, Chapter 9 references and adopts numerous National Fire Protection Association (NFPA) standards, including the acceptance testing criteria within the standard. The referenced standards will also contain more specific design and installation criteria than are found in this chapter. As noted in Section 102.7, where differences occur between code requirements and the referenced standard, the code provisions apply.

Purpose

Fire protection systems may serve one or more purposes in providing adequate protection from fire and hazardous material exposure. The purpose of Chapter 9 is to prescribe the minimum requirements for an active system or systems of fire protection to perform the following functions: to detect a fire, to alert the occupants or fire department of a fire emergency, to control smoke and to control or extinguish the fire. Generally, the requirements are based on the occupancy and height and area of the building, as these are the factors that most affect fire-fighting capabilities and the relative hazard of a specific space or area.

SECTION 901 GENERAL

901.1 Scope. The provisions of this chapter shall specify where fire protection and life safety systems are required and shall apply to the design, installation, inspection, operation, testing and maintenance of all *fire protection systems*.

❖ Chapter 9 contains requirements for fire protection systems that may be installed or located in a building. These include automatic suppression systems, standpipe systems, fire alarm and detection systems, smoke control systems, smoke and heat vents, and portable fire extinguishers. Besides indicating the conditions under which respective systems are required, this chapter contains the design, installation, maintenance, testing and operational criteria for fire protection systems. While the code requires proper maintenance for the reliability of the systems, the actual maintenance provisions (periodic testing, inspections and maintenance) may be contained in one of the referenced standards.

Chapter 9 is intended to apply to buildings of new construction or where deemed applicable because of a change in occupancy or an addition, unless specifically indicated to be applicable to existing buildings only. The scoping provisions in Chapter 1 should be consulted for determining the proper requirements for additions, alterations and remodelings.

This chapter also addresses the requirements for fire command centers, fire department connections, fire pumps and emergency radio systems. These features all directly relate to the proper function of fire protection systems.

901.2 Construction documents. The *fire code official* shall have the authority to require *construction documents* and calculations for all *fire protection systems* and to require permits be issued for the installation, rehabilitation or modification of any *fire protection system*. *Construction documents* for *fire protection systems* shall be submitted for review and approval prior to system installation.

❖ The construction documents and related calculations for all fire protection systems must be reviewed before a permit is issued. The review is performed to determine compliance with the code requirements and the applicable provisions in the referenced standards.

Typical shop drawings for fire protection systems are usually not prepared during the initial submittal for a construction permit. Many jurisdictions require a separate submittal and issue a separate permit to the contractor installing the system (see Section 901.3). Factors such as classification of the hazard; amount of agent or water supply available; and the design criteria, including the density or concentration to be achieved by the system, are to be included with the shop drawings. Specific equipment data sheets identifying sprinklers, pipe dimensions, power requirements for smoke detectors, and so on must also be included with the submittal in addition to any required calculations. See also the commentary to Section 907.1.1 regarding fire alarm system construction documents and Section 907.1.2 regarding fire alarm system shop drawings.

901.2.1 Statement of compliance. Before requesting final approval of the installation, where required by the *fire code official*, the installing contractor shall furnish a written statement to the *fire code official* that the subject *fire protection system* has been installed in accordance with *approved* plans and has been tested in accordance with the manufacturer's specifications and the appropriate installation standard. Any deviations from the design standards shall be noted and copies of the approvals for such deviations shall be attached to the written statement.

❖ A certificate or other approved written statement must be submitted to the fire code official with the proper documentation from the installing contractor specifying that the fire protection system has been installed in accordance with the requirements of the code. The certificate should also indicate that all required inspections and tests of the system have been conducted at the time of application for a certificate of occupancy.

The written statement is to indicate that the system has been installed in accordance with code requirements. As previously stated, contractors may have certificates that specify the criteria of the referenced standards since many of them contain sample certificates. While such certificates may be used, the contractor is required to certify that the system complies with the provisions of the code, which in some instances may vary from the referenced standards. These variations and any other variations involved in the installation, whether by change order, variance or field condition, must also be included with the written statement.

901.3 Permits. Permits shall be required as set forth in Sections 105.6 and 105.7.

❖ Section 105 requires permits of two separate but related types. Section 105.6 requires an operational permit. These permits are required to conduct certain types of business or hazardous operations that require a higher level of scrutiny from the fire code official. The second type of permit, required by Section 105.7, is the construction permit, which is required for the installation and modification of all fire protection systems.

901.4 Installation. *Fire protection systems* shall be maintained in accordance with the original installation standards for that system. Required systems shall be extended, altered or augmented as necessary to maintain and continue protection where the building is altered, remodeled or added to. *Alterations* to *fire protection systems* shall be done in accordance with applicable standards.

❖ This section emphasizes that systems installed and maintained in compliance with the codes and standards in effect at the time they were placed in service must remain operational at all times. It is not the intent of the code to require existing systems that are otherwise not being altered to comply with current code and standard requirements. An existing system, even if it does not meet current standards, is allowed to continue in service as long as it continues to provide no less quality in service than what was originally in place. Hence, if an alteration or expansion of the system is proposed, the key is whether or not the level of protection afforded by the system is the same or greater than what it was before the alteration or expansion was considered. Any added sections of the system must meet the requirements for new fire protection according to the system involved.

901.4.1 Required fire protection systems. *Fire protection systems* required by this code or the *International Building Code* shall be installed, repaired, operated, tested and maintained in accordance with this code. A *fire protection system* for which a design option, exception or reduction to the provisions of this code or the *International Building Code* has been granted shall be considered to be a required system.

❖ Fire protection systems that are required by Chapter 9 or by another section of either the IBC or the code must be considered as required systems. The fire protection system is an integral component of the protection features of the building and must be properly installed, repaired, operated, tested and maintained in accordance with the code. Improperly installed or maintained systems can fail to provide the anticipated protection and, in some cases, create a hazard in itself.

Although the code may not require a fire protection system for a specific building or portion of a building because of its occupancy, the fire protection system would still be considered a required system if some other code alternative, exception or reduction was taken based on the installation of that fire protection system. For example, a typical small office building may not require an automatic sprinkler system solely because of its Group B occupancy classification. However, if an exit access corridor fire-resistance-rating reduction is taken as allowed by Table 1020.1 for buildings equipped throughout with an NFPA 13 sprinkler system, that sprinkler system is now considered a required system. Code trade-offs, exceptions, reductions or other design options are not unique to the IBC. Such trade-offs occur more than 60 times in the code.

901.4.2 Nonrequired fire protection systems. A *fire protection system* or portion thereof not required by this code or the *International Building Code* shall be allowed to be furnished for partial or complete protection provided that such installed system meets the applicable requirements of this code and the *International Building Code*.

❖ A building owner or designer may elect to install a fire protection system that is not required in the code. Even though such a system is not required, it must comply with the applicable requirements of Chapter 9. This requirement is based on the concept that any fire protection system not installed as required by the code is lacking because it could give a false impression of properly installed protection.

For example, if a building owner chooses to install sprinkler protection in a certain area and that protection is not required by any provisions of the code, the system must be installed in accordance with NFPA 13 or 13R, as applicable, and other applicable requirements of the code, such as water supply and supervision. The extent of the protection provided would not be regulated. Once the system is installed, it is subject to the same code requirements for maintenance and testing with which any other system would be required to comply.

If the optional sprinkler system is intended to be used to provide alternatives found elsewhere in the code, the system would cease to be voluntary. In such a case, it becomes a required system and subject to Section 901.4.1.

901.4.3 Fire areas. Where buildings, or portions thereof, are divided into *fire areas* so as not to exceed the limits established for requiring a *fire protection system* in accordance with this chapter, such *fire areas* shall be separated by *fire barriers* constructed in accordance with Section 707 of the *International Building Code* or *horizontal assemblies* constructed in accordance with Section 711 of the *International Building Code*, or both, having a fire-resistance rating of not less than that determined in accordance with Section 707.3.10 of the *International Building Code*.

❖ This section provides specific guidance on how a building needs to be divided into fire areas in order to avoid requiring a fire protection system to be installed. A single occupancy group would require fire barriers or horizontal assemblies in order to create multiple fire areas (see Table 707.3.10 of the IBC), each having an area below the threshold for fire protection system installation.

901.4.4 Additional fire protection systems. In occupancies of a hazardous nature, where special hazards exist in addition to the normal hazards of the occupancy, or where the *fire code official* determines that access for fire apparatus is unduly difficult, the *fire code official* shall have the authority to require additional safeguards. Such safeguards include, but shall not be limited to, the following: automatic fire detection systems, fire alarm systems, automatic fire-extinguishing systems, standpipe systems, or portable or fixed extinguishers. Fire protection equipment required under this section shall be installed in accordance with this code and the applicable referenced standards.

❖ This section allows the fire code official to require fire protection safeguards beyond the minimum requirement of Chapter 9 where warranted by potential unsafe conditions. The provisions of the code cannot anticipate every occupancy condition. Hazardous material occupancies or buildings with limited fire department access are potentially a greater hazard to both building occupants and fire fighters. Any additional safeguards should be those needed to abate potential hazards. This section does not give the fire code official the right to require additional systems without cause. If the condition is adequately addressed by the code, then additional safeguards are not warranted. Should additional safeguards be deemed necessary, then the fire protection components regulated by this section must be considered required systems.

901.4.5 Appearance of equipment. Any device that has the physical appearance of life safety or fire protection equipment but that does not perform that life safety or fire protection function shall be prohibited.

❖ All required or provided life safety or fire protection-related equipment must be continued in use and be maintained to meet the requirements in effect at the time of the original installation. Nonrequired equipment that has been taken out of service or cannot function as intended must be dismantled and removed to prevent creating a false impression of protection.

Simply because a nonrequired system does not meet the current standards is neither cause to require its removal (see Section 901.4), nor a reason to require the system to be upgraded. As long as the system is maintained in the manner in which it was intended when installed, it can be allowed to continue.

901.4.6 Pump and riser room size. Where provided, fire pump rooms and *automatic sprinkler system* riser rooms shall be designed with adequate space for all equipment necessary for the installation, as defined by the manufacturer, with sufficient working space around the stationary equipment. Clearances around equipment to elements of permanent construction, including other installed equipment and appliances, shall be sufficient to allow inspection, service, repair or replacement without removing such elements of permanent construction or disabling the function of a required fire-resistance-rated assembly. Fire pump and *automatic sprinkler system* riser rooms shall be provided with doors and unobstructed passageways large enough to allow removal of the largest piece of equipment.

❖ Section 901.4.6 establishes that, where a pump or riser room is necessary, those rooms housing fire protection system risers or fire pumps and their components have adequate space to facilitate their maintenance. This section does not require the construction of a room to house fire protection systems; however, if a room is provided, this section requires that it be adequately sized to allow for maintenance.

Instead of prescribing arbitrary dimensions, this provision bases the room area on clearances specified by the equipment manufacturers to ensure adequate space is available for its installation or removal. The design must provide enough area so that walls, finish materials and doors are not required to be removed during maintenance activities. The provision also prescribes that the size of the door serving a riser or pump room is of a size to accommodate the removal of the largest piece of equipment.

Given that the design of fire protection systems generally commences during the period that building construction drawings and specifications are being reviewed by the jurisdiction, it will be especially important for the building's designer to establish dialogue with the fire protection system contractor early in the design process to ensure that the room and passageways can accommodate the largest equipment and provide the space needed for maintenance.

901.4.6.1 Access. Automatic sprinkler system risers, fire pumps and controllers shall be provided with ready access. Where located in a fire pump room or automatic sprinkler system riser room, the door shall be permitted to be locked provided that the key is available at all times.

❖ This section requires that there is available access at all times to the fire pump and system control valves for the purposes of fire-fighting operations, inspection and testing requirements, and maintenance on the system. Where located in a locked room in order to provide a secure location away from malicious mischief and vandalism, the key must always be available for use by authorized individuals for entry.

901.4.6.2 Marking on access doors. Access doors for automatic sprinkler system riser rooms and fire pump rooms shall be labeled with an approved sign. The lettering shall be in contrasting color to the background. Letters shall have a minimum height of 2 inches (51 mm) with a minimum stroke of $^3/_8$ inch (10 mm).

❖ Proper identification of the room is critical in order to allow for quick access for fire fighters. The specific requirements of color and lettering size are to ensure that the identification will be uniform at all locations and can be easily read from a distance.

901.4.6.3 Environment. Automatic sprinkler system riser rooms and fire pump rooms shall be maintained at a temperature of not less than 40°F (4°C). Heating units shall be permanently installed.

❖ The specific requirement for a minimum temperature of the room provides protection from freezing for the sprinkler system and fire pump. Where heating is required to maintain the room temperature, it shall be installed permanently so that it is automatic in operation and dependable when it is necessary.

901.4.6.4 Lighting. Permanently installed artificial illumination shall be provided in the automatic sprinkler system riser rooms and fire pump rooms.

❖ Sufficient illumination in the fire pump and system control valve room is required to be installed permanently so that it is always available to provide visibility to the equipment within the room for inspection and operation.

901.5 Installation acceptance testing. Fire detection and alarm systems, emergency alarm systems, gas detection systems, fire-extinguishing systems, fire hydrant systems, fire standpipe systems, fire pump systems, private fire service mains and all other *fire protection systems* and appurtenances thereto shall be subject to acceptance tests as contained in the installation standards and as *approved* by the *fire code official*. The *fire code official* shall be notified before any required acceptance testing.

❖ All of the systems listed must pass an acceptance test to determine that they will operate as required by the code. Acceptance tests are usually part of the final inspection procedures. The referenced standards contain specific acceptance test procedures. In most instances, the acceptance test procedures require 100-percent operation of the testable system components to determine that they are operational and functioning as required. Often, the design professional may require additional testing that may be beyond the code requirements to verify that the system operates as designed. The design professional may also establish the appropriate testing criteria for special systems, such as smoke control systems. These proposed testing protocols, where not addressed elsewhere in the code, must be approved by the fire code official before being performed.

The inclusion of the requirement for acceptance tests in the code is not intended to assign responsibility for witnessing the tests. The responsibility to witness the acceptance test is an administrative issue that each municipality must address. Because the acceptance test is critical during design and construction and is a requirement of occupancy, the requirement is located in the code. The section also clarifies that it is the owner or owner's authorized agent's responsibility to conduct the test and the role of the fire code official to witness—not conduct—the test. Typically, the owner will assign the responsibility of conducting the test to the installing contractor.

901.5.1 Occupancy. It shall be unlawful to occupy any portion of a building or structure until the required fire detection, alarm and suppression systems have been tested and *approved*.

❖ Partial occupancy of any structure must not be permitted unless all fire protection systems for the occupied areas have been tested and approved. Even so, the code assumes that full protection for all areas will be provided as quickly as possible. The installation of many fire protection systems and the associated code alternatives permitted for a given occupancy assume complete building protection and not just in the occupied areas. All partial occupancy conditions are subject to the final approval of the fire code official. Section 105.3.4 allows the fire code official to issue conditional occupancy permits.

If the building becomes vacant, this section would be applicable again. Here, occupancy is based on a certificate of occupancy. If the vacancy is in a tenant space of an otherwise fully protected building, then the fire protection system must be continued. The other tenants of the building are subject to the necessary continuation of the fire protection system. This is similar to partial occupancy. On the other hand, if a building is vacated completely and the certificate of occupancy is forfeited, then the entire building can be considered as unoccupied, and the fire protection systems can be discontinued. At such time, utilities can be disconnected and the building be declared nonhabitable. This option carries with it the burden of reuse because if the vacant, nonhabitable building is intended to be used again, it is subject to provisions in the IBC that would require the building to be certified as a new structure and may involve significant modifications in order to receive a new certificate of occupancy.

Often, insurance companies will require that automatic sprinkler systems be kept in operation during a vacancy. If such is the case, utilities will likely need to be kept in place in order to keep the system within operating temperature requirements. Buildings in which occupancy is discontinued for an extended period of time may be considered hazardous and require action to remediate the problem, possibly by demolition.

If the system being installed is a nonrequired system, then this section is not applicable and partial occupancy can be granted.

901.6 Inspection, testing and maintenance. Fire detection and alarm systems, emergency alarm systems, gas detection systems, fire-extinguishing systems, mechanical smoke exhaust systems and smoke and heat vents shall be maintained in an operative condition at all times, and shall be replaced or repaired where defective. Nonrequired *fire protection systems* and equipment shall be inspected, tested and maintained or removed.

❖ Adequate maintenance, inspection and periodic testing of all of the listed systems, equipment and devices, including equipment and systems related to mechanical smoke exhaust and smoke and heat vents, is necessary so that they are ready to perform their intended functions should fire occur.

An inspection consists of a visual check of a system or device to verify that it is in operating condition and free from defects or damage. Indicating valves, gauges and indicator lamps are a few of the features required by the codes to facilitate this activity. Obvious damage and the general condition of the system, particularly the presence of corrosion, both external and internal, must always be noted and recorded. Partially because they are less detailed, inspections are conducted more frequently than tests and maintenance. Because special knowledge and tools are not required, inspections may be performed by any reasonably competent person.

Periodic tests following standardized methods are intended to confirm the results of inspections and determine that all components function properly and that systems meet their original design specifications. Tools, equipment or devices are usually required for these tests.

Because tests are more detailed than inspections, they are usually conducted only once or twice per year in most cases. Some tests, however, may be required as frequently as bimonthly or quarterly (for example, some fire alarm system equipment) or as infrequently as 5-, 6- or 12-year intervals (for example, portable fire-extinguisher hydrostatic tests). Since specialized knowledge and equipment are required, testing is usually done by technicians or specialists trained in the proper conduct of the test methods involved.

Periodic maintenance keeps systems in good working order and may be used to repair damage or defects discovered during inspections or testing. Specialized tools and training are required to perform maintenance. Only properly trained technicians or specialists should perform required periodic maintenance. Most maintenance is required only as needed, but many manufacturers suggest or require regular periodic replacement of parts subject to wear or abuse.

Nonrequired fire protection systems, where installed, require the same level of maintenance as required systems. If required maintenance is not being done, there is no way to determine if the system will function as intended. Therefore, inadequately maintained, nonrequired systems must be removed to avoid creating a false impression of adequate protection.

901.6.1 Standards. *Fire protection systems* shall be inspected, tested and maintained in accordance with the referenced standards *listed* in Table 901.6.1.

❖ Specific requirements related to inspection practices, testing schedules and maintenance procedures are dependent on the type of fire protection system and its corresponding referenced NFPA standard as indicated in Table 901.6.1.

TABLE 901.6.1
FIRE PROTECTION SYSTEM MAINTENANCE STANDARDS

SYSTEM	STANDARD
Portable fire extinguishers	NFPA 10
Carbon dioxide fire-extinguishing system	NFPA 12
Halon 1301 fire-extinguishing systems	NFPA 12A
Dry-chemical extinguishing systems	NFPA 17
Wet-chemical extinguishing systems	NFPA 17A
Water-based fire protection systems	NFPA 25
Fire alarm systems	NFPA 72
Smoke and heat vents	NFPA 204
Water-mist systems	NFPA 750
Clean-agent extinguishing systems	NFPA 2001

❖ This table lists the NFPA referenced standards to be used for the inspection, testing and maintenance criteria for various fire protection systems. Many of the testing and maintenance requirements are included elsewhere in Chapter 9 of the code.

901.6.2 Integrated testing. Where two or more fire protection or life safety systems are interconnected, the intended response of subordinate fire protection and life safety systems shall be verified when required testing of the initiating system is conducted. In addition, integrated testing shall be performed in accordance with Sections 901.6.2.1 and 901.6.2.2.

❖ The code intends to require proper operation of integrated features of fire protection and life safety systems. In some cases, such as a fire alarm system initiating a complex response of doors, dampers, elevators and fans in a high-rise building, the integration is highly complex, involving cooperation of many different trades, controls and systems. In other cases, such as notifying a monitoring service when a fire sprinkler operates, the integration is relatively simple. The intent of this section is that the required testing of integrated features is scaled in a manner that is reasonable for a wide range of applications.

901.6.2.1 High-rise buildings. For high-rise buildings, integrated testing shall comply with NFPA 4, with an integrated test performed prior to issuance of the certificate of occupancy and at intervals not exceeding 10 years, unless otherwise specified by an integrated system test plan prepared in accordance with NFPA 4. If an equipment failure is detected during integrated testing, a repeat of the integrated test shall not be required, except as necessary to verify operation of fire protection or life safety functions that are initiated by equipment that was repaired or replaced.

❖ NFPA 4 is referenced for compliance in this section for the integrated testing of fire protection systems in high-rise buildings. The integrated test is to be completed before the building is allowed to be occupied and additionally every 10 years or less to ensure that the required fire protection systems continue to function as intended. In addition, it is stated that a repeat of the entire integrated test is not required when failed initiating equipment is repaired or replaced.

901.6.2.2 Smoke control systems. Where a fire alarm system is integrated with a smoke control system as outlined in Section 909, integrated testing shall comply with NFPA 4, with an integrated test performed prior to issuance of the certificate of occupancy and at intervals not exceeding 10 years, unless otherwise specified by an integrated system test plan prepared in accordance with NFPA 4. If an equipment failure is detected during integrated testing, a repeat of the integrated test shall not be required, except as necessary to verify operation of fire protection or life safety functions that are initiated by equipment that was repaired or replaced.

❖ NFPA 4 is referenced for compliance in this section for the integrated testing of fire alarm systems that are required to operate in combination with smoke control systems. The integrated test is to be completed before the building is allowed to be occupied and additionally every 10 years or less to ensure that the required fire protection systems continue to function as intended. In addition, it is stated that a repeat of the entire integrated test is not required when failed initiating equipment is repaired or replaced.

901.6.3 Records. Records of all system inspections, tests and maintenance required by the referenced standards shall be maintained.

❖ Accurate, up-to-date records are required to document the history of system inspection, testing and maintenance. Record keeping is not intended simply to prove to the fire code official that required inspection, testing and maintenance are being performed, but to assist the owner or his or her agent in performing these functions. A well-kept log helps an owner or technician determine how the system is performing over time and how changes inside and outside of the protected premises are affecting system performance. For example, automatic sprinkler system main drain test results may indicate whether the public water supply is being degraded by development, thereby impairing sprinkler system capabilities. Similarly, a history of accidental alarms at a specific smoke detector may indicate that the device requires cleaning or maintenance.

901.6.3.1 Records information. Initial records shall include the name of the installation contractor, type of components installed, manufacturer of the components, location and number of components installed per floor. Records shall include the manufacturers' operation and maintenance instruction manuals. Such records shall be maintained for the life of the installation.

❖ When the fire protection systems are first installed, an accurate inventory must be compiled so that future owners and officials can refer back to the documents for maintenance and operational requirements. Additionally, if a recall is required, the installation inventory will be able to identify if any of the components subject to the recall are installed. By including the installation contractor's information in the list, a resolution of any legal aspects of defective components can be more readily obtained. Also, if operations or maintenance change during the life of the installation and a public notice is provided, the building owner will have the information necessary to know and apply the new requirements. The requirement to collect and maintain this information is already within many of the standards referenced in the code. This requirement gives the fire code official enforcement language and assists the building owner in understanding the responsibilities associated with having these fire protection systems installed in the building.

901.7 Systems out of service. Where a required *fire protection system* is out of service, the fire department and the *fire code official* shall be notified immediately and, where required by the *fire code official*, the building shall be either evacuated or an *approved* fire watch shall be provided for all occupants left unprotected by the shutdown until the *fire protection system* has been returned to service.

Where utilized, fire watches shall be provided with not less than one *approved* means for notification of the fire department and their only duty shall be to perform constant patrols of the protected premises and keep watch for fires.

❖ The protection afforded by a required fire protection system must not be diminished in any existing building except for the purpose of conducting tests, maintenance or repairs. The length of service interruptions must be kept to a minimum. The fire department and the fire code official must be notified of any service interruptions. They must carefully evaluate the continued operation or occupancy of buildings and structures where protection is interrupted. Whenever possible, all unaffected portions of the system should be kept in service. Until protection is restored, hazardous processes or operations should be suspended and alternative special protection should be considered in addition to an approved fire watch.

The code text only addresses when a required system is placed out of service. However, if a system is in place, even though it is not required by the code or the IBC, it would be an appropriate courtesy to inform the fire department of any fire protection system being discontinued or temporarily taken out of service. If the nonrequired system is to be placed out of service for an extended period of time, the fire code official has the authority to address the condition under Section 901.4.5 and require that the system be either placed back into operation or removed so as not to create a false impression of protection.

901.7.1 Impairment coordinator. The building *owner* shall assign an impairment coordinator to comply with the requirements of this section. In the absence of a specific designee, the *owner* shall be considered to be the impairment coordinator.

❖ The impairment coordinator is the person responsible for maintaining the building fire protection systems. The impairment coordinator may be the building owner or other designee, such as the plant manager or building engineer, if he or she is trained to comply with the provisions of Section 901.7.

901.7.2 Tag required. A tag shall be used to indicate that a system, or portion thereof, has been removed from service.

❖ When any fire protection system is taken out of service, it must be clearly identified with a visible tag that indicates the conditions of the impairment and who to notify. The tag is intended to alert building occupants and fire department personnel that the system in question is impaired. It must remain visibly in place until full protection is restored.

901.7.3 Placement of tag. The tag shall be posted at each fire department connection, system control valve, fire alarm control unit, fire alarm annunciator and *fire command center*, indicating which system, or part thereof, has been removed from service. The *fire code official* shall specify where the tag is to be placed.

❖ This section specifies some of the impaired locations where a tag must be used. Tagging a fire department connection, for example, is intended to alert the responding fire department that a normal operating condition does not exist for the portion of the system beyond the connection. While it is also important to tag system control valves, an impairment tag in the sprinkler riser room may not get noticed until accessed by fire department personnel. The final location of all impairment tags is subject to the approval of the fire code official.

901.7.4 Preplanned impairment programs. Preplanned impairments shall be authorized by the impairment coordinator. Before authorization is given, a designated individual shall be responsible for verifying that all of the following procedures have been implemented:

1. The extent and expected duration of the impairment have been determined.
2. The areas or buildings involved have been inspected and the increased risks determined.
3. Recommendations have been submitted to management or the building *owner*/manager.
4. The fire department has been notified.
5. The insurance carrier, the alarm company, the building *owner*/manager and other authorities having jurisdiction have been notified.
6. The supervisors in the areas to be affected have been notified.
7. A tag impairment system has been implemented.
8. Necessary tools and materials have been assembled on the impairment site.

❖ This section specifies the procedures that must be followed in a thorough preplanned impairment program. These procedures must be followed whenever systems are purposely impaired, such as for routine sprinkler system alarm testing. Proper notification of responsible parties eliminates the chance of false alarms, reduces disruption of normal business activities and encourages quick resumption of normal operations.

901.7.5 Emergency impairments. Where unplanned impairments occur, appropriate emergency action shall be taken to minimize potential injury and damage. The impairment coordinator shall implement the steps outlined in Section 901.7.4.

❖ Unplanned impairments, of course, go beyond typical testing and maintenance procedures but are also not necessarily indicative of a fire event. For example, an unplanned emergency impairment might occur if a sprinkler head or pipe was found leaking or was accidentally impacted by a forklift. To reduce water damage and to repair the sprinkler system, the valve controlling the water supply to the affected area would need to be closed, thereby impairing protection to the area protected by that portion of the sprinkler system. The impairment coordinator must follow the procedures in Section 901.7.4 to restore protection in minimum time.

901.7.6 Restoring systems to service. Where impaired equipment is restored to normal working order, the impairment coordinator shall verify that all of the following procedures have been implemented:

1. Necessary inspections and tests have been conducted to verify that affected systems are operational.
2. Supervisors have been advised that protection is restored.
3. The fire department has been advised that protection is restored.
4. The building *owner*/manager, insurance carrier, alarm company and other involved parties have been advised that protection is restored.
5. The impairment tag has been removed.

❖ Regardless of whether a system is taken out of service for either a planned impairment or for an emergency, this section specifies the procedures to follow when restoring a system to service. By following these procedures, all responsible parties who were informed of the initial impairment will also be made aware that the system is now fully operational. Restoring the system to service assumes the affected part of the system has been corrected and is in proper working condition.

901.8 Removal of or tampering with equipment. It shall be unlawful for any person to remove, tamper with or otherwise disturb any fire hydrant, fire detection and alarm system, fire suppression system or other fire appliance required by this code except for the purposes of extinguishing fire, training, recharging or making necessary repairs or where *approved* by the *fire code official*.

❖ Tampering or otherwise unauthorized altering of any fire protection system or component is illegal. A person who unlawfully tampers with equipment could face potential criminal charges. Tampering could include intentionally pulling a manual fire alarm box when no emergency exists, playing with matches to set off a smoke detector or flowing a city fire hydrant. The use of fire protection systems, equipment and other fire appliances is limited to those people authorized to conduct repairs and maintenance unless approved by the fire code official.

901.8.1 Removal of or tampering with appurtenances. Locks, gates, doors, barricades, chains, enclosures, signs, tags or seals that have been installed by or at the direction of the *fire code official* shall not be removed, unlocked, destroyed, tampered with or otherwise vandalized in any manner.

❖ Tampering with or vandalizing appurtenances that are in place to prevent tampering with the system components is also prohibited. For example, sprinkler system control valves are routinely chained and locked in the open position in addition to being equipped with electronically monitored tamper switches. Gates at fire apparatus roads, authorized by Section 503.6 of the code, must not have the locks changed or operation altered unless approved by the fire code official. Any unauthorized removal or tampering with these types of devices is strictly prohibited.

901.8.2 Removal of existing occupant-use hose lines. The *fire code official* is authorized to permit the removal of existing occupant-use hose lines where both of the following conditions exist:

1. The hose line would not be utilized by trained personnel or the fire department.
2. The remaining outlets are compatible with local fire department fittings.

❖ The current code and the IBC do not require occupant-use hoses in as many locations as were required in previous editions of the codes and referenced standards. There also has been a shift in the philosophy of fire service leaders as to whether occupants should attempt to extinguish the fire via occupant-use hose stations or evacuate the structure. Most of the population is now being taught to evacuate the building, not to fight the fire. This shift is mainly due to the safety risk of having an untrained person attempting to fight a fire with more than a fire extinguisher. Another consideration was the ongoing cost to building owners to comply with maintenance and testing requirements for the hoses and their racks. Many jurisdictions have enacted local legislation or code changes to address this issue, and the addition of this new section updates the code to reflect conventional wisdom on this topic. This section provides safeguards in the form of several conditions for the fire code official to consider in formulating an approval for removal of occupant-use hoses. The first condition assumes that there is not a trained fire brigade on the premises that might be qualified to use the hose stations as first responders in, for example, an industrial setting. Condition 1 also recognizes that fire departments typically will not use private hose stations for fire attack due to the questionable quality of their maintenance. Condition 2 was included to ensure that any outlets that remain are useable by the fire department by requiring that their threads be compatible with local fire department fire hose fittings, such as American National Fire Hose Connection Screw Threads (NH).

901.9 Termination of monitoring service. For fire alarm systems required to be monitored by this code, notice shall be made to the *fire code official* whenever alarm monitoring services are terminated. Notice shall be made in writing by the provider of the monitoring service being terminated.

❖ This section requires the monitoring service itself to notify the fire code official of service being terminated. Although the ultimate responsibility rests with the building owner, he or she is not cited in this section since if they discontinued the service, they would likely not understand the implications, and if they did would have no incentive to contact the fire code official.

901.10 Recall of fire protection components. Any *fire protection system* component regulated by this code that is the subject of a voluntary or mandatory recall under federal law shall be replaced with *approved*, *listed* components in compliance with the referenced standards of this code. The *fire code official* shall be notified in writing by the building *owner* when the recalled component parts have been replaced.

❖ This section provides the fire code official with a valuable tool for monitoring recalls. Under this provision, a code section can be cited that will allow the fire code official to enforce the provisions of the recall on systems within the jurisdiction. Product listings and compliance with referenced standards are paramount in the effectiveness of fire protection systems. Companies may be under an agreement with federal agencies to "voluntarily" recall certain components or face legal action. While this is technically voluntary, it in no way reduces the need for the recall. To the extent that the company's livelihood depends on the recall being performed properly, the action is not voluntary. This section allows the fire code official to compel the building owner to comply with the recall and replace the component with one that is not subject to suspicion.

SECTION 902
DEFINITIONS

902.1 Definitions. The following terms are defined in Chapter 2:

ALARM NOTIFICATION APPLIANCE.

ALARM SIGNAL.

ALARM VERIFICATION FEATURE.

ANNUNCIATOR.

AUDIBLE ALARM NOTIFICATION APPLIANCE.

AUTOMATIC.

AUTOMATIC FIRE-EXTINGUISHING SYSTEM.

AUTOMATIC SMOKE DETECTION SYSTEM.

AUTOMATIC SPRINKLER SYSTEM.

AUTOMATIC WATER MIST SYSTEM.

AVERAGE AMBIENT SOUND LEVEL.

CARBON DIOXIDE EXTINGUISHING SYSTEM.

CLEAN AGENT.

COMMERCIAL MOTOR VEHICLE.

CONSTANTLY ATTENDED LOCATION.

DELUGE SYSTEM.

DETECTOR, HEAT.

DRY-CHEMICAL EXTINGUISHING AGENT.

ELEVATOR GROUP.

EMERGENCY ALARM SYSTEM.

EMERGENCY VOICE/ALARM COMMUNICATIONS.

FIRE ALARM BOX, MANUAL.

FIRE ALARM CONTROL UNIT.

FIRE ALARM SIGNAL.

FIRE ALARM SYSTEM.

FIRE AREA.

FIRE DETECTOR, AUTOMATIC.

FIRE PROTECTION SYSTEM.

FIRE SAFETY FUNCTIONS.

FIXED BASE OPERATOR (FBO).

FOAM-EXTINGUISHING SYSTEM.

GAS DETECTION SYSTEM.

HALOGENATED EXTINGUISHING SYSTEM.

IMPAIRMENT COORDINATOR.

INITIATING DEVICE.

MANUAL FIRE ALARM BOX.

MULTIPLE-STATION ALARM DEVICE.

MULTIPLE-STATION SMOKE ALARM.

NOTIFICATION ZONE.

NUISANCE ALARM.

PRIVATE GARAGE.

RECORD DRAWINGS.

SINGLE-STATION SMOKE ALARM.

SLEEPING UNIT.

SMOKE ALARM.

SMOKE DETECTOR.

STANDPIPE, TYPES OF.

- **Automatic dry.**
- **Automatic wet.**
- **Manual dry.**
- **Manual wet.**
- **Semiautomatic dry.**

STANDPIPE SYSTEM, CLASSES OF.

- **Class I system.**
- **Class II system.**
- **Class III system.**

SUPERVISING STATION.

SUPERVISORY SERVICE.

SUPERVISORY SIGNAL.

SUPERVISORY SIGNAL-INITIATING DEVICE.

TIRES, BULK STORAGE OF.

TRANSIENT AIRCRAFT.

TROUBLE SIGNAL.

VISIBLE ALARM NOTIFICATION APPLIANCE.

WET-CHEMICAL EXTINGUISHING AGENT.

WIRELESS PROTECTION SYSTEM.

ZONE.

ZONE, NOTIFICATION.

❖ Definitions of terms can help in the understanding and application of the code requirements. This section directs the code user to Chapter 2 for the proper application of the indicated terms used in this chapter. Terms may be defined in Chapter 2, in another International Code® as indicated in Section 201.3 or the dictionary meaning may be all that is needed (see also commentary, Sections 201 through 201.4).

Certain requirements in the code are based on code provisions in the IBC, *International Mechanical Code®* (IMC®) and *International Plumbing Code®* (IPC®). A review of definitions included in those codes will aid in the understanding of many of the requirements contained in the code.

SECTION 903
AUTOMATIC SPRINKLER SYSTEMS

903.1 General. *Automatic sprinkler systems* shall comply with this section.

❖ This section identifies the conditions requiring an automatic sprinkler system for all occupancies. The need for an automatic sprinkler system may depend on not only the occupancy but also the occupant load, fuel load, height and area of the building as well as fire-fighting capabilities. Section 903.2 addresses all occupancy conditions requiring an automatic sprinkler system. Section 903.3 contains the installation requirements for all sprinkler systems in addition to the requirements of NFPA 13, NFPA 13R and NFPA 13D. The supervision and alarm requirements for sprinkler systems are contained in Section 903.4, whereas Section 903.5 refers to testing and maintenance requirements for sprinkler systems found in Section 901 and NFPA 25. Section 903.6 addresses existing buildings and references Chapter 11.

Unless specifically allowed by the code or the IBC, residential sprinkler systems installed in accordance with NFPA 13R or NFPA 13D are not recognized for reductions or exceptions permitted by other sections of this code or the IBC. NFPA 13 systems provide the level of protection associated with adequate fire suppression for all occupancies. NFPA 13R and NFPA 13D systems are intended more to provide adequate time for egress but not necessarily for complete suppression of the fire. Commentary Figure 903.2 lists examples of where the various sprinkler thresholds differ in application.

The area values contained in this section are intended to apply to fire areas, which are comprised of all floor areas bounded by fire barriers, fire walls or exterior walls. The minimum required fire-resistance rating of fire barrier assemblies that define a fire area is specified in Table 707.3.10 of the IBC. Because the areas are defined as fire areas, fire barriers, horizontal assemblies, fire walls or exterior walls are the only acceptable means of subdividing a building into smaller areas instead of installing an automatic sprinkler system. Whereas fire barriers and exterior walls define multiple fire areas within a single building, a fire wall defines separate buildings within one structure. Also note that some of the threshold limitations result in a requirement to install an automatic sprinkler system throughout the building while others may require only specific fire areas to be sprinklered.

Another important point is that one fire area may include floor areas in more than one story of a building (see the commentary to the definition of "Fire area" in Section 202).

The application of mixed occupancies and fire areas must be carefully researched. Often the required separation between occupancies for the purposes of applying the separated mixed-use option in Section 508.4 of the IBC will result in a separation that is less than what is required to define the boundaries of a fire area. It is possible to have two different occupancies within a given fire area, treated as separated uses but with code requirements applicable to both occupancies since they are not separated by the rating required for fire areas.

903.1.1 Alternative protection. Alternative automatic fire-extinguishing systems complying with Section 904 shall be permitted instead of automatic sprinkler protection where recognized by the applicable standard and *approved* by the *fire code official.*

❖ This section permits the use of an alternative automatic fire-extinguishing system when approved by the fire code official as a means of compliance with the occupancy requirements of Section 903. Although the use of an alternative extinguishing system allowed by Section 904, such as a carbon dioxide system or clean-agent system, would satisfy the requirements of Section 903.2, it would not be considered an acceptable alternative for the purposes of exceptions, reductions or other code alternatives that would be applicable if an automatic sprinkler system were installed.

903.2 Where required. *Approved automatic sprinkler systems* in new buildings and structures shall be provided in the locations described in Sections 903.2.1 through 903.2.12.

Exception: Spaces or areas in telecommunications buildings used exclusively for telecommunications equipment, associated electrical power distribution equipment, batteries and standby engines, provided that those spaces or areas are equipped throughout with an automatic smoke detection system in accordance with Section 907.2 and are separated from the remainder of the building by not less than 1-hour *fire barriers* constructed in accordance with Section 707 of the *International Building Code* or not less than 2-hour *horizontal assemblies* constructed in accordance with Section 711 of the *International Building Code,* or both.

❖ Sections 903.2.1 through 903.2.12 identify the conditions requiring an automatic sprinkler system (see Commentary Figure 903.2). The type of sprinkler system must be one that is permitted for the specific occupancy condition. An NFPA 13R sprinkler system, for example, may not be installed to satisfy the sprinkler threshold requirements for a mercantile occupancy (see Section 903.2.7). As indicated in Section 903.3.1.2, the use of an NFPA 13R sprinkler system is limited to Group R occupancies not exceeding four stories in height.

There is one exception for those spaces or areas used exclusively for telecommunications equipment. The telecommunications industry has continually stressed the need for the continuity of telephone service, and the ability to maintain this service is of prime importance. This service is a vital link between the community and the various life safety services, including fire, police and emergency medical services. The integrity of this communications service can be jeopardized not only by fire, but also by water, from whatever the source.

It must be emphasized that the exception applies only to those spaces or areas that are used exclusively for telecommunications equipment. Historically, those spaces have a low incidence of fire events. Fires in telecommunications equipment are difficult to start and, if started, grow slowly, thus permitting early detection. Such fires are typically of the smoldering type, do not spread beyond the immediate area and generally self-extinguish.

Note, however, that this exception requires fire resistive separation from other portions of the building and, most importantly, that the building cannot qualify for any code trade-offs for fully sprinklered buildings.

903.2.1 Group A. An *automatic sprinkler system* shall be provided throughout buildings and portions thereof used as Group A occupancies as provided in this section.

❖ Group A occupancies are characterized by a significant number of people who are not familiar with their surroundings. The requirement for a suppression system reflects the additional time needed for egress. The extent of protection is also intended to extend to the occupants of the assembly group from unobserved fires in other building areas located between the story containing the assembly occupancy and all levels of exit discharge serving such occupancies. The only exception to the coverage is for Group A-5 occupancies that are open to the atmosphere. Such occupancies require only certain aspects to be sprinklered, such as concession stands (see commentary, Section 903.2.1.5).

The requirement for sprinklers is based on the location and function of the space. It is not dependent on whether the area is provided with exterior walls. IFC Committee Interpretation No. 25-05 to this section discusses this issue and states, in part, that "where no surrounding exterior walls are provided along the perimeter of the building, the building area is used to identify and determine applicable fire area." Outdoor areas, such as pavilions and patios, may have no walls but will have an occupant load and other factors that identify the assembly occupancy as such. If any of the thresholds are reached requiring sprinkler protection, then sprinkler protection must be provided whether there are exterior walls or not.

903.2.1.1 Group A-1. An *automatic sprinkler system* shall be provided throughout stories containing Group A-1 occupancies and throughout all stories from the Group A-1 occupancy to and including the levels of exit discharge serving that occupancy where one of the following conditions exists:

1. The *fire area* exceeds 12,000 square feet (1115 m^2).
2. The *fire area* has an *occupant load* of 300 or more.
3. The *fire area* is located on a floor other than a *level of exit discharge* serving such occupancies.
4. The *fire area* contains a multiple-theater complex.

❖ Group A-1 occupancies are identified as assembly occupancies with fixed seating, such as theaters. In addition to the high occupant load associated with these types of facilities, egress is further complicated by the possibility of low lighting levels customary during performances. The fuel load in these buildings is usually of a type and quantity that would support fairly rapid fire development and sustained duration.

Theaters with stages pose a greater hazard. Sections 410.7 and 410.8 require stages to be equipped with an automatic sprinkler system and standpipe system, respectively. The proscenium opening must also be protected. These features compensate for the additional hazards associated with stages in Group A-1 occupancies.

This section lists four conditions that require installing a suppression system in a Group A-1 occupancy including the entire story where the A-1 occupancy is located and all intervening floors. Condition 1 requires that, if any one fire area of Group A-1 exceeds 12,000 square feet (1115 m^2), the automatic sprinkler system is to be installed throughout the entire story where a Group A-1 occupancy is located, regardless of whether the building is divided into more than one fire area. However, if all fire areas are less than 12,000 square feet (1115 m^2) (and less than the other thresholds), then sprinklers would not be required. Compartmentalization into multiple fire areas in compliance with IBC Chapter 7 is deemed an adequate alternative to sprinkler protection.

Condition 2 establishes the minimum number of occupants for which an automatic sprinkler system is considered necessary. The determination of the actual occupant load must be based on Section 1004.

Occupancy	Threshold	Exception
All occupancies	Buildings with floor level ≥ 55 feet above or below fire department vehicle access and occupant load ≥ 30.	Open parking structures (F-2)
Assembly (A-1, A-3, A-4)	Fire area > 12,000 sq. ft. or fire area occupant load ≥ 300 or fire area above/below level of exit discharge. Multitheater complex (A-1 only).	None
Assembly (A-2)	Fire area > 5,000 sq. ft. or fire area occupant load ≥ 100 or fire area above/below level of exit discharge.	None
Assembly (A-5)	Accessory areas > 1,000 sq. ft. Enclosed spaces under grandstands or bleachers ≤ 1,000 sq. ft. and not constructed in accordance with Section 1029.1.1.1 or > 1,000 sq. ft.	None
Ambulatory care facility (B)	≥ 4 care recipients incapable of self preservation or any care recipients incapable of self preservation above or below level of exit discharge.	Floors classified as an open parking garage
Educational (E)	Fire area > 12,000 sq. ft. or on a floor other than a level of exit discharge serving such occupancies. Fire area occupant load ≥ 300.	Every classroom has not fewer than one exterior exit door at ground level, an automatic sprinkler system is not required in any area below the lowest level of exit discharge serving that area.
Factory (F-1) Mercantile (M) Storage (S-1)	Fire area > 12,000 sq. ft. or fire area located > three stories above grade, or combined fire area > 24,000 sq. ft. Woodworking > 2,500 sq. ft. (F-1 only) Manufacture > 2,500 sq. ft. (F1), display and sale > 5,000 sq. ft. (M), storage > 2,500 sq. ft. (S-1) of upholstered furniture or mattresses. Bulk storage of tires > 20,000 cu. ft. (S-1 only)	None
High-hazard (H-1, H-2, H-3, H-4, H-5)	Sprinklers required.	None
Institutional (I-1, I-2, I-3, I-4)	Sprinklers required.	Day care at level of exit discharge and each classroom has exterior exit door.
Residential (R)	Sprinklers required.	None
Repair garage (S-1)	Fire area > 12,000 sq. ft. or ≥ two stories above grade with fire area > 10,000 sq. ft. or repair garage servicing vehicles in basement or servicing commercial motor vehicles in fire area > 5,000 sq. ft.	None
Parking garage (S-1)	Commercial motor vehicles parking area > 5,000 sq. ft.	
Parking garage (S-2)	Fire area > 12,000 sq. ft. or fire area > 5,000 sq. ft. for storage of commercial motor vehicles; or beneath other groups (enclosed parking).	Not if beneath Group R-3.
Covered and open malls (914.2.1)	Sprinklers required.	Attached open parking structures.
High-rises (914.3.1)	Sprinklers required.	Open garages; certain telecommunications equipment buildings.
Unlimited area buildings (IBC 507)	A-3, A-4, B, F, M, S: one story. B, F, M, S: two story.	One story F-2 or S-2.

For SI: 1 foot = 304.8 mm, 1 square foot = 0.0929 m^2.

a. Thresholds located in Section 903.2 unless noted. See also Table 903.2.11.6 for additional required suppression systems.

Commentary Figure 903.2
SUMMARY OF OCCUPANCY-RELATED AUTOMATIC SPRINKLER THRESHOLDS[a]

Condition 3 accounts for occupant egress delay when traversing a stairway requiring a sprinkler system, regardless of the size of occupant load. In such cases, alternative emergency escape elements such as windows may not be available; making the suppression needs all the greater. It is not necessary for the occupant load to exceed 300 on a level other than the level of exit discharge serving such occupancy. Any number of Group A-1 occupants on the alternative level would be cause to apply the requirement for sprinklers. The text does not make reference to "story" but uses the term "floor," which could include mezzanines and basements.

Condition 4 states that a sprinkler system is required for multiplex theater complexes to account for the delay associated with the notification of adjacent compartmentalized spaces where the occupants may not be immediately aware of an emergency.

903.2.1.2 Group A-2. An *automatic sprinkler system* shall be provided throughout stories containing Group A-2 occupancies and throughout all stories from the Group A-2 occupancy to and including the levels of exit discharge serving that occupancy where one of the following conditions exists:

1. The *fire area* exceeds 5,000 square feet (464 m^2).
2. The *fire area* has an *occupant load* of 100 or more.
3. The *fire area* is located on a floor other than a *level of exit discharge* serving such occupancies.

❖ Group A-2 assembly occupancies are intended for food or drink consumption, such as banquet halls, nightclubs and restaurants. Occupancies in Group A-2 involve life safety factors such as a high occupant density, flexible fuel loading, movable furnishings and limited lighting; therefore, they must be protected with an automatic sprinkler system under any of the listed conditions.

In the case of an assembly use, the purpose of the automatic sprinkler system is to provide life safety from fire as well as preserving property. By requiring fire suppression in areas through which the occupants may egress, including the level of exit discharge serving such occupancies, the possibility of unobserved fire development affecting occupant egress is minimized.

The 5,000-square-foot (464 m^2) threshold for the automatic sprinkler system reflects the higher degree of life safety hazard associated with Group A-2 occupancies. As alluded to earlier, Group A-2 occupancies could have low lighting levels, loud music, late hours of operation, dense seating with ill-defined aisles and alcoholic beverage service. These factors in combination could delay fire recognition, confuse occupant response and increase egress time.

Although the calculated occupant load for a 5,000 square-foot (465 m^2) space at 15 square feet (1.4 m^2) per occupant would be over 100, the occupant load threshold in Condition 2 is meant to reflect the concern for safety in these higher density occupancies. Although the major reason for establishing the occupant threshold at 100 was because of several recent nightclub incidents, the requirement is not limited to nightclubs or banquet facilities but to all Group A-2 occupancies. Any restaurant with an occupant load greater than 100 would require sprinkler protection as well. This includes fast food facilities with no low lighting or alcohol sales. The similar intent of Condition 3 is addressed in the commentary to Section 903.2.1.1.

Note that as with Group A-1 occupancies, when sprinklers are required, they are required on the story where the Group A-2 occupancy is located and on all intervening floors leading to the levels of exit discharge.

903.2.1.3 Group A-3. An *automatic sprinkler system* shall be provided throughout stories containing Group A-3 occupancies and throughout all stories from the Group A-3 occupancy to and including the levels of exit discharge serving that occupancy where one of the following conditions exists:

1. The *fire area* exceeds 12,000 square feet (1115 m^2).
2. The *fire area* has an *occupant load* of 300 or more.
3. The *fire area* is located on a floor other than a *level of exit discharge* serving such occupancies.

❖ Group A-3 occupancies are assembly occupancies intended for worship, recreation or amusement and other assembly uses not classified elsewhere in Group A, such as churches, museums and libraries. While Group A-3 occupancies could potentially have a high occupant load, they normally do not have the same potential combination of life safety hazards associated with Group A-2 occupancies. As with most assembly occupancies, however, most of the occupants are typically not completely familiar with their surroundings. Where any of the three listed conditions are applicable, an automatic sprinkler system is required throughout the fire area containing the Group A-3 occupancy, including the entire story where the Group A-3 occupancy is located and throughout all floors between the Group A occupancy and exit discharge that serves that occupancy (see commentary, Sections 903.2.1 and 903.2.1.1).

903.2.1.4 Group A-4. An *automatic sprinkler system* shall be provided throughout stories containing Group A-4 occupancies and throughout all stories from the Group A-4 occupancy to and including the levels of exit discharge serving that occupancy where one of the following conditions exists:

1. The *fire area* exceeds 12,000 square feet (1115 m^2).
2. The *fire area* has an *occupant load* of 300 or more.
3. The *fire area* is located on a floor other than a *level of exit discharge* serving such occupancies.

❖ Group A-4 occupancies are assembly uses intended for viewing of indoor sporting events and activities such as arenas, skating rinks and swimming pools. The occupant load density may be high, depending on the extent and style of seating, such as bleachers or fixed seats, and the potential for standing-room viewing.

Where any of the three listed conditions are applicable, an automatic sprinkler system is required throughout the fire area containing the Group A-4 occupancy, including the entire story where the Group A-4 occupancy is located, and in all floors between the Group A occupancy and exit discharge (see commentary, Sections 903.2.1 and 903.2.1.1).

903.2.1.5 Group A-5. An *automatic sprinkler system* shall be provided for all enclosed Group A-5 accessory use areas in excess of 1,000 square feet (93 m^2).

❖ Group A-5 occupancies are assembly uses intended for viewing of outdoor activities. This occupancy classification could include amusement park structures, grandstands and open stadiums. A sprinkler system is not required in the open area of Group A-5 occupancies because the buildings would not accumulate smoke and hot gases. A fire in open areas would also be obvious to all spectators.

Enclosed areas such as retail areas, press boxes and concession stands require sprinklers if they are in excess of 1,000 square feet (93 m^2). The 1,000-square-foot (93 m^2) accessory use area is not intended to be an aggregate condition but rather per space. Thus, a press box that is 2,500 square feet (232 m^2) in area would need to be subdivided into areas less than 1,000 square feet (93 m^2) each in order to be below the threshold for sprinklers. There is no specific requirement for the separation of these spaces. It is assumed, however, that the separation would be a solid barrier of some type but without a required fire-resistance rating.

The provision is meant to mirror that in Section 1029.6.2.3, which exempts press boxes and storage facilities less than 1,000 square feet (93 m^2) in area from sprinkler requirements in smoke-protected assembly seating areas.

903.2.1.5.1 Spaces under grandstands or bleachers. Enclosed spaces under *grandstands* or *bleachers* shall be equipped with an *automatic sprinkler system* in accordance with Section 903.3.1.1 where either of the following exist:

1. The enclosed area is 1,000 square feet (93 m^2) or less and is not constructed in accordance with Section 1029.1.1.1.
2. The enclosed area exceeds 1,000 square feet (93 m^2).

❖ This section provides the area threshold for automatic sprinklers to be required in an enclosed space under grandstands or bleachers. Areas that are 1,000 square feet or less are required to be constructed in accordance with Section 1029.1.1.1 in order to be exempt from requiring automatic sprinkler protection. Enclosed areas that are greater than 1,000 square feet are to be protected with automatic sprinklers regardless of the construction type and level of separation.

903.2.1.6 Assembly occupancies on roofs. Where an occupied roof has an assembly occupancy with an *occupant load* exceeding 100 for Group A-2 and 300 for other Group A occupancies, all floors between the occupied roof and the *level of exit discharge* shall be equipped with an *automatic sprinkler system* in accordance with Section 903.3.1.1 or 903.3.1.2.

Exception: Open parking garages of Type I or Type II construction.

❖ Frequently, rooftops are being used and occupied as assembly occupancies. Building owners will provide an open air rooftop bar or lounge, or other use similar to a Group A-2 occupancy on the roof of a building. A roof does not meet the definition of a fire area. As such, protection of the occupants can be less than what would otherwise be required were the occupancy located on a floor rather than on the roof. In addition, even if a fire occurs within the building itself, it puts these occupants at risk. The provisions requiring sprinklers are based on the type of assembly occupancy located on the roof. The roof itself is not required to be sprinklered. The reference to Section 903.3.1.2 is added, since this use can occur on the roof of multifamily housing facilities.

The exception for open parking garages is consistent with the existing code requirement exception for open parking garages under Section 903.2.11.3 for "Buildings 55 feet or more in height." It is becoming more common in the urban renewal areas throughout the United States that jurisdictions are asking developers to provide additional recreational and green spaces for their citizens to enjoy within their own communities. Because of the limited space available, it is not uncommon for such recreational and green spaces to be provided on the roofs of open parking garages. Based on the existing wording of this section, these recreational and green spaces greater than 700 square feet (based on 7 square feet net per occupant) or 1,500 square feet (based on 15 square feet net per occupant) would now require the open parking garage to be sprinklered. In other words, an open recreational or green space on the roof of an open parking structure that is more than approximately 39 by 39 feet square would require the garage to be sprinklered with a dry pipe sprinkler system that is initially a major cost to the project as well as a major monthly and yearly maintenance expense. Such an expense would most likely have an adverse effect on developers doing major city urban renewal projects, deterring them from providing such amenities for the local jurisdiction.

Additionally, there are considerable data supporting the exception's elimination of automatic sprinkler systems in open parking garages. Two sample reports that evaluated fire behavior in parking garages are:

1. 2006 NFPA Fire Data Report, "Structure and Vehicle Fires in General Vehicle Parking Garages."
2. 2008 Parking Consultants Council Fire Safety Committee Report, "Parking Structure Fire Facts."

These reports provided the following conclusions:

- There was an average of only 660 fires per year in all types of parking garages in the United States. This represented a mere 0.006 percent of all fires annually.
- There were no fire fatalities in open parking garages of Type I or II construction. On average, there were only 2 injuries per year.
- There was no structural damage in 98.7 percent of the fires in parking garages.
- Vehicle fires in parking garages typically do not spread from vehicle to vehicle. Fire spread from vehicle to vehicle occurred in only 7 percent of the incidents.

Automatic sprinkler systems are required in occupancies other than open parking garages to protect the assembly occupancy above the fire and to protect the means of egress. Based on the inherent fire safety provided by open parking garages of Type I or II construction, an automatic sprinkler system is not required when an assembly use is located on the roof.

903.2.1.7 Multiple fire areas. An *automatic sprinkler system* shall be provided where multiple fire areas of Group A-1, A-2, A-3 or A-4 occupancies share exit or *exit access* components and the combined *occupant load* of these fire areas is 300 or more.

❖ There are two conditions required to trigger the requirements of this section. The first is that exit or exit access components of Group A-1, A-2, A-3 or A-4 fire areas are shared. The second is that the combined occupant load of the fire areas that share these components exceeds 300 persons.

This section addresses the issue of multiple small assembly occupancies placed in a single-story building and not triggering a sprinkler system requirement because of the installation of a rated corridor and separation walls. The code now requires that sprinkler systems be added when the convergence of more than 300 persons share an exit. This is consistent with the intent of automatic sprinkler systems being required for life safety and to maintain tenable exiting in a fire event. A fire event that is near an exit is the same whether there are 300 occupants in one room or three rooms with 100 occupants each sharing an exit. This is also consistent with the requirement in the “multi-theater complex” for Group A-1, which is a requirement for anytime two or more theaters are in the same tenancy and does not consider occupant load as a trigger.

This will still allow single-story buildings with multiple tenancies that have separate exits and that utilize the fire area separation concept, such as buildings with multiple restaurants with separate entrances and strip-style mall buildings.

903.2.2 Ambulatory care facilities. An *automatic sprinkler system* shall be installed throughout the entire floor containing an ambulatory care facility where either of the following conditions exist at any time:

1. Four or more care recipients are incapable of self-preservation.
2. One or more care recipients that are incapable of self-preservation are located at other than the level of exit discharge serving such a facility.

In buildings where ambulatory care is provided on levels other than the *level of exit discharge*, an *automatic sprinkler system* shall be installed throughout the entire floor as well as all floors below where such care is provided, and all floors between the level of ambulatory care and the nearest *level of exit discharge*, the *level of exit* discharge, and all floors below the *level of exit discharge*.

Exception: Floors classified as an open parking garage are not required to be sprinklered.

❖ Ambulatory care facilities are Group B occupancies, which have an enhanced set of requirements that account for the fact that patients may be incapable of self-preservation and require rescue by other occupants or fire personnel. There are several aspects to the enhanced features, including smoke compartments, sprinklers and fire alarms. More specifically, the requirements for sprinklers are based on the presence of four or more care recipients at any given time that are incapable of self-preservation or any number of care recipients that are incapable of self-preservation located on a floor other than the level of exit discharge that serves the ambulatory care facility. The sprinkler requirement is limited to the floor area that contains the Group B ambulatory care facility and any floors between the ambulatory care facility and level of exit discharge (see commentary, Section 422).

903.2.3 Group E. An *automatic sprinkler system* shall be provided for Group E occupancies as follows:

1. Throughout all Group E *fire areas* greater than 12,000 square feet (1115 m^2) in area.
2. The Group E fire area is located on a floor other than a level of exit discharge serving such occupancies.

   Exception: In buildings where every classroom has not fewer than one exterior exit door at ground level, an automatic sprinkler system is not required in any area below the lowest level of exit discharge serving that area.
3. The Group E fire area has an occupant load of 300 or more.

❖ Group E occupancies are limited to educational purposes through the 12th grade and day care centers serving children older than $2^1/_2$ years of age. The 12,000-square-foot (1115 m^2) fire area threshold for the sprinkler system was established to allow smaller schools and day care centers to be nonsprinklered to minimize the economic impact on these facilities. The 12,000-square-foot (1115 m^2) threshold is similar to that used for several other occupancies, such as Group M occupancies.

Sprinklers would also be required in portions of the building located below the level of exit discharge serving that occupancy. However, there is an exception that would allow the omission of the automatic sprinkler system for the Group E fire area if there is a direct exit to the exterior from each classroom at ground level. The occupants must be able to go from the classroom directly to the outside without passing through intervening corridors, passageways or interior exit stairways.

903.2.4 Group F-1. An *automatic sprinkler system* shall be provided throughout all buildings containing a Group F-1 occupancy where one of the following conditions exists:

1. A Group F-1 *fire area* exceeds 12,000 square feet (1115 m^2).
2. A Group F-1 *fire area* is located more than three stories above grade plane.
3. The combined area of all Group F-1 *fire areas* on all floors, including any mezzanines, exceeds 24,000 square feet (2230 m^2).
4. A Group F-1 occupancy used for the manufacture of upholstered furniture or mattresses exceeds 2,500 square feet (232 m^2).

❖ Group F-1 occupancies must meet several different conditions as to when the fire area or occupancy must be sprinklered. The first three conditions are related to the difficulty of manually suppressing a fire involving a large area. Therefore, occupancies of Group F-1 must be protected throughout with an automatic sprinkler system if the fire area is in excess of 12,000 square feet (1115 m^2); if the total of all fire areas is in excess of 24,000 square feet (2230 m^2); or if the fire area is located more than three stories above grade plane. This is one of the few locations in the code where the total floor area of the building is aggregated for application of a code requirement. The stipulated conditions for when an automatic sprinkler system is required also apply to Group M (see Section 903.2.7) and S-1 (see Section 903.2.9) occupancies. Condition 4 for sprinklering a Group F-1 occupancy relates to the requirement for Group F-1 occupancies in excess of 2,500 square feet (232 m^2) that are used for the manufacture of upholstered furniture or mattresses. Note that this requirement is based simply on the square footage of the Group F-1 occupancy and is not related to fire areas. Upholstered furniture has the potential for rapid-growing and high-heat-release fires. This hazard is increased substantially when there are numerous upholstered furniture items or mattresses being manufactured. Such fires put the occupants and emergency responders at risk. This requirement exists regardless of whether the upholstered furniture has passed any fire-retardant tests. See the commentary for Section 903.2.7 for more discussion on the subject of upholstered furniture. See the commentary to Section 903.2.9 for discussion of the formal interpretation and applicability to the code and the IBC.

The following examples illustrate how the criteria of this section are intended to be applied:

- If a building contains a single fire area of Group F-1 and the fire area is 13,000 square feet (1208 m^2), an automatic sprinkler system is required throughout the entire building; however, if this fire area is separated into two fire areas and neither is in excess of 12,000 square feet (1115 m^2), an automatic fire sprinkler system is not required. To be considered separate fire areas, the areas must be separated by fire barriers or horizontal assemblies having a fire-resistance rating as required in Table 707.3.10 of the IBC.
- If a 30,000-square-foot (2787 m^2) Group F-1 building is equally divided into separate fire areas of 10,000 square feet (929 m^2) each, an automatic sprinkler system would still be required throughout the entire building. Because the aggregate area of all fire areas exceeds 24,000 square feet (2230 m^2), additional compartmentation will not eliminate the need for an automatic sprinkler system. However, the use of a fire wall to separate the structure into two buildings would reduce the aggregate area of each building to less than 24,000 square feet (2230 m^2) and each fire area to less than 12,000 square feet (1115 m^2), which would offset the need for an automatic sprinkler system.

903.2.4.1 Woodworking operations. An *automatic sprinkler system* shall be provided throughout all Group F-1 occupancy *fire areas* that contain woodworking operations in excess of 2,500 square feet (232 m^2) in area that generate finely divided combustible waste or use finely divided combustible materials.

❖ Because of the potential amount of combustible dust that could be generated during woodworking operations, an automatic sprinkler system is required throughout a fire area when it contains a woodworking operation that exceeds 2,500 square feet (232 m^2) in area. Facilities where woodworking operations take place, such as cabinet making, are considered Group F-1 occupancies. The intent of the phrase "finely divided combustible waste" is to describe particle concentrations that are in the explosive range (see Chapter 22 for discussion of dust-producing operations).

The extent of sprinkler coverage is only intended to be for the Group F-1 occupancy involved in the woodworking activity. If the fire area is larger than 2,500 square feet (232 m^2) but the woodworking area is 2,500 square feet (232 m^2) or less, sprinklers are not required. It is not the intent to require the installation of sprinklers throughout the building but rather in the fire area where the hazard may be present.

903.2.5 Group H. *Automatic sprinkler systems* shall be provided in high-hazard occupancies as required in Sections 903.2.5.1 through 903.2.5.3.

❖ Group H occupancies are those intended for the manufacturing, processing or storage of hazardous materials that constitute a physical or health hazard. To be considered a Group H occupancy, the amount of hazardous materials is assumed to be in excess of the maximum allowable quantities permitted by Tables 5003.1.1(1) and 5003.1.1(2).

903.2.5.1 General. An *automatic sprinkler system* shall be installed in Group H occupancies.

❖ This section requires an automatic sprinkler system in all Group H occupancies. Even though in some instances the hazard associated with the occupancy may be one that is not a fire hazard, an automatic sprinkler system is still required to minimize the potential for fire spreading to the high-hazard use; that is, the sprinklers protect the high-hazard area from fire outside the area. This section does not prohibit the use of an alternative automatic fire-extinguishing system in accordance with Section 904. When a water-based system is not compatible with the hazardous materials involved and thus creates a dangerous condition, an alternative fire-extinguishing system should be used. For example, combustible metals, such as magnesium and titanium, have a serious record of involvement with fire and are typically not compatible with water (see commentary, Chapter 59).

Where control areas are used to regulate the quantity of hazardous material within a building, the building is not considered a Group H occupancy. Unless a building would be required by some other code provision to be protected with sprinklers, control areas can be used to control the allowable quantities of hazardous materials in a building so as to not warrant a Group H classification and its mandatory sprinkler requirements.

903.2.5.2 Group H-5 occupancies. An *automatic sprinkler system* shall be installed throughout buildings containing Group H-5 occupancies. The design of the sprinkler system shall be not less than that required under the *International Building Code* for the occupancy hazard classifications in accordance with Table 903.2.5.2.

Where the design area of the sprinkler system consists of a *corridor* protected by one row of sprinklers, the maximum number of sprinklers required to be calculated is 13.

❖ Group H-5 occupancies are structures that are typically used as semiconductor fabrication facilities and comparable research laboratory facilities that use hazardous production materials (HPM). Many of the materials used in semiconductor fabrication present unique hazards. Several of the materials are toxic, while some are corrosive, water reactive or pyrophoric. Fire protection for these facilities is aimed at preventing incidents from escalating and producing secondary threats beyond a fire, such as the release of corrosive or toxic materials. Because of the nature of Group H-5 facilities, the overall amount of hazardous materials can far exceed the maximum allowable quantities given in Tables 5003.1.1(1) and 5003.1.1(2). Although the amount of HPM is restricted in fabrication areas, the quantities of HPM in storage rooms normally will be in excess of those allowed by the tables. Additional requirements for Group H-5 facilities are located in Chapter 27 and Section 415.11 of the IBC.

This section also specifies the sprinkler design criteria, based on NFPA 13, for various areas in a Group H-5 occupancy (see commentary, Table 903.2.5.2). When the corridor design area sprinkler option is used, a maximum of 13 sprinklers must be calculated. This exceeds the requirements of NFPA 13 for typical egress corridors, which requires a maximum of either five or seven calculated sprinklers, depending on the extent of protected openings in the corridor. The increased number of calculated corridor sprinklers is based on the additional hazard associated with the movement of hazardous materials in corridors of Group H-5 facilities.

TABLE 903.2.5.2
GROUP H-5 SPRINKLER DESIGN CRITERIA

LOCATION	OCCUPANCY HAZARD CLASSIFICATION
Fabrication areas	Ordinary Hazard Group 2
Service corridors	Ordinary Hazard Group 2
Storage rooms without dispensing	Ordinary Hazard Group 2
Storage rooms with dispensing	Extra Hazard Group 2
Corridors	Ordinary Hazard Group 2

❖ Table 903.2.5.2 designates the appropriate occupancy hazard classification for the various areas within a Group H-5 facility. The listed occupancy hazard classifications correspond to specific sprinkler system design criteria in NFPA 13. Ordinary Hazard Group 2 occupancies, for example, require a minimum design density of 0.20 gpm/ft^2 (8.1 L/min/m^2) with a minimum design area of 1,500 square feet (139 m^2). An Extra Hazard Group 2 occupancy, in turn, requires a minimum design density of 0.40 gpm/ft^2 (16.3 L/min/m^2) with a minimum operating area of 2,500 square feet (232 m^2). The increased overall sprinkler demand for Extra Hazard Group 2 occupancies is based on the potential use and handling of substantial amounts of hazardous materials, such as flammable or combustible liquids.

903.2.5.3 Pyroxylin plastics. An *automatic sprinkler system* shall be provided in buildings, or portions thereof, where cellulose nitrate film or pyroxylin plastics are manufactured, stored or handled in quantities exceeding 100 pounds (45 kg).

❖ Cellulose nitrate (pyroxylin) plastics pose unusual and substantial fire risks. Pyroxylin plastics are the most dangerous and unstable of all plastic compounds. The chemically bound oxygen in their structure causes them to burn vigorously in the absence of atmospheric oxygen. Although these compounds produce approximately the same amount of energy as paper when they burn, pyroxylin plastics burn at a rate as much as 15 times greater than comparable common combustibles. When burning, these materials release highly flammable and toxic combustion by-products. Consequently, cellulose nitrate fires are very difficult to control. Although this section specifies a sprinkler threshold quantity of 100 pounds, the need for additional fire protection should be considered for pyroxylin plastics in any amount.

Although the code includes cellulose nitrate "film" in its requirements, cellulose nitrate motion picture film has not been used in the United States since the 1950s. All motion picture film produced since that time is what is typically called "safety film." Consequently, the only application for this section relative to motion picture film is where it may be used in laboratories or storage vaults that are dedicated to film restoration and archives. The protection of these facilities is addressed in Sections 306.2 and 6504.2.

903.2.6 Group I. An *automatic sprinkler system* shall be provided throughout buildings with a Group I *fire area.*

Exceptions:

1. An *automatic sprinkler system* installed in accordance with Section 903.3.1.2 shall be permitted in Group I-1, Condition 1 facilities.
2. An *automatic sprinkler system* is not required where Group I-4 day care facilities are at the *level of exit discharge* and where every room where care is provided has not fewer than one exterior *exit* door.
3. In buildings where Group I-4 day care is provided on levels other than the *level of exit discharge*, an *automatic sprinkler system* in accordance with Section 903.3.1.1 shall be installed on the entire floor where care is provided, all floors between the level of care and the *level of exit discharge* and all floors below the *level of exit discharge* other than areas classified as an open parking garage.

❖ The Group I occupancy is divided into four individual occupancy classifications based on the degree of detention, supervision and physical mobility of the occupants. The evacuation difficulties associated with the building occupants creates the need to incorporate a defend-in-place philosophy of fire protection in occupancies of Group I. For this reason, all such occupancies are to be protected with an automatic sprinkler system. Note that this section is applicable to the entire building that contains a Group I occupancy.

Of particular note, this section encompasses all Group I-3 occupancies where more than five persons are detained (see IBC Section 308.5). There has been considerable controversy concerning the use of automatic sprinklers in detention and correctional occupancies. Special design considerations can be taken into account to alleviate the perceived problems with sprinklers in sleeping units. Sprinklers that reduce the likelihood of vandalism as well as the potential to hang oneself are commercially available. Knowledgeable designers can incorporate certain design features to increase reliability and decrease the likelihood of damage to the system.

Group I-4 occupancies would include either adult-only care facilities or occupancies that provide personal care for more than five children $2^1/_2$ years of age or less on a less-than-24-hour basis. Because the degree of assistance and the time needed for egress cannot be gauged, an automatic sprinkler system is required.

There are three exceptions to this section. Exception 1 permits Group I-1 Condition 1 occupancies to be protected throughout with an NFPA 13R system instead of an NFPA 13 system. This is the lower risk condition for Group I-1 occupancies. Group I-1 Condition 2 occupancies would be required to use an NFPA 13 system.

Exception 2 exempts sprinkler systems completely if the day care center is at the level of exit discharge and every room has at least one exterior exit door. Note that day cares to which this section applies are considered by Section 308.6.1 to be Group E occupancies. An automatic sprinkler system would not be required unless dictated by the requirements in Section 903.2.2 (see the commentary for Section 308.6.1).

Exception 3 is also related to day cares that are still classified as Group I-4 by nature of the location in the building. In that case, an NFPA 13 system would be required on the floor where the center is located and all floors between and including the level of exit discharge. This is less stringent than the main requirement in Section 903.2.6 that requires the entire building to be sprinklered. As defined in Section 202, a Group I-4 child care facility located at the level of exit discharge and accommodating no more than 100 children, with each child care room having an exit directly to the exterior, would be classified as a Group E occupancy.

903.2.7 Group M. An *automatic sprinkler system* shall be provided throughout buildings containing a Group M occupancy where one of the following conditions exists:

1. A Group M *fire area* exceeds 12,000 square feet (1115 m^2).
2. A Group M *fire area* is located more than three stories above grade plane.
3. The combined area of all Group M *fire areas* on all floors, including any mezzanines, exceeds 24,000 square feet (2230 m^2).
4. A Group M occupancy used for the display and sale of upholstered furniture or mattresses exceeds 5,000 square feet (464 m^2).

❖ The sprinkler threshold requirements for Group M occupancies are identical to those of Group F-1 and S-1 occupancies (see commentary, Section 903.2.4). The one exception is that Group M occupancies are provided with an increased area for display of upholstered furniture and mattresses of 5,000 square feet (464 m^2) versus 2,500 square feet (232 m^2) required for Group F-1 and S-1 occupancies. As noted in the commentary for Group F-1 occupancies, upholstered furniture and mattresses have the potential for rapidly growing and high-heat-release fires. This hazard is increased substantially when there are numerous upholstered furniture items or mattresses on display. Such fires put the occupants and emergency responders at risk. This requirement exists regardless of whether the upholstered furniture has passed any fire-retardant tests.

The code does not specifically address what constitutes upholstered furniture, but by simple dictionary definition, upholstered furniture has seats covered with padding, springs, webbing and fabric or leather covers. The code does not make any distinction between levels of padding and upholstery provided on furniture, which was intentional. The proponent's reason statement for code change F135-07/08 stated, in part, "the American Home Furnishings Alliance (AHFA) and the National Home Furnishings Association (NHFA) have examined proposals for exempting vendors of certain constructions of furniture and concluded that such exemptions would be impractical for local code officials to enforce. This is the case because the internal construction of furniture cannot be established reliably without deconstructing it."

Note that, as with Group F-1 occupancies, the criteria is written such that any Group M occupancy, not the fire area, over 5,000 square feet (464 m^2) used for the display and sale of upholstered furniture and mattresses shall be sprinklered throughout. This is regardless of the quantity of upholstered furniture and mattresses actually available for purchase. The reason these requirements were placed into the code and the IBC was based on a large fire in Charleston, South Carolina, that killed nine fire fighters. The facility was a combination furniture showroom and associated storage area. The building did not provide an automatic sprinkler system. See the commentary to Section 903.2.9 for discussion of a formal interpretation dealing with Group S-1 occupancies and applicability to the code and the IBC.

Automatic sprinkler systems for mercantile occupancies are typically designed for an Ordinary Hazard Group 2 classification in accordance with NFPA 13. If high-piled storage (see Section 903.2.7.1) is anticipated, additional levels of fire protection may be required. Also, some merchandise in mercantile occupancies, such as aerosols, rubber tires, paints and certain plastic commodities, even at limited storage heights, are considered beyond the standard Class I through IV commodity classification assumed for mercantile occupancies in NFPA 13 and may warrant additional fire protection.

903.2.7.1 High-piled storage. An *automatic sprinkler system* shall be provided as required in Chapter 32 in all buildings of Group M where storage of merchandise is in high-piled or rack storage arrays.

❖ Regardless of the size of the Group M fire area, an automatic sprinkler system may be required in a high-piled storage area. High-piled storage includes piled, palletized, bin box, shelf or rack storage of Class I through IV commodities to a height greater than 12 feet (3658 mm) and certain high-hazard commodities greater than 6 feet (1829 mm). Chapter 23 provides a package of requirements that may include sprinkler protection, depending on the size of the high-piled storage area. The design standard for the sprinkler protection of high-piled storage is NFPA 13, which addresses the many different types and configurations of high-piled storage.

903.2.8 Group R. An *automatic sprinkler system* installed in accordance with Section 903.3 shall be provided throughout all buildings with a Group R *fire area.*

❖ This section requires sprinklers in any building that contains a Group R fire area. This includes uses such as hotels, apartment buildings, group homes and dormitories. There are no minimum criteria and no exceptions.

It should be noted that buildings constructed under the *International Residential Code*® (IRC®) are not included in Group R and would not, therefore, be subject to these particular requirements. The 2009 IRC requires sprinklers in all new townhouses and in all new one- and two-family dwellings. The IRC is a stand-alone code for the construction of detached one- and two-family dwellings and multiple single-family dwellings (townhouses) not more than three stories in height with a separate means of egress and addresses the requirements for sprinklers in a different way. That is, all of the provisions for new construction that affect those buildings are to be covered exclusively by the IRC and are not to be covered by another International Code. Buildings that do not fall within the scope of the IRC would be classified in Group R and be subject to these provisions. This is stated clearly in IFC Committee Interpretation No. 29-03.

With respect to life safety, the need for a sprinkler system is dependent on the occupants' proximity to the fire and the ability to respond to a fire emergency. Group R occupancies could contain occupants who may require assistance to evacuate, such as infants, those with a disability or who may simply be asleep. While the presence of a sprinkler system cannot always protect occupants in residential buildings who are aware of the ignition and either do not respond or respond inappropriately, it can prevent fatalities outside of the area of fire origin regardless of the occupants' response. Section 903.3.2 requires quick-response or residential sprinklers in all Group R occupancies. Full-scale fire tests have demonstrated the ability of quick-response and residential sprinklers to maintain tenability from flaming fires in the room of fire origin.

Where a different occupancy is located in a building with a residential occupancy, the provisions of this section still apply and the entire building is required to be provided with an automatic sprinkler system regardless of the type of mixed-use condition considered. This is consistent with the mixed-use provisions in IBC Chapter 5. The type of sprinkler system permitted in the different types of Group R occupancies is further clarified in Sections 903.2.8.1 through 903.2.8.4.

903.2.8.1 Group R-3. An *automatic sprinkler system* installed in accordance with Section 903.3.1.3 shall be permitted in Group R-3 occupancies.

❖ Group R-3 occupancies are essentially one- and two-family dwellings that fall outside the scope of the IRC; thus, an NFPA 13D system is appropriate. It should be noted there is no restriction on the use of NFPA 13 or NFPA 13R systems.

903.2.8.2 Group R-4, Condition 1. An *automatic sprinkler system* installed in accordance with Section 903.3.1.3 shall be permitted in Group R-4, Condition 1 occupancies.

❖ Group R-4, Condition 1 is the lesser of the risk categories for Group R-4 occupancies. The occupants are more capable of evacuating without assistance. Therefore, they are treated no differently than a Group R-3 occupancy.

903.2.8.3 Group R-4, Condition 2. An *automatic sprinkler system* installed in accordance with Section 903.3.1.2 shall be permitted in Group R-4, Condition 2 occupancies.

❖ In Group R-4, Condition 2 occupancies, the occupants need more assistance evacuating a building; therefore, an NFPA 13R system is required, which is more robust. It should be noted that there are some concerns with NFPA 13R systems not adequately addressing attic spaces as typically NFPA 13R systems focus primarily on the main habitable portion of the building. Specific compliance conditions are provided in Section 903.3.1.2.3.

903.2.8.4 Care facilities. An *automatic sprinkler system* installed in accordance with Section 903.3.1.3 shall be permitted in care facilities with five or fewer individuals in a single-family dwelling.

❖ This section is similar to Sections 903.2.8.1 and 903.2.8.2 and allows the use of an NFPA 13D system in place of an NFPA 13 or 13R system. In this case, it is specific to smaller care facilities with five or fewer residents. Again, while not technically a single-family dwelling, they are very similar in nature based on the type and actual use of the building.

903.2.9 Group S-1. An *automatic sprinkler system* shall be provided throughout all buildings containing a Group S-1 occupancy where one of the following conditions exists:

1. A Group S-1 *fire area* exceeds 12,000 square feet (1115 m^2).
2. A Group S-1 *fire area* is located more than three stories above grade plane.
3. The combined area of all Group S-1 *fire areas* on all floors, including any mezzanines, exceeds 24,000 square feet (2230 m^2).
4. A Group S-1 *fire area* used for the storage of commercial motor vehicles where the *fire area* exceeds 5,000 square feet (464 m^2).
5. A Group S-1 occupancy used for the storage of upholstered furniture or mattresses exceeds 2,500 square feet (232 m^2).

❖ An automatic sprinkler system must be provided throughout all buildings containing a Group S-1 occupancy fire area where the fire area exceeds 12,000 square feet (1115 m^2); is more than three stories above grade plane; combined, on all floors including mezzanines, exceeds 24,000 square feet (2230 m^2); or is used for the storage of commercial motor vehicles and exceeds 5,000 square feet (464 m^2). See the commentary to the definition of "Commercial motor vehicle" in Chapter 2.

The first three sprinkler threshold requirements for Group S-1 occupancies are identical to those of Groups F-1 and M (see commentary, Sections 903.2.4 and 903.2.7). Group S-1 occupancies, such as warehouses and self-storage buildings, are assumed to be used for the storage of combustible materials. While high-piled storage does not change the Group S-1 occupancy classification, sprinkler protection, if required, may have to comply with the additional requirements of Chapter 32. High-piled stock or rack storage in any occupancy must comply with the code and the IBC. The fifth sprinkler threshold is the same as for Group F-1 except that, in this case, upholstered furniture and mattresses are being stored and not manufactured. Group M has a similar threshold, but is required for larger occupancies containing such items with an area of 5,000 square feet (464 m^2) versus what is required for Group S-1 and F-1 occupancies of 2,500 square feet (232 m^2). See the commentary for Group M and Group F-1 definitions for more discussion on this issue. Again, it is important to note that the threshold is based on the square footage of the occupancy and not on the size of the fire area. A formal interpretation (IFC Interpretation 20-14) has been issued on this section. The formal interpretation addresses self-storage warehouses specifically and whether such a facility between 2,500 and 12,000 square feet would require an automatic sprinkler system. This is based on the fact that upholstered furniture may be stored in such units. The response provided noted that a sprinkler system would be required given that the requirements focus on the square footage of the occupancy and are not based on fire area or the amount of upholstered furniture or mattresses present.

903.2.9.1 Repair garages. An *automatic sprinkler system* shall be provided throughout all buildings used as repair garages in accordance with Section 406.8 of the *International Building Code*, as shown:

1. Buildings having two or more stories above grade plane, including *basements*, with a *fire area* containing a repair garage exceeding 10,000 square feet (929 m^2).
2. Buildings not more than one story above grade plane, with a *fire area* containing a repair garage exceeding 12,000 square feet (1115 m^2).
3. Buildings with repair garages servicing vehicles parked in *basements*.
4. A Group S-1 *fire area* used for the repair of commercial motor vehicles where the *fire area* exceeds 5,000 square feet (464 m^2).

❖ Automatic sprinklers may be required in repair garages, depending on the quantity of combustibles present, their location and floor area. In addition, any Group S-1 fire area intended for the repair of commercial motor vehicles that exceeds 5,000 square feet (464 m^2) would require sprinklers. This is the same criteria as Group S-1 occupancies and Group S-2 enclosed parking garages storing commercial motor vehicles. Repair garages may contain significant quantities of flammable liquids and other combustible materials. These occupancies are typically considered Ordinary Hazard Group 2 occupancies as defined in NFPA 13. Portions of repair garages used for parts cleaning using flammable or combustible liquids may require automatic sprinkler protection. If quantities of hazardous materials exceed the limitations in Section 307 for maximum allowable quantities per control area, the repair garage would be reclassified as a Group H occupancy. Note that the term "Commercial motor vehicles" is specifically defined in Chapter 2.

903.2.9.2 Bulk storage of tires. Buildings and structures where the area for the storage of tires exceeds 20,000 cubic feet (566 m^3) shall be equipped throughout with an *automatic sprinkler system* in accordance with Section 903.3.1.1.

❖ This section specifies when an automatic sprinkler system is required for the bulk storage of tires based on the volume of the storage area as opposed to a specific number of tires. Even in fully sprinklered buildings, tire fires pose significant problems to fire departments. Tire fires produce thick smoke and are difficult to extinguish by sprinklers alone. NFPA 13 contains specific fire protection requirements for the storage of rubber tires.

Whether the volume of tires is divided into different fire areas or not is irrelevant to the application of this section. If the total for all areas where tires are stored is great enough that the resultant storage volume exceeds 20,000 cubic feet (566 m^3), the building must be sprinklered throughout. See the commentary to the Section 202 definition of "Tires, bulk storage of" for further information.

903.2.10 Group S-2 enclosed parking garages. An *automatic sprinkler system* shall be provided throughout buildings classified as enclosed parking garages in accordance with Section 406.6 of the *International Building Code* where either of the following conditions exists:

1. Where the *fire area* of the enclosed parking garage exceeds 12,000 square feet (1115 m^2).
2. Where the enclosed parking garage is located beneath other groups.

Exception: Enclosed parking garages located beneath Group R-3 occupancies.

❖ Fire records have shown that fires in parking structures typically fully involve only a single automobile with minor damage to adjacent vehicles. An enclosed parking garage, however, does not allow the dissipation of smoke and hot gases as readily as an open parking structure, which is also considered a Group S-2 occupancy. If the enclosed parking garage has a fire area greater than 12,000 square feet (1115 m^2) or is located beneath another occupancy group, the enclosed parking garage must be protected with an automatic sprinkler system. This requirement that the enclosed parking garage located beneath other occupancy groups is required to be sprinklered is based on the potential for a fire to develop undetected, which would endanger the occupants of the other occupancy. The 12,000-square-foot (1115 m^2) threshold is similar to other occupancies such as Groups M and S-1.

It should be noted that while open parking garages are considered a Group S-2 occupancy, they are not required by the provisions of this section to be equipped with an automatic sprinkler system.

The exception exempts enclosed garages in buildings where the garages are located below a Group R-3 occupancy. The exception is essentially moot since the code requires all buildings with a Group R occupancy to be sprinklered throughout. Because the entire building with the residential occupancy is required to be sprinklered according to Section 903.2.8, the garage would be sprinklered as well. It should be noted that if the Group R-3 occupancy was protected with an NFPA 13D system, the enclosed parking garage would not require sprinklers.

903.2.10.1 Commercial parking garages. An *automatic sprinkler system* shall be provided throughout buildings used for storage of commercial motor vehicles where the *fire area* exceeds 5,000 square feet (464 m^2).

❖ Because of the larger-sized vehicles involved in commercial parking structures, such as those housing commercial motor vehicles as defined in Section 202, a more stringent sprinkler threshold is required. Bus garages may also be located adjacent to passenger terminals (Group A-3) that have a substantial occupant load. Commercial parking requires only a single vehicle in order to be classified as commercial parking.

The criterion for sprinkler protection is based on the size of the fire area and not the size of the commercial parking. If the commercial parking involves only 1,000 square feet (93 m^2) but the fire area exceeds 5,000 square feet (464 m^2), sprinkler protection is required.

903.2.11 Specific buildings areas and hazards. In all occupancies other than Group U, an *automatic sprinkler system* shall be installed for building design or hazards in the locations set forth in Sections 903.2.11.1 through 903.2.11.6.

❖ Sections 903.2.11.1 through 903.2.11.2 specify certain conditions under which an automatic sprinkler system is required, even in otherwise nonsprinklered buildings. As indicated, the listed conditions in the noted sections are applicable to all occupancies except Group U. Most structures that qualify as Group U do not typically have the type of conditions stipulated in Sections 903.2.11.1 through 903.2.11.1.3.

903.2.11.1 Stories without openings. An *automatic sprinkler system* shall be installed throughout all *stories*, including *basements*, of all buildings where the floor area exceeds 1,500 square feet (139 m^2) and where the story does not comply with the following criteria for exterior wall openings:

1. Openings below grade that lead directly to ground level by an exterior *stairway* complying with Section 1011 or an outside ramp complying with Section 1012. Openings shall be located in each 50 linear feet (15 240 mm), or fraction thereof, of *exterior wall* in the story on not fewer than one side. The required openings shall be distributed such that the lineal distance between adjacent openings does not exceed 50 feet (15 240 mm).
2. Openings entirely above the adjoining ground level totaling not less than 20 square feet (1.86 m^2) in each 50 linear feet (15 240 mm), or fraction thereof, of *exterior wall* in the story on not fewer than one side. The required openings shall be distributed such that the lineal distance between adjacent openings does not exceed 50 feet (15 240 mm). The height of the bottom of the clear opening shall not exceed 44 inches (1118 mm) measured from the floor.

❖ Because of both the lack of openings in exterior walls for access by the fire department for fire fighting and rescue and the problems associated with venting the products of combustion during fire suppression operations, all stories, including any basements of buildings that do not have adequate openings as defined in this section, must be equipped with an automatic sprinkler system. This section applies to stories without sufficient exterior openings where the floor area exceeds 1,500 square feet (139 m^2) and where the building is not otherwise required to be fully sprinklered. The requirement for an automatic sprinkler system in this section applies only to the affected area and does not mandate sprinkler protection throughout the entire building.

Stories without openings, as defined in this section, are stories that do not have at least 20 square feet (1.9 m^2) of opening leading directly to ground level in each 50 lineal feet (15 240 mm), or fraction thereof, on at least one side. Since exterior doors will provide openings of 20 square feet (1.9 m^2), or slightly less in some occupancies, exterior stairways and ramps in each 50 lineal feet (15 240 mm) are considered acceptable.

This section specifically states that the required openings be distributed such that the lineal distance between adjacent openings does not exceed 50 feet (15 240 mm). If the openings in the exterior wall are located without regard to the location of the adjacent openings, it is possible that segments of the exterior wall will not have the required access to the interior of the building for fire-fighting purposes. Any arrangement of required stairways, ramps or openings that results in a portion of the wall 50 feet (15 240 mm) or more in length with no openings to the exterior does not meet the intent of the code that access be provided in each 50 lineal feet (15 240 mm) (see Commentary Figure 903.2.11.1).

There is a further restriction on openings that are entirely above grade. More specifically, to support fire-fighting operations, the openings need to be accessible and usable. Therefore, Item 2 specifies that the maximum sill height be 44 inches (1118 mm) above the floor. This height is consistent with the height provided for emergency escape and rescue windows in Section 1030.3.

One application of this section has been addressed and is in the 2015 edition of *International Code Interpretations*. It addresses automotive service shops that have below-grade service areas where employees perform oil changes and other minor maintenance services. The below-grade areas are typically open to the grade-level service bays via openings providing access to the underside of the vehicles without requiring the vehicle to be lifted into the air. Inasmuch as the below-grade space has no openings directly to the exterior, the question was asked if it would be regulated as a windowless story and thus be required to be equipped with an automatic fire suppression system in accordance with Section 903.2.11.1.

The answer to that question is no. Because of the openness between the adjacent service levels, the below-grade area would be more appropriately regulated similar to a mezzanine rather than a story. A mezzanine is not regulated as a separate story but rather as part of the same story that it serves. Therefore, if the below-grade service level is in compliance with the applicable provisions of Section 505, the windowless story provisions of Section 903.2.11.1 would be evaluated based on the exterior wall openings of the main level and not the service mezzanine below. The direct interconnections between the two adjacent floor levels by multiple service openings provide access to the lower service area for fire-fighting and rescue operations. As such, it would not be regulated as a windowless story.

The requirement to sprinkler the basement is independent of mixed-use conditions. Whether the basement is separated or nonseparated is irrelevant to the need for sprinkler protection, nor does the requirement to provide sprinklers in the basement imply that sprinklers must be provided elsewhere. This requirement is applicable to the basement or any story without openings, irrespective of other code provisions.

Also, these provisions are not based on the size of a fire area but rather on the size of the basement. Thus, subdividing the basement into multiple fire areas would have no effect on the requirement. However, one benefit of the multiple fire areas could be that each fire area could have a separate limited area sprinkler system with less than 20 sprinklers.

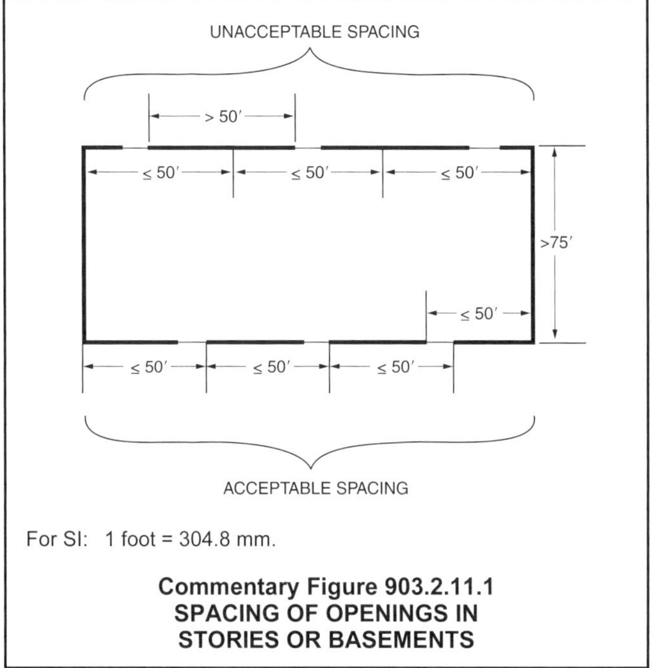

For SI: 1 foot = 304.8 mm.

Commentary Figure 903.2.11.1 SPACING OF OPENINGS IN STORIES OR BASEMENTS

903.2.11.1.1 Opening dimensions and access. Openings shall have a minimum dimension of not less than 30 inches (762 mm). *Access* to such openings shall be provided for the fire department from the exterior and shall not be obstructed in a manner such that fire fighting or rescue cannot be accomplished from the exterior.

❖ To qualify, an opening must not be less than 30 inches (762 mm) in least dimension and must be accessible to the fire department from the exterior. The minimum opening dimension gives fire department personnel access to the interior of the story or basement for fire-fighting and rescue operations and provides openings that are large enough to vent the products of combustion.

903.2.11.1.2 Openings on one side only. Where openings in a story are provided on only one side and the opposite wall of such story is more than 75 feet (22 860 mm) from such openings, the story shall be equipped throughout with an *approved automatic sprinkler system,* or openings shall be provided on not fewer than two sides of the story.

❖ If openings are provided on only one side, an automatic sprinkler system would still be required if the opposite wall of the story is more than 75 feet (22 860 mm) from existing openings. An alternative to providing the automatic sprinkler system would be to design openings on at least two sides of the exterior of the building. As long as the story being considered is not a basement, the openings on two sides can be greater than 75 feet (22 860 mm) from any portion of the floor. In basements, if any portion is more than 75 feet (22 860 mm) from the openings, the entire basement must be equipped with an automatic sprinkler system, as indicated in Section 903.2.11.1.3. Providing openings on more than one wall allows cross ventilation to vent the products of combustion [see Commentary Figures 903.2.11.1.2(1–4)].

903.2.11.1.3 Basements. Where any portion of a *basement* is located more than 75 feet (22 860 mm) from openings required by Section 903.2.11.1, or where walls, partitions or other obstructions are installed that restrict the application of water from hose streams, the *basement* shall be equipped throughout with an *approved automatic sprinkler system.*

❖ The 75-foot (22 860 mm) distance is intended to be measured in the line of travel—not in a straight line perpendicular to the wall. Where obstructions, such as walls or other partitions, are present in a basement, the walls and partitions enclosing any room or space must have openings that provide an equivalent degree of fire department access to that provided by the openings prescribed in Section 903.2.11.1 for exterior walls. When obstructions such as walls or partitions are installed in the basement, the ability to apply hose streams through these openings and reach the basement area is reduced or eliminated. The configuration and clear-opening requirements become useless when an interior wall or other obstruction is placed inside the basement. In that case, it is reasonable to require automatic fire sprinklers to provide adequate protection in the basement. If an equivalent degree of fire department access to all portions of the floor area is not provided, the basement would require an automatic sprinkler system.

903.2.11.2 Rubbish and linen chutes. An *automatic sprinkler system* shall be installed at the top of rubbish and linen chutes and in their terminal rooms. Chutes shall have additional sprinkler heads installed at alternate floors and at the lowest intake. Where a rubbish chute extends through a building more than one floor below the lowest intake, the extension shall have sprinklers installed that are recessed from the drop area of the chute and protected from freezing in accordance with Section 903.3.1.1. Such sprinklers shall be installed at alternate floors, beginning with the second level below the last intake and ending with the floor above the discharge. *Access* to sprinklers in chutes shall be provided for servicing.

❖ Gravity rubbish (waste) and linen chutes can pose a significant hazard to building occupants if they are not properly installed and protected. Generally, these systems are installed in high-occupancy buildings where the occupants will be sleeping or are incapable of self-rescue, such as in Group I, R-1 and R-2 occupancies. For occupant convenience, openings to the chutes are commonly provided in areas accessible to the public and, in older buildings, the chute opening may be located in an exit access corridor. In compari-

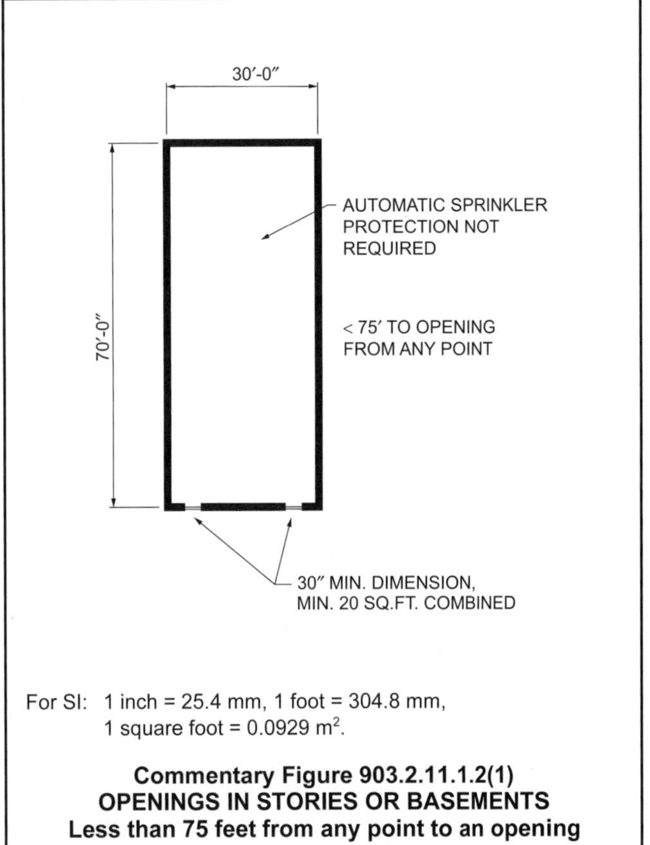

For SI: 1 inch = 25.4 mm, 1 foot = 304.8 mm,
1 square foot = 0.0929 m^2.

Commentary Figure 903.2.11.1.2(1)
OPENINGS IN STORIES OR BASEMENTS
Less than 75 feet from any point to an opening

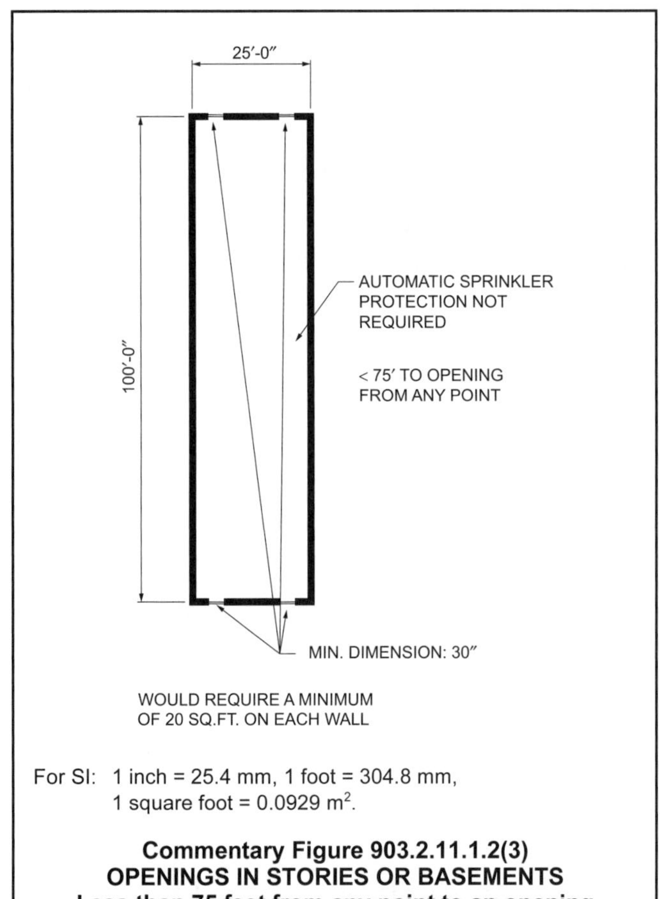

For SI: 1 inch = 25.4 mm, 1 foot = 304.8 mm,
1 square foot = 0.0929 m^2.

Commentary Figure 903.2.11.1.2(3)
OPENINGS IN STORIES OR BASEMENTS
Less than 75 feet from any point to an opening

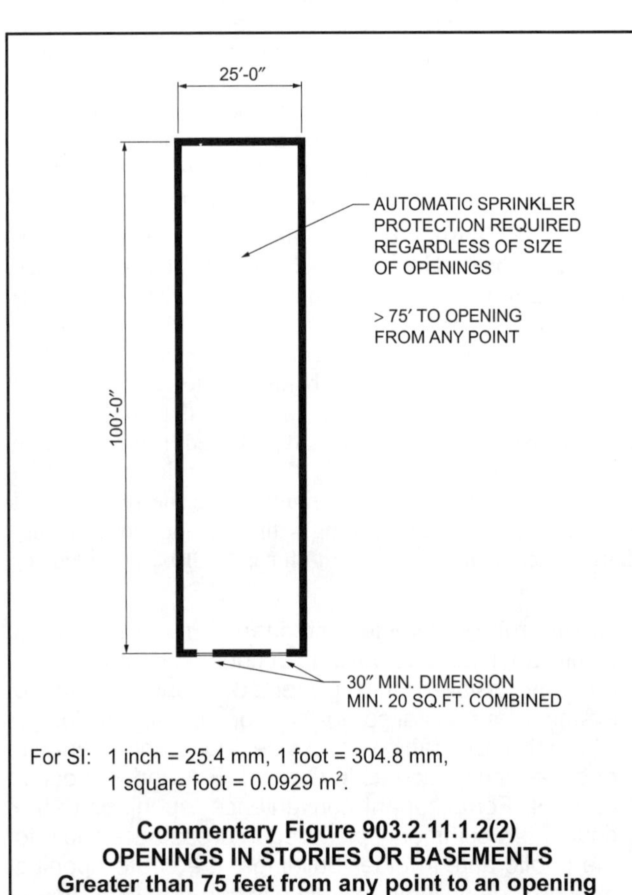

For SI: 1 inch = 25.4 mm, 1 foot = 304.8 mm,
1 square foot = 0.0929 m^2.

Commentary Figure 903.2.11.1.2(2)
OPENINGS IN STORIES OR BASEMENTS
Greater than 75 feet from any point to an opening

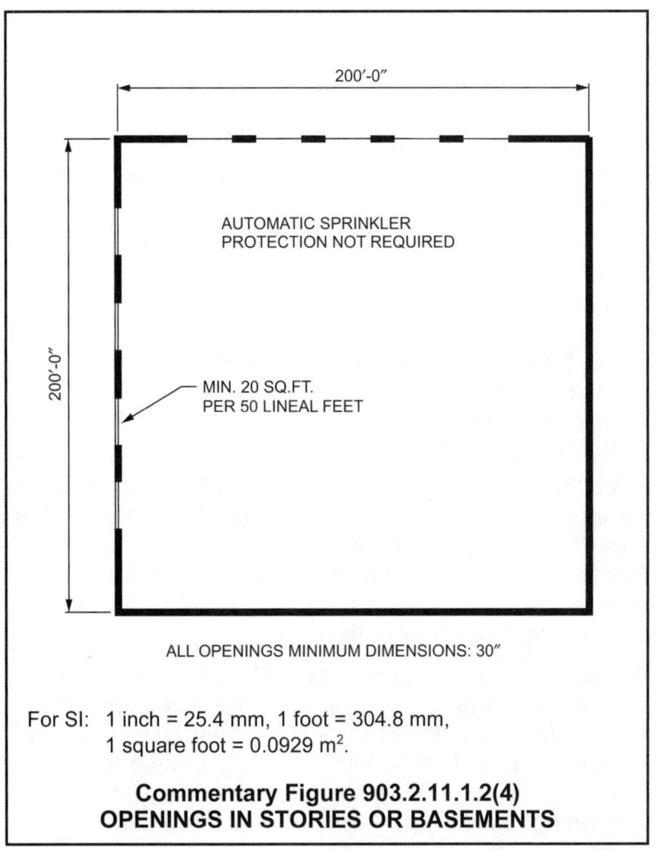

For SI: 1 inch = 25.4 mm, 1 foot = 304.8 mm,
1 square foot = 0.0929 m^2.

Commentary Figure 903.2.11.1.2(4)
OPENINGS IN STORIES OR BASEMENTS

son to other building shafts, gravity rubbish and linen chutes always contain fuel. As bags of waste debris or linen fall through the chute, they can deposit fluids such as waste cooking oil, which adheres to the shaft surface. This waste material and other debris provide fuel that can support and accelerate vertical fire spread. The greatest accumulation of fuel will be in the termination room; however, a significant amount of fuel that covers the interior surface area of the chute will be found in the sections of chutes closest to the collection or termination room. Therefore, it is important that the automatic sprinklers be properly placed and protected so they are available in the event of a fire in the termination room and to protect waste compaction equipment where such equipment is installed.

Installation of gravity chutes for rubbish or linen requires compliance with the code, the IBC and Chapter 6 of NFPA 82. Under the code, permanent rubbish and linen chutes are constructed inside of a fire-resistance-rated shaft assembly with a minimum 1-hour fire-resistance rating in buildings less than four stories in height; in buildings four or more stories in height, the fire-resistance rating is increased to 2 hours by Section 713.4. The design of the shaft system and its openings must also comply with the requirements in Sections 713.11 and 713.13, which require the termination room receiving the discharged material to be separated from the building by a fire-resistance rating equivalent to that of the shaft that it serves.

Section 713.13.6 requires the installation of an automatic sprinkler system in rubbish and linen chutes to comply with the requirements of Section 903.2.11.2. Section 903.2.11.2 correlates with the requirements in Chapter 22 of NFPA 13. Chapter 22 of NFPA 13 contains the special occupancy requirements for all buildings, including gravity waste and linen chutes. The provisions align the code and IBC requirements with those in NFPA 82 and NFPA 13.

A critical term in this section is "extension." The word was selected to address chutes installed in buildings of pedestal construction or other designs in which the fire-resistant construction shaft and chute pass through a less hazardous occupancy, such as a Group S-2 parking garage, or other floors that do not have access to the shaft. In these areas, chute openings are generally not provided. As a result, this section now contains a specific provision that may impose a requirement for sprinklers in the portion of the chute that serves as an extension beyond the last intake and the termination room or discharge area.

Because objects will be falling through the chute, the code requires the chute sprinklers to be recessed and protected from impact. Sprinklers are not required at every story housing a chute. The code requires automatic sprinklers at the top of the chute and at its termination. In addition, sprinkler heads are required at alternate floors within the chute, with a head being installed at the floor level with the lowest intake point into the chute. Previously, these additional sprinkler heads were only required where the shaft extended through three or more floors. These revisions, plus the previously discussed requirements for extensions, may result in additional sprinkler heads within some shafts as compared to the previous requirements.

Sprinklers in chutes that are in locations subject to freezing require freeze protection in accordance with the requirements of Section 903.3.1.1 and, therefore, the NFPA 13 standard. This can be accomplished using a dry-pendant sprinkler or constructing a dry-pipe sprinkler system.

903.2.11.3 Buildings 55 feet or more in height. An *automatic sprinkler system* shall be installed throughout buildings that have one or more stories with an *occupant load* of 30 or more located 55 feet (16 764 mm) or more above the lowest level of fire department vehicle access, measured to the finished floor.

Exceptions:

1. Open parking structures.
2. Occupancies in Group F-2.

❖ Because of the difficulties associated with manual suppression of a fire in mid-rise buildings in excess of 55 feet (16 764 mm) above the lowest level of fire department vehicle access, an automatic sprinkler system is required throughout the building, regardless of occupancy. Buildings that qualify for a sprinkler system under this section are not necessarily high-rise buildings as defined in Section 202 and are focused also on those with occupants located on the upper floors. These provisions apply only to buildings with occupied floors having an occupant load of 30 or more located on stories 55 feet or greater from fire department vehicle access. The 55 feet is measured to the finished floor (see Commentary Figure 903.2.11.3).

The listed exceptions are occupancies that, based on height only, do not require an automatic sprinkler system. Open parking structures are also exempt from the high-rise provisions of Section 403. Although an automatic sprinkler system is not required in open parking structures, a sprinkler system may still be needed, depending on the building construction type and the area and number of parking tiers (see Table 406.3.5 of the IBC).

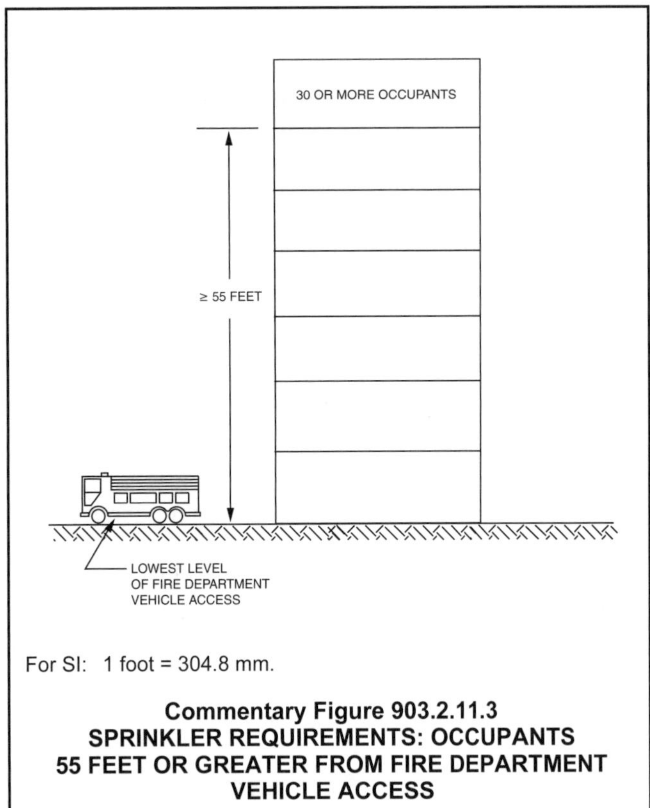

For SI: 1 foot = 304.8 mm.

Commentary Figure 903.2.11.3
SPRINKLER REQUIREMENTS: OCCUPANTS 55 FEET OR GREATER FROM FIRE DEPARTMENT VEHICLE ACCESS

903.2.11.4 Ducts conveying hazardous exhausts. Where required by the *International Mechanical Code*, automatic sprinklers shall be provided in ducts conveying hazardous exhaust or flammable or combustible materials.

Exception: Ducts where the largest cross-sectional diameter of the duct is less than 10 inches (254 mm).

❖ Section 510 of the IMC addresses the requirements for hazardous exhaust systems. To protect against the spread of fire within a hazardous exhaust system and to prevent a duct fire from involving the building, an automatic sprinkler system must be installed to protect the exhaust duct system. Where materials conveyed in the ducts are not compatible with water, alternative extinguishing agents should be used. The fire suppression requirement is intended to apply to exhaust systems having an actual fire hazard. An automatic sprinkler system in the duct would be of little value for an exhaust system that conveys only nonflammable or noncombustible materials, fumes, vapors or gases.

The exception recognizes the reduced hazard associated with smaller ducts and the impracticality of installing sprinkler protection. Another exception in the IMC indicates that laboratory hoods that meet specific provisions of the IMC are not required to be suppressed. Because the IMC is more specific in this regard, it should be consulted for the proper application of the exception.

903.2.11.5 Commercial cooking operations. An *automatic sprinkler system* shall be installed in commercial kitchen exhaust hood and duct systems where an *automatic sprinkler system* is used to comply with Section 904.

❖ An automatic suppression system is required for commercial kitchen exhaust hood and duct systems where required by Section 609 or by the IMC to have a Type I hood. Type I hoods are required for commercial cooking equipment that produces grease-laden vapors or smoke. Section 904.12 recognizes that alternative extinguishing systems other than an automatic sprinkler system may be used. Where an automatic sprinkler system is used for commercial cooking operations, it must comply with the requirements identified in Section 904.12.4.

903.2.11.6 Other required suppression systems. In addition to the requirements of Section 903.2, the provisions indicated in Table 903.2.11.6 require the installation of a fire suppression system for certain buildings and areas.

❖ In addition to Section 903.2, requirements for automatic fire suppression systems are also found elsewhere in the code as indicated in Table 903.2.11.6.

TABLE 903.2.11.6. See page 9-27.

❖ Table 903.2.11.6 identifies other sections of the code that require an automatic fire suppression system based on the specific occupancy or use because of the unique hazards of such use or occupancy. The table does not identify the various sections of the code that contain design alternatives based on the use of an automatic fire suppression system, typically an automatic sprinkler system.

903.2.12 During construction. *Automatic sprinkler systems* required during construction, *alteration* and demolition operations shall be provided in accordance with Section 3314.

❖ Chapter 33 of the code and Chapter 33 of the IBC address fire safety requirements during construction, alteration or demolition work. Working sprinkler systems should remain operative at all times unless it is absolutely necessary to shut down the system because of the proposed work. All sprinkler system impairments should be rectified as quickly as possible unless specific prior approval has been obtained from the fire code official. Buildings with a required sprinkler system should not be occupied unless the sprinkler system has been installed and tested consistent with Section 901.5. If the system must be placed out of service, the requirements of Section 901.7 are necessary to address the temporary impairment to the fire protection system.

903.3 Installation requirements. *Automatic sprinkler systems* shall be designed and installed in accordance with Sections 903.3.1 through 903.3.8.

❖ Specific design, installation and testing criteria are given for automatic sprinkler systems in the sections and subsections that follow, as well as an indication of the applicability of a nationally recognized standard in the area. The information required to complete a thorough review of an automatic sprinkler system is listed in Commentary Figure 903.3.

TABLE 903.2.11.6
ADDITIONAL REQUIRED FIRE SUPPRESSION SYSTEMS

SECTION	SUBJECT
914.2.1	Covered and open mall buildings
914.3.1	High-rise buildings
914.4.1	Atriums
914.5.1	Underground structures
914.6.1	Stages
914.7.1	Special amusement buildings
914.8.2	Airport traffic control towers
914.8.3, 914.8.6	Aircraft hangars
914.9	Flammable finishes
914.10	Drying rooms
914.11.1	Ambulatory care facilities
1029.6.2.3	Smoke-protected assembly seating
1103.5.1	Existing Group A occupancies
1103.5.2	Pyroxylin plastic storage in existing buildings
1103.5.3	Existing Group I-2 occupancies
1103.5.4	Existing Group I-2, Condition 2 occupancies
1103.5.4	Pyroxylin plastics
2108.2	Dry cleaning plants
2108.3	Dry cleaning machines
2309.3.1.5.2	Hydrogen motor fuel-dispensing area canopies
2404.2	Spray finishing in Group A, E, I or R
2404.4	Spray booths and spray rooms
2405.2	Dip-tank rooms in Group A, I or R
2405.4.1	Dip tanks
2405.9.4	Hardening and tempering tanks
2703.10	HPM facilities
2703.10.1.1	HPM work station exhaust
2703.10.2	HPM gas cabinets and exhausted enclosures
2703.10.3	HPM exit access corridor
2703.10.4	HPM exhaust ducts
2703.10.4.1	HPM noncombustible ducts
2703.10.4.2	HPM combustible ducts
2807.3	Lumber production conveyor enclosures
2808.7	Recycling facility conveyor enclosures
3006.1	Class A and B ovens
3006.2	Class C and D ovens
Table 3206.2	Storage fire protection
3206.4	Storage
3704.5	Storage of more than 1,000 cubic feet of loose combustible fibers
5003.8.4.1	Gas rooms
5003.8.5.3	Exhausted enclosures
5004.5	Indoor storage of hazardous materials

(continued)

TABLE 903.2.11.6—continued
ADDITIONAL REQUIRED FIRE SUPPRESSION SYSTEMS

SECTION	SUBJECT
5005.1.8	Indoor dispensing of hazardous materials
5104.4.1	Aerosol product warehouses
5106.3.2	Aerosol display and merchandising areas
5306.2.1	Exterior medical gas storage room
5306.2.2	Interior medical gas storage room
5306.2.3	Medical gas storage cabinet
5606.5.2.1	Storage of smokeless propellant
5606.5.2.3	Storage of small arms primers
5704.3.7.5.1	Flammable and combustible liquid storage rooms
5704.3.8.4	Flammable and combustible liquid storage warehouses
5705.3.7.3	Flammable and combustible liquid Group H-2 or H-3 areas
6004.1.2	Gas cabinets for highly toxic and toxic gas
6004.1.3	Exhausted enclosures for highly toxic and toxic gas
6004.2.2.6	Gas rooms for highly toxic and toxic gas
6004.3.3	Outdoor storage for highly toxic and toxic gas
6504.1.1	Pyroxylin plastic storage cabinets
6504.1.3	Pyroxylin plastic storage vaults
6504.2	Pyroxylin plastic storage and manufacturing

For SI: 1 cubic foot = 0.023 m^3.

903.3.1 Standards. Sprinkler systems shall be designed and installed in accordance with Section 903.3.1.1, unless otherwise permitted by Sections 903.3.1.2 and 903.3.1.3 and other chapters of this code, as applicable.

❖ Automatic sprinkler systems are to be installed to comply with the code and NFPA 13, 13R or 13D. As provided for in Section 102.4, where differences occur between the code and NFPA 13, 13R or 13D, the code applies. The fire code official also has the authority to approve the type of sprinkler system to be installed. See Commentary Figure 903.3.1 for typical design parameters for each type of sprinkler system.

This section also provides a pointer to other sections of the code that might provide more specific or detailed sprinkler requirements such as those found in Chapter 4 of the IBC.

903.3.1.1 NFPA 13 sprinkler systems. Where the provisions of this code require that a building or portion thereof be equipped throughout with an *automatic sprinkler system* in accordance with this section, sprinklers shall be installed throughout in accordance with NFPA 13 except as provided in Sections 903.3.1.1.1 and 903.3.1.1.2.

❖ NFPA 13 contains the minimum requirements for the design and installation of automatic water sprinkler systems and exposure protection sprinkler systems. The requirements contained in the standard include the character and adequacy of the water supply and the selection of sprinklers, piping, valves and all of

1. Information required on shop drawings includes:

— Name of owner and occupant
— Location, including street address
— Point of compass
— Graphic indication of scale
— Ceiling construction
— Full-height cross section
— Location of fire walls
— Location of partitions
— Occupancy of each area or room
— Location and size of blind spaces and closets
— Any questionable small enclosures in which no sprinklers are to be installed
— Size of city main in street, pressure and whether dead end or circulation and, if dead end, direction and distance to nearest circulating main, city main test results
— Other source of water supply, with pressure or elevation
— Make, type and orifice size of sprinkler
— Temperature rating and location of high-temperature sprinklers
— Limitations on extended coverage sprinklers or other special sprinkler types
— Number of sprinklers on each riser and on each system by floors and total area by each system on each floor
— Make, type, model and size of alarm or dry-pipe valve
— Make, type, model and size of preaction or deluge valve
— Type and location of alarm bells
— Backflow prevention method and details
— Total number of sprinklers on each dry-pipe system or preaction deluge system
— Approximate capacity in gallons or each dry-pipe system
— Setting for pressure-reducing valves
— Pipe size, type, and schedule of wall thickness
— Cutting lengths of pipe (or center-to-center dimensions)
— Type of fittings, riser nipples and size, and all welds and bends
— Type and location of hangers, inserts and sleeves
— Calculations of loads and details for sway bracing
— All control valves, checks, drain pipes, flushing, and test pipes
— Size and location of standpipe risers and hose outlets
— Small hand hose equipment
— Underground pipe size, length, location, weight, material, point of connection to city main; the type of valves, meters and valve pits; and the depth that top of the pipe is laid below grade
— Size and location of hydrants along with hose-houses
— Size and location of fire department connections
— When the equipment is to be installed as an addition to an old group of sprinklers without additional feed from the yard system, enough of the old system shall be indicated on the plans to show the total number of sprinklers to be supplied and to make all connections clear
— Information to be provided on the hydraulic nameplate
— Name, address and phone number of contractor and sprinkler designer
— Hydraulic reference points shall be shown by a number and/or letter designation and shall correspond with comparable reference points shown on the hydraulic calculation sheets
— System design criteria showing the minimum rate of water application (density), the design area of water application and the water required for hose streams both inside and outside
— Actual calculated requirements showing the total quantity of water and the pressure required at a common reference point for each system
— Elevation data showing elevations of sprinklers, junction points and supply or reference points
— Protected wall openings if room design method is used

2. Information required on calculations includes:

— Location
— Name of owner and occupant
— Building identification
— Description of hazard
— Name and address of contractor and designer
— Name of approving agency

3. System design requirements include:

— Design area of water application
— Minimum rate of water application (density)
— Area of sprinkler coverage
— Hazard or commodity classification
— Building height
— Storage height
— Storage method
— Total water requirements, as calculated, including allowance for hose demand water supply information and allowance for in-rack sprinklers
— Location and elevation static and residual test gauge with relation to the riser reference point
— Size and location of hydrants used for flow test data
— Flow location
— Static pressure, psi
— Residual pressure, psi
— Flow, gpm
— Date
— Time
— Test conducted by whom
— Sketch to accompany gridded system calculations to indicate flow quantities and directions for lines with sprinklers operated in the remote area

4. Additional information necessary for complete review includes:

— Sprinkler description and discharge constant (K-value)
— Hydraulic reference points
— Flow, gpm
— Pipe diameter (actual internal diameter)
— Pipe length
— Equivalent pipe length for fittings and components
— Friction loss in psi per foot of pipe
— Total friction loss between reference points
— Elevation difference between reference points
— Required pressure in psi at each reference point
— Velocity pressures and normal pressure if included in calculations
— Notes to indicate starting points, reference to other sheets or clarification of data
— Information on antifreeze solution (type and quantity)
— Water treatment system information including reason for treatment and program details

5. Included with the submittal must be a graph sheet showing water supply curves and system requirements including:

— Hose demand plotted on semilogarithmic graph paper so as to present a graphic summary of the complete hydraulic calculations
— Sprinkler system demand including in-rack sprinklers (if applicable)

Commentary Figure 903.3
SAMPLE SPRINKLER SYSTEM DRAWING AND DATA SUBMITTALS

the materials and accessories. The standard does not include requirements for installation of private fire service mains and their appurtenances, installation of fire pumps, or construction and installation of gravity and pressure tanks and towers.

NFPA 13 defines seven classifications or types of water sprinkler systems: wet-pipe [see Commentary Figure 903.3.1.1], dry pipe, preaction or deluge, combined dry pipe and preaction, antifreeze systems, sprinkler systems that are designed for a special purpose and outside sprinklers for exposure protection. While numerous variables must be considered in selecting the proper type of sprinkler system the wet-pipe sprinkler system is recognized as the most effective and efficient. The wet-pipe system is also the most reliable type of sprinkler system because water under pressure is available at the sprinkler. Therefore, wet-pipe sprinkler systems are recommended wherever possible.

The extent of coverage and distribution of sprinklers is based on the NFPA 13 standard. Numerous conditions exist in the standard where sprinklers are specifically required and also where they may or may not be located. Once it is determined that the sprinkler system is to be in accordance with NFPA 13, that standard must be reviewed for installation details. For example, exterior spaces such as combustible canopies are required to be equipped with sprinklers according to Section 8.15.7 of NFPA 13 where the canopy extends for a distance of 4 feet (1219 mm) or more. A 3-foot (914 mm) combustible canopy would not require sprinklers nor would a 6-foot (1829 mm) canopy constructed of noncombustible materials, provided there is no combustible storage under the canopy.

Because installation is required to be in accordance with NFPA 13, if the standard allows for the omission of sprinklers in any location, then the building is still considered as sprinklered throughout. For example, Section 8.15.8.1.1 of NFPA 13 allows sprinklers to be omitted from bathrooms in dwelling units in motels and hotels. If sprinklers are not provided in the bathrooms because of the conditions stipulated in NFPA 13, the building would still be considered as sprinklered throughout in accordance with the code, NFPA 13 and the IBC.

Exceptions for the use of NFPA 13R and 13D systems are addressed throughout the code when exceptions based on the use of sprinklers are provided. More specifically, if the use of these other standards is appropriate, it will be noted within the exception. For a building to be considered "equipped throughout" with an NFPA 13 sprinkler system, complete protection must be provided in accordance with the referenced standard, subject to the exempt locations indicated in Section 903.3.1.1.1. See Commentary Figure 904.2.1 for examples of requirements modified through the use of sprinkler systems.

903.3.1.1.1 Exempt locations. Automatic sprinklers shall not be required in the following rooms or areas where such rooms or areas are protected with an *approved* automatic fire detection system in accordance with Section 907.2 that will respond to visible or invisible particles of combustion. Sprinklers shall not be omitted from a room merely because it is damp, of fire-resistance-rated construction or contains electrical equipment.

1. A room where the application of water, or flame and water, constitutes a serious life or fire hazard.
2. A room or space where sprinklers are considered undesirable because of the nature of the contents, where *approved* by the *fire code official.*
3. Generator and transformer rooms separated from the remainder of the building by walls and floor/ceiling or roof/ceiling assemblies having a *fire-resistance rating* of not less than 2 hours.
4. Rooms or areas that are of noncombustible construction with wholly noncombustible contents.
5. Fire service access elevator machine rooms and machinery spaces.
6. Machine rooms, machinery spaces, control rooms and control spaces associated with occupant evacuation elevators designed in accordance with Section 3008 of the *International Building Code.*

❖ This section allows the omission of sprinkler protection in certain locations if an approved automatic fire detection system is installed. Buildings in compliance with

	NFPA 13	NFPA 13R	NFPA 13D
Extent of protection	Equip throughout (Section 903.3.1.1)	Occupied spaces (Section 903.3.1.2)	Occupied spaces (Section 903.3.1.3)
Scope	All occupancies	Low-rise residential	One- and two-family dwellings
Sprinkler design	Density/area concept	4-head design	2-head design
Sprinklers	All types	Residential only	Residential only
Duration	30 minutes (minimum)	30 minutes	10 minutes
Advantages	Property and life protection	Life safety/tenability	Life safety/tenability

Commentary Figure 903.3.1
NFPA 13, NFPA 13R, NFPA 13D SYSTEMS

one of the six listed conditions would still be considered fully sprinklered throughout in compliance with the code and NFPA 13 and thus are eligible for all applicable code alternatives, exceptions or reductions. Elimination of the sprinkler system in a sensitive area is subject to the approval of the fire code official.

Condition 1 addresses restrictions where the application of water could create a hazardous condition. For example, sprinkler protection is to be avoided where it is not compatible with certain stored materials (i.e., some water-reactive hazardous materials such as calcium carbide). Combustible metals, such as magnesium and aluminum, may burn so intensely that the use of water to attempt fire control will only intensify the reaction.

It is not the intent of Condition 2 to omit sprinklers solely because of a potential for water damage. A desire to not sprinkler a certain area (such as a computer room or operating room) does not fall within the limitations of the exception unless there is something unique about the space that would result in water being incompatible. A computer room can be adequately protected using an automatic sprinkler system or an alternative gaseous suppression agent system or a combination of these systems. The intent of Condition 2 is to consider whether the contents would react adversely to the application of water. It is important to note that the fire code official must approve the use of this item. Note also that with respect to computer rooms, NFPA 75 (*Protection of Information Technology Equipment*) (not a referenced standard) recognizes automatic sprinklers as the primary fire protection system for computer rooms.

Condition 3 recognizes the low fuel load and low occupancy hazards associated with generator and transformer rooms and, therefore, allows the omission of sprinkler protection if the rooms are separated from adjacent areas by 2-hour fire-resistance-rated construction. This condition assumes the room is not used for any combustible storage. This condition is similar to Section 8.15.11.3 of NFPA 13, which exempts electrical equipment rooms from sprinkler protection, provided the room is dedicated to the use of dry-type electrical equipment, is constructed as a 2-hour fire-resistance-rated enclosure, and is not used for combustible storage.

Condition 4 requires the construction of the room or area, as well as the contents, to be noncombustible. An example would be an area in an unprotected steel-frame building (Type IIB construction) used for steel or concrete block storage. Neither involves any significant combustible packaging or sources of ignition, and few combustibles are present (see Commentary Figure 903.3.1).

Condition 5 addresses the concern for elevator machine rooms and machinery spaces associated with fire service access elevators, as required by Sections 403.6.1 and 3007, for buildings with occupied floors greater than 120 feet (36.58 m) from the lowest level of fire department access. These elevators need to work

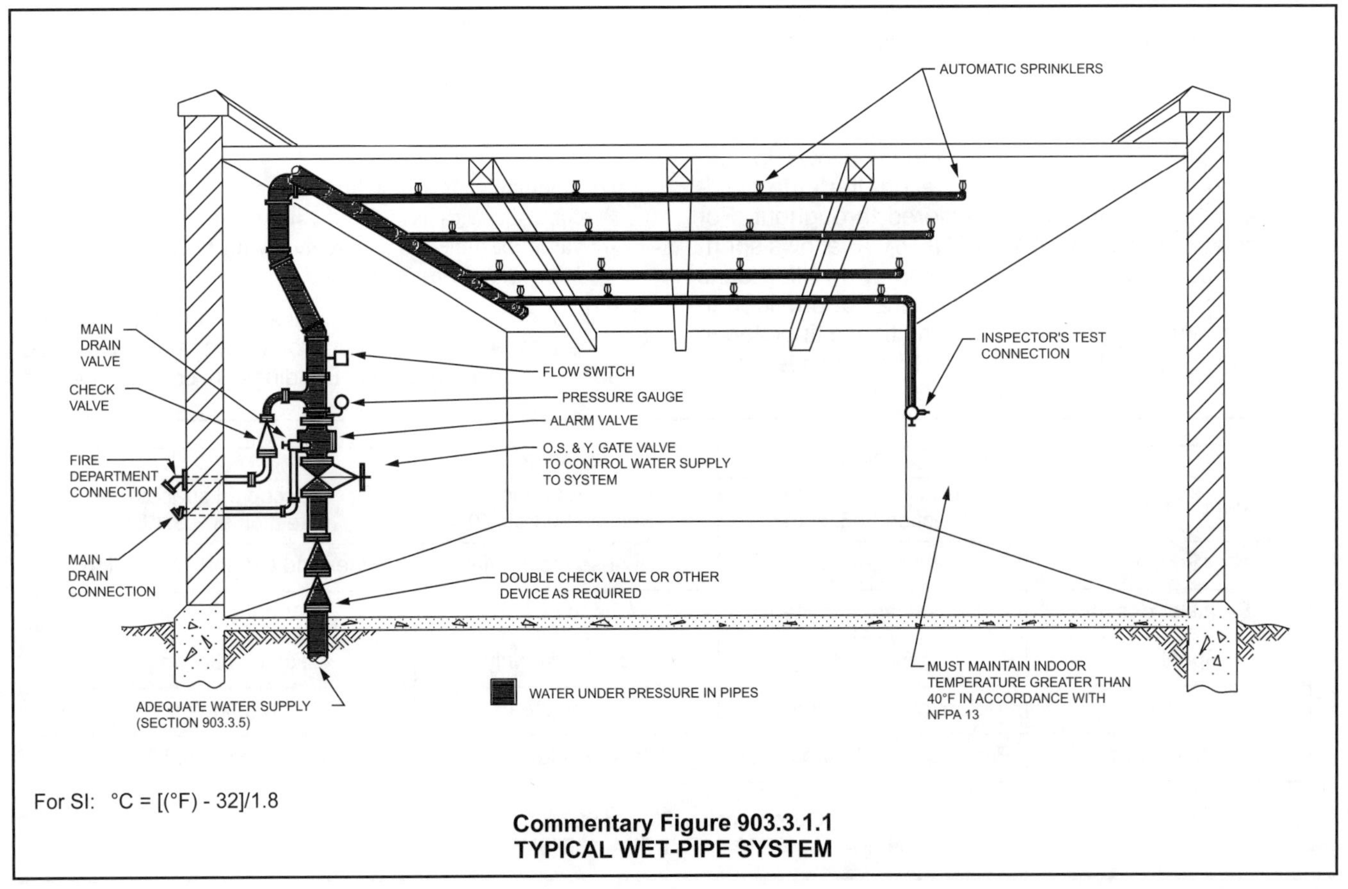

Commentary Figure 903.3.1.1
TYPICAL WET-PIPE SYSTEM

during fire situations and their operation cannot be threatened by the activation of a sprinkler in a machine room or space that may affect the operation of the elevators. Fire service access elevators are required to be continuously monitored at the fire command center in accordance with Section 3007.7.

Condition 6, similar to Condition 5, exempts sprinklers from the machine rooms, machinery spaces, control rooms and control spaces for occupant evacuation elevators. Like fire service access elevators, these elevators need to work during fire situations and their operation cannot be threatened by the activation of a sprinkler in machine rooms, machinery spaces, control rooms and control spaces. Such elevators are required to be monitored at the fire command center in accordance with Section 3008.7.

903.3.1.1.2 Bathrooms. In Group R occupancies, sprinklers shall not be required in bathrooms that do not exceed 55 square feet (5 m^2) in area and are located within individual *dwelling units* or *sleeping units*, provided that walls and ceilings, including the walls and ceilings behind a shower enclosure or tub, are of noncombustible or limited-combustible materials with a 15-minute thermal barrier rating.

❖ This provision was added to the code to reinstate an exception of NFPA 13 that had been in existence since 1976 but was deleted for all but dwelling units in motels and hotels (NFPA 8.15.8.1.1) from the 2013 edition of NFPA 13. Although reinstating the small bathroom exception will have a limited impact on new construction because many modern bathrooms exceed the 55-square-foot area limit to accommodate wheelchair access, the more important consequence will be removing an unnecessary cost increase for building owners who choose to retrofit existing properties with small bathrooms that were built before it was common to provide wheelchair access. Codes and standards should not erect any unnecessary barriers to retrofitting sprinklers into existing properties, such as existing high-rise buildings.

In the 1976 edition of the Life Safety Code (NFPA 101), to encourage cost-effective fire protection systems for apartment buildings, Section 11-3.8.3.4.1 provided an exception to permit bathrooms that did not exceed 55 square feet within individual dwelling units to omit sprinklers when the apartment building was sprinklered in accordance with NFPA 13. The basis of the 55-square-foot area is that this area accommodates a "typical" small bathroom that contains a standard tub, a toilet, a sink and nothing more. This exception was later duplicated from NFPA 101 into the 1991 edition of NFPA 13 with the understanding that the next edition of NFPA 101 (1994) could delete the exception since NFPA 13 would have it covered. NFPA 101-1994 then, as planned, deleted the exception.

The history of apartment unit bathroom fires is statistically minimal. According to the NFPA Home Structure Fire Report, January 2009, Table 9B, "Reported Apartment Structure Fires by Area of Origin 2003–2006 Annual Averages," out of 113,000 fires/year, only 1,600 (1 percent) are in bathrooms. Given that there is more than 35 years of experience with the bathroom sprinkler exception being in place (since it was put into NFPA 101 in 1976), it would certainly be reasonable to expect anecdotal or statistical experience to indicate the existence of a problem if there were one.

903.3.1.2 NFPA 13R sprinkler systems. *Automatic sprinkler systems* in Group R occupancies up to and including four stories in height in buildings not exceeding 60 feet (18 288 mm) in height above grade plane shall be permitted to be installed throughout in accordance with NFPA 13R.

The number of stories of Group R occupancies constructed in accordance with Sections 510.2 and 510.4 of the *International Building Code* shall be measured from the horizontal assembly creating separate buildings.

❖ NFPA 13R contains design and installation requirements for a sprinkler system to aid in the detection and control of fires in low-rise (four stories or less) residential occupancies.

Sprinkler systems designed in accordance with NFPA 13R are intended to prevent flashover (total involvement) in the room of fire origin and to improve the chance for occupants to escape or be evacuated. The design criteria in NFPA 13R are similar to those in NFPA 13 except that sprinklers may be omitted from areas in which fatal fires in residential occupancies do not typically originate (bathrooms, closets, attics, porches, garages and concealed spaces).

A common question is whether a mixed-occupancy building that contains a Group R occupancy could still use NFPA 13R for the design. If one of the mixed-use occupancies would require a sprinkler system throughout the building in accordance with NFPA 13, then a 13R system would not be allowed. If, however, the only reason a sprinkler system is being installed is because there is a Group R fire area within the building, then an NFPA 13R system would be an appropriate design choice. The areas that are not classified as Group R would require protection in accordance with NFPA 13.

It must be noted that although the building would be considered sprinklered throughout in accordance with NFPA 13R, not all of the code sprinkler alternatives could be applied. Any alternative that requires the installation of an NFPA 13 system would not be applicable if a portion of the building utilizes an NFPA 13R system.

The code provisions that allow for an increase in building height according to Section 504.3 do not compound this section. NFPA 13R is applicable to buildings that are up to four stories and 60 feet (18 288 mm) in height above grade plane. If the design of a residential building intends to take advantage of the sprinkler height increase so that the building is five stories or more, the sprinkler system must be an NFPA 13 system. Because this section limits the height to four stories, that is the maximum height for a building that can utilize an NFPA 13R system.

This is consistent with the scoping provisions in the NFPA 13R standard.

The limitation of four stories in height is to be measured with respect to the established grade plane, which is consistent with IFC Interpretation No. 43-03. As such, a basement would not be considered a story above grade for purposes of determining the applicability of this section.

The second paragraph recognizes the application of the requirements of Sections 510.2 and 510.4, which are essentially exceptions to the height and area requirements. They are based on providing a horizontal fire separation similar to the concept of a fire wall to create separate buildings. This establishes that the height in stories can be measured from the horizontal assembly instead of from grade plane. The height, in feet, would still be limited to being measured from grade plane. Such buildings are often referred to as "pedestal buildings."

903.3.1.2.1 Balconies and decks. Sprinkler protection shall be provided for exterior balconies, decks and ground floor patios of *dwelling units* and *sleeping units* where either of the following conditions exists:

1. The building is of Type V construction, provided that there is a roof or deck above.
2. Exterior balconies, decks and ground floor patios of dwelling units and sleeping units are constructed in accordance with Section 705.2.3.1, Exception 3 of the *International Building Code*.

Sidewall sprinklers that are used to protect such areas shall be permitted to be located such that their deflectors are within 1 inch (25 mm) to 6 inches (152 mm) below the structural members and a maximum distance of 14 inches (356 mm) below the deck of the exterior balconies and decks that are constructed of open wood joist construction.

❖ Balconies, decks and patios in buildings of Type V construction and used for Group R occupancies are required to have sprinkler protection when there is a roof or deck above. This is in addition to the requirements of NFPA 13R, which primarily addresses the life safety of occupants and not property protection. The intent is to address hazards such as grilling and similar activities. Since NFPA 13R does not require such coverage, there is potential that a fire on a balcony could grow much too large for the system within the building to handle. The concern is that a potential exterior balcony fire could spread to unprotected floor/ceiling assemblies and attic spaces and result in major property damage. Section 308.1.4 specifically addresses restrictions on open flame cooking devices used on combustible balconies. Note that sprinklers are not intended to be provided in closets found on such balconies.

Regardless of whether the exterior walking surface is attached to the building and called a balcony or is a freestanding structure such as a deck or patio, the concern for fire ignition in the area adjacent to the exterior wall is the same. Sidewall sprinklers should be selected based on the area of coverage and climate. If the potential for freezing exists, a dry sidewall sprinkler should be used. Where the overhanging deck or balcony is extensive, an extended coverage sprinkler should be selected.

903.3.1.2.2 Open-ended corridors. Sprinkler protection shall be provided in *open-ended corridors* and associated *exterior stairways* and *ramps* as specified in Section 1027.6, Exception 3.

❖ This section is simply emphasizing the fact that, since there is no separation from the exterior exit stairways, sprinklers would be required when using an NFPA 13R system. Section 1027.6, Exception 3 allows the separation between the open-ended corridor and exterior exit stairway to be omitted, but only where several conditions are met. The primary condition is that the corridor be sprinklered. A definition of "Open-ended corridor" is provided in Chapter 2. See Commentary Figure 903.3.1.2.2 for an example of an open-ended corridor.

Commentary Figure 903.3.1.2.2
OPEN-ENDED CORRIDOR

903.3.1.2.3 Attics. Attic protection shall be provided as follows:

1. Attics that are used or intended for living purposes or storage shall be protected by an *automatic sprinkler system.*
2. Where fuel-fired equipment is installed in an unsprinklered attic, not fewer than one quick-response interme-

diate temperature sprinkler shall be installed above the equipment.

3. Where located in a building of Type III, Type IV or Type V construction designed in accordance with Section 510.2 or 510.4 of the *International Building Code*, attics not required by Item 1 to have sprinklers shall comply with one of the following if the roof assembly is located more than 55 feet (16 764 mm) above the lowest level of required fire department vehicle access:
   3.1. Provide *automatic sprinkler system* protection.
   3.2. Construct the attic using noncombustible materials.
   3.3. Construct the attic using fire-retardant-treated wood complying with Section 2303.2 of the *International Building Code*.
   3.4. Fill the attic with noncombustible insulation.

   The height of the roof assembly shall be determined by measuring the distance from the lowest required fire vehicle access road surface adjacent to the building to the eave of the highest pitched roof, the intersection of the highest roof to the exterior wall, or the top of the highest parapet, whichever yields the greatest distance. For the purpose of this measurement, required fire vehicle access roads shall include only those roads that are necessary for compliance with Section 503.

4. Group R-4, Condition 2 occupancy attics not required by Item 1 to have sprinklers shall comply with one of the following:
   4.1. Provide *automatic sprinkler system* protection.
   4.2. Provide a heat detection system throughout the attic that is arranged to activate the building fire alarm system.
   4.3. Construct the attic using noncombustible materials.
   4.4. Construct the attic using fire-retardant-treated wood complying with Section 2303.2 of the *International Building Code*.
   4.5. Fill the attic with noncombustible insulation.

❖ This section clarifies that if the attic is used for living purposes or if fuel-fired equipment or storage is in these areas, full coverage in accordance with NFPA 13R is required. In attics where people are not expected and where storage or fuel-fired equipment is not located, some protection is required in addition to what NFPA 13R would require. Four different options of protection are provided. The first is simply to provide more warning time to the occupants if a fire should occur in the attic via a heat detector that activates the fire alarm system. The second is simply to reduce the risk of fire by requiring noncombustible construction materials. The third, similar to the second, is reducing the fire hazard by using fire-retardant-treated wood. This will slow the growth of a fire should one occur or prevent the start of a fire. The final option is simply to provide sprinkler protection to the attic. However if a sprinkler system is provided in the attic, issues such as freezing temperatures need to be addressed.

903.3.1.3 NFPA 13D sprinkler systems. *Automatic sprinkler systems* installed in one- and two-family *dwellings*; Group R-3; Group R-4, Condition 1; and *townhouses* shall be permitted to be installed throughout in accordance with NFPA 13D.

❖ NFPA 13D contains design and installation requirements for a sprinkler system to aid in the detection and control of fires in one- and two-family dwellings, mobile homes and townhouses. This section also specifically allows the use of an NFPA 13D system for occupancies classified as Group R-3 and Group R-4, Condition 1. Group R-3 occupancies are one- and two-family dwellings that fall outside the scope of the IRC and also those buildings housing small congregate living facilities and boarding houses. These facilities operate very similarly to a single-family home, and the level of the ability of the occupants is such that little assistance is needed for self-evacuation. This is consistent with the NFPA 13D requirements and is also consistent with FHA court cases based on nondiscrimination for group homes.

Similar to NFPA 13R, sprinkler systems designed in accordance with NFPA 13D are intended to prevent flashover (total involvement) in the room of fire origin and to improve the chance for occupants to escape or be evacuated. Although the allowable omission of sprinklers in certain areas of the dwelling unit in NFPA 13D is similar to that in NFPA 13R, the water supply requirements are less restrictive. NFPA 13D uses a two-head sprinkler design with a 10-minute duration requirement, while NFPA 13R uses a four-head sprinkler design with a 30-minute duration requirement. The decreased water supply requirement emphasizes the main intent of NFPA 13D to control the fire and maintain tenability during evacuation of the residence.

Since the fire code official has the authority to approve the type of sprinkler system, this section may be used to prevent the use of a specific type of sprinkler system that may be inappropriate for a particular type of occupancy.

903.3.2 Quick-response and residential sprinklers. Where *automatic sprinkler systems* are required by this code, quick-response or residential automatic sprinklers shall be installed in all of the following areas in accordance with Section 903.3.1 and their listings:

1. Throughout all spaces within a smoke compartment containing care recipient *sleeping units* in Group I-2 in accordance with the *International Building Code*.
2. Throughout all spaces within a smoke compartment containing treatment rooms in ambulatory care facilities.

3. *Dwelling units* and *sleeping units* in Group I-1 and R occupancies.
4. Light-hazard occupancies as defined in NFPA 13.

❖ This section requires the use of either listed quick-response or residential automatic sprinklers, depending on the type of sprinkler system required to achieve faster and more effective suppression in certain areas. Residential sprinklers are required in all types of residential buildings that would permit the use of an NFPA 13R or 13D sprinkler system.

Quick-response and residential sprinklers are similar in nature. They use a lighter material for the operating mechanism, thus reducing the heat lag in the element. The faster the heat can be absorbed, the sooner the sprinkler will begin to discharge water. Quick-response sprinklers have shown that they operate up to 25 percent faster than traditional sprinklers and create conditions in the room of origin that significantly increase the tenability of the environment. In tests performed by Factory Mutual (FM) for the Federal Emergency Management Agency (FEMA), the gas temperature in the room of origin was 550°F (288°C) with quick-response sprinklers, while it was 1,470°F (799°C) for conventional sprinklers at the time of sprinkler activation. More importantly, while the carbon monoxide (CO) level was 1,860 ppm for conventional sprinklers, the CO level when tested with quick-response sprinklers was only around 350 ppm. Comparatively, the National Institute of Occupational Safety and Health (NIOSH) considers the IDLH (immediately dangerous to life and health) level of CO to be 1,200 ppm. Thus, quick-response sprinklers have been shown to add significantly to the life safety effects of standard sprinkler systems.

Condition 1 requires the use of approved quick-response or residential sprinklers in smoke compartments containing care recipient sleeping units in Group I-2 occupancies. Even though properly operating standard sprinklers are effective, the extent of fire growth and smoke production that can occur before sprinkler activation creates the need for early warning to enable faster response by care providers and initiation of egress that is critical in occupancies containing persons incapable of self-preservation. The faster response time associated with quick-response or residential sprinklers increases the probability that the sprinklers will actuate before the care recipient's life would be threatened by a fire in his or her room.

Condition 2 requires the use of approved quick-response or residential sprinklers in smoke compartments containing treatment rooms in ambulatory care facilities. The justification is the same as that for Condition 1. When there is a potential for care recipients to be incapable of self-preservation, the use of residential sprinklers or quick-response sprinklers is critical.

Because of the kind of occupants sleeping in Group R and I-1 occupancies, as indicated in Condition 3, a faster responding type of sprinkler is desirable. Similar to the first condition, because occupants will be sleeping, the use of quick-response sprinklers creates additional safety by reducing sprinkler response time, thereby increasing the time available for egress and allowing for the time necessary for occupants to wake up and recognize the emergency event.

Condition 4 recognizes light-hazard occupancies in accordance with NFPA 13. These could include restaurants, schools, office buildings, places of religious worship and similar occupancies where the fire load and potential heat release of combustible contents are low.

903.3.3 Obstructed locations. Automatic sprinklers shall be installed with regard to obstructions that will delay activation or obstruct the water distribution pattern and shall be in accordance with the applicable *automatic sprinkler system* standard that is being used. Automatic sprinklers shall be installed in or under covered kiosks, displays, booths, concession stands or equipment that exceeds 4 feet (1219 mm) in width. Not less than a 3-foot (914 mm) clearance shall be maintained between automatic sprinklers and the top of piles of *combustible fibers*.

Exception: Kitchen equipment under exhaust hoods protected with a fire-extinguishing system in accordance with Section 904.

❖ To provide adequate sprinkler coverage, sprinkler protection must be extended under any obstruction that exceeds 4 feet (1219 mm) in width. Large air ducts are another common obstruction where sprinklers are routinely extended beneath the duct. The 3-foot (914 mm) storage clearance requirement for combustible fibers is caused by their potential high heat release. Most storage conditions require only a minimum 18-inch (457 mm) storage clearance to combustibles, depending on the type of sprinklers used and their actual storage conditions.

The exception recognizes that an alternative extinguishing system is permitted for commercial cooking systems in place of sprinkler protection for exhaust hoods that may be more than 4 feet (1219 mm) wide.

The application of this section is more critical to the ongoing use of the space. The obstruction conditions, therefore, should have already been addressed during plan review and installation inspection. This section gives the fire code official and building owner adequate information to avoid the most typical obstruction-related issues in terms of proper sprinkler coverage.

903.3.4 Actuation. *Automatic sprinkler systems* shall be automatically actuated unless specifically provided for in this code.

❖ The intent of this section is to eliminate the need for occupant intervention during a fire. As such, it is assumed that it will not be necessary for a person to manually open a valve or perform some other physical activity in order to allow the sprinkler system to activate.

Wet-pipe and dry-pipe sprinkler systems, for example, are essentially fail-safe systems in the sense that, if the system is in proper operating condition, it will operate once a sprinkler fuses. Dry systems have an inherent time lag for water to reach the sprinkler; therefore, the response is not as fast as for a wet-pipe system. Other types of sprinkler systems, such as preaction and deluge, rely on the actuation of a detection system to operate the sprinkler valve.

903.3.5 Water supplies. Water supplies for *automatic sprinkler systems* shall comply with this section and the standards referenced in Section 903.3.1. The potable water supply shall be protected against backflow in accordance with the requirements of this section and the *International Plumbing Code*. For connections to public waterworks systems, the water supply test used for design of fire protection systems shall be adjusted to account for seasonal and daily pressure fluctuations based on information from the water supply authority and as approved by the *fire code official*.

❖ To be effective, all sprinkler systems must have an adequate supply of water. The criteria for an acceptable water supply are contained in the standards referenced in Section 903.3.1. For example, NFPA 13 contains criteria for different types of water supplies as well as the methods to determine the pressure, flow capabilities and capacity necessary to get the intended performance from a sprinkler system. An acceptable water supply could consist of a reliable municipal supply, a gravity tank or a fire pump with a pressure tank or a combination of these.

This section also establishes the requirements for protecting the potable water system against a nonpotable source, such as stagnant water retained within the sprinkler piping. As stated in Section 608.16.4 of the IPC, an approved double check valve device or reduced pressure principle backflow preventer is required.

The other issue addressed by this section is fluctuations in water pressure. Information on pressure fluctuation is necessary to not only ensure that the minimum required pressure will be available for the automatic sprinkler system, but also to ensure that high pressures do not exceed the pressure limitations of the sprinkler system. If the water pressure on a sprinkler system exceeds 100 psi, changes in the hanging methods are required. Also, if a fire pump is provided, it might be possible to exceed 175 psi, which is typically considered the maximum working pressure for a sprinkler system. These are just additional reasons why it is critical to account for pressure fluctuations in the water supply. Obviously, fire flows can be affected by this, as well as other water-based fire protection systems, such as standpipes, which require a minimum 100 psi at the roof of high-rise buildings, and such may not be available due to pressure fluctuations. With regards to gathering of data, this requirement is simply intended to make sure that pressure fluctuations are addressed in accordance with the water supply authority to the extent that such information is available. Further authority is provided to the fire code official to accept other documentation.

903.3.5.1 Domestic services. Where the domestic service provides the water supply for the *automatic sprinkler system*, the supply shall be in accordance with this section.

❖ This section establishes the scope of domestic services for residential combination services. Essentially, compliance with Section 903.3.5 is required.

903.3.5.2 Residential combination services. A single combination water supply shall be allowed provided that the domestic demand is added to the sprinkler demand as required by NFPA 13R.

❖ NFPA 13R permits a common supply main to a building to serve both the sprinkler system and domestic services if the domestic demand is added to the sprinkler demand. NFPA 13R systems do not provide the same level of property protection as NFPA 13 systems.

903.3.6 Hose threads. Fire hose threads and fittings used in connection with *automatic sprinkler systems* shall be as prescribed by the *fire code official*.

❖ The threads on connections and fittings that the fire department will use to connect a hose must be compatible with the fire department threads.

Design documents must specify the type of thread to be used in order to be compatible with the local fire department equipment after consultation and coordination with the fire code official. The criteria typically apply to fire department connections for sprinkler and standpipe systems, standpipe hose connections, yard hydrants and wall hydrants.

The majority of fire departments in the United States use the American National Fire Hose Connection Screw Threads, also commonly known as NST and NS. NFPA 1963 gives the screw thread dimensions and the thread size of threaded connections, with nominal sizes ranging from $^3/_4$ inch (19 mm) to 6 inches (152 mm) for the NS thread. Although efforts to standardize fire hose threads began after the Boston conflagration in 1872, there are still many different screw threads, some of which give the appearance of compatibility with the NH thread. While NFPA 1963 may be used as a guide, the code does not require that any particular standard be used. Rather, it is important that the fire code official be consulted for the appropriate thread selection. The intent is that the threads match those of the local department identically so that adapters are not required within the fire department's own district.

903.3.7 Fire department connections. Fire department connections for *automatic sprinkler systems* shall be installed in accordance with Section 912.

❖ Section 912, to which this section points, provides a comprehensive set of requirements for fire department connections (FDCs), reducing the opportunity for any of its requirements to be overlooked. See the commentary for Section 912.

903.3.8 Limited area sprinkler systems. Limited area sprinkler systems shall be in accordance with the standards listed in Section 903.3.1 except as provided in Sections 903.3.8.1 through 903.3.8.5.

❖ The use of limited area sprinkler systems is restricted to cases in which the code requires a limited number of sprinklers to protect a specific hazard or area and not a complete automatic sprinkler system. For example, limited area sprinkler systems may be used to protect areas including, but not limited to, stages, storage and workshop areas, painting rooms, trash rooms and chutes, furnace rooms, kitchens and hazardous exhaust systems, and incidental uses as regulated in Section 509 of the IBC.

903.3.8.1 Number of sprinklers. Limited area sprinkler systems shall not exceed six sprinklers in any single fire area.

❖ In the 2015 edition of the code, the number of sprinklers allowed on a limited area sprinkler system in a fire area has been reduced to only six. In previous editions, up to 19 sprinklers were allowed. This reduced number will limit the type of applications for such systems. In the past, 19 sprinklers may have been able to address an entire building, depending on the system design, more easily allowing the use of the domestic water supply.

903.3.8.2 Occupancy hazard classification. Only areas classified by NFPA 13 as Light Hazard or Ordinary Hazard Group 1 shall be permitted to be protected by limited area sprinkler systems.

❖ The use of limited area systems is restricted to only the two lowest hazard occupancy classifications in accordance with NFPA 13. Such systems are fairly limited and can only contain six sprinklers per fire area. Because of this, the types of hazards protected should be limited.

903.3.8.3 Piping arrangement. Where a limited area sprinkler system is installed in a building with an automatic wet standpipe system, sprinklers shall be supplied by the standpipe system. Where a limited area sprinkler system is installed in a building without an automatic wet standpipe system, water shall be permitted to be supplied by the plumbing system provided that the plumbing system is capable of simultaneously supplying domestic and sprinkler demands.

❖ Two options are provided for how water to the limited area sprinkler system is to be supplied. If the building contains automatic wet standpipes, then the system must be supplied by the standpipe system. If there is no standpipe system available, connection to the domestic water supply is permitted. The water supply must be analyzed to determine if it is sufficient to supply simultaneously both domestic usage and the sprinkler system demand. This will mean looking at peak water use throughout the day. See Section 903.3.5 and the *International Plumbing Code*.

903.3.8.4 Supervision. Control valves shall not be installed between the water supply and sprinklers unless the valves are of an *approved* indicating type that are supervised or secured in the open position.

❖ No shutoff valves are permitted in the sprinkler system piping unless the valves are specifically approved and are either supervised or secured in the open position. These restrictions increase the likelihood that the sprinkler system will be operational should a fire occur. Valve supervision or securing a valve in the open position are considered equally reliable by this section.

903.3.8.5 Calculations. Hydraulic calculations in accordance with NFPA 13 shall be provided to demonstrate that the available water flow and pressure are adequate to supply all sprinklers installed in any single *fire area* with discharge densities corresponding to the hazard classification.

❖ Hydraulic calculations are required to be in accordance with NFPA 13 to demonstrate that the water system is adequate to supply the sprinkler demand in any particular fire area.

903.4 Sprinkler system supervision and alarms. Valves controlling the water supply for *automatic sprinkler systems*, pumps, tanks, water levels and temperatures, critical air pressures and waterflow switches on all sprinkler systems shall be electrically supervised by a *listed* fire alarm control unit.

Exceptions:

1. *Automatic sprinkler systems* protecting one- and two-family *dwellings*.
2. Limited area sprinkler systems in accordance with Section 903.3.8.
3. *Automatic sprinkler systems* installed in accordance with NFPA 13R where a common supply main is used to supply both domestic water and the *automatic sprinkler system*, and a separate shutoff valve for the *automatic sprinkler system* is not provided.
4. Jockey pump control valves that are sealed or locked in the open position.
5. Control valves to commercial kitchen hoods, paint spray booths or dip tanks that are sealed or locked in the open position.
6. Valves controlling the fuel supply to fire pump engines that are sealed or locked in the open position.
7. Trim valves to pressure switches in dry, preaction and deluge sprinkler systems that are sealed or locked in the open position.

❖ The reliability data on automatic sprinkler systems clearly indicate that a closed valve is the leading cause of sprinkler system failure. There are also a number of other critical elements that contribute to successful sprinkler system operation, including, but not limited to, pumps, water tanks and air pressure maintenance devices; therefore, this section requires that the various critical elements that contribute to an available water supply and to the function of the sprinkler system be electrically supervised.

Automatic sprinkler systems in one- and two-family dwellings are typically designed to comply with NFPA 13D, which does not require electrical supervision (see Exception 1).

Limited area sprinkler systems are generally supervised by their connection to the domestic water service, although the use of a supervised indicating valve is permitted. Compliance with Section 903.3.8 means that the alarm provisions of this section are not applicable to limited area systems. Consequently, limited area sprinkler systems do not require local alarms or supervision. Again, electrical supervision is required only if a control valve is installed between the riser control valve and the sprinkler system piping (see Exception 2).

Similar to limited area sprinkler systems, electrical supervision is not required for NFPA 13R residential combination services when a shutoff valve is not installed (see Exception 3). NFPA 13R sprinkler systems are supervised in that the only way to shut off the sprinkler system is to also shut off the domestic water supply.

The valves discussed in Exceptions 4 through 7 can be sealed or locked in the open position because they do not control the sprinkler system water supply.

903.4.1 Monitoring. Alarm, supervisory and trouble signals shall be distinctly different and shall be automatically transmitted to an *approved* supervising station or, where *approved* by the *fire code official*, shall sound an audible signal at a constantly attended location.

Exceptions:

1. Underground key or hub valves in roadway boxes provided by the municipality or public utility are not required to be monitored.
2. Backflow prevention device test valves located in limited area sprinkler system supply piping shall be locked in the open position. In occupancies required to be equipped with a fire alarm system, the backflow preventer valves shall be electrically supervised by a tamper switch installed in accordance with NFPA 72 and separately annunciated.

❖ Automatic sprinkler systems must be supervised as a means of determining that the system is operational. A valve supervisory switch operating as a normally open or normally closed switch is usually used. NFPA 72 does not permit valve supervisory switches to be connected to the same zone circuit as the waterflow switch unless it is specifically arranged to actuate a signal that is distinctive from the circuit trouble condition signal.

Required sprinkler systems are to be monitored by an approved supervising service to comply with NFPA 72. Types of supervising stations recognized in NFPA 72 include central stations, remote supervising stations or proprietary supervising stations.

A central station is an independent, off-site facility operated and maintained by personnel whose primary business is to furnish, maintain, record and supervise a signaling system. A proprietary system is similar to a central station system; however, a proprietary system is typically an on-site facility monitoring a number of buildings on the same site for the same owner. A remote station system has an alarm signal that is transmitted to a remote location acceptable to the authority having jurisdiction and that is attended 24 hours a day. The receiving equipment is usually located at a fire station, police station, regional emergency communications center or telephone answering service. An alternative use to the three previous supervising methods is an audible signal that can be transmitted to a constantly attended location approved by the fire code official.

Exception 1 recognizes that underground key or hub valves in roadway boxes are not normally supervised or required to be supervised by this section or NFPA 13.

Exception 2 acknowledges that local water utilities and environmental authorities in many instances require, by local ordinances, that backflow prevention devices be installed in limited-area sprinkler system piping. To make the testing and maintenance of backflow prevention devices easier, test valves are installed on each side of the device. These valves are typically indicating-type valves and can function as shutoff valves for the sprinkler system, and therefore require some level of supervision.

Because these infrequently used valves may be the only feature of protection requiring supervision in occupancies not otherwise required to be equipped with a fire alarm system, Exception 2 permits these valves to be locked in the open position; however, if the occupancy is protected by a fire alarm system, these valves must be equipped with approved valve supervisory devices connected to the fire alarm control panel on a separate (supervisory) zone so that the supervisory signal is transmitted to the designated receiving station. Installation and testing of backflow preventers in sprinkler systems are regulated in Sections 312.10 (testing) and 608.16.4 (devices) of the IPC.

903.4.2 Alarms. An approved audible device, located on the exterior of the building in an *approved* location, shall be connected to each *automatic sprinkler system*. Such sprinkler waterflow alarm devices shall be activated by water flow equivalent to the flow of a single sprinkler of the smallest orifice size installed in the system. Where a fire alarm system is installed, actuation of the *automatic sprinkler system* shall actuate the building fire alarm system.

❖ The audible alarm, sometimes referred to as the "outside ringer" or "water-motor gong," sounds when the sprinkler system has activated. The alarm device may be electrically operated or it may be a true water-motor gong operated by a paddle-wheel-type attachment to the sprinkler system riser that responds to the flow of water in the piping. Though no longer the alarm device of choice, water-motor gongs do have the advantage of not being subject to power failures within or outside the protected building (see Sections 6.9 and 8.17 of NFPA 13 for further information on these devices). The alarm must be installed on the exterior of the building in a location approved by the fire code official. This location is often in close proximity to the fire department connection (FDC), serving a collateral function of helping the responding fire apparatus engineer more promptly locate the FDC.

The alarm is not intended to be an evacuation alarm. The requirement is also not intended to be an indirect requirement for a fire alarm system. Unless a fire alarm system is required by some other code provision, only the exterior alarm device is required. However, when a fire alarm system is installed, the sprinkler system must also be interconnected with the fire alarm system so that when the sprinkler system actuates, it sounds the evacuation alarms required for the fire alarm system.

The primary purpose of the exterior alarm is to notify people outside the building that the sprinkler system is in operation. Originally, it was to act as a supplemental alert so that passersby could notify the fire department of the condition. However, because the code now requires electronic supervision of sprinkler systems, that function is mostly moot. The exterior notification now primarily serves the function of alerting the arriving fire department of which building or sprinkler system is in operation before staging firefighting activities for the building.

903.4.3 Floor control valves. *Approved* supervised indicating control valves shall be provided at the point of connection to the riser on each floor in high-rise buildings.

❖ In high-rise buildings, sprinkler control valves with supervisory initiating devices must be installed at the point of connection to the riser on each floor. Sprinkler control valves on each floor are intended to permit servicing activated systems without impairing the water supply to large portions of the building.

903.5 Testing and maintenance. Sprinkler systems shall be tested and maintained in accordance with Section 901.

❖ Section 901 contains requirements for the testing and maintenance of sprinkler systems. Acceptance tests are necessary to verify that the system performs as intended by design and by the code. Periodic testing and maintenance are essential to verify that the level of protection designed into the building will be operational whenever a fire occurs. Water-based extinguishing systems must be tested and maintained as required by NFPA 25.

903.6 Where required in existing buildings and structures. An *automatic sprinkler system* shall be provided in existing buildings and structures where required in Chapter 11.

❖ Chapter 11 of this code, specifically Section 1103.5, requires sprinklers for existing buildings used for the manufacture and storage of pyroxylin plastics in certain Group A-2 occupancies and in existing Group I-2 occupancies. See the commentary for Sections 1103.5.1 through 1103.5.4 for more detail on the retroactive sprinkler requirements.

SECTION 904
ALTERNATIVE AUTOMATIC FIRE-EXTINGUISHING SYSTEMS

904.1 General. Automatic fire-extinguishing systems, other than *automatic sprinkler systems*, shall be designed, installed, inspected, tested and maintained in accordance with the provisions of this section and the applicable referenced standards.

❖ Section 904 covers alternative fire-extinguishing systems that use extinguishing agents other than water. Alternative automatic fire-extinguishing systems include wet-chemical, dry-chemical, foam, carbon dioxide, halon and clean-agent suppression systems. In addition to the provisions of Section 904, the indicated referenced standards include specific installation, maintenance and testing requirements for all systems.

904.1.1 Certification of service personnel for fire-extinguishing equipment. Service personnel providing or conducting maintenance on automatic fire-extinguishing systems, other than *automatic sprinkler systems*, shall possess a valid certificate issued by an *approved* governmental agency, or other *approved* organization for the type of system and work performed.

❖ Maintenance of fire protection systems and devices are minimum Chapter 9 requirements. Fire protection systems, like other technologies, have advanced new designs that require a clear understanding of their construction and maintenance. To ensure that systems and devices are properly maintained, the code now requires individuals performing these activities be certified. Certification must be issued by an approved organization or governmental agency.

These provisions align the code with NFPA standards governing the design, construction, inspection and maintenance of alternative automatic fire-extinguishing systems and portable fire extinguishers. The personnel qualification requirements specified by the applicable NFPA standards for the various alternative automatic fire-extinguishing systems are summarized in Commentary Figure 904.1.1.

Several organizations offer certifications that will confirm to code officials that individuals are qualified to perform maintenance on alternative automatic fire-extinguishing systems and portable fire extinguishers. The International Code Council® (ICC®), in conjunction with the National Association of Fire Equipment Distributors (NAFED), offers certifications to individuals who service and inspect portable fire extinguishers and pre-engineered alternative fire-extinguishing systems protecting commercial kitchen hoods or industrial equipment such as spray booths. The National Institute for Certification in Engineering Technologies (NICET) offers four progressive levels of certification for individuals who design, erect and inspect special hazard suppression systems. Special hazard suppression systems include all of the various systems recognized in Section 904 and Commentary Figure 904.1.1. Finally, most manufacturers of these systems offer corporate certifications to individuals who will design, install and inspect them. Such certifications are beneficial to code officials because they confirm the individuals are qualified to install or maintain fire protection equipment produced by a specific manufacturer.

904.2 Where permitted. Automatic fire-extinguishing systems installed as an alternative to the required *automatic sprinkler systems* of Section 903 shall be *approved* by the *fire code official.*

❖ One of the main considerations in selecting an extinguishing agent should be the compatibility of the agent with the hazard. The fire code official is responsible for approving an alternative extinguishing agent. The approval should be based on the compatibility of the agent with the hazard and the potential effectiveness of the agent to suppress a fire involving the hazards present.

904.2.1 Restriction on using automatic sprinkler system exceptions or reductions. Automatic fire-extinguishing systems shall not be considered alternatives for the purposes of exceptions or reductions allowed for *automatic sprinkler systems* or by other requirements of this code.

❖ Although Section 904.2 allows the use of alternative fire-extinguishing systems with specific approval, this section prohibits the use of such systems as alternatives to reductions or exceptions allowed for automatic sprinkler systems throughout the code. Therefore, the building will not be considered as equipped throughout with an automatic sprinkler system when using systems such as automatic water mist or other alternative systems. See Commentary Figure 904.2.1.

904.2.2 Commercial hood and duct systems. Each required commercial kitchen exhaust hood and duct system required by Section 607 to have a Type I hood shall be protected with an *approved* automatic fire-extinguishing system installed in accordance with this code.

❖ This section requires an effective suppression system to combat fire on the cooking surfaces of grease-producing appliances and within the hood and exhaust system of a commercial kitchen installation. Type I hoods, including the duct system, must be protected with an approved automatic fire-extinguishing system because they are used for handling grease-laden vapors or smoke, whereas Type II hoods handle fumes, steam, heat and odors. Type I hoods are typically required for commercial food heat-processing equipment, such as deep fryers, griddles, charbroilers, broilers and open burner stoves and ranges. For additional guidance on the requirements for Type I and II hoods, see the commentary to Section 507 of the IMC.

904.3 Installation. Automatic fire-extinguishing systems shall be installed in accordance with this section.

❖ The installation of automatic fire-extinguishing systems must comply with the requirements of Sections 904.3.1 through 904.3.5 in addition to the installation criteria contained in the referenced standard for the proposed type of alternative extinguishing system.

NFPA STANDARD NUMBER & EDITION	SUBJECT	SECTION	PERSONNEL QUALIFICATION REQUIREMENT
12, 2011	Carbon dioxide	4.4.1.1	Specifications for carbon dioxide fire-extinguishing systems shall be prepared under the supervision of a person fully experienced and qualified in the design of carbon dioxide extinguishing systems and with the advice of the authority having jurisdiction.
12A, 2009	Halon 1301	5.1.2.1	Plans and calculations shall be submitted for approval to the authority having jurisdiction before installation begins. Their preparation shall be entrusted only to persons fully experienced and qualified in the design of Halon 1301 extinguishing systems.
17, 2013	Dry chemical	1.6	Only trained persons shall be considered competent to design or lay out, install and service dry-chemical systems.
17A, 2013	Wet chemical	1.7	Only trained persons shall be considered competent to design or lay out, install, and service wet chemical systems.
2001, 2012	Clean agent	7.6.1	All persons who could be expected to inspect, test, maintain, or operate fire-extinguishing systems shall be thoroughly trained and kept thoroughly trained in the functions they are expected to perform.

Commentary Figure 904.1.1
PERSONNEL QUALIFICATION REQUIREMENTS BY TYPE OF FIRE-EXTINGUISHING AGENT

CODE SECTION[a]	MODIFICATION	NFPA 13	NPFA 13R	NFPA 13D
Increases				
504.3 and Table 504.3	Height increase in feet	yes	yes	no
504.4 and Table 504.4	Height increase in number of stories	yes	yes	no
506.2 and Table 506.2	Area increase	yes	yes	no
1005.3.1, 1005.3.2[b]	Egress width	yes	yes	no
Table 1017.2[b]	Travel distance	yes	yes	no
Rating Reductions				
Table 508.4	Separated occupancies	yes	no	no
708.3	Fire partitions (dwelling units, sleeping units)	yes	no	no
Table1020.1[b]	Corridor walls	yes	yes	no
Miscellaneous				
Tables 307.1(1), 307.1(2)	Hazardous material increase	yes	no	no
404.2	Atriums	yes	no	no
507.4, 507.5	Unlimited area buildings	yes	no	no
Table 705.8	Allowable area of openings	yes	no	no
705.8.5	Vertical separation of openings	yes	yes	no
718.3.2	Residential floor/ceiling draftstopping	yes	yes[c]	no
718.3.3	Nonresidential draftstopping	yes	no	no
718.4.2	Groups R-1, R-2 attic draftstopping	yes	yes[c]	no
718.4.3	Other group draftstopping	yes	no	no
Table 803.9	Interior finish	yes	yes	no
804.4.2	Floor finish	yes	yes	no
907.2.1–907.2.10[b]	Manual fire alarm system	yes (A, B, E, F, M)	yes (R-1, R-2)	no
1009.2.1[b]	Accessible egress	yes	yes	no
1028.1[b]	Exit discharge	yes	yes	no
1406.3	Balconies	yes	yes[c, d]	yes[c]

a. Section numbers refer to sections in the code.
b. Section numbers in Chapters 9 and 10 apply to both the IBC and the code.
c. Sprinkler protection must be extended to the affected areas.
d. For additional balcony requirements, see Section 903.3.1.2.1.

Commentary Figure 904.2.1
SELECTED EXAMPLES OF REQUIREMENTS MODIFIED THROUGH USE OF AUTOMATIC SPRINKLER SYSTEMS

904.3.1 Electrical wiring. Electrical wiring shall be in accordance with NFPA 70.

❖ NFPA 70 regulates the design and installation of electrical systems and equipment. All electrical work must also be in compliance with any specific electrical classifications and conditions contained in the referenced standards for each type of system.

Chapter 27 of the IBC and Section 605 contain provisions that also reference NFPA 70. Those sections also contain additional information that must be applied when addressing electrical issues.

904.3.2 Actuation. Automatic fire-extinguishing systems shall be automatically actuated and provided with a manual means of actuation in accordance with Section 904.12.1. Where more than one hazard could be simultaneously involved in fire due to their proximity, all hazards shall be protected by a single system designed to protect all hazards that could become involved.

Exception: Multiple systems shall be permitted to be installed if they are designed to operate simultaneously.

❖ Section 904.3.2 requires alternative fire-extinguishing systems to be designed for automatic activation. Activation commonly occurs when a heat, fire or smoke detection system activates. In Type I commercial kitchen hoods, Section 904.12 requires a manual and automatic means of activating the fire-extinguishing system. Designing a fire-extinguishing system to operate only upon manual actuation is prohibited by the code and many of the NFPA fire protection system standards.

The requirements for fire-extinguishing system actuation correlate with the requirements of NFPA 17 and NFPA 17A. The requirement prescribes that when a hazard is protected by two or more fire-extinguishing systems, all of the systems must be designed to operate simultaneously. The reason for the revision is that a typical alternative automatic fire-extinguishing system has a limited amount of fire-extinguishing agent. The amount of agent that is available is based on the area or volume of the hazard and the fire behavior of the fuel. Because the amount of agent is limited, the simultaneous operation of all the fire-extinguishing systems ensures that enough agent is applied to extinguish the fire and prevent its spread from the area of origin.

It is fairly common for a single hazard to be protected by two or more alternative automatic fire-extinguishing systems. For example, protection of a spray booth used for the application of flammable finishes using dry chemical commonly requires two or three alternative automatic fire-extinguishing systems. The reason is that many dry-chemical and all wet-chemical systems are preengineered systems. Utilizing listed nozzles, preengineered systems are designed and constructed based on the manufacturer's installation requirements. Because these systems are assembled using listed nozzles and extinguishing agents, one system may not be able to protect the spraying space and exhaust plenum. As a result, two or more systems may be required as a provision of an extinguishing system's listing to protect certain hazards.

Another example is commercial kitchen cooking operations. Consider a flat grill broiler and a deep fat fryer located beneath the same Type I hood. It is quite common for each of these commercial cooking appliances to be protected by separate automatic fire-extinguishing systems. Based on the revision to Section 904.3.2, both extinguishing systems must simultaneously operate in the event a fire involves either of the example appliances.

904.3.3 System interlocking. Automatic equipment interlocks with fuel shutoffs, ventilation controls, door closers, window shutters, conveyor openings, smoke and heat vents and other features necessary for proper operation of the fire-extinguishing system shall be provided as required by the design and installation standard utilized for the hazard.

❖ Shutting off fuel supplies will eliminate potential ignition sources in the protected area. Automatic door and window closers and dampers for forced-air ventilation systems are intended to maintain the desired concentration level of the extinguishing agent in the protected area. See the commentary for Section 904.12.2 for information on system interconnections in commercial cooking fire-extinguishing systems.

904.3.4 Alarms and warning signs. Where alarms are required to indicate the operation of automatic fire-extinguishing systems, distinctive audible, visible alarms and warning signs shall be provided to warn of pending agent discharge. Where exposure to automatic-extinguishing agents poses a hazard to persons and a delay is required to ensure the evacuation of occupants before agent discharge, a separate warning signal shall be provided to alert occupants once agent discharge has begun. Audible signals shall be in accordance with Section 907.5.2.

❖ Safeguards are necessary to prevent injury or death to personnel in areas where the atmosphere will be made hazardous by oxygen depletion due to agent discharge in a confined space. The "where alarms are required" phrase is referring to requirements that will be found in the referenced installation standards indicated in Sections 904.5 through 904.12, as applicable. Predischarge alarms that will operate on fire detection system activation must be installed within and at entrances to the affected areas.

Where required by the appropriate installation standard, an extinguishing agent discharge delay feature shall also be provided to allow evacuation of personnel prior to agent discharge. Warning and instructional signs are also to be posted, preferably at the entrances to and within the protected area. See Section 4.5.6.1 of NFPA 12 for additional information on carbon dioxide system alarms, Section 4.3.5 of NFPA 12A for additional information on Halon system alarms and Section 4.3.5 of NFPA 2001 for additional information on clean agent system alarms.

904.3.5 Monitoring. Where a building fire alarm system is installed, automatic fire-extinguishing systems shall be monitored by the building fire alarm system in accordance with NFPA 72.

❖ Automatic fire-extinguishing systems need not be electrically supervised unless the building is equipped with a fire alarm system. This section recognizes the fact that a fire alarm system is not required in all buildings. However, because most alternative fire-extinguishing systems require the space to be evacuated before the system is discharged, they are equipped with evacuation alarms. Interconnection of the fire-extinguishing system evacuation alarm with the building evacuation alarm results in an increased level of hazard notification for the occupants in addition to the electrical supervision of the fire-extinguishing system.

904.4 Inspection and testing. Automatic fire-extinguishing systems shall be inspected and tested in accordance with the provisions of this section prior to acceptance.

❖ The completed installation must be tested and inspected to determine that the system has been installed in compliance with the code and will function as required. Full-scale acceptance tests must be conducted as required by the applicable referenced standard.

904.4.1 Inspection. Prior to conducting final acceptance tests, all of the following items shall be inspected:

1. Hazard specification for consistency with design hazard.
2. Type, location and spacing of automatic- and manual-initiating devices.
3. Size, placement and position of nozzles or discharge orifices.
4. Location and identification of audible and visible alarm devices.
5. Identification of devices with proper designations.
6. Operating instructions.

❖ This section identifies those items that need to be verified or visually inspected prior to the final acceptance tests. All equipment should be listed, approved and installed in accordance with the manufacturer's recommendations.

904.4.2 Alarm testing. Notification appliances, connections to fire alarm systems and connections to *approved* supervising stations shall be tested in accordance with this section and Section 907 to verify proper operation.

❖ Components of fire-extinguishing systems related to alarm devices and their supervision must be tested before the system is approved. Alarm devices must be tested to satisfy the requirements of NFPA 72.

904.4.2.1 Audible and visible signals. The audibility and visibility of notification appliances signaling agent discharge or system operation, where required, shall be verified.

❖ This section requires verification, upon completion of the system installation, of the audibility and visibility of notification appliances in the area affected by the extinguishing agent discharge of the alternative automatic fire-extinguishing system.

904.4.3 Monitor testing. Connections to protected premises and supervising station fire alarm systems shall be tested to verify proper identification and retransmission of alarms from automatic fire-extinguishing systems.

❖ Where monitoring of fire-extinguishing systems is required, such as by Section 904.3.5, all connections related to the supervision of the system must be tested to verify they are in proper working order.

904.5 Wet-chemical systems. Wet-chemical extinguishing systems shall be installed, maintained, periodically inspected and tested in accordance with NFPA 17A and their listing. Records of inspections and testing shall be maintained.

❖ NFPA 17A contains minimum requirements for the design, installation, operation, testing and maintenance of wet-chemical preengineered extinguishing systems. Equipment that is typically protected with wet-chemical extinguishing systems includes restaurant, commercial and institutional hoods, plenums, ducts, and associated cooking equipment. Strict compliance with the manufacturer's installation instructions is vital for a viable installation.

Wet-chemical solutions used in extinguishing systems are relatively harmless and there is usually no lasting significant effect on a person's skin, respiratory system or clothing. These solutions may produce a mild, temporary irritation, but the symptoms will usually disappear when contact is eliminated.

This section also specifically requires that records be maintained of inspections and testing to increase the effectiveness of such systems. Without records of such inspections and testing, it is more difficult to determine if the systems will be effective when activated and when future inspection and testing is necessary.

904.5.1 System test. Systems shall be inspected and tested for proper operation at six-month intervals. Tests shall include a check of the detection system, alarms and releasing devices, including manual stations and other associated equipment. Extinguishing system units shall be weighed and the required amount of agent verified. Stored pressure-type units shall be checked for the required pressure. The cartridge of cartridge-operated units shall be weighed and replaced at intervals indicated by the manufacturer.

❖ This section specifies the frequency for inspection and testing of wet-chemical extinguishing systems. The system and its essential components must be inspected and checked every six months to determine that the system is in full operating condition.

904.5.2 Fusible link maintenance. Fixed temperature-sensing elements shall be maintained to ensure proper operation of the system.

❖ Wet-chemical extinguishing systems are commonly used to protect commercial cooking equipment. The fusible metal alloy sensing elements are subject to the accumulation of grease or other contaminants that could affect the operation of the fusible link. The sensing elements must be inspected routinely and replaced as needed.

904.6 Dry-chemical systems. Dry-chemical extinguishing systems shall be installed, maintained, periodically inspected and tested in accordance with NFPA 17 and their listing. Records of inspections and testing shall be maintained.

❖ NFPA 17 contains the minimum requirements for the design, installation, testing, inspection, approval, operation and maintenance of dry-chemical extinguishing systems.

The fire code official has the authority to approve the type of dry-chemical extinguishing system to be used. NFPA 17 identifies three types of dry-chemical extinguishing systems: total flooding, local application and hand hose-line systems. Only total flooding and local application systems are considered automatic extinguishing systems.

The types of hazards and equipment that can be protected with dry-chemical extinguishing systems include: flammable and combustible liquids and combustible gases; combustible solids, which melt when involved in a fire; electrical hazards, such as transformers or oil circuit breakers; textile operations subject to flash surface fires; ordinary combustibles such as wood, paper or cloth; and restaurant and commercial hoods, ducts and associated cooking appliance hazards, such as deep fat fryers and some plastics, depending on the type of material and configuration.

Total flooding dry-chemical extinguishing systems are used only where there is a permanent enclosure surrounding the hazard that is adequate to enable the required concentration to be built up. The total area of unclosable openings must not exceed 15 percent of the total area of the sides, top and bottom of the enclosure. Consideration must be given to eliminating the probable sources of reignition within the enclosure because the extinguishing action of dry-chemical systems is transient.

Local application of dry-chemical extinguishing systems is to be used for extinguishing fires where the hazard is not enclosed or where the enclosure does not conform to the requirements for total-flooding systems. Local application systems have successfully protected hazards involving flammable or combustible liquids, gases and shallow solids, such as paint deposits.

NFPA 17 also discusses pre-engineered dry-chemical systems consisting of components designed to be installed in accordance with pretested limitations as tested and labeled by a testing agency. Pre-engineered systems must be installed within the limitations that have been established by the testing agency and may include total flooding, local application or a combination of both types of systems.

The type of dry chemical used in the extinguishing system is a function of the hazard to be protected. The type of dry chemical used in a system should not be changed unless it has been proven changeable by a testing laboratory, is recommended by the manufacturer of the equipment and is acceptable to the fire code official for the hazard being protected. Additional guidance on the use of various dry-chemical agents can be found in NFPA 17.

This section also specifically requires that records be maintained of inspections and testing to increase the effectiveness of such systems. Without records of such inspections and testing, it is more difficult to determine if the systems will be effective when activated and when future inspection and testing is necessary.

904.6.1 System test. Systems shall be inspected and tested for proper operation at six-month intervals. Tests shall include a check of the detection system, alarms and releasing devices, including manual stations and other associated equipment. Extinguishing system units shall be weighed, and the required amount of agent verified. Stored pressure-type units shall be checked for the required pressure. The cartridge of cartridge-operated units shall be weighed and replaced at intervals indicated by the manufacturer.

❖ This section specifies the frequency for inspection and testing of dry-chemical extinguishing systems. The system and its essential components must be inspected and checked every six months to determine that the system is in full operating condition.

904.6.2 Fusible link maintenance. Fixed temperature-sensing elements shall be maintained to ensure proper operation of the system.

❖ Dry-chemical extinguishing systems are commonly used to protect commercial cooking systems and other hazardous use conditions. In these applications, the fusible metal alloy sensing elements are subject to the accumulation of grease or other contaminants that could affect the operation of the fusible link. The sensing elements must be inspected routinely and replaced as needed.

904.7 Foam systems. Foam-extinguishing systems shall be installed, maintained, periodically inspected and tested in accordance with NFPA 11 and NFPA 16 and their listing. Records of inspections and testing shall be maintained.

❖ NFPA 11 covers the characteristics of foam-producing materials used for fire protection and the requirements for design, installation, operation, testing and maintenance of equipment and systems, including those used in combination with other fire-extinguishing agents. The minimum requirements are covered for flammable and combustible liquid hazards in local areas within buildings, storage tanks and indoor and outdoor processing areas.

Low-expansion foam is defined as an aggregation of air-filled bubbles resulting from the mechanical expansion of a foam solution by air with a foam-to-solution volume ratio of less than 20:1. It is most often used to protect flammable and combustible liquid hazards. Also, low-expansion foam may be used for heat radiation protection. Combined-agent systems involve the application of low-expansion foam to a hazard simultaneously or sequentially with dry-chemical powder.

NFPA 11 gives minimum requirements for the installation, design, operation, testing and maintenance of medium- and high-expansion foam systems. Medium-expansion foam is defined as an aggregation of air-filled bubbles resulting from the mechanical expansion of a foam solution by air or other gases with a foam-to-solution volume ratio of 20:1 to 200:1. High-expansion foam has a foam-to-solution volume ratio of 200:1 to approximately 1,000:1.

Medium-expansion foam may be used on solid fuel and liquid fuel fires where some degree of in-depth coverage is necessary (for example, for the total flooding of small, enclosed or partially enclosed volumes, such as engine test cells, transformer rooms, etc.). High-expansion foam is most suitable for filling volumes in which fires exit at various levels. For example, high-expansion foam can be used effectively against high-rack storage fires in enclosures such as in underground passages, where it may be dangerous to send personnel to control fires involving liquefied natural gas (LNG) and liquefied petroleum gas (LP-gas), and to provide vapor dispersion control for LNG and ammonia spills. High-expansion foam is particularly suited for indoor fires in confined spaces, since it is highly susceptible to wind and lack-of-confinement effects.

NFPA 16 contains the minimum requirements for open-head deluge-type foam-water sprinkler systems and foam-water spray systems. The systems are especially applicable to the protection of most flammable liquid hazards and have been used successfully to protect aircraft hangars and truck loading racks.

This section also specifically requires that records be maintained of inspections and testing to increase the effectiveness of such systems. Without records of such inspections and testing, it is more difficult to determine if the systems will be effective when activated and when future inspection and testing is necessary.

904.7.1 System test. Foam-extinguishing systems shall be inspected and tested at intervals in accordance with NFPA 25.

❖ Although Section 904.7.1 references NFPA 25 as the standard for the inspection and testing of foam-extinguishing systems, NFPA 25 is limited to water-based extinguishing systems. NFPA 25 technically addresses only foam-water sprinkler systems as specified in NFPA 16. NFPA 11 should be consulted for inspection and testing intervals for low-, medium- and high-expansion foam systems.

As with other alternative fire-extinguishing systems, the inspection and testing of foam systems is necessary to determine that the system is fully operational. In addition to general maintenance of equipment, the condition of the foam concentrate and its storage tanks or containers should be inspected at least once a year to verify adequate quality. The desired concentration of the foam concentrate in a stagnant storage situation may deteriorate over time.

904.8 Carbon dioxide systems. Carbon dioxide extinguishing systems shall be installed, maintained, periodically inspected and tested in accordance with NFPA 12 and their listing. Records of inspections and testing shall be maintained.

❖ NFPA 12 provides minimum requirements for the design, installation, testing, inspection, approval, operation and maintenance of carbon dioxide extinguishing systems.

Carbon dioxide extinguishing systems are useful in extinguishing fires in specific hazards or equipment in occupancies where an inert electrically nonconductive medium is essential or desirable and where cleanup of other extinguishing agents, such as dry-chemical residue, presents a problem. Carbon dioxide systems have satisfactorily protected the following: flammable liquids; electrical hazards, such as transformers, oil switches, rotating equipment and electronic equipment; engines using gasoline and other flammable liquid fuels; ordinary combustibles, such as paper, wood and textiles; and hazardous solids.

The fire code official has the authority to approve the type of carbon dioxide system to be installed. NFPA 12 defines four types of carbon dioxide systems: total flooding, local application, hand hose lines and standpipe and mobile supply systems. Only total flooding and local application systems are automatic suppression systems.

Total-flooding systems may be used where there is a permanent enclosure around the hazard that is adequate to allow the required concentration to be built up and maintained for the required period of time, which varies for different hazards. Examples of hazards that have been successfully protected by total-flooding systems include rooms, vaults, enclosed machines, ducts, ovens, and containers and their contents.

Local application systems may be used for extinguishing surface fires in flammable liquids, gases and shallow solids where the hazard is not enclosed or the enclosure does not conform to the requirements for a total-flooding system. Examples of hazards that have been successfully protected by local application systems include dip tanks, quench tanks, spray booths, oil-filled electric transformers and vapor vents.

This section also specifically requires that records be maintained of inspections and testing to increase the effectiveness of such systems. Without records of such inspections and testing, it is more difficult to determine if the systems will be effective when activated and when future inspection and testing is necessary.

904.8.1 System test. Systems shall be inspected and tested for proper operation at 12-month intervals.

❖ To determine adequate operation, carbon dioxide systems must be inspected and tested at least once a year.

904.8.2 High-pressure cylinders. High-pressure cylinders shall be weighed and the date of the last hydrostatic test shall be verified at six-month intervals. Where a container shows a loss in original content of more than 10 percent, the cylinder shall be refilled or replaced.

❖ Because of the potential for unobserved leakage of high-pressure cylinders, they need to be weighed semiannually to verify the concentration level is always within at least 10 percent of the original content.

904.8.3 Low-pressure containers. The liquid-level gauges of low-pressure containers shall be observed at one-week intervals. Where a container shows a content loss of more than 10 percent, the container shall be refilled to maintain the minimum gas requirements.

❖ A weekly visual observation of the liquid-level gauges of low-pressure containers is required to verify that there has been no significant leakage.

904.8.4 System hoses. System hoses shall be examined at 12-month intervals for damage. Damaged hoses shall be replaced or tested. At five-year intervals, all hoses shall be tested.

❖ The maintenance of system hoses is essential to ensuring the reliability of their use in an emergency. Although system hoses need to be visually checked on an annual basis only, a complete pressure test as indicated in Section 904.8.4.1 must be performed every five years.

904.8.4.1 Test procedure. Hoses shall be tested at not less than 2,500 pounds per square inch (psi) (17 238 kPa) for high-pressure systems and at not less than 900 psi (6206 kPa) for low-pressure systems.

❖ Every five years, system hoses for both high-pressure/low-pressure systems must be pressure tested to verify they are still in proper operating condition. The test typically involves filling the hose with water. The hose is then pressurized at the desired test pressure for at least 1 minute to observe any potential distortions or leakage in the hose. All hose assemblies that do not pass the test should be marked, destroyed and replaced with new hose assemblies. Hose assemblies that pass the test should be marked, dated and returned to service.

904.8.5 Auxiliary equipment. Auxiliary and supplementary components, such as switches, door and window releases, interconnected valves, damper releases and supplementary alarms, shall be manually operated at 12-month intervals to ensure that such components are in proper operating condition.

❖ The effectiveness of the carbon dioxide extinguishing system is also dependent on the operation of its auxiliary components. These components must also be manually operated at least once a year.

904.9 Halon systems. Halogenated extinguishing systems shall be installed, maintained, periodically inspected and tested in accordance with NFPA 12A and their listing. Records of inspections and testing shall be maintained.

❖ NFPA 12A contains minimum requirements for the design, installation, testing, inspection, approval, operation and maintenance of Halon 1301 extinguishing systems. Halon 1301 fire-extinguishing systems are useful in specific hazards, equipment or occupancies where an electrically nonconductive medium is essential or desirable and where cleanup of other extinguishing agents presents a problem.

Halon 1301 systems have satisfactorily protected gaseous and liquid flammable materials; electrical hazards, such as transformers, oil switches and rotating equipment; engines using gasoline and other flammable fuels; ordinary combustibles, such as paper, wood and textiles; and hazardous solids. Halon 1301 systems have also satisfactorily protected electronic computers, data processing equipment and control rooms.

The fire code official has the authority to approve the type of halogenated extinguishing system to be installed. NFPA 12A defines two types of halogenated extinguishing systems: total flooding and local application. Total-flooding systems may be used where there is a fixed enclosure around the hazard that is adequate to enable the required halon concentration to be built up and maintained for the required period of time to enable the effective extinguishing of the fire. Total-flooding systems may provide fire protection for rooms, vaults, enclosed machines, ovens, containers, storage tanks and bins.

Local application systems are used where there is not a fixed enclosure around the hazard or where the fixed enclosure around the hazard is not adequate to enable an extinguishing concentration to be built up and maintained in the space. Hazards that may be successfully protected by local application systems include dip tanks, quench tanks, spray booths, oil-filled electric transformers and vapor vents.

Two other considerations in selecting the proper extinguishing system are ambient temperature and the personnel hazards associated with the agent. The ambient temperature of the enclosure for a total-flooding system must be above 70°F (21°C) for Halon 1301 systems. Special consideration must also be given to the use of Halon systems when the temperatures are in excess of 900°F (482°C) because halon will readily decompose at such temperatures and the products of decomposition can be extremely irritating if inhaled, even in small amounts.

Halon 1301 total-flooding systems must not be used in concentrations greater than 10 percent in normally occupied areas. Where personnel cannot vacate the area within 1 minute, Halon 1301 total-flooding systems must not be used in normally occupied areas with concentrations greater than 7 percent. Halon 1301 total-flooding systems may be used with concentrations of up to 15 percent if the area is not normally occupied and the area can be evacuated within 30 seconds.

The use of halogenated extinguishing systems has become a concern with respect to the potential environmental effects of halon. Halongenated fire-extinguishing agents have been identified as a source of emissions, resulting in the depletion of the stratospheric ozone layer and, in accordance with the Montreal Protocol, the ceasing of its production in January 1994. Therefore, the supply of halon is limited and new supplies of halogenated extinguishing agents will not be available in the future. Existing supplies of halon can, however, continue to be used in existing, undischarged systems or to recharge discharged systems. This newfound need for halon supplies has given rise to new industries geared to the ranking, recycling and reclamation of existing halon supplies. Alternative "clean agent" extinguishing agents have been developed to replace halogenated agents (see Section 904.10).

This section also specifically requires that records be maintained of inspections and testing to increase the effectiveness of such systems. Without records of such inspections and testing, it is more difficult to determine if the systems will be effective when activated and when future inspection and testing is necessary.

904.9.1 System test. Systems shall be inspected and tested for proper operation at 12-month intervals.

❖ To determine proper operation, Halon systems must be inspected and tested at least once a year.

904.9.2 Containers. The extinguishing agent quantity and pressure of containers shall be checked at six-month intervals. Where a container shows a loss in original weight of more than 5 percent or a loss in original pressure (adjusted for temperature) of more than 10 percent, the container shall be refilled or replaced. The weight and pressure of the container shall be recorded on a tag attached to the container.

❖ Because of the potential for unobserved leakage of the Halon containers, they must be checked at least semi-annually to verify the original weight and pressure are within the designated tolerances. When necessary, containers must be refilled or replaced when the desired levels are not maintained. The containers should also be checked for evidence of corrosion or mechanical damage.

904.9.3 System hoses. System hoses shall be examined at 12-month intervals for damage. Damaged hoses shall be replaced or tested. At five-year intervals, all hoses shall be tested.

❖ Maintenance of system hoses is essential to ensuring the reliability of their use in an emergency. System hoses need to be visually checked annually. A complete pressure test as indicated in Section 904.9.3.1 must be performed every five years.

904.9.3.1 Test procedure. For Halon 1301 systems, hoses shall be tested at not less than 1,500 psi (10 343 kPa) for 600 psi (4137 kPa) charging pressure systems and not less than 900 psi (6206 kPa) for 360 psi (2482 kPa) charging pressure systems. For Halon 1211 hand-hose line systems, hoses shall be tested at 2,500 psi (17 238 kPa) for high-pressure systems and 900 psi (6206 kPa) for low-pressure systems.

❖ Every five years, system hoses must be pressure tested to verify they are still in proper operating condition. This section specifies the test pressure for the various types of Halon systems. The pressure test is intended to check for any potential distortion or leaking in the hose (see commentary, Section 904.8.4.1).

904.9.4 Auxiliary equipment. Auxiliary and supplementary components, such as switches, door and window releases, interconnected valves, damper releases and supplementary alarms, shall be manually operated at 12-month intervals to ensure such components are in proper operating condition.

❖ The effectiveness of halogenated extinguishing systems is also dependent on the operation of its auxiliary components. These components must be manually operated at least once a year.

904.10 Clean-agent systems. Clean-agent fire-extinguishing systems shall be installed, maintained, periodically inspected and tested in accordance with NFPA 2001 and their listing. Records of inspections and testing shall be maintained.

❖ NFPA 2001 contains minimum requirements for the design, installation, testing, inspection and operation of clean-agent fire-extinguishing systems. A clean agent is an electrically nonconducting suppression agent that is volatile or gaseous at discharge and does not leave a residue on evaporation. Clean-agent fire-extinguishing systems are installed in locations that are enclosed and have openings in the protected area that can be sealed on activation of the alarm to provide effective clean-agent concentrations. A clean-agent fire-extinguishing system should not be installed in locations that cannot be sealed unless testing has shown that adequate concentrations can be developed and maintained.

The two categories of clean agents are halocarbon compounds and inert gas agents. Halocarbon compounds include bromine, carbon, chlorine, fluorine, hydrogen and iodine. Halocarbon compounds suppress fire by a combination of breaking the chemical chain reaction of the fire, reducing the oxygen supporting the fire and reducing the ambient temperature of the fire origin to reduce the propagation of the fire. Inert gas agents contain primary components consisting of helium, neon, argon or a combination of these. Inert gases work by reducing the oxygen concentration around the fire origin to a level that does not support combustion.

Clean-agent fire-extinguishing systems were developed in response to the demise of halon as an acceptable fire-extinguishing agent because of its harmful effect on the environment. Although the original hope for a halon substitute was that these new clean agents could be directly and proportionally substituted for halon agents in existing systems (drop-in replacements), research has shown that clean agents are less efficient in extinguishing fires than are the halons they were intended to replace and require approximately 60 percent more agent by weight and volume in storage to do the same job. Additionally, the physical and chemical characteristics of clean agents differ sufficiently from halon to require different nozzles in addition to the need for larger storage vessels. Existing piping systems should be salvaged for use with clean agents only if they are carefully evaluated and determined to be hydraulically compatible with the flow characteristics of the new agent.

This section also relies on strict adherence to the system manufacturer's design and installation instructions for code compliance. As with many of the alternative fire suppression systems covered in this chapter, clean-agent systems are, for the most part, subjected by their manufacturers to a testing and listing program conducted by an approved testing agency. In such testing and listing programs, the clean agent is listed for use with specific equipment and equipment is listed for use with specific clean agents. The resultant listings include reference to the manufacturer's installation manuals, thereby giving the fire code official another valuable resource for reviewing and approving clean-agent systems.

Although clean agents have found a limited market for local application uses, such as a replacement for Halon 1211 in portable fire extinguishers, their primary application is in total-flooding systems, and they are available in both engineered and preengineered configurations.

Engineered clean-agent systems are specifically designed for protection of a particular hazard, whereas preengineered systems are designed to operate within predetermined limitations up to the noted maximums, thus allowing broader applicability to a variety of hazard applications.

Total-flooding systems are used where there is a fixed enclosure around the hazard that is adequate to enable the required clean-agent concentration to build up and be maintained within the space long enough to extinguish the fire. Such applications can include vaults, ovens, containers, tanks, computer rooms, paint lockers or enclosed machinery. In selecting the clean agent to be used in a given application, careful consideration must be given to whether the protected area is a normally occupied space, because different agents have different levels of concentration at which they may be a health hazard to occupants of the area.

The fire code official has the authority to approve the type of clean-agent system to be installed and should become familiar with the unique characteristics and hazards of clean-agent extinguishing systems using all available resources on the subject.

This section also specifically requires that records be maintained of inspections and testing to increase the effectiveness of such systems. Without records of such inspections and testing, it is more difficult to determine if the systems will be effective when activated and when future inspection and testing is necessary.

904.10.1 System test. Systems shall be inspected and tested for proper operation at 12-month intervals.

❖ To determine proper operation, all clean-agent systems must be inspected and tested at least once a year.

904.10.2 Containers. The extinguishing agent quantity and pressure of the containers shall be checked at six-month intervals. Where a container shows a loss in original weight of more than 5 percent or a loss in original pressure, adjusted for temperature, of more than 10 percent, the container shall be refilled or replaced. The weight and pressure of the container shall be recorded on a tag attached to the container.

❖ Because of the potential for unobserved leakage of the clean-agent containers, they must be checked at least semi-annually to verify the original weight and pressure are within the designated tolerances. When necessary, containers must be refilled or replaced when the desired levels are not maintained.

904.10.3 System hoses. System hoses shall be examined at 12-month intervals for damage. Damaged hoses shall be replaced or tested. All hoses shall be tested at five-year intervals.

❖ The maintenance of system hoses is essential to ensuring their reliability in an emergency. System hoses must be visually checked annually. A complete pressure test must be performed every five years.

904.11 Automatic water mist systems. *Automatic water mist systems* shall be permitted in applications that are consistent with the applicable listing or approvals and shall comply with Sections 904.11.1 through 904.11.3.

❖ This section provides the ability to use automatic water mist systems in specific applications. These installations are required to be consistent with the listings or approvals to which such systems have been tested. See Commentary Figure 904.11 for a picture showing the discharge of a water mist nozzle.

Commentary Figure 904.11
WATER MIST NOZZLE DISCHARGE

904.11.1 Design and installation requirements. *Automatic water mist systems* shall be designed and installed in accordance with Sections 904.11.1.1 through 904.11.1.4.

❖ The subsections that follow provide the various installation and design requirements related to water mist systems. This relates to the systems themselves and providing a reliable water supply.

904.11.1.1 General. *Automatic water mist systems* shall be designed and installed in accordance with NFPA 750 and the manufacturer's instructions.

❖ This section simply provides reference to the subsections with the detailed requirements related to the design and installation of water mist systems.

904.11.1.2 Actuation. *Automatic water mist systems* shall be automatically actuated.

❖ If a water mist system is used, it is required to be automatically activated.

904.11.1.3 Water supply protection. Connections to a potable water supply shall be protected against backflow in accordance with the *International Plumbing Code*.

❖ The water supply quality is more critical with automatic water mist systems than automatic sprinkler systems. Backflow prevention is required as it would be for water supply for automatic sprinkler systems.

904.11.1.4 Secondary water supply. Where a secondary water supply is required for an *automatic sprinkler system*, an *automatic water mist system* shall be provided with an *approved* secondary water supply.

❖ Since these systems work to protect buildings and spaces in a fashion similar to a sprinkler system and possibly as an alternative to automatic sprinkler systems, the water supply must be appropriate. If an automatic sprinkler system is required to have a secondary water supply in accordance with Section 403.3.3, then the water mist system must also provide an approved secondary water supply.

904.11.2 Water mist system supervision and alarms. Supervision and alarms shall be provided as required for *automatic sprinkler systems* in accordance with Section 903.4.

❖ This section plays a similar role to an automatic sprinkler system with regard to supervision and alarms. It is critical to make sure valves are open. In addition, an alarm to notify of an activation must be provided as it is for a sprinkler system. Note that this is not intended to be an occupant notification system. See the commentary to Section 903.4.

904.11.2.1 Monitoring. Monitoring shall be provided as required for *automatic sprinkler systems* in accordance with Section 903.4.1.

❖ See the commentary to Sections 903.4.1 and 904.11.2.

904.11.2.2 Alarms. Alarms shall be provided as required for *automatic sprinkler systems* in accordance with Section 903.4.2.

❖ Again, this is not intended to be occupant notification but to simply alert someone that the system has activated. See the commentary to Sections 903.4.2 and 904.11.2.

904.11.2.3 Floor control valves. Floor control valves shall be provided as required for *automatic sprinkler systems* in accordance with Section 903.4.3.

❖ See the commentary to Section 903.4.3.

904.11.3 Testing and maintenance. *Automatic water mist systems* shall be tested and maintained in accordance with Section 901.6.

❖ Testing and maintenance are critical to the long-term viability of automatic water mist systems. The code focuses not simply on initial installation but also on maintenance.

904.12 Commercial cooking systems. The automatic fire-extinguishing system for commercial cooking systems shall be of a type recognized for protection of commercial cooking equipment and exhaust systems of the type and arrangement protected. Preengineered automatic dry- and wet-chemical extinguishing systems shall be tested in accordance with UL 300 and *listed* and *labeled* for the intended application. Other types of automatic fire-extinguishing systems shall be *listed* and *labeled* for specific use as protection for commercial cooking operations. The system shall be installed in accordance with this code, NFPA 96, its listing and the manufacturer's installation instructions. Automatic fire-extinguishing systems of the following types shall be installed in accordance with the referenced standard indicated, as follows:

1. Carbon dioxide extinguishing systems, NFPA 12.
2. *Automatic sprinkler systems*, NFPA 13.
3. Automatic water mist systems, NFPA 750.

4. Foam-water sprinkler system or foam-water spray systems, NFPA 16.
5. Dry-chemical extinguishing systems, NFPA 17.
6. Wet-chemical extinguishing systems, NFPA 17A.

Exception: Factory-built commercial cooking recirculating systems that are tested in accordance with UL 710B and *listed*, *labeled* and installed in accordance with Section 304.1 of the *International Mechanical Code*.

❖ The history of commercial kitchen exhaust systems shows that the mixture of flammable grease and effluents carried by such systems and the potential for the cooking equipment to act as an ignition source contribute to a higher level of hazard for kitchen exhaust systems than is normally found in many other exhaust systems. Furthermore, fire in a grease exhaust duct can produce temperatures of 2,000°F (1093°C) or more and heat radiating from the duct can ignite nearby combustibles. As a result, the code requires exhaust systems serving grease-producing equipment to include fire suppression to protect the cooking surfaces, hood, filters and exhaust duct to confine a fire to the hood and duct system, thus reducing the likelihood of it spreading to the structure.

In addition to the general requirements of this section, five industry standards are referenced for the installation of fire-extinguishing systems protecting commercial food heat-processing equipment and kitchen exhaust systems. Design professionals should specify and design fire-extinguishing systems to comply with these referenced standards. Only the installation of fire-extinguishing systems is regulated by these references. Where preengineered automatic dry- and wet-chemical extinguishing systems are installed, they must be listed and labeled for the specific cooking operation and tested in accordance with UL 300. Design and construction requirements for the specific types of fire-extinguishing systems are found in the respective sections of the referenced standards.

Regulatory requirements for the approval and installation of fire-extinguishing systems are the same as the approval required for all mechanical equipment and appliances. This section, therefore, requires extinguishing systems to be listed and labeled by an approved agency and installed in accordance with their listing and the manufacturer's installation instructions.

The exception allows factory-built commercial cooking recirculating systems to be installed if they have been tested and listed in accordance with UL 710B. It is important that they be installed in accordance with the manufacturer's installation instructions so that the listing requirements are met. An improper installation could result in hazardous vapors being discharged back into the kitchen.

Commercial cooking recirculating systems consist of an electric cooking appliance and an integral or matched packaged hood assembly. The hood assembly consists of a fan, collection hood, grease filter, fire damper, fire-extinguishing system and air filter, such as an electrostatic precipitator. These systems are tested for fire safety and emissions. The grease vapor (condensable particulate matter) in the effluent at the system discharge is not allowed to exceed a concentration of 5.0 mg/m^3. Recirculating systems are not used with fuel-fired appliances because the filtering systems do not remove combustion products. Kitchens require ventilation in accordance with Chapter 4 of the IMC.

Although the provisions in Section 904.12 address many of the specifics for commercial kitchens, additional information regarding commercial cooking suppression systems is located in Sections 904.3.2 and 904.3.3. This information is supplemental to that and should be considered together in developing the design for commercial cooking suppression systems.

904.12.1 Manual system operation. A manual actuation device shall be located at or near a *means of egress* from the cooking area not less than 10 feet (3048 mm) and not more than 20 feet (6096 mm) from the kitchen exhaust system. The manual actuation device shall be installed not more than 48 inches (1200 mm) nor less than 42 inches (1067 mm) above the floor and shall clearly identify the hazard protected. The manual actuation shall require a maximum force of 40 pounds (178 N) and a maximum movement of 14 inches (356 mm) to actuate the fire suppression system.

Exception: *Automatic sprinkler systems* shall not be required to be equipped with manual actuation means.

❖ The manual device, usually a pull station, mechanically activates the suppression system. The typical system uses a mechanical circuit of cables under tension to hold the system in the armed (cocked) mode. Melting of a fusible link or actuation of a manual pull station causes the cable to lose tension, which, in turn, starts the discharge of the suppression agent. The manual actuation device must be readily and easily usable by the building occupants; therefore, the device must not require excessive force or range of movement to cause actuation.

In order to allow the actuation device to be used most effectively, the specified mounting height is intended to be consistent with the NFPA 17A standards and be handicapped accessible. This includes the requirement to identify the actuation device with the hazard protected. Where multiple kitchen appliances are provided, properly identifying which device relates to which appliance is very important. Required signage should be readily visible in the hazard area and capable of conveying information quickly and concisely.

Manual actuation is not required for automatic sprinkler systems because the typical system design will employ closed heads and wet system piping. A manual actuation valve would serve no purpose because sprinkler heads are already supplied with pressurized water and will discharge water only when the individual fusible elements open the heads.

904.12.2 System interconnection. The actuation of the fire extinguishing system shall automatically shut down the fuel or electrical power supply to the cooking equipment. The fuel and electrical supply reset shall be manual.

❖ The actuation of any fire suppression system must automatically shut off all sources of fuel or power to all cooking equipment located beneath the exhaust hood protected by the suppression system. This requirement is intended to shut off all heat sources that could reignite or intensify a fire. Shutting off a fuel and power supply to cooking appliances will eliminate an ignition source and allow the cooking surfaces to cool down. This shutdown is accomplished with mechanical or electrical interconnections between the suppression system and a shutoff valve or switch located on the fuel or electrical supply.

Common fuel shutoff valves include mechanical-type gas valves and electrical solenoid-type gas valves. Contactor-type switches or shunt-trip circuit breakers can be used for electrically heated appliances. The fuel or electric source must not be automatically restored after the suppression system has been actuated.

Chemical-type fire-extinguishing systems discharge for only a limited time and can discharge only once before recharge and reset; therefore, precautions must be taken to prevent a fire from reigniting. After a fire is detected and the initial suppressant discharge begins, the fuel and power supply will be locked out, thereby preventing the operation of the appliances until all systems are again ready for operation. Fuel and power supply shutoff must be manually restored by resetting a mechanical linkage or holding/latching-type circuit.

904.12.3 Carbon dioxide systems. Where carbon dioxide systems are used, there shall be a nozzle at the top of the ventilating duct. Additional nozzles that are symmetrically arranged to give uniform distribution shall be installed within vertical ducts exceeding 20 feet (6096 mm) and horizontal ducts exceeding 50 feet (15 240 mm). Dampers shall be installed at either the top or the bottom of the duct and shall be arranged to operate automatically upon activation of the fire-extinguishing system. Where the damper is installed at the top of the duct, the top nozzle shall be immediately below the damper. Automatic carbon dioxide fire-extinguishing systems shall be sufficiently sized to protect all hazards venting through a common duct simultaneously.

❖ This section states specific design requirements for nozzle locations, dampers and ducts for carbon dioxide extinguishing systems that may be used to protect commercial cooking systems. These requirements are intended to supersede similar, more general provisions in NFPA 12. Because carbon dioxide (CO_2) is a gaseous suppressant, dampers are required in the ductwork to define the atmosphere where the fire event would be. A specific concentration of CO_2 is necessary and dampers are required to define and contain the suppressant. The discharge cools exposed surfaces in addition to depriving the fire of oxygen. Although not mentioned specifically in this section, the applicable provisions of NFPA 12 should also be applied because the system is a CO_2 system as referenced in Section 904.8.

904.12.3.1 Ventilation system. Commercial-type cooking equipment protected by an automatic carbon dioxide extinguishing system shall be arranged to shut off the ventilation system upon activation.

❖ Shutting down the ventilation system upon activation of the CO_2 extinguishing system maintains the desired concentration of carbon dioxide to suppress the fire. Leakage of gas from the protected area should be kept to a minimum. Where leakage is anticipated, additional quantities of carbon dioxide must be provided to compensate for any losses.

904.12.4 Special provisions for automatic sprinkler systems. *Automatic sprinkler systems* protecting commercial-type cooking equipment shall be supplied from a separate, indicating-type control valve that is identified. *Access* to the control valve shall be provided.

❖ This section requires a separate control valve in the water line to the sprinklers protecting the cooking and ventilating system. The additional valve allows the flexibility to shut off the system for repairs or for cleanups after sprinkler discharge without taking the entire system out of service.

904.12.4.1 Listed sprinklers. Sprinklers used for the protection of fryers shall be tested in accordance with UL 199E, *listed* for that application and installed in accordance with their listing.

❖ Sprinklers specifically listed for such use must be used when protecting deep fat fryers. These specially listed sprinklers use finer water droplets than standard spray sprinklers. The water spray lowers the temperature below a point where the fire can sustain itself and reduces the possibility of the fire expanding. UL 199E addresses these special sprinklers and includes performance tests for deep fat fryer extinguishment and also deep fat fryer cooking temperature splash. The selection of inappropriate sprinklers for deep fat fryer protection can increase the hazards during water application rather than suppressing the fire.

904.12.5 Operations and maintenance. Automatic fire-extinguishing systems protecting commercial cooking systems shall be maintained in accordance with Sections 904.12.5.1 through 904.12.5.3.

❖ Most fires in commercial kitchens involve the cooking appliance and exhaust system in some way. Proper operation of the system in accordance with the IMC, as well as routine maintenance, can reduce the hazards related to the collection and removal of smoke and grease-laden vapors.

904.12.5.1 Existing automatic fire-extinguishing systems. Where changes in the cooking media, positioning of cooking equipment or replacement of cooking equipment occur in existing commercial cooking systems, the automatic fire-extinguishing system shall be required to comply with the applicable provisions of Sections 904.12 through 904.12.4.

❖ The provisions of Section 904.12 have long required new commercial cooking systems with preengineered fire-extinguishing systems to be tested in accordance with UL 300 and listed and labeled for that use. The question has often arisen, however, as to whether or how those provisions should be applied to existing systems. This section provides guidance and adds clarity as to when existing automatic fire-extinguishing systems protecting commercial cooking operations need to be modified, upgraded or replaced to meet UL 300 requirements. These provisions are thought to be consistent with provisions adopted by some states and local jurisdictions on this topic.

904.12.5.2 Extinguishing system service. Automatic fire-extinguishing systems shall be serviced not less frequently than every six months and after activation of the system. Inspection shall be by qualified individuals, and a certificate of inspection shall be forwarded to the *fire code official* upon completion.

❖ Range hood fire-extinguishing systems must be inspected and serviced at regular intervals to determine that they are ready to perform the intended function. Obviously, service is required after the suppression system discharges. The extent of service and maintenance depends on the type of fire-extinguishing system installed. The NFPA standard corresponding to the installed extinguishing agent should be consulted for additional service requirements (see commentary, Section 904.12).

904.12.5.3 Fusible link and sprinkler head replacement. Fusible links and automatic sprinkler heads shall be replaced annually, and other protection devices shall be serviced or replaced in accordance with the manufacturer's instructions.

Exception: Frangible bulbs are not required to be replaced annually.

❖ Because of the potential accumulation of grease or other contaminants that could adversely affect proper operation, fusible links and automatic sprinkler heads must be replaced at least annually. The sensing elements of the fusible link devices as well as the sprinkler heads must be routinely visually inspected and replaced as needed, at least annually.

The exception allows frangible bulb-type sprinklers to not be replaced as long as the annual examination shows no accumulation of grease or other contaminants.

904.13 Domestic cooking systems. Cooktops and ranges installed in the following occupancies shall be protected in accordance with Section 904.13.1:

1. In Group I-1 occupancies where domestic cooking facilities are installed in accordance with Section 420.8 of the *International Building Code*.
2. In Group I-2, Condition 1 occupancies where domestic cooking facilities are installed in accordance with Section 407.2.6 of the *International Building Code*.
3. In Group R-2 college dormitories where domestic cooking facilities are installed in accordance with Section 420.10 of the *International Building Code*.

❖ As nursing homes move away from institutional models, it is critical to have a functioning kitchen that can serve as the "hearth of the home." Instead of a large, centralized, institutional kitchen where all meals are prepared and delivered to a central dining room or the resident's room, the new "household model" nursing home uses de-centralized kitchens and small dining areas to create the feeling and focus of home. For persons with dementia, it is particularly important to have spaces that look familiar, like the kitchen in their former home, to increase their understanding and ability to function at their highest level. This section addresses the fire protection system needs for these kitchens. Note that these occupancies already contain quick-response sprinklers. This section provides the requirements for the hood fire-extinguishing system needed for the cooking hood located over the cooktop or range. That system is required to be in compliance with UL 300A.

904.13.1 Protection from fire. Cooktops and ranges shall be protected in accordance with Section 904.13.1.1 or 904.13.1.2.

❖ There are two options available for the protection of cooktops and ranges. The first is to provide an automatic fire-extinguishing system in accordance with Section 904.13.1.1 and the second is to provide burners that have been tested and listed to prevent ignition of cooking oil in accordance with Section 904.13.1.2.

904.13.1.1 Automatic fire-extinguishing system. The domestic recirculating or exterior vented cooking hood provided over the cooktop or range shall be equipped with an approved automatic fire-extinguishing system complying with the following:

1. The automatic fire-extinguishing system shall be of a type recognized for protection of domestic cooking equipment. Preengineered automatic fire-extinguishing systems shall be listed and labeled in accordance with UL 300A and installed in accordance with the manufacturer's instructions.
2. Manual actuation of the fire-extinguishing system shall be provided in accordance with Section 904.12.1.
3. Interconnection of the fuel and electric power supply shall be in accordance with Section 904.12.2.

❖ The first option for the protection of cooktops and ranges is to provide an approved automatic fire-extinguishing system. The system is to conform to the three conditions listed. It is to be listed in accordance with UL 300A and installed in conformance with the manufacturer's written instructions. A means of manual operation is to be provided in conformance with Section 904.12.1. In addition, the fuel and electric power supply are to be interconnected as stated in Section 904.12.2.

904.13.1.2 Ignition prevention. Cooktops and ranges shall include burners that have been tested and listed to prevent ignition of cooking oil with burners turned on to their maximum heat settings and allowed to operate for 30 minutes.

❖ The second option for the protection of cooktops and ranges is to use specifically listed ignition resistant burners that do not allow cooking oils to ignite during testing. If these burners are used, an automatic cooktop fire-extinguishing system is not required. Recent work by the Fire Protection Research Foundation confirms that burners meeting these specifications are highly unlikely to ignite cooking materials. The UL 858 Standard for Safety for Household Electric Ranges was recently revised to include a new Section 60A, Abnormal Operation—Coil Surface Unit Cooking Oil Ignition Test that evaluates the ability of coiled surface units to not ignite cooking oil.

904.14 Aerosol fire-extinguishing systems. Aerosol fire-extinguishing systems shall be installed, periodically inspected, tested and maintained in accordance with Sections 901 and 904.4, NFPA 2010, and in accordance with their listing.

Such devices and appurtenances shall be listed and installed in compliance with manufacturer's instructions.

❖ This section provides the requirements for the use of aerosol fire-extinguishing systems intended for total-flooding applications. As stated, the installation is to conform to Sections 901 and 904.4 as well as NFPA 2010 and the specific system listing. The appropriate UL standard is 2775 for Fixed Condensed Aerosol Extinguishing System Units.

Condensed aerosol fire suppression systems can be used as an alternative to other fire suppression systems for the protection of Class A (surface), Class B, and Class C hazards. These systems do not use compressed gas cylinders or pressure-rated piping. Generally, they are electrically operated when integrated with IFC-approved fire alarm and releasing control systems and approved/listed releasing panels, or are deployed as automatic stand-alone fire-extinguishing units. Typically these extinguishing units are designed as disposable devices with a minimum 10-year shelf life.

904.14.1 Maintenance. Not less than semiannually, an inspection shall be conducted by a trained person to assess whether the system is in working order. Not less than annually, a certified fire suppression contractor having knowledge of and training in the installation, operation and maintenance of the specific fire-extinguishing system shall inspect, test, service and maintain such system in accordance with this section and the manufacturer's specifications and servicing manuals.

❖ This section provides the maintenance frequency for aerosol fire-extinguishing systems. The systems are required to be inspected by a trained person at least twice a year. Note that the person performing the inspection should be trained by the installing certified fire suppression contractor or system manufacturer's representative. The annual maintenance requirements are to be as prescribed by the specific manufacturer's specifications and servicing manual and must be completed by a fire suppression contractor that is certified by the system manufacturer.

SECTION 905 STANDPIPE SYSTEMS

905.1 General. Standpipe systems shall be provided in new buildings and structures in accordance with Sections 905.2 through 905.11. In buildings used for *high-piled combustible storage*, fire protection shall be in accordance with Chapter 32.

❖ Standpipe systems are required in buildings to provide a quick, convenient water source for fire department use where hose lines would otherwise be impractical, such as in high-rise buildings. Standpipe systems can also be used prior to deployment of hose lines from fire department apparatus. The requirements for standpipes are based on practical requirements of typical fire-fighting operations and the nationally recognized standard NFPA 14.

The threads on connections to which the fire department may connect a hose must be compatible with the fire department hose threads (see commentary, Section 903.3.6). Chapter 23 requires a Class I standpipe system in exit passageways of buildings used for high-piled storage. Note that if a building containing high-piled storage does not contain an exit passageway, then standpipes would not be required. High-piled storage involves the solid-piled, bin box, palletized or rack storage of Class I through IV commodities over 12 feet (3658 mm) high. High-hazard commodities stored higher than 6 feet (1829 mm) are also considered high piled.

905.2 Installation standard. Standpipe systems shall be installed in accordance with this section and NFPA 14. Fire department connections for standpipe systems shall be in accordance with Section 912.

❖ This section requires the installation of standpipe systems to comply with the applicable provisions of NFPA 14 in addition to Section 905. NFPA 14 contains the minimum requirements for the installation of standpipe and hose systems for buildings and structures. The standard addresses additional requirements not addressed in the code, such as pressure limitations, minimum flow rates, piping specifications, hose connection details, valves, fittings, hangers and the testing and inspection of standpipes. The periodic inspection, testing and maintenance of standpipe systems must comply with NFPA 25.

Section 905 and NFPA 14 recognize three classes of standpipe systems: Class I, II or III. The type of system required depends on building height, building area, type of occupancy and the extent of automatic sprinkler protection. Section 905 also recognizes five types of standpipe systems: automatic dry, automatic wet, manual dry, manual wet and semiautomatic dry. The use of each type of system is limited to the building conditions and locations identified in Section 905.3. The classes and types of standpipe systems are defined in Section 202.

Section 912, to which this section refers, provides a comprehensive set of requirements for FDCs, reducing the opportunity for any of its requirements to be overlooked. See the commentary to Section 912.

905.3 Required installations. Standpipe systems shall be installed where required by Sections 905.3.1 through 905.3.8. Standpipe systems are allowed to be combined with *automatic sprinkler systems*.

Exception: Standpipe systems are not required in Group R-3 occupancies.

❖ Standpipe systems are installed in buildings based on the occupancy, fire department accessibility and special conditions that may require manual fire suppression exceeding the capacity of a fire extinguisher. Standpipe systems are most commonly required for buildings that exceed the height threshold requirement in Section 905.3.1; for buildings with certain features of a specific occupancy; or for buildings such as covered and open mall buildings, stages and underground buildings.

This section also states that a standpipe system does not have to be separate from an installed sprinkler system. It is common practice in multiple-story buildings for the standpipe system risers to also serve as risers for the automatic sprinkler systems.

In these instances, precautions need to be taken so that the operation of one system will not interfere with the operation of the other system. Therefore, control valves for the sprinkler system must be installed where the sprinklers are connected to the standpipe riser at each floor level. This allows the standpipe system to remain operational, even if the sprinkler system is shut off at the floor control valve.

The exception recognizes that standpipe systems in Group R-3 occupancies would be of minimal value to the fire department and would send the wrong message to the occupants of a dwelling unit. In the case of multiple single-family dwellings, each dwelling unit has a separate entrance and is separated from the other units by 1-hour fire partitions. These conditions permit ready access to fires and also provide for a degree of fire containment through compartmentation, which is not always present in other occupancies.

905.3.1 Height. Class III standpipe systems shall be installed throughout buildings where any of the following conditions exist:

1. Four or more stories are above or below grade plane.
2. The floor level of the highest story is located more than 30 feet (9144 mm) above the lowest level of the fire department vehicle access.
3. The floor level of the lowest story is located more than 30 feet (9144 mm) below the highest level of fire department vehicle access.

Exceptions:

1. Class I standpipes are allowed in buildings equipped throughout with an *automatic sprinkler system* in accordance with Section 903.3.1.1 or 903.3.1.2.
2. Class I standpipes are allowed in Group B and E occupancies.
3. Class I manual standpipes are allowed in open parking garages where the highest floor is located not more than 150 feet (45 720 mm) above the lowest level of fire department vehicle access.
4. Class I manual dry standpipes are allowed in open parking garages that are subject to freezing temperatures, provided that the hose connections are located as required for Class II standpipes in accordance with Section 905.5.
5. Class I standpipes are allowed in *basements* equipped throughout with an *automatic sprinkler system*.
6. Class I standpipes are allowed in buildings where occupant-use hose lines will not be utilized by trained personnel or the fire department.
7. In determining the lowest level of fire department vehicle access, it shall not be required to consider either of the following:
   7.1. Recessed loading docks for four vehicles or less.
   7.2. Conditions where topography makes access from the fire department vehicle to the building impractical or impossible.

❖ Given the available manpower on the fire department vehicle, standard fire-fighting operations and standard hose sizes, four or more stories above or below grade plane or a 30-foot (9144 mm) vertical distance above or below the lowest or highest level of the fire department vehicle access is generally considered the maximum distance to which a typical fire department engine company can practically and readily extend its hose lines. Thus, the maximum vertical travel (height) threshold is based on the time it would take a typical fire department engine (pumper) company to manually suppress a fire. The standpipe connection reduces the time needed for the fire department to extend hose lines up or down stairways to advance and apply water to the fire. For this use, a minimum Class III standpipe system is required.

With respect to the height of the building, the threshold is measured from the level at which the fire department can gain access to the building directly from its vehicle and begin vertical movement. Floor levels above grade are measured from the lowest level of fire department vehicle access to the highest floor level above [see Commentary Figure 905.3.1(1)]. If a building contains floor levels below the level of fire department vehicle access, the measurement is made from the highest level of fire department vehicle access to the lowest floor level. In cases where a building has more than one level of fire department vehicle access, the most restrictive measurement is used because it is not known at which level the fire department will access the building. In other words, the vertical distance is to be measured from the more restrictive level of fire department vehicle access to the level of the highest (or lowest, if below) floor [see Commentary Figure 905.3.1(2)].

The threshold based on the height of the building is independent of the occupancy of the building, the area of the building or the presence of an automatic sprinkler system. This is based on the universal need to be able to provide a water supply for fire suppression in any building and on the limitations of the physical effort necessary to extend hose lines vertically.

Before discussing the exceptions, it is important to understand the differences between the different classes and operational characteristics of standpipes. More detailed information is included in Section 202 for the definitions of the different classes and types of standpipes.

Standpipes can be dry or wet, manual, automatic or semiautomatic. Automatic systems can be either wet or dry. Manual systems can be either wet or dry. A semiautomatic system is always in association with a dry system.

The code is written such that it could be assumed the default is an automatic wet system. This is, however, not the case. The requirement is left to the design standard, NFPA 14. Section 5.4.1.1 of NFPA 14 indicates that Class I standpipes can be manual if the building is not a high-rise. Section 5.4.1.4 of the standard indicates that a Class I standpipe must be wet except where the pipe is subject to freezing. Thus, where a Class I standpipe is installed, possibly as a part of Exception 1, the system can be manual wet if the building is not a high-rise. This is consistent with IFC Committee Interpretation No. 33-03. As long as the building is not a high-rise, it can be provided with a Class I standpipe system that is manual wet.

Class II and III standpipes are required to be automatic wet types or semiautomatic wet types except where the piping is subject to freezing, according to Section 5.4.2 of NFPA 14. They cannot be manual. Only Class I standpipes can be manual and can only be used under the conditions noted in this code. Note that other sections of the code may specify whether the system must be automatic. If the requirement is not noted elsewhere in the code, then the decision to use an automatic or manual system is left to the designer.

Exception 1 recognizes that with a fully operational automatic sprinkler system, the time that the fire department has to extend hoses within the building is substantially increased and that the amount of effort required is greatly reduced. Consequently, a single Class I connection can be provided. The second, $1^1/_2$-inch (38 mm) connection is allowed to be omitted. NFPA 14 also has a similar provision but is more restrictive as it only eliminates the hose station and additionally requires a $2^1/_2$ inch by $1^1/_2$ inch (65 mm by 40 mm) reducer and a cap attached with a chain (see NFPA 14, Section 7.3.4.1). In accordance with Section 102.4, the code would take precedence and the reducer and cap would not be required.

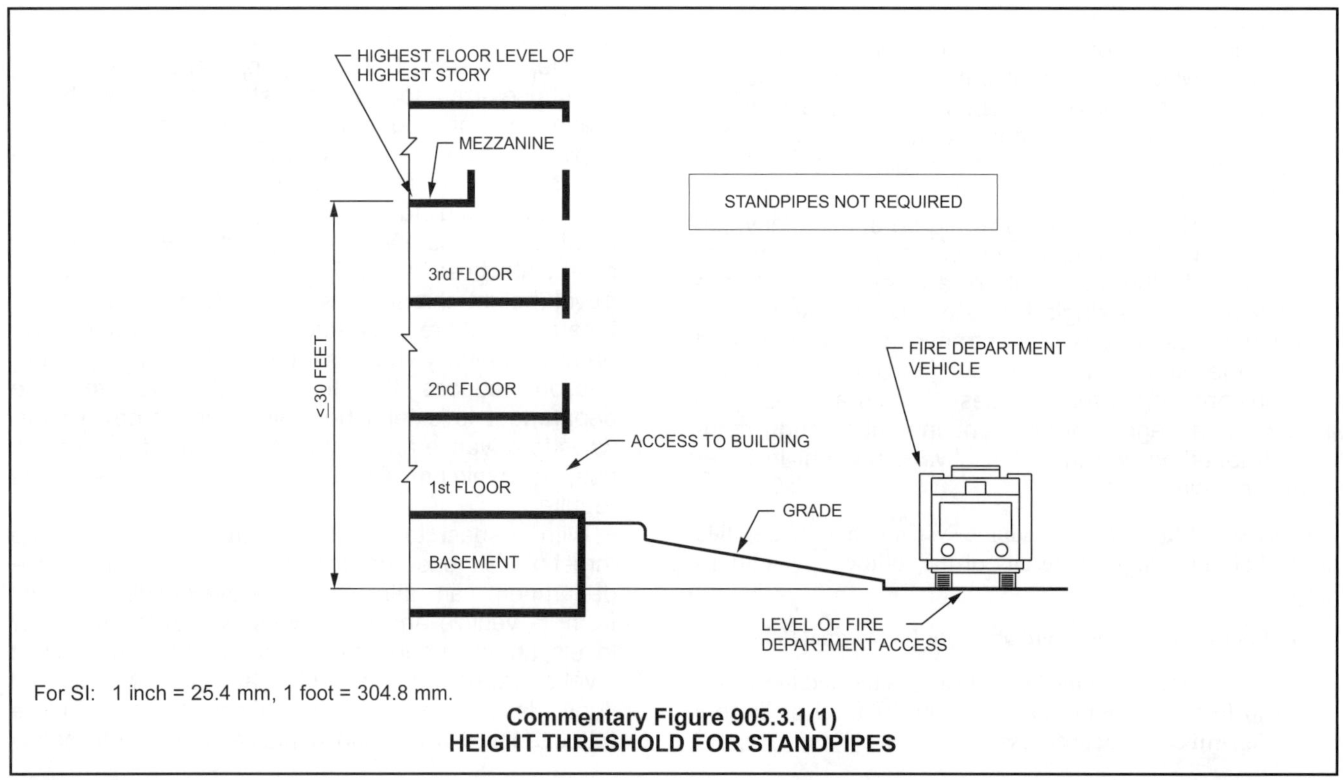

For SI: 1 inch = 25.4 mm, 1 foot = 304.8 mm.

Commentary Figure 905.3.1(1)
HEIGHT THRESHOLD FOR STANDPIPES

Exception 2 allows for the use of Class I standpipes in Group B and E occupancies. Occupant-use hose stations are considered to be a legacy method of fire protection, existing for decades in model code requirements. In recent years, many fire safety and evacuation plans have all but abandoned occupant-use hoses in their training of building occupants, relying instead on fire extinguisher training (which is required in all new and existing Group B and E occupancies) as the primary focus of evacuation. Also, fire behavior can be different in these occupancies due to compartment fire loading. This creates fires that develop faster, create more heat in most situations, and produce greater amounts of toxic smoke. Collectively, the ability for occupants to safely and effectively utilize occupant-use hoses without fire-fighting gear and respiratory protection is considered to be greatly minimized. Occupant-use hose is permitted to not be installed in sprinkler-protected buildings that otherwise require standpipes. Even though this may seem to be a trade-off, the determination of whether to replace the manual method (occupant-use hose) with an automatic sprinkler system should be based on the occupants' ability to suppress a fire manually.

Exception 3 identifies one of the issues relative to open parking garages. This exception allows for the garage, when not more than 150 feet (45 720 mm) in height above the lowest level of fire department access, to have a wet standpipe but without additional operating pressure until the fire department connects and begins pumping into the system. This makes sense since normal operations typically do not begin until after the fire department is on the scene and has made its initial assessments. This is generally considered to be the maximum safe height for pumpers to overcome the hydrostatic head presented by 150 feet (45 720 mm) of water. Careful considerations should be made since not all fire departments have equipment capable of this type of pumping capacity.

Exception 4 is similar to the prior exception but with the added provision that the standpipe can be dry if subject to freezing, regardless of height. Because the standpipe will be without water and be dependent on the fire department to provide both water and pressure, standpipe outlets must be spaced more frequently, as noted in Section 905.5 for Class II standpipes, so that fire fighters can connect and begin operations quicker. The exception does not require Class II outlets; only that the spacing be consistent with the requirement for Class II.

Exception 5 is similar to Exception 1 but only addresses sprinklers in the basement. Thus, it is possible to use this exception if only the basement is protected by automatic sprinklers. However, Class I connections can only be provided in the basements—not on the upper floors. The exception cannot be used for stories above grade unless the entire building is sprinklered and, therefore, compliant with Exception 1.

Exception 6 allows for the use of Class I standpipes in place of Class III standpipes in buildings where occupant-use hose lines will not be used by trained personnel or the fire department. If occupants are not trained in their use and the fire department will not utilize them, then occupant-use hose lines serve no purpose and could potentially slow down the

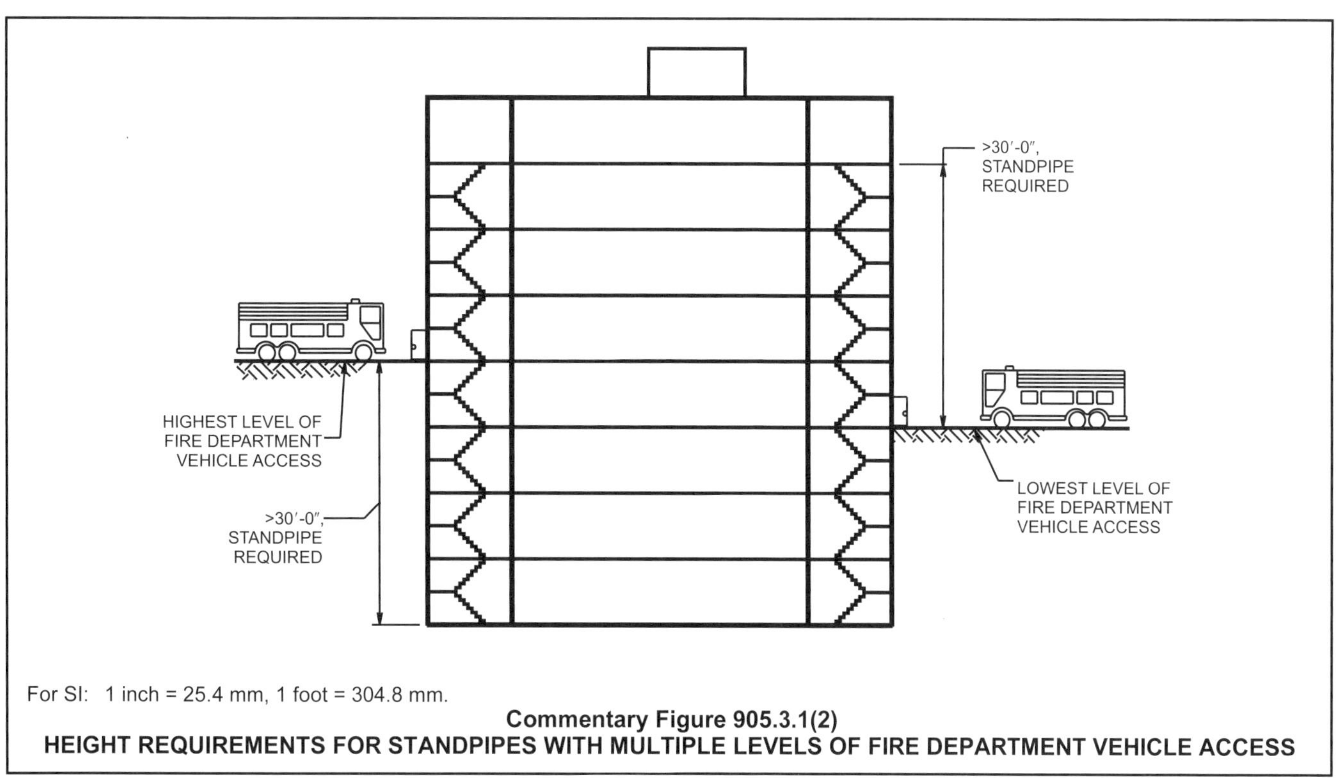

For SI: 1 inch = 25.4 mm, 1 foot = 304.8 mm.

Commentary Figure 905.3.1(2)
HEIGHT REQUIREMENTS FOR STANDPIPES WITH MULTIPLE LEVELS OF FIRE DEPARTMENT VEHICLE ACCESS

fire department's attempt to connect its own hose to the $2^1/_2$-inch (64 mm) hose valve outlet. Thus, a Class I standpipe can be used in this situation.

Exception 7 provides additional information about what must be considered when determining building height with respect to the level of fire department vehicle access. The first item is a practical one that excludes loading docks of a limited size. The second item notes that although it may be possible to have a fire department vehicle arrive adjacent to the building at a low level, it may not be possible for the fire department to access the building from that level. An example of this condition would be where a road surface is located below a building built on a bluff. Although the fire department vehicles can approach from the lower road, fire department personnel cannot access the building from that lower level. Thus, the standpipe requirement would not be based on the road below the bluff.

905.3.2 Group A. Class I automatic wet standpipes shall be provided in nonsprinklered Group A buildings having an *occupant load* exceeding 1,000 persons.

Exceptions:

1. Open-air-seating spaces without enclosed spaces.
2. Class I automatic dry and semiautomatic dry standpipes or manual wet standpipes are allowed in buildings that are not high-rise buildings.

❖ The main concern in assembly occupancies with a high occupant load is evacuation. Many occupants may not be familiar with either their surroundings or the egress arrangement in the building. This section also assumes the building is not sprinklered; therefore, control and suppression of the fire is left to the fire department.

Exception 1 exempts open-air seating without enclosed spaces, such as grandstands and bleachers. In such occupancies, a buildup of smoke and hot gases is not possible because these structures are open to the atmosphere.

Exception 2 states that in lieu of a Class I automatic wet standpipe, automatic dry and semiautomatic dry Class I standpipes are permitted in buildings that are not considered to be a high-rise.

905.3.3 Covered and open mall buildings. Covered mall and open mall buildings shall be equipped throughout with a standpipe system where required by Section 905.3.1. Mall buildings not required to be equipped with a standpipe system by Section 905.3.1 shall be equipped with Class I hose connections connected to the *automatic sprinkler system* sized to deliver water at 250 gallons per minute (946.4 L/min) at the hydraulically most remote hose connection while concurrently supplying the automatic sprinkler system demand. The standpipe system shall be designed not to exceed a 50 pounds per square inch (psi) (345 kPa) residual pressure loss with a flow of 250 gallons per minute (946.4 L/min) from the fire department connection to the hydraulically most remote hose connection. Hose connections shall be provided at each of the following locations:

1. Within the mall at the entrance to each exit passageway or corridor.
2. At each floor-level landing within *interior exit stairways* opening directly on the mall.
3. At exterior public entrances to the mall of a covered mall building.
4. At public entrances at the perimeter line of an open mall building.
5. At other locations as necessary so that the distance to reach all portions of a tenant space does not exceed 200 feet (60 960 mm) from a hose connection.

❖ Covered and open mall buildings are only required to have a standpipe system if Section 905.3.1 requires such features. If standpipes are not required because of building height, Class I hose connections that are connected to the automatic sprinkler system are still required. Also, to ensure that both the sprinkler system and hose connections will function at an acceptable level, the system must be sized for both the sprinkler demand and the hose connection demand. This section specifies a minimum flow rate and a maximum pressure loss to the most remote hose connection so that the fire department can gain full use of the hose connection during a fire. Hose connections are required when a standpipe system is not at key locations, such as entrances to exit passageways and at entrances to the covered or open mall. Note that these locations are essentially the same locations required for Class I hose connections in Section 905.4, except that this section also requires that the distance to reach any portion of a tenant space from a hose connection must not exceed 200 feet (60 960 mm).

905.3.4 Stages. Stages greater than 1,000 square feet (93 m^2) in area shall be equipped with a Class III wet standpipe system with $1^1/_2$-inch and $2^1/_2$-inch (38 mm and 64 mm) hose connections on each side of the stage.

Exception: Where the building or area is equipped throughout with an *automatic sprinkler system*, a $1^1/_2$-inch (38 mm) hose connection shall be installed in accordance with NFPA 13 or in accordance with NFPA 14 for Class II or III standpipes.

❖ Because of the potentially large fuel load and three-dimensional aspect of the fire hazard associated with stages greater than 1,000 square feet (93 m^2) in area, Class III standpipes are required on each side of these large stages. The standpipes must be equipped with a $1^1/_2$-inch (38 mm) hose connection and a $2^1/_2$-inch (64 mm) hose connection. The $1^1/_2$-inch (38 mm) connection is for the hose requirement in Section 905.3.4.1. The $2^1/_2$-inch (64 mm) connection is to provide greater flexibility for the fire department in its fire-fighting operations.

Stages, as used in this section, are those stages defined in Section 410.2, which include overhead hanging curtains, drops, scenery or stage effects other than lighting and sound. These were traditionally referred to as "legitimate stages." It is not an appropriate application of this section to require standpipes for elevated areas in banquet rooms or theatrical platforms where the higher fuel loads associated with a legitimate stage do not exist.

The exception recognizes the benefit of the building or area being sprinklered. If so, then only a single $1^1/_2$-inch (38 mm) connection is required. This hose connection is intended to be used by the fire department and apply less water from the hose because of the suppression activity of the sprinkler system. Hose threads must be compatible with those of the fire department as required in Section 903.3.6.

In a fully sprinklered building, it is acceptable to supply the hose connections through the same standpipe as the sprinklers. This is reflected in the reference to both NFPA 13, which acknowledges this concept, and NFPA 14, which contains similar provisions. If the provisions of NFPA 14 are used, although the standpipe must be wet and Class II in its installation, the design of the water supply and interconnection of systems can be in accordance with the requirements for Class II as well as for Class III standpipes.

905.3.4.1 Hose and cabinet. The $1^1/_2$-inch (38 mm) hose connections shall be equipped with sufficient lengths of $1^1/_2$-inch (38 mm) hose to provide fire protection for the stage area. Hose connections shall be equipped with an *approved* adjustable fog nozzle and be mounted in a cabinet or on a rack.

❖ The $1^1/_2$-inch (38 mm) standpipe hose installed for stages greater than 1,000 square feet (93 m^2) in area is intended for use by stage personnel who have been trained to use it. The length of hose provided is a function of the size and configuration of the stage. This includes by definition the entire performance area and adjacent backstage and support areas not fire separated from the performance area. The effective reach of the fire stream from the fog nozzle is a function of the available water supply, and in particular, the pressure. Fog nozzles typically require 100 pounds per square inch (psi) (690 kPa) for optimum performance.

905.3.5 Underground buildings. Underground buildings shall be equipped throughout with a Class I automatic wet or manual wet standpipe system.

❖ Underground buildings pose unique hazards to life safety because of their isolation and inaccessibility. Additional fire protection and fire-fighting measures for the fire department are required to compensate for the lack of exterior access for fire suppression and rescue operations (see Section 405).

905.3.6 Helistops and heliports. Buildings with a rooftop *helistop* or *heliport* shall be equipped with a Class I or III standpipe system extended to the roof level on which the *helistop* or *heliport* is located in accordance with Section 2007.5.

❖ Buildings containing rooftop helistops or heliports are required to be equipped with a Class I or III standpipe. A heliport is a distinct hazard that will involve flammable fuels. In the event of an emergency, rapid deployment of hand hose lines will be necessary to attack a resulting fire, effectuate rescue and protect exposures and the remainder of the building.

The requirement results in a standpipe system throughout the building, not just a connection at the roof level. This is critical in fire-fighting operations because many times the connection below the rooftop level may be needed just to gain access to the roof. If the only connection is on the roof, it is of no use if the fire fighters cannot get to it.

Additionally, a heliport includes fueling operations. It is entirely possible for a spill to not only affect the rooftop, but also floors below as the liquid fuel spreads. The standpipe system will again be utilized in these situations.

Section 2007.5 requires a $2^1/_2$-inch (64 mm) standpipe outlet to be within 150 feet (45 675 mm) of all portions of the heliport or helistop area and be either Class I or III.

905.3.7 Marinas and boatyards. Standpipes in marinas and boatyards shall comply with Chapter 36.

❖ Section 3604.2 contains the specifics as to when standpipes are required at marinas. Marinas and boatyards have unique challenges for fire fighting. Although there is water readily available, it is not easily or effectively capable of being applied to a fire at such a facility. A fire in such facilities can spread from structure to structure and from vessel to vessel with no effective way to attack and control it. Section 3604.2 references NFPA 303 for the standpipe requirements and additionally requires that no point on the marina pier or float system exceeds 150 feet (45 720 mm) from a standpipe hose connection (see commentary, Section 3604.2).

905.3.8 Rooftop gardens and landscaped roofs. Buildings or structures that have rooftop gardens or landscaped roofs and that are equipped with a standpipe system shall have the standpipe system extended to the roof level on which the rooftop garden or landscaped roof is located.

❖ This section requires that if the building is equipped with a standpipe system, whether or not such systems are required, it must be extended to a roof containing a garden or that which is landscaped. These requirements relate to the requirements in Section 317 that address the increased fuel load being added to roofs.

905.4 Location of Class I standpipe hose connections. Class I standpipe hose connections shall be provided in all of the following locations:

1. In every required *interior exit stairway*, a hose connection shall be provided for each story above and below grade plane. Hose connections shall be located at the

main floor landing unless otherwise *approved* by the *fire code official.*

Exception: A single hose connection shall be permitted to be installed in the open corridor or open breezeway between open stairs that are not greater than 75 feet (22 860 mm) apart.

2. On each side of the wall adjacent to the *exit* opening of a horizontal *exit.*

   Exception: Where floor areas adjacent to a horizontal *exit* are reachable from an *interior exit stairway* hose connection by a 30-foot (9144 mm) hose stream from a nozzle attached to 100 feet (30 480 mm) of hose, a hose connection shall not be required at the horizontal *exit.*

3. In every *exit* passageway, at the entrance from the exit passageway to other areas of a building.

   Exception: Where floor areas adjacent to an exit passageway are reachable from an *interior exit stairway* hose connection by a 30-foot (9144 mm) hose stream from a nozzle attached to 100 feet (30 480 mm) of hose, a hose connection shall not be required at the entrance from the exit passageway to other areas of the building.

4. In covered mall buildings, adjacent to each exterior public entrance to the mall and adjacent to each entrance from an *exit* passageway or *exit corridor* to the mall. In open mall buildings, adjacent to each public entrance to the mall at the perimeter line and adjacent to each entrance from an exit passageway or exit corridor to the mall.

5. Where the roof has a slope less than four units vertical in 12 units horizontal (33.3-percent slope), a hose connection shall be located to serve the roof or at the highest landing of an *interior exit stairway* with access to the roof provided in accordance with Section 1011.12.

6. Where the most remote portion of a nonsprinklered floor or story is more than 150 feet (45 720 mm) from a hose connection or the most remote portion of a sprinklered floor or story is more than 200 feet (60 960 mm) from a hose connection, the *fire code official* is authorized to require that additional hose connections be provided in *approved* locations.

❖ Hose connections are required for the fire department to make use of the standpipe system. Since the fire department will typically access the building using the stairways, and most fire departments do not permit entry to the fire floor without an operating hose line, a hose connection must be installed for each floor level of each required enclosed stairway.

Item 1 also specifies that the hose connections are to be located at the main floor landing. The hose connections, however, are permitted to be at the intermediate landing instead of at the main floor landing if this arrangement is approved by the fire code official. In the specific case of an open corridor or open breezeway that is located in between open stairs, a single hose connection is permitted to be installed within the open corridor or open breezeway.

Because horizontal exits are also primary entrances to the fire floor, Item 2 states that hose connections must also be provided at each horizontal exit. The construction of the fire separation assembly used as the horizontal exit will protect the fire fighters while they are connecting to the standpipe system. The hose connections are to be located on each side of the horizontal exit to enable fire fighters to be in a protected area, regardless of the location of the fire. The exception acknowledges that there may already be a hose connection in close proximity to the horizontal exit if there is a stairway adjacent to the horizontal exit. The intent is to allow fewer standpipe outlets if the area can be adequately covered by the standpipes in stairways since those are the standpipes typically used by the fire department.

Item 3 states that an exit passageway in a building required to have a standpipe system is typically used as an extension of a required exit stairway. This allows use of the exit passageway for fire-fighting staging operations in the same way as an exit stair. The exception acknowledges that there may already be a hose connection in close proximity to the exit passageway. If there is a stairway containing a hose connection in close proximity to the exit passageway that can meet the 30-foot (9144 mm) hose stream from a nozzle attached to 100 feet (30 480 mm) of hose, then an additional standpipe is not required. The intent is to allow fewer standpipe outlets if the area can be adequately covered by the standpipes in stairways since those are the standpipes typically used by the fire department.

In covered and open mall buildings, Item 4 requires hose connections at each entrance to an exit passageway or exit corridor. In addition, covered mall buildings would be required to have connections at each exterior public entrance. Open malls would require connections at the public entrance perimeter line. These locations allow fire personnel to have a support line as soon as they enter the building.

Item 5 is consistent with NFPA 14 regarding the installation of Class I standpipe hose connections on the roofs of buildings. This requirement requires only one standpipe to extend to the roof level or highest landing of the stairway serving the roof. This coordinates with Section 1011.12, which only requires one stairway to extend to the roof.

Hose connections in each interior exit stairway result in hose connections being located based on the travel distances permitted in Table 1017.2, which recognizes that most fire departments carry standpipe hose packs with 150 feet (45 720 mm) of hose or possibly with 100 feet (30 480 mm) of hose and an additional 50-foot (15 240 mm) section that could be easily connected.

With the typical travel distance permitted in nonsprinklered buildings of 200 feet (60 960 mm), reasonable coverage is provided when the effective reach of a fire stream is considered. Depending on the arrangement of the floor, however, all areas may not be effectively protected. Although this situation could easily be corrected by locating additional hose connections on the floor, such connections may rarely be used because of the difficulty in identifying their location during a fire and the fact that most fire departments require an operational hose line before they enter the fire floor. Because longer travel distances are allowed in sprinklered buildings, the problem is increased, but the need for prompt manual suppression is reduced by the presence of the sprinkler system. Item 6 gives the fire code official the authority to require additional hose connections if needed.

905.4.1 Protection. Risers and laterals of Class I standpipe systems not located within an *interior exit stairway* shall be protected by a degree of *fire resistance* equal to that required for vertical enclosures in the building in which they are located.

Exception: In buildings equipped throughout with an *approved automatic sprinkler system*, laterals that are not located within an *interior exit stairway* are not required to be enclosed within fire-resistance-rated construction.

❖ To minimize the potential for damage to the standpipe systems from a fire, the risers and laterals (i.e., the horizontal segments of standpipe system piping) must be located in an enclosure having the same fire-resistance rating as required for a vertical or shaft enclosure within the building. The required fire-resistance rating for the enclosure can be determined as detailed in Section 713.4.

The exception states that the enclosure for laterals is not required if the building is equipped throughout with an approved automatic sprinkler system. The potential for damage to the standpipe system is minimized by the protection provided by the sprinkler system. The automatic sprinkler system may be either an NFPA 13 or 13R system, depending on what was permitted for the building occupancy.

If the interior exit stairway is not required to have a rated enclosure, such as in an open parking garage, the laterals are similarly not required to be in an enclosure. The protection afforded the vertical riser in the stairway must be the same as that afforded the laterals. If the stairway is not required by other sections of the code to be located in a rated enclosure, then the laterals are not required to be in rated protection either.

905.4.2 Interconnection. In buildings where more than one standpipe is provided, the standpipes shall be interconnected in accordance with NFPA 14.

❖ In cases where there are multiple Class I standpipe risers, the risers must be supplied from and interconnected to a common supply line. The required fire department connection must serve all of the sprinklers or standpipes in the building.

905.5 Location of Class II standpipe hose connections. Class II standpipe hose connections shall be located so that all portions of the building are within 30 feet (9144 mm) of a nozzle attached to 100 feet (30 480 mm) of hose. Class II standpipe hose connections shall be located where they will have *ready access*.

❖ Sections 905.5.1 through 905.5.3 specify the requirements for Class II standpipe hose connections. Class II standpipe systems are primarily intended for use by the building occupants.

This section for Class II standpipes does not specifically require the hose station and uses the term "hose connection" with a location based on 100 feet (30 480 mm) of hose. However, the definition of Class II and III standpipes and Section 7.3.3.1 of NFPA 14 specifically require hose stations. Section 905.2 specifically references NFPA 14.

Although NFPA 14 requires a hose station, the decision as to whether a hose station is required may be one that is affected by the policies and procedures of the local fire department. It should be remembered that Class II hose connections and hose stations are intended for occupant use and not necessarily for fire department use. The fire department typically uses the Class I connection that is compatible with $2^1/_2$-inch (64 mm) hose.

905.5.1 Groups A-1 and A-2. In Group A-1 and A-2 occupancies with *occupant loads* of more than 1,000, hose connections shall be located on each side of any stage, on each side of the rear of the auditorium, on each side of the balcony and on each tier of dressing rooms.

❖ Because of the high occupant load density in Group A-1 and A-2 occupancies, providing additional means for controlling fires in their initial stage is important to enable prompt evacuation of the building. This section is independent of the Class I standpipe requirement for stages based on square footage as indicated in Section 905.3.4.

905.5.2 Protection. Fire-resistance-rated protection of risers and laterals of Class II standpipe systems is not required.

❖ Class II standpipe systems are normally not located in exit stairways; standpipe hose connections are located near the protected area to allow quick access. Therefore, it is likely that neither the risers nor the laterals would be located in any enclosure.

905.5.3 Class II system 1-inch hose. A minimum 1-inch (25 mm) hose shall be allowed to be used for hose stations in light-hazard occupancies where investigated and *listed* for this service and where *approved* by the *fire code official*.

❖ This section permits the use of 1-inch (25 mm) listed noncollapsible hose as an alternative to $1^1/_2$-inch (38 mm) hose, subject to the approval of the fire code official. This alternative is limited to light-hazard occupancies, such as office buildings and certain assembly occupancies that tend to have lower fuel loads, since a smaller hose generally discharges less water.

905.6 Location of Class III standpipe hose connections. Class III standpipe systems shall have hose connections located as required for Class I standpipes in Section 905.4

and shall have Class II hose connections as required in Section 905.5.

❖ Class III standpipe systems that have both a $2^1/_2$-inch (64 mm) hose connection and a $1^1/_2$-inch (38 mm) hose connection must comply with the applicable requirements of Sections 905.4, 905.5 and 905.6. Thus, it is necessary to review and comply with all applicable provisions.

905.6.1 Protection. Risers and laterals of Class III standpipe systems shall be protected as required for Class I systems in accordance with Section 905.4.1.

❖ Because Class III standpipe systems are intended for use by fire-suppression personnel, they must be located in construction that has a fire-resistance rating equivalent to that of the vertical or shaft enclosure requirements of the building (see commentary, Section 905.4.1).

905.6.2 Interconnection. In buildings where more than one Class III standpipe is provided, the standpipes shall be interconnected in accordance with NFPA 14.

❖ As indicated in Section 905.4.2 for Class I standpipe systems, multiple standpipe risers must be interconnected with a common supply line. An indicating valve is typically installed at the base of each riser so that individual risers can be taken out of service without affecting the water supply or the operation of other standpipe risers.

905.7 Cabinets. Cabinets containing fire-fighting equipment, such as standpipes, fire hose, fire extinguishers or fire department valves, shall not be blocked from use or obscured from view.

❖ This section does not require that cabinets be provided to contain fire protection equipment. However, if they are provided, cabinets must be readily visible and accessible at all times. Sections 905.7.1 and 905.7.2 contain additional criteria for the construction and identification of the cabinets. Where cabinets are located in fire-resistance-rated assemblies, the integrity of the assembly must be maintained. Cabinet design for hose connections, control valves or other devices that require manual operation should be such that there is sufficient clearance between the cabinet body and the device to allow grasping of the device (quite likely with a gloved hand) and prompt operation of it.

905.7.1 Cabinet equipment identification. Cabinets shall be identified in an *approved* manner by a permanently attached sign with letters not less than 2 inches (51 mm) high in a color that contrasts with the background color, indicating the equipment contained therein.

Exceptions:

1. Doors not large enough to accommodate a written sign shall be marked with a permanently attached pictogram of the equipment contained therein.
2. Doors that have either an *approved* visual identification clear glass panel or a complete glass door panel are not required to be marked.

❖ This section specifies the minimum criteria to make the signs readily visible. Different color combinations may be approved by the fire code official if the color contrast between the letters and the background is vivid enough to make the sign visible at an approved distance. The exceptions address alternatives to letter signage if the cabinet is still conspicuously identified or the contents are readily visible.

905.7.2 Locking cabinet doors. Cabinets shall be unlocked.

Exceptions:

1. Visual identification panels of glass or other *approved* transparent frangible material that is easily broken and allows access.
2. *Approved* locking arrangements.
3. Group I-3 occupancies.

❖ Ready access to all fire-fighting equipment in the cabinet is essential. The exceptions, however, recognize the need to lock cabinets for security reasons and to prevent theft or vandalism (see commentary, Section 906.8).

905.8 Dry standpipes. Dry standpipes shall not be installed.

Exception: Where subject to freezing and in accordance with NFPA 14.

❖ Wet standpipe systems are preferred because they tend to be the most reliable type of standpipe system; therefore, dry standpipes are prohibited unless subject to freezing. For example, Class I manual standpipe systems, which do not have a permanent water supply, are permitted in open parking structures. This recognizes that open parking structures are not heated and that most fires are limited to the vehicle of origin. The use of any dry standpipe system instead of a wet standpipe should take into consideration the added response time and its effect on the occupancy characteristics of the building.

905.9 Valve supervision. Valves controlling water supplies shall be supervised in the open position so that a change in the normal position of the valve will generate a supervisory signal at the supervising station required by Section 903.4. Where a fire alarm system is provided, a signal shall be transmitted to the control unit.

Exceptions:

1. Valves to underground key or hub valves in roadway boxes provided by the municipality or public utility do not require supervision.
2. Valves locked in the normal position and inspected as provided in this code in buildings not equipped with a fire alarm system.

❖ As with sprinkler systems, water control valves for standpipe systems must be electrically supervised as a means of determining that the system is operational (see commentary, Section 903.4).

Exception 1 recognizes that underground key or hub valves in roadway boxes are not normally supervised or need to be supervised, whether the building contains a standpipe system or an automatic sprinkler system.

Exception 2 does not require the control valves for the standpipes to be electrically monitored if they are locked in the normal position and a fire alarm system is not installed in the building. When a fire alarm system is installed, the control valves for the standpipes must be electrically monitored and tied into the supervision required for the fire alarm system.

905.10 During construction. Standpipe systems required during construction and demolition operations shall be provided in accordance with Section 3313.

❖ As stated in Section 3311, at least one standpipe is required during construction of buildings four stories or more in height or during demolition of standpipe-equipped buildings. Standpipe systems must be accessible and operable during construction and demolition operations to assist in any potential fire (see commentary, Sections 3311.1 and 3311.2 of the IBC, and Sections 3313.1 and 3313.2 of the code).

905.11 Locking standpipe outlet caps. The *fire code official* is authorized to require locking caps on the outlets on dry standpipes where the responding fire department carries key wrenches for the removal that are compatible with locking FDC connection caps.

❖ Standpipe connection caps are vulnerable to theft. Vandalism is a concern when trash and debris are introduced into the outlet. The debris will flow directly to the fire fighters' nozzle, creating a life safety issue for fire fighters. The other problem that exists is with dry systems. When one or more valves are open within the system, and the fire department pumps to the system, the correct flow and pressure will not reach the fire fighters, causing a delay in the application of water. This delay can create increased property damage and life safety issues. This provision, when applied, will require the protected FDC and protected standpipe caps to have a compatible and standard opening mechanism.

905.12 Existing buildings. Where required in Chapter 11, existing structures shall be equipped with standpipes installed in accordance with Section 905.

❖ This section simply refers to Chapter 11 which addresses all requirements that apply to existing buildings (see commentary, Section 1103.6).

SECTION 906
PORTABLE FIRE EXTINGUISHERS

906.1 Where required. Portable fire extinguishers shall be installed in all of the following locations:

1. In new and existing Group A, B, E, F, H, I, M, R-1, R-2, R-4 and S occupancies.

   Exceptions:

   1. In Group R-2 occupancies, portable fire extinguishers shall be required only in locations specified in Items 2 through 6 where each dwelling unit is provided with a portable fire extinguisher having a minimum rating of 1-A:10-B:C.
   2. In Group E occupancies, portable fire extinguishers shall be required only in locations specified in Items 2 through 6 where each classroom is provided with a portable fire extinguisher having a minimum rating of 2-A:20-B:C.
2. Within 30 feet (9144 mm) distance of travel from commercial cooking equipment and from domestic cooking equipment in Group I-1; I-2, Condition 1; and R-2 college dormitory occupancies.
3. In areas where flammable or combustible liquids are stored, used or dispensed.
4. On each floor of structures under construction, except Group R-3 occupancies, in accordance with Section 3315.1.
5. Where required by the sections indicated in Table 906.1.
6. Special-hazard areas, including but not limited to laboratories, computer rooms and generator rooms, where required by the *fire code official*.

❖ Portable fire extinguishers are required in certain instances to give the occupants the means to suppress a fire in its incipient stage. The capability for manual fire suppression can contribute to the protection of the occupants, especially if there are evacuation difficulties associated with the occupancy or the specific hazard in the area. To be effective, personnel must be properly trained in the use of portable fire extinguishers.

Because of the high-hazard nature of building contents, portable fire extinguishers are required in occupancies in Group H.

Portable fire extinguishers are required in occupancies in Groups A, B, E, F, H, I, M, R-1, R-2, R-4 and S because of the need to control the fire in its early stages and because evacuation can be slowed by the density of the occupant load, the capability of the occupants to evacuate or the overall fuel load in the building. Because the code typically focuses on new buildings, this section is applicable to new buildings.

Portable fire extinguishers are required in areas containing special hazards, such as commercial cooking equipment, and specific hazardous operations, as indicated in Table 906.1. Because of the potentially extreme fire hazard associated with such areas or occupancy conditions, prompt extinguishment of the fire is critical.

Portable fire extinguishers are required in all buildings under construction, except in occupancies in Group R-3. The extinguishers are intended for use by construction personnel to suppress a fire in its incipient stages.

Portable fire extinguishers are also required in laboratories, computer rooms and other work spaces in which fire hazards may exist based on the use of the space. Many of these will be addressed by the required occupancy group criteria or by the specific hazard provisions of Table 906.1. Laboratories, for example, may not be considered Group H, but still use limited amounts of hazardous materials that would make manual means of fire extinguishment desirable.

The first exception to Item 1 permits smaller portable fire extinguishers (PFEs) in dwelling units of Group R-2 occupancies instead of larger PFEs in the common areas. Under the exception, the installation of 1-A:10-B:C PFEs within individual dwelling units allows apartment owners to eliminate their installation in common areas such as corridors, laundry rooms and swimming pool areas. PFEs in these areas are susceptible to vandalism or theft. Another issue is that larger PFEs are more difficult for the infirm and elderly to safely deploy and operate.

The second exception to Item 1 permits PFEs in Group E occupancies to be installed in only the locations listed in Items 2 through 6 if each classroom is provided with an extinguisher having a rating of 2-A:20-B:C. The reason for this option is that where schools are required to develop lockdown plans to protect students and faculty from intruders, these plans effectively prevent access to portable fire extinguishers normally located in hallways during lockdown situations. Locating extinguishers in classrooms provides accessibility during normal conditions as well as when a school is forced to go into lockdown. This exception provides an option for schools implementing lockdown plans to relocate extinguishers from hallways to classrooms.

For the period of 2003 through 2007, NFPA reported that approximately 38,000 fires occurred annually in apartment buildings. Sixty percent of these fires occurred inside of dwelling units versus 14 percent that occurred in common areas covered by Items 3 and 6 of Section 906.1. It is more logical to place PFEs inside dwelling units versus common areas because it locates the extinguisher in an area where statistically most fires occur. If the occupant cannot control the fire using the PFE, he or she can escape and allow the automatic sprinkler system to operate and control the fire. This exception improves the safety of Group R-2 residents because it does not require them to leave a dwelling involved in a fire, find a PFE and then return to the fire-involved dwelling unit to attempt incipient fire attack.

Including this requirement in the code alerts designers and building officials that the extinguishers are required. This will allow designers to plan for thicker walls where recessed cabinets may be used or to design locations where the extinguishers will not project into or obstruct the egress or circulation path.

TABLE 906.1. See page 9-63.

❖ Table 906.1 lists those sections that represent specific occupancy conditions requiring portable fire extinguishers for incipient fire control. Wherever the code requires a fire extinguisher because of one of the listed occupancy conditions, it may identify the required rating of the extinguisher that is compatible with the hazard involved in addition to referencing Section 906.

906.2 General requirements. Portable fire extinguishers shall be selected, installed and maintained in accordance with this section and NFPA 10.

Exceptions:

1. The distance of travel to reach an extinguisher shall not apply to the spectator seating portions of Group A-5 occupancies.
2. Thirty-day inspections shall not be required and maintenance shall be allowed to be once every 3 years for dry-chemical or halogenated agent portable fire extinguishers that are supervised by a *listed* and *approved* electronic monitoring device, provided that all of the following conditions are met:
   - 2.1. Electronic monitoring shall confirm that extinguishers are properly positioned, properly charged and unobstructed.
   - 2.2. Loss of power or circuit continuity to the electronic monitoring device shall initiate a trouble signal.
   - 2.3. The extinguishers shall be installed inside of a building or cabinet in a noncorrosive environment.
   - 2.4. Electronic monitoring devices and supervisory circuits shall be tested every 3 years when extinguisher maintenance is performed.
   - 2.5. A written log of required hydrostatic test dates for extinguishers shall be maintained by the *owner* to verify that hydrostatic tests are conducted at the frequency required by NFPA 10.

TABLE 906.1
ADDITIONAL REQUIRED PORTABLE FIRE EXTINGUISHERS

SECTION	SUBJECT
303.5	Asphalt kettles
307.5	Open burning
308.1.3	Open flames—torches
309.4	Powered industrial trucks
2005.2	Aircraft towing vehicles
2005.3	Aircraft welding apparatus
2005.4	Aircraft fuel-servicing tank vehicles
2005.5	Aircraft hydrant fuel-servicing vehicles
2005.6	Aircraft fuel-dispensing stations
2007.7	Heliports and helistops
2108.4	Dry cleaning plants
2305.5	Motor fuel-dispensing facilities
2310.6.4	Marine motor fuel-dispensing facilities
2311.6	Repair garages
2404.4.1	Spray-finishing operations
2405.4.2	Dip-tank operations
2406.4.2	Powder-coating areas
2804.3	Lumberyards/woodworking facilities
2808.8	Recycling facilities
2809.5	Exterior lumber storage
2903.5	Organic-coating areas
3006.3	Industrial ovens
3104.12	Tents and membrane structures
3206.10	High-piled storage
3315.1	Buildings under construction or demolition
3317.3	Roofing operations
3408.2	Tire rebuilding/storage
3504.2.6	Welding and other hot work
3604.4	Marinas
3703.6	Combustible fibers
5703.2.1	Flammable and combustible liquids, general
5704.3.3.1	Indoor storage of flammable and combustible liquids
5704.3.7.5.2	Liquid storage rooms for flammable and combustible liquids
5705.4.9	Solvent distillation units
5706.2.7	Farms and construction sites—flammable and combustible liquids storage
5706.4.10.1	Bulk plants and terminals for flammable and combustible liquids
5706.5.4.5	Commercial, industrial, governmental or manufacturing establishments—fuel dispensing
5706.6.4	Tank vehicles for flammable and combustible liquids
5906.5.7	Flammable solids
6108.2	LP-gas

3. In Group I-3, portable fire extinguishers shall be permitted to be located at staff locations.

❖ NFPA 10 contains minimum requirements for the selection, installation and maintenance of portable fire extinguishers. Portable fire extinguishers are investigated and rated in conformance to NFPA 10 and listed under a variety of standards. Portable fire extinguishers must be labeled and rated for use on fires of the type, severity and hazard class protected.

NFPA 10 notes that more frequent inspections may be necessary where conditions warrant. For existing installations, a history of recent fires, vandalism, physical abuse and theft should be considered in determining if more frequent inspections are needed. For both existing and new facilities, determining the frequency of inspections should take into account the environmental conditions in which the extinguisher will be located, including corrosiveness and temperature variations, and the possibility of obstructions that may place the extinguisher out of reach in case of an emergency.

Exception 1 recognizes the openness to the atmosphere associated with Group A-5 occupancies. A fire in open areas is more obvious to all spectators. Group A-5 occupancies also do not accumulate smoke and hot gases because they are not enclosed spaces. These reasons, in addition to the large and expansive layout within seating areas, make it reasonable and practical not to apply the distance of travel to a PFE criteria in Group A-5. Revised distance of travel allowances would need to be approved by the fire code official. Group A-5 occupancies also tend to be more subject to the corrosive conditions of an outdoor environment, and may include freeze/thaw cycles that can be detrimental to fire extinguishers.

Exception 2 acknowledges a 30-day inspection interval similar to NFPA 10. An electronic monitoring device can determine whether the fire extinguisher is still present and whether its contents are still at the proper charge. The use of such devices, being relatively new, is allowed if it is limited to dry-chemical and halogenated agents with the additional safeguards noted in the list. Where inspections may be at more frequent intervals, as discussed earlier, the use of electronic monitoring may have even greater benefit and is acknowledged as such in NFPA 10. The log, noted in Exception 2.5, can be a written log or a printout of the electronic log maintained by the electronic monitoring device. This exception provides the building owner with an alternative to the contract inspections popularly used.

Exception 3 recognizes that portable fire extinguishers located throughout the facility are at times tampered with, removed or used for weapons by inmates in a detention or correctional setting. This exception would protect the extinguishers from damage or removal by inmates while still making them available to staff and employees for use in an emergency situation.

906.2.1 Certification of service personnel for portable fire extinguishers. Service personnel providing or conducting maintenance on portable fire extinguishers shall possess a valid certificate issued by an *approved* governmental agency, or other *approved* organization for the type of work performed.

❖ Maintenance of fire protection systems and devices are minimum Chapter 9 requirements. Fire protection systems, like other technologies, have advanced, new designs that require a clear understanding of their construction and maintenance. To ensure that systems and devices are properly maintained, the code now requires individuals performing these activities be certified. Certification must be issued by an approved organization or governmental agency.

These provisions align the code with NFPA standards governing the inspection and maintenance of portable fire extinguishers.

Qualifications for individuals who service portable fire extinguishers are established in the 2018 edition of NFPA 10. Section 7.1.2.1 of NFPA 10 requires individuals inspecting and servicing portable fire extinguishers be trained and certified to reliably perform these activities.

906.3 Size and distribution. The size and distribution of portable fire extinguishers shall be in accordance with Sections 906.3.1 through 906.3.4.

❖ Proper selection and distribution of portable fire extinguishers are essential to having adequate protection for the building structure and the occupancy conditions within. This section introduces the sections that provide those requirements. Determination of the desired type of portable fire extinguisher depends on the character of the fire anticipated, building occupancy, specific hazards and ambient temperature conditions [see commentary, Tables 906.3(1) and 906.3(2)].

906.3.1 Class A fire hazards. The minimum sizes and distribution of portable fire extinguishers for occupancies that involve primarily Class A fire hazards shall comply with Table 906.3(1).

❖ Class A fires generally involve materials considered to be "ordinary combustibles," such as wood, cloth, paper, rubber and most plastics [see commentary, Table 906.3(1)].

TABLE 906.3(1)
FIRE EXTINGUISHERS FOR CLASS A FIRE HAZARDS

	LIGHT (Low) HAZARD OCCUPANCY	ORDINARY (Moderate) HAZARD OCCUPANCY	EXTRA (High) HAZARD OCCUPANCY
Minimum-rated single extinguisher	2-A[c]	2-A	4-A[a]
Maximum floor area per unit of A	3,000 square feet	1,500 square feet	1,000 square feet
Maximum floor area for extinguisher[b]	11,250 square feet	11,250 square feet	11,250 square feet
Maximum distance of travel to extinguisher	75 feet	75 feet	75 feet

For SI: 1 foot = 304.8 mm, 1 square foot = 0.0929 m^2, 1 gallon = 3.785 L.

a. Two $2^1/_2$-gallon water-type extinguishers shall be deemed the equivalent of one 4-A rated extinguisher.

b. Annex E.3.3 of NFPA 10 provides more details concerning application of the maximum floor area criteria.

c. Two water-type extinguishers each with a 1-A rating shall be deemed the equivalent of one 2-A rated extinguisher for Light (Low) Hazard Occupancies.

❖ Table 906.3(1), which parallels Table 6.2.1.1 of NFPA 10, establishes the minimum number and rating of fire extinguishers for Class A fires in any particular occupancy. The occupancy classifications are further defined in NFPA 10. The maximum area that a single fire extinguisher can protect is determined based on the rating of the fire extinguisher. The distance of travel limitation of 75 feet (22 860 mm) is intended to be the actual walking distance along a normal path of travel to the extinguisher. For this reason, it is necessary to select fire extinguishers that comply with both the distribution criteria and distance of travel limitation for a specific occupancy classification.

906.3.2 Class B fire hazards. Portable fire extinguishers for occupancies involving flammable or *combustible liquids* with depths less than or equal to 0.25 inch (6.4 mm) shall be selected and placed in accordance with Table 906.3(2).

Portable fire extinguishers for occupancies involving flammable or *combustible liquids* with a depth of greater than 0.25-inch (6.4 mm) shall be selected and placed in accordance with NFPA 10.

❖ Class B fires involve flammable and combustible liquids, oil-based paints, alcohols, solvents, flammable gases and similar materials. Selection of these extinguishers is made based on the depth of the liquid that could become involved in a fire. If the depth is 0.25-inch (6 mm) or less, selection is made using Table 906.3(2). Class B extinguishers for greater liquid depth, characterized in NFPA 10 as "appreciable depth," must be selected and installed in accordance with Section 6.3.2 of NFPA 10 [see commentary, Table 906.3(2)].

TABLE 906.3(2)
FIRE EXTINGUISHERS FOR FLAMMABLE OR COMBUSTIBLE LIQUIDS WITH DEPTHS OF LESS THAN OR EQUAL TO 0.25 INCH[a]

TYPE OF HAZARD	BASIC MINIMUM EXTINGUISHER RATING	MAXIMUM DISTANCE OF TRAVEL TO EXTINGUISHERS (feet)
Light (Low)	5-B 10-B	30 50
Ordinary (Moderate)	10-B 20-B	30 50
Extra (High)	40-B 80-B	30 50

For SI: 1 inch = 25.4 mm, 1 foot = 304.8 mm.

a. For requirements on water-soluble flammable liquids and alternative sizing criteria, see Section 5.5 of NFPA 10.

❖ Fires involving flammable or combustible liquids present a severe hazard challenge regardless of occupancy. Table 906.3(2), which parallels Table 6.3.1.1 of NFPA 10, prescribes the minimum portable fire extinguisher requirements where flammable or combustible liquids are limited in depth [0.25 inch (6 mm) or less]. As can be seen in the table, the size of the extinguisher is directly related to the distance of travel to the extinguisher for each given occupancy classification. These fire extinguisher provisions are independent of whether other fixed automatic fire-extinguishing systems are installed. For occupancy conditions involving flammable or combustible liquids in potential depths greater than 0.25 inch (6 mm), the selection and spacing criteria of NFPA 10 must be used in addition to any applicable requirements in Chapter 57 and NFPA 30.

906.3.3 Class C fire hazards. Portable fire extinguishers for Class C fire hazards shall be selected and placed on the basis of the anticipated Class A or B hazard.

❖ Class C fires involve energized electrical equipment where the electrical nonconductivity of the extinguishing agent is critical. The need for this class of extinguisher is simply based on the presence of the hazard in an occupancy and no numerical rating is required.

906.3.4 Class D fire hazards. Portable fire extinguishers for occupancies involving combustible metals shall be selected and placed in accordance with NFPA 10.

❖ Class D fires involve flammable solids, the bulk of which are combustible metals including, but not limited to, magnesium, potassium, sodium and titanium. Most Class D extinguishers will have a special low-velocity nozzle or discharge wand to gently apply the agent in large volumes to avoid disrupting any finely divided burning materials. Extinguishing agents are also available in bulk and can be applied with a scoop or shovel. While Class D extinguishers are often referred to as "dry chemical" fire extinguishers, they are more properly called "dry powder" fire extinguishers because their mechanism of extinguishment is by a smothering action rather than by chemical reaction with the combustion process.

There are several Class D fire-extinguisher agents available—some will handle multiple types of metal fires, others will not. Sodium carbonate-based extinguishers are used to control sodium, potassium, and sodium-potassium alloy fires but have limited use on other metals. This material smothers and forms a crust. Sodium chloride-based extinguishers contain sodium chloride salt and a thermoplastic additive. The plastic melts to form an oxygen-excluding crust over the metal, and the salt dissipates heat. This powder is useful on most alkali metals, including magnesium, titanium, aluminum, sodium, potassium and zirconium. Graphite-based extinguishers contain dry graphite powder that smothers burning metals. Unlike sodium chloride powder extinguishers, the graphite powder fire extinguishers can be used on very hot burning metal fires such as lithium, but the powder will not stick to and extinguish flowing or vertical lithium fires. The graphite powder acts as a heat sink as well as a means of smothering the metal fire. See the commentary to Section 5906.5.7 for a discussion of extinguishing flammable solid fires.

906.4 Cooking equipment fires. Fire extinguishers provided for the protection of cooking equipment shall be of an approved type compatible with the automatic fire-extinguishing system agent. Cooking equipment involving solid fuels or vegetable or animal oils and fats shall be protected by a Class K-rated portable extinguisher in accordance with Sections 906.1, Item 2, 906.4.1 and 906.4.2 as applicable.

❖ The combination of high-efficiency cooking appliances and hotter burning cooking media creates a potentially severe fire hazard. Although commercial cooking systems must have an approved exhaust hood and be protected by an approved automatic fire-extinguishing system, a manual means of extinguishment is desirable to attack a fire in its incipient stage.

As indicated in Section 906.1, Item 2, a Class K-rated portable fire extinguisher must be located within 30 feet (9144 mm) of travel distance of commercial-type cooking equipment. Class K-rated extinguishers have been specifically tested on commercial cooking appliances using vegetable or animal oils or fats. These portable fire extinguishers are usually of sodium bicarbonate or potassium bicarbonate dry-chemical type.

906.4.1 Portable fire extinguishers for solid fuel cooking appliances. Solid fuel cooking appliances, whether or not under a hood, with fireboxes 5 cubic feet (0.14 m3) or less in volume shall have a minimum 2.5-gallon (9 L) or two 1.5-gallon (6 L) Class K wet-chemical portable fire extinguishers located in accordance with Section 906.1.

❖ The fuels used in solid fuel-fired cooking appliances present significantly more potential burning surface area than the flat surface of a grill or deep fat fryer. This surface area is also often shielded by other solid fuel elements. As a result, a large extinguisher or two moderate-sized extinguishers are required. The $2^1/_2$-

gallon (9 L) extinguisher roughly equates to a 2A rating. The K-rating is necessary rather than using a water-based agent because the discharge from water-based extinguishers is usually in the form of a straight stream rather than a less concentrated, flooding type of coverage. A straight stream can dislodge the burning solid fuel material and possibly spread the burning coals to other areas where they could pose both a secondary fire risk, as well as a life safety hazard. The same travel distance to an extinguisher is required for solid fuel extinguishers as for deep fat fryer extinguishers so that manual suppression can be provided, if necessary, in a reasonable time. See the commentary to Section 904.12.5.2 for further discussion of Class K extinguishers.

906.4.2 Class K portable fire extinguishers for deep fat fryers. Where hazard areas include deep fat fryers, listed Class K portable fire extinguishers shall be provided as follows:

1. For up to four fryers having a maximum cooking medium capacity of 80 pounds (36.3 kg) each: one Class K portable fire extinguisher of a minimum 1.5-gallon (6 L) capacity.
2. For every additional group of four fryers having a maximum cooking medium capacity of 80 pounds (36.3 kg) each: one additional Class K portable fire extinguisher of a minimum 1.5-gallon (6 L) capacity shall be provided.
3. For individual fryers exceeding 6 square feet (0.55 m^2) in surface area: Class K portable fire extinguishers shall be installed in accordance with the extinguisher manufacturer's recommendations.

❖ Newer commercial cooking operations use improved, more efficient deep fat fryer-type cooking appliances and more healthful, unsaturated cooking oils that require a much higher cooking temperature than the former saturated oils. The Class K extinguishing agent and extinguishers were developed to deal with this new hazard. Class K extinguishers use a wet-chemical, potassium acetate-based agent that has proven to be more effective in fighting these fires and provides a cooling effect for the deep fat fryer hazard. Though primarily intended for cooking fires, many Class K extinguishers can also be effectively used on Class A, B and C hazards.

Class K fire extinguishers do not have letter ratings similar to other types of extinguishers. The capacity of the Class K extinguisher becomes the effective rating. Based on the extinguishing capability of a moderate-sized Class K extinguisher, the maximum quantity of typical fat frying medium can be determined. This quantity is determined by weight based on the typical deep fat fryer. A fryer capacity of 80 pounds (36.3 kg) can provide a surface area between $4^1/_2$ to 6 square feet (0.42 to 0.55 m^2), depending on the manufacturer. Where the surface area exceeds 6 square feet (0.55 m^2), guidelines for Class K extinguishers are no longer applicable. Consequently, for the larger surface area fryers, the size of Class K extinguisher should be based on the manufacturer's recommendations. Although not specifically indicated in the code text, the understanding is that if the weight capacity of the fryer exceeds 80 pounds (36.3 kg) but the surface area is less than 6 square feet (0.55 m^2), the manufacturer's recommendations should be applied for those conditions as well.

906.5 Conspicuous location. Portable fire extinguishers shall be located in conspicuous locations where they will have *ready access* and be immediately available for use. These locations shall be along normal paths of travel, unless the *fire code official* determines that the hazard posed indicates the need for placement away from normal paths of travel.

❖ Fire extinguishers must be located in readily accessible locations along normal egress paths. This increases the occupants' familiarity with the location of the fire extinguishers. When considering location, the most frequent occupants should be considered. These are the occupants who would become most familiar with the fire-extinguisher placement. For most buildings, it is the employees who are most familiar with their surroundings; therefore, a good understanding of employee operations is important for proper extinguisher placement.

906.6 Unobstructed and unobscured. Portable fire extinguishers shall not be obstructed or obscured from view. In rooms or areas in which visual obstruction cannot be completely avoided, means shall be provided to indicate the locations of extinguishers.

❖ Portable fire extinguishers must be located where they are readily visible at all times. If visual obstruction cannot be avoided, the location of the extinguishers must be marked by an approved means of identification. This could include additional signage, lights, arrows or other means approved by the fire code official. Unobstructed does not necessarily mean visible from all angles within the space. Often, columns or furnishings may obscure the extinguisher from one direction or another. These are not by themselves obstructions. The intent is that the extinguisher is not hidden but rather can be readily found. If the extinguisher is placed in the wall behind a door, it is clearly obstructed since it cannot be easily viewed. An extinguisher on a wall that is visible from most of the space would be considered unobstructed.

906.7 Hangers and brackets. Hand-held portable fire extinguishers, not housed in cabinets, shall be installed on the hangers or brackets supplied. Hangers or brackets shall be securely anchored to the mounting surface in accordance with the manufacturer's installation instructions.

❖ Portable fire extinguishers not housed in cabinets are usually mounted on walls or columns using securely fastened hangers. Brackets must be used where the fire extinguishers need to be protected from impact or other potential physical damage.

906.8 Cabinets. Cabinets used to house portable fire extinguishers shall not be locked.

Exceptions:

1. Where portable fire extinguishers subject to malicious use or damage are provided with a means of ready access.
2. In Group I-3 occupancies and in mental health areas in Group I-2 occupancies, access to portable fire extinguishers shall be permitted to be locked or to be located in staff locations provided that the staff has keys.

❖ Cabinets housing fire extinguishers must not be locked in order to provide quick access in an emergency. Exception 1, however, allows the cabinets to be locked in occupancies where vandalism, theft or other malicious behavior is possible. Exception 2 also permits cabinets housing fire extinguishers to be locked or to be located in staff locations in Group I-3 occupancies and mental health areas in Group I-2 occupancies. Occupants in Group I-3 areas of jails, prisons or similar restrained occupancies should not have access to fire extinguishers because they could possibly be used as a weapon or be subject to vandalism. Staff members who have been adequately trained in the use of fire extinguishers are assumed to have ready access to the keys for the cabinets at all times.

906.9 Extinguisher installation. The installation of portable fire extinguishers shall be in accordance with Sections 906.9.1 through 906.9.3.

❖ This section introduces the installation criteria for portable fire extinguishers based on the weight of the unit.

906.9.1 Extinguishers weighing 40 pounds or less. Portable fire extinguishers having a gross weight not exceeding 40 pounds (18 kg) shall be installed so that their tops are not more than 5 feet (1524 mm) above the floor.

❖ Because of the varying height and physical strength levels of persons who might be called on to operate a portable fire extinguisher, the mounting height of the extinguisher must be commensurate with its weight so that it may be easily retrieved by anyone from its mounting location and placed into use.

906.9.2 Extinguishers weighing more than 40 pounds. Hand-held portable fire extinguishers having a gross weight exceeding 40 pounds (18 kg) shall be installed so that their tops are not more than 3.5 feet (1067 mm) above the floor.

❖ See the commentary to Section 906.9.1.

906.9.3 Floor clearance. The clearance between the floor and the bottom of installed hand-held portable fire extinguishers shall be not less than 4 inches (102 mm).

❖ The clearance between the floor and the bottom of installed hand-held extinguishers must not be less than 4 inches (102 mm) to facilitate cleaning beneath the unit and reduce the likelihood of the extinguisher becoming dislodged during cleaning operations (floor mopping, sweeping, etc.).

906.10 Wheeled units. Wheeled fire extinguishers shall be conspicuously located in a designated location.

❖ Wheeled fire extinguishers consist of a large-capacity (up to several hundred pounds of agent) fire extinguisher assembly (either stored-pressure or pressure-transfer type) equipped with a carriage and wheels and discharge hose. They are constructed so that one able-bodied person could move the unit to the fire area and begin extinguishment unassisted. Wheeled fire extinguishers are capable of delivering greater flow rates and stream range for various extinguishing agents than hand-held portable fire extinguishers. Wheeled fire extinguishers are generally more effective in high-hazard areas and, as with any extinguisher, must be readily available and stored in an approved location. The wheeled fire extinguisher should be located a safe distance from the hazard area so that it will not become involved in the fire or access to it compromised by a fire. These units are typically found at airport fueling ramps, refineries, bulk plants and similar locations where high-challenge fires may be encountered. The extinguishing agents available in wheeled units include carbon dioxide, dry chemical, dry powder and foam.

SECTION 907 FIRE ALARM AND DETECTION SYSTEMS

907.1 General. This section covers the application, installation, performance and maintenance of fire alarm systems and their components in new and existing buildings and structures. The requirements of Section 907.2 are applicable to new buildings and structures. The requirements of Section 907.9 are applicable to existing buildings and structures.

❖ Fire alarm systems, which typically include manual fire alarm systems and automatic fire detection systems, must be installed in accordance with Section 907 and NFPA 72. As indicated in this section, only Section 907.9 is intended to be applicable to existing buildings and structures.

Manual fire alarm systems are installed in buildings to limit fire casualties and property losses. Fire alarm systems do this by promptly notifying the occupants of the building of an emergency, which increases the time available for evacuation. Similarly, when fire alarm systems are supervised, the fire department will be promptly notified and its response time relative to the onset of the fire will be reduced.

Automatic fire detection systems are required under certain conditions to increase the likelihood that a fire is detected and occupants are given an early warning. The detection system is a system of devices and associated hardware that activates the alarm system. The automatic detecting devices are to be smoke detectors, unless a condition exists that calls for the use of a different type of detector.

907.1.1 Construction documents. *Construction documents* for fire alarm systems shall be of sufficient clarity to indicate the location, nature and extent of the work proposed and show in detail that it will conform to the provisions of this code, the *International Building Code* and relevant laws, ordinances, rules and regulations, as determined by the *fire code official*.

❖ Construction documents for fire alarm systems must be submitted for review to determine compliance with the code, the IBC and NFPA 72. All of the information required by this section may not be available during the design stage and initial permit process. Later submission of more detailed shop drawings may be required in accordance with Section 907.1.2. These provisions are intended to reflect the minimum scope of information needed to determine code compliance. When the work can be briefly described on the application form, the fire code official may utilize judgment in determining the need for more detailed documents.

907.1.2 Fire alarm shop drawings. Shop drawings for fire alarm systems shall be prepared in accordance with NFPA 72 and submitted for review and approval prior to system installation.

❖ Since the fire protection contractor(s) may not have been selected at the time a permit is issued for construction of a building, detailed shop drawings for fire alarm systems may not be available. Because they provide the information necessary to determine code compliance, as specified in this section, they must be submitted and approved by the fire code official before the contractor can begin installing the system.

907.1.3 Equipment. Systems and components shall be *listed* and *approved* for the purpose for which they are installed.

❖ The components of the fire alarm system must be approved for use in the planned system. NFPA 72 requires all devices, combinations of devices, appliances and equipment to be labeled for their proposed use. The testing agency will test the components for use in various types of systems and stipulate the use of the component on the label. Evidence of listing and labeling of the system components must be submitted with the shop drawings. In some instances, the entire system may be labeled.

At least one major testing agency, Underwriters Laboratories, Inc. (UL), has a program in which alarm installation and service companies are issued a certificate and become listed by the agency as being qualified to design, install and maintain local, auxiliary, remote station or proprietary fire alarm systems. The listed companies may then issue a certificate showing that the system is in compliance with Section 907. Terms of the company certification by UL include the company being responsible for keeping accurate system documentation, including as-built record drawings, acceptance test records and complete maintenance records on a given system. The company is also responsible for the required periodic inspection and testing of the system under contract with the owner. A similar program has been available for many years for central station alarm service, whereas the UL program is relatively new to the industry. Even though this company and system listing program is not required by the code or NFPA 72, it can be a valuable tool for the fire code official in determining compliance with the referenced standard.

Another issue that must be considered is the compatibility of the system components as required by NFPA 72. The labeling of system components discussed previously should include any compatibility restrictions for components. Compatibility is primarily an issue of the ability of smoke detectors and fire alarm control panels (FACPs) to function properly when interconnected and affects the two-wire type of smoke detectors, which obtain their operating power over the same pair of wires used to transmit signals to the FACP (the control unit initiating device circuits). Laboratories will test for component compatibility either by actual testing or by reviewing the circuit parameters of both the detector and the FACP. Generally, if both the two-wire detector and the FACP are of the same brand, there should not be a compatibility problem. Nevertheless, the fire code official must be satisfied that the components are listed as being compatible. Failure to comply with the compatibility requirements of NFPA 72 can lead to system malfunction or failure at a critical time.

907.2 Where required—new buildings and structures. An *approved* fire alarm system installed in accordance with the provisions of this code and NFPA 72 shall be provided in new buildings and structures in accordance with Sections 907.2.1 through 907.2.23 and provide occupant notification in accordance with Section 907.5, unless other requirements are provided by another section of this code.

Not fewer than one manual fire alarm box shall be provided in an *approved* location to initiate a fire alarm signal for fire alarm systems employing automatic fire detectors or waterflow detection devices. Where other sections of this code allow elimination of fire alarm boxes due to sprinklers, a single fire alarm box shall be installed.

Exceptions:

1. The manual fire alarm box is not required for fire alarm systems dedicated to elevator recall control and supervisory service.
2. The manual fire alarm box is not required for Group R-2 occupancies unless required by the *fire code official* to provide a means for fire watch personnel to initiate an alarm during a sprinkler system impairment event. Where provided, the manual fire alarm box shall not be located in an area that is open to the public.

❖ This section specifies the occupancies or conditions in new buildings or structures that require some form of fire alarm system that is either a manual fire alarm system (manual fire alarm boxes) or an automatic smoke detection system. These systems must, upon activation, provide occupant notification throughout the area protected by the system unless other alternative provisions are allowed by this section.

Manual fire alarm systems must be installed in certain occupancies, depending on the number of occupants, capabilities of the occupants and height of the building. An automatic smoke detection system must be installed in those occupancies and conditions where the need to detect the fire is essential to evacuation or protection of the occupants. The requirements for automatic smoke detection are generally based on the evacuation needs of the occupants and whether the occupancy includes sleeping accommodations.

Fire alarm systems must be installed in accordance with the code and NFPA 72. NFPA 72 identifies the minimum performance, location, mounting, testing and maintenance requirements for fire alarm systems. Smoke detectors must be used, except when ambient conditions would prohibit their use. In that case, other detection methods may be used. The manufacturer's literature will identify the limitations on the use of smoke detectors, including environmental conditions such as humidity, temperature and airflow.

Only certain occupancies are required to have either a manual fire alarm or automatic fire detection system installed (see Commentary Figure 907.2). The need for either system is generally determined by the number of occupants, the height of the building or the ability of the occupants for self-preservation.

Note that generally the fire alarm requirements are based on occupancy and not on fire area. Commentary Figure 907.2 contains the conditions that require where either system must be installed in a building. The extent that an alarm system must be installed in a building once it has been determined that such a system is required is based on several factors. One, if it is the only occupancy in the building, then it would be required throughout the building. Two, if the building is a mixed occupancy, it can either be separated or nonseparated. If the occupancy is separated in accordance with Section 508.4, then the alarm system is only required within that separated portion of the building. If the building is considered a nonseparated, mixed-occupancy building, then Section 508.3.1 states that the code applies to each portion of the building based on the occupancy classification of that space and that the most restrictive provisions of Chapter 9 shall apply to the building or portion thereof in which the nonseparated occupancies are located. Therefore, if you have a Group A occupancy in a nonseparated mixed occupancy (containing other occupancies such as Groups B and M) where the Group A occupancy exceeds an occupant load of 300, then the entire nonseparated mixed occupancy would require the alarm system. Note that Section 508.3.1 focuses on each space to determine occupancy and requirements. Once the occupant load is determined, then any requirements, such as fire alarms, would be required throughout.

The code does not address whether a nonseparated mixed occupancy has a completely independent means of egress such as in a strip mall. Additionally, in a building containing primarily Group A occupancies, the code does not clearly address whether such occupancies within a building should be looked at as an aggregate or individual space. This issue has been clarified in the 2012 edition of the code through the use of the fire area concept for Group A occupancies, but only for the basic manual fire alarm requirements in Section 907.2.1. The emergency voice/alarm communication requirements in Section 907.2.1.1 provide a criteria of 1,000 or more occupants in a Group A occupancy. A building with multiple Group A occupancies without separation of egress paths would need to be reviewed in aggregate. Fire area separation could not be used to provide separation of occupancies in this case.

Commentary Figure 907.2 contains the threshold requirements for where a manual fire alarm system or an automatic fire detection system is required based on the occupancy group. It is important to remember that although the requirement for manual pull stations may not apply (e.g., sprinklered buildings), alarm and occupant notification may still be required. Sections 907.2.11 through 907.2.23 contain additional requirements for fire alarm systems, depending on special occupancy conditions such as atriums, high-rise buildings or covered mall buildings.

The single manual fire alarm box required by this section is needed to provide a means of manually activating a fire alarm system that only contains automatic devices such as sprinkler waterflow switches or smoke detectors. Its primary use is for alarm system maintenance technicians to be able to manually activate the fire alarm system in the event of a fire during the time the system or portions of the system are down for maintenance. Note that this requirement is not subject to any of the exceptions in Sections 907.2.1 through 907.2.23 that might waive the need for manual fire alarm boxes in certain buildings.

Exception 1 recognizes the specialized nature of fire alarm systems installed only for emergency elevator control and supervision.

Exception 2 waives the single manual fire alarm box but gives the fire code official authority to require it in sprinklered buildings for use by fire watch personnel or sprinkler maintenance personnel to be able to manually activate the fire alarm system in the event of a fire during the time the sprinkler system is down for maintenance.

907.2.1 Group A. A manual fire alarm system that activates the occupant notification system in accordance with Section 907.5 shall be installed in Group A occupancies where the occupant load due to the assembly occupancy is 300 or more, or where the Group A occupant load is more than 100 persons above or below the *lowest level of exit discharge*. Group A occupancies not separated from one another in accordance with Section 707.3.10 of the *International Building Code* shall be considered as a single occupancy for the purposes of applying this section. Portions of Group E occupancies occupied for assembly purposes shall be provided with a fire alarm system as required for the Group E occupancy.

Exception: Manual fire alarm boxes are not required where the building is equipped throughout with an automatic sprinkler system installed in accordance with Section 903.3.1.1 and the occupant notification appliances will activate throughout the notification zones upon sprinkler water flow.

❖ Group A occupancies are typically occupied by a significant number of people who are not completely familiar with their surroundings. The provisions of this section address three separate situations regarding the application of the alarm requirements for Group A occupancies. The three situations addressed by the provisions are: (1) where an assembly occupancy and another occupancy are involved; (2) where multiple assembly areas exist in a building; and (3) where the assembly use occurs in and is a part of a Group E occupancy.

In situations where an assembly area and another occupancy are involved, the code specifies that it is the occupant load "due to the assembly occupancy" that would need to be 300 or more before the manual alarm system is required. For example, if the building

MANUAL FIRE ALARM SYSTEM	
Occupancy Group(s)	**Threshold**
Assembly (A-1, A-2, A-3, A-4, A-5)	All with an occupant load of ≥ 300; or, > 100 above or below the lowest level of exit discharge (907.2.1)
Business (B)	Total Group B occupant load of ≥ 500; or, > 100 above or below the lowest level of exit discharge; or, in Group B fire areas containing an ambulatory care facility (907.2.2)
Educational (E)	> 50 occupants (several exceptions for manual fire alarm box placement) (907.2.3)
Factory (F-1, F-2)	≥ 2 stories with occupant load of ≥ 500 above or below the lowest level of exit discharge (exception for sprinklers) (907.2.4)
High hazard (H)	Group H-5 occupancies and occupancies used for manufacture of organic coatings (907.2.5)
Institutional (I-1, I-2, I-3, I-4)	All (exceptions for I-1 and I-2 manual fire alarm box placement and private mode signaling) (907.2.6)
Mercantile (M)	Total Group M occupant load of ≥ 500; or, occupant load of > 100 above or below the lowest level of exit discharge (907.2.7)
Hotels (R-1)	All (exceptions for ≤ 2 stories with sleeping units having exit directly to exterior; sprinklers) (907.2.8.1)
Multiple family (R-2)	If units ≥ 3 stories above lowest level of exit discharge; or, > 1 story below the highest level of exit discharge; or, > 16 units (exceptions for ≤ 2 stories with sleeping units having exit directly to exterior; sprinklers; open ended corridors/no corridor) (907.2.9.1)
Residential care/assisted living (R-4)	All (exceptions for sprinklers, manual fire alarm boxes at staff locations, direct exit to exterior, < 2 stories) (907.2.10.2)
AUTOMATIC SMOKE DETECTION SYSTEM	
Business (B) Ambulatory care facilities	Facility plus public use areas outside of it including public corridors and elevator lobbies (exception for sprinklers) (907.2.2.1)
High hazard (H)	Highly toxic gases, organic peroxides, oxidizers (907.2.5)
Institutional (I-1, I-2, I-3)	All, in specific areas by occupancy (907.2.6.1, 907.2.6.2, 907.2.6.3.3)
Hotels (R-1)	All, in interior corridors (exception for buildings without interior corridors and with sleeping units having exit directly to exterior) (907.2.8.2)
Residential care/assisted living (R-4)	All, in corridors, waiting areas open to corridors, nonsleeping area habitable spaces and kitchens (907.2.10.2)
College and university buildings (R-2 dormatories)	Common spaces; laundry, mechanical and storage rooms; interior corridors (exception for no interior corridors and each room has direct exit) (907.2.9.3)

Commentary Figure 907.2
SUMMARY OF MANUAL FIRE ALARM AND AUTOMATIC SMOKE DETECTION SYSTEM THRESHOLDS

is constructed with an assembly occupancy, such as a restaurant, with an occupant load of 250 and an adjacent office area with an occupant load of 100, the assembly space would not require an alarm system because the occupant load "due to the assembly occupancy" is less than 300. This is simply a clarification of the way the provisions were intended to be applied. This would be the intended way to apply the provision whether the building was constructed using the accessory-, separated- or nonseparated-occupancy requirements of IBC Chapter 5.

In buildings that contain multiple assembly areas, the second portion of the code text requires that the aggregate occupant load of the assembly areas is used unless the spaces are separated as required for fire areas in Section 707.3.10. Consider two examples to address this portion of the requirements. In a multiple-theater complex, the auditoriums are generally not separated from each other by the 2-hour fire-resistance rating that Table 707.3.10 would require; therefore, the aggregate occupant load of all of the assembly spaces would be used to determine if the occupant load was 300 or more. If it was, then the manual alarm would be required in all of the assembly spaces. As another example, consider a strip mall shopping center with a restaurant at one end of the building with an occupant load of 200 and a different restaurant with an occupant load of 150 at the other end of the building. Even though these are two completely separate establishments and have an amount of retail occupancy between them, the occupant load of the assembly areas does exceed 300. Therefore, unless a 2-hour fire-resistance-rated separation complying with Section 707.3.10 is provided somewhere between the two restaurants to separate them into different fire areas, a manual fire alarm would be required in the Group A occupancies. If a complying separation is provided at some point in the building, then each assembly space can be reviewed independently and would not require the installation of the alarm system. Be aware that the separation of assembly spaces or the need to aggregate the occupant loads from them could occur not only on the same floor within a building, but also to assembly uses located on different stories.

The exception allows the omission of manual fire alarm boxes in buildings equipped throughout with an automatic sprinkler system if activation of the sprinkler system will activate the building evacuation alarms associated with the manual fire alarm system.

This section also permits assembly-type areas in Group E occupancies to comply with Section 907.2.3 instead of the requirements of this section. A typical high school, for example, contains many areas used for assembly purposes such as a gymnasium, cafeteria, auditorium or library; however, they all exist to serve as an educational facility as their main function. The exception does not eliminate the fire alarm system and occupant notification system, but rather permits them to be initiated automatically by the sprinkler waterflow switch(es) instead of by the manual fire alarm boxes. It also reduces the possibility of mischievous or malicious false alarms being turned on by way of manual fire alarm boxes in venues where large numbers of people congregate.

907.2.1.1 System initiation in Group A occupancies with an occupant load of 1,000 or more. Activation of the fire alarm in Group A occupancies with an *occupant load* of 1,000 or more shall initiate a signal using an emergency voice/alarm communications system in accordance with Section 907.5.2.2.

> **Exception:** Where *approved*, the prerecorded announcement is allowed to be manually deactivated for a period of time, not to exceed 3 minutes, for the sole purpose of allowing a live voice announcement from an *approved*, constantly attended location.

❖ In order to afford authorized personnel the ability to selectively evacuate or manage occupant relocation in large assembly venues, this section requires the fire alarm system to operate through an emergency voice/alarm communications system. The exception allows the automatic alarm signals to be overridden for live voice instructions if the live voice instructions do not exceed 3 minutes. The location from which the live voice announcement originates must be constantly attended and approved by the fire code official (see also commentary, Section 907.5.2.2). In terms of the applicability of this section, it is not as specific as Section 907.2.1. More specifically, the concept of fire areas does not apply. Credit is not given to reduce the occupant load through the use of the fire area concept (see commentary, Section 907.2).

907.2.1.2 Emergency voice/alarm communication system captions. Stadiums, arenas and grandstands required to caption audible public announcements shall be in accordance with Section 907.5.2.2.4.

❖ A 2008 US Federal Court case prompted a change to the code and the IBC. The court ruled that persons with hearing impairments who attend events at stadiums, grandstands and arenas require a means of equivalent communications in lieu of the public address system. Providing occupant notification in these structures is challenging because of the building area and the number and diversity of occupants. Provisions were added in the code to require captioned messages in these buildings and grandstands when public address (PA) systems are prescribed by the accessibility requirements.

IBC Section 1108.2.7.3 sets forth requirements for audible PA systems in stadiums, arenas and grandstands. It requires that equivalent text information be provided to the audience and that the delivery time for these messages be the same as those broadcast from the PA system. The requirements apply to prerecorded and real-time messages. Section 1108.2.7.3 of the IBC also requires captioning of messages in stadiums, arenas and grandstands that have more than 15,000 fixed seats.

Because messages being broadcast can include instructions to building or site occupants explaining the actions they need to take in the event of an emergency, the requirements of NFPA 72 are applicable for captioning systems. Such a system falls within the scope of Chapter 24 of NFPA 72 entitled "Emergency Communication Systems." NFPA 72 defines an emergency communications system (ECS) as a system designed for life safety that indicates the existence of an emergency and communicates the appropriate response and action. The ECS is required to be classified as either a one- or two-way path system. It can be within a building or over a wide area or can be targeted to a particular group of recipients. The messages that will be broadcast are based on an emergency response plan developed during a risk analysis by the project stakeholders and approved by the fire code official.

The NFPA 72 ECS requirements are based on in-building or wide-area occupant notification. Wide-area systems could include the entire area of a jurisdiction. For stadium, arena and grandstand captioning, NFPA 72 defines these as mass notification systems (MNS). In the context of the NFPA 72 requirements, this particular code change requires a one-way MNS where instructions are broadcasted by personnel authorized to distribute messages. This could include fire fighters during a fire event; also, the system could be used by law enforcement officers during a domestic terrorism incident or a weather event like a tornado warning.

The design of the compliant MNS Chapter 24 of NFPA 72 is not prescriptive—an MNS is a performance-based design. Accordingly, fire code officials should require their design to be sealed by a registered professional engineer. Section 24.7 of the standard requires the preparation of a risk analysis based on the nature and anticipated risks of the facility. The risk analysis is part of the design brief, which will serve as the basis of the system design and is a required design document. NFPA 72 requires the following elements be included in the risk analysis:

- The number of persons within the building, area, space, campus or region.
- The character of the occupancy, such as unique hazards and the rate at which the hazard can develop.
- The anticipated threats, including natural, technological and intentional events.
- The reliability and performance of the MNS.
- Security of the MNS and its components.
- How the building or staff implements the risk analysis, including the use of the MNS.
- How emergency services, such as the fire service and law enforcement agencies, can employ the MNS.

In a stadium or arena, the captioning system is required to be a component of the emergency voice/alarm communications system (EV/ACS). Such a system is required by Section 907.2.1.1 in Group A occupancies with an occupant load of 1,000 or more.

The requirement in Section 907.5.2.2.4 specifies the captioning system would be connected to the EV/ACS. The fire alarm control unit will require a listed interface unit capable of displaying text messages. Textual visible appliances are allowed by NFPA 72 when used in conjunction with audible, visual or both types of notification appliances. In the public mode, textual visible appliances are located to ensure readability by the building occupants. Such a system can display messages using televisions or light emitting diode (LED) marquee signs.

The design concept of MNS is relatively new in the design community. Captioning systems might utilize components that are not listed for fire alarm service so the design will be required to comply with Chapter 24 of NFPA 72 for textual visible notification appliances. Emergency textual messages take precedence over any nonemergency text messages. Under NFPA 72, these devices require a primary and secondary power supply. If the devices are not monitored for integrity or loss of communications by an autonomous control or a fire alarm control unit, the appliance must clearly display its status. The size of characters displayed must comply with the requirements in NFPA 72. The NFPA 72 size, character and font requirements are based on the location of the display in relation to the height and distance from the persons viewing it.

907.2.2 Group B. A manual fire alarm system shall be installed in Group B occupancies where one of the following conditions exists:

1. The combined Group B *occupant load* of all floors is 500 or more.
2. The Group B *occupant load* is more than 100 persons above or below the lowest *level of exit discharge*.
3. The *fire area* contains an ambulatory care facility.

Exception: Manual fire alarm boxes are not required where the building is equipped throughout with an *automatic sprinkler system* installed in accordance with Section 903.3.1.1 and the occupant notification appliances will activate throughout the notification zones upon sprinkler water flow.

❖ Group B occupancies generally involve individuals or groups of people in separate office areas. As a result, the occupants are not necessarily aware of what is going on in other parts of the building. Group B buildings with large occupant loads, even in single-story buildings or where a substantial number of occupants are above or below the level of exit discharge, increase the difficulty of alerting the occupants of a fire. This is especially true in nonsprinklered buildings with given occupant load thresholds. Group B occupancies include a specific use called ambulatory care facilities, which present a higher level of life hazard than the typical Group B occupancy. The fact that the care recipients of such facilities may be rendered incapable of self-preservation for limited periods of time makes the need for a fire alarm system critical. Section 907.2.2 requires a manual alarm system any time a fire area contains an ambulatory care facility. See the commentary to Section 202, definition of "Ambulatory care facility" and Section 907.2.2.1.

The exception does not eliminate the fire alarm system, but rather permits it to be initiated automatically by the sprinkler waterflow switch(es) instead of by the manual fire alarm boxes.

907.2.2.1 Ambulatory care facilities. *Fire areas* containing ambulatory care facilities shall be provided with an electronically supervised automatic smoke detection system installed within the ambulatory care facility and in public use areas outside of tenant spaces, including public *corridors* and elevator lobbies.

Exception: Buildings equipped throughout with an *automatic sprinkler system* in accordance with Section 903.3.1.1 provided that the occupant notification appliances will activate throughout the notification zones upon sprinkler water flow.

❖ Years ago, few surgical procedures were performed outside of a hospital. Today, complex outpatient surgeries conducted outside of a hospital are commonplace. They are performed in facilities often called "day surgery centers" or "ambulatory surgical centers" because patients are able to walk in and walk out the same day. Procedures render care recipients temporarily incapable of self-preservation by application of nerve blocks, sedation or anesthesia; however, they do typically recover quickly.

The code identifies health care Group I occupancies as including a 24-hour stay. Without a 24-hour stay, these surgery centers were classified as Group B, which allowed the care providers to render an unlimited number of people incapable of self-preservation with no more protection than a business office. Since these types of facilities contain distinctly different hazards to life safety than other Group B occupancies, they are now required to have a higher level of life safety and fire protection as evidenced by the requirements of this section as well as Section 903.2.2 and the construction provisions of the code.

This section more specifically states that any time a fire area contains an ambulatory care facility, the fire area should be provided with a supervised smoke detection system in the ambulatory care facility and in public use areas outside of tenant spaces. Therefore, in a medical office building, for example, the ambulatory care facility contained within would have a full coverage system. The other offices in the building would not require smoke detection in the individual tenant spaces, but instead in the public areas, such as lobby or lounge areas.

The exception does not eliminate the fire alarm system, but rather permits it to be initiated automatically by the sprinkler waterflow switch(es) instead of by the smoke detection system.

907.2.3 Group E. A manual fire alarm system that initiates the occupant notification signal utilizing an emergency voice/alarm communication system meeting the requirements of Section 907.5.2.2 and installed in accordance with Section 907.6 shall be installed in Group E occupancies. Where *automatic sprinkler systems* or smoke detectors are installed, such systems or detectors shall be connected to the building fire alarm system.

Exceptions:

1. A manual fire alarm system is not required in Group E occupancies with an *occupant load* of 50 or less.
2. Emergency voice/alarm communication systems meeting the requirements of Section 907.5.2.2 and installed in accordance with Section 907.6 shall not be required in Group E occupancies with occupant loads of 100 or less, provided that activation of the manual fire alarm system initiates an *approved* occupant notification signal in accordance with Section 907.5.
3. Manual fire alarm boxes are not required in Group E occupancies where all of the following apply:
   - 3.1. Interior *corridors* are protected by smoke detectors.
   - 3.2. Auditoriums, cafeterias, gymnasiums and similar areas are protected by *heat detectors* or other *approved* detection devices.
   - 3.3. Shops and laboratories involving dusts or vapors are protected by *heat detectors* or other *approved* detection devices.
4. Manual fire alarm boxes shall not be required in Group E occupancies where all of the following apply:
   - 4.1. The building is equipped throughout with an *approved automatic sprinkler system* installed in accordance with Section 903.3.1.1.
   - 4.2. The emergency voice/alarm communication system will activate on sprinkler water flow.
   - 4.3. Manual activation is provided from a normally occupied location.

❖ Section 404.2.3 addresses the development and implementation of lockdown plans. These requirements were developed to ensure that the level of life safety inside of the building is not reduced or compromised during a lockdown. In order for a building to safely function in a lockdown condition, the code requires a means of communication between the established central location and each secured area. Section 404.3.3.1 does not prescribe the means of communication, which could include the use of text messages to cell phones/mobile devices, email messages or the use of preestablished audio or visual signals. The provisions in Section 404.2.3 are not specific to Group E occupancies—they are applicable to all occupancies that develop and implement lockdown plans.

Because of concerns of school campus safety serving kindergarten through 12th grade students, specific requirements were put into the 2012 edition of the code and the IBC for enhanced communication between the school administrators, teachers and students when a lockdown plan is activated in Group E occupancies. As a result, emergency voice/alarm communications systems (EV/ACS) are prescribed in Group E occupancies. Previously, the code permitted the manual fire alarm system to use audible and visible alarm notification appliances but did not require the added capabilities that an EV/ACS provides.

Section 907.2.3 sets forth the requirements for automatic fire alarm and detection system requirements in Group E occupancies and prescribes the installation of an EV/ACS as opposed to a traditional horn/strobe occupant notification system.

Exception 1 exempts Group E occupancies from requiring a fire alarm system when the occupant load is 50 or less. This would exempt small day care centers that serve children older than $2^1/_2$ years of age or a small Sunday school classroom at a place of religious worship.

Exception 2 provides relief for smaller schools. If the occupant load is 100 or less, notification is not required to be via an emergency voice/alarm communications system. A school with 100 occupants only has a couple of classrooms of children. Communication is simplified and an emergency voice/alarm communications system is considered to be excessive.

Exception 3 exempts manual fire alarm boxes in interior corridors, laboratories, auditoriums, cafeterias, gymnasiums and similar spaces based on the installation of heat/smoke detectors. This is not an exception from the EV/ACS but simply an exemption of locations requiring manual fire alarm boxes. The applicability of Exception 2 is independent of whether an automatic sprinkler system is installed. If an automatic smoke detection system is installed, it must be connected to the building fire alarm system.

Exception 4 allows the omission of the manual fire alarm boxes in Group E occupancies equipped throughout with an automatic sprinkler system if the actuation of the sprinkler system will activate the EV/ACS. See Section 903.2.3 for sprinkler requirements in Group E buildings.

907.2.4 Group F. A manual fire alarm system that activates the occupant notification system in accordance with Section 907.5 shall be installed in Group F occupancies where both of the following conditions exist:

1. The Group F occupancy is two or more stories in height.
2. The Group F occupancy has a combined *occupant load* of 500 or more above or below the lowest *level of exit discharge*.

Exception: Manual fire alarm boxes are not required where the building is equipped throughout with an *automatic sprinkler system* installed in accordance with Section 903.3.1.1 and the occupant notification appliances will activate throughout the notification zones upon sprinkler water flow.

❖ This section is intended to apply to large multiple-story manufacturing facilities. For this reason, a manual fire alarm system would be required only if the building were at least two stories in height and had 500 or more occupants above or below the level of exit discharge. An unlimited area, two-story Group F occupancy complying with Section 507.5 of the IBC would be indicative of an occupancy requiring a manual fire alarm system.

Buildings in compliance with Section 507.5 of the IBC, and large manufacturing facilities in general, however, must be fully sprinklered and would thus be eligible for the exception. The exception does not eliminate the fire alarm system but rather permits it to be initiated automatically by the sprinkler system waterflow switch(es) instead of by the manual fire alarm boxes.

907.2.5 Group H. A manual fire alarm system that activates the occupant notification system in accordance with Section 907.5 shall be installed in Group H-5 occupancies and in occupancies used for the manufacture of organic coatings. An automatic smoke detection system shall be installed for highly toxic gases, organic peroxides and oxidizers in accordance with Chapters 60, 62 and 63, respectively.

❖ Because of the nature and potential quantity of hazardous materials in Group H-5 occupancies, a manual means of activating an occupant notification system is essential for the safety of the occupants. In accordance with Section 2703.11, the activation of the alarm system must initiate a local alarm and transmit a signal to the emergency control station. The manual fire alarm system requirement for the building is in addition to the emergency alarm requirements in Section 2703.12 (see also Section 908.2).

Occupancies involved in the manufacture of organic coatings present special hazardous conditions because of the unstable character of the materials, such as nitrocellulose. Good housekeeping and control of ignition sources is critical. Chapter 29 contains additional requirements for organic coating manufacturing processes.

This section also requires an automatic smoke detection system in certain occupancy conditions involving either highly toxic gases or organic peroxides and oxidizers. The need for the automatic smoke detection system may depend on the class of materials and additional levels of fire protection provided. This requirement also assumes the quantity of materials is in excess of the maximum allowable quantities shown in Tables 5003.1.1(1) and 5003.1.1(2).

907.2.6 Group I. A manual fire alarm system that activates the occupant notification system in accordance with Section 907.5 shall be installed in Group I occupancies. An automatic smoke detection system that activates the occupant notification system in accordance with Section 907.5 shall be provided in accordance with Sections 907.2.6.1, 907.2.6.2 and 907.2.6.3.3.

Exceptions:

1. Manual fire alarm boxes in *sleeping units* of Group I-1 and I-2 occupancies shall not be required at *exits* if located at all care providers' control stations or other constantly attended staff locations, provided that such manual fire alarm boxes are visible and provided with *ready access,* and the distances of travel required in Section 907.4.2.1 are not exceeded.
2. Occupant notification systems are not required to be activated where private mode signaling installed in accordance with NFPA 72 is *approved* by the *fire code official* and staff evacuation responsibilities are included in the fire safety and evacuation plan required by Section 404.

❖ Because the protection and possible evacuation of the occupants in Group I occupancies are most often dependent on the response by care providers, occupancies in Group I must be protected with a manual fire alarm system and in certain instances, as described in Sections 907.2.6.1, 907.2.6.2 and 907.2.6.3, an automatic smoke detection system. In Group I-1, smoke alarms are also required in accordance with Section 907.2.6.1.1.

It is not the intent of this section to require a smoke detection system throughout all Group I occupancies. Smoke detectors are only generally required in the corridors and in waiting rooms that are open to corridors, unless noted otherwise. IFC Committee Interpretation No. 36-03 makes it clear that the Group I provisions only require a manual fire alarm system with smoke detectors in selected areas. To reduce the potential for unwanted alarms, manual fire alarm boxes may be located at the care providers' control stations or another constantly attended location.

Exception 1 reduces the likelihood of accidental or malicious false alarm system activations by manual means by allowing the pull stations to be located in a more controlled area. It assumes the approved location is always accessible by care providers and within a distance of travel of 200 feet (60 960 mm).

Exception 2 allows the common practice in Group I occupancies of notifying only the care providers instead of all building occupants in the event of a fire, subject to the approval of the fire code official. In order to have confidence that the actions taken will be appropriate, the code also requires that the responsibilities of the staff be documented in the fire safety and evacuation plan for the facility. These requirements are found in Section 404. This will increase the likelihood for any staff training to be linked to the allowance of private mode signaling.

907.2.6.1 Group I-1. An automatic smoke detection system shall be installed in *corridors*, waiting areas open to *corridors* and *habitable spaces* other than *sleeping units* and kitchens. The system shall be activated in accordance with Section 907.5.

Exceptions:

1. For Group I-1, Condition 1 occupancies, smoke detection in *habitable spaces* is not required where the facility is equipped throughout with an *automatic sprinkler system* installed in accordance with Section 903.3.1.1.
2. Smoke detection is not required for exterior balconies.

❖ Occupancies in Group I-1 tend to be compartmentalized into small rooms so that a fire in one area of the building would not easily be noticed by occupants in another part of the building. Therefore, smoke detection is required in areas other than sleeping units and kitchens. Sleeping units are required by Section 907.2.6.1.1 to be equipped with single- and multiple-station smoke alarms in accordance with Section 907.2.10.

Given that Group I-1 occupancies may not be supervised by care providers, and to reduce the likelihood that a fire within a waiting area open to a corridor or within the corridor itself could develop beyond the incipient stage, thereby jeopardizing the building egress, these areas must be equipped with automatic smoke detection.

Exception 1 allows smoke detectors to be eliminated from habitable spaces of Group I-1, Condition 1 occupancies if the building is equipped throughout with an NFPA 13 automatic sprinkler system. The sprinkler system should control any fire and perform occupant notification through actuation of the waterflow switch and subsequent activation of the building alarm notification appliances. A sprinkler system is required for all Group I occupancies in accordance with Section 903.2.6. It should be noted that Group I-1, Condition 1 is the lower risk Group I-1 occupancy where residents are able to evacuate without assistance. See the commentary to Section 308.3 of the IBC.

Exception 2 allows for omitting smoke detectors from exterior balconies for environmental reasons and does not require the installation of an alternative type of detector. The exterior balconies are assumed to be sufficiently open to the atmosphere to readily allow the dissipation of smoke and hot gases.

907.2.6.1.1 Smoke alarms. Single- and multiple-station smoke alarms shall be installed in accordance with Section 907.2.11.

❖ As with dwelling units or sleeping units in any occupancy, this section requires that single- and multiple-station smoke alarms be installed in accordance with Section 907.2.10. Section 907.2.10.2 deals specifically with the requirements for Group I-1.

907.2.6.2 Group I-2. An automatic smoke detection system shall be installed in *corridors* in Group I-2, Condition 1 facilities and spaces permitted to be open to the *corridors* by Section 407.2 of the *International Building Code*. The system shall be activated in accordance with Section 907.4. Group I-2, Condition 2 occupancies shall be equipped with an automatic smoke detection system as required in Section 407 of the *International Building Code*.

Exceptions:

1. *Corridor* smoke detection is not required in smoke compartments that contain *sleeping units* where such units are provided with smoke detectors that comply with UL 268. Such detectors shall provide a visual display on the *corridor* side of each *sleeping unit* and shall provide an audible and visual alarm at the care providers' station attending each unit.
2. *Corridor* smoke detection is not required in smoke compartments that contain *sleeping units* where *sleeping unit* doors are equipped with automatic door-closing devices with integral smoke detectors on the unit sides installed in accordance with their listing, provided that the integral detectors perform the required alerting function.

❖ Automatic smoke detection is required in areas permitted to be open to corridors in occupancies classified as Group I-2, Condition 2 and corridors in Group I-2, Condition 1 occupancies (e.g., nursing homes, long-term care facilities and detoxification facilities). In recognition of quick-response sprinkler technology and the fact that the sprinkler system is electronically supervised, and because the doors to care recipients' sleeping units are continuously supervised by care providers when in the open position, smoke detectors are not required for adequate fire safety in care recipient sleeping units.

In Group I-2, Condition 1 occupancies (nursing homes, long-term care facilities and detoxification facilities), some redundancy is appropriate because such facilities typically have less control over furnishings and personal items, thereby resulting in a less predictable and usually higher fire hazard load than Group I-2, Condition 2 occupancies (hospitals). Also, there is generally less care provider's supervision in these facilities than in other health care facilities and thus less control over care recipient smoking and other fire causes. Therefore, to provide additional protection against fires spreading from the room of origin, smoke detection is required in corridors of nursing homes, long-term care facilities and detoxification facilities.

Smoke detection is not required in corridors of Group I-2, Condition 2 occupancies except where otherwise specifically required in the code. Similarly, because areas open to the corridor very often are the room of fire origin, and such areas are no longer required by the code to be under visual supervision by care providers, some redundancy to protection by the sprinkler system is requested. Accordingly, all areas open to corridors must be protected by an automatic smoke detection system. This requirement provides an additional level of protection against sprinkler system failures or lapses in care provider supervision.

These requirements are not applicable to Group I-2, Condition 2 (hospitals). The scope of this section clearly indicates that its provisions are only applicable to detoxification facilities and nursing homes (Group I-2, Condition 1). Hospitals are noted as being subject to the provisions in Section 407.2 of the IBC. IFC Committee Interpretation No. 37-03 addresses this issue. Section 407.2 of the IBC notes that smoke detection is only required for spaces open to corridors, such as waiting areas and mental health treatment areas where patients are not capable of self-preservation (see commentary, IBC Section 407.2).

There are two exceptions to the requirement for an automatic fire detection system in corridors of nursing homes, long-term care facilities and detoxification facilities. Both exceptions provide an alternative method for redundant protection in care recipient sleeping units. For this reason, they provide either a backup to the notification of a fire or containment of fire in the room of origin.

Exception 1 requires smoke detectors in sleeping units that activate both a visual display on the corridor side of the care recipient sleeping unit and visual and audible alarms at the care provider's station serving the room. Detectors complying with UL 268 are intended for open area protection and for connection to a normal power supply or as part of a fire alarm system. This exception, however, is specifically designed to not require the detectors to activate the building fire alarm system where approved care recipient sleeping unit smoke detectors are installed and where visual and audible alarms are provided. This is in response to the concern over unwanted alarms. The required alarm signals will not necessarily indicate to care providers that a fire emergency exists because the care provider call system may typically be used to identify numerous conditions within the room.

Exception 2 addresses the situation where smoke detectors are incorporated within automatic door-closing devices. The units are acceptable as long as the required alarm functions are still provided. Such units are usually listed as combination door closer and hold-open devices.

907.2.6.3 Group I-3 occupancies. Group I-3 occupancies shall be equipped with a manual fire alarm system and automatic smoke detection system installed for alerting staff.

❖ Because of the evacuation difficulties associated with Group I-3 occupancies and the dependence on adequate staff response, a manual fire alarm system and an automatic smoke detection system are required subject to the special occupancy conditions in Sections 907.2.6.3.1 through 907.2.6.3.3. This section recognizes that the evacuation of Group I-3 occupancies depends on an effective staff response. Chapter 4 and specifically Section 403.8.3 contain the requirements for an emergency plan, including employee training, staff availability, the need for occupants to notify staff and the need for the proper keys for unlocking doors for staff in Group I-3 occupancies.

907.2.6.3.1 System initiation. Actuation of an automatic fire-extinguishing system, *automatic sprinkler system*, a manual fire alarm box or a fire detector shall initiate an approved fire alarm signal that automatically notifies staff.

❖ This section specifies the systems that, upon activation, must initiate the required alarm signal immediately and automatically to the staff so that staff will respond in a timely manner.

907.2.6.3.2 Manual fire alarm boxes. Manual fire alarm boxes are not required to be located in accordance with Section 907.4.2 where the fire alarm boxes are provided at staff-attended locations having direct supervision over areas where manual fire alarm boxes have been omitted.

❖ Because of the potential for intentional false alarms and the resulting disruption to the facility, manual fire alarm boxes in Group I-3 occupancies may be either locked or made inaccessible to the occupants.

907.2.6.3.2.1 Manual fire alarms boxes in detainee areas. Manual fire alarm boxes are allowed to be locked in areas occupied by detainees, provided that staff members are present within the subject area and have keys readily available to operate the manual fire alarm boxes.

❖ The locking of manual fire alarm boxes is permitted only in areas where staff members are present and keys are readily available to them to unlock the boxes, or where the alarm boxes are located in a manned staff location that has direct supervision of the Group I-3 area.

907.2.6.3.3 Automatic smoke detection system. An automatic smoke detection system shall be installed throughout resident housing areas, including *sleeping units* and contiguous day rooms, group activity spaces and other common spaces normally open to residents.

Exceptions:

1. Other *approved* smoke detection arrangements providing equivalent protection, including, but not limited to, placing detectors in exhaust ducts from cells or behind protective guards *listed* for the purpose, are allowed where necessary to prevent damage or tampering.
2. *Sleeping units* in Use Conditions 2 and 3 as described in Section 308 of the *International Building Code*.
3. Smoke detectors are not required in *sleeping units* with four or fewer occupants in smoke compartments that are equipped throughout with an *automatic sprinkler system* installed in accordance with Section 903.3.1.1.

❖ Evacuation of Group I-3 facilities is impractical because of the need to maintain security. An automatic smoke detection system is therefore required to provide early warning of a fire.

As indicated in Exception 1, the installation of automatic smoke detectors must take into account the need to protect the detector from vandalism by residents. As a result, detectors may have to be located in return air ducts or be protected by a substantial physical barrier.

Since occupants in Use Condition 2 or 3 are not locked in their sleeping units, Exception 2 reduces the need for smoke detection.

Exception 3 allows smoke detectors to be omitted in sleeping units housing no more than four occupants on the basis that in a building that is protected throughout with an approved automatic sprinkler system, the system will provide both detection and suppression functions. Group I facilities are assumed to be fully sprinklered throughout in accordance with NFPA 13 as required by Section 903.2.6. The limitation of four occupants reduces the potential fuel load (mattresses, clothes, etc.) and the likelihood of involvement over an extended area.

907.2.7 Group M. A manual fire alarm system that activates the occupant notification system in accordance with Section 907.5 shall be installed in Group M occupancies where one of the following conditions exists:

1. The combined Group M *occupant load* of all floors is 500 or more persons.
2. The Group M *occupant load* is more than 100 persons above or below the lowest *level of exit discharge*.

Exceptions:

1. A manual fire alarm system is not required in covered or open mall buildings complying with Section 402 of the *International Building Code*.
2. Manual fire alarm boxes are not required where the building is equipped throughout with an *automatic sprinkler system* installed in accordance with Section 903.3.1.1 and the occupant notification appliances will automatically activate throughout the notification zones upon sprinkler water flow.

❖ Group M occupancies have the potential for large numbers of occupants who may not be familiar with their surroundings. The installation of a fire alarm system increases the ability to alert the occupants of a fire. Note that the occupant thresholds must be considered independently. If the total occupant load is 500 or more persons, a manual fire alarm system is required. If more than 100 persons are above or below the level of exit discharge, a manual fire alarm system is required.

This section also specifies that the manual fire alarm boxes must, upon activation, provide occupant notification throughout the Group M occupancy.

The extent of fire alarm application is based on the area in which the Group M occupancy is located. If the building is considered as a separated mixed occupancy, then the fire alarm system is only required in the individual occupancy in which the occupant load exceeds the threshold quantity. The rest of the building would not require a fire alarm system. This approach is noted in IBC Section 508.4.1, which states that each separated space must comply with the code based on the occupancy classification of that portion of the building. If the Group M occupancy was part of a nonseparated mixed-use building, then the alarm system would be required in the entire building in accordance with IBC Section 508.3.1. The determination as to when such a system is required would be based solely on the Group M occupant load.

Exception 1 recognizes the increased level of fixed automatic protection inherently required in covered mall buildings, including an automatic sprinkler system and possibly a smoke control system. Covered mall buildings are also required to contain an emergency voice communication system (see Section 907.2.19).

Exception 2 does not eliminate the fire alarm system, but rather allows it to be initiated automatically by sprinkler system waterflow switch(es) instead of by manual fire alarm boxes. Buildings with a fire area containing a Group M occupancy in excess of 12,000 square feet (1115 m^2) must be equipped with an automatic sprinkler system complying with Section 903.2.7.

907.2.7.1 Occupant notification. During times that the building is occupied, the initiation of a signal from a manual fire alarm box or from a waterflow switch shall not be required to activate the alarm notification appliances when an alarm signal is activated at a constantly attended location from which evacuation instructions shall be initiated over an emergency voice/alarm communication system installed in accordance with Section 907.5.2.2.

❖ Occupants in a mercantile occupancy may assume the alarm is a false alarm or act inappropriately and thus delay evacuation of the building. To prevent such a dangerous situation, the manual fire alarm system may be part of an EV/ACS. The signal is to be sent to a constantly attended location on-site from which evacuation instructions can be given.

It should be noted that, although the alarm notification alternative allows for the manual use of an EV/ACS, the alternative does not remove the requirement for audible and visual notification devices.

907.2.8 Group R-1. Fire alarm systems and smoke alarms shall be installed in Group R-1 occupancies as required in Sections 907.2.8.1 through 907.2.8.3.

❖ Because residents of Group R-1 occupancies may be asleep and are usually transients who are unfamiliar with the building, and because such buildings contain numerous small rooms where occupants may not notice a fire in another part of the building, occupancies in Group R-1 must have a manual fire alarm system and an automatic smoke detection system installed throughout. Requirements for single- or multiple-station smoke alarms in sleeping units are contained in Section 907.2.11.1.

907.2.8.1 Manual fire alarm system. A manual fire alarm system that activates the occupant notification system in accordance with Section 907.5 shall be installed in Group R-1 occupancies.

Exceptions:

1. A manual fire alarm system is not required in buildings not more than two stories in height where all individual *sleeping units* and contiguous attic and crawl spaces to those units are separated from each other and public or common areas by not less than 1-hour *fire partitions* and each individual *sleeping unit* has an *exit* directly to a *public way*, *egress court* or yard.
2. Manual fire alarm boxes are not required throughout the building where all of the following conditions are met:
   - 2.1. The building is equipped throughout with an *automatic sprinkler system* installed in accordance with Section 903.3.1.1 or 903.3.1.2.
   - 2.2. The notification appliances will activate upon sprinkler water flow.
   - 2.3. Not fewer than one manual fire alarm box is installed at an *approved* location.

❖ This section is specific to manual fire alarm systems and requires such systems in all Group R-1 occupancies, with two exceptions.

Exception 1 eliminates the requirement for a manual fire alarm system if the sleeping units have an exit discharging directly to a public way, exit court or yard. Even though the building may be two stories in height, the sleeping units on each floor must have access directly to an approved exit at grade level. The use of an exterior exit access balcony with exterior stairs serving the second floor does not constitute an exit directly at grade. The minimum 1-hour fire-resistance rating required for adequate separation of the sleeping units must be maintained.

Exception 2 does not omit the fire alarm system but rather permits it to be initiated automatically by sprinkler system waterflow switch(es) in lieu of manual fire alarm boxes. The sprinkler system must activate the occupant notification system, and at least one manual fire alarm box shall be installed at an approved location. See the commentary to Section 907.2 for a discussion of the single manual fire alarm box.

The exceptions do not affect the independent provision in Section 907.2.10 for single- or multiple-station smoke alarms.

907.2.8.2 Automatic smoke detection system. An automatic smoke detection system that activates the occupant notification system in accordance with Section 907.5 shall be installed throughout all interior *corridors* serving *sleeping units*.

Exception: An automatic smoke detection system is not required in buildings that do not have interior *corridors* serving *sleeping units* and where each *sleeping unit* has a *means of egress* door opening directly to an *exit* or to an exterior *exit access* that leads directly to an *exit*.

❖ This section requires an automatic smoke detection system within interior corridors. Such systems make use of smoke detectors for alarm initiation in accordance with Section 907.2, with one exception.

The exception provides that automatic fire detectors are not required in motels and hotels that do not have interior corridors and in which sleeping units have a door opening directly to an exterior exit access that leads directly to the exits. The intent of the exception is that the exit access from the sleeping unit door be exterior and not require reentering the building prior to entering the exit. Since the exit access is outside, the need for detectors other than the smoke alarms required by Section 907.2.8.3 in sleeping units is greatly reduced.

907.2.8.3 Smoke alarms. Single- and multiple-station smoke alarms shall be installed in accordance with Section 907.2.10.

❖ The actual requirements for single- and multiple-station smoke alarms are located in Section 907.2.10. That section requires that the single- and multiple-station smoke alarms within sleeping units be connected to the emergency electrical system. Automatic activation of the fire alarm system is avoided to reduce unnecessary alarms within such buildings.

907.2.9 Group R-2. Fire alarm systems and smoke alarms shall be installed in Group R-2 occupancies as required in Sections 907.2.9.1 and 907.2.9.3.

❖ This section introduces the fire alarm system and smoke alarm requirements for Group R-2 occupancies. This includes Group R-2 occupancies in general and also Group R-2 college and university buildings.

907.2.9.1 Manual fire alarm system. A manual fire alarm system that activates the occupant notification system in accordance with Section 907.5 shall be installed in Group R-2 occupancies where any of the following conditions apply:

1. Any *dwelling unit* or *sleeping unit* is located three or more stories above the lowest *level of exit discharge*.
2. Any *dwelling unit* or *sleeping unit* is located more than one story below the highest *level of exit discharge* of *exits* serving the *dwelling unit* or *sleeping unit*.
3. The building contains more than 16 *dwelling units* or *sleeping units*.

Exceptions:

1. A fire alarm system is not required in buildings not more than two stories in height where all *dwelling units* or *sleeping units* and contiguous attic and crawl spaces are separated from each other and public or common areas by not less than 1-hour *fire partitions* and each *dwelling unit* or *sleeping unit* has an *exit* directly to a *public way*, *egress court* or yard.
2. Manual fire alarm boxes are not required where the building is equipped throughout with an *automatic sprinkler system* installed in accordance with Section 903.3.1.1 or 903.3.1.2 and the occupant notification appliances will automatically activate throughout the notification zones upon a sprinkler water flow.
3. A fire alarm system is not required in buildings that do not have interior *corridors* serving *dwelling units* and are protected by an *approved automatic sprinkler system* installed in accordance with Section 903.3.1.1 or 903.3.1.2, provided that *dwelling units* either have a *means of egress* door opening directly to an exterior *exit access* that leads directly to the *exits* or are served by open-ended *corridors* designed in accordance with Section 1027.6, Exception 3.

❖ The occupants of Group R-2 occupancies are not considered to be as transient as those of Group R-1, which increases the probability that residents can more readily notify each other of a fire. Therefore, Group R-1 occupancies must have a manual fire alarm system with audible and visual notification appliances subject to the exceptions in Section 907.2.8.1, whereas Group R-2 occupancies are required to have only a manual fire alarm system as stipulated in one of the three listed conditions. The threshold conditions are meant to be applied independently of each other.

Exception 1 eliminates the requirement for a manual fire alarm system if the sleeping units have an exit discharging directly to a public way, exit court or yard. Even though the building may be two stories in height, the sleeping units on each floor must have access directly to an approved exit at grade level. The use of an exterior exit access balcony with exterior stairs serving the second floor does not constitute an exit directly at grade. The minimum 1-hour fire-resistance rating required for adequate separation of the sleeping units must be maintained.

Exception 2 does not omit the fire alarm system but rather permits it to be initiated automatically by sprinkler system waterflow switch(es) in lieu of manual fire alarm boxes. The sprinkler system must activate the occupant notification system. This exception does not affect the independent provisions of Section 907.2.10.

Exception 3 allows the omission of a fire alarm system in fully sprinklered buildings (NFPA 13 or 13R) with no interior corridors and that exit directly to an exterior exit access or have open-ended corridors. The important thing to note is that the sprinkler system is not required to activate alarm notification appliances since a fire alarm system would not be required. Only the sprinkler alarms required by Section 903.4 would be required.

907.2.9.2 Smoke alarms. Single- and multiple-station smoke alarms shall be installed in accordance with Section 907.2.10.

❖ The actual requirements for single- and multiple-station smoke alarms are located in Section 907.2.10. That section requires that the single- and multiple-station smoke alarms within sleeping units be connected to the emergency electrical system. Automatic activation of the fire alarm system is avoided to reduce unnecessary alarms within such buildings.

907.2.9.3 Group R-2 college and university buildings. An automatic smoke detection system that activates the occupant notification system in accordance with Section 907.5 shall be installed in Group R-2 occupancies operated by a college or university for student or staff housing in all of the following locations:

1. Common spaces outside of *dwelling units* and *sleeping units*.
2. Laundry rooms, mechanical equipment rooms and storage rooms.
3. All interior corridors serving *sleeping units* or *dwelling units*.

Exception: An automatic smoke detection system is not required in buildings that do not have interior *corridors* serving *sleeping units* or *dwelling units* and where each *sleeping unit* or *dwelling unit* either has a *means of egress* door opening directly to an exterior *exit access* that leads directly to an *exit* or a *means of egress* door opening directly to an *exit*.

Required smoke alarms in *dwelling units* and *sleeping units* in Group R-2 occupancies operated by a college or university for student or staff housing shall be interconnected with the fire alarm system in accordance with NFPA 72.

❖ This section requires an automatic smoke detection system be provided in Group R-2 occupancies operated by a college or university for student or staff housing. It also requires the smoke alarms in individual units to be interconnected with the fire alarm system. This interconnection is only for the purpose of making occupants within each unit aware of the fire alarm activation in the building. The intent is not to activate the building fire alarm system by smoke alarms in each unit. This is more restrictive than a Group R-2 occupancy in general, as typically the requirements are limited to a manual fire alarm system and smoke alarms in the individual sleeping or dwelling units.

The smoke detection system is focused on common areas, such as interior corridors, lounge areas, laundry rooms, and areas such as mechanical rooms, which could be the source of a fire, especially in these specific types of Group R-2 occupancies.

In a study completed by the New York State Governor's Task Force on Campus Fire Safety, it was cited that 43 percent of fires in college dormitories are located in dorm rooms or kitchens, leaving the other 57 percent located in areas that would not require smoke detection under the current code. The study also showed that there were approximately 300 fires on college campuses over a three-year period, while only 160 were reported to the fire department. The Center for Campus Fire Safety states that 99 deaths have been "reported" in fires in student housing since 2000.

An NFPA study on student housing showed 3,300 structural fires in dormitories, fraternities, sororities and barracks between 2002 and 2005. Since 1980, there has been an increase of 3 percent in reported fires in dormitory-type occupancies, while there has been a 52-percent decrease in overall reported structural fires.

The requirements in this section are very similar to the recommendations of the study done in New York State. It is important to note that the recommendations for that study were specifically aimed at the properties of the colleges and universities so it was not the study's intent to cover off-campus housing in this particular regard. There were recommendations for off-campus housing, such as sororities and fraternities, to have annual inspections. This particular distinction was not addressed in detail during the code development process initially; however, since this is somewhat of a continuation of requirements that were added into Chapter 4 of the 2006 edition of the IFC for emergency preparedness and planning, and those requirements were intended to deal with buildings that were college or university property, it seemed reasonable to interpret that this requirement is also limited to the buildings that are college or university property and does not apply to Group R-2 occupancies that are not college or university property. This has since been clarified through the code development process and the section now specifically notes that the Group R-2 occupancies are specifically operated by a college or university.

The exception allows for the elimination of the smoke detection system in the specific situation where there are no interior corridors and the occupants essentially exit directly to the outside. The lack of interior corridors and exterior exits reduces the amount of smoke one unit will expose to another. Note that smoke alarms within the units are still required by Section 907.2.10.2. Note also that it is entirely possible that some areas that are required to have smoke detection may have ambient conditions that warrant a different type of alarm-initiating device. Section 907.4.3 addresses this concern.

907.2.10 Single- and multiple-station smoke alarms. *Listed* single- and multiple-station smoke alarms complying with UL 217 shall be installed in accordance with Sections 907.2.10.1 through 907.2.10.7 and NFPA 72.

❖ Single- and multiple-station smoke alarms have evolved as one of the most important fire safety features in residential and similar occupancies having sleeping occupants. The value of early fire warning in these occupancies has been repeatedly demonstrated in fires involving both successful and unsuccessful smoke alarm performance.

For successful smoke alarm operation and performance, single- and multiple-station smoke alarms must be listed in accordance with UL 217 and installed to comply with the code and Chapter 11 of NFPA 72, which contains the minimum requirements for the selection, installation, operation and maintenance of fire warning equipment for use in family living units. These devices are called "smoke alarms" rather than "smoke detectors" because they are independent of a fire alarm system and include an integral alarm notification device.

907.2.10.1 Group R-1. Single- or multiple-station smoke alarms shall be installed in all of the following locations in Group R-1:

1. In sleeping areas.
2. In every room in the path of the *means of egress* from the sleeping area to the door leading from the *sleeping unit*.
3. In each story within the *sleeping unit*, including *basements*. For *sleeping units* with split levels and without an intervening door between the adjacent levels, a smoke alarm installed on the upper level shall suffice for the adjacent lower level provided that the lower level is less than one full story below the upper level.

❖ Because the occupants of a sleeping unit or suite may be asleep and unaware of a fire developing in the room or in the egress path, single- or multiple-station smoke alarms must be provided in the sleeping unit and in any intervening room between the sleeping unit and the exit access door from the room. If the sleeping unit or suite involves more than one level, a smoke alarm must also be installed on every level. See the commentary to Section 202, definition of "Sleeping unit."

Smoke alarms are required in split-level arrangements, except those that meet the conditions described in Item 3. In accordance with Section 907.2.10.5, all smoke alarms within a sleeping unit or suite must be interconnected so that actuation of one alarm will actuate all smoke alarms within the sleeping unit or suite.

907.2.10.2 Groups R-2, R-3, R-4 and I-1. Single or multiple-station smoke alarms shall be installed and maintained in Groups R-2, R-3, R-4 and I-1 regardless of *occupant load* at all of the following locations:

1. On the ceiling or wall outside of each separate sleeping area in the immediate vicinity of bedrooms.
2. In each room used for sleeping purposes.
3. In each story within a *dwelling unit*, including *basements* but not including crawl spaces and uninhabitable attics. In *dwellings* or *dwelling units* with split levels and without an intervening door between the adjacent levels, a smoke alarm installed on the upper level shall suffice for the adjacent lower level provided that the lower level is less than one full story below the upper level.

❖ Because the occupants of a dwelling unit may be asleep and unaware of a fire developing in the room or in an area within the dwelling unit that will affect their ability to escape, single- or multiple-station smoke alarms must be installed in every bedroom, in the vicinity of all bedrooms (e.g., hallways leading to the bedrooms) and on each story of the dwelling unit (see Commentary Figure 907.2.10.2 and the commentary to Section 202 definition of "Dwelling unit").

If a sprinkler system is installed throughout the building in accordance with NFPA 13, 13R or 13D, if applicable, smoke alarms would still be required in the bedrooms even if residential sprinklers are used.

Smoke alarms are required in split-level arrangements. As required by Section 907.2.10.5, all smoke alarms within a dwelling unit must be interconnected so that actuation of one alarm will actuate the alarms in all detectors within the dwelling unit.

These provisions do not apply to one- and two-family dwellings and multiple single-family dwellings (townhouses) not more than three stories in height with a separate means of egress that are regulated by the IRC. The IRC is intended to be a stand-alone document, but if the residential units do not fall within the scope of the IRC or for other reasons are intended to be subject to this code, then the requirements of this section would apply. IFC Committee Interpretation No. 42-03 addresses this condition and contains additional explanatory information about the IRC and its relationship to the other International Codes.

Although the occupants of a sleeping unit in a Group I-1 occupancy may be asleep, they are still considered capable of self-preservation. Regardless, smoke alarms are required in sleeping units. The exception allows single- or multiple-station smoke alarms to be eliminated in the room if an automatic fire detection system that includes in-room system smoke detectors is installed as required by Section 907.2.6.

907.2.10.3 Installation near cooking appliances. Smoke alarms shall not be installed in the following locations unless this would prevent placement of a smoke alarm in a location required by Section 907.2.10.1 or 907.2.10.2:

1. Ionization smoke alarms shall not be installed less than 20 feet (6096 mm) horizontally from a permanently installed cooking appliance.
2. Ionization smoke alarms with an alarm-silencing switch shall not be installed less than 10 feet (3048 mm) horizontally from a permanently installed cooking appliance.
3. Photoelectric smoke alarms shall not be installed less than 6 feet (1829 mm) horizontally from a permanently installed cooking appliance.

❖ This requirement is intended to reduce nuisance alarms attributed to locating smoke alarms in close proximity to cooking appliances and bathrooms in which steam is produced. These provisions are based on the findings in the Task Group Report "Minimum Performance Requirements for Smoke Alarm Detection Technology," February 22, 2008, and are consistent with similar requirements included in Section 29.8.3.4 of NFPA 72.

907.2.10.4 Installation near bathrooms. Smoke alarms shall be installed not less than 3 feet (914 mm) horizontally from the door or opening of a bathroom that contains a bathtub or shower unless this would prevent placement of a smoke alarm required by Section 907.2.10.1 or 907.2.10.2.

❖ See the commentary to Section 907.2.10.3. Sections 907.2.10.3 and 907.2.10.4 are provided to reduce nuisance alarms.

907.2.10.5 Interconnection. Where more than one smoke alarm is required to be installed within an individual *dwelling unit* or *sleeping unit* in Group R or I-1 occupancies, the smoke alarms shall be interconnected in such a manner that the activation of one alarm will activate all of the alarms in the individual unit. Physical interconnection of smoke alarms shall not be required where listed wireless alarms are installed and all alarms sound upon activation of one alarm. The alarm shall be clearly audible in all bedrooms over background noise levels with all intervening doors closed.

❖ The installation of smoke alarms in areas remote from the sleeping area will be of minimal value if the alarm is not heard by the occupants. Interconnection of multiple smoke alarms within an individual dwelling unit or sleeping unit is required in order to alert a sleeping occupant of a remote fire within the unit before the combustion products reach the smoke alarm in the sleeping area and thus provide additional time for evacuation.

The term "interconnection" refers to either hard-wired systems or listed wireless systems. UL has listed smoke detectors that use this technology. It is presumed that on safely evacuating the unit or room of fire origin, an occupant will notify other occupants by actuating the manual fire alarm system or using other available means. Section 907.7.1 addresses the testing of the smoke alarms to demonstrate that interconnection of such smoke alarms is properly functioning.

Similar requirements can now be found in the IRC, IBC and *International Existing Building Code*® (IEBC®) for both new and existing buildings to allow interconnection with wireless technology of smoke alarms. All wirelessly interconnected smoke alarms are listed to UL 217 and are classified by NFPA 72 as low-power systems.

907.2.10.6 Power source. In new construction, required smoke alarms shall receive their primary power from the building wiring where such wiring is served from a commercial source and shall be equipped with a battery backup. Smoke alarms with integral strobes that are not equipped with battery back-up shall be connected to an emergency electrical system in accordance with Section 1203. Smoke alarms shall emit a signal when the batteries are low. Wiring shall be permanent and without a disconnecting switch other than as required for overcurrent protection.

Exception: Smoke alarms are not required to be equipped with battery backup where they are connected to an emergency electrical system that complies with Section 604.

❖ Smoke alarms are required to use AC as a primary power source and battery power as a secondary source to improve their reliability. For example, during a power outage, the probability of fire is increased because of the use of candles or lanterns for temporary light. Required backup battery power is intended to provide continued functioning of the smoke alarms. Smoke alarms are commonly designed to emit a recurring signal when batteries are low and need to be replaced.

Certain occupancies may already have an emergency electrical system in the building to monitor other building system conditions. The emergency electrical system provides a level of reliability equivalent to battery backup.

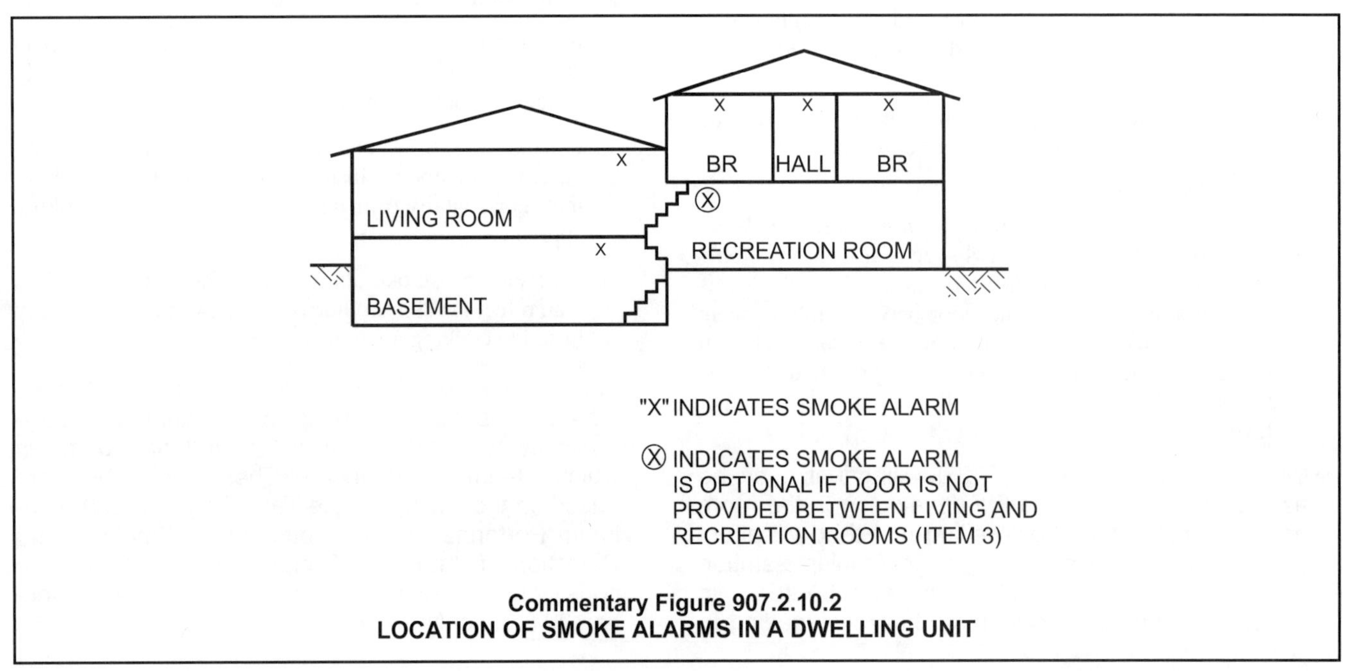

Commentary Figure 907.2.10.2
LOCATION OF SMOKE ALARMS IN A DWELLING UNIT

907.2.10.7 Smoke detection system. Smoke detectors listed in accordance with UL 268 and provided as part of the building fire alarm system shall be an acceptable alternative to single- and multiple-station *smoke alarms* and shall comply with the following:

1. The fire alarm system shall comply with all applicable requirements in Section 907.
2. Activation of a smoke detector in a *dwelling unit* or *sleeping unit* shall initiate alarm notification in the *dwelling unit* or *sleeping unit* in accordance with Section 907.5.2.
3. Activation of a smoke detector in a *dwelling unit* or *sleeping unit* shall not activate alarm notification appliances outside of the *dwelling unit* or *sleeping unit*, provided that a supervisory signal is generated and monitored in accordance with Section 907.6.6.

❖ This section specifically allows the use of an automatic smoke detection system as an alternative to smoke alarms. In the past, when this concept was proposed, it was only allowed through an alternative method and materials approach (see Section 104.9 of this code), even though, in concept, it provided the same level of protection. Such systems provide the same safety features necessary for occupants but are simply part of a fire alarm system. Note that if a detector activates within a sleeping or dwelling unit, the occupant notification system is not intended to activate. This is consistent with the operation of smoke alarms. Item 3 specifically requires the notification to be only to occupants of the sleeping unit or dwelling unit.

907.2.11 Special amusement buildings. An automatic smoke detection system shall be provided in special amusement buildings in accordance with Sections 907.2.11.1 through 907.2.11.3.

❖ Special amusement buildings are buildings in which the means of egress is not readily apparent, is intentionally confounded or is not readily available. Special amusement buildings must also comply with the provisions of Section 411 of the IBC.

The approved automatic smoke detection system is required to provide early warning of a fire. The detection system is required regardless of the presence of staff in the building.

907.2.11.1 Alarm. Activation of any single smoke detector, the *automatic sprinkler system* or any other automatic fire detection device shall immediately activate an audible and visible alarm at the building at a constantly attended location from which emergency action can be initiated, including the capability of manual initiation of requirements in Section 907.2.11.2.

❖ On activation of either a smoke detector or other automatic fire detection device or the automatic sprinkler system, an alarm must activate both an audible and visible alarm at a constantly attended location. The staff at the location is expected to be capable of then providing the required egress illumination, stopping the conflicting or confusing sounds and distractions, and activating the exit marking required by Section 907.2.11.2. The staff is also expected to be capable of preventing additional people from entering the building.

907.2.11.2 System response. The activation of two or more smoke detectors, a single smoke detector equipped with an alarm verification feature, the *automatic sprinkler system* or other *approved* fire detection device shall automatically do all of the following:

1. Cause illumination of the *means of egress* with light of not less than 1 footcandle (11 lux) at the walking surface level.
2. Stop any conflicting or confusing sounds and visual distractions.
3. Activate an *approved* directional *exit* marking that will become apparent in an emergency.
4. Activate a prerecorded message, audible throughout the special amusement building, instructing patrons to proceed to the nearest exit. Alarm signals used in conjunction with the prerecorded message shall produce a sound that is distinctive from other sounds used during normal operation.

❖ Once a fire has been detected, measures must be taken to stop the confusion or distractions. Additionally, the egress path must be illuminated and marked. These measures must occur automatically on detection of the fire or sprinkler water flow. A prerecorded message that can be heard throughout the building instructing the occupants to proceed to the nearest exit must be automatically activated. The message and alarm signals should be designed to prevent panic. The prerecorded message capability is in addition to the EV/ACS requirement of Section 907.2.11.3. The wiring of all devices must comply with NFPA 72.

907.2.11.3 Emergency voice/alarm communication system. An emergency voice/alarm communication system, which is allowed to serve as a public address system, shall be installed in accordance with Section 907.5.2.2 and be audible throughout the entire special amusement building.

❖ Because of the problem associated with evacuating special amusement buildings, an emergency voice/alarm communications system is required (see also Section 907.5.2.2). This section allows the system to also serve as a public address (PA) system to have the capability to alert the occupants of a fire and give them evacuation instructions. The system must be designed so that once the voice alarm is activated, the typical public address function is superseded by the voice alarm. Because a manual override must be provided, it is possible that the same microphone used for the public address can be used for the override. However, a separate action would be necessary so that the override function can be used once the voice alarm is active.

907.2.12 High-rise buildings. High-rise buildings shall be provided with an automatic smoke detection system in accordance with Section 907.2.12.1, a fire department communication system in accordance with Section 907.2.12.2 and an emergency voice/alarm communication system in accordance with Section 907.5.2.2.

Exceptions:

1. Airport traffic control towers in accordance with Section 907.2.21 of this code and Section 412 of the *International Building Code.*
2. Open parking garages in accordance with Section 406.5 of the *International Building Code.*
3. Buildings with an occupancy in Group A-5 in accordance with Section 303.1 of the *International Building Code.*
4. Low-hazard special occupancies in accordance with Section 503.1.1 of the *International Building Code.*
5. Buildings with an occupancy in Group H-1, H-2 or H-3 in accordance with Section 415 of the *International Building Code.*
6. In Group I-1 and I-2 occupancies, the alarm shall sound at a constantly attended location and occupant notification shall be broadcast by the emergency voice/alarm communication system.

❖ High-rise buildings require additional fire protection systems because of the difficulties with smoke movement, egress time and fire department access. As a result, this section requires both an automatic fire alarm system and an emergency voice/alarm communications system (see commentary, Section 907.5.2.2). Exceptions 1 through 5 are the same as those in Section 403.1 regarding the applicability of the high-rise provisions.

Exception 1 addresses airport traffic control towers and is based on the limited fuel load and the limited number of persons occupying the tower.

Open parking garages and places of outdoor assembly (Group A-5) are exempted by Exceptions 2 and 3, respectively, because of the free ventilation to the outside that exists in such structures.

In Exception 4, low-hazard special industrial occupancies may be exempted when approved by the fire code official. Such buildings should be evaluated based on the occupant load and the hazards of the occupancy and its contents to determine whether the protection features required by Section 403 of the code are necessary.

Buildings with occupancies in Groups H-1, H-2 and H-3 are excluded from the requirements of this section by Exception 5 because the fire hazard characteristics of these occupancies have not yet been considered in high-rise buildings.

Exception 6 recognizes the supervised environment typical of institutional uses and the reliance placed on staff to act appropriately in an emergency. As is the case for most voice alarms, the key is in being able to deliver specific information to the people who can affect a safe egress—whether it be the public, employees, or both.

907.2.12.1 Automatic smoke detection. Automatic smoke detection in high-rise buildings shall be in accordance with Sections 907.2.12.1.1 and 907.2.12.1.2.

❖ This section simply introduces the fire alarm and detection system requirements for high-rise buildings.

907.2.12.1.1 Area smoke detection. Area smoke detectors shall be provided in accordance with this section. Smoke detectors shall be connected to an automatic fire alarm system. The activation of any detector required by this section shall activate the emergency voice/alarm communication system in accordance with Section 907.5.2.2. In addition to smoke detectors required by Sections 907.2.1 through 907.2.9, smoke detectors shall be located as follows:

1. In each mechanical equipment, electrical, transformer, telephone equipment or similar room that is not provided with sprinkler protection.
2. In each elevator machine room, machinery space, control room and control space and in elevator lobbies.

❖ Automatic smoke detectors are required in all high-rise buildings in certain locations so that a fire will be detected in its early stages of development. The detectors must be connected to the automatic fire alarm system and be capable of initiating operation of the EV/ACS.

This section divides the automatic smoke detection requirement into two categories. Smoke detectors must be installed in rooms that are not typically occupied. This includes rooms used for mechanical equipment, electrical equipment, transformer equipment and telephone equipment where such rooms do not have automatic sprinkler protection. In most cases, these rooms will have sprinkler protection by virtue of being in a high-rise building and will therefore not require smoke detectors. However, in elevator machine rooms, machinery spaces, control rooms, control spaces and elevator lobbies, smoke detectors are required regardless of sprinkler protection.

Note that smoke detection and smoke alarms may be required based on occupancy-related requirements elsewhere in Section 907.2.

907.2.12.1.2 Duct smoke detection. Duct smoke detectors complying with Section 907.3.1 shall be located as follows:

1. In the main return air and exhaust air plenum of each air-conditioning system having a capacity greater than 2,000 cubic feet per minute (cfm) (0.94 m^3/s). Such detectors shall be located in a serviceable area downstream of the last duct inlet.

2. At each connection to a vertical duct or riser serving two or more stories from a return air duct or plenum of an air-conditioning system. In Group R-1 and R-2 occupancies, a smoke detector is allowed to be used in each return air riser carrying not more than 5,000 cfm (2.4 m^3/s) and serving not more than 10 air-inlet openings.

❖ Smoke detectors must be installed in the main return air and exhaust air plenum of each air-conditioning system having a design capacity exceeding 2,000 cubic feet per minute (cfm) (0.94 m^3/s). Systems with design capacities equal to or less than 2,000 cfm (0.94 m^3/s) are exempt from this requirement because their small size limits their capacity for spreading smoke to parts of the building not already involved with fire.

The area that could be served by a 2,000-cfm (0.94 m^3/s) system (approximately 5 tons of cooling capacity) is comparatively small; therefore, the distribution of smoke in a system of that size would be minimal. Smoke detectors must be located so that they monitor the total airflow within the system. If a single detector is unable to sample the total airflow at all times, then multiple detectors are required. The smoke detectors must be made accessible for maintenance and inspection. Many failures and false alarms are caused by a lack of maintenance and cleaning of the smoke detectors.

Consistent with Section 606.2.3 of the IMC, return air risers serving two or more stories must have smoke detectors installed at each story. Item 2 allows the use of a single listed smoke detector in each return air riser in a Group R-1 or R-2 occupancy if the capacity of each riser does not exceed 5,000 cfm (2.4 m^3/s) and does not serve more than 10 air-inlet openings. This alternative allows smaller buildings that have residential occupancies to only monitor the return air from each return air riser.

907.2.12.2 Fire department communication system. Where a wired communication system is *approved* in lieu of an emergency responder radio coverage system in accordance with Section 510, the wired fire department communication system shall be designed and installed in accordance with NFPA 72 and shall operate between a *fire command center* complying with Section 508, elevators, elevator lobbies, emergency and standby power rooms, fire pump rooms, areas of refuge and inside *interior exit stairways*. The fire department communication device shall be provided at each floor level within the *interior exit stairway*.

❖ High-rise buildings have posed a challenge to the traditional communication systems used by the fire service for fire-to-ground communications to assist fire ground officers in communicating with the fire fighters working in various areas of the building. Where testing of the emergency responder radio coverage system required by Section 403.4.5 of the code shows that the signal strengths are not satisfactory, Section 510.1, Exception 1, allows for the alternative of installation of a wired communication system designed in accordance with this section. The system must be capable of operating between the fire command center and every elevator, elevator lobby, emergency/standby power room, fire pump room, area of refuge and interior exit stairway. Note that this section does not offer specific criteria as to what constitutes an acceptable wired communication system or its components. It could be a component of an emergency voice/alarm communications system that complies with Section 907.5.2.2 or a building's telephone system. In any event, when applying Section 510.1, Exception 1, and this section, the concurrent approval of the fire and building code officials is required.

907.2.12.3 Multiple-channel voice evacuation. In buildings with an occupied floor more than 120 feet (36 576 mm) above the lowest level of fire department vehicle access, voice evacuation systems for high-rise buildings shall be multiple-channel systems.

❖ This section requires multiple-channel voice evacuation systems in high-rise buildings when the buildings have an occupied floor more than 120 feet above the lowest level of fire department vehicle access. Having a multiple-channel system allows the emergency responders to deliver different live messages to various areas of the building at one time, which can lead to more detailed and more efficient emergency communications to the occupants.

For example, if a fire occurs on the sixth floor of a high-rise building, a multiple-channel system can be used by the emergency responders to direct the occupants of the fifth, sixth, and seventh floors to immediately egress via the nearest exit stairway, while at the same time separately informing the occupants of the eighth and higher levels of the situation and directing them to stand by. This type of ability can help the emergency responders control crowding within the exit stairways. Additionally, the benefits of the multiple-channel system are not limited to fire evacuations only, as these systems can also be used effectively in active-shooter and other emergencies.

907.2.13 Atriums connecting more than two stories. A fire alarm system shall be installed in occupancies with an atrium that connects more than two stories, with smoke detection in locations required by a rational analysis in Section 909.4 and in accordance with the system operation requirements in Section 909.17. The system shall be activated in accordance with Section 907.5. Such occupancies in Group A, E or M shall be provided with an emergency voice/alarm communication system complying with the requirements of Section 907.5.2.2.

❖ Buildings containing an atrium that connects more than two stories are to be equipped with a fire alarm system that can be used to notify building occupants to begin evacuating in case of a fire. The other critical part of such fire alarm systems is to activate the smoke control system. The system is to be activated by smoke detection designed and installed in accordance with the rational analysis as required in Section 909.4. More specifically, smoke control systems are engineered systems that are activated by carefully placed and zoned smoke detection. If improperly designed and installed, the system may not be effective. For instance, wrongly placed or inappropriate smoke detection technology may not activate fast enough and the smoke control system would be overwhelmed. This section goes on to state that the alarm system must be initiated in accordance with Section 907.5, which requires that the alarm system is to be initiated by the sprinkler system and any automatic or manual fire alarm-initiating devices in the building. It does not intend to require certain features to be installed within the atrium but rather is simply requiring that any such features present initiate the occupant notification system. It would not necessarily be appropriate to also initiate the smoke control system on activation of the alarm system within a building containing an atrium (see Section 909.12.3). The alarm system needs to be carefully zoned in such buildings to avoid an inappropriate activation of the smoke control system from a space not associated with the atrium.

Groups A, E and M must have an emergency voice/alarm communications system that complies with Section 907.5.2.2 because of the number of persons to be evacuated and the lack of familiarity with the location of exits that is typical of occupants in Groups A and M.

907.2.14 High-piled combustible storage areas. An automatic smoke detection system shall be installed throughout *high-piled combustible storage* areas where required by Section 3206.5.

❖ Section 3206.5 requires an automatic fire detection system in high-piled combustible storage areas, depending on the commodity class, the size of the high-piled storage area and the presence of an automatic sprinkler system. High-piled storage is the storage of Class I through IV commodities in piles, bin boxes, on pallets or in racks more than 12 feet (3658 mm) high or for high-hazard commodities stored higher than 6 feet (1829 mm). Chapter 32 and NFPA 13 contain additional requirements for all high-piled storage conditions.

907.2.15 Aerosol storage uses. Aerosol product rooms and general-purpose warehouses containing aerosol products shall be provided with an *approved* manual fire alarm system where required by this code.

❖ Chapter 32 and NFPA 30B contain additional guidance on the storage of and fire protection requirements for aerosol products. The requirements for storing the various levels of aerosol products are dependent on the level of sprinkler protection, the type of storage and the quantity of aerosol products. Although aerosol product fires generally involve property loss as opposed to loss of life, installation of a manual fire alarm system could aid in the prompt evacuation of the occupants. Fires involving aerosol products can spread rapidly through a building that is not properly protected and controlled.

907.2.16 Lumber, wood structural panel and veneer mills. Lumber, wood structural panel and veneer mills shall be provided with a manual fire alarm system.

❖ Any facility using mechanical methods to process wood into finished products produces debris and the potential for combustible dust. Such facilities include mills that produce solid wood lumber and wood veneers as well as those that manufacture structural wood panels such as waferboard, oriented strandboard, composite wood panels or plywood. Good housekeeping and control of ignition sources are therefore essential. To aid in the quick evacuation of occupants in an emergency, Section 2804.2.1 requires a manual fire alarm system in lumber, wood structural panel and veneer mills that contain product dryers because of their potential as a source of ignition. A manual fire alarm system is not required, however, if the dryers and all other potential sources of ignition are protected by a supervised automatic sprinkler system.

907.2.17 Underground buildings with smoke control systems. Where a smoke control system is installed in an underground building in accordance with the *International Building Code*, automatic smoke detectors shall be provided in accordance with Section 907.2.17.1.

❖ As indicated in Section 405.5.2, each compartment of an underground building must have a smoke control/exhaust system that can be activated both automatically and manually. Floor levels more than 60 feet (18 288 mm) below the lowest level of exit discharge must be compartmented. Compartmentation is a key element in the egress and fire access plan for floor areas in an underground building. The smoke control system must not only facilitate egress during a fire, but also improve fire department access to the fire source by maintaining visibility that would be otherwise impaired given the inability of the fire service to manually ventilate the underground portion of the building (see commentary, IBC Section 405.4.1).

907.2.17.1 Smoke detectors. Not fewer than one smoke detector *listed* for the intended purpose shall be installed in all of the following areas:

1. Mechanical equipment, electrical, transformer, telephone equipment, elevator machine or similar rooms.
2. Elevator lobbies.
3. The main return and exhaust air plenum of each air-conditioning system serving more than one story and located in a serviceable area downstream of the last duct inlet.
4. Each connection to a vertical duct or riser serving two or more floors from return air ducts or plenums of heating, ventilating and air-conditioning systems, except that in Group R occupancies, a *listed* smoke detector is allowed to be used in each return air riser carrying not

more than 5,000 cfm (2.4 m^3/s) and serving not more than 10 air inlet openings.

❖ Automatic smoke detectors are required in certain locations in all underground buildings so that a fire will be detected in its early stages of development. Underground buildings are similar to high-rise buildings in that they present an unusual hazard by being virtually inaccessible to exterior fire department suppression and rescue operations with the increased potential to trap occupants inside the structure. For this reason, the smoke detector location requirements for underground buildings are similar to those in Section 907.2.12.1 for high-rise buildings (see commentary, Section 907.2.12.1).

The requirement for a smoke detector in the main return and exhaust air plenum of an air-conditioning system in an underground building, however, differs from that of a high-rise building in that it is not a function of capacity [2,000 cfm (0.94 m^3/s)] but rather a function of whether the system serves more than one floor level. There is more concern over the threat of smoke movement from floor to floor because the products of combustion cannot be vented directly to the atmosphere.

907.2.17.2 Alarm required. Activation of the smoke control system shall activate an audible alarm at a constantly attended location.

❖ The audible alarm is required to notify qualified personnel immediately that the smoke control system has been activated and to put emergency procedures into action quickly.

907.2.18 Deep underground buildings. Where the lowest level of a structure is more than 60 feet (18 288 mm) below the finished floor of the lowest *level of exit discharge*, the structure shall be equipped throughout with a manual fire alarm system, including an emergency voice/alarm communication system installed in accordance with Section 907.5.2.2.

❖ The ability to communicate and offer warning of a fire can increase the time available for egress from the building. Underground structures located more than 60 feet (18 288 mm) below the level of exit discharge must therefore have a manual fire alarm system. An emergency voice/alarm communications system is also required as part of this system (see commentary, Section 907.5.2.2).

907.2.19 Covered and open mall buildings. Where the total floor area exceeds 50,000 square feet (4645 m^2) within either a covered mall building or within the perimeter line of an open mall building, an emergency voice/alarm communication system shall be provided. *Access* to emergency voice/alarm communication systems serving a mall, required or otherwise, shall be provided for the fire department. The system shall be provided in accordance with Section 907.5.2.2.

❖ Because of the potentially large number of occupants and their unfamiliarity with their surroundings, an EV/ACS, accessible by the fire department, is required to aid in evacuation of covered mall buildings exceeding 50,000 square feet (4645 m^2) in total floor area or an open mall exceeding 50,000 square feet (4645 m^2) measured within the perimeter lines of the open mall. Anchor stores are not included as part of the covered or open mall building (see commentary, Section 202 for the definition of "Covered mall building").

907.2.20 Residential aircraft hangars. Not fewer than one single-station smoke alarm shall be installed within a residential aircraft hangar as defined in Chapter 2 of the *International Building Code* and shall be interconnected into the residential smoke alarm or other sounding device to provide an alarm that will be audible in all sleeping areas of the *dwelling*.

❖ Residential aircraft hangars are assumed to be on the same property as a one- or two-family dwelling. Section 412.5 of the IBC contains additional requirements for the construction of residential aircraft hangars. The hangar could be located immediately adjacent to the dwelling unit if it is separated by 1-hour fire-resistance-rated construction. Because of the potentially close proximity of the aircraft and its flammability and fuel source, at least one smoke alarm is required in the hangar that is interconnected to the residential smoke alarms. It should be noted, however, that the requirement for a smoke alarm is also applicable to residential aircraft hangars that are detached from the dwelling unit. Because a minimum separation distance is not specified, a fire in the hangar could still present a serious fire hazard to the dwelling unit.

907.2.21 Airport traffic control towers. An automatic smoke detection system that activates the occupant notification system in accordance with Section 907.5 shall be provided in airport control towers in accordance with Sections 907.2.21.1 and 907.2.21.2.

Exception: Audible appliances shall not be installed within the control tower cab.

❖ Airport traffic control towers must be designed to comply with IBC Section 412.3. These structures are unique in that they can be built to excessive heights and are often permitted to have one exit stairway. IBC Section 412.3 requires that airport traffic control towers with an occupied floor more than 35 feet above fire department vehicle access be equipped throughout with an automatic sprinkler system. The requirements for detection systems and associated occupant notification are addressed based on whether the airport traffic control tower is equipped throughout with an automatic sprinkler system and whether multiple exits are provided.

The exception recognizes the sensitive nature of the operations that take place in the cab located at the top of the tower and prohibits the installation of audible alarm notification devices there. Notification of occupants within the cab is to be by visual notification appliances only.

907.2.21.1 Airport traffic control towers with multiple exits and automatic sprinklers. Airport traffic control towers with multiple *exits* and equipped throughout with an *auto-*

matic sprinkler system in accordance with Section 903.3.1.1 shall be provided with smoke detectors in all of the following locations:

1. Airport traffic control cab.
2. Electrical and mechanical equipment rooms.
3. Airport terminal radar and electronics rooms.
4. Outside each opening into *interior exit stairways*.
5. Along the single *means of egress* permitted from observation levels.
6. Outside each opening into the single *means of egress* permitted from observation levels.

❖ This section addresses airport traffic control towers that are equipped throughout with both an automatic sprinkler system and multiple exits. The requirements are less restrictive than Section 907.2.21.2 because two important safety aspects are provided.

The first three items address occupiable or equipment-related rooms where the fires are more likely to start. The last two items address the paths of egress. Item 4 requires one detector outside each entrance to the interior stairway. Item 5 is specific to providing detection along the entire means of egress path from the observation levels.

907.2.21.2 Other airport traffic control towers. Airport traffic control towers with a single *exit* or where sprinklers are not installed throughout shall be provided with smoke detectors in all of the following locations:

1. Airport traffic control cab.
2. Electrical and mechanical equipment rooms.
3. Airport terminal radar and electronics rooms.
4. Office spaces incidental to the tower operation.
5. Lounges for employees, including sanitary facilities.
6. *Means of egress*.
7. Utility shafts where *access* to smoke detectors can be provided.

❖ This section addresses airport traffic control towers that have only a single exit or where an automatic sprinkler system is not provided. Essentially all of the items addressed are the areas permitted in an airport traffic control tower in accordance with Section 412.3. Items 1 through 3 are the same as Section 907.2.21.1. These are the critical occupiable spaces and equipment spaces where fires have the greatest effect on the operation of airport traffic control towers. Since this is a single exit tower and possibly not equipped throughout with an automatic sprinkler system, other occupiable areas such as offices and lounges for employees must also provide smoke detection. Since there are limited exits or no systems able to control the fire, early warning of a fire becomes more critical. Item 6 requires smoke detection along the means of egress path. The intent is to address the exit access path leading to the interior exit stairway. Finally, Item 7 addresses the potential for fires in any utility shaft that may be accessible to building occupants.

907.2.22 Battery rooms. An automatic smoke detection system shall be installed in areas containing stationary storage battery systems as required in Section 1206.2.

❖ Stationary lead-acid battery systems are commonly used for standby power, emergency power or uninterrupted power supplies. The release of hydrogen gas during battery system operation is usually minimal. Adequate ventilation will disperse the small amounts of liberated hydrogen. Because standby power and emergency power systems control many important building emergency systems and functions, a supervised automatic smoke detection system is required for early warning notification of a hazardous condition. Section 608 contains additional requirements, including the need for safety venting, room enclosure requirements, spill control and neutralization provisions, ventilation criteria, signage and seismic protection. Section 509 also requires that such rooms in certain occupancies be separated by 1-hour construction.

907.2.23 Capacitor energy storage systems. An automatic smoke detection system shall be installed in areas containing capacitor energy storage systems as required by Section 1206.3.

❖ This section requires that an automatic smoke detection system be installed in areas containing capacitor energy storage systems.

907.3 Fire safety functions. Automatic fire detectors utilized for the purpose of performing fire safety functions shall be connected to the building's fire alarm control unit where a fire alarm system is required by Section 907.2. Detectors shall, upon actuation, perform the intended function and activate the alarm notification appliances or activate a visible and audible supervisory signal at a constantly attended location. In buildings not equipped with a fire alarm system, the automatic fire detector shall be powered by normal electrical service and, upon actuation, perform the intended function. The detectors shall be located in accordance with NFPA 72.

❖ When the code requires installation of automatic fire detectors to perform a specific function, such as elevator recall or smokeproof enclosure ventilation, or when detectors are installed to comply with a permitted alternative, such as door-closing devices, these detectors must be connected to the building's automatic fire alarm system if the building is required by the code to have such a system.

In addition to performing its intended function (for example, closing a door), if a detector is activated, it must also activate either the building alarm devices (if present) or a supervisory signal at a constantly attended location. This requirement recognizes that these detectors and the devices they control are part of the building fire protection system and are expected to perform as designed. If they are connected to a fire alarm system, they will have the supervision necessary for operational reliability. If they are not connected to and supervised by a fire alarm system, they still must be supervised through the constantly attended location.

For buildings not required to have a fire alarm system, the fire safety function detectors must be powered by the building electrical system and be located as required by NFPA 72. Without this stipulation, these detectors could not be expected to perform as intended because there would be no power supply.

907.3.1 Duct smoke detectors. Smoke detectors installed in ducts shall be *listed* for the air velocity, temperature and humidity present in the duct. Duct smoke detectors shall be connected to the building's fire alarm control unit where a fire alarm system is required by Section 907.2. Activation of a duct smoke detector shall initiate a visible and audible supervisory signal at a *constantly attended location* and shall perform the intended fire safety function in accordance with this code and the *International Mechanical Code*. In facilities that are required to be monitored by a supervising station, duct smoke detectors shall report only as a supervisory signal and not as a fire alarm. They shall not be used as a substitute for required open area detection.

Exceptions:

1. The supervisory signal at a constantly attended location is not required where duct smoke detectors activate the building's alarm notification appliances.
2. In occupancies not required to be equipped with a fire alarm system, actuation of a smoke detector shall activate a visible and an audible signal in an *approved* location. Smoke detector trouble conditions shall activate a visible or audible signal in an *approved* location and shall be identified as air duct detector trouble.

❖ It is not the intent of this section to send a signal to the fire department or to activate the alarm notification devices within a building. Instead, this section requires that a supervisory signal be sent to a constantly attended location. Smoke detectors must be connected to a fire alarm system where such systems are installed. Connection to the fire alarm system will activate a visible and audible supervisory signal at a constantly attended location, which will alert building supervisory personnel that a smoke alarm has activated and will also provide electronic supervision of the duct detectors, thereby indicating any problems that may develop in the detector system circuitry or power supply.

Exception 1 allows activation of the building alarm notification appliances in place of a supervisory signal. Causing the occupant notification system to sound would alert the occupants of the building that an alarm condition exists within the air distribution system, thereby performing the same function as a supervisory signal sent to a constantly attended location.

Exception 2 recognizes that not all buildings are required to have a fire alarm system. A visible and audible signal must be activated at an approved location that will alert building supervisory personnel to take action. Additionally, the duct smoke detectors must be electronically supervised to indicate trouble (system fault) in the detector system circuitry or power supply. A trouble condition must activate a distinct visible or audible signal at a location that will alert the responsible personnel.

907.3.2 Special locking systems. Where special locking systems are installed on means of egress doors in accordance with Section 1010.1.9.7 or 1010.1.9.8, an automatic detection system shall be installed as required by that section.

❖ This section alerts the code user to additional requirements in Sections 1010.1.9.6 and 1010.1.9.7 that tie the operation of egress doors into the activation of an automatic fire detection system. A smoke or heat detection system is required to unlock delayed egress locks upon activation. The heat detection system can be the sprinkler system. For example, a similar requirement is found in Section 1010.1.4.3 that requires horizontal sliding doors used as a component of the means of egress, where required to be rated, to be self-closing or automatic-closing upon smoke detection. Also, electrically locked egress doors in occupancies as required by Section 1010.1.9.8 must be capable of being automatically unlocked by activation of an automatic fire detection system, if one is installed.

907.3.3 Elevator emergency operation. Automatic fire detectors installed for elevator emergency operation shall be installed in accordance with the provisions of ASME A17.1/CSA B44 and NFPA 72.

❖ This section provides correlation with Section 607.1 by making it clear that automatic fire detection devices used to initiate Phase I emergency recall of elevators are to be installed in accordance with both ASME A17.1 and NFPA 72.

907.3.4 Wiring. The wiring to the auxiliary devices and equipment used to accomplish the fire safety functions shall be monitored for integrity in accordance with NFPA 72.

❖ In order to provide a reasonable level of integrity and reliability to the installation of automatic fire detection devices and related equipment installed to perform various fire safety functions in accordance with Section 907.3, this section requires that all wiring interconnecting such devices and equipment be monitored for integrity in accordance with NFPA 72.

907.4 Initiating devices. Where manual or automatic alarm initiation is required as part of a fire alarm system, the initiating devices shall be installed in accordance with Sections 907.4.1 through 907.4.3.1.

❖ This section introduces Sections 907.4.1 through 907.4.3.1, which contain requirements for the various types of manual or automatic fire alarm-initiating devices.

907.4.1 Protection of fire alarm control unit. In areas that are not continuously occupied, a single smoke detector shall be provided at the location of each fire alarm control unit, notification appliance circuit power extenders and supervising station transmitting equipment.

Exception: Where ambient conditions prohibit installation of smoke detector, a *heat detector* shall be permitted.

❖ This section requires a smoke detector at the fire alarm control unit. This is consistent with Section 10.4.4 of NFPA 72. This smoke detector will activate the fire alarm control unit and allow it to either notify occupants or transmit a signal to a remote monitoring location before the fire impairs the fire alarm control unit. The exception parallels Section 907.4.3 by allowing a heat detector to be installed in lieu of a smoke detector in areas where the ambient environment is hostile to smoke detectors and could lead to unwanted alarm activations. This exception is also allowed by NFPA 72.

907.4.2 Manual fire alarm boxes. Where a manual fire alarm system is required by another section of this code, it shall be activated by fire alarm boxes installed in accordance with Sections 907.4.2.1 through 907.4.2.6.

❖ This section specifies the requirements for manual fire alarm boxes that are part of a required manual fire alarm system.

907.4.2.1 Location. Manual fire alarm boxes shall be located not more than 5 feet (1524 mm) from the entrance to each *exit*. In buildings not protected by an *automatic sprinkler system* in accordance with Section 903.3.1.1 or 903.3.1.2, additional manual fire alarm boxes shall be located so that the distance of travel to the nearest box does not exceed 200 feet (60 960 mm).

❖ Manual fire alarm boxes must be located in the path of egress and be readily accessible to the occupants. They must be located within 5 feet (1524 mm) of the entrance to each exit on every story of the building. This would include the need to locate manual fire alarm boxes near each horizontal exit, as well as entrances to stairs and exit doors to the exterior.

Manual fire alarm boxes are located near exits so that an adequate number of devices are available in the path of egress to transmit an alarm in a timely manner. These locations also encourage the actuation of a manual fire alarm box on the fire floor prior to entering the stair, resulting in the alarm being received from the actual fire floor and not another floor along the path of egress.

The location also presumes that individuals will be evacuating the area where the fire originated. When evacuation of the fire area is unlikely, consideration could be given to putting manual fire alarm boxes in more convenient places. Examples of such instances would be officer stations in Group I-3 occupancies and care provider's stations in Group I-2 occupancies.

The 200-foot (60 960 mm) exit access travel distance limitation is consistent with the exit access travel distance permitted for most nonsprinklered occupancies. If the 200-foot (60 960 mm) travel distance to a manual fire alarm box is exceeded in a nonsprinklered building, additional manual fire alarm boxes would be required.

907.4.2.2 Height. The height of the manual fire alarm boxes shall be not less than 42 inches (1067 mm) and not more than 48 inches (1372 mm) measured vertically, from the floor level to the activating handle or lever of the box.

❖ Manual fire alarm boxes must be reachable by the occupants of the building. They must also be mounted high enough to reduce the likelihood of damage or false alarms from something accidentally striking the device. Therefore, manual fire alarm boxes must be mounted a minimum of 42 inches (1067 mm) and a maximum of 48 inches (1372 mm) above the floor level. The 48-inch (1372 mm) measurement corresponds to the maximum unobstructed side-reach height by a person in a wheelchair.

907.4.2.3 Color. Manual fire alarm boxes shall be red in color.

❖ Manual fire alarm boxes are to be painted or manufactured in a distinctive and traditional red color to provide a visual cue to help building occupants identify the device.

907.4.2.4 Signs. Where fire alarm systems are not monitored by a supervising station, an *approved* permanent sign shall be installed adjacent to each manual fire alarm box that reads: WHEN ALARM SOUNDS—CALL FIRE DEPARTMENT.

Exception: Where the manufacturer has permanently provided this information on the manual fire alarm box.

❖ This section has limited application because, as indicated in Section 907.6.6, fire alarm systems generally must be monitored by an approved supervising station. Where a system is not monitored, such as with a fire alarm system that is not required by code, adequate signage must be displayed to tell occupants what response actions must be taken. Most building occupants assume that when an alarm device is activated, the fire department will automatically be notified as well. The sign must be conspicuously located next to the manual fire alarm box unless it is mounted on the manual fire alarm box itself by the manufacturer.

907.4.2.5 Protective covers. The *fire code official* is authorized to require the installation of *listed* manual fire alarm box protective covers to prevent malicious false alarms or to provide the manual fire alarm box with protection from physical damage. The protective cover shall be transparent or red in color with a transparent face to permit visibility of the manual fire alarm box. Each cover shall include proper operating instructions. A protective cover that emits a local alarm signal shall not be installed unless *approved*. Protective covers shall not project more than that permitted by Section 1003.3.3.

❖ Although manual fire alarm boxes must be readily available to all occupants in buildings required to have a manual fire alarm system, this section allows the use of protective covers if they are approved by the fire code official. Protective covers are commonly used to reduce either the potential for intentional false alarms or vandalism. They also provide protection in locations where the manual fire alarm boxes may be exposed to physical damage, such as in gymnasiums, indoor tennis courts and the like.

907.4.2.6 Unobstructed and unobscured. Manual fire alarm boxes shall be provided with *ready access*, unobstructed, unobscured and visible at all times.

❖ This section addresses the concern that manual fire alarm boxes be kept clear and unobstructed. It is recommended that a minimum of 3 feet (914 mm) be kept clear but more may be needed. NFPA 72 addresses the need for manual fire alarm boxes to be unobstructed in Section 17.14.8.2 and states that manual fire alarm boxes be conspicuous, unobstructed and accessible. This requirement will assist during the design, construction, inspection and future maintenance of manual fire alarm boxes, helping ensure they are located where they will be provided with enough space for access and will not be obstructed.

907.4.3 Automatic smoke detection. Where an automatic smoke detection system is required it shall utilize smoke detectors unless ambient conditions prohibit such an installation. In spaces where smoke detectors cannot be utilized due to ambient conditions, *approved* automatic *heat detectors* shall be permitted.

❖ Smoke detectors must be used, except when ambient conditions would prohibit their use. This section would allow a heat detector to be installed in lieu of a smoke detector in areas where the ambient environment is hostile to smoke detectors and could lead to unwanted alarm activations. The smoke detector manufacturer's literature will identify the limitations on the use of smoke detectors, including environmental conditions such as humidity, temperature and airflow.

907.4.3.1 Automatic sprinkler system. For conditions other than specific fire safety functions noted in Section 907.3, in areas where ambient conditions prohibit the installation of smoke detectors, an *automatic sprinkler system* installed in such areas in accordance with Section 903.3.1.1 or 903.3.1.2 and that is connected to the fire alarm system shall be *approved* as automatic heat detection.

❖ This section states that automatic heat detection is not required when buildings are fully sprinklered in accordance with NFPA 13 or 13R. The presence of a sprinkler system exempts areas where a heat detector can be installed in place of a smoke detector, such as in storage or furnace rooms. The sprinkler head in this case essentially acts as a heat detection device. Note that this provision does not apply to the fire safety functions indicated in Section 907.3.

907.5 Occupant notification systems. A fire alarm system shall annunciate at the fire alarm control unit and shall initiate occupant notification upon activation, in accordance with Sections 907.5.1 through 907.5.2.3.3. Where a fire alarm system is required by another section of this code, it shall be activated by:

1. Automatic fire detectors.
2. Automatic sprinkler system waterflow devices.
3. Manual fire alarm boxes.
4. Automatic fire-extinguishing systems.

Exception: Where notification systems are allowed elsewhere in Section 907 to annunciate at a constantly attended location.

❖ This section makes it clear that fire alarm system activation begins first by activating the fire alarm control unit, then by notifying the occupants of an alarm condition and then goes on to introduce all of the components of an occupant notification system contained in Sections 907.5.1 through 907.5.2.3.3.

It also lists the system components that are to act as alarm initiation devices. The exception is a recognition that there are places in the code where an alternative to occupant notification is an alarm notification at a constantly attended location. The exception is intended to clarify the code so that there is no question as to whether this general provision for alarm activation is superseded by the other sections addressing the alarm notification at a constantly attended location.

907.5.1 Presignal feature. A presignal feature shall not be installed unless *approved* by the *fire code official*. Where a presignal feature is provided, a signal shall be annunciated at a constantly attended location *approved* by the *fire code official*, so that occupant notification can be activated in the event of fire or other emergency.

❖ A presignal feature on a fire alarm system allows the occupant notification devices to activate in selected, constantly attended locations only and from which human intervention is required to activate a general occupant notification signal. Alternatively, this feature can be programmed to delay the general alarm notification for more than 1 minute before it will automatically be activated by the control panel. In either presignal scenario, remote transmission of the alarm signal to the fire department is immediate. See NFPA 72 for additional information on the presignal feature.

Improper use of the presignal feature has been a contributing factor in several multiple-death fire incidents. In most instances, the staff failed to activate the general alarm quickly and the occupants of the building were unaware of the fire. Therefore, the use of a presignal feature is discouraged by the code. A presignal feature may be used only if it is approved by the fire code official and the fire department.

907.5.2 Alarm notification appliances. Alarm notification appliances shall be provided and shall be *listed* for their purpose.

❖ The code requires that fire alarm systems be equipped with approved alarm notification appliances so that in an emergency, the fire alarm system will notify the occupants of the need for evacuation or implementation of the fire emergency plan. Alarm notification devices required by the code are of two general types: visible and audible. Except for voice/alarm signaling systems, once the system has been activated, all visible and audible alarms are required to activate. Voice/alarm signaling systems are special signaling systems that are activated selectively in response to specific emergency conditions.

907.5.2.1 Audible alarms. Audible alarm notification appliances shall be provided and emit a distinctive sound that is not to be used for any purpose other than that of a fire alarm.

Exceptions:

1. Audible alarm notification appliances are not required in critical care areas of Group I-2, Condition 2 occupancies that are in compliance with Section 907.2.6, Exception 2.
2. A visible alarm notification appliance installed in a nurses' control station or other continuously attended staff location in a Group I-2, Condition 2 suite shall be an acceptable alternative to the installation of audible alarm notification appliances throughout the suite in Group I-2, Condition 2 occupancies that are in compliance with Section 907.2.6, Exception 2.
3. Where provided, audible notification appliances located in each enclosed occupant evacuation elevator lobby in accordance with Section 3008.9.1 of the *International Building Code* shall be connected to a separate notification zone for manual paging only.

❖ To attract the attention of building occupants, audible alarms must be distinctive, using a sound that is unique to the fire alarm system and used for no other purpose than alerting occupants to a fire emergency. Other emergencies, such as tornados, must be signaled by another sound different from the fire signal.

Exception 1 recognizes that the occupants in critical care areas of Group I-2 occupancies are usually incapacitated. The audible alarms may have the effect of unnecessarily disrupting the care recipients who are most likely not capable of self-preservation. Likewise, audible alarms in operating theaters of hospitals could be hazardous because an alarm activation could startle a surgeon during a delicate procedure. Critical care areas are also assumed to be adequately staffed at all times. Section 907.2.6, Exception 2 allows the use of private mode signaling in accordance with NFPA 72 and also requires that staff evacuation responsibilities be included in the fire safety and evacuation plan. See the commentary to Section 907.2.6. In private mode, as permitted by Section 907.2.6, there is still a requirement for an audible alarm notification from appliances, though at a much lower decibel level meant to alert staff of the alarm activation. Allowing the audible alarm to be eliminated from critical care areas (operating rooms) in exchange for a visual notification device is also not appropriate since the visual signal device also creates a distraction in critical care areas that may not be able to immediately stop a patient procedure. The emergency action plan would include provisions for alerting critical area staff and initiating the actions to be taken.

Exception 2 allows hospital care suites to eliminate audible alarms where visible alarm notification appliances are located at a continuously attended staff location or nurses control station. In a suite arrangement, the "control area" is the centrally manned location for staff monitoring patients in the separate rooms. An alarm indicator at this location will alert staff for response in a more effective and efficient manner. Similar to Exception 1, audible alarms can unnecessarily disrupt the care recipients. In addition, simply providing visible alarm notification throughout the suite is not appropriate. The patients' evacuation depends on staff since they are not capable of self-preservation. As with Exception 1, compliance with Exception 2 to Section 907.2.6 would be required in order to take advantage of this exception.

Exception 3 is intended to address the concern that automatic emergency voice/alarm messages do not interfere with operation of the two-way communication associated with the occupant evacuation elevators. Live voice messages would be appropriate in the lobbies.

907.5.2.1.1 Average sound pressure. The audible alarm notification appliances shall provide a sound pressure level of 15 decibels (dBA) above the average ambient sound level or 5 dBA above the maximum sound level having a duration of not less than 60 seconds, whichever is greater, in every occupiable space within the building.

❖ To attract the attention of building occupants, this section requires that the distinctive audible alarms must be capable of being heard above the ambient noise level in a space. The indicated levels are considered the minimum pressure differential that will be perceivable by most people. It prescribes that the sound pressure level (SPL) for notification appliances shall be a minimum of 15 decibels measured in the A-scale (dBA) above the ambient SPL or 5 dBA above the maximum SPL in every space that can be occupied in a building. These SPLs are based on a minimum 1-minute measurement period. SPLs for Group R and I-1 occupancies, mechanical rooms and other occupancies are no longer stipulated as they had been in previous editions of the code.

The values mandated in Section 907.5.2.1.1 in previous editions of the code were not consistent with the notification appliance SPL requirements in NFPA 72. NFPA 72 requirements for the audible notification appliances are based on if the devices emit alert or evacuation tones, voice messages or audible notifications for exit markings. The provisions in Section 907.5.2.1.1 would apply to all notification appliances designed to operate in either public or private mode. In sleeping areas, the minimum SPL is no longer specified in Section 907.5.2.1.1; however, for smoke alarms, NFPA 72 requires a minimum 75 dBA SPL at the pillow.

Also note that the 2010 Americans with Disabilities Act *Standards for Accessible Design* has an exception for medical care facilities following industry practice that will allow a dependence on staff. The activation of either audible or visible alarms could be detrimental to the care recipients in locations like operating rooms and intensive or critical care units.

907.5.2.1.2 Maximum sound pressure. The maximum sound pressure level for audible alarm notification appliances shall be 110 dBA at the minimum hearing distance from the audible appliance. Where the average ambient noise is greater than 95 dBA, visible alarm notification appliances shall be provided in accordance with NFPA 72 and audible alarm notification appliances shall not be required.

❖ In no case may the sound pressure level exceed 110 dBA at the minimum hearing distance from the audible appliance. This is consistent with Americans with Disabilities Act (ADA) requirements. Sound pressures above that level can cause pain or even permanent hearing loss. In such cases, audible alarms are not required to be installed but visual alarms would be necessary to compensate for the lack of audibility.

It should also be noted that in certain work areas, the Occupational Safety and Health Administration (OSHA) requires employees to wear hearing protection, possibly preventing them from hearing an audible alarm. Additionally, the noise factor in these areas is high enough that an audible alarm may not be discernible. In these areas, as well as in others, the primary method of indicating a fire can be by a visible signal. Employees must be capable of identifying such a signal as indicating a fire.

907.5.2.2 Emergency voice/alarm communication systems. Emergency voice/alarm communication systems required by this code shall be designed and installed in accordance with NFPA 72. The operation of any automatic fire detector, sprinkler waterflow device or manual fire alarm box shall automatically sound an alert tone followed by voice instructions giving *approved* information and directions for a general or staged evacuation in accordance with the building's fire safety and evacuation plans required by Section 404. In high-rise buildings, the system shall operate on at least the alarming floor, the floor above and the floor below. Speakers shall be provided throughout the building by paging zones. At a minimum, paging zones shall be provided as follows:

1. Elevator groups.
2. *Interior exit stairways.*
3. Each floor.
4. *Areas of refuge* as defined in Chapter 2.

Exception: In Group I-1 and I-2 occupancies, the alarm shall sound in a constantly attended area and a general occupant notification shall be broadcast over the overhead page.

❖ The primary purpose of an emergency voice/alarm communications system is to provide dedicated manual and automatic facilities for the origination, control and transmission of information and instructions pertaining to a fire alarm emergency to the occupants of a building. This section identifies that notification speakers are required throughout the building with a minimum of one speaker in each paging zone when an emergency voice/alarm communications system is required. The system may sound a general alarm or be a selective system in which only certain areas of the building receive the alarm indication for staged evacuation. See Chapter 4 for evacuation plan requirements. The intent is to provide the capability to send out selective messages to individual areas; however, it does not prohibit the same message to be sent to all areas. In high-rise buildings, a minimum area of notification must include the alarming floor and one floor above and one floor below it.

This section also identifies the minimum paging zone arrangement. This does not preclude further zone divisions for logical staged evacuation in accordance with an approved evacuation plan.

This section also indicates that the emergency voice/alarm system is to be initiated as all other fire alarm systems are initiated. The functional operation of the system begins with an alert tone (usually 3 to 10 seconds in duration) followed by the evacuation signal (message). It is important to remember that the voice alarm system is not an "audible alarm." It has its own specific criteria for installation and approval according to NFPA 72. Consequently, the sound pressure requirements for audible alarms do not apply to voice alarm systems. For voice alarm systems, the intent is communication and an understanding of what is being said, not volume.

The exception is similar to Exception 2 of Section 907.5.2.1, and recognizes the supervised environment typical of institutional uses and the reliance placed on staff to act appropriately in an emergency. As is the case for most voice alarms, the key is in being able to deliver specific information to the people who can affect a safe egress—whether this is the public, employees or both.

907.5.2.2.1 Manual override. A manual override for emergency voice communication shall be provided on a selective and all-call basis for all paging zones.

❖ The intent of this section is to provide the ability to transmit live voice instructions over any previously initiated signals or prerecorded messages for all zones. This would include the ability to override the voice message at once throughout the building or to be able to select individual paging zones for the message override.

907.5.2.2.2 Live voice messages. The emergency voice/alarm communication system shall have the capability to broadcast live voice messages by paging zones on a selective and all-call basis.

❖ This would include the ability to provide the live voice message at once throughout the building or to be able to select individual paging zones to receive the message. Speakers used for background music must not be used unless specifically listed for fire alarm system use. NFPA 72 has additional requirements for the placement, location and audibility of speakers used as part of an emergency voice/alarm communications system.

907.5.2.2.3 Alternative uses. The emergency voice/ alarm communication system shall be allowed to be used for other announcements, provided that the manual fire alarm use takes precedence over any other use.

❖ In certain circumstances that should be approved by the fire code officials, the emergency voice/alarm communications system could be used to convey information other than fire alarm-related items. This could include severe weather warnings that might require evacuation or relocation, lockdown instructions (see commentary, Section 404.2.3) and similar approved messages. In the event of such usage, the system must respond immediately to manual fire alarm box activations.

907.5.2.2.4 Emergency voice/alarm communication captions. Where stadiums, arenas and grandstands have 15,000 fixed seats or more and provide audible public announcements, the emergency/voice alarm communication system shall provide pre-recorded or real-time captions. Prerecorded or live emergency captions shall be from an *approved* location constantly attended by personnel trained to respond to an emergency.

❖ This provision links the EV/ACS with the requirements for captioning in IBC Section 1108.2.7.3. IBC Section 1108.2.7.3 requires that stadiums, arenas and grandstands with 15,000 or more fixed seats provide captioning for audible announcements (see commentary, Section 907.2.1.2).

907.5.2.2.5 Emergency power. Emergency voice/ alarm communications systems shall be provided with emergency power in accordance with Section 1203. The system shall be capable of powering the required load for a duration of not less than 24 hours, as required in NFPA 72.

❖ Because the emergency voice/alarm communications system is a critical aid in evacuating a building, the system must be connected to an approved emergency power source complying with Section 2702 of the IBC. The section also clarifies that the duration of the load for EV/ACS is a minimum of 24 hours.

907.5.2.3 Visible alarms. Visible alarm notification appliances shall be provided in accordance with Sections 907.5.2.3.1 through 907.5.2.3.3.

Exceptions:

1. Visible alarm notification appliances are not required in *alterations*, except where an existing fire alarm system is upgraded or replaced, or a new fire alarm system is installed.
2. Visible alarm notification appliances shall not be required in *exits* as defined in Chapter 2.
3. Visible alarm notification appliances shall not be required in elevator cars.
4. Visual alarm notification appliances are not required in critical care areas of Group I-2, Condition 2 occupancies that are in compliance with Section 907.2.6, Exception 2.

❖ This section contains alarm system requirements for occupants who are hearing impaired. Visible alarm notification appliances are to be installed in conjunction with the audible devices and located and oriented so that they will display alarm signals throughout a space. It is not the intent of the code to offer visible alarm signals as an option to audible alarm signals. Both are required. However, the code acknowledges conditions when audible alarms may be of little or no value, such as when the ambient sound level exceeds 105 dBA. In such cases, Section 907.5.2.1.2, similar to NFPA 72, allows for visible alarm notification appliances in the area.

Exception 1 states that visible alarm devices are not required in previously approved existing fire alarm systems or as part of minor alterations to existing fire alarm systems. Extensive modifications to an existing fire alarm system such as an upgrade or replacement would require the installation of visible alarm devices even if the previous existing system neither had them nor required them. The main reason is a combination of simple economics and practical application. Many existing systems that do not have visible signal devices do not have the wiring capability to include such devices. To make the necessary changes to the existing system, a total replacement of the existing system may need to take place. In many cases, this is cost prohibitive. Thus, if the alteration is small, the system can be left as is, without the visual devices. The second consideration is scope. If the alteration involves only a limited area, it could be confusing to have part of the area equipped with visual devices and part without. This is not good practice, as the alarm could be confusing. If an entire floor is being altered, then it becomes subject to consideration for an upgrade to an alarm system with visual devices. If only an office is being remodeled, then the implication is that the upgrade to visual devices may not be warranted. This determination will be subjective in many cases and should be applied based on the life safety benefit and financial expenses involved and whether adequate audible devices are present for full coverage.

In Exception 2, visible alarm devices are not required in exit elements because of the potential distraction during evacuation. Exits, as defined in Chapter 2, could include interior exit stairways or exit passageways but not exit access corridors. In tall buildings, exiting may be phased based on alarm zone. If the alarm floor and adjacent floors are notified of the emergency but the remainder of the building is not, then a visual device in the stairway would be confusing to those people who may not be coming from the alarm floor.

Previously, some jurisdictions were requiring visible alarm notification appliances to be installed in elevator cars since there was no exception in the code or NFPA 72 to allow omission of this type of notification appliance in elevator cars. Exception 3 eliminates any confusion regarding the need to install visible notification appliances in elevator cars. The rationale for not installing visible notification appliances in elevator cars is the same as for interior exit stairways; high light intensity from these notification appliances may cause confusion and disorientation. Also, elevator passengers are "captive" in that they cannot respond to such devices until the elevator arrives at its destination or is recalled by the Phase I emergency recall feature, which could lead to passenger panic.

Exception 4 was added to eliminate visual alarm notification appliances in critical care areas of Group I-2, Condition 2 occupancies (hospitals) because of the hazards they may pose to the occupants. Such occupancies already have staff procedures in place during fires that more than compensate for visual alarm notification appliances. In addition, in these areas of the hospital, the patients are not typically ambulatory. This allowance includes specific requirements for detailing of the staff evacuation responsibilities based on the requirements in Section 907.2.6. See also the commentary to Exception 1 of Section 907.5.2.1.

907.5.2.3.1 Public use areas and common use areas. Visible alarm notification appliances shall be provided in *public use areas* and *common use areas*.

Exception: Where employee work areas have audible alarm coverage, the notification appliance circuits serving the employee work areas shall be initially designed with not less than 20-percent spare capacity to account for the potential of adding visible notification appliances in the future to accommodate hearing-impaired employee(s).

❖ Visible alarm notification appliances must provide coverage in all areas open to the public (use areas) as well as all shared or common use areas (e.g., corridors, public restrooms, shared offices, classrooms, medical exam rooms, etc.). Areas where visible alarm notification appliances are not required include private offices, mechanical rooms or similar spaces. The intent with this section is to replicate the provisions included in the Americans with Disabilities Act *Standards for Accessible Design*.

The exception allows employee work areas to provide only for spare capacity on notification circuits to allow for those with hearing impairments to be accommodated as necessary. This spare capacity is intended to eliminate the potential for overloading notification circuits when a hearing-impaired person is hired and needs to be accommodated, but reduces the initial construction cost as such alarm notification appliances may not be necessary in every situation.

907.5.2.3.2 Groups I-1 and R-1. Habitable spaces in dwelling units and sleeping units in Group I-1 and R-1 occupancies in accordance with Table 907.5.2.3.2 shall be provided with visible alarm notification. Visible alarms shall be activated by the in-room smoke alarm and the building fire alarm system.

❖ Fire alarm systems in Group I-1 and R-1 sleeping accommodations must be equipped with visible alarms to the extent stated in Table 907.5.2.3.2. The visible alarm notification devices in these rooms are to be activated by both the required in-room smoke alarm and the building fire alarm system. All visible alarm notification appliances in a building, however, need not be activated by individual room smoke alarms. It is not a requirement that the accessible sleeping units be provided with visible alarm notification appliances even though some elderly patients or residents may be both mobility and hearing impaired.

TABLE 907.5.2.3.2
VISIBLE ALARMS

NUMBER OF SLEEP UNITS	SLEEPING ACCOMMODATIONS WITH VISIBLE ALARMS
6 to 25	2
26 to 50	4
51 to 75	7
76 to 100	9
101 to 150	12
151 to 200	14
201 to 300	17
301 to 400	20
401 to 500	22
501 to 1,000	5% of total
1,001 and over	50 plus 3 for each 100 over 1,000

❖ This table specifies the minimum number of sleeping units that are to be equipped with visible and audible alarms. The numbers are based on the total number of sleeping accommodations in the facility. The requirements in this table are intended to be consistent with the *2010 ADA Standards for Accessible Design*.

907.5.2.3.3 Group R-2. In Group R-2 occupancies required by Section 907 to have a fire alarm system, each *story* that contains *dwelling units* and *sleeping units* shall be provided with the future capability to support visible alarm notification appliances in accordance with Chapter 10 of ICC A117.1. Such capability shall accommodate wired or wireless equipment. The future capability shall include one of the following:

1. The interconnection of the building fire alarm system with the unit smoke alarms.
2. The replacement of audible appliances with combination audible/visible appliances.
3. The future extension of the existing wiring from the unit smoke alarm locations to required locations for visible appliances.

❖ Group R-2 occupancies with a fire alarm system are required to have the capability to support visual alarm notification appliances in accordance with Chapter 10 of ICC A117.1. This requirement has been in the IBC, and the language added in the 2012 edition is intended to provide more specific guidance as to what is meant by "capability." Note that this requirement includes all dwelling and sleeping units, not just those classified as either Type A or B. Sections 1006.2 through 1006.4.4 of ICC A117.1 address smoke and fire alarm requirements as they pertain to accessible communication features. More specifically, Section 1006.2 states that when unit smoke detection is provided, it shall provide audible notification in compliance with NFPA 72. Section 1006.3 is focused on buildings where fire alarm systems are provided. If a fire alarm system is provided in the building, ICC A117.1 requires that the wiring be extended to a point within the unit in the vicinity of the smoke detection system. Based on the type of unit and the strategy used by the designer, this location may vary. Section 1006.4 addresses the visible alarm requirements specifically and has various issues it addresses, as follows:

1. Complies with Section 702 of ICC A117.1, which focuses on the requirements of NFPA 72, and that such notification devices be hardwired.
2. Addresses the fact that all visible notification devices be activated within the unit, either when the smoke alarms in the unit activate or when that portion of the building fire alarm system in that portion of the building activates.
3. Allows the same visible notification for the smoke alarms in the unit and the building fire alarm system.
4. Prohibits the use of the visible notification for anything other than the operation of the smoke alarms in the unit or the building fire alarm system.

In terms of the specific capability requirements, this section has been clarified to provide direction as to what may be meant by bringing the wiring to the unit. There has been confusion in the past when it was interpreted that all units are required to be prewired for visible appliances, which was not the intent of ICC A117.1. More specifically, now the requirements provide essentially three options for future capability, as follows:

- Potential for future interconnection of the building fire alarm system with the unit smoke alarms.
- Replacement of audible appliance with combination audible/visible appliances.
- Extension of wiring from the unit smoke alarm locations to required locations of visible appliances.

It is important to remember that the location of visible notification devices, if installed, are driven by the requirements of NFPA 72 and may vary the approach taken, based on the configuration of the space.

907.6 Installation and monitoring. A fire alarm system shall be installed and monitored in accordance with Sections 907.6.1 through 907.6.6.2 and NFPA 72.

❖ This section specifies the requirements for fire alarm system installation and monitoring and also references the installation requirements of NFPA 72.

907.6.1 Wiring. Wiring shall comply with the requirements of NFPA 70 and NFPA 72. Wireless protection systems utilizing radio-frequency transmitting devices shall comply with the special requirements for supervision of low-power wireless systems in NFPA 72.

❖ Wiring for fire alarm systems must be installed so that it is secure and will function reliably in an emergency. The code requires that the wiring for fire alarm systems meet the requirements of NFPA 70 and NFPA 72. This requirement is in addition to the general requirements for electrical installations set forth in Chapter 27 of the IBC. For reliability, systems that use radio-frequency transmitting devices for signal transmission are required to have supervised transmitting and receiving equipment that conforms to the special requirements contained in NFPA 72. This requirement is in addition to the general requirements for supervision in Section 907.6.6.

907.6.2 Power supply. The primary and secondary power supply for the fire alarm system shall be provided in accordance with NFPA 72.

Exception: Backup power for single-station and multiple-station smoke alarms as required in Section 907.2.10.6.

❖ The operation of fire alarm systems is essential to life safety in buildings and must be reliable in the event the normal power supply fails. For proper operation of fire alarm systems, this section requires that the primary and secondary power supplies comply with NFPA 72. This is in addition to the general requirements for electrical installations in Chapter 27. NFPA

72 offers three alternatives for secondary supply: a 24-hour storage battery, storage batteries with a 4-hour capacity and a generator or multiple generators.

NFPA 72 requires that the primary and secondary power supplies for remotely located control equipment essential to the system operation must conform to the requirements for primary and secondary power supplies for the main system. Also, NFPA 72 contains requirements for monitoring the integrity of primary power supplies and requires a backup power supply.

907.6.3 Initiating device identification. The fire alarm system shall identify the specific initiating device address, location, device type, floor level where applicable and status including indication of normal, alarm, trouble and supervisory status, as appropriate.

Exceptions:

1. Fire alarm systems in single-story buildings less than 22,500 square feet (2090 m^2) in area.
2. Fire alarm systems that only include manual fire alarm boxes, waterflow initiating devices and not more than 10 additional alarm-initiating devices.
3. Special initiating devices that do not support individual device identification.
4. Fire alarm systems or devices that are replacing existing equipment.

❖ Current technology makes identification of alarm-initiating devices much easier. This section takes advantage of this technology to improve the ability of emergency responders to rapidly identify the location and status of initiating devices at the time of an emergency. It will also help identify problematic alarm-initiating devices and thus reduce nuisance alarms. It also eliminates the requirements for providing zone indication of system status. This is considered particularly important in high-rise buildings, where the number of initiating devices and the geometry of the building warrant a need for point monitoring of individual devices, which is not currently accommodated by single floor zones.

This section allows the building official the flexibility to not require individual detection device identification in smaller buildings where the source of alarm and trouble signals can be more easily determined.

The 22,500-square-foot limitation noted in Exception 1 relates to the size of a typical fire alarm zone (see Section 907.6.4) and represents a small building. Exception 2 addresses manual fire alarm systems in which the location of initiation may not be an indicator of where the fire actually is or an automatic sprinkler waterflow alarm-initiating device that could be annunciating an entire building, along with a very limited number of other alarm initiating devices Exception 3 recognizes that some devices will not work with this requirement. Finally, Exception 4 provides flexibility to existing system replacement. Replacement should be encouraged, and requiring identification of alarm-initiating device locations is considered onerous.

907.6.3.1 Annunciation. The initiating device status shall be annunciated at an *approved* on-site location.

❖ This section specifically notes that the alarm-initiating device status of trouble versus alarm needs to be provided in an approved location to enable rapid identification of problematic devices or alarm conditions by first responders.

907.6.4 Zones. Each floor shall be zoned separately and a zone shall not exceed 22,500 square feet (2090 m^2). The length of any zone shall not exceed 300 feet (91 440 mm) in any direction.

Exception: *Automatic sprinkler system* zones shall not exceed the area permitted by NFPA 13.

❖ Since the fire alarm system also aids emergency personnel in locating the fire, the system must be zoned to shorten response time to the fire location. Zoning is also critical if the fire alarm system initiates certain other fire protection systems or control features, such as smoke control systems.

At a minimum, each floor of a building must constitute one zone of the system. If the floor area exceeds 22,500 square feet (2090 m^2), additional zones per floor are required. The maximum length of a zone is 300 feet (91 440 mm).

The exception states that NFPA 13 defines the maximum areas to be protected by one sprinkler system and that the sprinkler system need not be designed to meet the 22,500-square-foot (2090 m^2) area limitations for a fire alarm system zone. For example, NFPA 13 permits a sprinkler system riser in a light-hazard occupancy to protect an area of 52,000 square feet (4831 m^2) per floor. In accordance with the exception, a single waterflow switch, and consequently a single fire alarm system zone, would be acceptable. If other alarm-initiating devices are present on the floor, they would need to be zoned separately to meet the 22,500-square-foot (2090 m^2) limitation.

It is not intended that this section apply to sprinkler systems. This section only applies where a fire alarm system is required in accordance with Section 907. Unless the building is categorized as a high rise and must comply with Section 907.6.4.2, the code does not mandate the zoning of sprinkler systems per floor. With today's fully addressable fire alarm systems, each detector effectively becomes its own zone. The intent with zoning is to identify and limit the search area for fire alarm systems. Addressable devices will indicate the precise location of the alarm condition, thereby eliminating the need for the zoning contemplated by this section when approved by the fire code official in accordance with Section 104.11.

907.6.4.1 Zoning indicator panel. A zoning indicator panel and the associated controls shall be provided in an *approved* location. The visual zone indication shall lock in until the system is reset and shall not be canceled by the operation of an audible alarm-silencing switch.

❖ The zoning indicator panel, which can be the fire alarm control unit or a separate fire alarm annunciator panel (FAAP), must be installed in a location approved by the fire code official. One of the key considerations in determining panel placement is whether the panel is located to permit ready access by emergency responders. Once an alarm-initiating device within a zone has been activated, the annunciation of the zone must lock in until the system is reset.

907.6.4.2 High-rise buildings. In high-rise buildings, a separate zone by floor shall be provided for each of the following types of alarm-initiating devices where provided:

1. Smoke detectors.
2. Sprinkler waterflow devices.
3. Manual fire alarm boxes.
4. Other *approved* types of automatic fire detectiondevices or suppression systems.

❖ High-rise buildings must have a separate zone by floor for each indicated type of alarm-initiating device. Although this feature may be desirable in all buildings, the incremental cost difference is substantially higher in low-rise buildings in which basic fire alarm systems are installed. State-of-the-art fire alarm systems installed in high-rise buildings are addressable and by their nature automatically provide this minimum zoning.

907.6.5 Access. Access shall be provided to each fire alarm device and notification appliance for periodic inspection, maintenance and testing.

❖ Automatic fire detectors, especially smoke detectors, require periodic cleaning to reduce the likelihood of malfunction. Section 907.8 and NFPA 72 require inspection and testing at regular intervals. Access to perform the required inspections, necessary maintenance and testing is a particularly important consideration for those detectors that are installed within a concealed space, such as an air duct.

907.6.6 Monitoring. Fire alarm systems required by this chapter or by the *International Building Code* shall be monitored by an *approved* supervising station in accordance with NFPA 72.

Exception: Monitoring by a supervising station is not required for:

1. Single- and multiple-station smoke alarms required by Section 907.2.10.
2. Smoke detectors in Group I-3 occupancies.
3. *Automatic sprinkler systems* in one- and two-family dwellings.

❖ Fire alarm systems required by Section 907 are required to be electrically supervised by one of the methods prescribed in NFPA 72.

Exception 1 exempts single- and multiple-station smoke alarms from being supervised because of the potential for unwanted false alarms.

Exception 2 recognizes a similar problem in Group I-3 occupancies. Accordingly, because of the concern over unwanted alarms, smoke detectors in Group I-3 occupancies need only sound an approved alarm signal that automatically notifies staff (see Section 907.2.6.3.1). Smoke detectors in such occupancies are typically subject to misuse and abuse, and frequent unwanted alarms would negate the effectiveness of the system.

Exception 3 clarifies that sprinkler systems in one- and two-family dwellings are not part of a dedicated fire alarm system and are typically designed in accordance with NFPA 13D, which does not require electrical supervision.

907.6.6.1 Automatic telephone-dialing devices. Automatic telephone-dialing devices used to transmit an emergency alarm shall not be connected to any fire department telephone number unless *approved* by the fire chief.

❖ On initiation of an alarm, supervisory or trouble signal, an automatic telephone-dialing device takes control of the telephone line for the reliability of transmission of all signals. The device, however, must not be connected to the fire department telephone number unless specifically approved by the fire department because that could disrupt any potential emergency (911) calls. NFPA 72 contains additional guidance on such devices, including digital alarm-communicator systems.

907.6.6.2 Termination of monitoring service. Termination of fire alarm monitoring services shall be in accordance with Section 901.9.

❖ This is simply a cross link to a requirement in the IFC related to the termination of monitoring service. Section 901.9 requires the monitoring service itself to notify the fire code official of the service being terminated. Although the ultimate responsibility rests with the building owner, he or she is not cited in this section since if they discontinued the service, they would likely not understand the implications, and if they did, would have no incentive to contact the fire code official.

907.7 Acceptance tests and completion. Upon completion of the installation, the fire alarm system and all fire alarm components shall be tested in accordance with NFPA 72.

❖ A complete performance test of the fire alarm system must be conducted to determine that the system is operating as required by the code. The acceptance test must include a test of each circuit, alarm-initiating device, alarm notification appliance and any supplementary functions, such as activation of closers and dampers. The operation of the primary and secondary (emergency) power supplies must also be tested, as well as the supervisory function of the control panel. Section 901.5 assigns responsibility for conducting the acceptance tests to the owner or the owner's representative.

NFPA 72 contains specific acceptance test procedures. Additional guidance on periodic testing and inspection can also be obtained from Section 907.8 and NFPA 72.

907.7.1 Single- and multiple-station alarm devices. When the installation of the alarm devices is complete, each device and interconnecting wiring for multiple-station alarm devices shall be tested in accordance with the smoke alarm provisions of NFPA 72.

❖ To determine that smoke alarms have been properly installed and are ready to function as intended, they must be actuated during an acceptance test. The test also confirms that interconnected detectors will operate simultaneously as required. The responsibility for conducting the acceptance tests rests with the owner or the owner's representative as stated in Section 901.5.

907.7.2 Record of completion. A record of completion in accordance with NFPA 72 verifying that the system has been installed and tested in accordance with the *approved* plans and specifications shall be provided.

❖ In accordance with NFPA 72, this section requires a written statement from the installing contractor that the fire alarm system has been tested and installed in compliance with the approved plans and the manufacturer's specifications. Any deviations from the approved plans or the applicable provisions of NFPA 72 are to be noted in the record of completion.

907.7.3 Instructions. Operating, testing and maintenance instructions and record drawings ("as builts") and equipment specifications shall be provided at an *approved* location.

❖ To permit adequate testing, maintenance and troubleshooting of the installed fire alarm system, an owner's manual with complete installation instructions must be kept on-site or in another approved location. The instructions include a description of the system, operating procedures, and testing and maintenance requirements.

907.8 Inspection, testing and maintenance. The maintenance and testing schedules and procedures for fire alarm and fire detection systems shall be in accordance with Sections 907.8.1 through 907.8.5 and NFPA 72. Records of inspection, testing and maintenance shall be maintained.

❖ Fire alarms and smoke detection systems are to be inspected, tested and maintained in accordance with Sections 907.8.1 through 907.8.5 and the applicable requirements of NFPA 72. It is the building owner's responsibility to keep these systems operable at all times.

907.8.1 Maintenance required. Where required for compliance with the provisions of this code, devices, equipment, systems, conditions, arrangements, levels of protection or other features shall thereafter be continuously maintained in accordance with applicable NFPA requirements or as directed by the *fire code official*.

❖ Periodic maintenance keeps systems in good working order or allows repair of defects discovered during inspections or testing. Because specialized tools and training are needed, only properly trained technicians or specialists should perform required periodic maintenance. Most maintenance is required only as needed, but many manufacturers suggest or require regular periodic replacement of parts subject to wear or abuse.

907.8.2 Testing. Testing shall be performed in accordance with the schedules in NFPA 72 or more frequently where required by the *fire code official*. Records of testing shall be maintained.

Exception: Devices or equipment that are inaccessible because of safety considerations shall be tested during scheduled shutdowns where *approved* by the *fire code official*, but not less than every 18 months.

❖ NFPA 72 includes schedules for testing frequencies of fire alarm and fire detection systems and their components. Periodic tests that follow standardized methods are intended to confirm the results of inspections, determine that all components function properly and determine that systems meet their original design specifications. Tools, devices or equipment are usually required to perform tests. Because tests are more detailed than inspections, they are usually done only once or twice per year in most cases. Some tests, however, may be required as frequently as bimonthly or quarterly. Because specialized knowledge and equipment are required, tests must usually be performed by technicians or specialists trained in the test methods involved.

Although Section 907.8.2 specifically addresses testing, NFPA 72 also contains schedules for visual inspection frequencies. An inspection consists of a visual check of a system or device to verify it is in operating condition and free from visible defects or damage.

Obvious damage and the general condition of the system must always be noted and recorded. Partly because of their cursory nature, inspections are conducted more frequently than tests and maintenance. Because special knowledge and tools are not required, inspections may be done by any competent person.

The exception recognizes the impracticality of testing every device or piece of equipment related to a fire alarm or fire detection system. Some devices may be inaccessible for safety considerations, such as those in continuous process operations. Testing, however, must be done during scheduled shutdowns.

907.8.3 Smoke detector sensitivity. Smoke detector sensitivity shall be checked within one year after installation and every alternate year thereafter. After the second calibration test, where sensitivity tests indicate that the detector has remained within its *listed* and marked sensitivity range (or 4-percent obscuration light gray smoke, if not marked), the length of time between calibration tests shall be permitted to be extended to not more than 5 years. Where the frequency is extended, records of detector-caused nuisance alarms and subsequent trends of these alarms shall be maintained. In zones or areas where nuisance alarms show any increase over the previous year, calibration tests shall be performed.

❖ Usually, changes in detector sensitivity are caused by inadequate maintenance. Regular sensitivity testing is intended to determine whether detectors require recalibration, maintenance or replacement. This section prescribes the intervals for testing smoke detector sensitivity. Where two successful tests have been conducted, the frequency of the calibration tests can be extended to a maximum of five years. This interval extension recognizes the stability of both the environment and the detector. However, if nuisance alarms occur during this time interval extension, calibration tests may be needed because of potential changes in the environment where the detector is located or in the performance of the detector itself.

907.8.4 Sensitivity test method. To verify that each smoke detector is within its *listed* and marked sensitivity range, it shall be tested using one of the following methods:

1. A calibrated test method.
2. The manufacturer's calibrated sensitivity test instrument.
3. *Listed* control equipment arranged for the purpose.
4. A smoke detector/control unit arrangement whereby the detector causes a signal at the control unit where the detector's sensitivity is outside its acceptable sensitivity range.
5. Another calibrated sensitivity test method acceptable to the *fire code official*.

Detectors found to have a sensitivity outside the *listed* and marked sensitivity range shall be cleaned and recalibrated or replaced.

Exceptions:

1. Detectors *listed* as field adjustable shall be permitted to be either adjusted within the *listed* and marked sensitivity range and cleaned and recalibrated or they shall be replaced.
2. This requirement shall not apply to single-station smoke alarms.

❖ This section prescribes acceptable test methods to verify that each smoke detector is within its listed and marked sensitivity range; any of the listed test methods may be used.

With regard to a calibration test method, many manufacturers have designed their devices to be tested by the application of a magnet at a test point on the outside of the detector. This activates a reed switch or pulls a fine wire into the detection chamber to simulate a predetermined level of obscuration.

Another test method may require that a test device such as a key-type tool be inserted in a test port. This either activates a test switch or produces the desired level of obscuration directly.

One detector manufacturer supplies an interface device for connecting a volt-ohm-amp meter to a test port. Pressing a button on the interface device permits a direct reading of detector chamber voltage in an alarm condition.

Other detectors must be removed and inserted in or connected to a device used to calibrate and test the device. The calibrated sensitivity test instrument must satisfy the manufacturer's recommendation for a specific detector.

Addressable/analog-type detectors produce direct readings of the chamber voltage by the control unit. Many of these systems permit sensitivity adjustments within acceptable limits from the control unit as well. This test method essentially allows remote sensitivity testing.

A system control/detector combination unit detects changes in the environment and in the detector by comparing current readings to previously stored information in the memory of the control unit. Significant changes would indicate that the stability of either the environment or the detector has changed and that further maintenance or recalibration is required.

Any other method or device that permits the user to check the voltage drop across a smoke detection chamber is acceptable, subject to the approval of the fire code official. Test devices should be manufactured and supplied by the smoke detector manufacturer.

Exception 1 recognizes that some smoke detectors may be listed as being field adjustable. If, however, such devices cannot be adjusted to their listed sensitivity, then they must be replaced.

Exception 2 exempts single-station smoke alarms from sensitivity testing because these devices are not designed with the same level of technical sophistication as system smoke detectors. Smoke alarm manufacturers also recommend that the devices be discarded and replaced at regular intervals to reduce the likelihood of failure.

907.8.4.1 Sensitivity testing device. Smoke detector sensitivity shall not be tested or measured using a device that administers an unmeasured concentration of smoke or other aerosol into the detector.

❖ Functional testing using smoke or a smoke substitute, such as aerosols, must comply with the manufacturer's recommended test procedures. A precisely measured amount of smoke or other aerosol product must be used to adequately determine detector sensitivity. Some detector manufacturers do not accept testing with aerosol products and void detector warranties where this product is used. The functional test method selected should not permanently affect detector performance.

907.8.5 Inspection, testing and maintenance. The building *owner* shall be responsible to maintain the fire and life safety systems in an operable condition at all times. Service personnel shall meet the qualification requirements of NFPA 72 for inspection, testing and maintenance of such systems. Records of inspection, testing and maintenance shall be maintained.

❖ This section clearly indicates that it is the responsibility of the building owner to maintain all fire alarm systems in proper working order. Often, an outside agency that employs adequately trained personnel will provide any maintenance and testing that is needed. NFPA 72 contains additional guidance on the qualifications for service personnel. Some examples include factory-trained and factory-certified individuals, individuals certified for fire alarm testing and inspection by NICET, or other individuals tested and certified by the local authority. Proper maintenance of fire alarm systems is essential so that the systems will perform as intended.

Inspection and test records provide a means for determining compliance with the requirements of the code. Inspectors should be prepared to determine that inspection, test and maintenance logs are accurate and complete. Records must include the nature of the activity or service performed, when the activity occurred, who performed the activity and who witnessed testing or approved the work upon completion.

907.9 Where required in existing buildings and structures. An *approved* fire alarm system shall be provided in existing buildings and structures where required in Chapter 11.

❖ Retroactive requirements for fire alarms are found in Section 1103.7. All the retroactive code requirements are found in Chapter 11 for convenience and to help with consistent enforcement.

907.10 Smoke alarm maintenance. Smoke alarms shall be tested and maintained in accordance with the manufacturer's instructions. Smoke alarms shall be replaced when they fail to respond to operability tests, or when they exceed 10 years from the date of manufacture, unless an earlier replacement is specified in the manufacturer's published instructions.

❖ This section states that smoke alarms shall be replaced when they fail to respond to operability tests, or when they exceed 10 years from the date of manufacture, unless an earlier replacement is specified in the manufacturer's published instructions. The replacement of smoke alarms when they exceed 10 years from the date of manufacture is considered to be an operational and maintenance requirement for new and existing smoke alarms and not a construction requirement. It is the intent of this section to maintain a fully operational smoke alarm system, and the 10-year replacement criterion is a maximum equipment life span.

SECTION 908 EMERGENCY ALARM SYSTEMS

908.1 Group H occupancies. Emergency alarms for the detection and notification of an emergency condition in Group H occupancies shall be provided as required in Chapter 50.

❖ Emergency alarm systems provide indication and warning of emergency situations involving hazardous materials. An emergency alarm system is required in all Group H occupancies as indicated in Sections 5004.9 and 5005.4.4, as well as Group H-5 HPM facilities, as indicated in Section 908.2. The Group H occupancy classification assumes the storage or use of hazardous materials exceeds the maximum allowable quantities specified in Tables 5003.1.1(1) and 5003.1.1(2).

An emergency alarm system should include an emergency alarm-initiating device outside each interior door of hazardous material storage areas, a local alarm device and adequate supervision.

Even though ozone gas generator rooms (Section 6005.3.2), repair garages (Section 2311.8.9) and refrigeration systems (Section 605.8) are not typically classified as Group H occupancies, the potential hazards associated with these occupancy conditions are great enough to require additional means of early warning detection.

908.2 Group H-5 occupancy. Emergency alarms for notification of an emergency condition in an HPM facility shall be provided as required in Section 2703.12.

❖ In addition to hazardous material storage areas as regulated by Section 5004.9, Section 2703.12.1 also requires emergency alarms for service corridors, exit access corridors and interior exit stairways because of the potential transport of hazardous materials through these areas. Section 2703.13 requires a continuous gas detection system for early detection of leaks in areas where HPM gas is used. Gas detection systems are required to initiate a local alarm and transmit a signal to the emergency control station upon detection (see commentary, Sections 2703.12 and 2703.13).

SECTION 909 SMOKE CONTROL SYSTEMS

909.1 Scope and purpose. This section applies to mechanical or passive smoke control systems where they are required for new buildings or portions thereof by provisions of the *International Building Code* or this code. The purpose of this section is to establish minimum requirements for the design, installation and acceptance testing of smoke control systems that are intended to provide a tenable environment for the evacuation or relocation of occupants. These provisions are not intended for the preservation of contents, the timely restoration of operations or for assistance in fire suppression or overhaul activities. Smoke control systems regulated by this section serve a different purpose than the smoke- and heat-removal provisions found in Section 910. Mechanical smoke control systems shall not be considered exhaust systems under Chapter 5 of the *International Mechanical Code*.

❖ This section is clarifying the intent of smoke control provisions, which is to provide a tenable environment to occupants during evacuation and relocation and not to protect the contents, enable timely restoration of operations or facilitate fire suppression and overhaul activities. It should also be understood that a smoke control system cannot maintain tenable conditions within the immediate area of fire origin. There are provisions for high-rise buildings in IBC Section 403.4.7 that are focused on the removal of smoke for post-fire and overhaul operations, which is very different than the smoke control provisions in Section 909. Another element addressed in this section is that smoke control systems serve a different purpose than smoke and heat vents (see Section 910). This eliminates any confusion that smoke and heat vents can be used as a substitution for smoke control. Additionally, a clarification is provided to note that smoke control systems are not considered an exhaust system in accordance with Chapter 5 of the IMC. This is because such systems are unique in their operation and are not necessarily designed to exhaust smoke but are focused on tenability for occupants during egress. It should be noted that the smoke control provisions are duplicated in Chapter 5 of the IMC.

It is important to note that these provisions only apply when smoke control is required by other sections of the code. The code requires smoke management within atrium spaces (see IBC Section 404.5) and underground buildings (see IBC Section 405.5). High-rise facilities require smokeproof exit enclosures in accordance with Sections 909.20 and 1023.11 (see IBC Section 403.5.4). Also, covered mall buildings that contain atriums that connect more than two stories require smoke control (see IBC Section 402.7.2). Underground buildings with floors used for human occupancy that are greater than 30 feet below the floor of the level of exit discharge are required to be provided with smoke control (see IBC Section 405.5). I-3 detention occupancies that are in windowless buildings are also required to be provided with smoke control compliant with Section 909 (see IBC Section 408.9).

Section 909 focuses primarily on mechanical smoke control systems, but there are many instances within the code where smoke is required to be managed in a passive way through the use of concepts such as smoke compartments. Smoke compartments are formed through the use of smoke barriers in accordance with IBC Section 709. Smoke barriers can be used simply as a passive smoke management system or can be a design component of a mechanical smoke control system in accordance with Section 909. Some examples of occupancies requiring passive systems include hospitals, nursing homes and similar facilities (Group I-2 occupancies) and detention facilities (Group I-3 occupancies) (see IBC Sections 407.5 and 408.6).

In some cases, mechanical smoke control in accordance with Section 909 is allowed as an option for compliance. More specifically, if a Group I-3 contains windowless areas of the facility, natural or mechanical smoke management is required (see IBC Section 408.9).

Over time, smoke control provisions have become more complex. The reason is related to the fact that smoke is a complex problem. There are numerous parameters that need to be considered when designing a smoke control system, including factors such as buoyancy; expansion of gases; wind; the geometry of the space and of communicating spaces; the dynamics of the fire, including heat-release rate; the production and distribution of smoke; and the interaction of the building systems. The means of egress from the space is also a major consideration and time to egress is a factor in designing for tenability. The historical cookbook approach of providing six air changes or four air changes based on volume of the communicating space does not take these factors into consideration.

Smoke control systems can be either passive or active. Active systems are sometimes referred to as mechanical. Passive smoke control systems take advantage of smoke barriers surrounding the zone in which the fire event occurs or high bay areas that act as reservoirs to control the movement of smoke to other areas of the building. Active systems utilize pressure differences to contain smoke within the event zone or exhaust flow rates sufficient to slow the descent of the upper-level smoke accumulation to some predetermined position above necessary means of egress paths through the zone of fire origin. On rare occasions, there is also a possibility of controlling the movement of smoke horizontally by opposed airflow.

Essentially, there are three methods of mechanical or active smoke control that can be used separately or in combination within a design: pressurization, exhaust and opposed airflow.

Of course, all of these active approaches can be used in combination with the passive method.

Typically, the mechanical pressurization method is used in high-rise buildings when pressurizing shafts (interior exit stairways or elevator hoistways) and for zoned smoke control. Pressurization is not practical in large open spaces such as atriums or malls, since it is difficult to develop the required pressure differences due to the large volume of the space.

The exhaust method is typically used in large open spaces such as atriums and malls. The opposed airflow method, which basically uses a velocity of air horizontally to slow the movement of smoke, is typically applied in combination with either a pressurization method or exhaust method within hallways or openings into atriums and malls.

The application of each of these methods will be dependent on the specifics of the building design. Smoke control within a building is fundamentally an architecturally driven problem. Different architectural geometries first dictate the need, or lack thereof, for smoke control, and then define the bounds of available solutions to the problem.

909.2 General design requirements. Buildings, structures, or parts thereof required by the *International Building Code* or this code to have a smoke control system or systems shall have such systems designed in accordance with the applicable requirements of Section 909 and the generally accepted and well-established principles of engineering relevant to the design. The *construction documents* shall include sufficient information and detail to describe adequately the elements of the design necessary for the proper implementation of the smoke control systems. These documents shall be accompanied with sufficient information and analysis to demonstrate compliance with these provisions.

❖ This section simply states that when smoke control systems are required by the code, the design is required to be in accordance with the provisions of this section. As noted in the commentary to Section 909.1, there are instances within the code that have smoke management systems that are purely passive in nature and do not reference Section 909.

This section stresses that designs in accordance with this section need to follow "generally accepted and well-established principles of engineering relevant to the design," essentially requiring a certain level of qualifications in the applicable areas of engineering to prepare such designs. The primary engineering disciplines tend to be fire engineering and mechanical engineering. It should be noted that each state in the United States typically requires minimum qualifications to undertake engineering design. Two important resources when designing smoke control systems are the International Code Council's (ICC) *A Guide to Smoke Control in the 2006 IBC®* and American Society of Heating, Refrigerating and Air-Conditioning Engineers' (ASHRAE) *Handbook of Smoke Control Engineering*. Additionally, Section 909.8 requires the use of NFPA 92 for the design of smoke control systems using the exhaust method. This standard has many relevant aspects beyond the design of exhaust method systems that are also beneficial to the system designer. In particular, Annex B provides resources in terms of determination of fire size for design. ICC's *A Guide to Smoke Control in the 2006 IBC®* also provides guidance on design fires.

A key element covered in this section is the need for detailed and clear construction documents so that the system is installed correctly. In most complex designs, the key to success is appropriate communication to the contractors as to what needs to be installed. The more complex a design becomes, the more likely there is to be construction errors. Most smoke control systems are complex, which is why special inspections in accordance with Section 909.3 and Chapter 17 of the IBC are critical for smoke control systems. Additionally, in order for the design to be accepted, analyses and justifications need to be provided in enough detail to evaluate for compliance. Adequate documentation is critical to the commissioning, inspection, testing and maintenance of smoke control systems and significantly contributes to the overall reliability and effectiveness of such systems.

909.3 Special inspection and test requirements. In addition to the ordinary inspection and test requirements that buildings, structures and parts thereof are required to undergo, smoke control systems subject to the provisions of Section 909 shall undergo special inspections and tests sufficient to verify the proper commissioning of the smoke control design in its final installed condition. The design submission accompanying the *construction documents* shall clearly detail procedures and methods to be used and the items subject to such inspections and tests. Such commissioning shall be in accordance with generally accepted engineering practice and, where possible, based on published standards for the particular testing involved. The special inspections and tests required by this section shall be conducted under the same terms as in Section 1704 of the *International Building Code*.

❖ Because of the complexity and uniqueness of each design, special inspection and testing must be conducted. The designer needs to provide specific recommendations for special inspection and testing within his or her documentation. In fact, the code specifies in Chapter 17 of the IBC that special inspection agencies for smoke control have expertise in fire protection engineering, mechanical engineering and certification as air balancers. Since the designs are unique to each building, there probably will not be a generic approach available to inspect and test such systems. The designer can and should, however, use any available published standards or guides when developing the special inspection and testing requirements for that particular design. ICC's *A Guide to Smoke Control in the 2006 IBC®* provides some background on such inspections, Also, ASHRAE Guideline 5 is a good starting place, but only as a general outline. In addition, NFPA 92 also has extensive testing, documentation and maintenance requirements that may be a good resource. NFPA 92 is referenced in Sections 909.7 and 909.8 for the design of smoke control systems using the airflow method and exhaust method. Each system will require a unique commissioning plan that can be developed only after careful and thoughtful examination of the final design and all of its components and interrelationships. Generally, these provisions may be included in design standards or engineering guides.

909.4 Analysis. A rational analysis supporting the types of smoke control systems to be employed, the methods of their operations, the systems supporting them and the methods of construction to be utilized shall accompany the *construction documents* submission and include, but not be limited to, the items indicated in Sections 909.4.1 through 909.4.7.

❖ This section indicates that simply determining airflow, exhaust rates and pressures to maintain tenable conditions is not adequate. There are many factors that could alter the effectiveness of a smoke control system, including stack effect, temperature effect of fire, wind effect, heating, ventilating and air-conditioning (HVAC) system interaction and climate, as well as the placement, quantity of inlets/outlets and velocity of supply and exhaust air, changes in building occupancy, placement of fuel loads, and type of fuels may have significant impact on the suitability of a smoke control system. The underlying physics related to how these factors impact the design of a smoke control system are discussed in the *SFPE Handbook of Fire Protection Engineering*, 5th edition, Chapters 50 and 51. These factors are addressed in the sections that follow. Additionally, the duration of operation of any smoke control system is mandated at a minimum of 20 minutes or 1.5 times the egress time, whichever is less. The code cannot reasonably anticipate every conceivable building arrangement and condition the building may be subject to over its life and must depend on such factors being addressed through a rational analysis.

909.4.1 Stack effect. The system shall be designed such that the maximum probable normal or reverse stack effect will not adversely interfere with the system's capabilities. In determining the maximum probable stack effect, altitude, elevation, weather history and interior temperatures shall be used.

❖ Stack effect is the tendency for air to rise within a heated shaft when the temperature is colder on the exterior of the building. Air in the building has a buoyant force because it is warmer and less dense than the outside air. This buoyant force causes air to rise within the shafts of buildings. Reverse stack effect is the tendency for air to flow downward within a building when the interior is cooler than the exterior of the building. Stack effect can have a significant impact on smoke flow during building fires and can affect the intended operation of a smoke control system. If stack effect is great enough, it may overcome the pressures determined during the design analyses and allow smoke to enter areas outside the zone of origin (see Commentary Figure 909.4.1).

909.4.2 Temperature effect of fire. Buoyancy and expansion caused by the design fire in accordance with Section 909.9 shall be analyzed. The system shall be designed such that these effects do not adversely interfere with the system's capabilities.

❖ This section requires that the design account for the effect temperature may have on the success of the system. When air or any gases are heated, they will expand. This expansion makes the gases lighter and therefore more buoyant. The buoyancy of hot gases is important when the design is to exhaust such gases from a location in or close to the ceiling; therefore, if sprinklers are part of the design, as required by Section 909, the gases may be significantly cooler than an unsprinklered fire, making it more difficult to remove the smoke and alter the plume dynamics. The fact that air expands when heated needs to be accounted for in the design.

When using the pressurization method, the expansion of hot gases needs to be accounted for, since it will take a larger volume of air to create the necessary pressure differences to maintain the area of fire origin in negative pressure. The expansion of the gases has the effect of pushing the hot gases out of the area of fire origin. Since sprinklers will tend to cool the gases, the effect of expansion is lower. The pressure difference required in Section 909.6.1 is specifically based on a sprinklered building. If the building is nonsprinklered, higher pressure differences may be required. The minimum pressure difference for certain unsprinklered ceiling height buildings is as follows:

Ceiling height (feet)	Minimum pressure difference (inch water gage)
9	0.10
15	0.14
21	0.18

This is a very complex issue that needs to be part of the design analysis. It needs to address the type

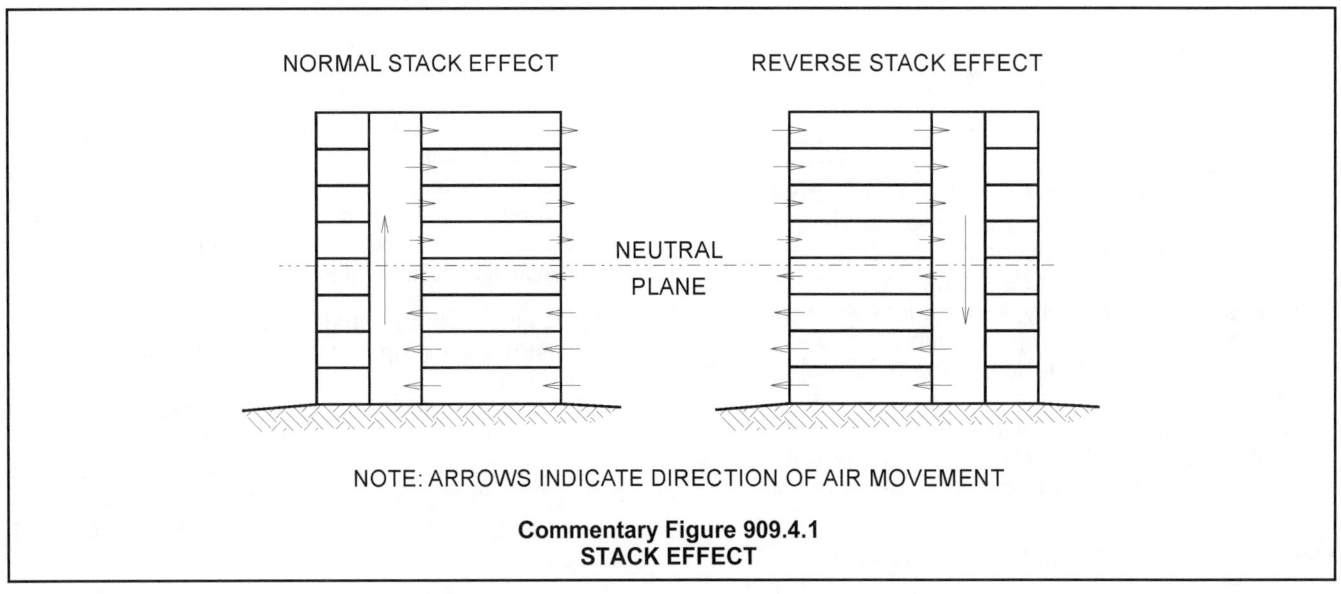

Commentary Figure 909.4.1
STACK EFFECT

and reaction of the fire protection systems, ceiling heights and the size of the design fire.

909.4.3 Wind effect. The design shall consider the adverse effects of wind. Such consideration shall be consistent with the wind-loading provisions of the *International Building Code.*

❖ The effect of wind on a smoke control system within a building is very complex. It is generally known that wind exerts a load on a building and that wind has a pronounced impact on smoke movement within a building. The loads are looked at as windward (positive pressure) and leeward (negative pressure). The velocity of winds will vary based on the terrain and the height above grade; therefore, the height of the building and surrounding obstructions will have an effect on these velocities. These pressures alter the operation of fans, especially propeller fans, thus altering the pressure differences and airflow direction in the building. There is not an easy solution to dealing with these effects. In fact, little research has been done in this area.

It should be noted that in larger buildings a wind study is normally undertaken for the structural design. The data from those studies can be used in the analysis of the effects on the pressures and airflow within the building with regard to the performance of the smoke control system.

909.4.4 Systems. The design shall consider the effects of the heating, ventilating and air-conditioning (HVAC) systems on both smoke and fire transport. The analysis shall include all permutations of systems status. The design shall consider the effects of the fire on the heating, ventilating and air-conditioning systems.

❖ If not properly configured to shut down or be included as part of the design, the HVAC system can alter the smoke control design. More specifically, if dampers are not provided between smoke zones within the HVAC system ducts, smoke could be transported from one zone to another. Additionally, if the HVAC system places more supply air than assumed for the smoke control system design, the velocity of the air may adversely affect the fire plume or a positive pressure may be created. Generally, an analysis of the smoke control design and the HVAC system in all potential modes should occur and be noted within the design documentation as well as incorporated into inspection, testing and maintenance procedures. This is critical as these systems need to be maintained and tested to help ensure that they operate and shut down systems as required.

909.4.5 Climate. The design shall consider the effects of low temperatures on systems, property and occupants. Air inlets and exhausts shall be located so as to prevent snow or ice blockage.

❖ This section is focused on properly protecting equipment from weather conditions that may affect the reliability of the design. For instance, extremely cold or hot air may damage critical equipment within the system when pulled directly from the outside. Some listings of duct smoke detectors are for specific temperature ranges; therefore, placing such detectors within areas exposed to extreme temperatures may void the listing. Also, the equipment and air inlets and outlets should be designed and located so as to not collect snow and ice that could block air from entering or exiting the building.

909.4.6 Duration of operation. All portions of active or engineered smoke control systems shall be capable of continued operation after detection of the fire event for a period of not less than either 20 minutes or 1.5 times the calculated egress time, whichever is greater.

❖ The intent of the smoke control provisions is to provide a tenable environment for occupants to either evacuate or relocate to a safe place. Evacuation and relocation activities include a pre-evacuation period (notifying occupants, seeking information, decision time, preparing to evacuate) and the movement period. In order to achieve this goal, the code has established 20 minutes or 1.5 times the calculated egress time, whichever is greater, as a minimum time for evacuation or relocation. Basically this allows a designer to undertake an analysis to more closely determine the necessary time required. The code provides a safety factor of 1.5 times the egress time to account for uncertainty related to human behavior. It is stressed that the 20-minute duration as well as the calculated egress time, whichever approach is chosen, begins after the detection of the fire event and notification to the building occupants to evacuate have occurred, since occupants need to be alerted before evacuation can happen. The calculation of evacuation time needs to include delays with notification and the start of evacuation (i.e., pre-evacuation time). It is stressed that the code states 20 minutes or 1.5 times the egress time, whichever is greater (i.e., 20 minutes is a minimum). Egress of occupants can be addressed through hand calculations or through the use of computerized evacuation models. Some of the more advanced models can address a variety of factors, including the building layout, different sizes of people, different movement speeds and different egress paths available. With these types of models, the actual time can be even more precisely calculated. Of course it is cautioned that in many cases these models provide the optimal time for egress. The safety factor of 1.5 within the code is intended to address many of these uncertainties.

Note that this section applies to all types of smoke control designed in accordance with Section 909. Also, most smoke control systems will typically have the ability to run for much longer than 20 minutes as they are on standby power and may be able to continue to achieve the tenability goals.

System response as required in Section 909.17 needs to be accounted for when determining the ability of the smoke control system to keep the smoke layer interface at the appropriate level (see commentary, Section 909.17).

909.4.7 Smoke control system interaction. The design shall consider the interaction effects of the operation of multiple smoke control systems for all design scenarios.

❖ The focus of this section is related to the interaction of multiple mechanical smoke control systems by asking for a specific analysis of the interaction of such systems similar to that required for the interaction of HVAC systems. Where hoistway pressurization is chosen as an option for compliance with the hoistway opening protection requirements, the potential exists for a pressurized stair system to also be present. These two systems need to be able to operate at the same time without a negative impact on either system. It is also possible that an atrium with a smoke control system is located in a building containing a stair pressurization system.

909.5 Smoke barrier construction. *Smoke barriers* required for passive smoke control and a smoke control system using the pressurization method shall comply with Section 709 of the *International Building Code.* The maximum allowable leakage area shall be the aggregate area calculated using the following leakage area ratios:

1. Walls: $A/A_w = 0.00100$
2. Interior *exit stairways* and *ramps* and *exit passageways*: $A/A_w = 0.00035$
3. Enclosed *exit access stairways* and *ramps* and all other shafts: $A/A_w = 0.00150$
4. Floors and roofs: $A/A_F = 0.00050$

where:

A = Total leakage area, square feet (m^2).

A_F = Unit floor or roof area of barrier, square feet (m^2).

A_w = Unit wall area of barrier, square feet (m^2).

The leakage area ratios shown do not include openings due to gaps around doors and operable windows. The total leakage area of the *smoke barrier* shall be determined in accordance with Section 909.5.1 and tested in accordance with Section 909.5.2.

❖ Part of the strategy of smoke control systems, particularly smoke control systems using the pressurization method (often termed "zoned smoke control"), is the use of smoke barriers to divide a building into separate smoke zones (or compartments). This strategy is used in both passive and mechanical systems. It should be noted that not all walls, ceilings or floors would be considered smoke barriers. Only walls that designate separate smoke zones within a building need to be constructed as smoke barriers. This section is simply providing requirements for walls, floors and ceilings that are used as smoke barriers. It should be noted that it is possible that a smoke control system utilizing the exhaust method may not need to utilize a smoke barrier to divide the building into separate smoke zones; therefore, the evaluation of barrier construction and leakage area may not be necessary and is primarily focused on designs using a passive approach or the pressurization method.

In order for smoke to not travel from one smoke zone to another, specific construction requirements are necessary in accordance with the code. It should be noted that openings such as doors and windows are dealt with separately within Section 909.5.3 from openings such as cracks or penetrations.

909.5.1 Total leakage area. Total leakage area of the barrier is the product of the *smoke barrier* gross area multiplied by the allowable leakage area ratio, plus the area of other openings such as gaps around doors and operable windows.

❖ It is impossible for walls and floors to be constructed that are completely free from openings that may allow the migration of smoke; therefore, leakage needs to be compensated for within the design by calculating the leakage area of walls, ceilings and floors. The factors provided in Section 909.5, which originate from ASHRAE's provisions on leaky buildings, are used to calculate the total leakage area. The total leakage area is then used in the design process to determine the proper amount of air to create the required pressure differences across these surfaces that form smoke zones.

Additionally, Section 909.5 provides ratios to determine the maximum allowable leakage in walls, interior exit stairways, shafts, floors and roofs. These leakage areas are critical in determining whether the proper pressure differences are provided when utilizing the pressurization method of smoke control. Pressure differences will decrease as the openings get larger.

909.5.2 Testing of leakage area. Compliance with the maximum total leakage area shall be determined by achieving the minimum air pressure difference across the barrier with the system in the smoke control mode for mechanical smoke control systems utilizing the pressurization method. Compliance with the maximum total leakage area of passive smoke control systems shall be verified through methods such as door fan testing or other methods, as *approved* by the *fire code official.*

❖ These leakage criteria need to be evaluated through testing. For the case of a pressurization system, pressure differences need to be verified when the system is in smoke control mode. In the case of passive smoke control systems, pressure testing through tests such as the door fan method is necessary.

909.5.3 Opening protection. Openings in *smoke barriers* shall be protected by automatic-closing devices actuated by the required controls for the mechanical smoke control system. Door openings shall be protected by fire door assemblies complying with Section 716 of the *International Building Code.*

Exceptions:

1. Passive smoke control systems with automatic-closing devices actuated by spot-type smoke detectors *listed* for releasing service installed in accordance with Section 907.3.

2. Fixed openings between smoke zones that are protected utilizing the airflow method.
3. In Group I-1, Condition 2; Group I-2; and ambulatory care facilities, where a pair of opposite-swinging doors are installed across a corridor in accordance with Section 909.5.3.1, the doors shall not be required to be protected in accordance with Section 716 of the *International Building Code*. The doors shall be close-fitting within operational tolerances and shall not have a center mullion or undercuts in excess of $^3/_4$-inch (19.1 mm) louvers or grilles. The doors shall have head and jamb stops and astragals or rabbets at meeting edges and, where permitted by the door manufacturer's listing, positive-latching devices are not required.
4. In Group I-2 and ambulatory care facilities, where such doors are special-purpose horizontal sliding, accordion or folding door assemblies installed in accordance with Section 1010.1.4.3 and are automatic closing by smoke detection in accordance with Section 716.2.6.6 of the *International Building Code*.
5. Group I-3.
6. Openings between smoke zones with clear ceiling heights of 14 feet (4267 mm) or greater and bank-down capacity of greater than 20 minutes as determined by the design fire size.

❖ Similar to concerns of smoke leakage between smoke zones, openings may compromise the necessary pressure differences between smoke zones. Openings in smoke barriers, such as doors and windows, must be either constantly or automatically closed when the smoke control system is operating. This section requires that doors be automatically closed through the activation of an automatic-closing device linked to the smoke control system. Essentially, when the smoke control system is activated, all openings are automatically closed. This most likely would mean that the mechanism that activates the smoke control system would also automatically close all openings. The smoke control system will be activated by a specifically zoned smoke detection or sprinkler system as required by Sections 909.12.3 and 909.12.4.

In terms of actual opening protection, Section 909.5.3 is simply referring the user to IBC Section 716 for specific construction requirements for doors located in smoke barriers. Note that smoke barriers are different from fire barriers, since the intended measure of performance is different. One is focused on fire spread from the perspective of heat, the other from the perspective of smoke passage. Smoke barriers do require a 1-hour fire-resistance rating.

There are several exceptions to this particular section. Exception 1 is specifically for passive systems. Passive systems, as noted, are systems in which there is no use of mechanical systems. Instead, the system operates primarily on the configuration of barriers and layout of the building to provide smoke control. Passive systems can use spot-type detectors to close doors that constitute portions of a smoke barrier. Essentially, this means a full fire alarm system would not be required. Instead, single station detectors would be allowed to close the doors. Such doors would need to fail in the closed position if power is lost. The specifics as to approved devices would be found in NFPA 72.

Exception 2 is based on the fact that some systems take advantage of the opposed airflow method such that smoke is prevented from migrating past the doors. Therefore, since the design already accounts for potential smoke migration at these openings through the use of air movement, it is unnecessary to require the barrier to be closed.

Exception 3 is specifically related to the unique requirements for Group I-1, Condition 2; I-2 occupancies; and ambulatory care occupancies. Essentially, a very specific alternative, which meets the functional needs of these occupancy types, is provided. Opposite-swinging doors are allowed without meeting the specific requirements of Section 716. Note that Group I-2 and ambulatory care facilities utilize the concept of smoke compartments, which is a form of a passive smoke control system. The requirements of this section are focused on openings in smoke barriers that need to close upon activation of a pressurization system.

Exception 4 provides a specific allowance for horizontal sliding doors in Group I-2, Condition 2 occupancies and ambulatory care occupancies. These doors are commonly used in such occupancies and have very specific installation requirements in Section 1010.1.4.3. These doors are an alternative to pivoted or side-hinged, swinging-type doors. This exception requires compliance with Section 716.5.9.3 for automatic closing upon detection of smoke.

Exception 5 allows an exemption from the automatic-closing requirements for all Group I-3 occupancies. This is because facilities that have occupants under restraint or with specific security restrictions have unique requirements in accordance with Section 408 of the code. These requirements accomplish the intent of providing reliable barriers between each smoke zone since, for the most part, such facilities will have a majority of doors closed and in a locked position because of the nature of the facility. The staff very closely controls these types of facilities.

Exception 6 relates to the behavior of smoke. The assumption is that smoke rises because of the buoyancy of hot gases, and if the ceiling is sufficiently high, the smoke layer will be contained for a longer period of time before it begins to move into the next smoke zone. Therefore, it is not as critical that the doors automatically close. This allowance is dependent on the specific design fire for a building. See Section 909.9 for more information on design fire determination. Different size design fires create different amounts of smoke that, depending on the layout of the building, may migrate in different ways throughout the building. This section mandates that smoke cannot begin to migrate into the next smoke zone for at least 20 minutes. This is consistent with the 20-minute minimum duration of operation of smoke control systems required in Section 909.4.6. It should be noted that a minimum of 14-foot (4267 mm) ceilings are required to take advantage of this exception. This exception would require an engineering analysis.

909.5.3.1 Group I-1, Condition 2; Group I-2; and ambulatory care facilities. In Group I-1, Condition 2; Group I-2; and *ambulatory care facilities*, where doors are installed across a *corridor*, the doors shall be automatic closing by smoke detection in accordance with Section 716.2.6.6 of the *International Building Code* and shall have a vision panel with fire-protection-rated glazing materials in fire-protection-rated frames, the area of which shall not exceed that tested.

❖ Part of the alternative allowed for horizontal sliding doors in Exception 3 of Section 909.5.3 for Group I-1, Condition 2; Group I-2; and ambulatory care facilities is the requirement that vision panels be provided. These vision panels need to be approved fire-protection-rated glazing and be within frames of a size that does not exceed the frame size that was used for testing of the glazing.

909.5.3.2 Ducts and air transfer openings. Ducts and air transfer openings are required to be protected with a minimum Class II, 250°F (121°C) smoke damper complying with Section 717 of the *International Building Code*.

❖ Another factor that adds to the reliability of smoke barriers is the protection of ducts and air transfer openings within smoke barriers. Left open, these openings may allow the transfer of smoke between smoke zones. These ducts and air transfer openings most often are part of the HVAC system. Damper operation and the reaction with the smoke control system will be evaluated during acceptance testing. It should be noted that there are duct systems used within a smoke control design that are controlled by the smoke control system and should not automatically close upon detection of smoke via a smoke damper.

It should be noted that a smoke damper works differently than a fire damper. Fire dampers react to heat via a fusible link, while smoke dampers activate upon the detection of smoke. The smoke dampers used should be rated as Class II, 250°F (121°C). The class of the smoke damper refers to its level of performance relative to leakage. The temperature rating is related to its ability to withstand the heat of smoke resulting from a fire. It should be noted that although smoke barriers are only required to utilize smoke dampers, there may be many instances where a fire damper is also required. For instance, the smoke barrier may also be used as a fire barrier. Also, IBC Section 717.5.3 would require penetration of shafts to contain both a smoke damper and a fire damper. Therefore, in some cases both a smoke damper and fire damper would be required. There are listings specific to combination smoke and fire dampers. IBC Section 717.5.3, Exception 1.3 recognizes that dampers may inhibit the performance of a smoke control system. This exception allows duct penetrations without dampers if they will inhibit the performance of the smoke control system.

More specific requirements about dampers can be found in Chapter 7 of the IBC and Chapter 6 of the IMC.

909.6 Pressurization method. The primary mechanical means of controlling smoke shall be by pressure differences across *smoke barriers*. Maintenance of a tenable environment is not required in the smoke-control zone of fire origin.

❖ There are several methods or strategies that may be used to control smoke movement. One of these methods is pressurization, wherein the system primarily utilizes pressure differences across smoke barriers to control the movement of smoke. Basically, if the area of fire origin maintains a negative pressure, then the smoke will be contained to that smoke zone. A typical approach used to obtain a negative pressure is to exhaust the fire floor. This is a fairly common practice in high-rise buildings. Interior exit stairways also utilize the concept of pressurization by keeping the interior exit stairways under positive pressure. The pressurization method in large open spaces, such as malls and atria, is impractical since it would take a large quantity of supply air to create the necessary pressure differences. It should be noted that pressurization is mandated as the primary method for mechanical smoke control design, but this is related to the primary methods historically used for smoke control in high-rise buildings. Currently high-rise buildings do not require smoke control. Airflow and exhaust methods are only allowed when appropriate. The exhaust method is the most commonly applied method based on the use of the atrium provisions in IBC Section 404.5.

The pressurization method does not require that tenable conditions be maintained in the smoke zone where the fire originates. Maintaining this area tenable would be impossible, because pressures from the surrounding smoke zones would be placing a negative pressure within the zone of origin to keep the smoke from migrating.

Pressurization is used often with interior exit stairways. This method provides a positive pressure within the interior exit stairways to resist the passage of smoke. Stair pressurization is one method of compliance for stairways in high-rise or underground buildings where the floor surface is located more than 75 feet (22 860 mm) above the lowest level of fire department vehicle access or more than 30 feet (9144 mm) below the floor surface of the lowest level of exit discharge. It should be noted that there are two methods found in the code that address smoke movement—smokeproof enclosures or pressurized stairs. A smokeproof enclosure requires a certain fire-resistance rating along with access through a ventilated vestibule or an exterior balcony. The vestibule can be ventilated in two ways: using natural ventilation or mechanical ventilation as outlined in Sections 909.20.3 and 909.20.4. The pressurization method requires a sprinklered building and a minimum pressure difference of 0.15 inch (37 Pa) of water and a maximum of 0.35 inch (87 Pa) of water. These pressure differences are to be available with all doors closed under maximum stack pressures (see Sections 909.20 and 1023.11 for more details).

As noted, the pressurization method utilizes pressure differences across smoke barriers to achieve control of smoke. Sections 909.6.1 and 909.6.2 provide the criteria for smoke control design in terms of minimum and maximum pressure differences.

In summary, the pressurization method is used in two ways. The first is through the use of smoke zones where the zone of origin is exhausted, creating a negative pressure. The second is stair pressurization that creates a positive pressure within the stair to avoid the penetration of smoke. Note that the code allows the use of a smokeproof enclosure instead of pressurization.

909.6.1 Minimum pressure difference. The pressure difference across a *smoke barrier* used to separate smoke zones shall be not less than 0.05-inch water gage (0.0124 kPa) in fully sprinklered buildings.

In buildings permitted to be other than fully sprinklered, the smoke control system shall be designed to achieve pressure differences not less than two times the maximum calculated pressure difference produced by the design fire.

❖ The minimum pressure difference is established as 0.05-inch water gage (12 Pa) in fully sprinklered buildings. This particular criterion is related to the pressures needed to overcome buoyancy and the pressures generated by the fire, which include expansion. This particular criterion is based on a sprinklered building. The pressure difference would need to be higher in a building that is not sprinklered. Additionally, the pressure difference needs to be provided based on the possible stack and wind effects present.

909.6.2 Maximum pressure difference. The maximum air pressure difference across a *smoke barrier* shall be determined by required door-opening or closing forces. The actual force required to open *exit* doors when the system is in the smoke control mode shall be in accordance with Section 1010.1.3. Opening and closing forces for other doors shall be determined by standard engineering methods for the resolution of forces and reactions. The calculated force to set a side-hinged, swinging door in motion shall be determined by:

$$F = F_{dc} + K(WA\Delta P)/2(W - d) \qquad \textbf{(Equation 9-1)}$$

where:

A = Door area, square feet (m^2).

d = Distance from door handle to latch edge of door, feet (m).

F = Total door opening force, pounds (N).

F_{dc} = Force required to overcome closing device, pounds (N).

K = Coefficient 5.2 (1.0).

W = Door width, feet (m).

ΔP = Design pressure difference, inches of water (Pa).

❖ The maximum pressure difference is based primarily on the force needed to open and close doors. The code establishes maximum opening forces for doors. This maximum opening force cannot be exceeded, taking into account the pressure differences across a doorway in a pressurized environment. Essentially, based on the opening force requirements of Section 1010.1.3, the maximum pressure difference can be calculated in accordance with Equation 9-1. In accordance with Chapter 10, the maximum opening force of a door has three components, including:

Door latch release:
Maximum of 15 pounds (67 N)

Set door in motion:
Maximum of 30 pounds (134 N)

Swing to full open position:
Maximum of 15 pounds (67 N)

Equation 9-1 is used to calculate the total force to set the door into motion when in the smoke control mode; therefore, the limiting criteria would be 30 pounds (134 N). It should be noted that although the accessibility requirements related to door opening force are more restrictive in Section 404.2.8 of ICC A117.1, fire doors do not require compliance with these requirements.

909.6.3 Pressurized stairways and elevator hoistways. Where stairways or elevator hoistways are pressurized, such pressurization systems shall comply with Section 909 as smoke control systems, in addition to the requirements of Section 909.21 of this code and Section 909.20 of the *International Building Code*.

❖ The purpose of this section is to clarify that pressurized stairways and pressurized hoistways are smoke control systems and must be addressed in the same way that a pressurization system in accordance with Section 909.6 addresses such systems. This would require compliance with various sections but in particular the requirements for a rational analysis in accordance with Section 909.4.

909.7 Airflow design method. Where *approved* by the *fire code official*, smoke migration through openings fixed in a permanently open position, which are located between smoke control zones by the use of the airflow method, shall be permitted. The design airflow shall be in accordance with this section. Airflow shall be directed to limit smoke migration from the fire zone. The geometry of openings shall be considered to prevent flow reversal from turbulent effects. Smoke control systems using the airflow method shall be designed in accordance with NFPA 92.

❖ This method is allowed only where approved by the building official. As the title states, this method utilizes airflow to avoid the migration of smoke across smoke barriers. This has been referred to as opposed airflow. Specifically, this method is suited for the protection of smoke migration through doors and related openings fixed in a permanently open position. This method consists of providing a particular velocity of air based on the temperature of the smoke and the height of the opening. The temperature of the smoke will depend on the design fire that is established for the particular building. The higher the temperature of the smoke and the larger the opening, the higher the velocity necessary to maintain the smoke from migrating into the smoke zone. It should be noted that the airflow method seldom works for large openings, since the velocity to oppose the smoke becomes too high. This method tends to work better for smaller openings, such as pass-through windows. Reference is made to NFPA 92 to determine the minimum velocity required to limit smoke spread.

909.7.1 Prohibited conditions. This method shall not be employed where either the quantity of air or the velocity of the airflow will adversely affect other portions of the smoke control system, unduly intensify the fire, disrupt plume dynamics or interfere with exiting. Airflow toward the fire shall not exceed 200 feet per minute (1.02 m/s). Where the calculated airflow exceeds this limit, the airflow method shall not be used.

❖ The airflow method has a limitation on maximum velocity. This limitation is because air may distort the flame and cause additional entrainment and turbulence; therefore, having a high velocity of air entering the zone of fire origin has the potential of increasing the amount of smoke produced. The velocity may also interact with other portions of the smoke control design. For instance, the pressure differences in other areas of the building may be altered, which may exceed the limitations of Sections 909.6.1 and 909.6.2. This section requires that when a velocity of over 200 feet per minute (1.02 m/sec) is calculated at the design fire, the airflow method is not allowed. The solution may result in requiring a barrier such as a wall or door.

If the airflow design method is chosen to protect areas communicating with an atrium, the air added to the smoke layer needs to be accounted for in the exhaust rate.

909.8 Exhaust method. Where *approved* by the *fire code official*, mechanical smoke control for large enclosed volumes, such as in atriums or malls, shall be permitted to utilize the exhaust method. Smoke control systems using the exhaust method shall be designed in accordance with NFPA 92.

❖ This method is allowed only where approved by the fire code official. The primary application of the exhaust method is in large volume spaces, such as atriums, arenas, convention centers, airport terminals and malls, and is the most widely used method in the IBC. The strategy of this method is to maintain tenable conditions in a large-volume space. This is primarily accomplished through exhausting smoke. The amount of exhaust depends on the design fire [see Commentary Figure 909.8(1)] and the geometry of the space under consideration. Essentially, fires produce different amounts and properties of smoke based on the material being burned, and size and placement of the fire; therefore, NFPA 92 is referenced for the design of such systems. NFPA 92 presents several ways to address the control of smoke, which includes the use of the following tools:

- Scale Modeling (Small-scale testing)—Utilizes the concept of scaling to allow small-scale tests to be conducted to understand smoke movement within a space.
  - Benefits—More realistic understanding of smoke movement in spaces with unusual configurations or projections than algebraic calculations.
  - Disadvantages—Expensive and the application of results is limited to the uniqueness of the space being analyzed.
- Algebraic Calculations—Empirically derived (based on testing) modeling in its simplest form.
  - Benefits—Simple, cost-effective analysis.
  - Disadvantages—Limited applicability because of the range of values they were derived from. Only appropriate with certain types of design fires, typically over conservative outputs that increase equipment needs and equipment costs and can impact aesthetics and architectural design.
- Computer Modeling [Computational Fluid Dynamics (CFD) or zone models]—Combination of theory and empirical values to determine the smoke movement and fire-induced conditions within a space and effectiveness of the smoke control system.
  - Benefits—More realistic understanding of smoke movement in spaces with unusual configurations or projections and less expensive than scale modeling. Helps significantly in designing smoke control systems tailored to spaces and achieving cost-effective designs, and can help limit the impact to architectural design.

- Disadvantages—Computing time and cost can be greater than algebraic calculations but benefits typically outweigh this disadvantage. Early planning is important and can limit these adverse impacts.

In terms of computer models, as noted, there are essentially two methods that include zone models and CFD models. Generally, zone models are based on the unifying assumption that in any compartment where the effects of the fire are present, there are distinct control volumes (hot upper layer, cool lower layer). In real life, such distinct layers do not exist. An example of a zone model used in such applications include the Consolidated Model of Fire Growth and Smoke Transport (CFAST). See Chapter 31 of the *SFPE Handbook of Fire Protection Engineering, 5th edition* for further information on zone models. CFD models take this much further and actually divide the space into thousands or millions of interconnected "control volumes" ("three-dimensional cells" or "fields"). The model then yields time-varying predictions of temperature, gas velocity, gas species concentrations, etc. in each individual cell and how it interacts with those adjacent to it. The use of such models becomes more accurate with more numerous and smaller cells, but the computing power and expertise required is much higher than for zone models. See Chapter 32 of the *SFPE Handbook of Fire Protection Engineering, 5th edition* for further information of CFD models. As noted, the use of either type of model can be advantageous, but such use must be undertaken by someone qualified. Proper review and verification of the input and output is critical. As stated in the SFPE Engineering Guide, *Guidelines for Substantiating a Fire Model for a Given Application*, determining the suitability of a fire model is part of a five-step process that includes:

1. Defining the problem of interest.
2. Selecting a candidate model.
3. Verification and validation.
4. User effect.
5. Documentation.

A commonly used CFD model is the Fire Dynamics Simulator (FDS) developed by NIST. Other models such as ANSYS Fluent are sometimes used (Fluent Inc.).

Depending on the space being evaluated, some design strategies may provide a better approach than others. Past editions of the code smoke control provisions for the exhaust method mandated the use of the algebraic method with a steady fire. This also mandated that a mechanical system be used, whereas NFPA 92 allows an overall review of smoke layer movement and whether the design goals, which in this case are mandated by the code, can be met. Therefore, if it can be shown that the smoke layer interface can be held at 6 feet (1829 mm) above the highest level of egress as mandated in Section 909.8.1 for the design operation time required by Section 909.4.6 without mechanical ventilation, then the space would comply with Section 909. NFPA 92 presents several design approaches. This allows more flexibility in design than that found in previous editions of the code.

NFPA 92 as a standard does not set the minimum smoke layer interface height or duration for system operation. Such criteria are found within Sections 909.8.1 and 909.4.6, respectively. See the commentary for those sections.

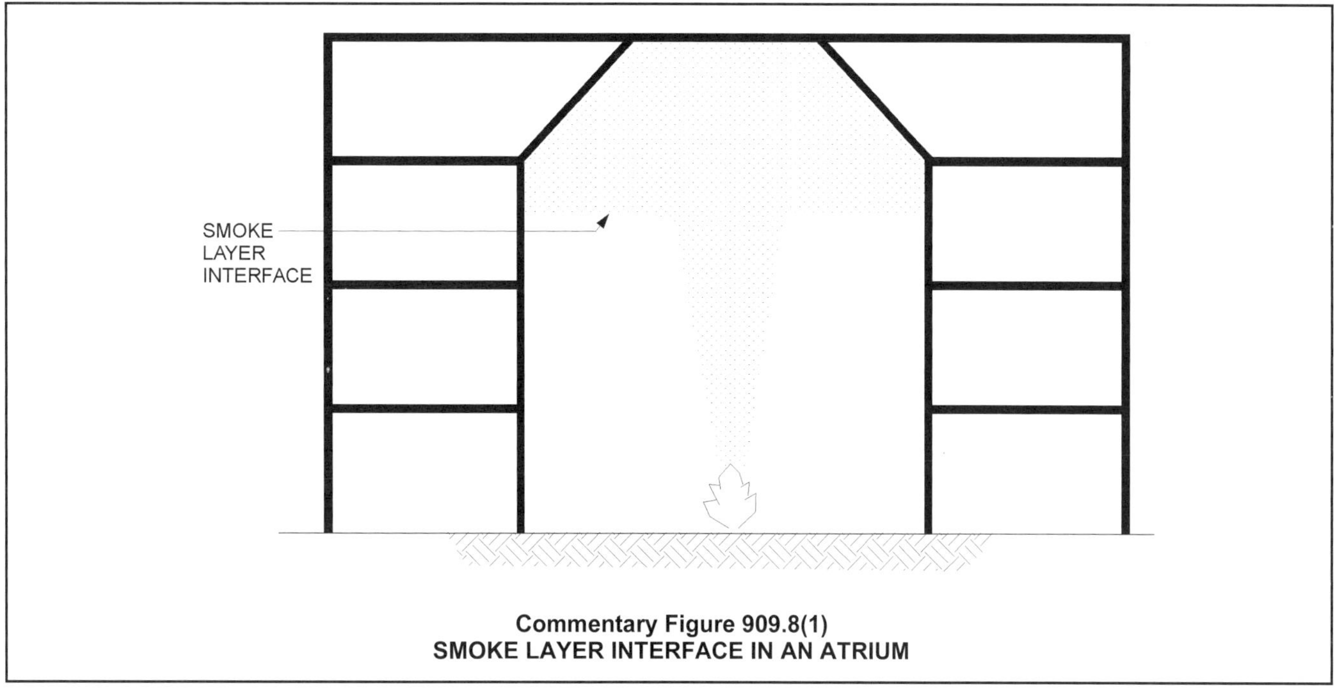

Commentary Figure 909.8(1)
SMOKE LAYER INTERFACE IN AN ATRIUM

If the algebraic approach is used, consideration of three types of fire plumes may be required to determine which one is the most demanding in terms of smoke removal needs based on the space being assessed. They include:

Axisymmetric plumes—Smoke rises unimpeded by walls, balconies or similar projections [see Commentary Figure 909.8(2)].

Balcony spill plumes—Smoke flows under and around edges of a horizontal projection [see Commentary Figure 909.8(3)].

Window plumes—Smoke flows through an opening into a large-volume space [see Commentary Figure 909.8(4)].

It should be noted that prior to the reference to NFPA 92 in the code, the balcony spill and window plume calculations had been eliminated from the smoke control requirements of the code because of concerns with the applicability of those calculations. The major difference is that NFPA 92 does not mandate the use of such equations as did previous editions of the IBC. The use of such equations will depend on the design fires agreed upon for the particular design and whether an algebraic approach is chosen. These equations are used to determine a mass flow rate of smoke to ultimately determine the required exhaust volume for that space. If the potential for balcony or window spill plumes is known to exist within the space, then appropriate measures need to be taken to address these, as they typically result in more onerous exhaust and supply requirements. Part of the reason for the initial deletion of these equations was the fact that such scenarios are not as likely or their impact is significantly reduced in sprinklered buildings. There is also some concern with the applicability of the balcony spill plume equation in a variety of applications. These potential fire scenarios and resulting plumes may further the need to undertake a CFD analysis to address such hazards more appropriately and effectively.

Commentary Figure 909.8(2)
AXISYMMETRIC PLUME

Another key aspect that NFPA 92 included within the algebraic method is equations to determine that a minimum number of exhaust inlets are available to prevent plugholing. Plugholing occurs when the exhaust capacity at a single point is sufficiently large enough to draw air from the lower layer in addition to smoke. As such, less smoke is removed by the exhaust fans and

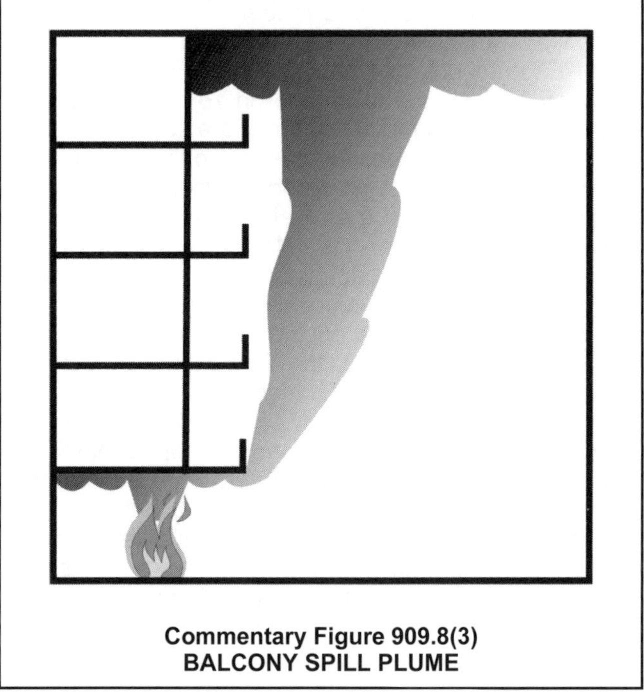

Commentary Figure 909.8(3)
BALCONY SPILL PLUME

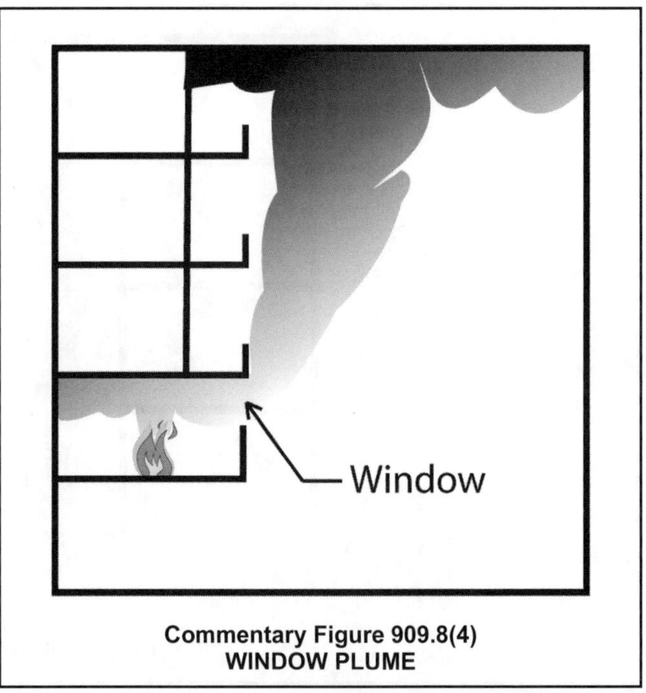

Commentary Figure 909.8(4)
WINDOW PLUME

a deeper layer results. If plugholing occurs, some of the fan capacity is used to exhaust air rather than smoke and thus can affect the ability to maintain the smoke layer at or above the design height. Scale modeling and computer fire modeling would demonstrate these potential problems during the testing and analysis, respectively [see Commentary Figure 909.8(5)].

It should be noted that this section specifically references NFPA 92 for the design of smoke control using the exhaust method. Therefore, the requirements in NFPA 92 related to testing, documentation and maintenance would not be applicable though they may be a good resource. Equipment and controls would be part of the design; therefore, related provisions of NFPA 92 would apply. Generally, the code addresses equipment and controls in a similar fashion.

909.8.1 Smoke layer. The height of the lowest horizontal surface of the smoke layer interface shall be maintained not less than 6 feet (1829 mm) above a walking surface that forms a portion of a required egress system within the smoke zone.

❖ The design condition to be used when applying NFPA 92 is to maintain the smoke layer interface at least 6 feet (1829 mm) above any walking surface that is considered part of the required egress within the particular smoke zone, such as an atrium, for 20 minutes or 1.5 times the calculated egress time (see Section 909.4.6). Chapter 10 considers the majority of occupiable space as part of the means of egress system. Also keep in mind that the criteria of 6 feet (1829 mm) does not apply just to the main floor surface of the mall or atrium but to any level where occupants may be exposed (for example, balconies) [see Commentary Figure 909.8.1(1)].

The code uses the terminology "lowest horizontal surface of the smoke layer interface." NFPA 92 has several definitions related to smoke layer, which include the following:

Smoke layer. The accumulated thickness of smoke below a physical barrier.

Smoke layer interface. The theoretical boundary between a smoke layer and the smoke-free air. (Note: This boundary is at the beginning of the transition zone.)

First indication of smoke. The boundary between the transition zone and the smoke-free air.

Transition zone. The layer between the smoke layer interface and the first indication of smoke in which the smoke layer temperature decreases to ambient. The transition zone may be several feet thick (large open space) or may barely exist (small area with intense fire).

See also Commentary Figure 909.8.1(2).

NFPA 92 provides algebraic equations to determine the first indication of smoke but is limited to very specific conditions such as a uniform cross section, specific aspect ratios, steady or unsteady fires and no smoke exhaust operating. When using algebraic equations for smoke layer interface by looking at different types of plumes, the smoke layer interface terminology is used and the user enters the desired smoke layer interface height. Zone models use simplifying assumptions so the layers are distinct from one another. In contrast, when CFD or scale modeling is used, the data must be analyzed to verify that the smoke layer interface is located at or above 6 feet (1829 mm) during the event. This is not a simple

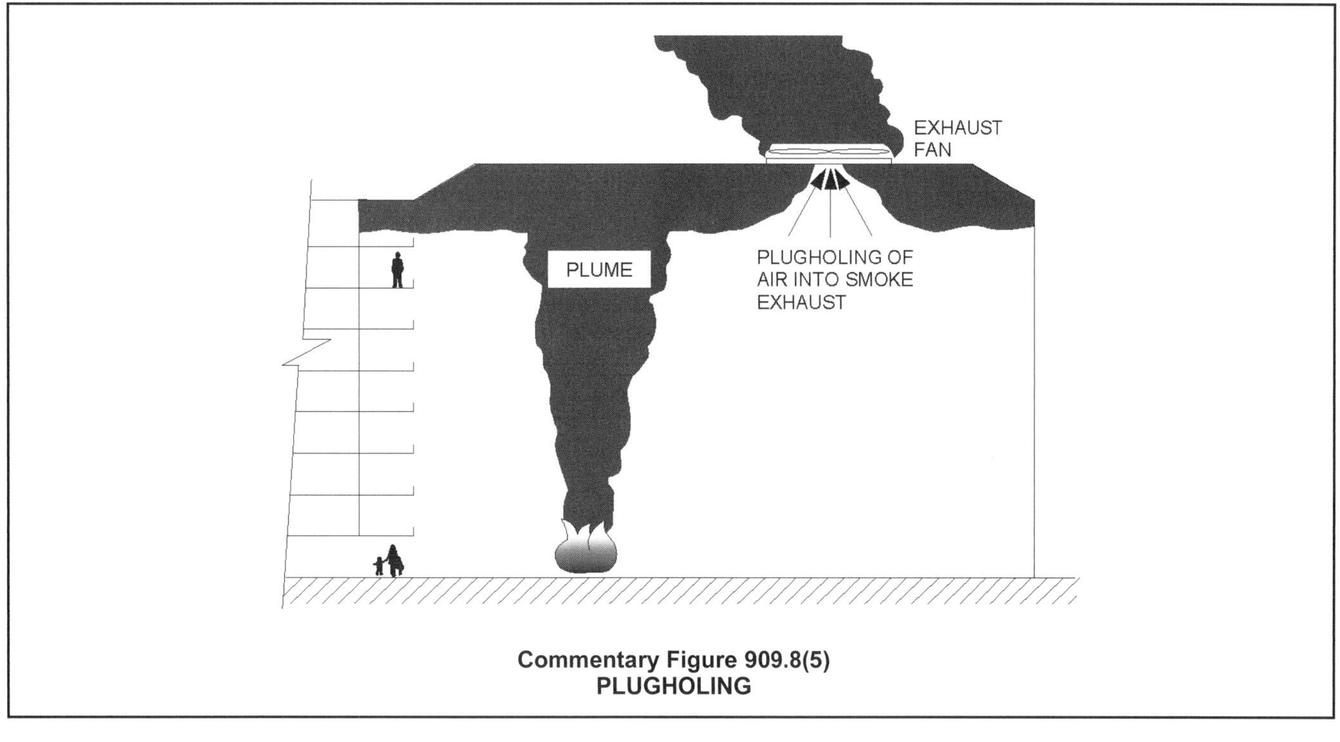

Commentary Figure 909.8(5)
PLUGHOLING

analysis, as CFD and scale modeling provide more detail on actual smoke behavior; therefore, the location of the smoke layer interface may not be initially clear without some level of analysis. Again it depends on the depth of the transition layer. This may require reviewing tenability within the transition zone. Tenability limits need to be agreed upon by the stakeholders involved. The *SFPE Handbook of Fire Protection Engineering, 5th edition,* Chapters 61 and 62 provide guidance on how to define tenability limits. Using CFD or scale modeling would likely need to occur through the alternative methods and materials section (see Section 104.11) because of the need to review tenability limits. It should be noted that NFPA 92 Annex A suggests that there are methods to determine where the smoke layer interface and first indication of smoke are located when undertaking CFD and scale modeling using a limited number of point measurements.

Also, Section 909.8.1 specifies a minimum distance for the smoke layer interface from any walking surface whereas Section 4.5.4.2 of NFPA 92 has provisions that simply allow the analysis to demonstrate tenability regardless of where the layer height is located above the floor. Defining tenability can be more difficult as there is not a standard definition. Any design using that approach would need to be addressed through Section 104.11.

Note that the response time of the system components (detection, activation, ramp-up time, shutting down HVAC, opening/closing doors and dampers, etc.) needs to be accounted for when analyzing the location of the smoke layer interface in relation to the duration of operations stated in Section 909.4.6 (see commentary, Section 909.17).

909.9 Design fire. The design fire shall be based on a rational analysis performed by the registered design professional and *approved* by the *fire code official*. The design fire shall be based on the analysis in accordance with Section 909.4 and this section.

❖ Estimating the design fire is the most critical element in the smoke control system design; several design fire types and/or locations should be considered in the design of most systems. The fire is what produces the smoke to be controlled by the system; thus, the size of the fire directly impacts the quantity of smoke being produced. This section ensures that the design fire be determined through a rational analysis by a registered design professional with knowledge in this area. Such professionals should have experience in the area of fire dynamics, fire engineering and general building design, including mechanical systems. When determining the design fire, the designer should work with various stakeholders to determine the types of hazards and combustible materials (fire scenarios) on

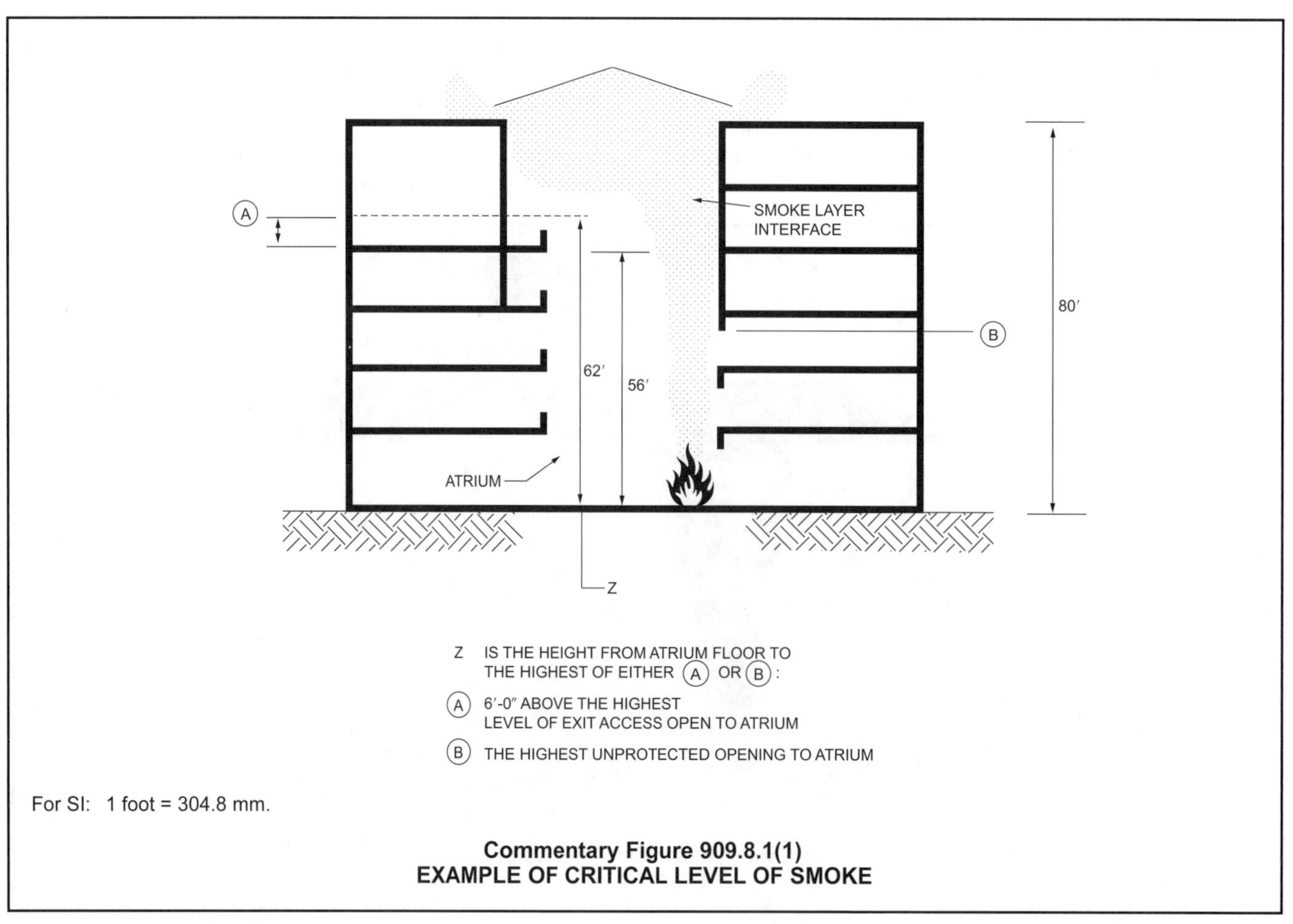

Commentary Figure 909.8.1(1)
EXAMPLE OF CRITICAL LEVEL OF SMOKE

a permanent as well as temporary basis (i.e., Christmas/holiday decorative materials or scenery, temporary art exhibits) that may be present throughout the use of the building once occupied. Fire scenarios describe a sequence of possible events and set of conditions that describe the development of fire and the spread of combustion products throughout a building or part of a building. Those hazards then need to be translated to potential design fires to be used when determining the smoke layer interface height for the duration as determined by Section 909.4.6. See the commentary for Section 909.9.3 for potential sources when determining design fires.

This section also does not mandate the type of fire (i.e., steady versus unsteady). A steady fire assumes a constant heat-release rate over a period of time, where unsteady fires do not. An unsteady fire includes the growth and decay phases of the fire, as well as the peak heat-release rate. An unsteady fire will hit a peak heat-release rate when burning in the open, like an axisymmetric fire. An unsteady fire is a more realistic view of how fires actually burn. It should be noted that fires can be a combination of unsteady and steady fires when sufficient fuel is available. In other words, the fire initially grows (unsteady) then reaches a steady state and burns for some time at a particular heat-release rate before decay occurs.

Design fire information should therefore typically include growth rate, peak heat-release rate, duration and decay as well as information related to fire locations and products of combustion yield (CO, smoke, etc.) that are produced by the various design fires that are deemed credible for the space.

To provide an order of magnitude of fire sizes obtained from various combustibles, the following data from fire tests are provided. The following heat-release rates, found in Section 3, Chapter 3-1 of the 4th edition of the *SFPE Handbook of Fire Protection Engineering*, are peak heat-release rates:

- Plastic trash bags/paper trash:
  Approximately 120–350 kW
- Latex foam pillow:
  Approximately 120 kW
- Dry Douglas fir Christmas tree:
  Approximately 3000 kW at 20% moisture
- Polyurethane foam (PVC Ticking material) Mattress:
  Approximately 2630 kW
- Plywood wardrobe:
  Approximately 2900–6400 kW

909.9.1 Factors considered. The engineering analysis shall include the characteristics of the fuel, fuel load, effects included by the fire and whether the fire is likely to be steady or unsteady.

❖ This section simply provides more detail on the factors that should be taken under consideration when determining the design fire size. To determine the appropriate fire size, an engineering analysis is necessary that takes into account the following elements: fuel (potential burning rates), fuel load (how much), effects included by the fire (smoke particulate size and density), steady or unsteady (burn steadily or simply peak and dissipate), and likelihood of sprinkler activation (based on height and distance from the fire).

909.9.2 Design fire fuel. Determination of the design fire shall include consideration of the type of fuel, fuel spacing and configuration.

❖ The design fire size may also be affected by surrounding combustibles, which may have the effect of increasing the fire size. More specifically, there is concern that if sufficient separation is not maintained between combustibles, then a larger design fire is likely. The code does not provide extensive detail on this as such determination is left to the rational analysis undertaken by the design professional. NFPA 92 provides one method in which to determine the critical separation distance, *R*. This is based on fire size and the critical radiant heat flux for nonpiloted ignition. Nonpiloted ignition means the radiated heat from the fire without direct flame contact will ignite adjacent combustibles.

909.9.3 Heat-release assumptions. The analysis shall make use of best available data from *approved* sources and shall not be based on excessively stringent limitations of combustible material.

❖ This section stresses that data obtained for use in a rational analysis need to come from relevant and appropriate sources. Data can be obtained from groups such as NIST or from Annex B of NFPA 92. Data from fire tests are available and are a good resource for such analysis. As noted earlier, such data are not prevalent (see also Chapter 8, Analysis of Design Fires, from *A Guide to Smoke Control in the 2006 IBC®* and Chapter 26 of the *SFPE Handbook of Fire Protection Engineering, 5th edition*).

909.9.4 Sprinkler effectiveness assumptions. A documented engineering analysis shall be provided for conditions that assume fire growth is halted at the time of sprinkler activation.

❖ This section raises a few questions regarding activation of sprinklers and their impact on the fire both in terms of their ability to "control" as well as "extinguish" a fire. The first is concerning an assumption that sprinklers will immediately control the fire as soon as they are activated (i.e., control results in limiting further growth and maintaining the heat-release rate at approximately the same fire size as when the sprinklers activated). This assumption may be true in some cases, but for high ceilings, the sprinkler may not activate or may be ineffective. Sprinklers may be ineffective in high spaces, since by the time they are activated, the fire is too large to control. Essentially, the fire plume may push away and evaporate the water before it actually reaches the seat of the fire. In addition, the fire may be shielded from sprinkler spray so that insufficient quantities of water reach the fuel. These are common problems with high-piled storage as well as other fires, including retail, and has been shown in actual tests. Also, if the fire becomes too large before the sprinklers are activated, the available water supply and pressure for the system may be compromised. Additionally, based on the layout of the room and the movement of the fire effluents, the wrong sprinklers could be activated, which leads to a larger fire size and depletion of the available water supply and pressure.

Another issue is whether the sprinklers "control" or "extinguish" the fire. Typical sprinklers are assumed only to control fires as opposed to extinguishing them. Sprinklers may be able to extinguish the fire, but it should not automatically be assumed. A fire that is controlled will achieve steady state and maintain a certain fire size, which is very different from a fire that is actually extinguished.

Based on these concerns, each scenario needs to be looked at individually to determine whether sprinklers would be effective in halting the growth or extinguishing the fire. More specifically, the evaluation should include droplet size, density and area of coverage and should also be based on actual test results.

909.10 Equipment. Equipment including, but not limited to, fans, ducts, automatic dampers and balance dampers shall be suitable for their intended use, suitable for the probable exposure temperatures that the rational analysis indicates, and as *approved* by the *fire code official.*

❖ Section 909.10 and subsequent sections are primarily related to the reliability of the system components to provide a smoke control system that works according to the design. One of the largest concerns when using smoke control provisions is the overall reliability of the system. Such systems have many different components, such as smoke and fire dampers, fans, ducts and controls associated with such components. The more components a system has, the less reliable it becomes. In fact, one approach in providing a higher level of reliability is utilizing the normal building systems such as the HVAC to provide the smoke control system. Basically, systems used every day are more likely to be working appropriately, since they are essentially being tested daily; however, there are many components that are specific to the smoke control system, such as exhaust fans in an atrium or the smoke control panel.

Also, there is not a generic prescriptive set of requirements as to how all smoke control system elements should operate, since each design may be fairly unique. The specifics on operation of such a system need to be included within the design and construction documents. Most components used in smoke control systems are elements used in many other applications such as HVAC systems; therefore, the basic mechanisms of a fan used in a smoke control system may not be different, although they may be applied differently.

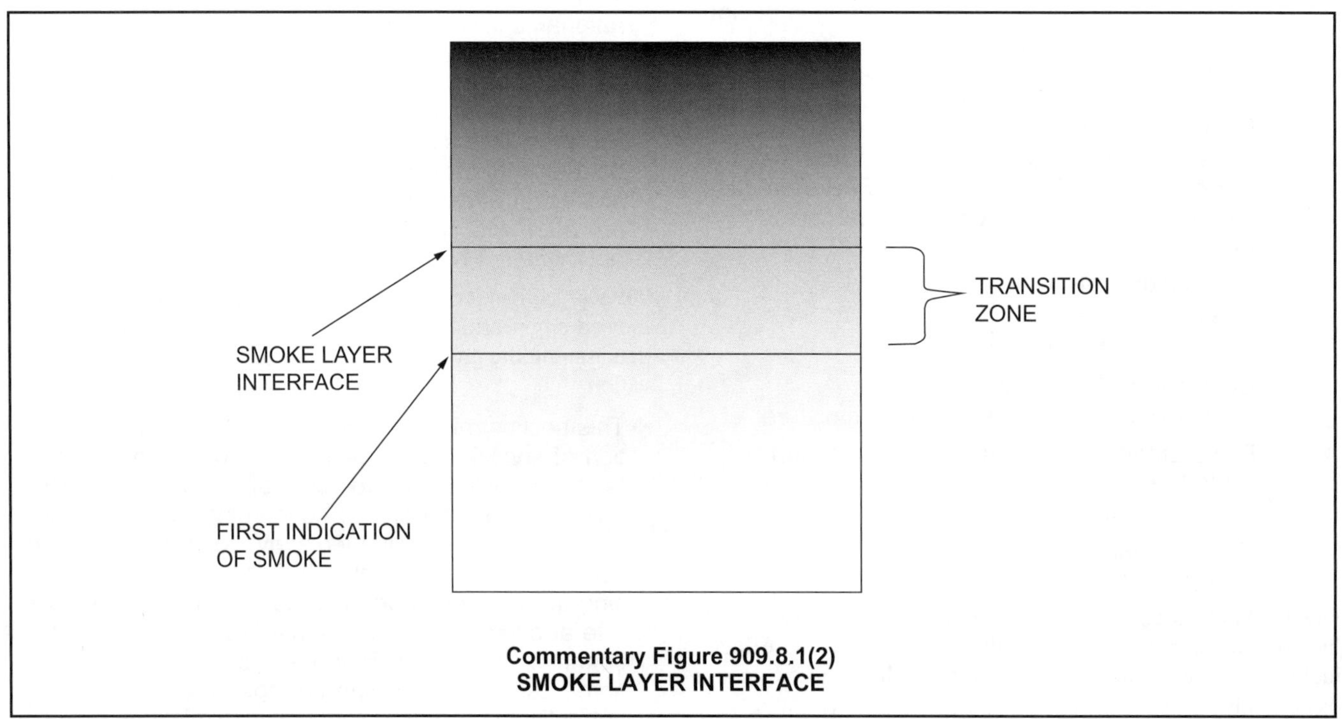

Commentary Figure 909.8.1(2)
SMOKE LAYER INTERFACE

909.10.1 Exhaust fans. Components of exhaust fans shall be rated and certified by the manufacturer for the probable temperature rise to which the components will be exposed. This temperature rise shall be computed by:

$$T_s = (Q_c/mc) + (T_a) \qquad \textbf{(Equation 9-2)}$$

where:

c = Specific heat of smoke at smoke layer temperature, Btu/lb°F (kJ/kg · K).

m = Exhaust rate, pounds per second (kg/s).

Q_c = Convective heat output of fire, Btu/s (kW).

T_a = Ambient temperature, °F (K).

T_s = Smoke temperature, °F (K).

Exception: Reduced T_s as calculated based on the assurance of adequate dilution air.

❖ Fans used for smoke control systems must be able to tolerate the possible elevated temperatures to which they will be exposed. Again, like many other factors, this depends on the specifics of the design fire. Essentially, Equation 9-2 requires the calculation of the potential temperature rise. The exhaust fans must be specifically rated and certified by the manufacturer to be able to handle these rises in temperature. There is an exception that allows reduction of the temperature if it can be shown that adequate temperature reduction will occur. In many cases, if the exhaust fans are near the ceiling, the smoke will be much cooler than the value resulting from Equation 9-2 since the smoke may cool considerably by the time it reaches the ceiling. Also, sprinkler activation will assist in cooling the smoke further.

909.10.2 Ducts. Duct materials and joints shall be capable of withstanding the probable temperatures and pressures to which they are exposed as determined in accordance with Section 909.10.1. Ducts shall be constructed and supported in accordance with the *International Mechanical Code.* Ducts shall be leak tested to 1.5 times the maximum design pressure in accordance with nationally accepted practices. Measured leakage shall not exceed 5 percent of design flow. Results of such testing shall be a part of the documentation procedure. Ducts shall be supported directly from fire-resistance-rated structural elements of the building by substantial, noncombustible supports.

Exception: Flexible connections, for the purpose of vibration isolation, complying with the *International Mechanical Code* and that are constructed of *approved* fire-resistance-rated materials.

❖ The next essential component of a smoke control system is the integrity of the ducts to transport supply and exhaust air. The integrity of ducts is also important for an HVAC system, but is more critical in this case since it is not simply a comfort issue but one of life safety. The key concern with ducts in smoke control systems is that they can withstand elevated temperatures and that there will be minimal leakage. The concern with leakage is the potential of leaking smoke into another smoke zone or not providing the proper amount of supply air to support the system.

More specifically, all ducts need to be leak tested to 1.5 times the maximum static design pressure. The leakage resulting should be no more than 5 percent of the design flow. For example, a duct that has a design flow of 300 cubic feet per minute (cfm) (0.141 m^3/s) would be allowed 15 cfm (0.007 m^3/s) of leakage when exposed to a pressure equal to 1.5 times the design pressure for that duct. The tests should be in accordance with nationally accepted practices. This criterion will often limit ductwork for smoke control systems to lined systems, since the amount of leakage in such systems is much less.

As part of the concern for possible exposure to fire and fire products, the ducts are required to be supported by way of substantial noncombustible supports connected to the fire-resistance-rated structural elements of the building. As noted, the system needs to able to run for 20 minutes starting from the detection of the fire. The exception to this section is really more of an acknowledgment that flexible connections for vibration isolation are acceptable when constructed of approved fire-resistance-rated materials. More specifically, it is often necessary to use such connections for connecting the duct to the fan. These connections cannot necessarily meet the requirements of the main section, but are a minimal part of the ductwork and as long as they perform adequately with regard to fire resistance, they are permitted. Note that the term "approved" is used to determine the required fire resistance; therefore, flexibility is provided. The code does not specifically address this determination but perhaps a relationship to the duration or operation and these flexible connections could be made to determine the necessary performance.

909.10.3 Equipment, inlets and outlets. Equipment shall be located so as to not expose uninvolved portions of the building to an additional fire hazard. Outside air inlets shall be located so as to minimize the potential for introducing smoke or flame into the building. Exhaust outlets shall be so located as to minimize reintroduction of smoke into the building and to limit exposure of the building or adjacent buildings to an additional fire hazard.

❖ The intent of this section is to minimize the likelihood of smoke being reintroduced into the building due to poorly placed outdoor air inlets and exhaust air outlets; therefore, placing one right next to the other on the exterior of the building would be inappropriate. In addition, wind and other adverse conditions should be considered when choosing locations for these inlets and outlets. Particular attention should be paid to introducing exhausted smoke into another smoke zone. Also, smoke should be exhausted in a direction that will not introduce it into surrounding buildings or facilities. Within the building itself, the supply air and exhaust outlets should also be strategically located. The exhaust inlets and supply air should be evenly distributed to reduce the likelihood of a high velocity of air that may disrupt the fire plume and also push smoke back into occupied areas. See the commentary to Section 909.8 for discussion on avoiding plugholing.

909.10.4 Automatic dampers. Automatic dampers, regardless of the purpose for which they are installed within the smoke control system, shall be *listed* and conform to the requirements of *approved* recognized standards.

❖ This section addresses the reliability of any dampers used within a smoke control system. This particular provision requires that the dampers be listed and conform to the appropriate recognized standards. More specifically, Section 717 contains more detailed information on the specific requirements for smoke and fire dampers. Smoke and fire dampers should be listed in accordance with UL 555S and 555, respectively. Also, remember that each smoke control design is unique and the sequence and methods used to activate the dampers may vary from design to design. This information needs to be addressed in the construction documents.

Another factor to take into account, with regard to timing of the system, is the fact that some dampers react more quickly than others, simply due to the particular smoke damper characteristics. Additionally, during the commissioning of the system, the damper is going to be exposed to many repetitions. These repetitions need to be accounted for in the overall reliability of the system.

909.10.5 Fans. In addition to other requirements, belt-driven fans shall have 1.5 times the number of belts required for the design duty with the minimum number of belts being two. Fans shall be selected for stable performance based on normal temperature and, where applicable, elevated temperature. Calculations and manufacturer's fan curves shall be part of the documentation procedures. Fans shall be supported and restrained by noncombustible devices in accordance with the structural design requirements of Chapter 16 of the *International Building Code.*

Motors driving fans shall not be operated beyond their nameplate horsepower (kilowatts) as determined from measurement of actual current draw and shall have a minimum service factor of 1.15.

❖ Part of the overall reliability requires that fans used to provide supply air and exhaust capacity will be functioning when necessary; therefore, a safety factor of 1.5 is placed on the required belts for fans. All fans used as part of a smoke control system must provide 1.5 times the number of required belts with a minimum of two belts for all fans.

This section also points out that the fan chosen should fit the specific application. It should be able to withstand the temperature rise as calculated in Section 909.10.1 and generally be able to handle typical exposure conditions, such as location and wind. For instance, propeller fans are highly sensitive to the effects of wind. When located on the windward side of a building, wall-mounted, nonhooded propeller fans are not able to compensate for wind effects. Additionally, even hooded propeller fans located on the leeward side of the building may not adequately compensate for the decrease in pressure caused by wind effects. In general, when designing a system, it should be remembered that field conditions might vary from the calculations; therefore, flexibility should be built into the design that would account for things such as variations in wind conditions.

Finally, this section stresses that fan motors not be operated beyond their rated horsepower.

909.11 Standby power. Smoke control systems shall be provided with standby power in accordance with Section 1203.

❖ This section references Chapter 12 for the specifics as to what is required for standby power. As with any life safety system, a level of redundancy with regard to power supply is required to enable the functioning of the system during a fire. The primary source is the building's normal power system. The secondary power system is by means of standby power. One of the key elements is that standby power systems are intended to operate within 60 seconds of loss of primary power. It should be noted that the primary difference between standby power and emergency power is that emergency power must operate within 10 seconds of loss of primary power versus 60 seconds.

909.11.1 Equipment room. The standby power source and its transfer switches shall be in a room separate from the normal power transformers and switch gears and ventilated directly to and from the exterior. The room shall be enclosed with not less than 1-hour fire barriers constructed in accordance with Section 707 of the *International Building Code* or horizontal assemblies constructed in accordance with Section 711 of the *International Building Code*, or both.

❖ This section requires isolation from normal building power systems via a 1-hour fire barrier, 1-hour horizontal assembly, or both, depending on the location within the building. This increases the reliability and reduces the likelihood that a single event could remove both power supplies. The intent of the ventilation is focused on the proper function of the standby power source in terms of engine-driven generators having appropriate cooling air and combustion air. The requirement that it be from the outside is related to the protection of such ventilation from the effects of fire.

909.11.2 Power sources and power surges. Elements of the smoke control system relying on volatile memories or the like shall be supplied with uninterruptable power sources of sufficient duration to span 15-minute primary power interruption. Elements of the smoke control system susceptible to power surges shall be suitably protected by conditioners, suppressors or other *approved* means.

❖ Smoke control systems have many components, sometimes highly sensitive electronics, that are adversely affected by any interruption in or sudden surges of power. Therefore, Section 909.11.2 requires that any components of a smoke control system, such as volatile memories, be supplied with an uninterruptible power system for the first 15 minutes of loss of primary power. Volatile memory components will lose memory upon any loss of power, no matter how short the time period. Once the 15 minutes elapse, these elements can be transitioned to the already operating standby power supply.

With regard to components sensitive to power surges, they need to be provided with surge protection in the form of conditioners, suppressors or other approved means.

909.12 Detection and control systems. Fire detection systems providing control input or output signals to mechanical smoke control systems or elements thereof shall comply with the requirements of Section 907. Such systems shall be equipped with a control unit complying with UL 864 and *listed* as smoke control equipment.

❖ This section is focused on proper monitoring of the fire detection systems that activate the smoke control system through compliance with Section 907 and UL 864. This requires a specific listing of the fire alarm control unit as smoke control equipment. UL 864 has a subcategory (UUKL) specific to fire alarm control panels for smoke control system applications.

909.12.1 Verification. Control systems for mechanical smoke control systems shall include provisions for verification. Verification shall include positive confirmation of actuation, testing, manual override and the presence of power downstream of all disconnects. A preprogrammed weekly test sequence shall report abnormal conditions audibly, visually and by printed report. The preprogrammed weekly test shall operate all devices, equipment, and components used for smoke control.

Exception: Where verification of individual components tested through the preprogrammed weekly testing sequence will interfere with, and produce unwanted effects to, normal building operation, such individual components are permitted to be bypassed from the preprogrammed weekly testing, where *approved* by the *fire code official* and in accordance with both of the following:

1. Where the operation of components is bypassed from the preprogrammed weekly test, presence of power downstream of all disconnects shall be verified weekly by a listed control unit.
2. Testing of all components bypassed from the preprogrammed weekly test shall be in accordance with Section 909.20.6.

❖ This section addresses the function of the mechanical elements of the smoke control system once the system is activated. In particular, there is a focus on verification of activities. Verification would include the following two aspects:

1. The system is able to verify actuations, testing, manual overrides and the presence of power downstream. This would require information reported back to the smoke control panel, which can be accomplished via the weekly test sequence or through full electronic monitoring of the system.
2. Conduct a preprogrammed weekly test that simulates an actual (smoke) event to test the components of the system. These components would include elements such as smoke dampers, fans and doors. Abnormal conditions need to be reported in three ways:

   a. Audibly.

   b. Visually.

   c. Printed report.

It should be noted that electrical monitoring of the control components is not required (supervision). Such supervision verifies integrity of the conductors from a fire alarm control unit to the control system input. The weekly test is considered sufficient verification of system performance and is often termed "end-to-end verification." In other words, the control system input provides the expected results. Verification can be accomplished through any sensor that is calibrated to distinguish the difference between proper operation and a fault condition. For fans, proper operation means that the fan is moving air within the intent of its design. Fault conditions include power failure, broken fan belts, adverse wind effects, a locked rotor condition and/or filters or large ducts that are blocked, causing significantly reduced airflow. In addition to differential pressure transmitters and sail switches, this can be accomplished by state-of-the-art current sensors. There is more discussion on verification for elements such as ducts and fire doors in Chapter 9 of *A Guide to Smoke Control in the 2006 IBC®*.

Also, the fact that a smoke control system is nondedicated (integrated with an HVAC system) does not mean that it is automatically being tested on a daily basis. It is cautioned that simply depending on occupant discomfort, for example, is sometimes an insufficient indicator of a fully functioning smoke control system. There may be various modes in which the HVAC system could operate that may not exercise the smoke control features and the sequence in which the system should operate. An example is an air-conditioning system operating only in full recirculating mode versus exhaust mode. This failure will likely not affect occupants and will not exercise the exhaust function. Plus, doors, which may be part of the smoke barrier, may not need to be closed in normal building operations but would need to be closed during smoke control system operation. This is why this section does not necessarily differentiate between dedicated and nondedicated smoke control systems and requires the system components to be tested.

It is important to note that this weekly test sequence is not an actual smoke event and is only intended to activate the system to ensure that the components are working correctly.

The exception addresses the impracticality of requiring a weekly test for many buildings. For many systems, the weekly test requires the introduction of untreated air into the smoke zone. This can be impractical in areas with cold or hot climates and for buildings that require close control of temperature and humidity, such as art museums and similar facilities. The introduction of the untreated air can also result in wasting energy to reheat, recool, humidify, or dehumidify the smoke control zone.

The intent of the exception is to provide means to verify that the required systems will be available when needed. The code requires control units to comply with UL 864; thus, all components of the control system will be supervised. The exception includes requirements for verification of the power downstream of all disconnects, such as power breakers, power disconnects, automatic transfer switches, motor starters, and motor controls. This will provide reasonable assurance that power will be available for all smoke control components, such as fans, dampers, doors, and windows. The exception also adds the semi-annual requirement for a complete system test by reference to Section 909.20.6. This allows the building owner to schedule complete system testing on days that will reduce the impact to the building and energy needs. The combination of additional supervision and additional testing provides a reasonable alternative to weekly testing.

909.12.2 Wiring. In addition to meeting requirements of NFPA 70, all wiring, regardless of voltage, shall be fully enclosed within continuous raceways.

❖ Wiring is required to be placed within continuous raceways, which provides an additional level of reliability for the system. The definition of the term "raceway" in NFPA 70 lists several acceptable types of complying raceway that can be used; however, manufactured cable assemblies such as metal-clad cable (Type MC) or armored cable (Type AC) are not included.

909.12.3 Activation. Smoke control systems shall be activated in accordance with this section.

❖ The activation of a smoke control system is dependent on when such a system is required. Mechanical smoke control systems, which could include pressurization, airflow or exhaust methods, require an automatic activation mechanism. When using a passive system that depends on compartmentation, spot-type detectors are acceptable for the release of door closers and similar openings. With more complex mechanical systems, such activation needs to go beyond single-station detectors and be part of an automatic coordinated system.

909.12.3.1 Pressurization, airflow or exhaust method. Mechanical smoke control systems using the pressurization, airflow or exhaust method shall have completely automatic control.

❖ Automatic activation of such systems is especially critical as tenability is much more difficult to achieve if a delay occurs waiting for manual activation of the system. See Sections 909.6 for the pressurization method, 909.7 for the airflow design method and 909.8 for the exhaust method.

909.12.3.2 Passive method. Passive smoke control systems actuated by *approved* spot-type detectors *listed* for releasing service shall be permitted.

❖ This section recognizes that a passive system does not address smoke containment through mechanical means; therefore, it does not need to be "automatically activated" except in cases where smoke barriers have openings. These openings would be required to have smoke detectors to close openings where required by the design. Although spot-type detectors are technically automatic, they are not part of a more coordinated system of activation as needed for mechanical smoke control systems. Such detectors are simply standalone devices that fail in the fail-safe position. In other words, if the power were lost, a door on a magnetic hold would simply close.

909.12.4 Automatic control. Where completely automatic control is required or used, the automatic-control sequences shall be initiated from an appropriately zoned *automatic sprinkler system* complying with Section 903.3.1.1, manual controls provided with *ready access* for the fire department and any smoke detectors required by the engineering analysis.

❖ Where automatic activation is required, it must be accomplished by a properly zoned automatic sprinkler system and/or smoke detection where required by this code, or other initiation methods if the engineering analysis requires them. Manual control for the fire department needs to be provided. An important point with this particular requirement is that smoke control systems are engineered systems and a prescribed smoke detection system may not fit the needs of the specific design. Other types of detectors, such as beam detectors (within an atrium), may be used and could be more useful and more practical from a maintenance standpoint. Also, it may not be practical or appropriate for the building's fire alarm system to activate such systems, as it may alter the effectiveness of the system by pulling smoke through the building versus removing or containing the smoke. For example, a building with an atrium may have several floors below the space. If a fire occurs in one of the floors not associated with the atrium, the atrium smoke control system could possibly pull smoke throughout the building if the detection is zoned incorrectly.

909.13 Control air tubing. Control air tubing shall be of sufficient size to meet the required response times. Tubing shall be flushed clean and dry prior to final connections and shall be adequately supported and protected from damage. Tubing passing through concrete or masonry shall be sleeved and protected from abrasion and electrolytic action.

❖ Control tubing is a method that uses pneumatics to operate components such as the opening and closing of dampers. Because of the sophistication of electronic systems today, control tubing is becoming less common.

These particular requirements provide the criteria for properly designing and installing control tubing. Essentially, it is up to the design professional to determine the size requirements and to properly design appropriate supports. This information needs to be detailed within the construction documents. Additionally, because of the effect of moisture and other contaminants on control tubing, it must be flushed clean and then dried before installation.

909.13.1 Materials. Control air tubing shall be hard drawn copper, Type L, ACR in accordance with ASTM B42, ASTM B43, ASTM B68, ASTM B88, ASTM B251 and ASTM B280. Fittings shall be wrought copper or brass, solder type, in accordance with ASME B16.18 or ASME B16.22. Changes in direction shall be made with appropriate tool bends. Brass compression-type fittings shall be used at final connection to devices; other joints shall be brazed using a BCuP5 brazing alloy with solidus above 1,100°F (593°C) and liquidus below 1,500°F (816°C). Brazing flux shall be used on copper-to-brass joints only.

Exception: Nonmetallic tubing used within control panels and at the final connection to devices, provided that all of the following conditions are met:

1. Tubing shall comply with the requirements of Section 602.2.1.3 of the *International Mechanical Code*.
2. Tubing and the connected device shall be completely enclosed within a galvanized or paint-grade steel enclosure having a minimum thickness of 0.0296 inch (0.7534 mm) (No. 22 gage). Entry to the enclosure shall be by copper tubing with a protective grommet of neoprene or Teflon or by suitable brass compression to male-barbed adapter.
3. Tubing shall be identified by appropriately documented coding.
4. Tubing shall be neatly tied and supported within the enclosure. Tubing bridging cabinets and doors or moveable devices shall be of sufficient length to avoid tension and excessive stress. Tubing shall be protected against abrasion. Tubing connected to devices on doors shall be fastened along hinges.

❖ This section addresses the materials allowed for control air tubing along with approved methods of connection. All of this information needs to be documented, as it will be subject to review by the special inspector.

909.13.2 Isolation from other functions. Control tubing serving other than smoke control functions shall be isolated by automatic isolation valves or shall be an independent system.

❖ This section requires separation of control tubing used for other functions through the use of isolation valves or a completely separate system. This is necessary due to the difference in requirements for control tubing used in a smoke control system versus other building systems. The isolation of the control air tubing for a smoke control system needs to be specifically noted on the construction documents.

909.13.3 Testing. Control air tubing shall be tested at three times the operating pressure for not less than 30 minutes without any noticeable loss in gauge pressure prior to final connection to devices.

❖ As part of the acceptance testing of the smoke control system, the control air tubing will be pressure tested three times the operating pressure for 30 minutes or more. The performance criterion as to whether the control tubing is considered a failure is when there is any noticeable loss in gauge pressure prior to final connection of devices during the 30-minute duration test.

909.14 Marking and identification. The detection and control systems shall be clearly marked at all junctions, accesses and terminations.

❖ This section requires that all portions of the fire detection system that activate the smoke control system be marked and identified appropriately. This includes all applicable fire alarm-initiating devices, the respective junction boxes, all data-gathering panels and fire alarm control panels. Additionally, all components of the smoke control system, which are not considered a fire detection system, are required to be properly identified and marked. This would include all applicable junction boxes, control tubing, temperature control modules, relays, damper sensors, automatic door sensors and air movement sensors.

909.15 Control diagrams. Identical control diagrams showing all devices in the system and identifying their location and function shall be maintained current and kept on file with the *fire code official*, the fire department and in the *fire command center* in a format and manner *approved* by the *fire code official*.

❖ The purpose of control diagrams is to provide consistent information on the system in several key locations, including the building department, the fire department and the fire command center. If a fire command center is not required or provided, the diagrams need to be located such that they can be readily accessed during an emergency. Some possible locations may be the security office, the building manager's office or, if possible, within the smoke control panel. This information is intended to assist in the use and operation of the smoke control system. The format of the control diagram is as approved by the fire chief. This is necessary since the fire department is the agency that will be using such a system during a fire and when the system is tested in the future. The more clearly the information is communicated, the more effective the smoke control system will be.

It should be noted that the fire department may want all smoke control systems within a jurisdiction to follow a particular protocol for control diagrams. Generally, the control diagrams should indicate the required reaction of the system in all scenarios. The status or position of every fan and damper in every scenario must be clearly identified.

909.16 Fire fighter's smoke control panel. A fire fighter's smoke control panel for fire department emergency response purposes only shall be provided and shall include manual control or override of automatic control for mechanical smoke control systems. The panel shall be located in a *fire command center* complying with Section 508 in high-rise buildings or buildings with smoke-protected assembly seating. In all other buildings, the fire fighter's smoke control panel shall be installed in an *approved* location adjacent to the fire alarm control panel. The fire fighter's smoke control panel shall comply with Sections 909.16.1 through 909.16.3.

❖ One of the elements that makes a smoke control system effective is that its activity is successfully communicated to the fire department and the fire department is able to manually operate the system. The following sections provide requirements for a control panel specifically for smoke control systems. This panel is required to be located within a fire command center when it is located in a high-rise building or there is smoke-protected seating. Section 508.1 would require a fire command center for high-rise buildings. Smoke-protected seating does not require a fire command center in Chapter 10, but this provision would ensure that one exists and contains the smoke control panel. Facilities with smoke-protected seating tend to be larger facilities that, at the very least, would already have a central security center if not a fire command center as required by the jurisdiction. All other locations would only need to provide the panel in an approved location as long as it is located with the fire alarm panel. The specific location will depend on the needs of the fire department in that jurisdiction. The reason not all fire fighter's smoke control panels need to be located in a fire command center is that many smoke control systems are located in a building containing an atrium that may only be three stories in height. A 200-square-foot (19 m^2) fire command center would be excessive for such buildings. There are two components that include the requirements for the display and for the controls. This control panel will provide an ability to override any other controls, whether manual or automatic, within the building as they relate to the smoke control system.

Note that the publication *A Guide to Smoke Control in the 2006 IBC®* goes into more detail about the fire fighter's smoke control panel requirements.

909.16.1 Smoke control systems. Fans within the building shall be shown on the fire fighter's control panel. A clear indication of the direction of airflow and the relationship of components shall be displayed. Status indicators shall be provided for all smoke control equipment, annunciated by fan and zone and by pilot-lamp-type indicators as follows:

1. Fans, dampers and other operating equipment in their normal status—WHITE.
2. Fans, dampers and other operating equipment in their off or closed status—RED.
3. Fans, dampers and other operating equipment in their on or open status—GREEN.
4. Fans, dampers and other operating equipment in a fault status—YELLOW/AMBER.

❖ This section denotes what should be displayed on the control panel. The display is required to include all fans, an indication of the direction of airflow and the relationship of the components. Also, status lights are required, and this section sets out specific standardized colors to indicate normal status, closed status, open status and fault status. A standardized approach increases the likelihood that the fire department will be able to quickly become familiar with a system. Since the fire department has the ability to override the automatic functions of the system, this information is critical.

909.16.2 Smoke control panel. The fire fighter's control panel shall provide control capability over the complete smoke control system equipment within the building as follows:

1. ON-AUTO-OFF control over each individual piece of operating smoke control equipment that can be controlled from other sources within the building. This includes *stairway* pressurization fans; smoke exhaust fans; supply, return and exhaust fans; elevator shaft fans; and other operating equipment used or intended for smoke control purposes.
2. OPEN-AUTO-CLOSE control over individual dampers relating to smoke control and that are controlled from other sources within the building.
3. ON-OFF or OPEN-CLOSE control over smoke control and other critical equipment associated with a fire or smoke emergency and that can only be controlled from the fire fighter's control panel.

Exceptions:

1. Complex systems, where *approved*, where the controls and indicators are combined to control and indicate all elements of a single smoke zone as a unit.
2. Complex systems, where *approved*, where the control is accomplished by computer interface using *approved*, plain English commands.

❖ This section sets the requirements as to which controls need to be provided for the fire department on the control panel.

There are two aspects to the controls. The controls will include ON-AUTO-OFF and OPEN-AUTO-CLOSE settings or will be strictly ON-OFF or OPEN-CLOSE. If the system or component can be set on automatic (AUTO), it can be controlled from other locations beyond the fire command center. This would include control from an automatic smoke detection system or by manual activation. If a control contains only ON-OFF or OPEN-CLOSE settings, the only way the system component can be controlled is in the fire command center.

It should be noted that components such as fans are usually associated with ON-OFF-type controls, whereas components such as dampers are associated with OPEN-CLOSE-type controls.

909.16.3 Control action and priorities. The fire fighter's control panel actions shall be as follows:

1. ON-OFF and OPEN-CLOSE control actions shall have the highest priority of any control point within the building. Once issued from the fire fighter's control panel, automatic or manual control from any other control point within the building shall not contradict the control action. Where automatic means are provided to interrupt normal, nonemergency equipment operation or produce a specific result to safeguard the building or equipment including, but not limited to, duct freezestats, duct smoke detectors, high-temperature cutouts, temperature-actuated linkage and similar devices, such means shall be capable of being overridden by the fire fighter's control panel. The last control action as indicated by each fire fighter's control panel switch position shall prevail. Control actions shall not require the smoke control system to assume more than one configuration at any one time.

   Exception: Power disconnects required by NFPA 70.

2. Only the AUTO position of each three-position fire-fighter's control panel switch shall allow automatic or manual control action from other control points within the building. The AUTO position shall be the NORMAL, nonemergency, building control position. Where a fire fighter's control panel is in the AUTO position, the actual status of the device (on, off, open, closed) shall continue to be indicated by the status indicator described in Section 909.16.1. Where directed by an automatic signal to assume an emergency condition, the NORMAL position shall become the emergency condition for that device or group of devices within the zone. Control actions shall not require the smoke control system to assume more than one configuration at any one time.

❖ This section clarifies that when a component of the system is placed in an ON-OFF or OPEN-CLOSE configuration, no other control point in the building, whether automatic or manual, can override the action established in the fire command center. If a system component is configured in AUTO mode, it can be controlled from locations within the building beyond the fire command center. Some controls are specifically designed to only allow an action from the fire command center.

909.17 System response time. Smoke-control system activation shall be initiated immediately after receipt of an appropriate automatic or manual activation command. Smoke control systems shall activate individual components (such as dampers and fans) in the sequence necessary to prevent physical damage to the fans, dampers, ducts and other equipment. For purposes of smoke control, the fire fighter's control panel response time shall be the same for automatic or manual smoke control action initiated from any other building control point. The total response time, including that necessary for detection, shutdown of operating equipment and smoke control system startup, shall allow for full operational mode to be achieved before the conditions in the space exceed the design smoke condition. The system response time for each component and their sequential relationships shall be detailed in the required rational analysis and verification of their installed condition reported in the required final report.

❖ This particular section provides the criteria as to when the smoke control system is required to begin operation. Whether or not the activation is manual or automatic, these criteria clarify that the system be initiated immediately. Also, it requires that components activate in a sequence that will not potentially damage the fans, dampers, ducts and other equipment. Unrealistic timing of the system has the potential of creating an unsuccessful system. Delays in the system can be seen in slow dampers, fans that ramp up or down, systems that poll slowly and intentional built-in delays. These factors can add significantly to the reaction time of the system and may hamper achieving the design goals.

The key element is that the system be fully operational before the smoke conditions exceed the design parameters. The design should include these possible delays when analyzing the smoke layer interface location. The sequence of events needs to be justified within the design analysis and described clearly in the construction documents.

909.18 Acceptance testing. Devices, equipment, components and sequences shall be individually tested. These tests, in addition to those required by other provisions of this code, shall consist of determination of function, sequence and, where applicable, capacity of their installed condition.

❖ In order to achieve a certain level of performance, the smoke control system needs to be thoroughly tested. Section 909.18 requires that all devices, equipment components and sequences be individually tested.

909.18.1 Detection devices. Smoke or fire detectors that are a part of a smoke control system shall be tested in accordance with Chapter 9 in their installed condition. Where applicable, this testing shall include verification of airflow in both minimum and maximum conditions.

❖ Detection devices are required to be tested in accordance with the fire protection requirements found in Chapter 9. Also, since such detectors may be subject to higher air velocities than typical detectors, their operation needs to be verified in the minimum and maximum anticipated airflow conditions.

909.18.2 Ducts. Ducts that are part of a smoke control system shall be traversed using generally accepted practices to determine actual air quantities.

❖ This section requires ducts that are part of the smoke control system to be tested to show that the proper amount of air is flowing. It should be noted that Section 909.10.2 requires that the ducts be leak tested to 1.5 times the maximum design pressure. Such leakage is not allowed to exceed 5 percent of the design flow.

909.18.3 Dampers. Dampers shall be tested for function in their installed condition.

❖ This section notes that all dampers need to be inspected to meet the function for which they are installed. For instance, a damper that is to be open when the system is in smoke control mode should be verified to be open when testing the system. Also, a damper may have a specific timing associated with its operation that would need to be verified through testing.

909.18.4 Inlets and outlets. Inlets and outlets shall be read using generally accepted practices to determine air quantities.

❖ Similar to ducts, the appropriate amount of air that is entering or exiting the inlets and outlets, respectively, must be checked.

909.18.5 Fans. Fans shall be examined for correct rotation. Measurements of voltage, amperage, revolutions per minute and belt tension shall be made.

❖ This section requires the testing of fans for the following: correct rotation, voltage, amperage, revolutions per minute and belt tension. These features are key to having the system run as designed.

A common problem with fans is that they are often installed in the reverse direction. Also, to verify the reliability of the fans, elements such as the appropriate voltage and belt tension need to be tested.

909.18.6 Smoke barriers. Measurements using inclined manometers or other *approved* calibrated measuring devices shall be made of the pressure differences across *smoke barriers*. Such measurements shall be conducted for each possible smoke control condition.

❖ As discussed in Section 909.5.2, the testing of pressure differences across smoke barriers needs to be measured in the smoke control mode. As noted in Section 909.18.6, such testing is to be performed for every possible smoke control condition, and the measurements will be taken using an inclined manometer or other approved methods. Electronic devices are also available. Qualified individuals must calibrate these types of devices. Additionally, before using an alternative method of testing, the building official needs to approve such a method.

909.18.7 Controls. Each smoke zone equipped with an automatic-initiation device shall be put into operation by the actuation of one such device. Each additional device within the zone shall be verified to cause the same sequence without requiring the operation of fan motors in order to prevent damage. Control sequences shall be verified throughout the system, including verification of override from the fire fighter's control panel and simulation of standby power conditions.

❖ This section requires the overall testing of the system. More specifically, each zone needs to individually initiate the smoke control system by the activation of an automatic initiation device. Once that has occurred, it needs to be verified that all other devices within each zone will activate the system, but to avoid damage, the fans do not need to be activated.

In addition to determining that all of the appropriate devices initiate the system, it must also be verified that all of the controls on the fire fighter's control panel initiate the appropriate aspects of the smoke control system, including the override capability.

Finally, the initiation and availability of the standby power system need to be verified.

909.18.8 Testing for smoke control. Smoke control systems shall be tested by a special inspector in accordance with Section 1705.18 of the *International Building Code*.

❖ Smoke control systems require testing by a special inspector since they are unique and complex life safety systems. Section 1705.18 of the IBC provides the same requirements for testing as presented in Sections 909.18.8.1 and 909.18.8.2.

909.18.8.1 Scope of testing. Testing shall be conducted in accordance with the following:

1. During erection of ductwork and prior to concealment for the purposes of leakage testing and recording of device location.
2. Prior to occupancy and after sufficient completion for the purposes of pressure-difference testing, flow measurements, and detection and control verification.

❖ Special inspections need to occur at two different stages during construction to facilitate the necessary inspections. The first round of testing occurs before concealment of the ductwork or fire protection elements. The special inspector needs to verify the leakage in accordance with Section 909.10.2. Additionally, the location of all fire protection devices needs to be verified and documented at this time.

The second round of testing occurs just prior to occupancy. The testing includes the verification of pressure differences across smoke barriers, as required in Sections 909.5.2 and 909.18.6; the verification of appropriate volumes of airflow, as noted in the design; and finally the verification of the appropriate operation of the detection and control mechanisms, as required in Sections 909.18.1 and 909.18.7. These tests need to occur just prior to occupancy, since the test results will more clearly represent actual conditions. This also makes a strong design and quality assurance during construction critical, as it is very costly and difficult in most cases to make changes at this stage. Note that the test does not actually place smoke into the space or demonstrate the smoke layer interface location. Instead, the testing is focused on all of the elements of the design such as airflow and duct closure as prescribed by the specific design.

909.18.8.2 Qualifications. *Approved* agencies for smoke control testing shall have expertise in fire protection engineering, mechanical engineering and certification as air balancers.

❖ As noted in Section 909.3, special inspections are required for smoke control systems. This means a certain level of qualification that would include the need for expertise in fire protection engineering, mechanical engineering and certification as air balancers.

909.18.8.3 Reports. A complete report of testing shall be prepared by the *approved* agency. The report shall include identification of all devices by manufacturer, nameplate data, design values, measured values and identification tag or mark. The report shall be reviewed by the responsible registered design professional and, when satisfied that the design intent has been achieved, the responsible registered design professional shall sign, seal and date the report.

❖ Once the testing by the special inspector is complete, documentation of the activity is required. This documentation is to be prepared in the form of a report that identifies all devices by manufacturer, nameplate data, design values, measured values and identification or mark.

909.18.8.3.1 Report filing. A copy of the final report shall be filed with the *fire code official* and an identical copy shall be maintained in an *approved* location at the building.

❖ The report needs to be reviewed, approved and then signed, sealed and dated. This report is to be provided to the building official and a copy is also to remain in the building in an approved location. When a fire command center is required, this is the best location for such documents. Otherwise, a location such as the security office or building manager's office might be appropriate.

909.18.9 Identification and documentation. Charts, drawings and other documents identifying and locating each component of the smoke control system, and describing their proper function and maintenance requirements, shall be maintained on file at the building as an attachment to the report required by Section 909.18.8.3. Devices shall have an *approved* identifying tag or mark on them consistent with the other required documentation and shall be dated indicating the last time they were successfully tested and by whom.

❖ Additional documentation that needs to be maintained includes charts, drawings and other related documentation that assists in the identification of each aspect of the smoke control system. This documentation is where information, such as the last time a device or component was successfully tested and by whom, is recorded. This will serve as the main documentation for the system. Again, the fire command center, if required, is the most appropriate location for such information (see commentary, Section 909.18.8.3.1).

909.19 System acceptance. Buildings, or portions thereof, required by this code to comply with this section shall not be issued a certificate of occupancy until such time that the *fire code official* determines that the provisions of this section have been fully complied with and that the fire department has received satisfactory instruction on the operation, both automatic and manual, of the system and a written maintenance program complying with the requirements of Section 909.20.1 has been submitted and *approved* by the *fire code official.*

Exception: In buildings of phased construction, a temporary certificate of occupancy, as *approved* by the *fire code official*, shall be allowed, provided that those portions of the building to be occupied meet the requirements of this section and that the remainder does not pose a significant hazard to the safety of the proposed occupants or adjacent buildings.

❖ This section stipulates that the certificate of occupancy cannot be issued unless the smoke control system has been accepted. It is essential that the system be inspected and approved since it is a life safety system. There is an exception for buildings that are constructed in phases where a temporary certificate of occupancy is allowed. For example, a building where the portion requiring smoke control is not yet occupied so egress concerns through that space are not relevant. This space needs to be separated by smoke barriers (different smoke zone). The code also requires a maintenance program for smoke control systems since the long-term success of such systems depends heavily on proper maintenance in addition to rigorous acceptance testing. The IBC simply provides a reference to that section of the code.

909.20 Maintenance. Smoke control systems shall be maintained to ensure to a reasonable degree that the system is capable of controlling smoke for the duration required. The system shall be maintained in accordance with the manufacturer's instructions and Sections 909.20.1 through 909.20.6.

❖ Routine maintenance and testing of smoke control systems is essential to ensure their performance, as designed, under fire conditions. Maintenance practices must be consistent with the manufacturer's recommendations and as indicated in Sections 909.20.1 through 909.20.6. Note that Section 909.12.1 requires weekly preprogrammed tests that report abnormal conditions.

909.20.1 Schedule. A routine maintenance and operational testing program shall be initiated immediately after the smoke control system has passed the acceptance tests. A written schedule for routine maintenance and operational testing shall be established.

❖ Operational testing and maintenance must be performed on the smoke control system periodically to verify that it still operates as required by the approved design. A written schedule must be maintained.

909.20.2 Records. Records of smoke control system testing and maintenance shall be maintained. The record shall include the date of the maintenance, identification of the servicing personnel and notification of any unsatisfactory condition and the corrective action taken, including parts replaced.

❖ This section prescribes the desired content of the written record for the smoke control testing and maintenance program. Test results and maintenance activities should be clearly documented. The written record should be available for inspection and reviewed by the fire code official.

909.20.3 Testing. Operational testing of the smoke control system shall include all equipment such as initiating devices, fans, dampers, controls, doors and windows.

❖ Smoke control systems are made up of components and equipment that are an integral part of other building systems such as fire alarm systems; heating, ventilating and air-conditioning (HVAC) equipment; and automatic sprinkler systems. For this reason, operational testing of all related system components must ensure that the system as a whole will perform as intended.

909.20.4 Dedicated smoke control systems. Dedicated smoke control systems shall be operated for each control sequence semiannually. The system shall be tested under standby power conditions.

❖ Because dedicated smoke control systems are designed for smoke control only, the operation of these systems does not adversely affect other building systems or operations. The control sequence for these systems must be tested semiannually to check for system component failures that may not get noticed because dedicated smoke control systems are independent of building HVAC systems.

909.20.5 Nondedicated smoke control systems. Non-dedicated smoke control systems shall be operated for each control sequence annually. The system shall be tested under standby power conditions.

❖ Contrary to dedicated smoke control systems identified in Section 909.20.4, smoke control systems that are not dedicated share system components with other building systems, including the HVAC system. Consequently, testing of the control sequence of systems that are not dedicated can be done annually, rather than semiannually, because equipment failures related to other building systems would most likely be noticed and corrected when those other systems are tested or maintained.

Simply because a system is nondedicated does not guarantee that failures will be detected any easier. This relates to the fact that when a system is in smoke control mode, it may have very different demands than when simply operating as a traditional HVAC system (see commentary, Section 909.12).

909.20.6 Components bypassing weekly test. Where components of the smoke control system are bypassed by the preprogrammed weekly test required by Section 909.12.1, such components shall be tested semiannually. The system shall be tested under standby power conditions.

❖ This section is specifically linked to the exception in Section 909.12.1 that allows the elimination of the weekly test of the system. In order to allow the elimination of the weekly test, Section 909.12.1 provides additional monitoring features and requires more frequent testing of the overall system by a special inspector. This will primarily affect nondedicated systems that are currently only required to be tested annually. Dedicated systems are already required to be tested semiannually.

[BF] 909.21 Elevator hoistway pressurization alternative. Where elevator hoistway pressurization is provided in lieu of required enclosed elevator lobbies, the pressurization system shall comply with Sections 909.21.1 through 909.21.11.

❖ This section sets out the requirements for hoistway pressurization when used as a method to protect hoistway openings as required in Section 3006 of the IBC. The minimum and maximum pressures are similar to those for pressurized stairs in Section 909.20.5 of the IBC. The provisions are located in Section 909 to group all the smoke control techniques and requirements into the same section. This will promote more consistency in code application when addressing smoke control.

[BF] 909.21.1 Pressurization requirements. Elevator hoistways shall be pressurized to maintain a minimum positive pressure of 0.10 inch of water (25 Pa) and a maximum positive pressure of 0.25 inch of water (67 Pa) with respect to adjacent occupied space on all floors. This pressure shall be measured at the midpoint of each hoistway door, with all elevator cars at the floor of recall and all hoistway doors on the floor of recall open and all other hoistway doors closed. The pressure differentials shall be measured between the hoistway and the adjacent elevator landing. The opening and closing of hoistway doors at each level must be demonstrated during this test. The supply air intake shall be from an outside, uncontaminated source located a minimum distance of 20 feet (6096 mm) from any air exhaust system or outlet.

Exceptions:

1. On floors containing only Group R occupancies, the pressure differential is permitted to be measured between the hoistway and a *dwelling unit* or *sleeping unit*.
2. Where an elevator opens into a lobby enclosed in accordance with Section 3007.6 or 3008.6 of the *International Building Code*, the pressure differential is permitted to be measured between the hoistway and the space immediately outside the door(s) from the floor to the enclosed lobby.
3. The pressure differential is permitted to be measured relative to the outdoor atmosphere on floors other than the following:
   3.1. The fire floor.
   3.2. The two floors immediately below the fire floor.
   3.3. The floor immediately above the fire floor.
4. The minimum positive pressure of 0.10 inch of water (25 Pa) and a maximum positive pressure of 0.25 inch of water (67 Pa) with respect to occupied floors is not required at the floor of recall with the doors open.

❖ This section states the minimum and the maximum positive pressure that must be achieved by the smoke control mechanical pressurization system. The minimum positive pressure is 0.10 inch of water column (25 Pa), the same as required for stairway pressurization in Section 909.20.5. The maximum pressure is 0.25 inch of water column (62 Pa), which is a little less than the maximum allowed for stairway pressurization. The minimum pressure is to ensure that the stack effect is overcome and the maximum pressure is an upper limit to ensure that the doors will operate properly. This section requires a test when the system is complete. The pressures are measured at the midpoint of each hoistway door with all elevator cars at the recall floor and all the hoistway doors open on that level. This simulates the Phase I recall requirements in IBC Section 3003.2. Hoistway doors are then tested on each level to ensure proper operation.

The supply air intake for the pressurization system must be located at least 20 feet (6096 mm) away from any source of contamination to ensure that the hoistway remains tenable through the fire event or well into it before the elevators can no longer be used. Also, if smoke is drawn into the supply air, the system will only spread smoke and not prevent its spread.

There are four exceptions to the requirements of Section 909.21.1. The first two provide exceptions as to where the pressure differential can be measured. Exception 3 allows the pressure differences only to be measured at the fire floor and several designated floors. Finally, Exception 4 allows the pressure differential measurement to be omitted for the floor of recall.

The first three exceptions originated from the City of Seattle, Washington, which has had a long history of requiring pressurized hoistways in high-rise buildings to prevent smoke migration. In 2005, the City of Seattle Department of Planning & Development (DPD) convened a committee, which included representatives from industry, the Seattle Fire Department, and DPD, to decide whether to recommend changes to the high-rise smoke migration control requirements in place at that time. The committee also consulted with Dr. John Klote, who suggested the approach that Seattle eventually adopted with some small modifications. These requirements are an adaptation of the Seattle approach.

During the 2009/2010 code change cycle, a proposal was made to delete the hoistway pressurization requirements in the IBC without substitution (FS51-09/10), based on a study conducted by Drs. Miller and Beasley. This study showed that requiring the pressure differential of 0.10 inch of water column to be maintained at the recall floor with the elevator doors in the open position resulted in overpressurization of all the other floors—meaning the current standards in the code cannot be met. Based on further modeling by Dr. Miller, the proponent for FS51-09/10 submitted a public comment introducing Seattle's requirements into the IBC. The reason statement for the public comment stated Dr. Miller "concluded that the 'Seattle approach' does indeed meet all the prescriptive requirements of the IBC 2009." The proposal and its public comment were ultimately withdrawn by the proponent in anticipation of further review of the overall elevator lobby provisions.

The intent of the code is to keep smoke out of the hoistway, so the pressure should be measured between the elevator hoistway and the elevator landing/lobby. However, Exception 1 allows the pressure to be measured between the hoistway and sleeping or dwelling units in residential buildings, since they are highly compartmented. In addition, the fire source is most likely to be in the dwelling or sleeping unit, and providing positive pressure in the corridor/hallway outside the units (via leakage through the elevator hoistway doors) will help reduce the smoke migrating from the affected unit. Exception 2, which is specific to elevator lobbies associated with fire service access elevators (FSAE) and occupant evacuation elevators, allows the pressure to be measured between the hoistway and the space on the outside of the smoke barrier that forms the lobby. It should be noted that hoistway pressurization is not a design alternative to enclosed lobbies for FSAEs and occupant evacuation elevators. Enclosed elevator lobbies are always required for these types of elevators. This exception would only apply if such a system was provided.

Exception 3 allows the 0.10-inch-water-column pressure differential between the hoistway and the floor be met only on the four most critical floors—the floor of fire origin, the two floors immediately below, and one floor immediately above. For all other stories, the pressure differential is allowed to be measured between the hoistway and the outside of the building. The purpose of this requirement is to maintain a slightly positive pressure in the building relative to atmospheric, so as to lower the neutral pressure plane in the building, which then reduces the driving force of stack effect. This exception is intended to be permitted to be used in conjunction with Exceptions 1 and 2. The engineers who design this system begin by modeling one floor as the "notionalized" fire floor, and designing the system (fans, dampers, etc.) accordingly. Each floor is subsequently modeled as the notionalized fire floor, and the system is checked to make sure the maximum and minimum pressure differentials are met. (Note that actual models may not have to be run for each floor if it is clear the worst case has been covered.) Ultimately, the system will need to be designed so it will correctly configure itself for a fire originating on any floor in the building.

The fourth exception omits the need to measure the pressure differential at the floor of elevator recall where the door is typically open. Section 909.21.1 requires the pressure difference, required for the pressurization alternative, to be measured at the midpoint of each hoistway door, with all elevator cars at the floor of recall and all hoistway doors on the floor of recall open and all other hoistway doors closed.

Elevator hositway pressurization is intended to minimize smoke movement into an elevator shaft when a lobby is not provided. Meeting the required pressure difference on the recall floor with the hoistway doors open is not necessary because the recall floor is protected by smoke detectors that will not allow the hoistway doors to open if smoke is present.

The pressurization method is based on using pressure differences produced by fans to minimize the spread of smoke across a barrier. A barrier will not exist on the recall floor when the hoistway doors are open, and smoke detectors used for elevator recall prevent the doors from opening when smoke is present.

[BF] 909.21.1.1 Use of ventilation systems. Ventilation systems, other than hoistway supply air systems, are permitted to be used to exhaust air from adjacent spaces on the fire floor, two floors immediately below and one floor immediately above the fire floor to the building's exterior where necessary to maintain positive pressure relationships as required in Section 909.21.1 during operation of the elevator shaft pressurization system.

❖ This section allows the use of the general building HVAC system to exhaust air to create/maintain the required pressure differential. It is to be noted that the requirements of the rest of Section 909.21, in particular, Section 909.21.10 regarding protection of equipment, would still apply to these components.

[BF] 909.21.2 Rational analysis. A rational analysis complying with Section 909.4 shall be submitted with the *construction documents*.

❖ Section 909.4 recognizes that there are many factors involved in a smoke control system, including stack effect due to height, temperature effect of fire, wind effect, interaction of the HVAC system, the weather, and the egress time, all of which must be evaluated. The report must be submitted with the permit documents. Most importantly, the duration of operation of the smoke control system is a function of 1.5 times the egress time or 20 minutes, whichever is less. More discussion on the duration of operation is found in the commentary for Section 909.4.6.

[BF] 909.21.3 Ducts for system. Any duct system that is part of the pressurization system shall be protected with the same *fire-resistance rating* as required for the elevator shaft enclosure.

❖ All ductwork necessary for hoistway pressurization must be protected from the effects of fire by enclosure in fire-resistance-rated construction equivalent to that required for the elevator hoistway shaft enclosure.

[BF] 909.21.4 Fan system. The fan system provided for the pressurization system shall be as required by Sections 909.21.4.1 through 909.21.4.4.

❖ This section details the requirements for the mechanical system used for pressurization of the hoistway enclosure.

[BF] 909.21.4.1 Fire resistance. Where located within the building, the fan system that provides the pressurization shall be protected with the same *fire-resistance rating* required for the elevator shaft enclosure.

❖ The only way to ensure that the mechanical pressurization system can operate during a fire is to locate it in a safe place. If located within the building, it must be in an enclosed room protected with the same fire-resistance-rated construction required for the hoistway enclosure.

[BF] 909.21.4.2 Smoke detection. The fan system shall be equipped with a smoke detector that will automatically shut down the fan system when smoke is detected within the system.

❖ The airflow must be free of smoke or it will only increase the likelihood of smoke spreading throughout the building. The smoke detector required by this section should be located on the intake side of the blower fan.

[BF] 909.21.4.3 Separate systems. A separate fan system shall be used for each elevator hoistway.

❖ This section requires that each hoistway enclosure have its own mechanical system. This provides a more redundant system and helps to increase the likelihood that fans will be operational during a fire.

[BF] 909.21.4.4 Fan capacity. The supply fan shall be either adjustable with a capacity of not less than 1,000 cfm (0.4719 m^3/s) per door, or that specified by a *registered design professional* to meet the requirements of a designed pressurization system.

❖ The fan capacity should be as specified by the registered design professional to meet the operational ranges of pressure at each door or be adjustable with a capacity of at least 1,000 cfm (0.4719 m^3/s) per hoistway door. In either case, it is subject to field testing and adjustments to meet the pressure ranges.

[BF] 909.21.5 Standby power. The pressurization system shall be provided with standby power in accordance with Section 1203.

❖ The elevator hoistway pressurization system is an emergency system and must have provisions for standby power like other emergency systems. Section 2702 of the IBC states the requirements that standby power systems must meet. It is consistent with other smoke control systems required by Section 909 in that such systems have standby power as they are life safety systems.

[BF] 909.21.6 Activation of pressurization system. The elevator pressurization system shall be activated upon activation of either the building fire alarm system or the elevator lobby smoke detectors. Where both a building fire alarm system and elevator lobby smoke detectors are present, each shall be independently capable of activating the pressurization system.

❖ This section requires that the pressurization system will be activated when the general building fire alarm system or an elevator lobby smoke detector is activated. All buildings using this pressurization option will more than likely be required to have both. High-rise buildings require elevator lobby smoke detectors, but other buildings may not. Section 909.12 requires smoke detectors to activate the pressurization system if the design requires it to operate to remove the smoke.

[BF] 909.21.7 Testing. Testing for performance shall be required in accordance with Section 909.18.8. System acceptance shall be in accordance with Section 909.19.

❖ Testing will be required to evaluate the performance of the completed system (see commentary, Sections 909.18 and 909.19).

[BF] 909.21.8 Marking and identification. Detection and control systems shall be marked in accordance with Section 909.14.

❖ See the commentary to Section 909.14.

[BF] 909.21.9 Control diagrams. Control diagrams shall be provided in accordance with Section 909.15.

❖ See the commentary to Section 909.15.

[BF] 909.21.10 Control panel. A control panel complying with Section 909.16 shall be provided.

❖ See the commentary to Section 909.16.

[BF] 909.21.11 System response time. Hoistway pressurization systems shall comply with the requirements for smoke control system response time in Section 909.17.

❖ See the commentary to Section 909.17.

SECTION 910 SMOKE AND HEAT REMOVAL

910.1 General. Where required by this code, smoke and heat vents or mechanical smoke removal systems shall conform to the requirements of this section.

❖ This section essentially requires either smoke and heat vents or a mechanical smoke removal system where required by Section 910.2. It should be noted that where high-piled combustible storage is involved, Chapter 32 also applies.

The purpose of smoke and heat vents or smoke removal systems has historically been related to the needs of fire fighters. More specifically, smoke and heat vents or smoke removal systems, when activated, have the potential effect of lifting the height of the smoke layer and providing more tenable conditions to undertake fire-fighting activities. Other potential benefits include a reduction in property damage and the creation of more tenable conditions for occupants.

These provisions are based on research on the interaction of sprinklers, roof vents and draft curtains funded by the National Fire Protection Research Foundation (NFPRF) and conducted at Underwriters Laboratories (UL) in 1997/1998. This research is summarized in a document referred to as *National Institute of Science and Technology Interagency Report* (NISTIR) 6196-1 dated September 1998. The current provisions were also based on the following:

- Provisions for the use of roof vents in sprinklered buildings included in the 2010 and 2013 editions of NFPA 13, including the substantiation statement for the NFPA 13 roof vent provisions.
- The capability of standard spray sprinklers to both control and extinguish a fire within 30 minutes of sprinkler operation without supplemental fire department activity has been documented.
- Recommendations contained in National Institute for Occupational Safety and Health (NIOSH) 2005-132, *Preventing Injuries and Deaths of Fire Fighters Due to Truss Systems*, and NIOSH 2010-153, *Preventing Deaths and Injuries of Fire Fighters Using Risk Management Principles at Structure Fires*.
- Recommendations contained in the Initial Report of the Federal Emergency Management Agency (FEMA)/National Fallen Firefighters Foundation (NFFF®) Firefighter Life Safety Summit held on April 14, 2004, in Tampa, Florida.

The primary purpose of smoke and heat removal from the perspective of the building code requirement is to assist fire-fighting operations after control of the fire has been achieved by the automatic sprinkler system. Automatic smoke and heat vents and automatic sprinkler systems were developed independently of one another and their interaction has been a concern for many years. Even today, there is no accepted method of analyzing their interaction and, therefore, the installation standards for each (NFPA 204 and NFPA 13, respectively) give cautions to the designers of buildings having both systems. Note that NFPA 204 is not referenced in Section 910.

Manually activated mechanical smoke removal systems can perform the same function as roof vents. Mechanical smoke removal systems as required in Section 910 provide fire-rated, grade-level enclosures for the control of the mechanical smoke removal system. This provides greater control of the system for the fire incident commander and reduces the need to place fire fighters on roofs or in other hazardous situations to operate smoke and heat venting systems. This methodology is consistent with the latest recommendations from NIOSH and NFFF for fire fighter safety, risk management and recommended fire-fighting tactics.

910.2 Where required. Smoke and heat vents or a mechanical smoke removal system shall be installed as required by Sections 910.2.1 and 910.2.2.

Exceptions:

1. Frozen food warehouses used solely for storage of Class I and II commodities where protected by an *approved automatic sprinkler system*.

2. Smoke and heat removal shall not be required in areas of buildings equipped with early suppression fast-response (ESFR) sprinklers.

3. Smoke and heat removal shall not be required in areas of buildings equipped with control mode special application sprinklers with a response time index of 50 $(m \cdot s)^{1/2}$ or less that are listed to control a fire in stored commodities with 12 or fewer sprinklers.

❖ Sections 910.2.1 and 910.2.2 provide the locations where such smoke removal or smoke and heat vents would be required. There are three overall exceptions to the application of Section 910.

Exception 1 recognizes the "building-within-a-building" nature of typical frozen food warehouses. As such, smoke from a fire within a freezer would be contained within the freezer, thus negating the usefulness of smoke and heat vents at the roof level.

Exception 2 recognizes the negative effect that smoke and heat vents can have on the operation of early suppression fast-response (ESFR) sprinklers. Those negative effects include diverting heat away from the sprinklers, which could delay their activation or result in the activation of more sprinklers in areas away from the source of the fire, which may overwhelm the system.

Exception 3 recognizes a new category of automatic sprinkler that shares the key characteristics of ESFR sprinklers, i.e., thermal elements that have a response time index (RTI) of 50 or less and are listed to protect a design area that involves 12 or fewer sprinklers. These control mode special application (CMSA) sprinklers, while not called ESFR, still require similar precautions to ESFR sprinklers with respect to not introducing unknowns, such as smoke and heat removal, that were not present in the full-scale fire tests that determined their listing parameters. Such unknowns can lead to sprinkler "skipping" and exceeding the 12 sprinkler design area, which was the exact concern that led to the ESFR-related provisions that are currently in this chapter and Chapter 32. Note that CMSA sprinklers must have both an RTI of 50 or less and be listed to control or suppress a fire with 12 or fewer sprinklers to qualify for this exception. Any sprinkler listed as "quick response" will satisfy the "50 RTI or less" criterion based on the definition of "quick response" in NFPA 13 Section 3.6.4.7. The number of operating sprinklers will be indicated in the listing criterion for each sprinkler.

910.2.1 Group F-1 or S-1. Smoke and heat vents installed in accordance with Section 910.3 or a mechanical smoke removal system installed in accordance with Section 910.4 shall be installed in buildings and portions thereof used as a Group F-1 or S-1 occupancy having more than 50,000 square feet (4645 m^2) of undivided area. In occupied portions of a building equipped throughout with an *automatic sprinkler system* in accordance with Section 903.3.1.1, where the upper surface of the story is not a roof assembly, a mechanical smoke removal system in accordance with Section 910.4 shall be installed.

Exception: Group S-1 aircraft repair hangars.

❖ Large-area buildings with moderate to heavy fire loads present special challenges to the fire department in disposing of the smoke generated in a fire. In order to provide the fire department with the ability to rapidly and efficiently dispose of smoke in large-area Group F-1 and S-1 buildings exceeding 50,000 square feet (4645 m2) in undivided area without exposing personnel to the dangers associated with cutting ventilation holes in the roof, smoke and heat vents or a smoke removal system must be provided. The code is not clear on what is meant by the term "undivided area." However, the intent is to provide the ability to manage the smoke in large spaces. Draft curtains or potentially any physical separation (regardless of rating) would provide such division. Draft curtains are typically constructed of sheet metal, lath and plaster, gypsum board or other materials that resist the passage of smoke. Typically draft curtains are at least 6 feet deep (1829 mm) from the ceiling. In keeping with the concern for managing smoke, the joints and connections should be smoke tight.

Based on the intent of "undivided area," a fire barrier, smoke barrier, fire partition or smoke partition would be more than what is required and would therefore be an acceptable method of dividing the area.

This requirement is independent of the requirements related to high-piled storage in Section 910.2.2. High-piled combustible storage is not occupancy specific.

This section also addresses multiple-story buildings where the Group F-1 or S-1 occupancy is not the uppermost story and therefore would not have a roof in which to place smoke and heat vents. This section would require that a smoke removal system be installed.

910.2.2 High-piled combustible storage. Smoke and heat removal required by Table 3206.2 for buildings and portions thereof containing high-piled combustible storage shall be installed in accordance with Section 910.3 in unsprinklered buildings. In buildings and portions thereof containing high-piled combustible storage equipped throughout with an *automatic sprinkler system* in accordance with Section 903.3.1.1, a smoke and heat removal system shall be installed in accordance with Section 910.3 or 910.4. In occupied portions of a building equipped throughout with an *automatic sprinkler system* in accordance with Section 903.3.1.1 where the upper surface of the story is not a roof assembly, a mechanical smoke removal system in accordance with Section 910.4 shall be installed.

❖ This section requires smoke and heat removal as it is required in Chapter 32 for high-piled combustible storage. Specifically Table 3206.2 sets out when smoke and heat removal is required. If Table 3206.2 does not require such protection, compliance with

Section 910 is not necessary. The requirement in Table 3206.2 is based primarily on the size of the high-piled combustible storage area and whether the area is equipped with an automatic sprinkler system.

There are several requirements provided within this section. The first addresses nonsprinklered high-piled storage areas. Such areas are required to use smoke and heat vents as mechanical smoke removal systems are designed for use in sprinklered buildings. The rationale for this provision is that a mechanical smoke removal system capable of handling temperatures between 1,000°F and 2,000°F cannot be practically provided at a reasonable cost.

Where high-piled storage areas are equipped with an automatic sprinkler system, smoke and heat vents or a smoke removal system is required to comply with this section. However, if the high-piled storage area is located in a multiple-story building where the storage area is not located on the uppermost story, this section requires that a smoke removal system be used.

910.3 Smoke and heat vents. The design and installation of smoke and heat vents shall be in accordance with Sections 910.3.1 through 910.3.3.

❖ This section simply sets out the subsections that must be addressed to comply with the requirements for the installation of smoke and heat vents.

910.3.1 Listing and labeling. Smoke and heat vents shall be *listed* and labeled to indicate compliance with UL 793 or FM 4430.

❖ This section specifically requires that all smoke and heat vents be both listed and labeled in accordance with UL 793 or FM 4430. This provides consistency and a level of quality where smoke and heat vents are required. The standard addresses smoke and heat vents that automatically operate during fires via nonelectrical means. Automatic vents listed and labeled to this standard can be operated both automatically and manually. There are two main mechanisms for activation that include a heat-responsive device or a plastic cover shrinking and falling out of place because of fire exposure.

910.3.2 Smoke and heat vent locations. Smoke and heat vents shall be located 20 feet (6096 mm) or more from adjacent *lot lines* and *fire walls* and 10 feet (3048 mm) or more from *fire barriers*. Vents shall be uniformly located within the roof in the areas of the building where the vents are required to be installed by Section 910.2, with consideration given to roof pitch, sprinkler location and structural members.

❖ This section has two functions, the first being to focus on hazards to adjacent buildings and the second being proper function of smoke and heat vents through proper placement.

In terms of adjacent properties, this section requires a minimum distance to lot lines and fire walls and then a minimum distance to fire barriers. The first set of distances focuses on separate buildings and exposures, whereas the distance to fire barriers is less restrictive since it focuses on different uses and occupancies within the same building (see Commentary Figure 910.3.2).

To enhance vent performance within the area containing the smoke and heat vents, such vents need to be uniformly spaced. Consideration of issues such as sprinkler location and roof pitch are also essential to proper vent location.

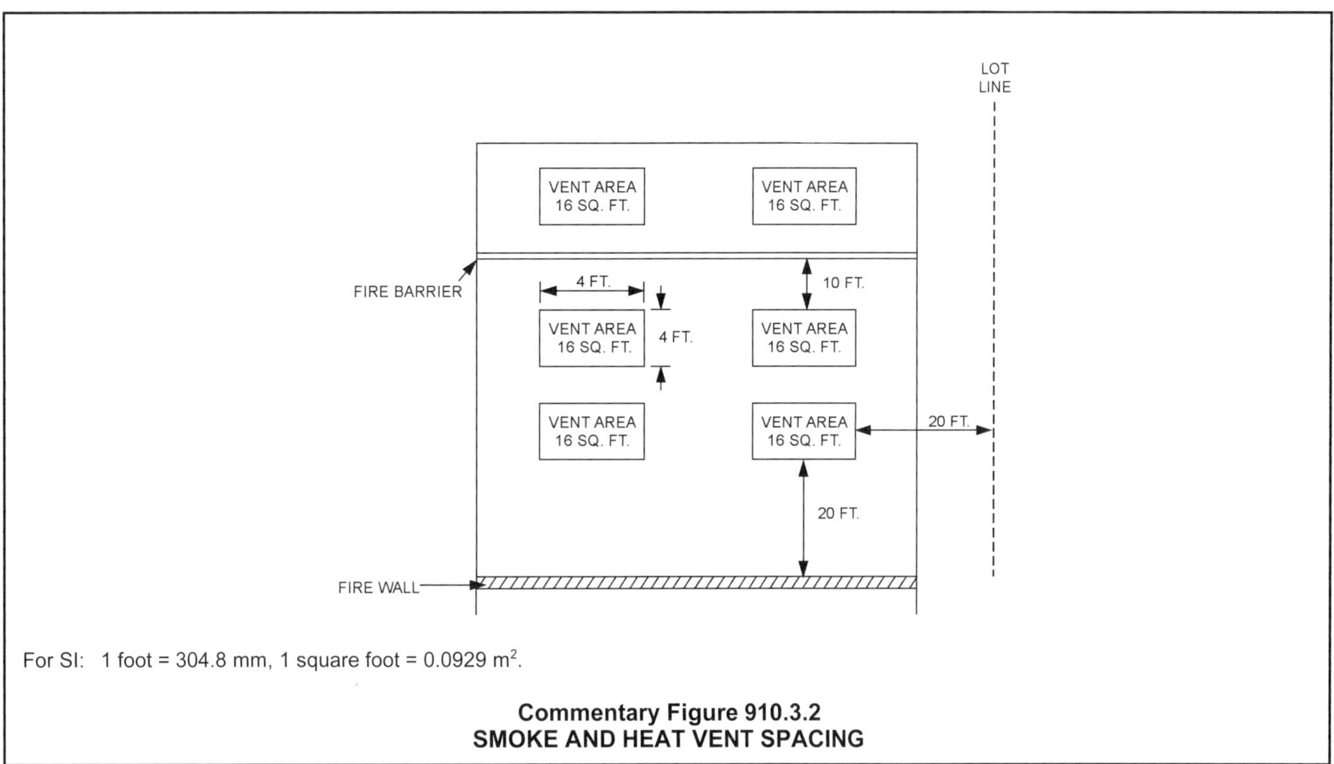

For SI: 1 foot = 304.8 mm, 1 square foot = 0.0929 m^2.

Commentary Figure 910.3.2
SMOKE AND HEAT VENT SPACING

910.3.3 Smoke and heat vents area. The required aggregate area of smoke and heat vents shall be calculated as follows:

For buildings equipped throughout with an *automatic sprinkler system* in accordance with Section 903.3.1.1:

$A_{VR} = V/9000$ **(Equation 9-3)**

where:

A_{VR} = The required aggregate vent area (ft^2).

V = Volume (ft^3) of the area that requires smoke removal.

For unsprinklered buildings:

$A_{VR} = A_{FA}/50$ **(Equation 9-4)**

where:

A_{VR} = The required aggregate vent area (ft^2).

A_{FA} = The area of the floor in the area that requires smoke removal.

❖ This section provides the design criteria to determine the required area of smoke and heat vents. The requirements are based on whether the area requiring smoke and heat vents is equipped with an automatic sprinkler system.

The design of roof vents in buildings protected by an automatic sprinkler system require that the area of roof vents provide equivalent venting to that required for the mechanical smoke removal system (two air changes per hour) based on an assumption that each square foot of vent area will provide 300 cubic feet per minute (cfm) of ventilation. The reason for this requirement is that the roof vents should at least provide venting equivalent to the minimum venting provided by the mechanical smoke removal system. A factor of 300 cfm of venting per square foot of vent area was included in the 2012 edition of the code, although the use of this conversion factor is questionable at best. The actual ventilation provided by each square foot of vent area will depend on the temperature differential between ambient conditions and the smoke layer under the roof deck or the pressure achieved if positive pressure ventilation is utilized. If the prescribed value is not practical for a given building design, designers have the option of demonstrating other values that provide the same performance under Section 104.11 of the code, which allows alternative methods and designs.

The design of roof vents in buildings not protected by a sprinkler system requires that the ratio of the area of the vents to the floor area be a minimum of 1:50. The rationale is that the case where roof vents will be provided without sprinkler protection will be rare (e.g., buildings that contain high-piled storage with an area between 2,500 and 12,000 square feet). Given that this situation will be rare, a complex analysis to determine the required area of roof vents was believed to be unnecessary. The ratio of vent area to floor area of 1:50 is conservative based on the requirements that were included in the 2012 IBC and the code.

910.4 Mechanical smoke removal systems. Mechanical smoke removal systems shall be designed and installed in accordance with Sections 910.4.1 through 910.4.7.

❖ Mechanical smoke removal systems are considered to be equivalent to smoke and heat vents in terms of code compliance. In multiple-story buildings, those areas requiring smoke and heat removal will require the use of a mechanical smoke removal system because of its location on stories other than the uppermost story. This section provides the various design requirements for such systems.

910.4.1 Automatic sprinklers required. The building shall be equipped throughout with an approved *automatic sprinkler system* in accordance with Section 903.3.1.1.

❖ The rationale for this provision is that a mechanical smoke removal system capable of handling temperatures between 1,000°F and 2,000°F cannot be practically provided at a reasonable cost. Therefore, in order to allow the use of a mechanical smoke removal system, the building is required to be equipped throughout with an automatic sprinkler system.

910.4.2 Exhaust fan construction. Exhaust fans that are part of a mechanical smoke removal system shall be rated for operation at 221°F (105°C). Exhaust fan motors shall be located outside of the exhaust fan air stream.

❖ This section requires exhaust fan motors to be located out of the exhaust stream to protect the mechanical equipment from excessive heat. Provisions for the mechanical smoke removal system permit the system to be designed to handle air at ambient temperature provided that the fan motors are located outside the air stream. The basis for this provision is the thermocouple temperature data for the large-scale fire tests conducted at UL in 1997/1998, specifically Tests P-1 and P-4. (In Tests P-1 and P-4, no vents opened so the ceiling temperatures recorded would be unaffected by the activation of vents. See pages 40 and 52 of the NISTIR 6196-1 report dated September 1998 for the thermocouple temperature data recorded as a function of time.)

The exposing temperatures and time periods were reviewed and not considered to pose a threat to the building structure, fans or power wiring.

The sprinkler activation times and ceiling temperature data for the five large-scale fire tests summarized in NISTIR 6196-1 indicate that the exposure of mechanical exhaust fans and ducts located at the ceiling to high temperatures will be relatively short. Since it is anticipated that the exhaust system will only be activated after the arrival of fire fighters at the scene (estimated to be 7 minutes or longer after ignition), ceiling temperatures should be reduced sufficiently to allow fans rated for only ambient temperatures to be used for the exhaust system.

910.4.3 System design criteria. The mechanical smoke removal system shall be sized to exhaust the building at a minimum rate of two air changes per hour based on the volume of the building or portion thereof without contents. The capacity of each exhaust fan shall not exceed 30,000 cubic feet per minute (14.2 m^3/s).

❖ Sections 910.4.3 and 910.4.3.1 specify the design requirements for the minimum number of air changes, maximum fan capacity, and the provision of makeup air.

These provisions require that the mechanical smoke removal system be sized to provide a minimum exhaust rate of two air changes per hour based on the enclosed volume of the building space to be exhausted, without any deductions for the space occupied by storage or equipment. An exhaust rate of two air changes per hour is based on an analysis assuming a conservative approach using a Factory Mutual Research Corporation Standard Plastic Commodity (polystyrene cups in compartmented cartons). This commodity is recognized to represent a severe fire hazard of high-density plastics.

In a calculation based on this commodity, a maximum of 68,960 cfm of smoke was generated by the design fire. Based on an empty building volume of 2.659 million cubic feet, the exhaust rate required to achieve two air changes per hour is 88,633 cfm. Because no single fan can exceed 30,000 cfm, this building required five fans, each exhausting 25,570 cfm for a total of 127,850 cfm. This exceeds the minimum two air changes per hour by more than 40 percent. Even at the minimum required rate of two air changes per hour, the calculation results show that the mechanical smoke removal system will be capable of removing the smoke from the building faster than it will be generated, ultimately removing smoke from the building.

910.4.3.1 Makeup air. Makeup air openings shall be provided within 6 feet (1829 mm) of the floor level. Operation of makeup air openings shall be manual or automatic. The minimum gross area of makeup air inlets shall be 8 square feet per 1,000 cubic feet per minute (0.74 m^2 per 0.4719 m^3/s) of smoke exhaust.

❖ In order for a mechanical smoke removal system to work properly, makeup air at the proper location and volume needs to be provided. Generally, makeup air inlets need to be located much lower than where the smoke is exhausted to get the proper movement of air. In this case, the required location is within 6 feet of the floor.

The derivation of the gross vent area is based on NFPA 92-2012. Specifically, Annex Section A-4.4.4.1.4 states that the maximum air velocity through the makeup air inlet is 1 m/sec or 200 ft/min. This is the same limitation found in Section 909.7.1, which is for the airflow method of smoke control. The area requirement is then derived as follows:

- Effective Vent Area = (1,000 ft^3/min)/(200 ft/min) = 5 ft^2 per 1,000 cfm
- Assume an orifice coefficient of 0.6
- Gross Vent Area = 5 ft^2/(0.6) = 8.33 ft^2 per 1,000 cfm, which is rounded down because of the conservative nature of the requirement

The reason for this limitation is to prevent significant deflection of the plume, which will cause more air entrainment into the plume and more smoke production. This criterion is conservative as the requirement assumes an active fire and the design philosophy for this requirement is to provide post-fire smoke exhaust.

910.4.4 Activation. The mechanical smoke removal system shall be activated by manual controls only.

❖ This section requires that mechanical systems are to be activated manually so that the fire department is in control of the system. In some situations, automatic operation could cause a fire to grow or spread, opening an excessive number of sprinklers. Automatic operation of the mechanical smoke removal system could also be detrimental to the operation of the sprinkler system in a manner similar to draft curtains. The effect of the automatic mechanical smoke removal system on sprinkler operation would depend on when the system was activated. The sooner the system is automatically activated, the greater the detrimental effect. The fire department will retain the option to shut down the exhaust system.

910.4.5 Manual control location. Manual controls shall be located where they are able to be accessed by the fire service from an exterior door of the building and separated from the remainder of the building by not less than 1-hour *fire barriers* constructed in accordance with Section 707 of the *International Building Code* or *horizontal assemblies* constructed in accordance with Section 711 of the *International Building Code*, or both.

❖ This section establishes the required placement, access and protection of the manual controls to ensure that fire fighters will have quick and protected access to them.

910.4.6 Control wiring. Wiring for operation and control of mechanical smoke removal systems shall be connected ahead of the main disconnect in accordance with Section 701.12E of NFPA 70 and be protected against interior fire exposure to temperatures in excess of 1,000°F (538°C) for a period of not less than 15 minutes.

❖ Unless the mechanical smoke removal system also functions as a component of a smoke control system, standby power is not specifically required (see commentary, Section 909.11 and IBC Section 2702). In order to provide an enhanced level of operational reliability, this section requires that the power supply to smoke exhaust fans must be provided from a circuit connected on the supply side (i.e., ahead) of the building's main electrical service disconnecting means. Note that this is one of the sources of standby power recognized by NFPA 70, Section 701.12(E). Such a circuit connected "ahead of the main" must still have its own approved overcurrent protection.

The provisions for the design of a mechanical smoke removal system indicate that wiring providing power to exhaust fans located in the interior of the building is to be protected by materials that will provide a 15-minute finish rating protection. The ceiling temperature data collected in the five large-scale fire tests summarized in NISTIR 6196-1 (cited earlier) show that temperatures at the ceiling will be far less than the exposure temperatures defined by the ASTM E119 time-temperature curve and that the ceiling temperatures will rapidly decrease once sprinklers activate. The ceiling temperature data included in NISTIR 6196-1 indicate that providing a 15-minute finish rating protection for the interior electrical power supply is more than adequate to prevent damage to the power supply wiring for the exhaust system.

910.4.7 Controls. Where building air-handling and mechanical smoke removal systems are combined or where independent building air-handling systems are provided, fans shall automatically shut down in accordance with the *International Mechanical Code*. The manual controls provided for the smoke removal system shall have the capability to override the automatic shutdown of fans that are part of the smoke removal system.

❖ This section requires that if a mechanical smoke removal system is integrated with a standard HVAC system, then the system must shut down upon detection of smoke as required by the IMC. This relates to the requirement in Section 910.4.4 that mechanical smoke removal systems shall be manually operated only.

The concern is that HVAC systems should not work against the intended operation of the smoke exhaust system. In some cases, the system may be a combination system where shutdown is not necessary or appropriate. It really depends on how the smoke exhaust system has been designed.

910.5 Maintenance and testing. Maintenance and testing of smoke and heat vents and mechanical smoke removal systems shall be in accordance with Sections 910.5.1 and 910.5.2. A written record of inspection, testing and maintenance that includes the date, identification of personnel involved, any unsatisfactory result, corrective action taken and replaced parts shall be maintained on the premises.

❖ Routine maintenance and testing of smoke removal systems is essential to ensure their performance, as designed, under fire conditions. Maintenance practices for these systems must be consistent with their design and any manufacturer's recommendations and as indicated in Section 910.5.1 or 910.5.2.

910.5.1 Smoke and heat vents. Smoke and heat vents shall be maintained in an operative condition. Inspection, testing and maintenance shall be in accordance with NFPA 204 except as follows:

1. Mechanically operated smoke and heat vents shall be inspected annually and operationally tested not less than every 5 years.
2. Gravity dropout smoke and heat vents shall be inspected annually.
3. Fused, damaged or painted fusible links shall be replaced.

❖ This section requires smoke and heat vents to be maintained in operating condition and incorporates NFPA 204 as the referenced standard for the maintenance of smoke and heat vents (see Section 901.6.1). Routine inspection, testing and maintenance of these devices are essential since they are typically only found in the largest commercial structures, and the amount of fire loading is usually very high (i.e., high-piled combustible storage). Ensuring that these devices are inspected, tested and maintained in proper working order by the building's owner also has positive effects on fire-fighter safety. These benefits include:

- Easy identification of the location of the fire within the structure.
- Release of excess heat within the structure.
- Decreasing fire severity.
- Increased visibility for fire fighters within the structure.
- Reduction of toxic products of combustion within the structure.

Additionally, the maintenance of these devices will have a mitigating effect on damage to the structure and/or its contents should a fire occur. These benefits include decreased likelihood of structural failure from heat retained within the structure and reduced damage to the structure and stored materials from smoke.

The sensing elements of fusible link devices installed as part of smoke and heat vents must be routinely visually inspected and replaced as needed to increase the likelihood that the vents will operate in a timely fashion when needed.

910.5.2 Mechanical smoke removal systems. Mechanical smoke removal systems shall be maintained in accordance with NFPA 204 and the equipment manufacturer's instructions except as follows:

1. Systems shall be inspected and operationally tested annually.
2. Testing shall include the operation of all system components, controls and ancillary equipment, such as makeup air openings.

3. A written schedule for routine maintenance and operational testing shall be established and testing shall be conducted in accordance with the schedule.

❖ This section references NFPA 204 with the exception of the three listed requirements. These have been added because it was determined that the maintenance requirements in NFPA 204 were not specific enough to ensure the necessary maintenance of the mechanical smoke removal systems.

Annual operational exercising of the entire mechanical smoke removal system must be performed to verify that it still operates as required by the approved design.

Because mechanical smoke removal systems are designed for smoke removal only, the operation of these systems does not adversely affect other building systems or operations. The control sequence for these systems must be included in the annual operational test to check for system component failures that may not get noticed because mechanical smoke removal systems are independent of building HVAC systems and operate only in emergency situations.

Routine operational testing and maintenance must be performed on the mechanical smoke removal system periodically to verify that it still operates as required by the approved design. A written schedule must be established and maintained.

This section prescribes the desired content of the written record for the mechanical smoke removal system testing and maintenance program. Test results and maintenance activities should be clearly documented. The written record should be available for inspection and reviewed by the fire code official.

SECTION 911
EXPLOSION CONTROL

911.1 General. Explosion control shall be provided in the following locations:

1. Where a structure, room or space is occupied for purposes involving explosion hazards as identified in Table 911.1.
2. Where quantities of hazardous materials specified in Table 911.1 exceed the maximum allowable quantities in Table 5003.1.1(1).

Such areas shall be provided with explosion (*deflagration*) venting, explosion (*deflagration*) prevention systems or *barricades* in accordance with this section and NFPA 69, or NFPA 495 as applicable. *Deflagration* venting shall not be utilized as a means to protect buildings from *detonation* hazards.

❖ It is usually impractical to design a building to withstand the pressure created by an explosion. Therefore, this section requires an explosion relief system for structures, rooms or spaces with occupancies involving explosion hazards. Explosions may result from the overpressurization of a containing structure, by physical/chemical means or by a chemical reaction. During an explosion, a sudden release of a high-pressure gas occurs and the energy is dissipated in the form of a shock wave.

Structures, rooms or spaces with occupancies involving explosion hazards must be equipped with some method of explosion control as required by the material-specific requirements in the code. Table 911.1 also specifies where explosion control is required based on certain materials or occupancies where the quantities of hazardous materials involved exceed the maximum allowable quantities in Table 5003.1.1(1). Section 911 recognizes explosion (deflagration) venting and explosion (deflagration) prevention systems as acceptable methods of explosion control, where appropriate. The use of barricades or other explosion protective devices, such as magazines, may be permitted as the means of explosion control where indicated in the code as an acceptable alternative and where approved by the fire code official.

TABLE 911.1. See page 9-136.

❖ This table designates where some methods of explosion control are required for specific material or special use conditions. This table applies where the quantities of hazardous materials involved exceed the maximum allowable quantities in Table 5003.1.1(1). Section 911.2 contains design criteria for explosion (deflagration) venting. Explosion prevention (suppression) systems, where used, must comply with NFPA 69. Barricade construction must be designed and installed to comply with NFPA 495. Chapters 50 through 67 of the code contain additional guidance on the applicability and design criteria for explosion control methods that depend on the specific type of hazardous material involved.

911.2 Required deflagration venting. Areas that are required to be provided with *deflagration* venting shall comply with the following:

1. Walls, ceilings and roofs exposing surrounding areas shall be designed to resist a minimum internal pressure of 100 pounds per square foot (psf) (4788 Pa). The minimum internal design pressure shall be not less than five times the maximum internal relief pressure specified in Item 5 of this section.
2. *Deflagration* venting shall be provided only in exterior walls and roofs.

   Exception: Where sufficient *exterior wall* and roof venting cannot be provided because of inadequate exterior wall or roof area, *deflagration* venting shall be allowed by specially designed shafts vented to the exterior of the building.
3. *Deflagration* venting shall be designed to prevent unacceptable structural damage. Where relieving a *deflagration*, vent closures shall not produce projectiles of

sufficient velocity and mass to cause life threatening injuries to the occupants or other persons on the property or adjacent *public ways*.

4. The aggregate clear area of vents and venting devices shall be governed by the pressure resistance of the construction assemblies specified in Item 1 of this section and the maximum internal pressure allowed by Item 5 of this section.
5. Vents shall be designed to withstand loads in accordance with the *International Building Code*. Vents shall consist of any one or any combination of the following to relieve at a maximum internal pressure of 20 pounds per square foot (958 Pa), but not less than the loads required by the *International Building Code*:
   - 5.1. *Exterior walls* designed to release outward.
   - 5.2. Hatch covers.
   - 5.3. Outward swinging doors.
   - 5.4. Roofs designed to uplift.
   - 5.5. Venting devices *listed* for the purpose.
6. Vents designed to release from the *exterior walls* or roofs of the building when venting a *deflagration* shall discharge directly to the exterior of the building where an unoccupied space not less than 50 feet (15 240 mm) in width is provided between the exterior walls of the building and the lot line.

   Exception: Vents complying with Item 7 of this section.
7. Vents designed to remain attached to the building when venting a *deflagration* shall be so located that the discharge opening shall be not less than 10 feet (3048 mm) vertically from window openings and *exits* in the building and 20 feet (6096 mm) horizontally from *exits* in the building, from window openings and *exits* in adjacent buildings on the same lot and from the lot line.

TABLE 911.1
EXPLOSION CONTROL REQUIREMENTS[f]

MATERIAL	CLASS	EXPLOSION CONTROL METHODS	
		Barricade construction	Explosion (deflagration) venting or explosion (deflagration) prevention systems
Hazard Category			
Combustible dusts[a]	—	Not required	Required
Cryogenic fluids	Flammable	Not required	Required
Explosives	Division 1.1 Division 1.2 Division 1.3 Division 1.4 Division 1.5 Division 1.6	Required Required Not required Not required Required Required	Not required Not required Required Required Not required Not required
Flammable gas	Gaseous Liquefied	Not required Not required	Required Required
Flammable liquids	IA[b] IB[c]	Not required Not required	Required Required
Organic peroxides	Unclassified detonable I	Required Required	Not permitted Not permitted
Oxidizer liquids and solids	4	Required	Not permitted
Pyrophoric	Gases	Not required	Required
Unstable (reactive)	4 3 detonable 3 nondetonable	Required Required Not required	Not permitted Not permitted Required
Water-reactive liquids and solids	3 2[e]	Not required Not required	Required Required
Special Uses			
Acetylene generator rooms	—	Not required	Required
Grain processing	—	Not required	Required
Liquefied petroleum gas distribution facilities	—	Not required	Required
Where explosion hazards exist[d]	Detonation Deflagration	Required Not required	Not permitted Required

a. Combustible dusts that are generated during manufacturing or processing. See definition of "Combustible dust" in Chapter 2.

b. Storage or use.

c. In open use or dispensing.

d. Rooms containing dispensing and use of hazardous materials where an explosive environment can occur because of the characteristics or nature of the hazardous materials or as a result of the dispensing or use process.

e. A method of explosion control shall be provided where Class 2 water-reactive materials can form potentially explosive mixtures.

f. Explosion venting is not required for Group H-5 Fabrication Areas complying with Chapter 27 and the *International Building Code*.

8. Discharge from vents shall not be into the interior of the building.

❖ This section prescribes the basic design criteria necessary for deflagration venting.

Deflagration venting limits the deflagration pressure in a certain area so that, in case of an explosion, the damage to that enclosed area is minimized or eliminated. Because there are so many variables involved for adequate deflagration venting, the parameters for each design should fit the individual situation. NFPA 68 contains additional guidance on the design and use of deflagration venting systems.

The area of the vent must be adequate to relieve the pressure before it reaches a level in excess of what can be withstood by the weakest building member. The vent area, therefore, is dependent on the actual construction of the enclosed area and the anticipated pressure. The vent panel should be of lightweight construction so that it can easily release at low pressures. Because the lightweight panels have little structural strength, railings may be required along the floor edge to prevent people or objects from falling against the panel.

Item 5 indicates that the vents are to be designed to relieve at a maximum internal pressure of 20 pounds per square foot (psf) (958 Pa), but not less than the load design requirements in Chapter 16 of the IBC. In areas commonly subject to high winds, the release pressure has to be increased accordingly to prevent the vents from being actuated by wind forces. Even though the release pressure should be as low as practical, it must always be higher than the external wind pressure.

Venting devices must be located to discharge directly to the open air or to an unoccupied space at least 50 feet (15 240 mm) in width on the same lot. To minimize damage and maintain the integrity of the existing system, window openings and egress facilities are not to be within 10 feet (3048 mm) vertically or 20 feet (6096 mm) horizontally of the vent. The spatial distance will permit the pressure to decrease and to not cause additional damage.

911.3 Explosion prevention systems. Explosion prevention systems shall be of an *approved* type and installed in accordance with the provisions of this code and NFPA 69.

❖ Depending on the conditions of the anticipated explosion hazard, the use of an explosion prevention system may be an effective means of explosion control. An explosion prevention system is most effective in confined spaces or enclosures in which combustible gases, mists or dusts are subject to deflagration in a gas-phase oxidant. Explosion prevention systems are intended to prevent an explosion hazard by combating the process of combustion in its incipient stage.

NFPA 69 contains further information on the installation, operation and design considerations for explosion prevention systems. Explosion prevention systems are commonly used to protect laboratory equipment, such as reactor vessels, mills and dust collectors.

911.4 Barricades. *Barricades* shall be designed and installed in accordance with NFPA 495.

❖ As indicated in Table 911.1, depending on the type of materials involved, barricade construction may be an acceptable method of explosion control. Barricade construction is an effective method of screening a building containing explosives from other buildings, magazines or public rights-of-way. The barricade could be either natural or artificial, where applicable, as specified in NFPA 495.

SECTION 912
FIRE DEPARTMENT CONNECTIONS

912.1 Installation. Fire department connections shall be installed in accordance with the NFPA standard applicable to the system design and shall comply with Sections 912.2 through 912.7.

❖ An FDC is required as part of a water-based suppression system as the auxiliary water supply. These connections give the fire department the capability of supplying the necessary water to the automatic sprinkler or standpipe system at a sufficient pressure. The FDC also serves as an alternative source of water should a valve in the primary water supply be closed. A fire department connection does not, however, constitute an automatic water source. See Commentary Figure 903.3.1.1 for a typical FDC arrangement on a wet-pipe sprinkler system.

The requirements for the FDC depend on the type of sprinkler system installed and whether a standpipe system is installed. NFPA 13 and 13R, for example, include design considerations for FDCs that are an auxiliary water supply source for automatic sprinkler systems; NFPA 14 is the design standard to use for FDCs serving standpipe systems. Threads for FDCs to sprinkler systems, standpipes, yard hydrants or any other fire hose connection must be approved (NFPA 1963 may be utilized as part of the approval or as otherwise approved) and be compatible with the connections used by the local fire department (see commentary, Sections 903.3.6 and 905.1).

912.2 Location. With respect to hydrants, driveways, buildings and landscaping, fire department connections shall be so located that fire apparatus and hose connected to supply the system will not obstruct access to the buildings for other fire apparatus. The location of fire department connections shall be *approved* by the *fire code official*.

❖ This section specifies that the FDC must be located so that vehicles and hose lines will not interfere with access to the building for the use of other fire department apparatus. The location of potential connected hose lines to the FDC and hydrants must be preplanned with the fire department. Many fire departments have a policy restricting the distance that a FDC may be from a fire hydrant. Some also have policies that indicate the maximum distance from the nearest point of fire department vehicle access (often, the curb). Since fireground operations are based on local operational procedures, it is only reasonable that the fire chief of the jurisdiction have approval authority over the location of and access to the FDC.

Landscaping can also be a hindrance to fire department operations. Even where the FDC is visible, the extensive use of landscaping may make access difficult. Landscaping also changes over time. What may not have been an obstruction when it was planted can sometimes grow into an obstruction over time.

912.2.1 Visible location. Fire department connections shall be located on the street side of buildings or facing *approved* fire apparatus access roads, fully visible and recognizable from the street, fire apparatus access road or nearest point of fire department vehicle access or as otherwise *approved* by the *fire code official*.

❖ FDCs must be readily visible and easily accessed. A local policy constituting what is readily visible and accessible needs to be established. While the intent is clearly understandable, its application can vary widely. A precise policy is the best way to avoid ambiguous directives that result in inconsistent and arbitrary enforcement. Usually, the policy will address issues such as location on the outside of the building and proximity to fire hydrants.

Landscaping is often used to hide the FDCs from the public. This can greatly hamper the efforts of the fire department in staging operations and supplying water to the fire protection systems. Landscaping must be designed so that it does not obstruct the visibility of the FDC. Since fireground operations are based on local operational procedures, it is only reasonable that the fire chief of the jurisdiction have final approval authority over the visibility of and access to the FDC.

912.2.2 Existing buildings. On existing buildings, wherever the fire department connection is not visible to approaching fire apparatus, the fire department connection shall be indicated by an *approved* sign mounted on the street front or on the side of the building. Such sign shall have the letters "FDC" not less than 6 inches (152 mm) high and words in letters not less than 2 inches (51 mm) high or an arrow to indicate the location. Such signs shall be subject to the approval of the *fire code official*.

❖ The section acknowledges that FDCs on existing buildings may not always be readily visible from the street or nearest point of fire department vehicle access. In those instances, the location of the connection must be clearly marked with signage. The FDC may be located on the side of the building or in an alley, not visible to arriving fire-fighting forces. A sign is necessary so that those driving the arriving apparatus know where to maneuver the vehicle to get close to the FDC.

912.3 Fire hose threads. Fire hose threads used in connection with standpipe systems shall be *approved* and shall be compatible with fire department hose threads.

❖ There are several sections in the code that contain requirements for fire department connections. This section simply correlates with those requirements by further clarifying that fire hose threads for standpipe systems must be approved.

912.4 Access. Immediate access to fire department connections shall be maintained at all times and without obstruction by fences, bushes, trees, walls or any other fixed or moveable object. Access to fire department connections shall be *approved* by the *fire code official*.

Exception: Fences, where provided with an access gate equipped with a sign complying with the legend requirements of Section 912.5 and a means of emergency operation. The gate and the means of emergency operation shall be *approved* by the *fire code official* and maintained operational at all times.

❖ The FDC must be readily accessible to fire fighters and allow fire-fighting personnel an adequate area to maneuver a hose for the connection. Landscaping design must not block a clear view of the FDC from arriving fire department vehicles. Depending on the type of landscaping materials, an active maintenance program may be necessary to maintain ready access over time. This section also recognizes that the obstructing objects regulated here can be either fixed or moveable (such as outdoor furnishings, shopping cart queue areas, etc.). Note that no specific dimension is given as was the case in previous editions of the code. This performance language avoids previous misinterpretations that the code intended to allow obstructions to FDC access as long as they were kept 3 feet (914 mm) away. Since fireground operations are based on local operational procedures, it is only reasonable that the fire chief of the jurisdiction have final approval authority over the access to the FDC.

The exception recognizes the practical fact that sometimes security or other considerations make installation of a fence around a building necessary as long as the fence meets the stated criteria. The sign requirement intends to provide a visual location cue to approaching fire apparatus where the height of the fence may obscure the visibility of the FDC.

912.4.1 Locking fire department connection caps. The *fire code official* is authorized to require locking caps on fire department connections for water-based *fire protection systems* where the responding fire department carries appropriate key wrenches for removal.

❖ This section allows for the FDC caps to be equipped with locks as long as the fire departments that respond to that building or facility have the appropriate key wrenches. This avoids vandalism and affords a more functional FDC when needed. Locking caps, even more so than regular FDC caps, need proper maintenance so that they can be removed when required. Any time that an additional mechanical function is added to something that is exposed to the elements, it must be done with the understanding that the corrosive nature of the elements can place the FDC out of commission if the cap cannot be removed (see Commentary Figure 912.4.1).

Commentary Figure 912.4.1
LOCKING FDC CAPS
(Photo courtesy of Knox Company)

912.4.2 Clear space around connections. A working space of not less than 36 inches (914 mm) in width, 36 inches (914 mm) in depth and 78 inches (1981 mm) in height shall be provided and maintained in front of and to the sides of wall-mounted fire department connections and around the circumference of free-standing fire department connections, except as otherwise required or *approved* by the *fire code official*.

❖ Care must be taken so that fences, utility poles, barricades and other obstructions do not prevent access to and use of FDCs. A clear space of 3 feet (914 mm) must be maintained in front of and to either side of wall-mounted FDCs and around free-standing FDCs to allow easy hose connections to the fitting and efficient use of spanner wrenches and other tools needed by the apparatus engineer.

Though not specifically mentioned in this section, it is also important that FDCs be installed with the hose connections well above adjoining grade to accommodate the free turning of a spanner wrench when connecting hoses to the FDC.

912.4.3 Physical protection. Where fire department connections are subject to impact by a motor vehicle, vehicle impact protection shall be provided in accordance with Section 312.

❖ Section 312 requires vehicle impact protection by placing steel posts filled with concrete around the FDC. Section 312 gives the specifications for the posts.

912.5 Signs. A metal sign with raised letters not less than 1 inch (25 mm) in size shall be mounted on all fire department connections serving automatic sprinklers, standpipes or fire pump connections. Such signs shall read: AUTOMATIC SPRINKLERS or STANDPIPES or TEST CONNECTION or a combination thereof as applicable. Where the fire department connection does not serve the entire building, a sign shall be provided indicating the portions of the building served.

❖ The purpose of the sign is to provide the responding fire fighters with the correct information on which portions of a building are served by the fire department connection. They identify the type of system or zone served by a given FDC. Many buildings include multiple sets of fire department connections that are not interconnected, such as separate connections for the building sprinkler system and the dry standpipe system in open parking structures. Some buildings may have only a partial sprinkler system, such as rehabilitated buildings where a sprinkler system is only installed on certain floors or a building that only has basement sprinklers in accordance with Section 903.2.11.

Signs may also distinguish FDCs from fire pump test headers. Usually, FDCs may be distinguished from fire pump test headers by the types of couplings provided. FDCs are customarily equipped with female couplings, while fire pump test headers usually have separately valved male couplings. Furthermore, fire pump test headers are equipped with one $2^{1}/_{2}$-inch (64 mm) outlet for each 250 gallon per minute (gpm) (16 L/s) of rated capacity.

Raised letters are required so that any repainting or fading of the colors on the sign will not affect its ability to be read. Each letter must be at least 1 inch (25 mm) in height so that the wording is clear. Often the wording may be abbreviated such that "AUTOMATIC SPRINKLERS" reads as "AUTO. SPKR." Existing signs may use language slightly different than that noted in the code. As long as the information is adequately communicated, there should be no reason to require new signage to replace existing ones (see Commentary Figure 912.5).

912.6 Backflow protection. The potable water supply to automatic sprinkler and standpipe systems shall be protected against backflow as required by the *International Plumbing Code*.

❖ Section 608.17.4 of the IPC requires all connections to automatic sprinkler systems and standpipe systems to be equipped with a means to protect the potable water supply. The means of backflow protection can be either a double check-valve assembly or a reduced-pressure-principle backflow preventer. This, in general, assumes an FDC is required. For example, a limited-area sprinkler system off the domestic supply does not necessarily require an FDC and would not require backflow protection.

Commentary Figure 912.5
FIRE DEPARTMENT CONNECTION WITH SIGN

912.7 Inspection, testing and maintenance. Fire department connections shall be periodically inspected, tested and maintained in accordance with NFPA 25. Records of inspection, testing and maintenance shall be maintained.

❖ Because FDCs are components of a water-based extinguishing system, NFPA 25 is applicable. Inspections must determine that connections are unobstructed, well-protected and in good working order. Plugs or covers must be installed to protect threads and pipe openings, and must be easily removed to permit connection of a fire hose.

Caps or plugs must be kept in place whenever the connection is not in use to discourage the insertion of objects into the connection openings. The interior of piping behind connection clappers must be checked for foreign material and obstructions.

Threads must be compatible with local fire service hose couplings and free of burrs, depressions and other flaws. Couplings must spin freely. Clappers, if installed in the pipe openings, must open easily and automatically return to the closed position.

Exposed piping, fittings, valves and couplings must be free of water where subject to freezing. Defects must be corrected without delay. These and other maintenance features are addressed in NFPA 25. This section also requires that written inspection and maintenance records be kept. Such records should indicate the date and time and the name of the person conducting the inspection or maintenance. These records must be maintained by the owner and should be made available to the fire code official for review when requested. This requirement relieves the fire code official of the administrative burden of maintaining test records.

SECTION 913
FIRE PUMPS

913.1 General. Where provided, fire pumps shall be installed in accordance with this section and NFPA 20.

❖ This section contains specific installation requirements for fire pumps supplying water to fire protection systems. Inspection, testing and maintenance requirements comply with NFPA 20 unless noted otherwise. Applicable maintenance standards are also identified.

Fire pumps are installed in sprinkler and standpipe systems to pressurize the water supply for the minimum required sprinkler and standpipe operation. They are considered a design feature or component of the system. Fire pumps can improve only the pressure of the incoming water supply, not the volume of water available.

Where the volume from a water supply is not adequate to supply sprinkler or standpipe demand, water tanks for private fire protection, improvements in the size and capacity of fire mains or water distribution systems, or all of these for the installation of a fire pump are needed.

Where fire pumps are required to meet the pressure requirements of sprinkler and standpipe systems, they must be installed and tested in accordance with NFPA 20.

913.2 Protection against interruption of service. The fire pump, driver and controller shall be protected in accordance with NFPA 20 against possible interruption of service through damage caused by explosion, fire, flood, earthquake, rodents, insects, windstorm, freezing, vandalism and other adverse conditions.

❖ This section lists hazards that must be taken into account when determining the extent of protection required for the fire pump and its auxiliary equipment. A pump room in a building that is protected against the listed hazards in compliance with the code would be considered in compliance. Because fire pumps are also typically located in separate detached structures, geographical and security issues must also be considered.

913.2.1 Protection of fire pump rooms. Rooms where fire pumps are located shall be separated from all other areas of the building in accordance with Section 913.2.1 of the *International Building Code*.

❖ The purpose of this section is to require indoor fire pump room separation by fire barriers and horizontal assemblies in accordance with the requirements in the IBC. See the commentary to Section 913.2.1 of the IBC for a complete discussion of the requirements.

913.2.2 Circuits supplying fire pumps. Cables used for survivability of circuits supplying fire pumps shall be protected using one of the following methods:

1. Cables used for survivability of required critical circuits shall be *listed* in accordance with UL 2196 and

shall have a *fire-resistance rating* of not less than 1 hour.

2. Electrical circuit protective systems shall have a *fire-restistance rating* of not less than 1 hour. Electrical circuit protective systems shall be installed in accordance with their listing requirements.

3. Construction having a *fire-resistance rating* of not less than 1 hour.

❖ This section is provided to better protect cables used for survivability of circuits associated with fire pumps by referencing the appropriate standard. UL 2196 is the ANSI-approved standard for tests of fire-resistive cables. NFPA 20 includes selective survivability requirements to ensure integrity of certain critical circuits. NFPA 70 does not specify the applicable standard within its mandatory provisions but recognizes electrical circuit protective systems as an alternative to listed cables. An electrical circuit protective system is a field assembly of components that must be installed according to the listing requirements and manufacturer's instructions in order to maintain the listing for the system. There are more than two dozen electrical circuit protective systems listed in the UL Fire Resistance Directory.

913.3 Temperature of pump room. Suitable means shall be provided for maintaining the temperature of a pump room or pump house, where required, above 40°F (5°C).

❖ As previously noted for sprinkler systems, standpipe systems and other water-based fire protection systems, pump rooms or pump houses must be maintained at a temperature of 40°F (4°C) or above to prevent the system from freezing. This is consistent with Section 5.12.2.1 of NFPA 20.

913.3.1 Engine manufacturer's recommendation. Temperature of the pump room, pump house or area where engines are installed shall never be less than the minimum recommended by the engine manufacturer. The engine manufacturer's recommendations for oil heaters shall be followed.

❖ The engine manufacturer's recommendation must be compiled with where the recommended minimum temperature is higher than the minimum established in Section 913.3. Maintaining the desired engine temperature enhances the startability of the engine. Maintaining water heaters and oil heaters as required for diesel engines, for example, will improve the starting capabilities of the fire pump and reduce engine wear and the drain on batteries.

913.4 Valve supervision. Where provided, the fire pump suction, discharge and bypass valves, and isolation valves on the backflow prevention device or assembly shall be supervised open by one of the following methods:

1. Central-station, proprietary or remote-station signaling service.

2. Local signaling service that will cause the sounding of an audible signal at a constantly attended location.

3. Locking valves open.

4. Sealing of valves and *approved* weekly recorded inspection where valves are located within fenced enclosures under the control of the *owner*.

❖ As was the case with sprinkler systems, water control valves that are a part of the fire pump installation must be supervised in the open position so that the system is operational when needed and also to reduce the chance of a system failure (see commentary, Section 903.4). In most cases the required water-based extinguishing system, of which the fire pump is an integral component, will be electrically supervised. Locking or sealing valves open as the only means of supervision may not be permitted, depending on the type of valve. Section 903.4, for example, specifically exempts jockey pump control valves from being electrically supervised if they are sealed or locked in the open position.

913.4.1 Test outlet valve supervision. Fire pump test outlet valves shall be supervised in the closed position.

❖ Fire pump test outlet valves are for performance testing of the fire pump and do not control the available water supply to either a sprinkler system or a standpipe system. These valves are normally in a closed position and are supervised accordingly.

913.5 Testing and maintenance. Fire pumps shall be inspected, tested and maintained in accordance with the requirements of this section and NFPA 25. Records of inspection, testing and maintenance shall be maintained.

❖ Fire pumps require periodic maintenance so that they will perform as required. Monthly maintenance includes running the pump at churn to exercise the pump and driver. Pump packings and relief valve settings must be adjusted as needed.

Annually, the pump must be retested to verify its proper performance. Pressure, flow, revolutions per minute, voltage and, for electric motor-driven pumps, voltage and amperage readings must be recorded, plotted and compared with original design criteria. Upon completion of testing and maintenance, the pump must be left in the automatic-start condition, ready for service. Because a fire pump is a component of a water-based extinguishing system, NFPA 25 is applicable. If the fire pump is powered by a liquid fuel, such as diesel, it is important that the fuel supply be replenished as soon as possible after the test.

913.5.1 Acceptance test. Acceptance testing shall be done in accordance with the requirements of NFPA 20.

❖ Chapter 14 of NFPA 20 details the procedure for conducting a fire pump acceptance test. This test is run to determine that the installation matches the sprinkler or standpipe system design criteria, the approved shop drawings and the pump manufacturer's performance specifications. The test is to be conducted in the presence of the building official in accordance with Section 901.5 by the installing contractor and representatives of the pump manufacturer and the controller manufacturer. Where the pump engine and/

or transfer switch are separately supplied components, their manufacturer representative must also be present.

913.5.2 Generator sets. Engine generator sets supplying emergency or standby power to fire pump assemblies shall be periodically tested in accordance with NFPA 110. Records of testing shall be maintained.

❖ This section does not require emergency or standby power for all fire pump installations, but rather requires the testing of on-site generator sets that are used for emergency or standby power to fire pump assemblies. The need for emergency or standby power is typically based on occupancy conditions as indicated in the IBC. Section 403.4.8 of the IBC, for example, requires standby power for all electrically powered fire pumps in high-rise buildings. A generator set is recognized as a permissible standby power source. NFPA 110 prescribes the operational testing requirements, including load tests, as well as the periodic inspection and maintenance for generator sets.

913.5.3 Transfer switches. Automatic transfer switches shall be periodically tested in accordance with NFPA 110. Records of testing shall be maintained.

❖ Automatic transfer switches are self-acting equipment that is used to transfer power from a normal source of electrical supply to an alternative supply, such as an engine generator set. NFPA 110 requires a test on each automatic transfer switch that simulates failure of the normal power source. Upon failure, the automatic transfer switch must then automatically transfer the load to the emergency power supply. Manual transfer switches are not permitted as the only means to transfer power between the normal supply and the alternative supply to the fire pump controller.

913.5.4 Pump room environmental conditions. Tests of pump room environmental conditions, including heating, ventilation and illumination, shall be made to ensure proper manual or automatic operation of the associated equipment.

❖ Maintaining suitable environmental conditions is essential to the proper starting capability, performance and safe operation of fire pumps and associated emergency power supplies, where required. Adequate ventilation, for example, is needed to maintain the ambient temperature in the pump room within the range recommended by the manufacturer for the emergency power supply equipment.

SECTION 914
FIRE PROTECTION BASED ON SPECIAL DETAILED REQUIREMENTS OF USE AND OCCUPANCY

914.1 General. This section shall specify where *fire protection systems* are required based on the detailed requirements of use and occupancy of the *International Building Code*.

❖ This section is intended to be a duplication of the fire protection system requirements included in Chapter 4 of the IBC located here in a single section of the code for ease of access by the user. It is organized based on the type of facility rather than the type of fire protection system required. Frequently, reference is made to other sections of the code where the requirements are to be found. Occasionally, administrative requirements are noted that do not appear in other sections. In all cases, the referenced section must be reviewed carefully since this section is intended to be subordinate to the main requirements found elsewhere in the code.

914.2 Covered and open mall buildings. Covered and open mall buildings shall comply with Sections 914.2.1 through 914.2.4.

❖ Various fire protection-related code sections from Section 402 of the IBC are included in the code so that the fire code official has convenient access to the necessary tools to address conditions and monitor new construction requirements related to fire protection systems in covered and open mall buildings. Not all covered and open mall provisions are included here. Specific information regarding kiosk placement, types of signage and other concerns are located in the IBC and can be consulted when the fire code official reviews the covered or open mall building. Although those provisions are not included here, they address issues that can have an adverse effect on the safety of occupants in the covered or open mall building.

914.2.1 Automatic sprinkler system. Covered and open mall buildings and buildings connected shall be equipped throughout with an automatic sprinkler system in accordance with Section 903.3.1.1, which shall comply with the all of the following:

1. The automatic sprinkler system shall be complete and operative throughout occupied space in the mall building prior to occupancy of any of the tenant spaces. Unoccupied tenant spaces shall be similarly protected unless provided with approved alternative protection.
2. Sprinkler protection for the mall of a covered mall building shall be independent from that provided for tenant spaces or anchor buildings.
3. Sprinkler protection for the tenant spaces of an open mall building shall be independent from that provided for anchor buildings.
4. Sprinkler protection shall be provided beneath exterior circulation balconies located adjacent to an open mall.
5. Where tenant spaces are supplied by the same system, they shall be independently controlled.

Exception: An *automatic sprinkler system* shall not be required in spaces or areas of open parking garages separated from the covered or open mall in accordance with Section 402.4.2.3 of the *International Building Code* and constructed in accordance with Section 406.5 of the *International Building Code*.

❖ The requirement for an automatic sprinkler system is found in Section 402.5 of the IBC. This reference provides the fire code official with the information and tools in order to work jointly with the building official in applying the sprinkler requirement for a covered and open mall building.

The covered or open mall building and connected buildings, such as anchor buildings, must be protected with an automatic sprinkler system to protect life and property effectively. As has been discussed throughout the section, numerous allowances (such as reduced tenant separations and elimination of area limitations) are based on the effectiveness of the automatic sprinkler system.

The sprinkler system is to be designed, installed, tested and maintained in accordance with Chapter 9 and NFPA 13. Additionally, the system must be installed such that any portion serving tenant spaces in a covered mall building may be shut down independently without affecting the operation of the systems protecting the mall area. This special feature is in recognition of the frequent need to shut down the system so that changes can be made to it as a result of tenant improvements and modifications.

In an open mall building, the sprinkler systems for the tenant spaces are to be separate from those provided for the anchor buildings. It is necessary that sprinkler protection for open mall buildings be extended to the underneath side of pedestrian walkways and exterior balconies used for circulation and egress purposes. Although the open mall itself does not require sprinkler protection, it is important that those areas below overhead walkways be provided with sprinklers.

Section 909.12.4 requires operation of the sprinkler system to automatically activate the mechanical smoke control system (where an automatic control system is utilized). It is imperative that the zoning of the sprinkler system match the zoning of the smoke control system. This is necessary so that the area where water flow has occurred will also be the area from which smoke is removed.

The exception clarifies that sprinkler protection need not be extended to complying open parking garages that are adequately separated from the covered mall building, open mall building or anchor store. The allowance is consistent with the automatic sprinkler provisions of Section 903.2 where no sprinkler protection is required in open parking garages based on a Group S-2 occupancy classification.

914.2.2 Standpipe system. The covered and open mall building shall be equipped throughout with a standpipe system as required by Section 905.3.3.

❖ The standpipe requirements for covered and open mall buildings exist in the code, as well as in Section 402.7.1 of the IBC, which refers to Section 905 for the requirements. For additional information regarding the requirements, see the commentary for Section 905.3.3.

914.2.3 Emergency voice/alarm communication system. Where the total floor area exceeds 50,000 square feet (4645 m^2) within either a covered mall building or within the perimeter line of an open mall building, an emergency voice/alarm communication system shall be provided. *Access* to emergency voice/alarm communication systems serving a mall, required or otherwise, shall be provided for the fire department. The system shall be provided in accordance with Section 907.5.2.2.

❖ This section is similar to Section 402.7.4 of the IBC. In covered and open mall buildings, there is a need to be able to control the large number of people that may be present. This can best be done when specific instructions are conveyed. Covered and open malls that are less than 50,000 square feet (4645 m^2) in area are not required to be provided with an emergency voice alarm system. If a public address system is provided in a smaller mall, it can serve the same purpose. See the commentary to Section 907.5.2.2 for additional information.

914.2.4 Fire department access to equipment. Rooms or areas containing controls for air-conditioning systems, automatic fire-extinguishing systems, *automatic sprinkler systems* or other detection, suppression or control elements shall be identified for use by the fire department.

❖ Section 402.7.5 of the IBC also states this requirement. The intent is that the fire department be able to access those systems that are critical to fire protection as well as those parts of the mechanical system that can aid in control of the ventilation system to use as conditions warrant. The text is included here so that the fire code official has a means for applying the requirement and approving the means by which identification of the rooms or areas will be provided.

914.3 High-rise buildings. High-rise buildings shall comply with Sections 914.3.1 through 914.3.7.

❖ High-rise buildings have unique challenges that set them apart from other buildings. Section 403 of the IBC establishes multiple fire protection requirements for such buildings.

914.3.1 Automatic sprinkler system. Buildings and structures shall be equipped throughout with an *automatic sprinkler system* in accordance with Section 903.3.1.1 and a secondary water supply where required by Section 914.3.2.

Exception: An *automatic sprinkler system* shall not be required in spaces or areas of:

1. Open parking garages in accordance with Section 406.5 of the *International Building Code*.
2. Telecommunications equipment buildings used exclusively for telecommunications equipment, associated electrical power distribution equipment, batteries and standby engines, provided that those spaces or areas are equipped throughout with an automatic fire detection system in accordance with Section 907.2 and are separated from the remainder

of the building by not less than 1-hour *fire barriers* constructed in accordance with Section 707 of the *International Building Code* or not less than 2-hour *horizontal assemblies* constructed in accordance with Section 711 of the *International Building Code*, or both.

❖ In order to provide protection for occupants and fire fighters, high-rise buildings are required to be equipped with an automatic sprinkler system. There are two exceptions that allow sprinkler protection to be omitted. Exception 1 is for an open parking garage that is a part of the high-rise building. This exception recognizes the relatively low life safety threat posed by fires in open parking garages. Additional information on open parking garages can be obtained in the commentary for Section 406 of the IBC.

Exception 2 acknowledges the water sensitivity of telecommunications systems. See commentary to the same exception in Section 903.2.

914.3.1.1 Number of sprinkler risers and system design. Each sprinkler system zone in buildings that are more than 420 feet (128 m) in height shall be supplied by not fewer than two risers. Each riser shall supply sprinklers on alternate floors. If more than two risers are provided for a zone, sprinklers on adjacent floors shall not be supplied from the same riser.

❖ The intent of this section is to increase the reliability of automatic sprinkler systems in very tall buildings, i.e., those that exceed 420 feet (128 m) in height, by requiring a minimum of two risers for each sprinkler system zone. The difficulty of fighting fires in very tall buildings ranges from difficult to virtually impossible with the sprinkler system impaired. Accordingly, the reliable functioning of sprinkler systems is critical. Various events could cause a sprinkler riser to be impaired, thereby leaving the structure vulnerable to fire. The NIST World Trade Center (WTC) Report documented that the proximate cause of the building's collapse was a building contents fire that raged out of control, in part at least, because the building's automatic sprinkler systems were nonfunctional due to the initial aircraft attack. Events far less dramatic could knock out or make a sprinkler riser inoperative, thereby leaving the structure highly vulnerable to fire.

Recommendation 12 of the NIST WTC Report calls for the redundancy of active fire suppression systems to be increased to accommodate the greater risks associated with increased building height and population. This section seeks to do that by requiring two risers designed such that, if one riser is taken out of service, the other will be able to supply sprinklers on the floors above and below. This will impede any fire spread and allow the fire department time to respond and extinguish the fire. At the One Meridian Plaza fire in Philadelphia, the further spread of an out-of-control fire occurring on floors not protected by sprinklers was prevented by the operation of 10 sprinklers when the fire reached a floor that had been retrofitted with sprinklers.

914.3.1.1.1 Riser location. Sprinkler risers shall be placed in interior exit stairways and ramps that are remotely located in accordance with Section 1007.

❖ This section requires the sprinkler risers to be located in protected interior exit stairways and ramps and specifies a separation distance to reduce the possibility that one incident could incapacitate both risers which is consistent with the approach used in the code for interior exit stairway separation. See commentary to Section 1007.

914.3.1.2 Water supply to required fire pumps. In buildings that are more than 420 feet (128 m) in *building height*, required fire pumps shall be supplied by connections to not fewer than two water mains located in different streets. Separate supply piping shall be provided between each connection to the water main and the pumps. Each connection and the supply piping between the connection and the pumps shall be sized to supply the flow and pressure required for the pumps to operate.

Exception: Two connections to the same main shall be permitted provided that the main is valved such that an interruption can be isolated so that the water supply will continue without interruption through not fewer than one of the connections.

❖ Fire pumps are installed in sprinkler and standpipe systems to pressurize the water supply for the minimum required sprinkler and standpipe operation. Fire pumps are only "required" to meet the system needs. Therefore, whether a particular high-rise building includes fire pumps will depend on interaction of the height of the building, the local water system and the designs of the sprinkler and standpipe systems in the building (see Section 913 for more information on fire pumps).

The difficulty of fighting fires in very tall buildings ranges from hard to virtually impossible. Accordingly, the reliable functioning of required sprinkler and standpipe systems is critically important.

Recommendation 12 of the NIST WTC Report called for the redundancy of active fire suppression systems to be increased to accommodate the greater risks associated with increasing building height and population. Where the systems require a fire pump and the building is more than 420 feet (128 m) in height, this section requires the fire pumps to be supplied by two water mains located in separate streets. The purpose of this is to increase the reliability of fire suppression systems in very tall buildings by requiring independent street-level water feeds such that the system will function as intended if one of those feeds is damaged or otherwise interrupted. Having two connections will greatly reduce the possibility of the loss of water due to a main break, given the valving that is a feature of a public water system. Each connection must be adequate to provide the flow and pressure needed for the fire pumps to operate. The exception is a performance-based provision that is not tied to any specific configuration.

914.3.2 Secondary water supply. An automatic secondary on-site water supply having a capacity not less than the hydraulically calculated sprinkler demand, including the hose stream requirement, shall be provided for high-rise buildings assigned to Seismic Design Category C, D, E or F as determined by the *International Building Code*. An additional fire pump shall not be required for the secondary water supply unless needed to provide the minimum design intake pressure at the suction side of the fire pump supplying the *automatic sprinkler system*. The secondary water supply shall have a duration of not less than 30 minutes as determined by the occupancy hazard classification in accordance with NFPA 13.

Exception: Existing buildings.

❖ The intent of this section is that a secondary water supply be provided on the high-rise building site in order to provide a high level of functional reliability for the fire protection systems if a seismic event disables the primary water supply for high-rise buildings assigned these Seismic Design categories. The categories are described in Section 1613 of the IBC.

The text's specific wording that the secondary supply be "on-site" rather than "to the site" would preclude the use, for example, of a secondary connection to the municipal supply to achieve compliance with this requirement.

The required amount of water is equal to the hydraulically calculated sprinkler demand plus hose stream demand for a minimum 30-minute period, dependent on the appropriate occupancy hazard classification in NFPA 13.

Note that the beginning of Section 914.3.2 requires that the secondary water supply be automatic; in other words, switchover to the secondary water source cannot occur manually. This is consistent with the definitions of "Automatic sprinkler system" and "Standpipe, types of" in that both systems are required to be connected to a reliable water supply.

Generally, this section does not automatically require a second fire pump, but if necessary, an additional pump may be required. A second pump would be necessary if the secondary water supply does not provide the necessary water pressure for intake into the primary fire pump.

914.3.3 Fire alarm system. A fire alarm system shall be provided in accordance with Section 907.2.12.

❖ See the commentary to Section 907.2.12.

914.3.4 Automatic smoke detection. Smoke detection shall be provided in accordance with Section 907.2.12.1.

❖ Section 907.2.12.1 indicates specific locations where smoke detection is required for a high-rise building. These requirements are due to the fact that the building is a high-rise and not necessarily dependent on the occupancy within. There may be additional requirements in other sections of the code that require specific detection due to the occupancy.

914.3.5 Emergency voice/alarm communication system. An emergency voice/alarm communication system shall be provided in accordance with Section 907.5.2.2.

❖ Due to the size of high-rise buildings, an emergency voice/alarm communications system is required so that specific commands can be given as necessary. See the commentary to Sections 907.2.12.1.1 and 907.5.2.2 for additional information.

914.3.6 Emergency responder radio coverage. Emergency responder radio coverage shall be provided in accordance with Section 510.

❖ The provisions of Section 510 are concerned with the reliability of portable radios used by emergency responders inside of buildings. This is in keeping with the philosophy inherent in the I-Codes that, when a facility grows too large or complex for effective fire response, fire protection features must be provided within the building. See the commentary to Section 510 for complete information on this topic.

914.3.7 Fire command. A *fire command center* complying with Section 508 shall be provided in a location *approved* by the fire department.

❖ Section 508 of the code contains the same information as Section 911 of the IBC on this subject. The fire command center must always be accessible to the fire service. See the commentary to Section 508 for additional information.

914.4 Atriums. Atriums shall comply with Sections 914.4.1 and 914.4.2.

❖ Atriums are addressed in Section 404 of the IBC, which identifies several fire protection systems that must be included in atriums. It is important to remember that these are requirements that are unique to the specific condition noted and the fire protection systems are a result of those conditions. These requirements are only partially related to the occupancies that may be present.

914.4.1 Automatic sprinkler system. An *approved automatic sprinkler system* shall be installed throughout the entire building.

Exceptions:

1. That area of a building adjacent to or above the atrium need not be sprinklered, provided that portion of the building is separated from the atrium portion by not less than a 2-hour *fire barrier* constructed in accordance with Section 707 of the *International Building Code* or *horizontal assemblies* constructed in accordance with Section 711 of the *International Building Code*, or both.
2. Where the ceiling of the atrium is more than 55 feet (16 764 mm) above the floor, sprinkler protection at the ceiling of the atrium is not required.

❖ Due to the possibility that smoke and fire could spread through an unprotected vertical opening, an automatic sprinkler system is required where an atrium is present in a building and must be installed throughout the building as a preventive measure. If, however, the atrium is treated more like a shaft and provided with a 2-hour enclosure, only the atrium itself must be sprinklered.

The assumption in Exception 1 is that the passive protection systems that isolate the atrium would be sufficient to compensate for the limited sprinkler coverage and be an acceptable alternative to sprinklers throughout the building.

Exception 2 allows for the omission of sprinklers in tall spaces for two reasons. First, due to the entrainment of cooler ambient air in the flame plume, the likelihood that sprinklers will activate diminishes greatly with increased atrium ceiling height. Secondly, the effectiveness of the sprinkler water discharging from such heights is also substantially diminished.

914.4.2 Fire alarm system. A fire alarm system shall be provided where required by Section 907.2.13.

❖ See the commentary for Section 907.2.13.

914.5 Underground buildings. Underground buildings shall comply with Sections 914.5.1 through 914.5.5.

❖ Section 405 of the IBC contains requirements for underground buildings. The fire protection features necessary for this type of building are also found elsewhere in this chapter but are reiterated in the following sections. Underground buildings present unique hazards in that the path of egress is upward, in the same direction as vertical fire movement. Fires in such buildings are also more challenging for fire fighters since there is no opportunity for an exterior fire attack. See the commentary for Section 405 of the IBC for additional information.

914.5.1 Automatic sprinkler system. The highest *level of exit discharge* serving the underground portions of the building and all levels below shall be equipped with an *automatic sprinkler system* installed in accordance with Section 903.3.1.1. Water-flow switches and control valves shall be supervised in accordance with Section 903.4.

❖ Underground buildings have occupiable levels that are more than 30 feet (9144 mm) below the lowest level of exit discharge. This requirement from the IBC indicates that sprinklers are required for the portions of the building that are below ground and the story at the highest level of exit discharge. The provision does not require sprinklers for any stories that may be above the highest level of exit discharge. If sprinklers were required for those areas, it would be due to provisions in other sections of the code. In some respects, this is an expansion of the general provisions for windowless stories in Section 903.2.11.1.

914.5.2 Smoke control system. A smoke control system is required to control the migration of products of combustion in accordance with Section 909 and provisions of this section. Smoke control shall restrict movement of smoke to the general area of fire origin and maintain *means of egress* in a usable condition.

❖ One common application for an underground building is to use excavated caverns for storage. In such a condition, there is no roof from which the fire service can attempt to vent the "building." Because occupants must egress in the same direction that smoke will vent itself, and because there are few, if any, openings by which to vent smoke to the exterior, the need for smoke control is greater than for traditional buildings. This section adds a degree of clarity to the design requirements of Section 909 in that the intent is to contain smoke to the general area of origin. Any method identified in Section 909 can be used, given that the intent is to allow for egress and limit smoke spread to areas of the building that are not involved in the fire event. See Section 909 for additional commentary on smoke control.

914.5.3 Compartment smoke control system. Where compartmentation is required by Section 405.4 of the *International Building Code*, each compartment shall have an independent smoke control system. The system shall be automatically activated and capable of manual operation in accordance with Section 907.2.17.

❖ Where buildings contain levels that are more than 60 feet (18 288 mm) below the lowest level of exit discharge, Section 405.4.1 of the IBC requires that there be at least two fire-resistance-rated compartments per floor and of approximately the same size. Because compartmentation exists, there is a need for additional safety with the smoke control system. Consequently, each compartment must have a smoke control system that is independent of that in the adjoining compartment. The word "independent" means that there can be no sharing of ductwork, mechanical equipment or power distribution. Connection to the standby system can be shared since that is consistent with the general intent of the smoke control system provisions in Section 909 and the IMC. See the commentary to Section 405.4 of the IBC.

914.5.4 Fire alarm system. A fire alarm system shall be provided where required by Sections 907.2.17 and 907.2.18.

❖ The threshold for requiring a fire alarm system is the same as that for compartmentation—an occupied floor level more than 60 feet (18 288 mm) below the level of exit discharge. The fire alarm requirements include the requirements for an emergency voice/alarm communications system. See the commentary to Sections 907.2.17 and 907.2.18 for additional information.

914.5.5 Standpipe system. The underground building shall be provided throughout with a standpipe system in accordance with Section 905.

❖ Section 905.3.1 requires a standpipe system where the building's lowest level is more than 30 feet (9144 mm) below the lowest level of fire department access. By definition, an underground building is one in which the lowest level is more than 30 feet (9144 mm) below the lowest level of exit discharge. One condition uses fire department vehicle access as the benchmark while the other uses the level of exit discharge. Care must be taken so that both conditions are addressed when determining standpipe system requirements for buildings that have levels below ground.

914.6 Stages. Stages shall comply with Sections 914.6.1 and 914.6.2.

❖ Section 410 of the IBC contains definitions and requirements for both stages and platforms. A stage, however, is a special condition, according to the IBC. It does not mean, for example, that an elevated platform in the front of the banquet hall is intended to be regulated the same as a stage. The term "stage," as used here, is traditionally considered a "legitimate stage"—one with scenery drops and a gridiron above. See the commentary to Section 410 of the IBC for further information.

914.6.1 Automatic sprinkler system. Stages shall be equipped with an *automatic sprinkler system* in accordance with Section 903.3.1.1. Sprinklers shall be installed under the roof and gridiron and under all catwalks and galleries over the stage. Sprinklers shall be installed in dressing rooms, performer lounges, shops and storerooms accessory to such stages.

Exceptions:

1. Sprinklers are not required under stage areas less than 4 feet (1219 mm) in clear height utilized exclusively for storage of tables and chairs, provided that the concealed space is separated from the adjacent spaces by Type X gypsum board not less than $^{5}/_{8}$ inch (15.9 mm) in thickness.
2. Sprinklers are not required for stages 1,000 square feet (93 m^2) or less in area and 50 feet (15 240 mm) or less in height where curtains, scenery or other combustible hangings are not retractable vertically. Combustible hangings shall be limited to a single main curtain, borders, legs and a single backdrop.
3. Sprinklers are not required within portable orchestra enclosures on stages.

❖ Stages contain significant quantities of combustible materials stored in, around and above the stage that are located in close proximity to large quantities of lighting equipment (i.e., scenery and lighting above the stage). There also is scenery on the sides and rear of the stage; shops located along the back and sides of the stage; and storage, props, trap doors and lifts under the stage floor. This combination of fuel load and ignition sources increases the potential for a fire. As such, stages and accessory areas, such as dressing rooms, workshops and storerooms, are required to be protected with an automatic sprinkler system (see commentary, IBC Section 410.6).

The exceptions are intended to be applied where the building would not otherwise be required to be provided with sprinklers. If the building must be sprinklered throughout, then the three exceptions are moot. Sprinkler installations must be in accordance with NFPA 13 and placed as required by that standard.

Exception 1 allows simple storage in the space below the stage, a space traditionally used for table and chair storage. The space must be compartmentalized so that a minimal thermal barrier is provided between the stored material and the areas outside the space. If the height of the space exceeds 4 feet (1219 mm) or the materials stored are other than those associated with table and chair storage, then sprinklers must be provided.

Exception 2 recognizes that small stage settings do not pose the same risk as larger stages. In schools where the stage may only be an elevated portion at the end of the cafeteria, for example, the exception gives a basis for determining whether sprinkler protection is required. If scenery is simply manually set in place or moved horizontally, the large fuel loads associated with stages is not present.

Exception 3 acknowledges the limited hazards associated with portable orchestra enclosures. These elements are temporary in nature and are intended to improve the acoustics of the stage performances. These temporary enclosures do not lend themselves to temporary sprinkler heads; therefore, none are required.

914.6.2 Standpipe system. Standpipe systems shall be provided in accordance with Section 905.

❖ Due to the historic fires on stages of theaters, the code requires that a standpipe system be provided for all stages greater than 1,000 square feet (93 m^2) in area. The design requirements are dependent on the extent of sprinkler protection. See the commentary to Section 905.3.4 for additional information about the standpipe requirements.

914.7 Special amusement buildings. Special amusement buildings shall comply with Sections 914.7.1 and 914.7.2.

❖ A special amusement building is one in which the egress is not readily apparent, is intentionally confounded or is not readily available. Due to those characteristics, special fire protection features are required. See the commentary to Section 411 of the IBC for additional information about these types of facilities.

914.7.1 Automatic sprinkler system. Special amusement buildings shall be equipped throughout with an *automatic sprinkler system* in accordance with Section 903.3.1.1. Where the special amusement building is temporary, the sprinkler water supply shall be of an *approved* temporary means.

Exception: Automatic sprinklers are not required where the total floor area of a temporary special amusement building is less than 1,000 square feet (93 m^2) and the *exit access* travel distance from any point to an *exit* is less than 50 feet (15 240 mm).

❖ Special amusement buildings do not normally have a readily identifiable means of egress. Consequently additional time for safe egress may be necessary. A sprinkler system will minimize the potential hazard to occupants by controlling fire development (see commentary, IBC Section 411).

914.7.2 Automatic smoke detection. Special amusement buildings shall be equipped with an automatic smoke detection system in accordance with Section 907.2.11.

❖ Section 907.2.11 indicates that a smoke detection system is required for special amusement buildings. See the commentary to Section 907.2.11 for additional information.

914.8 Aircraft-related occupancies. Aircraft-related occupancies shall comply with Sections 914.8.1 through 914.8.6.

❖ Aircraft related occupancies include air traffic control towers, residential and commercial hangars, and heliports and helistops. Hangars can be those for storage and "parking" of the aircraft or for repair and painting. All of these are addressed in Section 412 of the IBC.

While the following provisions do not identify fire protection requirements for heliports and helistops, Section 412.7 of the IBC requires that these facilities be designed in accordance with NFPA 418. That standard contains various provisions for fire protection including a foam fire-extinguishing system for rooftop landing pads and portable fire extinguishers. Section 2007 of the code contains fire protection requirements for helistops and heliports. Section 905.3.6 requires a standpipe system for helistops and heliports. Additional requirements for portable fire extinguishers in aviation facilities can be found in Section 2005 of the code.

914.8.1 Automatic smoke detection systems. Airport traffic control towers shall be provided with an automatic smoke detection system installed in accordance with Section 907.2.21.

❖ Airport traffic control towers are required to have an automatic fire detection system. Because the tower is designed so that people are elevated in the air, the vertical supports generally are narrow and contain little room for separated stairways. An early notification of a fire hazard is important in alerting the occupants so that fire safety operations can begin as quickly as possible. An automatic detection system is therefore required. Section 907.2.21.1 applies specifically to towers where sprinklers are provided and there are at least two means of egress. Where there is only a single means of egress, Section 907.2.21.2 specifies the coverage of the fire detection systems. Section 907.2.21.2 also applies to towers that are not sprinkler protected, although only towers with an occupied floor at a height of 35 feet (10 668 mm) or less would be without sprinklers (see IBC Section 412.2.4). Where suppression is not required by the code, the detection system is vital for the safety of the occupants. No requirements are included in Chapter 11 of the code to address existing airport traffic control towers.

914.8.2 Automatic sprinkler system for new airport traffic control towers. Where an occupied floor is located more than 35 feet (10 668 mm) above the lowest level of fire department vehicle access, new airport traffic control towers shall be equipped with an *automatic sprinkler system* in accordance with Section 903.3.1.1.

❖ Under Section 412.2.4 of the IBC, sprinkler systems are required for all towers being constructed once there is an occupied floor above 35 feet (10 668 mm). This height was selected because shorter towers should be reachable by ladders typically found at rural fire stations and smaller airports. These are also the types of airports that would have the shorter control towers. Due to the absence of aerial ladders or means to reach higher elevations at these locations, additional levels of fire protection are required. As such, life safety is positively affected by limiting the chance of smoke/fire spread and flashover in the facility where delayed evacuation of the cab may be required. In addition, property protection would allow earlier reuse of the structure.

914.8.3 Fire suppression for aircraft hangars. Aircraft hangars shall be provided with a fire suppression system designed in accordance with NFPA 409, based on the classification for the hangar given in Table 914.8.3.

Exception: Where a fixed base operator has separate repair facilities on site, Group II hangars operated by a fixed base operator used for storage of transient aircraft only shall have a fire suppression system, but the system shall be exempt from foam requirements.

❖ To minimize the fire hazards associated with aircraft hangars, most hangars are required to be protected with a fire suppression system. Where required, the fire suppression system must be designed and installed in accordance with the referenced standard, NFPA 409, which requires fire suppression based on the type and construction and the activities in a given hanger.

In the standard, the suppression requirements are broken down based on three categories: Group I, Group II and Group III hangars. Table 914.8.3 designates which Group category applies to various sizes of fire areas within a hangar and the type of construction. For example, a hanger that is 28,000 square feet (2601 m^2) in Type IIB construction would be a Group II hangar. Groups I and II hangers are required to have fire suppression as specified in NFPA 409. In general, Group III hangers are exempt from providing fire suppression unless one (or more) of the hazardous operations listed in Section 914.8.3.1 occurs within the hangar. In these situations, fire suppression based on the appropriate portion of the standard for either Group I or Group II is required.

The exception allows that the foam requirements for fire suppression do not need to be provided for Group II hangers if the hangar is essentially a parking garage for transient aircraft. The exception is only applicable where a larger airport facility has multiple hangars and separate hangars for repair operations.

TABLE 914.8.3. See below.

❖ This table is a correlation of the NFPA 409 construction and area limits with the IBC construction type requirements. It combines several tables in NFPA 409 into a single table that allows determination of the group type for aircraft hangars based on construction type and area before proceeding to the standard for the suppression requirements. Note a indicates that, regardless of size or construction type, any hangar with a door opening greater than 28 feet high (8534 mm) is required to have a fire suppression system as required for a Group I hangar. Note c provides a Group IV designation for any hangar located in a membrane structure.

914.8.3.1 Hazardous operations. Any Group III aircraft hangar in accordance with Table 914.8.3 that contains hazardous operations including, but not limited to, the following shall be provided with a Group I or II fire suppression system in accordance with NFPA 409 as applicable:

1. Doping.
2. Hot work including, but not limited to, welding, torch cutting and torch soldering.
3. Fuel transfer.
4. Fuel tank repair or maintenance not including defueled tanks in accordance with NFPA 409, inerted tanks or tanks that have never been fueled.
5. Spray finishing operations.
6. Total fuel capacity of all aircraft within the unsprinklered single *fire area* in excess of 1,600 gallons (6057 L).
7. Total fuel capacity of all aircraft within the maximum single *fire area* in excess of 7,500 gallons (28 390 L) for a hangar equipped throughout with an *automatic sprinkler system* installed in accordance with Section 903.3.1.1.

❖ Any of the operations listed in this section where they occur in a Group III hangar will require some level of fire suppression under NFPA 409. The hazardous operations on the list are straightforward. Additional information may be found as follows: Item 1 is discussed further in Section 914.8.4, Item 2 is regulated by Chapter 35, Items 3 and 4 are regulated by Chapter 57, Item 5 is regulated by Chapter 24.

914.8.3.2 Separation of maximum single fire areas. Maximum single *fire areas* established in accordance with hangar classification and construction type in Table 914.8.3 shall be separated by 2-hour *fire walls* constructed in accordance with Section 706 of the *International Building Code*. In determining the maximum single fire area as set forth in Table 914.8.3, ancillary uses that are separated from aircraft servicing areas by not less than a 1-hour *fire barrier* constructed in accordance with Section 707 of the *International Building Code* shall not be included in the area.

❖ Table 914.8.3 places a maximum size limit on hangars based on type of construction. For a hangar structure to exceed these sizes requires the construction of fire walls to establish fire areas that stay within the limits. This section is more stringent than the definition of "Fire area," which allows fire barriers to establish a fire area. For hangers, the fire areas must be created by the exterior walls of a building or a combination of exterior walls and fire walls. Note that there is some allowance for the use of fire barriers to create fire areas where separating ancillary uses such as business offices, maintenance shops and storage areas. The fire suppression requirements contained within NFPA 409 are primarily focused on the protection of aircraft within the servicing and storage area. The fire protection requirements in the

TABLE 914.8.3
HANGAR FIRE SUPPRESSION REQUIREMENTS[a, b, c]

MAXIMUM SINGLE FIRE AREA (square feet)	INTERNATIONAL BUILDING CODE TYPE OF CONSTRUCTION								
	IA	IB	IIA	IIB	IIIA	IIIB	IV	VA	VB
> 40,001	Group I	Group I	Group I	Group I	Group I	Group I	Group I	Group I	Group I
40,000	Group II	Group II	Group II	Group II	Group II	Group II	Group II	Group II	Group II
30,000	Group III	Group II	Group II	Group II	Group II	Group II	Group II	Group II	Group II
20,000	Group III	Group III	Group II	Group II	Group II	Group II	Group II	Group II	Group II
15,000	Group III	Group III	Group III	Group II	Group III	Group II	Group III	Group II	Group II
12,000	Group III	Group III	Group III	Group III	Group III	Group III	Group III	Group II	Group II
8,000	Group III	Group III	Group III	Group III	Group III	Group III	Group III	Group III	Group II
5,000	Group III	Group III	Group III	Group III	Group III	Group III	Group III	Group III	Group III

For SI: 1 square foot = 0.0929 m^2, 1 foot = 304.8 mm.

a. Aircraft hangars with a door height greater than 28 feet shall be provided with fire suppression for a Group I hangar regardless of maximum fire area.

b. Groups shall be as classified in accordance with NFPA 409.

c. Membrane structures complying with Section 3102 of the *International Building Code* shall be classified as a Group IV hangar.

ancillary areas are not as extensive as those required for the aircraft servicing and storage areas, and less restrictive separations are considered appropriate. This allowance is consistent with NFPA 409 requirements.

914.8.4 Finishing. The process of "doping," involving the use of a volatile flammable solvent, or of painting shall be carried on in a separate detached building equipped with automatic fire-extinguishing equipment in accordance with Section 903.

❖ Doping is a type of lacquer used to protect, waterproof and make taut the cloth surfaces of airplane wings. It is used on lighter-than-air, ultralight and some light aircraft. It is essentially painting on fabric. Doping is not used on metallic surfaces; however, the use of flammable paints is also addressed in this section. When flammable finishes are applied, the process must occur in a separate building not attached to the hangar. Because the code text refers to Section 903, the intent is for an automatic sprinkler system to be installed, unless otherwise approved (see commentary, IBC Section 412.3.5).

914.8.5 Residential aircraft hangar smoke alarms. Smoke alarms shall be provided within residential aircraft hangars in accordance with Section 907.2.20.

❖ A residential aircraft hangar, as defined in Section 202 of the IBC, is "... an accessory building less than 2,000 square feet (186 m^2) and 20 feet (6096 mm) in building height constructed on a one- or two-family property where aircraft are stored..." The requirements for the residential hangar are very similar to that for a residential garage. The hangar can be either detached or attached. If attached, it must be separated from the dwelling by construction with not less than a 1-hour fire-resistance rating. Section 907.2.20 requires a minimum of one smoke alarm in a residential aircraft hangar. See the commentary to Section 907.2.20 for additional information.

914.8.6 Aircraft paint hangar fire suppression. Aircraft paint hangars shall be provided with fire suppression as required by NFPA 409.

❖ To minimize the fire hazards associated with aircraft paint hangars, all such buildings are required to be protected with a fire suppression system. This requirement is applicable regardless of the size of the hangar in terms of height or area or the types and quantities of aircraft that are being cleaned or painted. The fire suppression system must be designed and installed in accordance with NFPA 409.

This section assumes the primary function of the hangar is as a paint hangar. Minor painting may constitute finishing in accordance with Section 914.8.4. While not referenced in the code, NFPA 410 provides additional guidance on aircraft maintenance, including the painting of aircraft.

914.9 Application of flammable finishes. An *automatic sprinkler system* or fire-extinguishing system shall be provided in all spray rooms and spray booths, and shall be installed in accordance with Chapter 9.

❖ Chapter 24 provides detailed information about spaces and rooms involved in the application of flammable finishes. This section references Chapter 9 for the appropriate type of fire-extinguishing system.

914.10 Drying rooms. Drying rooms designed for high-hazard materials and processes, including special occupancies as provided for in Chapter 4 of the *International Building Code*, shall be protected by an *approved* automatic fire-extinguishing system complying with the provisions of Chapter 9.

❖ This section reiterates the requirements from Section 417.4 of the IBC. See the commentary to Section 417.4 of the IBC for additional information.

914.11 Ambulatory care facilities. Occupancies classified as ambulatory care facilities shall comply with Sections 914.11.1 through 914.11.3.

❖ This section simply introduces the fire protection requirements for ambulatory care facilities. See also the commentary to Section 422 of the IBC.

914.11.1 Automatic sprinkler systems. An *automatic sprinkler system* shall be provided for ambulatory care facilities in accordance with Section 903.2.2.

❖ See the commentary to Section 903.2.2.

914.11.2 Manual fire alarm systems. A manual fire alarm system shall be provided for ambulatory care facilities in accordance with Section 907.2.2.

❖ See the commentary to Section 907.2.2.

914.11.3 Fire alarm systems. An automatic smoke detection system shall be provided for ambulatory care facilities in accordance with Section 907.2.2.1.

❖ See the commentary to Section 907.2.2.1.

SECTION 915
CARBON MONOXIDE DETECTION

915.1 General. Carbon monoxide detection shall be installed in new buildings in accordance with Sections 915.1.1 through 915.6. Carbon monoxide detection shall be installed in existing buildings in accordance with Section 1103.9.

❖ These provisions were added to the code and the IBC to be consistent with the requirements for carbon monoxide (CO) detectors in all new construction of one- and two-family dwellings that had been added to the IRC in the 2009 edition. Another reason for its approval was technical data in a 1998 article published by the *Journal of the American Medical Association* that stated that approximately 2,100 deaths occur annually as a result of CO poisoning. That annual number is based on the findings of a paper prepared by the US Department of Health Centers for Disease Control (CDC). That paper documented epidemiological research by two CDC physicians who examined 56,133 death certificates over a 10-year period. Excluding suicides, homicides, structure fires and deaths resulting from CO poisoning in motor vehicles, the death rate steadily decreased for the sample period, from a value of 1,513 people in 1979 to 878 in 1988. The highest death rates occurred in winter and among males, African Americans, the elderly and residents in northern states.

CO is a colorless, tasteless, odorless gas that interrupts the attachment of oxygen molecules to hemoglobin in blood cells and can cause headaches, confusion and dizziness. At higher concentrations, CO can cause loss of consciousness and eventual death. Exposures above 100 parts/million are dangerous to human health. It is not a toxic or highly toxic gas as defined in Chapter 2 but is classified as a flammable gas.

These provisions detail what occupancies require CO detection and where that detection is specifically to be located within the building. Also, flexibility on the use of single- and multiple-station alarms versus CO detection systems is provided.

Retroactive requirements are found in Chapter 11. These requirements are essentially the same except that Group E classrooms are not addressed and the CO alarms can be battery powered.

915.1.1 Where required. Carbon monoxide detection shall be provided in Group I-1, I-2, I-4 and R occupancies and in classrooms in Group E occupancies in the locations specified in Section 915.2 where any of the conditions in Sections 915.1.2 through 915.1.6 exist.

❖ CO detection is provided to protect occupants of dwelling units and sleeping units within Group I-1, I-4, and R occupancies and classrooms in Group E occupancies. These are locations where occupants are likely to be sleeping or that young children may be at risk. Sections 915.1.2 through 915.1.5 address the different scenarios that warrant CO detection and are more specific than past editions of the code and the IBC.

915.1.2 Fuel-burning appliances and fuel-burning fireplaces. Carbon monoxide detection shall be provided in *dwelling units*, *sleeping units* and classrooms that contain a fuel-burning appliance or a fuel-burning fireplace.

❖ This section clarifies that CO detection is required where the dwelling or sleeping unit or the classroom actually contains a fuel-burning appliance or fuel-burning fireplace. Section 915.1.3 discusses dwelling and sleeping units and classrooms that are served by fuel-burning, forced-air furnaces.

915.1.3 Fuel-burning forced-air furnaces. Carbon monoxide detection shall be provided in *dwelling units*, *sleeping units* and classrooms served by a fuel-burning, forced-air furnace.

Exception: Carbon monoxide detection shall not be required in *dwelling units*, *sleeping units* and classrooms where a carbon monoxide detector is provided in the first room or area served by each main duct leaving the furnace, and the carbon monoxide alarm signals are automatically transmitted to an approved location.

❖ This section addresses forced-air furnaces that physically move air. This potential source of CO is more indirect than having the fuel-burning appliance or fuel-burning fireplace within the space itself, but still creates a potential hazard.

The exception addresses the fact that if detection is provided closer to the source, then further detection within dwelling units, sleeping units and Group E classrooms is not necessary provided that a CO alarm signal is transmitted to an approved location from which emergency actions can be initiated and occupants in the portions of the building farther from the initial detection can be notified. The CO will continue to be generated until action is taken.

915.1.4 Fuel-burning appliances outside of dwelling units, sleeping units and classrooms. Carbon monoxide detection shall be provided in *dwelling units*, *sleeping units* and classrooms located in buildings that contain fuel-burning appliances or fuel-burning fireplaces.

Exceptions:

1. Carbon monoxide detection shall not be required in *dwelling units*, *sleeping units* and classrooms without communicating openings between the fuel-burning appliance or fuel-burning fireplace and the *dwelling unit*, *sleeping unit* or classroom.
2. Carbon monoxide detection shall not be required in *dwelling units*, *sleeping units* and classrooms where a carbon monoxide detector is provided in one of the following locations:
   - 2.1. In an approved location between the fuel-burning appliance or fuel-burning fireplace and the *dwelling unit*, *sleeping unit* or classroom.
   - 2.2. On the ceiling of the room containing the fuel-burning appliance or fuel-burning fireplace.

❖ This section focuses on the presence of fuel-burning equipment in buildings containing dwelling units, sleeping units and classrooms but with the fuel-burning equipment located outside of those areas. CO detection is required in every dwelling unit, sleeping unit and classroom, even if that equipment does not serve those spaces. A good example of this is a multiple-story hotel that has all electric HVAC in the sleeping units, but perhaps a fireplace in the lobby, forced-air heating in the common area, and a boiler in an equipment room.

There are two exceptions provided that recognize, based on several factors, that CO is a very low risk to the spaces required to be protected by Section 915.

Exception 1 addresses buildings where there are no communicating openings between the location of the fuel-burning appliance and dwelling units, sleeping units and classrooms. The intent is that if the appliance is not serving the space and has no communication with the space, CO should not enter those spaces. This covers situations where CO emanating from the fuel-burning appliance has no direct path to a dwelling unit or sleeping unit, such as a water heater in an equipment room that only has access from the exterior of the building, and no openings through which the CO can get to dwelling units or sleeping units. An interior door, between the equipment room and a dwelling unit, even if it is self-closing, would not allow this exception to be used.

Exception 2 is similar to the exception to Section 915.1.3. This exception requires the installation of one or more CO alarms in approved locations between fuel-burning appliances and the nearest dwelling unit, sleeping unit or classroom or on the ceiling of the room in which a fuel-burning appliance is located. CO alarms are only required where there are communicating openings including ducts, concealed spaces, interior hallways, stairs and spaces between the fuel-burning appliance or fuel-burning fireplace and the dwelling unit or sleeping unit where air can flow from the appliance to the dwelling unit or sleeping unit.

915.1.5 Private garages. Carbon monoxide detection shall be provided in *dwelling units*, *sleeping units* and classrooms in buildings with attached private garages.

Exceptions:

1. Carbon monoxide detection shall not be required in *dwelling units*, *sleeping units* and classrooms without communicating openings between the private garage and the *dwelling unit*, *sleeping unit* or classroom.
2. Carbon monoxide detection shall not be required in *dwelling units*, *sleeping units* and classrooms located more than one story above or below a private garage.
3. Carbon monoxide detection shall not be required where the private garage connects to the building through an open-ended corridor.
4. Where a carbon monoxide detector is provided in an approved location between openings to a private garage and *dwelling units*, *sleeping units* or classrooms.

❖ This section addresses attached private garages. Private garages, a term defined in Chapter 2, are often sources of CO generation. When attached to a building containing dwelling units, sleeping units or classrooms in Group E, CO detection is required.

There are several exceptions to the requirement for CO detection. These are similar to those found in Sections 915.1.3 and 915.1.4.

Exception 1 is similar to Exception 1 in Section 915.1.4. If there are no communicating openings, then CO detection is not required. The likelihood of CO entering the dwelling units, sleeping units or classrooms is greatly reduced.

Exception 2 addresses buildings where the dwelling units, sleeping units and classrooms are two stories above or below the location of a fuel-burning appliance. The CO would need to travel through an entire story before reaching the areas of concern.

Exception 3 does not require CO alarms to be provided where the private garage is attached to the building by an open-ended corridor (a term defined in Chapter 2 and the IBC, and commonly called a breezeway). This allows the CO concentration to dissipate before becoming a hazard to building occupants.

Exception 4 is similar to the exception to Section 915.1.3 and recognizes that the detection can be located closer to the source of the hazard rather than requiring detection in every dwelling unit, sleeping unit or classroom.

915.1.6 Exempt garages. For determining compliance with Section 915.1.5, an open parking garage complying with Section 406.5 of the *International Building Code* or an enclosed parking garage complying with Section 406.6 of the *International Building Code* shall not be considered a private garage.

❖ This section is only provided to distinguish open parking garages and enclosed parking garages from private garages. "Open parking garage" and "Private garage" are defined terms in Section 202 of the code.

915.2 Locations. Where required by Section 915.1.1, carbon monoxide detection shall be installed in the locations specified in Sections 915.2.1 through 915.2.3.

❖ Sections 915.2.1 through 915.2.3 provide more detail on where detection is specifically required to be installed. This is a clarification from previous editions. NFPA 720 does not provide enough detailed information as to where detection should be located, so specific direction is provided in the code. In some cases, the locations differ from that provided in NFPA 720.

915.2.1 Dwelling units. Carbon monoxide detection shall be installed in *dwelling units* outside of each separate sleeping area in the immediate vicinity of the bedrooms. Where a fuel-burning appliance is located within a bedroom or its attached bathroom, carbon monoxide detection shall be installed within the bedroom.

❖ The language is similar to that required for smoke alarms, but the detection is only required outside of each sleeping area. If the fuel-burning appliance is within the bedroom or the attached bathroom, detection is required within the bedroom itself. Commentary Figure 915.2.1 shows the layout of carbon monoxide alarms versus smoke alarms. Note that if they are combined (smoke and CO alarms), the smoke alarm placement would be more restrictive.

915.2.2 Sleeping units. Carbon monoxide detection shall be installed in *sleeping units*.

Exception: Carbon monoxide detection shall be allowed to be installed outside of each separate sleeping area in the immediate vicinity of the *sleeping unit* where the *sleeping* *unit* or its attached bathroom does not contain a fuel-burning appliance and is not served by a forced air furnace.

❖ The intent of this section is the same as Section 915.2.1 except that it is applicable to sleeping units. Sleeping units can be as simple as a hotel room or a suite-type layout. This allows the detection to be either in the sleeping area itself, as with a simple hotel room, or outside the sleeping area as is the case for dwelling units.

915.2.3 Group E occupancies. Carbon monoxide detectors shall be installed in classrooms in Group E occupancies. Carbon monoxide alarm signals shall be automatically transmitted to an on-site location that is staffed by school personnel.

Exception: Carbon monoxide alarm signals shall not be required to be automatically transmitted to an on-site location that is staffed by school personnel in Group E occupancies with an occupant load of 30 or less.

❖ This section clarifies that the detector is to be located within the classroom and that a signal from the CO detector be automatically transmitted to a location on-site where school personnel can react to the situation, such as the school office. The exception provides relief to small schools where it is very easy to communicate a hazardous situation throughout the building.

915.3 Carbon monoxide detection. Carbon monoxide detection required by Sections 915.1 through 915.2.3 shall be provided by carbon monoxide alarms complying with Section 915.4 or carbon monoxide detection systems complying with Section 915.5.

❖ This section provides the option of providing the CO detection through single- or multiple-station CO alarms or through a CO detection system. This is a similar concept to smoke alarms and smoke detection systems. Each type of CO detector is listed to a different UL standard, depending on whether it is to be used as a stand-alone or interconnected detector (UL 2034) or a detector that is part of a CO detection system (UL 2075). Section 915.4 addresses CO alarms and Section 915.5 addresses CO detection systems.

915.4 Carbon monoxide alarms. Carbon monoxide alarms shall comply with Sections 915.4.1 through 915.4.4.

❖ If the option of using CO alarms is chosen, compliance is required with Sections 915.4.1 through 915.4.4. CO alarms can be stand-alone or interconnected (single- or multiple-station). Section 915 does not address whether such alarms are required to be interconnected.

CO alarms are designed to initiate an audible alarm when the level of CO is still below that which can cause a loss of the ability to react to the dangers of CO exposure. UL specifies that CO alarms activate at a level where the CO concentration over a given period of time can achieve 10-percent carboxyhemo-

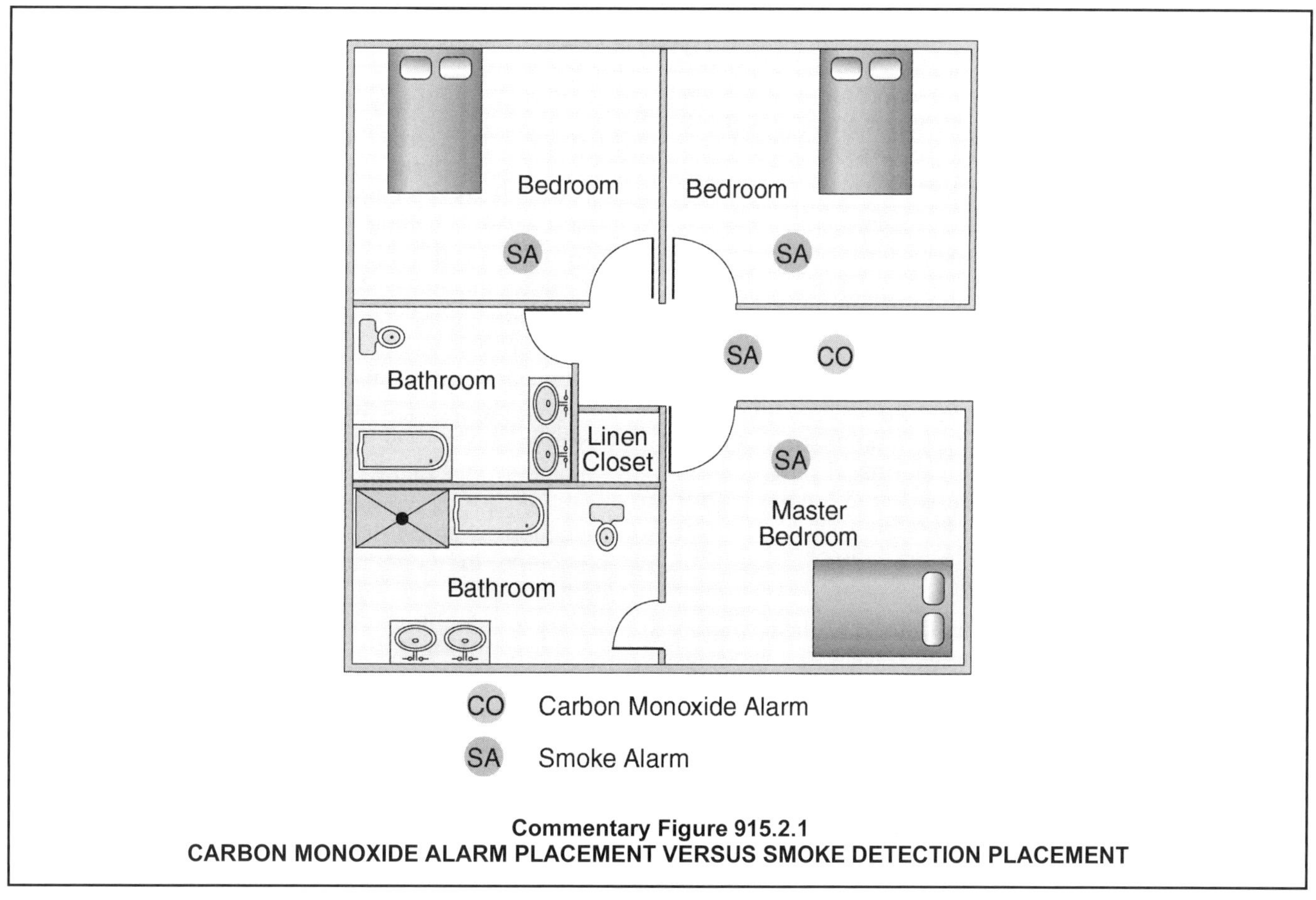

Commentary Figure 915.2.1
CARBON MONOXIDE ALARM PLACEMENT VERSUS SMOKE DETECTION PLACEMENT

globin (COHb) in the body. Ten-percent COHb will not cause physiological injury, but is a level at which increases in the CO concentration will begin to affect the human body.

915.4.1 Power source. Carbon monoxide alarms shall receive their primary power from the building wiring where such wiring is served from a commercial source, and when primary power is interrupted, shall receive power from a battery. Wiring shall be permanent and without a disconnecting switch other than that required for overcurrent protection.

> **Exception:** Where installed in buildings without commercial power, battery-powered carbon monoxide alarms shall be an acceptable alternative.

❖ This section is very similar to that required for smoke alarms (i.e., Section 907.2.10.6). The power supply must be provided by the building with battery backup. As with smoke alarms, the exception allows the use of battery power if commercial power is not available.

915.4.2 Listings. Carbon monoxide alarms shall be listed in accordance with UL 2034.

❖ Single- or multiple-station CO alarms are required to be listed in accordance with UL 2034. This standard is specific to CO alarms that provide both detection and notification.

915.4.3 Locations. Carbon monoxide alarms shall only be installed in *dwelling units* and in *sleeping units*. They shall not be installed in locations where the code requires carbon monoxide detectors to be used.

❖ This section provides the limits on the locations where carbon monoxide alarms can be installed and prohibits the substitution of carbon monoxide alarms in place of carbon monoxide detectors when the code requires that a detector be installed.

915.4.4 Combination alarms. Combination carbon monoxide/smoke alarms shall be an acceptable alternative to carbon monoxide alarms. Combination carbon monoxide/smoke alarms shall be listed in accordance with UL 2034 and UL 217.

❖ Since smoke alarms are required in many occupancies, often a single combination alarm is desired. In fact, in some jurisdictions the CO alarms are required to be combined with smoke alarms. To meet this requirement, the combination CO and smoke alarm must be listed to both UL 2034 and UL 217. See Commentary Figure 915.4.4 for an example of a combination CO and smoke alarm.

915.5 Carbon monoxide detection systems. Carbon monoxide detection systems shall be an acceptable alternative to carbon monoxide alarms and shall comply with Sections 915.5.1 through 915.5.3.

❖ If a CO detection system is preferred over CO alarms, compliance with Sections 915.5.1 through 915.5.3 is required.

Commentary Figure 915.4.4
COMBINATION CARBON MONOXIDE AND SMOKE ALARM

915.5.1 General. Carbon monoxide detection systems shall comply with NFPA 720. Carbon monoxide detectors shall be listed in accordance with UL 2075.

❖ There are two standards applicable to CO detection systems. The systems are required to comply with NFPA 720, and the detectors themselves are required to comply with UL 2075.

915.5.2 Locations. Carbon monoxide detectors shall be installed in the locations specified in Section 915.2. These locations supersede the locations specified in NFPA 720.

❖ This section is provided to clarify that the locations required for CO detectors in Section 915.2 differ from NFPA 720 and that those locations will supersede the standard. This simply reaffirms the provisions of Section 102.7.1 regarding conflicts between the code and a referenced standard.

915.5.3 Combination detectors. Combination carbon monoxide/smoke detectors installed in carbon monoxide detection systems shall be an acceptable alternative to carbon monoxide detectors, provided that they are listed in accordance with UL 2075 and UL 268.

❖ Similar to CO alarms, there is often a desire or a requirement to combine smoke detection and CO detection systems. If the detectors themselves are combined, they need to be listed in accordance with both UL 2075 and UL 268. NFPA 720 requires the CO alarm to be capable of transmitting a distinct audible signal that is different from the smoke alarm signal.

915.6 Maintenance. Carbon monoxide alarms and carbon monoxide detection systems shall be maintained in accordance with NFPA 720. Carbon monoxide alarms and carbon monoxide detectors that become inoperable or begin producing end-of-life signals shall be replaced.

❖ This section is simply a reference to the maintenance requirements of NFPA 720. In addition, when detectors become inoperable or start producing end-of-life signals, they are required to be replaced.

915.6.1 Enclosed parking garages. Carbon monoxide and nitrogen dioxide detectors installed in enclosed parking garages in accordance with the *International Mechanical Code*, Section 404.1 shall be maintained in accordance with the manufacturer's instructions and their listing. Detectors that become inoperable or begin producing end-of-life signals shall be replaced.

❖ This section is specific to carbon monoxide and nitrogen dioxide detectors. NFPA 720 does not address the maintenance of this type of detector. Thus, the required maintenance is to be provided by the manufacturer in their written instructions as well as the individual product listing. Also, similar to the previous section, when these detectors become inoperable or start producing end-of-life signals, they are required to be replaced.

SECTION 916 GAS DETECTION SYSTEMS

916.1 Gas detection systems. Gas detection systems required by this code shall comply with Sections 916.2 through 916.11.

❖ Gas detection systems are required for many different applications in the code. This section includes basic requirements for all gas detection systems and covers construction documents, equipment, power connections, emergency and standby power, sensor locations, gas sampling, system activation, signage, fire alarm system connections, maintenance, testing and sensor calibration. These are important safety requirements that are applicable to all gas detection systems, including those that are installed in a small operation up to those in large industrial facilities. Gas detection system equipment that can comply with these requirements is commercially available.

916.2 Permits. Permits shall be required as set forth in Section 105.7.11.

❖ A construction permit is required for the installation of gas detection systems. The requirements are located in Section 105.7.11.

916.2.1 Construction documents. Documentation of the gas detection system design and equipment to be used that demonstrates compliance with the requirements of this code shall be provided with the application for permit.

❖ The permit application must include the design drawings and equipment data sheets in order to document that the gas detection system conforms to the code requirements.

916.3 Equipment. Gas detection system equipment shall be designed for use with the gases being detected and shall be installed in accordance with manufacturer's instructions.

❖ The equipment to be used in the gas detection system is to be specific to the type of gas that is being used and detected. The system installation is to conform to the manufacturer's specific equipment instructions so that it will operate as required.

916.4 Power connections. Gas detection systems shall be permanently connected to the building electrical power supply or shall be permitted to be cord connected to an unswitched receptacle using an *approved* restraining means that secures the plug to the receptacle.

❖ The electric power supply for the gas detection system is to be installed permanently so that it will be able to operate continuously as required. As an alternative, subject to the approval of the fire code official, the power supply can be connected to an outlet that does not have a separate ON-OFF switch on the condition that it has an acceptable fixed restraint.

916.5 Emergency and standby power. Standby or emergency power shall be provided or the gas detection system shall initiate a trouble signal at an *approved* location if the power supply is interrupted.

❖ The gas detection system is to have a standby or emergency electric power supply. However, if it is not provided and the normal power supply is interrupted, the system is required to transmit a trouble signal to an approved location.

916.6 Sensor locations. Sensors shall be installed in approved locations where leaking gases are expected to accumulate.

❖ Each individual gas detection sensor is to be located where leaks are anticipated to occur. The locations are to be acceptable to the fire code official.

916.7 Gas sampling. Gas sampling shall be performed continuously. Sample analysis shall be processed immediately after sampling, except as follows:

1. For HPM gases, sample analysis shall be performed at intervals not exceeding 30 minutes.
2. For toxic gases that are not HPM, sample analysis shall be performed at intervals not exceeding 5 minutes, in accordance with Section 6004.2.2.7.
3. Where a less frequent or delayed sampling interval is *approved*.

❖ The required performance of the gas detection system sampling is that it is to be constant and without delay. However, this section provides three situations where the gas sampling is allowed to be less than continuous.

916.8 System activation. A gas detection alarm shall be initiated where any sensor detects a concentration of gas exceeding the following thresholds:

1. For flammable gases, a gas concentration exceeding 25 percent of the lower flammability limit (LFL).

2. For nonflammable gases, a gas concentration exceeding one-half of the IDLH, unless a different threshold is specified by the section of this code requiring a gas detection system.

Upon activation of a gas detection alarm, alarm signals or other required responses shall be as specified by the section of this code requiring a gas detection system. Audible and visible alarm signals associated with a gas detection alarm shall be distinct from fire alarm and carbon monoxide alarm signals.

❖ The required local alarm is intended to alert occupants to a hazardous condition in the vicinity of the inside storage room or area. The alarm is not intended to be an evacuation alarm; however, it is required to be monitored to hasten emergency personnel response.

916.9 Signage. Signs shall be provided adjacent to gas detection system alarm signaling devices that advise occupants of the nature of the signals and actions to take in response to the signal.

❖ This section requires informational signs in order to communicate the type of alarm and what action is to be taken upon activation.

916.10 Fire alarm system connections. Gas sensors and gas detection systems shall not be connected to fire alarm systems unless *approved* and connected in accordance with the fire alarm equipment manufacturer's instructions.

❖ This section requires that where gas sensors and gas detection systems are approved to be connected to a fire alarm system, they are only to be connected in conformance to the equipment manufacturer's written instructions. This ensures that the fire alarm system will operate as required in response to the independent operation of the gas detection system.

916.11 Inspection, testing and sensor calibration. Inspection and testing of gas detection systems shall be conducted not less than annually. Sensor calibration shall be confirmed at the time of sensor installation and calibration shall be performed at the frequency specified by the sensor manufacturer.

❖ This section provides the maximum allowable inspection and testing frequency. The requirement for an annual test and inspection provides confirmation that the system is operating properly and will function as designed. All systems components are to be verified at the time of the inspection with the exception of the sensor calibration. The required frequency of the calibration of the sensors is to be in accordance with the manufacturer's instructions.

SECTION 917 MASS NOTIFICATION SYSTEMS

917.1 College and university campuses. Prior to construction of a new building requiring a fire alarm system on a multiple-building college or university campus having a cumulative building occupant load of 1,000 or more, a mass notification risk analysis shall be conducted in accordance with NFPA 72. Where the risk analysis determines a need for mass notification, an *approved* mass notification system shall be provided in accordance with the findings of the risk analysis.

❖ This section does not specifically require that a mass notification system be installed. Instead it requires that a risk analysis be completed in accordance with NFPA 72 prior to the construction of a new building that requires a fire alarm system on a multiple-building college or university campus and has a cumulative building occupant load of 1,000 or more. If the results of the risk analysis state that a mass notification system shall be provided, then it is to be installed in accordance with the results and the acceptance of the fire code official.

Bibliography

The following resource materials were used in the preparation of the commentary for this chapter of the code:

Americans with Disabilities Act (ADA), Standard for Accessible Design 2010. Washington, DC: US Department of Justice, 2010.

ASHRAE Guideline 5-1994 (RA 2001), *Commissioning Smoke Management Systems*. Atlanta GA: American Society of Heating, Refrigerating and Air-Conditioning Engineers, 2001.

Cobb, Nathaniel and Ruth A. Etzel Ruth. "Unintentional Carbon Monoxide-Related Deaths in the United States, 1979 through 1988," *Journal of the American Medical Association*, August 7, 1991, Vol. 266, No. 5, pp. 659–663.

Fire Protection Handbook, 19th edition. Quincy, MA: National Fire Protection Association, 2003.

Grosshandler, William, *The Use of Portable Fire Extinguishers in Nightclubs*. Gaitherburg MD. National Institute of Science and Technology, July, 2008, pg. 5.

International Code Interpretations. Washington, DC: International Code Council, 2009.

Klote, J. and D. Evans. *A Guide to Smoke Control in the 2006 IBC*. Washington, DC: International Code Council, 2007.

Klote, J. and J. Milke. *Principles of Smoke Management*. Atlanta, GA: American Society of Heating, Refrigerating and Air-Conditioning Engineers, 2002.

NFPA 75-13, Standard for the Fire Protection of Information Technology Equipment. Quincy, MA: National Fire Protection Association, 2013.

NIST Special Publication 1066: Residential Kitchen Fire Suppression Research Needs, Madrzykowski, Hamins & Mehta, Feb. 2007.

NIST IR 6196-1 report dated September 1998.

Occupational Safety and Health (NIOSH) 2005-132, *Preventing Injuries and Deaths of Fire Fighters Due to Truss Systems*, and NIOSH 2010-153, *Preventing Deaths and Injuries of Fire Fighters Using Risk Management Principles at Structure Fires*.

Recommendations contained in the Initial Report of the Federal Emergency Management Agency (FEMA)/National Fallen Firefighters Foundation (NFFF®) Firefighter Life Safety Summit held on April 14, 2004, in Tampa, Florida.

SFPE *Engineering Guide to Performance-based Fire Protection Analysis and Design of Buildings*. Quincy, MA: National Fire Protection Association, 2004.

The SFPE Handbook of Fire Protection Engineering, 4th edition. Quincy, MA: National Fire Protection Association, 2008.

Chapter 10:
Means of Egress

General Comments

The general criteria set forth in Chapter 10 regulating the design of the means of egress are established as the primary method of protection for people in buildings. Chapter 10 provides the minimum requirements for means of egress in all buildings and structures. Both prescriptive and performance language is utilized in this chapter to provide for a basic approach in determining a safe exiting system for all occupancies. Chapter 10 addresses all portions of the egress system and includes design requirements as well as provisions regulating individual components. The requirements detail the size, arrangement, number and protection of means of egress components. Functional and operational characteristics also are specified for the components, which will permit their safe use without special knowledge or effort.

A zonal approach to egress provides the general basis for the chapter's format. A means of egress system has three parts: exit access, exit and exit discharge. Section 1001 includes administrative provisions. Section 1002 provides a list of defined terms that are primarily associated with Chapter 10. For commentary on these definitions, see Chapter 2.

Sections 1003 through 1015 include general provisions that apply to all three components of an egress system. This includes general means of egress requirements; occupant loads; means of egress sizing; the number of exits and exit access doorways and their configuration; illumination for the means of egress; specific requirements for accessible means of egress; doors, gates and turn-stiles; provisions for stairways and ramps along with their associated handrail and guard requirements; and exit signage (see commentary, Section 1003).

The exit access requirements are in Sections 1016 through 1021 (see commentary, Section 1016). This includes:

- General exit access requirements.
- Exit access travel distance.
- Aisles (for other than assembly spaces).
- Specific requirements for stairways and ramps.
- Corridors.
- Egress balconies.

The exit requirements are in Sections 1022 through 1027 (see commentary, Section 1022). Exit information includes provisions for:

- Exits.
- Interior and exterior stairways and ramps that serve as an exit element.
- Exit passageways.
- Luminious egress path markings that are required on the exit stairways in high-rise buildings (see IBC Section 403).
- Horizontal exits.

The exit discharge requirements are in Section 1028.

Section 1029 includes those means of egress requirements that are unique to spaces used for assembly purposes.

Emergency escape and rescue opening requirements are in Section 1030.

Sections 1003 through 1030 are duplicated text from Chapter 10 of the *International Building Code*® (IBC®) and are fully applicable to new buildings constructed after adoption of the code. The code has one additional section at the end of the chapter dealing with maintenance of the means of egress (see commentary, Section 1031). For means of egress requirements in existing buildings, refer to the *International Existing Building Code*® (IEBC®) or Chapter 11.

The evolution of means of egress requirements has been influenced by lessons learned from real fire incidents. While contemporary fires may reinforce some of these lessons, one must view each incident as an opportunity to assess critically the safety and reasonability of current regulations.

Cooperation among the developers of model codes and standards has resulted in agreement on many basic terms and concepts. The text of the code, including this chapter, is consistent with these national uniformity efforts.

National uniformity in an area such as means of egress has many benefits for the fire code official and other code users. At the top of the list are the lessons to be learned from national and international experiences, which can be reported in common terminology that everyone can relate to and clearly understand.

Purpose

A primary purpose of codes in general, and building and fire codes in particular, is to safeguard life in the presence of a fire. Integral to this purpose is the path of egress travel for occupants to escape and avoid a fire. Means of egress can be considered the lifeline of a building. The principles on which means of egress are based and that form the fundamental criteria for requirements provide a system that:

1. Will give occupants alternative paths of travel to a place of safety to avoid fire.
2. Will shelter occupants from fire and the products of combustion.
3. Will accommodate all occupants of a structure.
4. Is clear, unobstructed, well marked and illuminated and in which all components are under control of the user without requiring any tools, keys or effort.

History is marked with the severe loss of life from fire. Early as well as contemporary multiple-fatality fires can be traced to a compromise of one or more of the previous principles.

Life safety from fire is a matter of successfully evacuating or relocating the occupants of a building to a place of safety. As a result, life safety is a function of time: time for detection, time for notification and time for safe egress. The fire growth rate over a period of time is also a critical factor in addressing life safety. Other sections of the code, such as protection of vertical openings (Chapter 7), interior finishes (Chapter 8), fire suppression and detection systems (Chapter 9) and numerous others, also have an impact on life safety. This chapter addresses the issues related to the means available to relocate or evacuate building occupants.

SECTION 1001 ADMINISTRATION

1001.1 General. Buildings or portions thereof shall be provided with a *means of egress* system as required by this chapter. The provisions of this chapter shall control the design, construction and arrangement of *means of egress* components required to provide an *approved means of egress* from structures and portions thereof. Sections 1003 through 1030 shall apply to new construction. Section 1031 shall apply to existing buildings.

> **Exception:** Detached one- and two-family dwellings and multiple single-family dwellings (townhouses) not more than three stories above grade plane in height with a separate means of egress and their accessory structures shall comply with the *International Residential Code*.

❖ The minimum requirements for means of egress are to be incorporated in all structures as specified in this chapter. The system shall include exit access, exit, and exit discharge and address the needs of all occupants of the facility. Application would be effective on the date the code is adopted and placed into effect.

Fundamental to the level of life safety in any building, whether it is new or many years old, is the provision for an adequate egress system. It is for that reason that Section 1104 is retroactively applicable to existing buildings that are not undergoing changes, as regulated by the IEBC. The means of egress in existing buildings must also be properly maintained in accordance with Section 1031 if the intended level of safety is to remain for the life of the building.

Reflecting the correlation and compatibility that is a hallmark of the *International Codes*® (I-Codes®), the exception makes it clear that the means of egress in buildings that are within the scope of the *International Residential Code*® (IRC®) are to comply with those requirements instead of Chapter 10.

[BE] 1001.2 Minimum requirements. It shall be unlawful to alter a building or structure in a manner that will reduce the number of *exits* or the capacity of the *means of egress* to less than required by this code.

❖ A fundamental concept in life safety design is that the means of egress system is to be constantly available throughout the life of a building. Any change in the building or its contents, by physical reconstruction, alteration or a change of occupancy, is cause to review the resulting egress system. As a minimum, a building's means of egress is to be continued as initially approved. If a building or portion thereof has a change of occupancy, the complete egress system is to be evaluated and approved for compliance with the current code requirements for new occupancies (see the IEBC, Section 1031 and Chapter 11).

The means of egress in an existing building that experiences a change of occupancy, such as from Group S-2 (storage) to A-3 (assembly), requires reevaluation for code compliance based on the new occupancy. Similarly, the means of egress in an existing occupancy of Group A-3 in which additional seating is to be provided, thereby increasing the occupant load, requires reevaluation for code compliance based on the increased load.

The temptation is to temporarily remove egress components or other fire protection or life safety features from service during the alteration, repair or temporary occupancy of a building. During such times, a building is frequently more vulnerable to fire and the rapid spread of products of combustion. Either the occupants should not occupy those spaces where the means of egress has been compromised by the construction, or compensating fire safety features, providing equivalent safety for the occupants, should be considered. Occupants in adjacent areas may also require access to the egress facilities in the area under construction.

SECTION 1002 DEFINITIONS

[BE] 1002.1 Definitions. The following terms are defined in Chapter 2:

ACCESSIBLE MEANS OF EGRESS.

AISLE.

AISLE ACCESSWAY.

ALTERNATING TREAD DEVICE.

AREA OF REFUGE.

BLEACHERS.

BREAKOUT.

COMMON PATH OF EGRESS TRAVEL.

CORRIDOR.

DOOR, BALANCED.

EGRESS COURT.

EMERGENCY ESCAPE AND RESCUE OPENING.

EXIT.

EXIT ACCESS.

EXIT ACCESS DOORWAY.

EXIT ACCESS RAMP.

EXIT ACCESS STAIRWAY.

EXIT DISCHARGE.

EXIT DISCHARGE, LEVEL OF.

EXIT PASSAGEWAY.

EXTERIOR EXIT RAMP.

EXTERIOR EXIT STAIRWAY.

FIRE EXIT HARDWARE.

FIXED SEATING.

FLIGHT.

FLOOR AREA, GROSS.

FLOOR AREA, NET.

FOLDING AND TELESCOPIC SEATING.

GRANDSTAND.

GUARD.

HANDRAIL.

HORIZONTAL EXIT.

INTERIOR EXIT RAMP.

INTERIOR EXIT STAIRWAY.

LOW ENERGY POWER-OPERATED DOOR.

MEANS OF EGRESS.

MERCHANDISE PAD.

NOSING.

OCCUPANT LOAD.

OPEN-AIR ASSEMBLY SEATING.

OPEN-ENDED CORRIDOR.

PANIC HARDWARE.

PHOTOLUMINESCENT.

POWER-ASSISTED DOOR.

POWER-OPERATED DOOR.

PUBLIC WAY.

RAMP.

SCISSOR STAIRWAY.

SELF-LUMINOUS.

SMOKE-PROTECTED ASSEMBLY SEATING.

STAIR.

STAIRWAY.

STAIRWAY, SPIRAL.

WINDER.

❖ This section lists terms that are specifically associated with the subject matter of this chapter. It is important to emphasize that these terms are not exclusively related to this chapter, but may or may not also be applicable where the term is used elsewhere in the code.

Definitions of terms can help in the understanding and application of the code requirements. The purpose for including a list within this chapter is to provide more convenient access to terms that may have a specific or limited application within this chapter. For the complete definition and associated commentary, refer back to Chapter 2. Terms that are italicized provide a visual identification throughout the code that a definition exists for that term. The use and application of all defined terms are set forth in Section 201.

SECTION 1003 GENERAL MEANS OF EGRESS

[BE] 1003.1 Applicability. The general requirements specified in Sections 1003 through 1015 shall apply to all three elements of the *means of egress* system, in addition to those specific requirements for the *exit access*, the *exit* and the *exit discharge* detailed elsewhere in this chapter.

❖ The requirements in the chapter address the three parts of a means of egress system: the exit access, the exit and the exit discharge. This section specifies that the requirements of Sections 1003 through 1015 apply to the components of all three parts of the system. For example, the stair tread and riser dimensions in Section 1011 apply to interior exit access stairways, such as those leading from a mezzanine, and also apply to enclosed exit stairways per Section 1023, exterior exit stairways per Section 1027 and steps in the exit discharge per Section 1028.

The following sections are applicable for all parts of the means of egress:

- Section 1003 deals with the path for means of egress remaining free of obstructions and tripping hazards.
- Section 1004 provides criteria for determining occupant loads for a space. These numbers are used for determining means of egress, as a threshold for some suppression requirements and to determine the required plumbing fixture count.

- Section 1005 deals with the required size (i.e., width) of the path of travel for emergency evacuation. It is important not to create a "bottleneck" that could increase the amount of time necessary for occupants to exit the buildings.
- Section 1006 deals with the number of ways out of a space or off a floor, either by exit elements or exit access elements.
- Section 1007 provides placement and remoteness requirements for the exit and exit access elements prescribed in Section 1006.
- Section 1008 deals with illumination for the path of travel for the means of egress. Both general lighting and emergency backup lighting are addressed.
- Section 1009—IBC Chapter 11 provides accessibility requirements for how to get people with mobility impairments into a building. Section 1009 explains the options to allow people with mobility impairments to self-evacuate or to arrange for assisted rescue. The accessible means of egress is an important part of fire safety and evacuation plans (see Section 1002.2).
- Section 1010 includes requirements for doors, gates and turnstiles that are part of the path of travel from any occupied spaces. For example, doors that lead to a walk-in closet must comply with this section, but doors for reach-in closets are exempted.
- Section 1011 provides information on all types of stairways: from interior to exterior and from one riser to stairways with multiple flights and landings. Stepped aisles for areas within assembly seating are specifically addressed in Section 1029. For protection of stairways between stories, see Sections 1019, 1023 and 1027.
- Section 1012 deals with ramps. Ramped aisles serving assembly seating areas are specifically addressed in Section 1029. The ramp provisions are coordinated with ICC A117.1 and the *2010 ADA Standards for Accessible Design* [formerly the *Americans with Disabilities Act Accessibility Guidelines* (ADAAG), now referred to as the *2010 ADA Standards*]. For protection of ramps between stories, see Sections 1019, 1023 and 1027.
- Section 1013 describes where exit signs are required and what criteria they need to meet to be readily visible.
- Section 1014 describes handrail requirements for stairways and ramps. Handrails are important for guidance and to arrest a possible fall.
- Section 1015 provides criteria for the vertical portions of barriers that serve to protect people from possible falls at dropoffs greater than 30 inches (762 mm) along walking surfaces.

[BE] 1003.2 Ceiling height. The *means of egress* shall have a ceiling height of not less than 7 feet 6 inches (2286 mm) above the finished floor.

Exceptions:

1. Sloped ceilings in accordance with Section 1207.2 of the *International Building Code.*
2. Ceilings of *dwelling units* and *sleeping units* within residential occupancies in accordance with Section 1207.2 of the *International Building Code.*
3. Allowable projections in accordance with Section 1003.3.
4. *Stair* headroom in accordance with Section 1011.3.
5. Door height in accordance with Section 1010.1.1.
6. *Ramp* headroom in accordance with Section 1012.5.2.
7. The clear height of floor levels in vehicular and pedestrian traffic areas of public and private parking garages in accordance with Section 406.2.2 of the *International Building Code.*
8. Areas above and below *mezzanine* floors in accordance with Section 505.2 of the *International Building Code.*

❖ Generally, the specified ceiling height is the minimum allowed in any part of the egress path. The exceptions are intended to address conditions where the code allows the ceiling height to be lower than specified in this section.

This section is consistent with the minimum ceiling height for other areas as specified in IBC Section 1207. The exceptions are pointers to the lower headroom areas permitted in the code. For example, the headroom above and below a mezzanine is 7 feet (2134 mm) minimum.

[BE] 1003.3 Protruding objects. Protruding objects on *circulation paths* shall comply with the requirements of Sections 1003.3.1 through 1003.3.4.

❖ This section begins the provisions that apply to protruding objects and helps to improve awareness of these safety and accessibility-related provisions. The intent of the phrase "on circulation paths" is intended to allow for judgment determining where people walk versus all floor surfaces. For example, a drinking fountain in an alcove is over a floor, but it is not over a circulation path; therefore, it typically would not be considered a protruding object.

[BE] 1003.3.1 Headroom. Protruding objects are permitted to extend below the minimum ceiling height required by Section 1003.2 where a minimum headroom of 80 inches (2032 mm) is provided over any circulation paths, including walks, *corridors*, *aisles* and passageways. Not more than 50 percent of the ceiling area of a *means of egress* shall be reduced in height by protruding objects.

Exception: Door closers and stops shall not reduce headroom to less than 78 inches (1981 mm).

A barrier shall be provided where the vertical clearance above a circulation path is less than 80 inches (2032 mm) high above the finished floor. The leading edge of such a barrier shall be located 27 inches (686 mm) maximum above the finished floor.

❖ This provision is applicable to all routes that make up components of the means of egress. Specifically, the limitations in this section and those in Sections 1003.3.2 and 1003.3.3 provide a reasonable level of safety for people with vision impairments as well as for those exiting during emergency events when vision may be obscured by smoke or low lighting.

Minimum dimensions for headroom clearance are specified in this section. The minimum headroom clearance over all walking surfaces that are circulation paths is required to be maintained at 80 inches (2032 mm). This minimum headroom clearance is consistent with the requirements in Section 1011.3 for stairs and Section 1012.5.2 for ramps. Allowance must be made for door closers and stops, since their design and function necessitates placement within the door opening. The minimum headroom clearance for door closers and stops is allowed to be 78 inches (1981 mm) [see Commentary Figure 1003.3.1(1)]. The 2-inch (51 mm) projection into the doorway height is reasonable since these devices are normally mounted away from the center of the door opening, thus minimizing the potential for contact with a person moving through the opening. This is consistent with the exception to Section 1010.1.1.1.

The limitation on overhangs is of primary importance to individuals with visual impairments. Where vertical clearance along a walking surface is less than 80 inches (2032 mm), such as underneath the stairway on the ground floor, some sort of barrier that is detectable by a person using a cane must be provided. This can be a full-height wall, a rail at or below 27 inches (686 mm), a planter, fixed seating, and so on. A low curb is not effective as a barrier. A person with visual impairments might mistake it for a stair tread, step up onto it and strike their head. A rail at handrail height would not be detectable by a person using a cane, and he or she could possibly walk into the rail before detecting it. Also, when making decisions on the type of barrier, keep in mind that persons of shorter stature and children have a detectable range that may be below 27 inches (686 mm) [see Commentary Figure 1003.3.1(2)].

DOOR CLOSER

78" MIN.

For SI: 1 inch = 25.4 mm.

Commentary Figure 1003.3.1(1)
DOOR CLOSER HEADROOM PROTRUSIONS FOR CIRCULATION ROUTES

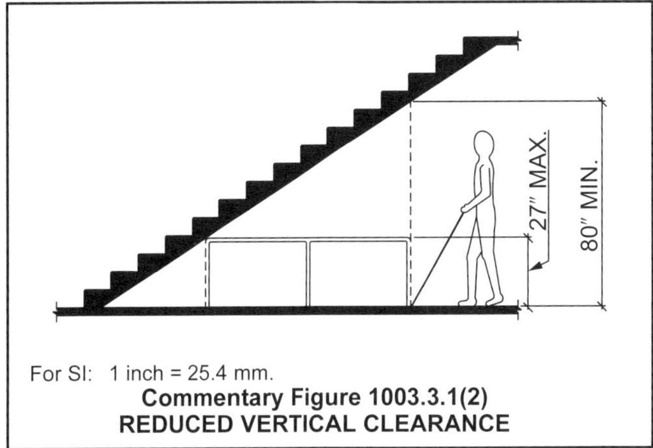

For SI: 1 inch = 25.4 mm.

Commentary Figure 1003.3.1(2)
REDUCED VERTICAL CLEARANCE

[BE] 1003.3.2 Post-mounted objects. A free-standing object mounted on a post or pylon shall not overhang that post or pylon more than 4 inches (102 mm) where the lowest point of the leading edge is more than 27 inches (686 mm) and less than 80 inches (2032 mm) above the finished floor. Where a sign or other obstruction is mounted between posts or pylons and the clear distance between the posts or pylons is greater than 12 inches (305 mm), the lowest edge of such sign or obstruction shall be 27 inches (686 mm) maximum or 80 inches (2032 mm) minimum above the finished floor or ground.

Exception: These requirements shall not apply to sloping portions of *handrails* between the top and bottom riser of *stairs* and above the *ramp* run.

❖ Post-mounted objects, such as signs or some types of drinking fountains or phone boxes, are not permitted to overhang more than 4 inches (102 mm) past the post where the bottom edge is located higher than 27 inches (686 mm) above the finished floor [see Commentary Figure 1003.3.2(1)]. Since the minimum required height of doorways, stairways and ramps in the means of egress is 80 inches (2032 mm), protruding objects located higher than 80 inches (2032 mm) above the finished floor are not regulated. Protrusions that are located lower than 27 inches (686 mm) above the finished floor are also permitted since they are more readily detected by a person using a long cane, provided that the minimum required width of the egress element is maintained. This is consistent with the post-mounted objects requirements in Section 307.3 of ICC A117.1, *Accessible and Usable Buildings and Facilities*. The intent is to reduce the potential for accidental impact for a person who is visually impaired.

Where signs are provided on multiple posts, the posts must be located closer than 12 inches (305 mm) apart, or the bottom edge of the sign must be lower than 27 inches (686 mm) so it is within detectable cane range or above 80 inches (2032 mm) so that it is above headroom clearances [see Commentary Figure 1003.3.2(2)].

The exception is intended for handrails that are located along the run of a stairway flight or ramp run. The extensions at the top and bottom of stairways and ramps must meet the requirements for protruding objects where people walk perpendicular to the stair or ramp.

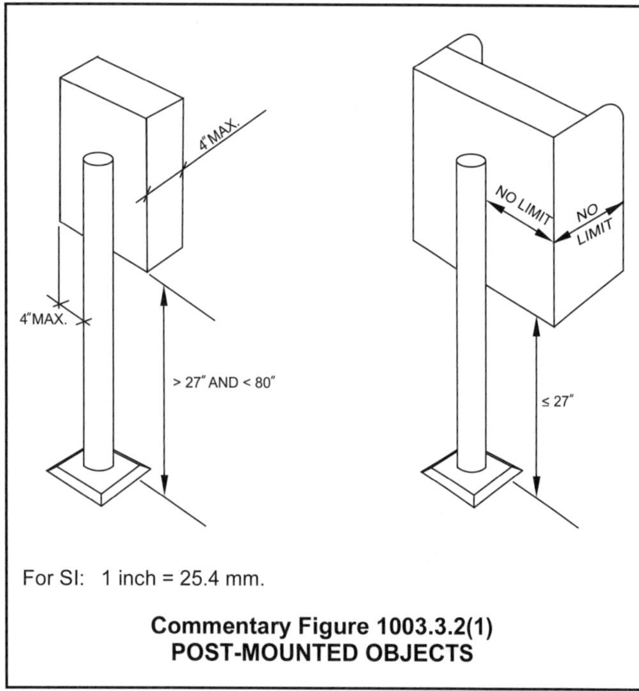

For SI: 1 inch = 25.4 mm.

Commentary Figure 1003.3.2(1)
POST-MOUNTED OBJECTS

[BE] 1003.3.3 Horizontal projections. Objects with leading edges more than 27 inches (685 mm) and not more than 80 inches (2030 mm) above the finished floor shall not project horizontally more than 4 inches (102 mm) into the *circulation path*.

Exception: *Handrails* are permitted to protrude $4^1/_2$ inches (114 mm) from the wall or *guard*.

❖ Protruding objects could slow the egress flow through a corridor or passageway and injure someone hurriedly passing by or someone with a visual impair-

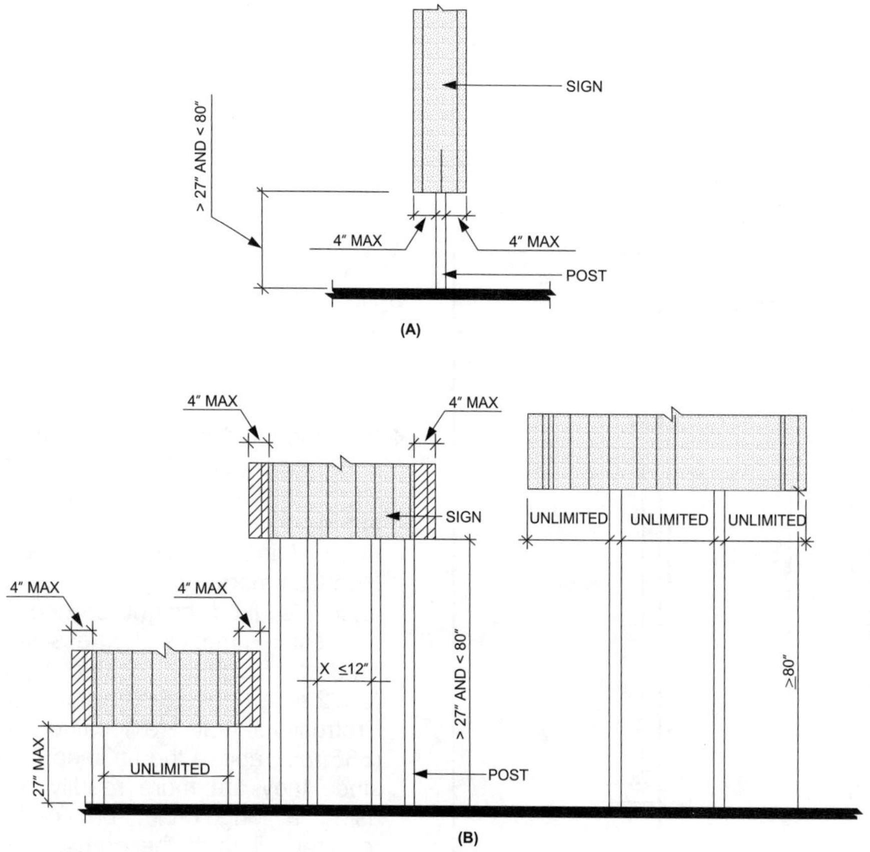

For SI: 1 inch = 25.4 mm.

Commentary Figure 1003.3.2(2)
POST-MOUNTED PROTRUDING OBJECTS

ment. Persons with a visual impairment who use a long cane for guidance must have sufficient warning of a protruding object. Where protrusions are located higher than 27 inches (686 mm) above the finished floor, the cane will most likely not encounter the protrusion before the person collides with the object.

Additionally, people with poor visual acuity or poor depth perception may have difficulty identifying protruding objects higher than 27 inches (686 mm). Therefore, objects such as lights, signs and door hardware, located between 27 inches (686 mm) and 80 inches (2032 mm) above the walking surface, are not permitted to extend more than 4 inches (102 mm) from each wall (see Commentary Figure 1003.3.3).

The requirement for protrusions into the door clear width in Section 1010.1.1.1 is different because it deals with allowances for panic hardware on a door. It is not the intent of this section to prohibit columns, pilasters or wing walls from projecting into a corridor as long as adequate egress width is maintained. These types of structural elements are detectable by persons using a long cane.

The exception is an allowance for handrails where they are provided along a wall, such as in some hospitals or nursing homes. The $4^1/_2$-inch (114 mm) measurement is intended to be consistent with projections by handrails into the required width of stairways and ramps in Section 1014.8. There are additional requirements regarding the required width (see Section 1005.2).

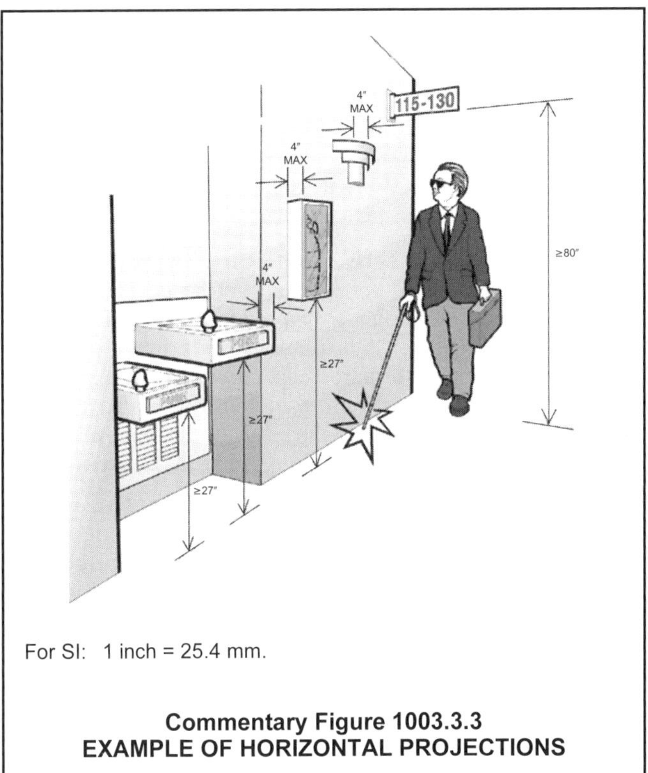

For SI: 1 inch = 25.4 mm.

Commentary Figure 1003.3.3
EXAMPLE OF HORIZONTAL PROJECTIONS

[BE] 1003.3.4 Clear width. Protruding objects shall not reduce the minimum clear width of *accessible routes*.

❖ This section is intended to limit the projections into an accessible route so that a minimum clear width of 36 inches (914 mm) is maintained along the route. ICC A117.1 is referenced by IBC Chapter 11 for technical requirements for accessibility. ICC A117.1, Section 403.5, allows the accessible route to be reduced in width to 32 inches (813 mm) for segments not to exceed 24 inches (610 mm) in length and spaced a minimum of 48 inches (1219 mm) apart. This allows for movement through a doorway or through a gap in planters or counters.

[BE] 1003.4 Slip-resistant surface. Circulation paths of the *means of egress* shall have a slip-resistant surface and be securely attached.

❖ As the pace of exit travel becomes hurried during emergency situations, the probability of slipping on smooth or slick floor surfaces increases. To minimize the hazard, all floor surfaces in the means of egress are required to be slip resistant. The use of hard floor materials with highly polished, glazed, glossy or finely finished surfaces should be avoided.

Field testing and uniform enforcement of the concept of slip resistance are not practical. One method used to establish slip resistance is that the static coefficient of friction between leather [Type 1 (Vegetable Tanned) of Federal Specification KK-L-165C] and the floor surface is greater than 0.5. Laboratory test procedures, such as ASTM D2047, can determine the static coefficient of resistance. Bulletin No. 4, "Surfaces," issued by the US Architectural and Transportation Barriers Compliance Board (ATBCB or Access Board) contains further information regarding slip resistance.

[BE] 1003.5 Elevation change. Where changes in elevation of less than 12 inches (305 mm) exist in the *means of egress*, sloped surfaces shall be used. Where the slope is greater than one unit vertical in 20 units horizontal (5-percent slope), *ramps* complying with Section 1012 shall be used. Where the difference in elevation is 6 inches (152 mm) or less, the *ramp* shall be equipped with either *handrails* or floor finish materials that contrast with adjacent floor finish materials.

Exceptions:

1. A single step with a maximum riser height of 7 inches (178 mm) is permitted for buildings with occupancies in Groups F, H, R-2, R-3, S and U at exterior doors not required to be *accessible* by Chapter 11 of the *International Building Code*.
2. A *stair* with a single riser or with two risers and a tread is permitted at locations not required to be *accessible* by Chapter 11 of the *International Building Code*, where the risers and treads comply with Section 1011.5, the minimum depth of the tread is 13 inches (330 mm) and not less than one *handrail* complying with Section 1014 is provided within 30 inches (762 mm) of the centerline of the normal path of egress travel on the *stair*.

3. A step is permitted in *aisles* serving seating that has a difference in elevation less than 12 inches (305 mm) at locations not required to be *accessible* by Chapter 11 of the *International Building Code*, provided that the risers and treads comply with Section 1029.14 and the *aisle* is provided with a *handrail* complying with Section 1029.16.

Throughout a story in a Group I-2 occupancy, any change in elevation in portions of the *means of egress* that serve nonambulatory persons shall be by means of a *ramp* or sloped walkway.

❖ Minor changes in elevation, such as a single step that is located in any portion of the means of egress (i.e., exit access, exit or exit discharge), may not be readily apparent during normal use or emergency egress and are considered to present a potential tripping hazard. Where the elevation change is less than 12 inches (305 mm), a ramp or sloped surface is specified to make the transition from higher to lower levels. This is intended to reduce accidental falls associated with the tripping hazard of an unseen step. Ramps must be constructed in accordance with Section 1012.1. Ramp provisions do not require handrails for ramps with a rise of 6 inches or less. However, the presence of the ramp must be readily apparent from the directions from which it is approached. Handrails are one method of identifying the change in elevation. In lieu of handrails, the surface of the ramp must be finished with materials that visually contrast with the surrounding floor surfaces. The walking surface of the ramp should contrast both visually and physically.

None of the exceptions are permitted along an accessible route required for either entry or egress from a space or building (see Section 1009 and IBC Chapter 11).

Exception 1 allows up to a 7-inch (178 mm) step at exterior doors in locations that are not used by the public on a regular basis (see Commentary Figure 1003.5). This exception is coordinated with Exception 2 of Section 1010.1.5, and is only applicable in occupancies that have relatively low occupant densities, such as factory and industrial structures. This exception is not applicable to exterior doors that are required to serve as an accessible entrance or that are part of a required accessible route. If this exception is utilized at a Group R-2 or R-3 occupancy, the designer may want to consider the issues of potential tripping hazards if this is a common entrance for a large number of occupants.

Exception 2 allows the transition from higher to lower elevations to be accomplished through the construction of stairs with one or two risers. The pitch of the stairway, however, must be shallower than that required for typical stairways (see Section 1011.5.2). Since the total elevation change is limited to 12 inches (305 mm), each riser must be approximately 6 inches (152 mm) in height. The elevation change must be readily apparent from the directions from which it is approached. At least one handrail is required. It must be constructed in accordance with Section 1014 and located so as to provide a graspable surface from the normal walking path.

Exception 3 is basically a cross reference to the assembly provisions for stepped aisles in Section 1029.

None of the exceptions are permitted in a Group I-2 occupancy (e.g., nursing home, hospital) in areas where nonambulatory persons may need access. The mobility impairments of these individuals require additional consideration.

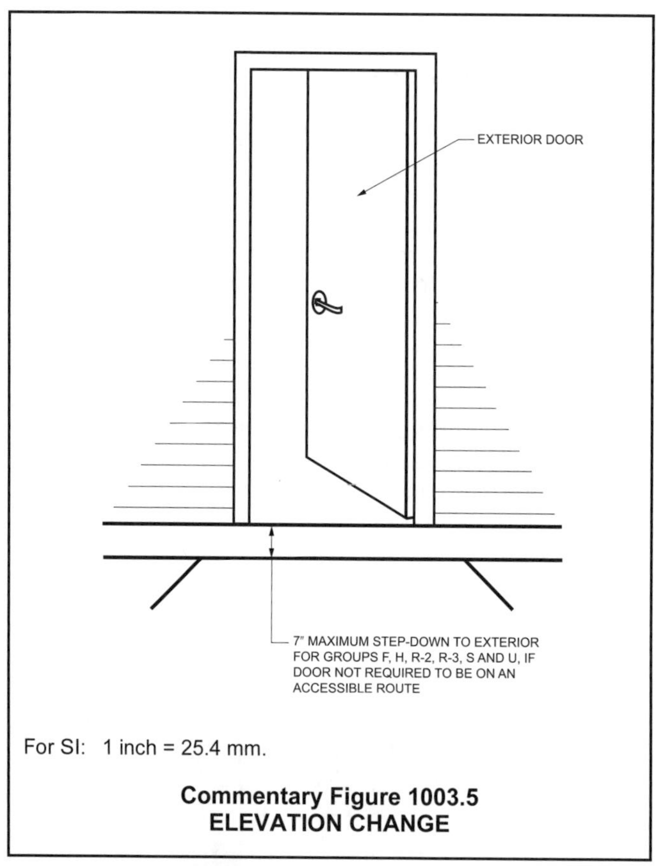

For SI: 1 inch = 25.4 mm.

Commentary Figure 1003.5
ELEVATION CHANGE

[BE] 1003.6 Means of egress continuity. The path of egress travel along a *means of egress* shall not be interrupted by a building element other than a *means of egress* component as specified in this chapter. Obstructions shall not be placed in the minimum width or required capacity of a *means of egress* component except projections permitted by this chapter. The minimum width or required capacity of a *means of egress* system shall not be diminished along the path of egress travel.

❖ This section requires that the entire means of egress path be clear of obstructions that could reduce the egress path to below the minimum width at any point. The egress path is also not allowed to be reduced in width such that the design occupant load (required capacity) would not be served. Note, however, that the egress path could be reduced in width in situations where it is wider than required by the code based on the occupant load. For example, if the required width of a corridor is 52 inches (1321 mm) based on the number of occupants using the corridor and the corridor provided is 96 inches (2438 mm) in width, the corridor would be allowed to be reduced to the minimum required width of 52 inches (1321 mm) since that width would still serve the number of occupants required by the code. In the context of this section, a "means of egress component" would most likely be a door or doorway.

[BE] 1003.7 Elevators, escalators and moving walks. Elevators, escalators and moving walks shall not be used as a component of a required *means of egress* from any other part of the building.

Exception: Elevators used as an *accessible means of egress* in accordance with Section 1009.4.

❖ Generally, the code does not allow elevators, escalators and moving sidewalks to be used as a required means of egress. The concern is that, because of possible power outages, escalators and moving sidewalks may not provide a safe and reliable means of egress that is available for use at all times.

Elevators are not typically used for unassisted evacuation during fire emergencies. However, in taller buildings, fire fighters use the elevators for both staging to fight the fire and assisted evacuation. They can verify that the shaft is not full of smoke, that the elevators will remain operational and, since they know the fire location, at which floors the elevator can be safely accessed. In accordance with the exception, elevators are allowed to be part of an accessible means of egress (i.e., assisted evacuation), provided they comply with the requirements of Section 1009.4. Where elevators are required to serve as part of the accessible means of egress is addressed in Section 1009.2.1. There are new provisions for fire service elevators and occupant evacuation elevators for high-rise buildings in IBC Sections 403, 3007 and 3008. These specific provisions will provide a level of safety that would meet the intent of the means of egress provisions in Chapter 10.

SECTION 1004
OCCUPANT LOAD

[BE] 1004.1 Design occupant load. In determining *means of egress* requirements, the number of occupants for whom *means of egress* facilities are provided shall be determined in accordance with this section.

❖ The design occupant load is the number of people intended to occupy a building or portion thereof at any one time; essentially, the number for which the means of egress is to be designed. It is the largest number derived by the application of Sections 1004.1 through 1004.8. Occupant density is limited to ensure a reasonable amount of freedom of movement (see Section 1004.5.1). The design occupant load is also utilized to determine the required plumbing fixture count (see commentary, Chapter 29) and other building requirements, such as automatic sprinkler systems and fire alarm and detection systems (see Chapter 9).

The intent of this section is to indicate the procedure by which design occupant loads are determined. This is particularly important because accurate determination of design occupant load is fundamental to the proper design of any means of egress system.

[BE] 1004.2 Cumulative occupant loads. Where the path of egress travel includes intervening rooms, areas or spaces, cumulative *occupant loads* shall be determined in accordance with this section.

❖ When occupants from an accessory area move through another area to exit, the combined number of occupants must be utilized to determine the capacity that the egress components must accommodate. It is not the intent of this section to "double count" occupants. For example, the means of egress from a lobby must be sized for the cumulative occupant load of the adjacent office spaces if the occupants must travel through the lobby to reach an exit. Likewise, if an adjacent room has an egress route independent of the lobby, the occupant load of that room would not be combined with the occupant loads of the other rooms that pass through the lobby. If a portion of the adjacent room's occupant load is to travel through the lobby, only that portion would be combined with the lobby occupant load for determining lobby egress (see Commentary Figure 1004.2). This is particularly important in determining the number of ways out of a space or off a story and the required capacity of those elements.

[BE] 1004.2.1 Intervening spaces or accessory areas. Where occupants egress from one or more rooms, areas or spaces through others, the design *occupant load* shall be the combined *occupant load* of interconnected accessory or intervening spaces. Design of egress path capacity shall be based on the cumulative portion of *occupant loads* of all rooms, areas or spaces to that point along the path of egress travel.

❖ An example of intervening spaces could be small tenant spaces within a large mercantile. It is common for banks or coffee shops to be located within large grocery stores. Another example would be a dentist's office where people in the staff and exam room areas would egress through the reception area.

[BE] 1004.2.2 Adjacent levels for mezzanines. That portion of the *occupant load* of a *mezzanine* with required egress through a room, area or space on an adjacent level shall be added to the *occupant load* of that room, area or space.

❖ The egress requirements for mezzanines that use exit access stairways to move to the ground level are handled similarly to those spaces with accessory areas addressed in Section 1004.2.1, versus the requirements for exiting from multiple stories in Sections 1004.2.3, 1005.3.1 and 1006. That is, that portion of the mezzanine occupant load that travels through the space below to get to the exit is to be added to the occupant load of the space on the floor below. The sizing and number of the egress components must reflect this combined occupant load. Section 505.2.3 contains additional criteria for the means of egress from mezzanines.

[BE] 1004.2.3 Adjacent stories. Other than for the egress components designed for convergence in accordance with Section 1005.6, the *occupant load* from separate stories shall not be added.

❖ Egress design for stories is typically not additive. For example, second-floor egress requirements that use exit access stairways to move to the ground level are coordinated with the requirements for exiting from multiple stories found in Sections 1005.3.1 and 1006. That is, the portion of the second floor occupant load that travels through the floor below to the exit is not to be added to the occupant load of the space on the floor below as you would for a mezzanine. The sizing and number of egress components do not have to reflect this combined occupant load. The exception to the rule is where there would be egress convergence of two stories at a level between the two stories (see Section 1005.6).

[BE] 1004.3 Multiple-function occupant load. Where an area under consideration contains multiple functions having different occupant load factors, the design *occupant load* for such area shall be based on the floor area of each function calculated independently.

❖ Table 1004.5, utilized for determining the occupant load for a space or a building, uses the term "function of space" instead of occupancy. The occupant load is determined by dividing either the net or gross floor area of the space by the occupant load factor. "Floor area, gross" and "Floor area, net" are defined in Chapter 2.

In buildings with different functions of space, the areas are considered separately. In other words, spaces with net floor area requirements are calculated and removed from the total area before applying gross floor area requirements. For example, an office building's 15-square-foot net floor area for loose tables and chairs would determine the occupant load in its conference rooms, and the 100-square-foot gross floor area for business would determine the occupant load for the rest of the areas in the building. There can be function areas within the same room. A fast-food restaurant is a good example of multiple uses in the same space. To determine occupant load, a designer could use a 7-square-foot net area for assembly standing space for the waiting area in front of the order counters; a combination 30-square-foot net area for unconcentrated assembly of loose tables and chairs and Section 1004.6 for fixed seating for the dining areas; and a 200-square-foot gross area for the commercial kitchen areas behind the counter. Not all buildings have occupant loads for all spaces. The fast-food restaurant example might not have an assigned occupant load for the toilet rooms or the corridor leading to the toilet rooms.

[BE] 1004.4 Multiple occupancies. Where a building contains two or more occupancies, the *means of egress* requirements shall apply to each portion of the building based on the occupancy of that space. Where two or more occupancies utilize portions of the same *means of egress* system, those egress components shall meet the more stringent requirements of all occupancies that are served.

❖ Since the means of egress systems are designed for the specific occupancy of a space, the provisions of this chapter are to be applied based on the actual occupancy conditions of the space served. See also Sections 508 and 1016.2.

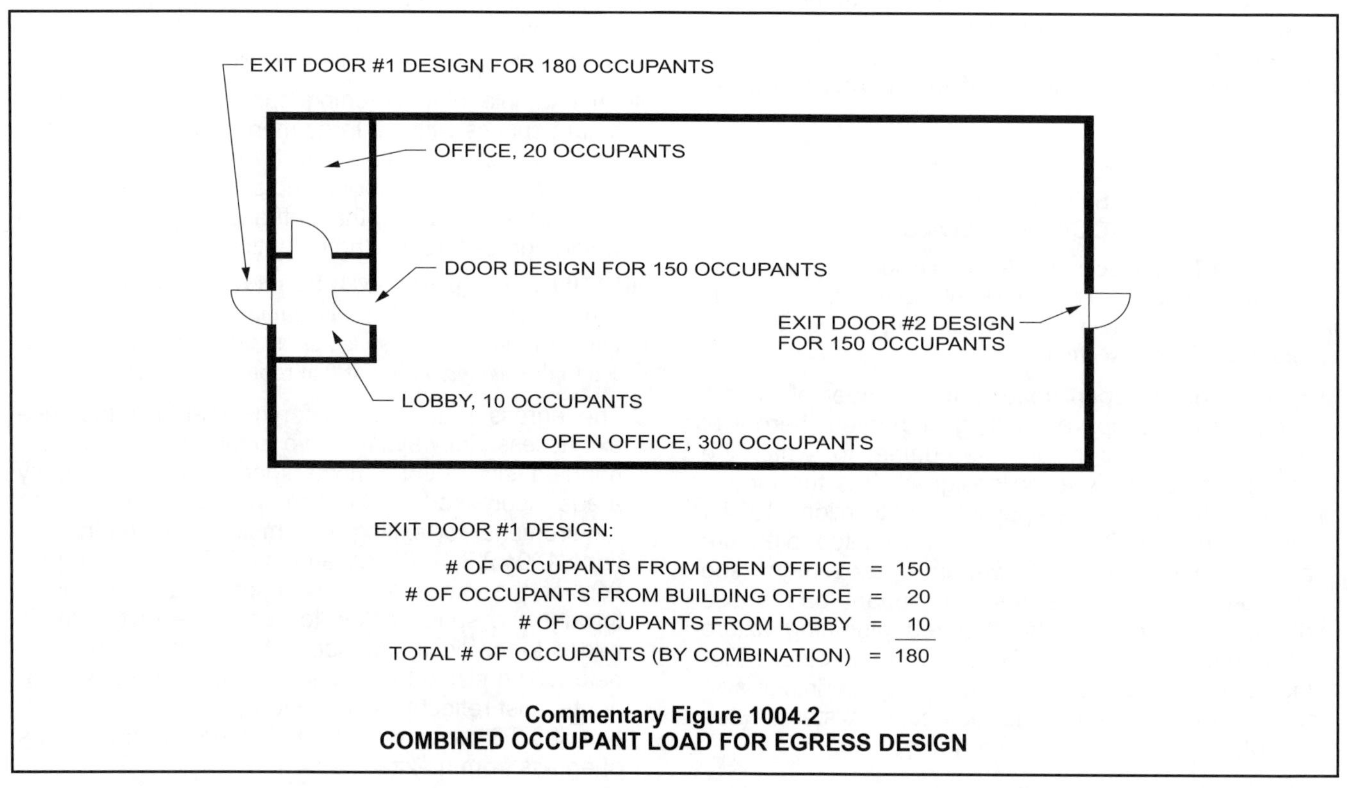

Commentary Figure 1004.2
COMBINED OCCUPANT LOAD FOR EGRESS DESIGN

For example, a hospital is classified as Group I-2. Patient care areas and the associated administrative or business functions can be in different areas or mixed together in the building. Chapter 3 would permit the entire building to be constructed to the more restrictive provisions for Group I-2; however, each area of the building need only have the means of egress designed in accordance with the actual occupancy conditions, such as Groups I-2 and B. If the corridor serves only the occupants in the business use (i.e., administrative staff), and is not intended to serve as a required means of egress for patients, the corridor need only be 36 or 44 inches (914 or 1118 mm) in width, depending on the occupant load.

Where the corridor is used by both Group I-2 and B occupancies, it must meet the most stringent requirement. For example, if a corridor in the business area is also used for the movement of beds (i.e., exit access from a patient care area), it would need to be a minimum of 96 inches (2438 mm) in clear width.

[BE] 1004.5 Areas without fixed seating. The number of occupants shall be computed at the rate of one occupant per unit of area as prescribed in Table 1004.5. For areas without *fixed seating*, the occupant load shall be not less than that number determined by dividing the floor area under consideration by the *occupant load* factor assigned to the function of the space as set forth in Table 1004.5. Where an intended function is not listed in Table 1004.5, the *fire code official* shall establish a function based on a listed function that most nearly resembles the intended function.

> **Exception:** Where *approved* by the *fire code official*, the actual number of occupants for whom each occupied space, floor or building is designed, although less than those determined by calculation, shall be permitted to be used in the determination of the design *occupant load*.

❖ The numbers for floor area per occupant load factor in Table 1004.5 reflect common and traditional occupant density based on empirical data for the density of similar spaces. The number determined using the occupant load factors in Table 1004.5 generally establishes the minimum occupant load for which the egress facilities of the rooms, spaces and building must be designed. The design occupant load is also utilized for other code requirements, such as determining the required plumbing fixture count (see commentary, IBC Chapter 29) and other building requirements, including automatic sprinkler systems and alarm and detection systems (see Chapter 9).

It is difficult to predict the many conditions by which a space within a building will be occupied over time. An assembly banquet room in a hotel, for example, could be arranged with rows of chairs to host a business seminar one day and with mixed tables and chairs to host a dinner reception the next day. In some instances, the room will be arranged with no tables and very few chairs to accommodate primarily standing occupants. In such a situation, the egress facilities must safely accommodate the maximum number of persons permitted to occupy the space. When determining the occupant load of this type of occupancy, the various arrangements (e.g., tables and chairs, chairs only, standing space) should be recognized. The worst-case scenario should be utilized to determine the requirements for the means of egress elements. This is consistent with the requirements for multiple-use spaces addressed in Section 302.1.

While some of the values in the table utilize the net floor area, most utilize the gross floor area. See the commentary to Table 1004.5 and the definitions for "Floor area, gross" and "Floor area, net" in Chapter 2 for additional discussion and examples.

The occupant load determined in accordance with this section is typically the minimum occupant load on which means of egress requirements are to be based. Some occupancies may not typically contain an occupant load totally consistent with the occupant load density factors of Table 1004.5. The exception is intended to address the limited circumstances where the actual occupant load is less than the calculated occupant load. Previously, designing for a reduced occupant load was permitted only through the variance process. With this exception, the building official can make a determination if a design that would use the actual occupant load was permissible. The building official may want to create specific conditions for approval. For example, the building official could choose to permit the actual occupant load to be utilized to determine the plumbing fixture count, but not the means of egress or sprinkler design; the determination could be that the reduced occupant load may be utilized in a specific area, such as in the storage warehouse, but not in the factory or office areas. Another point to consider would be the potential of the space being utilized for different purposes at different times, or the potential of a future change of tenancy without knowledge of the building department. Any special considerations for such unique uses must be documented and justified. Additionally, the owner must be aware that such special considerations will impact the future use of the building with respect to the means of egress and other protection features.

TABLE 1004.5. See page 10-12.

❖ Table 1004.5 establishes minimum occupant densities based on the function or actual use of the space (not group classification). The table presents the maximum floor area allowance per occupant (i.e., occupant load factor) based on studies and counts of the number of occupants in typical buildings. The use of this table, then, results in the minimum occupant load for which rooms, spaces and the building must be designed. While an assumed normal occupancy may be viewed as somewhat less than that determined by the use of the table factors, such a normal occupant load is not necessarily an appropriate design criterion. The greatest hazard to the occupants occurs where an unusually large crowd is present. The code does

[BE] TABLE 1004.5
MAXIMUM FLOOR AREA ALLOWANCES PER OCCUPANT

FUNCTION OF SPACE	OCCUPANT LOAD FACTOR[a]
Accessory storage areas, mechanical equipment room	300 gross
Agricultural building	300 gross
Aircraft hangars	500 gross
Airport terminal	
Baggage claim	20 gross
Baggage handling	300 gross
Concourse	100 gross
Waiting areas	15 gross
Assembly	
Gaming floors (keno, slots, etc.)	11 gross
Exhibit gallery and museum	30 net
Assembly with fixed seats	See Section 1004.4
Assembly without fixed seats	
Concentrated (chairs only – not fixed)	7 net
Standing space	5 net
Unconcentrated (tables and chairs)	15 net
Bowling centers, allow 5 persons for each lane including 15 feet of runway, and for additional areas	7 net
Business areas	150 gross
Concentrated business use areas	See Section 1004.8
Courtrooms – other than fixed seating areas	40 net
Day care	35 net
Dormitories	50 gross
Educational	
Classroom area	20 net
Shops and other vocational room areas	50 net
Exercise rooms	50 gross
Group H-5 fabrication and manufacturing areas	200 gross
Industrial areas	100 gross
Institutional areas	
Inpatient treatment areas	240 gross
Outpatient areas	100 gross
Sleeping areas	120 gross
Kitchens, commercial	200 gross
Library	
Reading rooms	50 net
Stack area	100 gross
Locker rooms	50 gross
Mall buildings – covered and open	See Section 402.8.2 of the *International Building Code*
Mercantile	60 gross
Storage, stock, shipping areas	300 gross
Parking garages	200 gross
Residential	200 gross
Skating rinks, swimming pools	
Rink and pool	50 gross
Decks	15 gross
Stages and platforms	15 net
Warehouses	500 gross

For SI: 1 square foot = 0.0929 m^2, 1 foot = 304.8 mm.

a. Floor area in square feet per occupant.

not limit the occupant load density of an area, except as provided for in Section 1004.5.1, but once the occupant load is established, the means of egress must be designed for at least that capacity. If it is intended that the occupant load will exceed that calculated in accordance with the table, then the occupant load is to be based on the estimated actual number of people, but not to exceed the maximum allowance in accordance with Section 1004.5.1. Therefore, the occupant load of the office or business areas in a storage warehouse or nightclub is to be determined using the occupant load factor most appropriate to that space—one person for each 150 square feet (13.9 m^2) of gross floor area.

The use of net and gross floor areas as defined in Chapter 2 is intended to provide a refinement in the occupant load determination. The gross floor area technique applied to a building only allows the deduction of the exterior walls, vent shafts and interior courts from the plan area of the building.

The net floor area permits the exclusion of certain spaces that would be included in the gross floor area. The net floor area is intended to apply to the actual occupied floor areas. The area used for permanent building components, such as shafts, fixed equipment, thicknesses of walls, corridors, stairways, toilet rooms, mechanical rooms and closets, is not included in net floor area. For example, consider a restaurant dining area with dimensions, measured from the inside of the enclosing walls, of 80 feet by 60 feet (24 384 mm by 18 288 mm) (see Commentary Figure 1004.5). Within the restaurant area is a 6-inch (152 mm) privacy wall running the length of the room [80 feet by 0.5 feet = 40 square feet (3.7 m^2)], a fireplace [40 square feet (3.7 m^2)] and a cloak room [60 square feet (5.6 m^2)]. Each of these areas is deducted from the restaurant area, resulting in a net floor area of 4,660 square feet (433 m^2). Since the restaurant intends to have unconcentrated seating that involves loose tables and chairs, the resulting occupant load is 311 persons (4,660 divided by 15). As the definition of "Floor area, net" indicates, certain spaces are to be excluded from the gross floor area to derive the net floor area. The key point in this definition is that the net floor area is to include the actual occupied area and does not include spaces uncharacteristic of that occupancy.

In determining the occupant load of a building with mixed groups, each floor area of a single occupancy must be separately analyzed, such as required by Section 1004.4. The occupant load of the business portion of an office/warehouse building is determined at a rate of one person for each 150 square feet (13.9 m^2) of office space, whereas the occupant load of the warehouse portion is determined at the rate of one person for each 300 square feet (28 m^2). There may even be different uses within the same room. For example, a restaurant dining room would have seating but may also have a waiting area with standing room, a take-out window with a queue line or employee areas behind a bar or reception desk.

If a specific type of facility is not found in the table, the occupancy it most closely resembles should be utilized. For example, a training room in a business office may utilize the 20-square-feet (1.86 m^2) net established for educational classroom areas, or a dance or karate studio may use the occupant load for rinks and pools for the studio areas.

Table 1004.5 presents a method of determining the absolute base minimum occupant load of a space that the means of egress is to accommodate.

The table occupant loads are based on the stereotypical configuration of spaces. For example, the dorm requirements were written based on dormitories with sleeping rooms with two to four students, a gang bathroom and a meeting/study lounge on each floor. Dormitory buildings that operate like army barracks may have a heavier occupant load, while facilities with groups of rooms with private bathrooms, living and even kitchenette areas may have a lower occupant load. Industrial facilities are based on typical fabricating plants. Warehouses are based on consistent in and out movement of product by employees. Factories with largely mechanized operations or warehouses that contain long-term storage are other examples where discussion with the building official and the application of the exception in Section 1004.5 might be considered.

In addition to the table, IBC Section 402 contains the basis for calculating the occupant load of a covered mall building; however, Table 1004.5 should be used for determining the occupant load of each anchor store.

[BE] 1004.5.1 Increased occupant load. The *occupant load* permitted in any building, or portion thereof, is permitted to be increased from that number established for the occupancies in Table 1004.5, provided that all other requirements of the code are met based on such modified number and the *occupant load* does not exceed one occupant per 7 square feet (0.65 m^2) of occupiable floor space. Where required by the *fire code official*, an *approved aisle*, seating or fixed equipment diagram substantiating any increase in *occupant load*

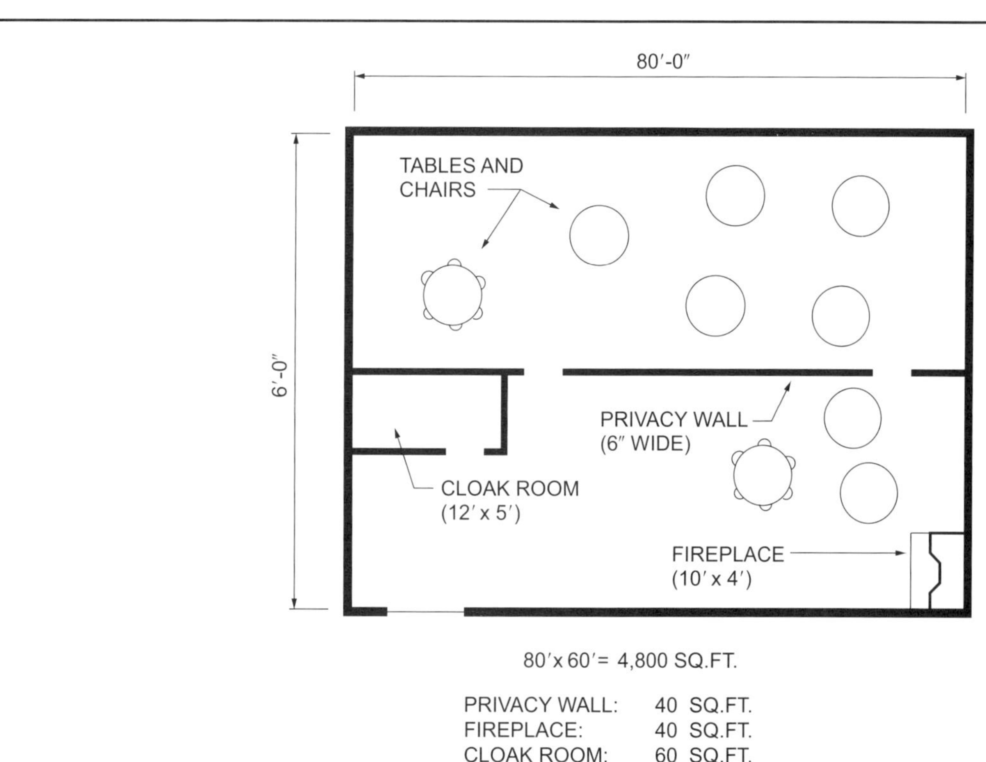

80′ x 60′ = 4,800 SQ.FT.

PRIVACY WALL:	40 SQ.FT.
FIREPLACE:	40 SQ.FT.
CLOAK ROOM:	60 SQ.FT.
TOTAL:	140 SQ.FT.

(TOTAL AREA WITHIN WALLS) - (EXCLUDED ITEMS) = (NET FLOOR AREA)
4,800 SQ.FT. - 140 SQ.FT. = 4,660 SQ.FT.

(NET FLOOR AREA)/(TABLE 1004.5 VALUE) = (OCCUPANT LOAD)
4,660 SQ.FT./15 SQ.FT. PER OCCUPANT = 311 OCCUPANTS

For SI: 1 inch = 25.4 mm, 1 foot = 304.8 mm, 1 square foot = 0.0929 m^2.

Commentary Figure 1004.5
TYPICAL NET FLOOR AREA OCCUPANT LOAD CALCULATION

shall be submitted. Where required by the *fire code official*, such diagram shall be posted.

❖ An increased occupant load is permitted above that developed by using Table 1004.5, for example, by utilizing the actual occupant load. However, if the occupant load exceeds that which is determined in accordance with Section 1004.5, the building official has the authority to require aisle, seating and equipment diagrams to confirm that all occupants have access to an exit, the exits provide sufficient capacity for all occupants and compliance with this section is attained.

The maximum area of 7 square feet (0.65 m^2) per occupant should allow for sufficient occupant movement in actual fire situations. This is not a conflict with the standing space provisions of 5 square feet (0.46 m^2) net area in accordance with Table 1004.5. Standing space is typically limited to a portion of a larger area, such as the area immediately in front of the bar or the waiting area in a restaurant, while the rest of the dining area would use 15 square feet (1.4 m^2) net area per occupant.

[BE] 1004.6 Fixed seating. For areas having *fixed seats* and *aisles*, the *occupant load* shall be determined by the number of *fixed seats* installed therein. The *occupant load* for areas in which *fixed seating* is not installed, such as waiting spaces, shall be determined in accordance with Section 1004.5 and added to the number of *fixed seats*.

The *occupant load* of wheelchair spaces and the associated companion seat shall be based on one occupant for each *wheelchair space* and one occupant for the associated companion seat provided in accordance with Section 1108.2.3 of the *International Building Code*.

For areas having *fixed seating* without dividing arms, the *occupant load* shall be not less than the number of seats based on one person for each 18 inches (457 mm) of seating length.

The *occupant load* of seating booths shall be based on one person for each 24 inches (610 mm) of booth seat length measured at the backrest of the seating booth.

❖ The occupant load in an area with fixed seats is readily determined. In spaces with a combination of fixed and loose seating, the occupant load is determined by a combination of the occupant density number from Table 1004.5 and a count of the fixed seats.

For bleachers, booths and other seating facilities without dividing arms, the occupant load is simply based on the number of people that can be accommodated in the length of the seat. Measured at the hips, an average person occupies about 18 inches (457 mm) on a bench. In a booth, additional space is necessary for "elbow room" while eating. In a circular or curved booth or bench, the measurement should be taken just a few inches from the back of the seat, which is where a person's hips would be located (see Commentary Figure 1004.6).

Some assembly spaces may have areas for standing or waiting. For example, some large sports stadiums have "standing room only" areas used for sell-out games. The Globe Theater in England has standing room in an area at the front of the theater. This

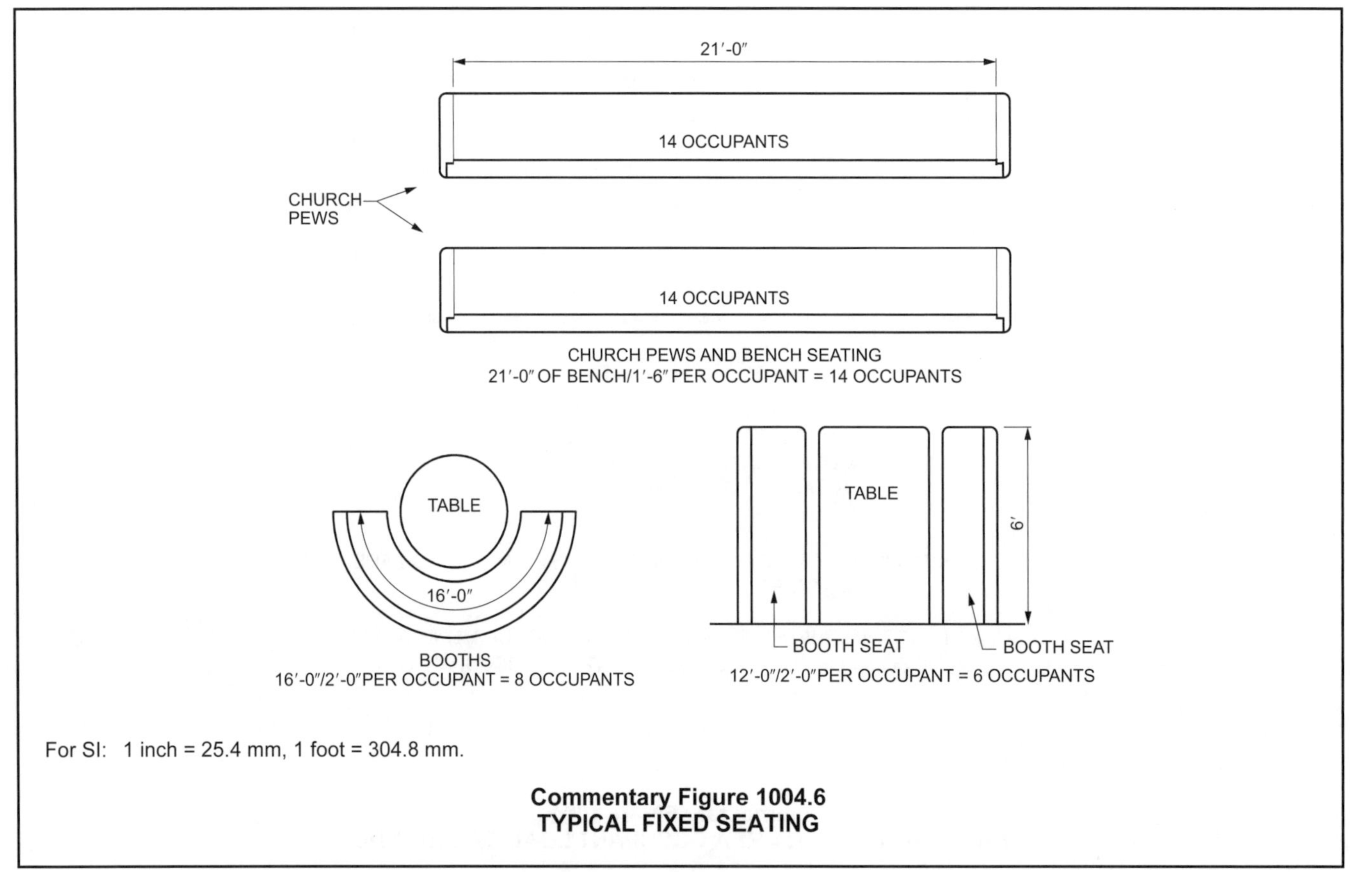

Commentary Figure 1004.6
TYPICAL FIXED SEATING

section is not intended to assign an occupant load to the typical circulation aisles in an assembly space. Occupant load for wheelchair spaces should be based on the number of wheelchairs and companion seats that the space was designed for. As specified in Section 1004.4, if the wheelchair spaces may also be utilized for standing space or removable seating, the occupant load must be determined by the worst-case scenario.

[BE] 1004.7 Outdoor areas. *Yards*, patios, occupied roofs, *courts* and similar outdoor areas accessible to and usable by the building occupants shall be provided with *means of egress* as required by this chapter. The *occupant load* of such outdoor areas shall be assigned by the *fire code official* in accordance with the anticipated use. Where outdoor areas are to be used by persons in addition to the occupants of the building, and the path of egress travel from the outdoor areas passes through the building, *means of egress* requirements for the building shall be based on the sum of the *occupant loads* of the building plus the outdoor areas.

Exceptions:

1. Outdoor areas used exclusively for service of the building need only have one *means of egress*.
2. Both outdoor areas associated with Group R-3 and individual dwelling units of Group R-2.

❖ This section addresses the means of egress of outdoor areas such as yards, patios, occupied roofs and courts. The primary concern is for those outdoor areas, used for functions that may include occupants other than the building occupants or the building occupants alone, where egress from the outdoor area is back through the building to reach the exit discharge. An example is an interior court of an office building where assembly functions are held during normal business hours for persons other than the building occupants. Where court occupants must egress from the interior court back through the building, the building's egress system is to be designed for the building occupants plus the assembly occupants from the interior court. Another example would be an outdoor dining area that exited back through the restaurant.

The occupant load is to be assigned by the building official based on the function of the space. It is suggested that the design occupant load be determined in accordance with Section 1004.5.

Exception 1 describes conditions where the occupant load is very limited, such as areas where an interior courtyard or roof has strictly plants or mechanical equipment. If the courtyard or roof is open for building occupants, other than maintenance personnel, to use the space, the space must be designed with the occupant loads in Table 1004.5. Balconies or patios associated with individual dwelling units, addressed in Exception 2, would typically be used by the occupants of the unit. Means of egress can be back through the building in accordance with Section 1016.2.

[BE] 1004.8 Concentrated business use areas. The occupant load factor for concentrated business use shall be applied to telephone call centers, trading floors, electronic data processing centers and similar business use areas with a higher density of occupants than would normally be expected in a typical business occupancy environment. Where approved by the code official, the occupant load for concentrated business use areas shall be the actual *occupant load*, but not less than one occupant per 50 square feet (4.65 m^2) of gross occupiable floor space.

❖ An average office space uses an occupant load factor of 150 square feet (13.9 m^2) per person. In recognition of the unique configurations and limited work space provided within businesses such as telephone call centers, trading floors and electronic data processing centers, a higher density of occupants is anticipated. The designer should provide information to the code official based on the actual occupant load anticipated for such areas. In no case should those numbers be less than 50 square feet (4.65 m^2) per person for determining the means of egress capacity and the numbers of plumbing fixtures.

[BE] 1004.9 Posting of occupant load. Every room or space that is an assembly occupancy shall have the *occupant load* of the room or space posted in a conspicuous place, near the main *exit* or *exit access* doorway from the room or space, for the intended configurations. Posted signs shall be of an *approved* legible permanent design and shall be maintained by the owner or the owner's authorized agent.

❖ Each room or space used for an assembly occupancy is required to display the approved occupant load. The placard must be posted in a visible location (near the main entrance) (see Commentary Figure 1004.9 for an example of an occupant load limit sign).

NOTICE
FOR YOUR SAFETY
OCCUPANCY
IS LIMITED TO:
428
PERSONS
BY ORDER OF
THE CODE OFFICIAL
Keep Posted Under Penalty Of Law

Commentary Figure 1004.9
EXAMPLE OF OCCUPANT LOAD LIMIT SIGN

The posting is required to provide a means by which to determine that the maximum approved occupant load is not exceeded. This permanent and readily visible sign provides a constant reminder to building personnel and is a reference for building officials during periodic inspections. The posted occupant load could also be an indication that the room was designed for a layout of just tables and chairs, not a layout of chairs only.

While the composition and organization of information in the sign are not specified, information must be recorded in a permanent manner. This means that a sign with changeable numbers would not be acceptable.

SECTION 1005
MEANS OF EGRESS SIZING

[BE] 1005.1 General. All portions of the *means of egress* system shall be sized in accordance with this section.

Exception: *Aisles* and *aisle accessways* in rooms or spaces used for assembly purposes complying with Section 1029.

❖ This section is a charging paragraph for sizing the means of egress system in a tenant space, floor or building. The exception is based on the understanding that means of egress paths within assembly areas have unique criteria based on the high occupant load and possibility of stepped or sloped aisles.

[BE] 1005.2 Minimum width based on component. The minimum width, in inches (mm), of any *means of egress* components shall be not less than that specified for such component, elsewhere in this code.

❖ The code requires the utilization of two methods to determine the minimum width of egress components. While this section provides a methodology for determining required widths based on the design occupant load calculated in accordance with Section 1004, other sections provide minimum widths of various components. The actual width that is provided is to be the larger of the two widths.

[BE] 1005.3 Required capacity based on occupant load. The required capacity, in inches (mm), of the *means of egress* for any room, area, space or story shall be not less than that determined in accordance with Sections 1005.3.1 and 1005.3.2.

❖ For this section, the sum of the capacities of the means of egress components that serve each space must equal or exceed the occupant load of that space. For example, the combined width of all of the exit stairways from a floor needs to be considered to determine if the stairways have adequate capacity for everyone to evacuate the building. All elements must meet the minimum width requirements specified in other sections (e.g., Section 1010.1.1 for doors, Sections 1009.3.2 and 1011.2 for stairs).

This section establishes the necessary width of each egress component on a "per-occupant" basis. Means of egress components are separated between "stairs" and "other," with "other" being doors, doorways, corridors, ramps, aisles, and so on.

The traditional unit of measurement of egress capacity was based on a "unit exit width" that was to simulate the body ellipse with a basic dimensional width of 22 inches (559 mm)—approximately the shoulder width of an average adult male. This unit exit width was combined with assumed egress movement (such as single file or staggered file) to result in an egress capacity per unit exit width for various occupancies. This assumption simplifies the dynamic egress process since contemporary studies have indicated that people do not egress in such precise and predictable movements. As traditionally used in the codes, the method of determining capacity per unit of clear width implies a higher level of accuracy than can realistically be achieved. The resulting factors preserve the features of the past practices that can be documented, while providing a more straightforward method of determining egress capacity.

[BE] 1005.3.1 Stairways. The capacity, in inches, of *means of egress stairways* shall be calculated by multiplying the *occupant load* served by such *stairways* by a *means of egress* capacity factor of 0.3 inch (7.6 mm) per occupant. Where *stairways* serve more than one story, only the *occupant load* of each story considered individually shall be used in calculating the required capacity of the *stairways* serving that story.

Exceptions:

1. For other than Group H and I-2 occupancies, the capacity, in inches, of *means of egress stairways* shall be calculated by multiplying the *occupant load* served by such *stairways* by a *means of egress* capacity factor of 0.2 inches (5.1 mm) per occupant in buildings equipped throughout with an *automatic sprinkler system* installed in accordance with Section 903.3.1.1 or 903.3.1.2 and an emergency voice/alarm communication system in accordance with Section 907.5.2.2.
2. Facilities with *smoke-protected assembly seating* shall be permitted to use the capacity factors in Table 1029.6.2 indicated for stepped *aisles* for *exit access* or *exit stairways* where the entire path for *means of egress* from the seating to the *exit discharge* is provided with a smoke control system complying with Section 909.
3. Facilities with *open-air assembly seating* shall be permitted to the capacity factors in Section 1029.6.3 indicated for stepped *aisles* for *exit access* or *exit stairways* where the entire path for *means of egress* from the seating to the *exit discharge* is open to the outdoors.

❖ The capacity factor for stairways is larger than "other egress components" because of the slowdown of travel to negotiate the steps. Where the required occupant capacity of an egress component is determined, multiplication by the appropriate factor results in the required clear width of the component in inches, based on capacity. Similarly, if the clear width of a component is known, division by the appropriate factor results in the permitted capacity of that component. In a multistory building, the size/capacity of the stairway is calculated using the occupant load from each story individually. While during an evacuation the persons closest to the stairway on upper floors may get to the same point on the stairway as a person who was farther into the building on a lower floor, studies have shown that using the occupant load for each floor separately is acceptable for calculation purposes. This is consistent with Section 1006.3.

Per Exception 1, other than in Group H or I-2, if the building is sprinklered and has an emergency voice/alarm communications system, the capacity factor for stairways is permitted to be reduced to 0.2 inch (5.1 mm) per occupant.

Venues with smoke-protected and open-air assembly seating are permitted to use a lower capacity number to determine the width of the egress components within the seating bowl. When designing the stepped aisles within the seating bowl, the provisions for Section 1029 are applicable. When designing components outside of the seating bowl, Section 1005.3 is applicable. Per Exceptions 2 and 3, if both the seating bowl and the entire route out of the building is smoke protected by mechanical means or open to the outside, the entire route can use the lower capacity numbers specified in Section 1029. For example, if an outdoor stadium has an enclosed concourse that spectators use to enter and exit the stadium seating, the lower open-air capacity numbers can be used to design the stepped aisles in the stadium, but the higher numbers for stairways must be used to size the stairways in the concourse. Only if the concourse is also open to the outside air can the lower open-air capacity numbers be used for the entire means of egress route. See the definitions of "Smoke-protected assembly seating" and "Open-air assembly seating" in Chapter 2. See also Sections 1029.6.2 and 1029.6.3.

The following examples illustrate typical calculations for stairways from a nonsprinklered, two-story, two-exit office building:

1. Determine the minimum required stairway width with a second-floor occupant load of 350:
   - 350 occupants multiplied by 0.3 inch (7.62 mm) = 105 inches (2667 mm) minimum.
   - 105 inches (2667 mm) divided by two stairways is $52^1/_2$ inches (1334 mm) minimum per stairway.
   - Section 1011.2 prescribes that the width of an interior stairway cannot be less than 44 inches (1118 mm).

For the first example, the capacity criteria are more restrictive; therefore, the minimum required width for each stairway is $52^1/_2$ inches (1334 mm).

2. Determine the minimum required stairway width with a second-floor occupant load of 90:
   - 90 occupants multiplied by 0.3 inch (7.62 mm) = 27 inches (686 mm) minimum.
   - 27 inches (686 mm) divided by two stairways is $13^1/_2$ inches (343 mm).
   - Section 1011.2 prescribes that the width of an interior stairway cannot be less than 44 inches (1118 mm). Note that the stair width reduction in Section 1011.2, Exception 1, is applicable only when the entire occupant load of a story is less than 50.

For the second example, the minimum clear width requirements are more restrictive; therefore, the minimum required width for each stairway is 44 inches (1118 mm).

The maximum capacity of a 44-inch (1118 mm) stairway is 44 inches divided by 0.3 inches (7.62 mm) per occupant = 146 occupants. Therefore, a floor level with two exit stairways could have 292 occupants before the capacity would control the stairway egress width.

Using the exception for sprinklered buildings, a 44-inch (1118 mm) stairway divided by 0.2 inch (5.08 mm) per occupant = 220 occupants. Therefore, a floor level with two exit stairways could have 440 occupants before the capacity would control the stairway egress width.

Keep in mind that accessible means of egress stairways in nonsprinklered buildings require a minimum clear width of 48 inches (1219 mm) between handrails (Section 1009.3.2).

[BE] 1005.3.2 Other egress components. The capacity, in inches, of *means of egress* components other than *stairways* shall be calculated by multiplying the *occupant load* served by such component by a *means of egress* capacity factor of 0.2 inch (5.1 mm) per occupant.

Exceptions:

1. For other than Group H and I-2 occupancies, the capacity, in inches, of *means of egress* components other than *stairways* shall be calculated by multiplying the *occupant load* served by such component by a *means of egress* capacity factor of 0.15 inches (3.8 mm) per occupant in buildings equipped throughout with an *automatic sprinkler system* installed in accordance with Section 903.3.1.1 or 903.3.1.2 and an emergency voice/alarm communication system in accordance with Section 907.5.2.2.
2. Facilities with *smoke-protected assembly seating* shall be permitted to use the capacity factors in Table 1029.6.2 indicated for level or ramped aisles for *means of egress* components other than *stairways* where the entire path for *means of egress* from the seating to the *exit discharge* is provided with a smoke control system complying with Section 909.

3. Facilities with *open-air assembly seating* shall be permitted to the capacity factors in Section 1029.6.3 indicated for level or ramped aisles for *means of egress* components other than *stairways* where the entire path for *means of egress* from the seating to the *exit discharge* is open to the outdoors.

❖ The capacity factor for "other egress components" (e.g., doors, gates, corridors, aisles, ramps) is less than stairways because of the slowdown of travel to negotiate the steps. When the required occupant capacity of an egress component is determined, multiplication by the appropriate factor results in the required clear width of the component in inches, based on capacity. Similarly, if the clear width of a component is known, division by the appropriate factor results in the permitted capacity of that component.

Per Exception 1, other than in Group H or I-2, if the building is sprinklered and has an emergency voice/alarm communications system, the capacity factor for doors, corridors, aisles, and so on, is permitted to be reduced to 0.15 inch (3.8 mm) per occupant.

Venues with smoke-protected and open-air seating are permitted to use a lower capacity number to determine the width of the egress components. When designing the ramped or level aisles and aisle accessways within the seating bowl, the provisions for Section 1029 are applicable. When designing components outside of the seating bowl, Section 1005.3 is applicable. Per Exceptions 2 and 3, if both the seating bowl and the entire route out of the building are smoke-protected by mechanical means or open to the outside, the entire route can use the lower capacity numbers. For example, if an outdoor stadium has an enclosed concourse that spectators use to enter and exit the stadium seating, the lower open-air capacity numbers can be used to design the ramped or level aisles in the stadium, but the higher numbers for other egress components must be used to size the corridors or ramps in the concourse. Only if the concourse is also open to the outside air can the lower open-air capacity numbers be used for the entire means of egress route. See the definitions of "Smoke-protected assembly seating" and "Open-air assembly seating" in Chapter 2. See also Sections 1029.6.2 and 1029.6.3.

For example, two exit access doorways from a room with an occupant load of 300 would each have a required capacity of not less than 150. Based on the minimum required clear door width [32-inch (813 mm) clear width per door divided by 0.2 inch (5.08 mm) per occupant = 160 occupants], two 32-inch (813 mm) clear width doors would meet both the minimum clear width (Section 1010.1.1) and the capacity requirements. Two exits from a space with an occupant load of 450 would each have a required capacity of not less than 225, necessitating more doors or larger door leaves.

Using Exception 1, the door capacity would increase [32-inch (813 mm) clear width per door divided by 0.15 inch (3.08 mm) per occupant = 213 occupants].

When determining the required capacity for the corridor, where the corridor runs in two directions to two different exits, similar to the room example, the number of occupants moving into the corridor to exit are divided by two. That is the number of occupants used to determine the minimum width. A 44-inch-wide corridor leading to two exits could have a total occupant load of 440 total (44-inch clear width divided by 0.2 inch per occupant = 220 occupants, multiplied by two directions = 440 total occupants) before a wider corridor would be required (see Section 1020.1 for minimum corridor width).

[BE] 1005.4 Continuity. The minimum width or required capacity of the *means of egress* required from any story of a building shall not be reduced along the path of egress travel until arrival at the *public way*.

❖ The requirement that both the minimum width and required capacity from any floor are to be provided along the entire exit to the termination, typically down the stairway to the exterior exit door at the level of exit discharge, results in an egress width that is adequate for the exit discharge.

The total capacity of the exits that serve a floor is not to be less than the occupant load of the floor as determined by Section 1004.1. If an exit, such as a stairway, also serves a second floor, and the required capacity of the exit serving the occupants of the second floor is greater than the first floor, the greater capacity would govern the egress components that the occupants of the floors share. For example, suppose an exit stairway serves two floors, with occupant loads of 300 on the lower floor and 500 on the upper floor. Assuming that two stairways serve each floor, and using the upper-floor occupant load of 500 as the basis of determination, the two stairways would be designed for a capacity of 250 people each. Note that the doors to the stairways on the lower floor would be designed for a capacity of 150 and the doors to the stairways on the upper floor would be designed for a capacity of 250. Reversing these two floors would result in the portion of the stairways that serves the upper floor to be designed for a capacity of 150 and the stairways that serve the lower floor to be designed for 250. Requiring the egress component to be designed for the largest tributary occupant load accommodates the worst-case situation.

Also note that the capacity of the exits is based on the occupant load of one floor. The occupant loads are not combined with other floors for the exit design. It is assumed that the peak demand or flow of occupants from more than one floor level will not occur simultaneously at a common point in the means of egress, except as provided for in Sections 1004.2.2 and 1005.6.

[BE] 1005.5 Distribution of minimum width and required capacity. Where more than one *exit*, or access to more than one *exit*, is required, the *means of egress* shall be configured such that the loss of any one *exit*, or access to one *exit*, shall not reduce the available capacity or width to less than 50 percent of the required capacity or width.

❖ It is critical that the distribution of both egress capacity and minimum width are examined. Where multiple means of egress are required, the loss of any one path cannot reduce the available capacity or width to less than 50 percent. The 50-percent minimum of the required egress capacity and width results in a fairly uniform distribution of egress paths. This requirement does not, however, require that the capacities be equally distributed where more than two means of egress are provided. An egress design with a dramatic imbalance of egress component capacities relative to occupant load distribution should be reviewed closely to avoid a needless delay in egressing a story or area. The balancing of the means of egress components, in accordance with the distribution of the occupant load, is reasonable and, in some cases, necessary for facilities having mixed occupancies with dramatically different occupant loads.

[BE] 1005.6 Egress convergence. Where the *means of egress* from stories above and below converge at an intermediate level, the capacity of the *means of egress* from the point of convergence shall be not less than the largest minimum width or the sum of the required capacities for the *stairways* or *ramps* serving the two adjacent stories, whichever is larger.

❖ Convergence of occupants can occur wherever the occupants of an upper floor travel down and occupants of a lower floor travel up and meet at a common, intermediate egress component on the route to the exit discharge. The intermediate component may or may not be another occupiable floor and, most often, is an exit door [see Commentary Figures 1005.6(1) and 1005.6(2)].

The entire premise of egress convergence is based on the assumption of simultaneous notification (i.e., all occupants of all floors begin moving toward the exits at the same time). As illustrated in Commentary Figure 1005.6(3), the occupants of the first floor will have exited the building by the time most of the occupants of the second floor have reached the exit discharge door. However, as illustrated in Commentary Figure 1005.6(1), the occupants of a basement will reach the discharge door simultaneously with the second-floor occupants, thereby creating a bottleneck and the need for sizing the affected component for a larger combined occupant load.

An egress convergence situation can also be created where an intermediate floor level is not present, as illustrated in Commentary Figure 1005.6(2). Again, under the assumption of simultaneous notification, occupants of both floors would reach the exit discharge door at approximately the same time, invoking the requirements for increased egress capacity.

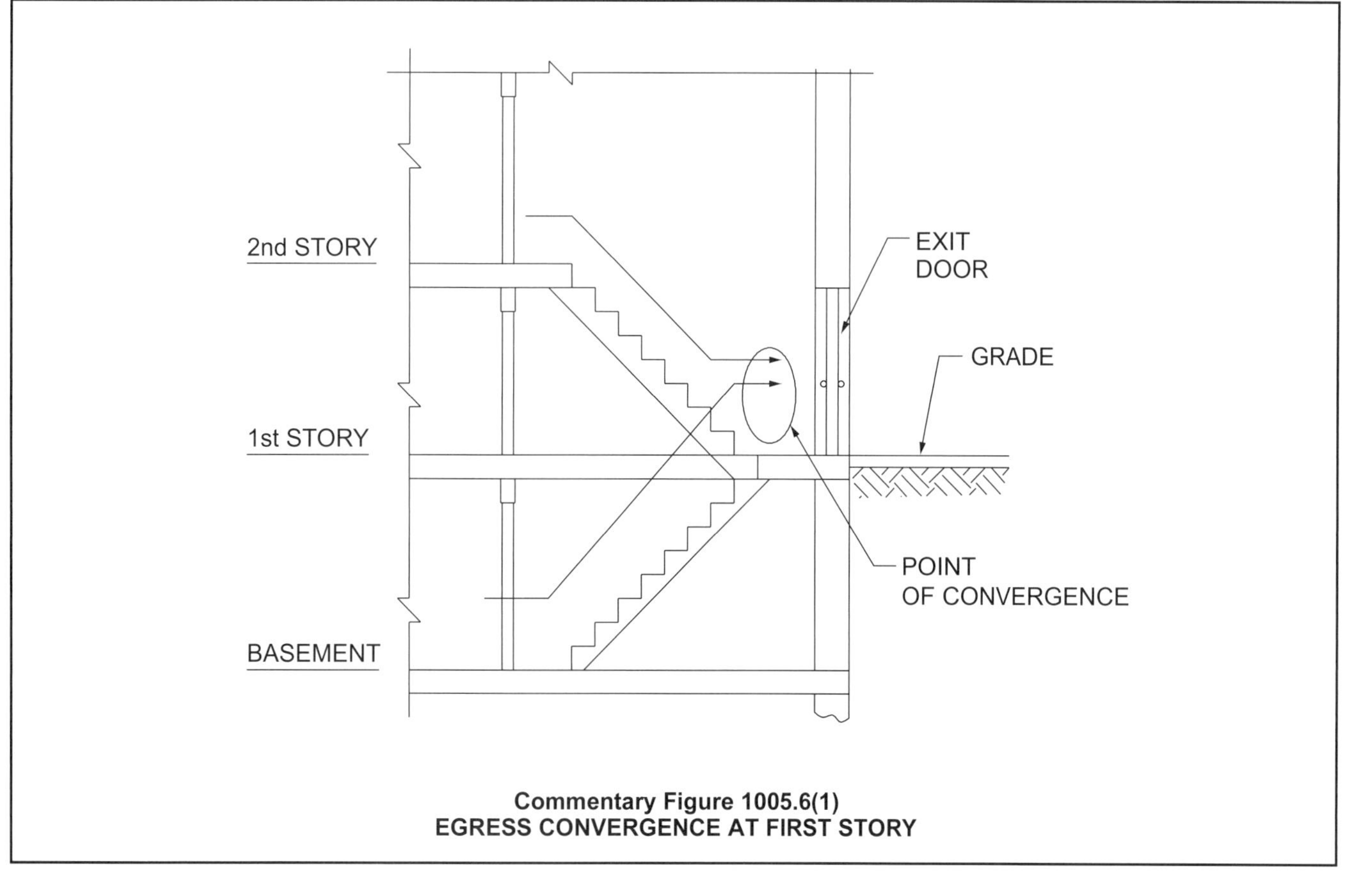

Commentary Figure 1005.6(1)
EGRESS CONVERGENCE AT FIRST STORY

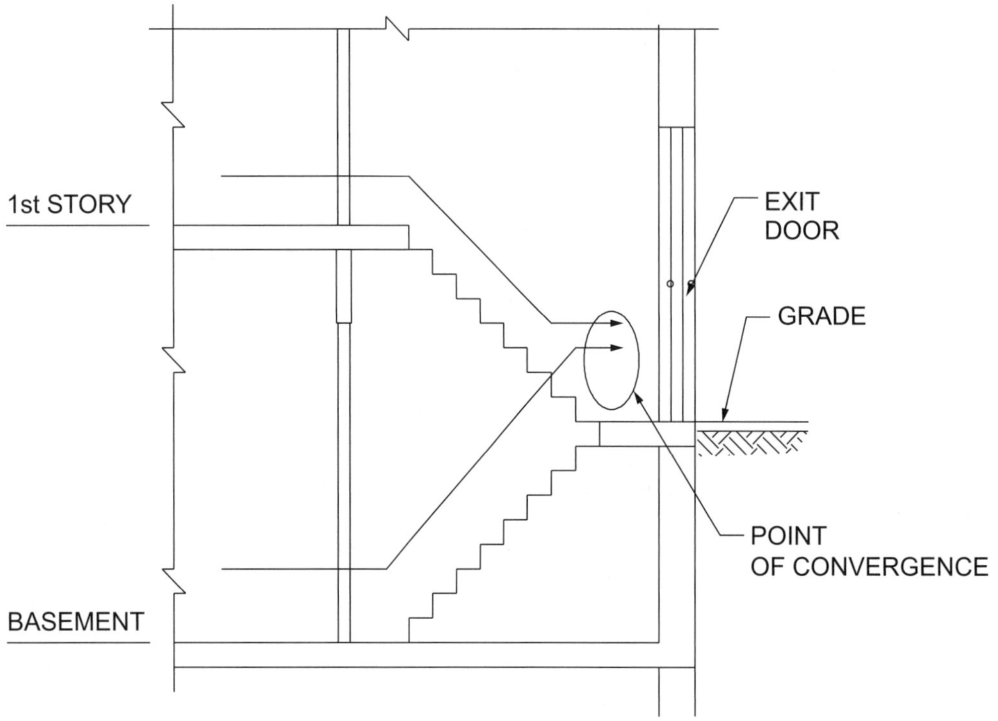

Commentary Figure 1005.6(2)
EGRESS CONVERGENCE AT INTERMEDIATE LEVEL

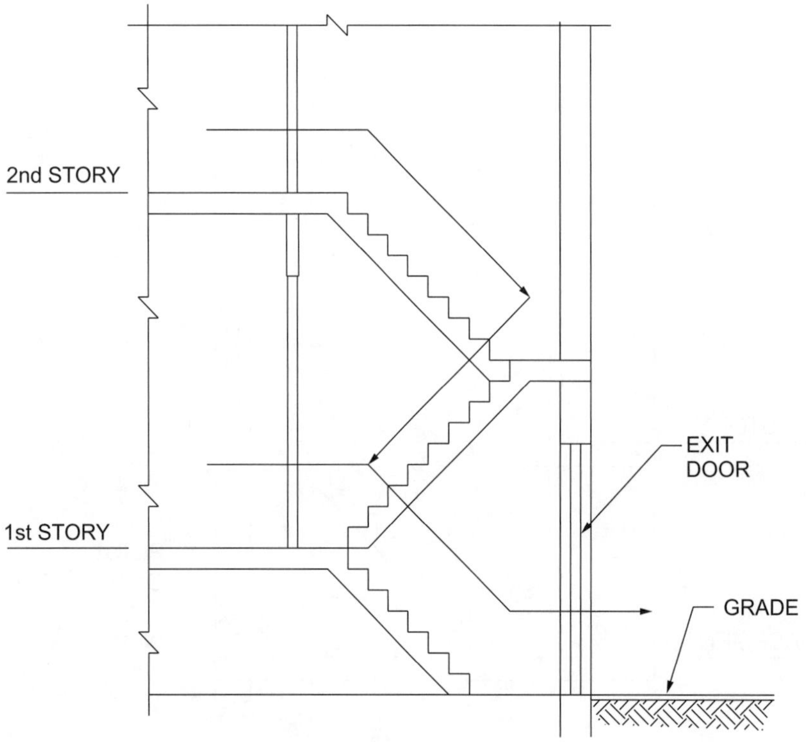

Commentary Figure 1005.6(3)
NO EGRESS CONVERGENCE

[BE] 1005.7 Encroachment. Encroachments into the required *means of egress* width shall be in accordance with the provisions of this section.

❖ This section addresses maximum encroachment into the required width along the path of travel for means of egress. Types of encroachment are door leaves, door hardware, handrails, trim and protruding objects. These requirements are referenced for aisles (Section 1018.1), corridors (Section 1020.3), exit passageways (Section 1024.2) and exit courts (Section 1028.4.1). Along stairways, handrail projections are permitted per Section 1014.8.

[BE] 1005.7.1 Doors. Doors, when fully opened, shall not reduce the required width by more than 7 inches (178 mm). Doors in any position shall not reduce the required width by more than one-half.

Exceptions:

1. Surface-mounted latch release hardware shall be exempt from inclusion in the 7-inch maximum (178 mm) encroachment where both of the following conditions exists:
   1.1. The hardware is mounted to the side of the door facing away from the adjacent wall where the door is in the open position.
   1.2. The hardware is mounted not less than 34 inches (865 mm) nor more than 48 inches (1219 mm) above the finished floor.
2. The restrictions on door swing shall not apply to doors within individual *dwelling units* and *sleeping units* of Group R-2 occupancies and *dwelling units* of Group R-3 occupancies.

❖ Projections or restrictions in the required width can impede and restrict occupant travel, causing egress to occur less efficiently than expected. The swinging of a door, such as from a room into a corridor, and any handrails along the route are permitted projections.

Historically, this section has looked at doors on one wall at a time. Doors located across the hall from one another are not considered additive when considering protrusion limits. Doors would not typically be opened to the full extent at exactly the same moment, nor can they remain open at 90 degrees and totally block the hall because of the maximum 7-inch (178 mm) encroachment limitation when fully open (typically approaching 180 degrees). Regarding door encroachment, there are two tests. The arc created by the door's outside edge cannot project into more than one-half of the required corridor width. When opened to its fullest extent, the door cannot project more than 7 inches (178 mm) into the required width, which is the dimension of the leaf thickness, excluding the hardware as shown in Commentary Figure 1005.7.1. Door hardware encroachment is addressed separately in Exception 1. These projections are permitted because they are considered to be temporary and do not significantly impede the flow. Occupants will compensate for the projection by a reduction in the natural cushion they retain between themselves and a boundary, known as the edge effect.

Per Exception 2, the door swing restrictions do not apply within dwelling units since the occupant load is very low. Based on the intent of this section, other situations that could be approved by the official having jurisdiction would be situations where the opening door would not block the egress, such as the door at the end of a corridor, or the room was not typically occupied, such as a janitor's closet.

The provision in Exception 1 indicates that hardware facing the corridor when the door is fully open need not be considered when determining the allowable door encroachment into a corridor of 7 inches (178 mm) maximum. The allowance is applicable pro-

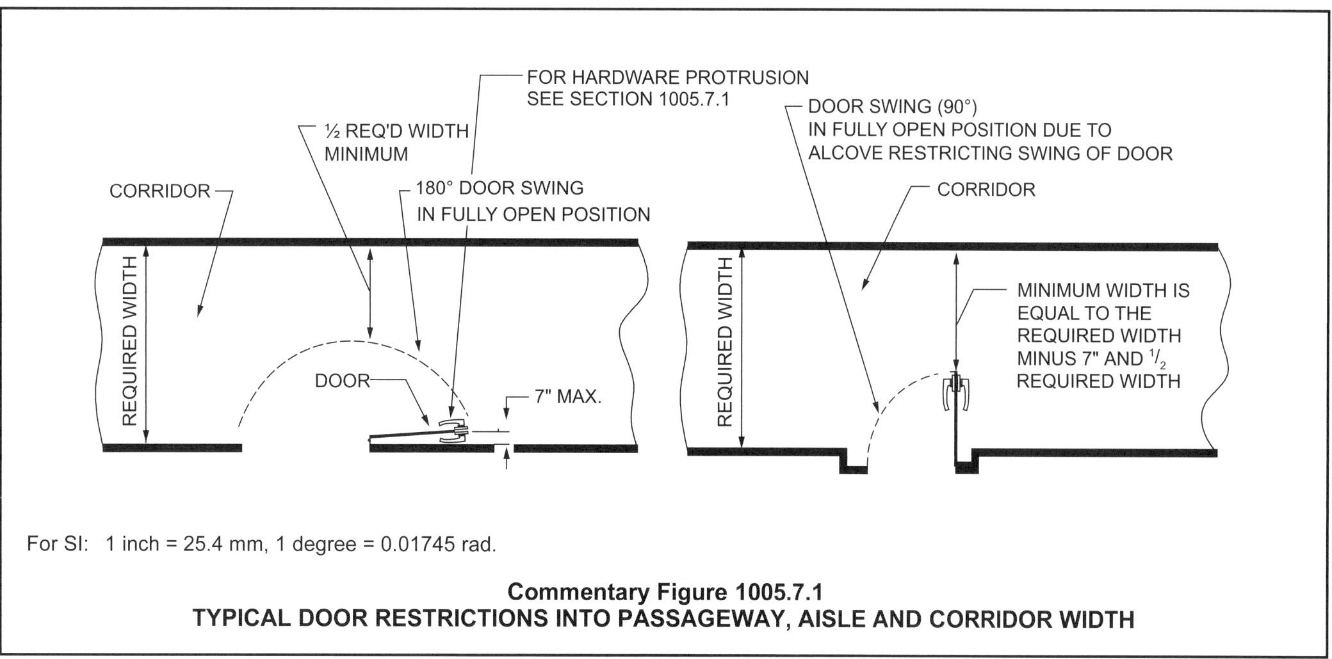

Commentary Figure 1005.7.1
TYPICAL DOOR RESTRICTIONS INTO PASSAGEWAY, AISLE AND CORRIDOR WIDTH

vided the hardware is mounted within a height range of 34 inches to 48 inches (865 to 1219 mm), which is consistent with the range for means of egress door hardware height as established in Section 1010.1.9.2. Where hardware extends across a door, such as panic hardware, the 4-inch (102 mm) projection in the door opening is addressed in Section 1010.1.1.1.

[BE] 1005.7.2 Other projections. *Handrail* projections shall be in accordance with the provisions of Section 1014.8. Other nonstructural projections such as trim and similar decorative features shall be permitted to project into the required width not more than $1^1/_2$ inches (38 mm) on each side.

Exception: Projections are permitted in corridors within Group I-2, Condition 1 in accordance with Section 407.4.3 of the *International Building Code*.

❖ Handrails are not required along corridors, level aisles, exit passageways and exit corridors; however, if provided, Section 1014.8 would be applicable. Handrails are sometimes provided along the hallways in hospitals or nursing homes to aid the residents. Bumper guards along the walls are not handrails.

Items such as baseboards, chair rails and pilasters are allowed to protrude over the required width of the corridor a maximum of $1^1/_2$ inches (38 mm); however, Section 1003.3.3 would be applicable for circulation paths where the corridors or aisles are wider than required.

The exception is in recognition of a situation unique to nursing homes (Group I-2, Condition 1). IBC Section 407.4.3 includes allowances for furniture in corridors to address patients needing a place to sit and rest as well as the new style of design that emphasizes the residential aspects of the environment.

[BE] 1005.7.3 Protruding objects. Protruding objects shall comply with the applicable requirements of Section 1003.3.

❖ This section is a reminder that requirements for protruding objects are applicable regarding encroachments into a confined path of travel. The difference, however, is that door and other projections are applied to the required minimum width, while protruding object provisions apply to circulation paths where aisles and corridors are wider than required.

SECTION 1006 NUMBERS OF EXITS AND EXIT ACCESS DOORWAYS

[BE] 1006.1 General. The number of *exits* or *exit access doorways* required within the *means of egress* system shall comply with the provisions of Section 1006.2 for spaces, including *mezzanines*, and Section 1006.3 for *stories* or occupied roofs.

❖ The criteria in this section to determine the number of ways to leave rooms or spaces (including mezzanines) and stories and occupied roofs are based on an empirical judgment of the associated risks. An occupied roof is a roof that can be used on a daily basis, such as a roof with a patio, pool or restaurant. A roof is not considered occupied if the only persons who typically access the roof are maintenance and service personnel.

[BE] 1006.2 Egress from spaces. Rooms, areas or spaces, including *mezzanines*, within a story or *basement* shall be provided with the number of *exits* or access to *exits* in accordance with this section.

❖ This section dictates the minimum number of paths of travel an occupant is to have available to avoid a fire incident in the occupied room or space. While providing multiple egress doorways from every room is unrealistic, a point does exist where alternative egress paths must be provided based on the number of occupants at risk, the distance any one occupant must travel to reach a doorway and the relative hazards associated with the occupancy of the space. Generally, the number of egress doorways required for any room or space coincides with the occupant load threshold criteria set forth for the minimum number of exits required for a story (see Section 1006.3). For the total exit access travel distance for these spaces, see Table 1017.2.

[BE] 1006.2.1 Egress based on occupant load and common path of egress travel distance. Two *exits* or *exit access doorways* from any space shall be provided where the design *occupant load* or the *common path of egress travel* distance exceeds the values listed in Table 1006.2.1. The cumulative *occupant load* from adjacent rooms, areas or spaces shall be determined in accordance with Section 1004.2.

Exceptions:

1. The number of exits from foyers, lobbies, vestibules or similar spaces need not be based on cumulative *occupant loads* for areas discharging through such spaces, but the capacity of the *exits* from such spaces shall be based on applicable cumulative *occupant loads*.
2. *Care suites* in Group I-2 occupancies complying with Section 407.4 of the *International Building Code*.

❖ The limiting criteria in Table 1006.2.1 for rooms or spaces permitted to have a single exit access doorway are based on an empirical judgment of the associated risks. For the total exit access travel distance for these space, see Table 1017.2.

If the occupants of a room are required to egress through another room, as permitted in Sections 1004.2 and 1016.2, the occupancies and egress travel distances of the rooms are to be combined to determine if multiple doorways are required from the combined rooms. For example, if a suite of offices shares a common reception area, the entire suite with the reception area must meet both the occupant load and the travel distance criteria. The same logic applies to a space with a mezzanine (see Section 1004.2.2). If the space is just a passage space, such as a vestibule, this is not considered a situation that is a cumulative occupant load (Exception 1).

It should be noted that where two doorways are required, the remoteness requirement of Section 1007.1 is applicable.

The common path of travel is the distance measured from the most remote point in a space to the point in the exit path where the occupant has access to two required exits in separate directions. The distance limitations are applicable to all paths of travel that lead out of a space or building where two exits are required. An illustration of this distance is found in Commentary Figure 1006.2.1. The illustration reflects two examples of a common path of travel where the occupants at points A and B are able to travel in only one direction before they reach a point at which they have a choice of two paths of travel to the required exits from the building. Note that from point A, the occupants have two available paths, but these merge to form a single path out of the space. This is also considered a common path of travel. The common path of travel is considered part of the overall travel distance limitations in Section 1017.2.

While a Group R-3 occupancy is typically a single-exit space, it is included in Table 1006.2.1 to address mixed-use buildings.

Exception 2 allows for hospital patient rooms and care suites to egress in accordance with the specific criteria in Section 407.4, including the common path of egress travel provisions (Table 1006.2.1, Note d). Other areas in Group I-2 occupancies are addressed in Table 1006.2.1.

TABLE 1006.2.1. See page 10-24.

❖ The table represents an empirical judgment of the risks associated with a single means of egress from a room or space based on the occupant load in the room, the travel distance to the exit access door and the inherent risks associated with the occupancy (such as occupant mobility, occupant familiarity with the building, occupant response and the fire growth rate). The number 49 is used for consistency with other occupant load thresholds, such as panic hardware (see Section 1010.1.10).

Since the occupants of Groups I and R may be sleeping and, therefore, not able to detect a fire in its early stages without staff supervision or room detectors, the number of occupants in a single egress unit is limited to 10 for Groups I and R-1 and 20 for Groups R-2, R-3 and R-4. See Section 1006.2.1, Exception 2, for Group I-2 patient rooms and care suites.

Because of the potential for rapidly developing hazardous conditions, the single egress condition in Groups H-1, H-2 and H-3 is limited to a maximum of three persons. Because the materials contained in Groups H-4 and H-5 do not represent the same fire hazard potential as those found in Groups H-1, H-2 and H-3, the occupant load for spaces with one means of egress is increased.

Because of the reduced occupant density in Group S and the occupants' normal familiarity with the building, the single egress condition is permitted with an occupant load of 29.

In nonsprinklered business, storage and utility buildings, the length of the common path of egress travel is greater for single-exit spaces where the occupant load for that space is 30 or less. Businesses, factories and nontransient residential buildings get an increase in the common path of travel in recognition of the additional fire safety offered by a fully sprinklered building. Common path of egress travel does not apply to stories or buildings with one exit. The definition for "Common path of egress travel" indicates the provisions are applicable only where access to two or more exits is required.

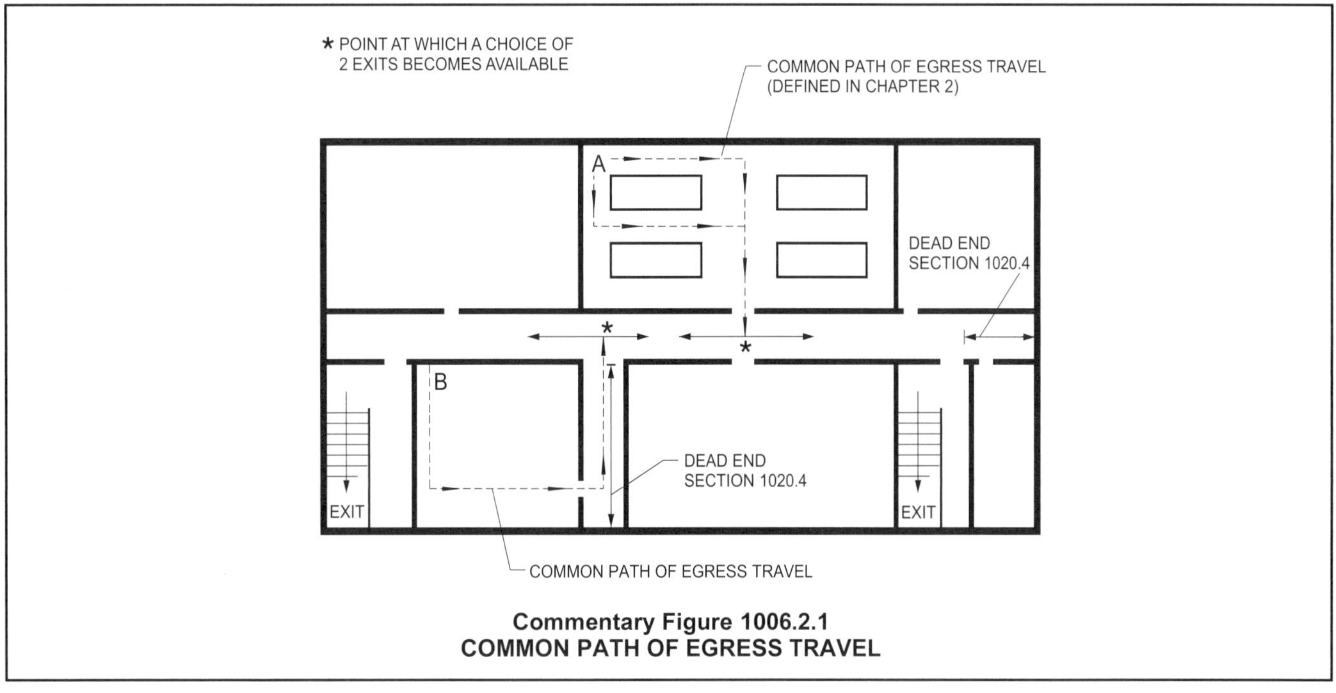

Commentary Figure 1006.2.1
COMMON PATH OF EGRESS TRAVEL

Note a indicates that the travel distance increase is based on an NFPA 13 or NFPA 13R sprinkler system being provided throughout the building, whichever is applicable to that occupancy. Note b is a general reminder for special requirements for sprinklers in Group H.

The reference in Note c to Section 1029.8 is to allow for the unique common path of egress travel requirements in spaces with assembly seating, such as in a lecture room or sports facility.

Note d is a reference to the common path of egress travel provisions specific to Group I-2 care rooms and suites that are specifically addressed in Section 407.4.

As indicated in Note e, while Group R-3 and R-4 dwellings are typically only required to have one exit (see Section 1006.3.3, Item 4), there can be a situation where a Group R-3 or R-4 unit is included in a mixed-use building. In these situations, the travel distance limitation of 125 feet for common path of egress travel given in the table is applicable. The total exit access travel distance can be 200 feet (see Table 1017.2). Keep in mind that Section 310.5 limits Group R-4 to 16 residents, excluding staff. This table is specific to an occupant load of 20 or fewer within the unit to allow for a single way out. For Group R-3 and R-4 units where an NFPA 13D sprinkler is permitted, see Section 1006.2.2.6 (per Note g).

Note f is an allowance for the common path of egress travel in an open parking garage to be up to 100 feet (30 480 mm) in length where the occupant load is greater than 30 and there is no sprinkler system provided. This is in recognition of the minimal possibility of smoke accumulation due to the openness requirements and low fuel loads of open parking garages.

[BE] 1006.2.1.1 Three or more exits or exit access doorways. Three *exits* or *exit access doorways* shall be provided from any space with an *occupant load* of 501 to 1,000. Four *exits* or *exit access doorways* shall be provided from any space with an *occupant load* greater than 1,000.

❖ Large facilities with high occupant loads are required to have more than two exits leading from each story. This is so that at least one exit will be available in case of a fire emergency and to increase the likelihood that a large number of occupants can be accommodated by the remaining exits where one exit is not available. Section 1005.5 specifies that the loss of one exit must not reduce the available exit capacity by more than 50 percent. This is reiterated in Sec-

TABLE 1006.2.1
SPACES WITH ONE EXIT OR EXIT ACCESS DOORWAY

OCCUPANCY	MAXIMUM OCCUPANT LOAD OF SPACE	MAXIMUM COMMON PATH OF EGRESS TRAVEL DISTANCE (feet)		
		Without Sprinkler System (feet)		With Sprinkler System (feet)
		Occupant Load		
		OL ≤ 30	OL > 30	
A[c], E, M	49	75	75	75[a]
B	49	100	75	100[a]
F	49	75	75	100[a]
H-1, H-2, H-3	3	NP	NP	25[b]
H-4, H-5	10	NP	NP	75[b]
I-1, I-2[d], I-4	10	NP	NP	75[a]
I-3	10	NP	NP	100[a]
R-1	10	NP	NP	75[a]
R-2	20	NP	NP	125[a]
R-3[e]	20	NP	NP	125[a, g]
R-4[e]	20	NP	NP	125[a, g]
S[f]	29	100	75	100[a]
U	49	100	75	75[a]

For SI: 1 foot = 304.8 mm.

NP = Not Permitted.

a. Buildings equipped throughout with an automatic sprinkler system in accordance with Section 903.3.1.1 or 903.3.1.2. See Section 903 for occupancies where automatic sprinkler systems are permitted in accordance with Section 903.3.1.2.

b. Group H occupancies equipped throughout with an automatic sprinkler system in accordance with Section 903.2.5.

c. For a room or space used for assembly purposes having fixed seating, see Section 1029.8.

d. For the travel distance limitations in Group I-2, see Section 407.4.

e. The common path of egress travel distance shall only apply in a Group R-3 occupancy located in a mixed occupancy building.

f. The length of common path of egress travel distance in a Group S-2 open parking garage shall be not more than 100 feet.

g. For the travel distance limitations in Groups R-3 and R-4 equipped throughout with an automatic sprinkler system in accordance with Section 903.3.1.3, see Section 1006.2.2.6.

tions 1029.2 and 1029.3 for spaces with assembly seating for more than 300 occupants. Exits should be separated in accordance with Section 1007.1.2. While an equal distribution of exit capacity among all the exits is not required, a proper design would consider occupant load distribution as well as reasonable capacity distribution so as to avoid a severe dependence on one exit or bottlenecks in anticipated high-use areas.

[BE] 1006.2.2 Egress based on use. The numbers of *exits* or access to *exits* shall be provided in the uses described in Sections 1006.2.2.1 through 1006.2.2.6.

❖ Six types of spaces, because of their levels of hazard, have egress requirements based on use rather than occupant load and travel distance.

[BE] 1006.2.2.1 Boiler, incinerator and furnace rooms. Two *exit access doorways* are required in boiler, incinerator and furnace rooms where the area is over 500 square feet (46 m^2) and any fuel-fired equipment exceeds 400,000 British thermal units (Btu) (422 000 KJ) input capacity. Where two *exit access doorways* are required, one is permitted to be a fixed ladder or an *alternating tread device*. *Exit access doorways* shall be separated by a horizontal distance equal to one-half the length of the maximum overall diagonal dimension of the room.

❖ This section requires two exit access doorways for the specified mechanical equipment spaces because of the level of hazards in this type of space. A fixed ladder or an alternating tread device is permitted for service personnel to egress where two doorways are required. The remoteness of the exit access doorways specified in this section provides two paths of travel to evacuate the room so that if one doorway is not available, the alternate path can be used.

[BE] 1006.2.2.2 Refrigeration machinery rooms. Machinery rooms larger than 1,000 square feet (93 m^2) shall have not less than two *exits* or *exit access doorways*. Where two *exit access doorways* are required, one such doorway is permitted to be served by a fixed ladder or an *alternating tread device*. *Exit access* doorways shall be separated by a horizontal distance equal to one-half the maximum horizontal dimension of the room.

All portions of machinery rooms shall be within 150 feet (45 720 mm) of an *exit* or *exit access doorway*. An increase in *exit access* travel distance is permitted in accordance with Section 1017.1.

Exit and *exit access doorways* shall swing in the direction of egress travel, regardless of the *occupant load* served. *Exit* and *exit access doorways* shall be tight fitting and self-closing.

❖ The reasons for these requirements are the same as for Section 1006.2.2.1. Travel distance can be increased where permitted in Table 1017.2. For example, where a sprinkler system is installed throughout the entire building in accordance with NFPA 13, the travel distance limit for a large refrigeration machinery room classified as Group F-1 could be increased to 250 feet (76 200 mm) based on Table 1017.2. The 150-foot (45 720 mm) travel distance is intended to be applied where a sprinkler system is not installed in order to shorten the time that occupants would be exposed to the hazards within the machinery room.

[BE] 1006.2.2.3 Refrigerated rooms or spaces. Rooms or spaces having a floor area larger than 1,000 square feet (93 m^2), containing a refrigerant evaporator and maintained at a temperature below 68°F (20°C), shall have access to not less than two *exits* or *exit access doorways*.

Exit access travel distance shall be determined as specified in Section 1017.1, but all portions of a refrigerated room or space shall be within 150 feet (45 720 mm) of an *exit* or *exit access doorway* where such rooms are not protected by an *approved automatic sprinkler system*. Egress is allowed through adjoining refrigerated rooms or spaces.

Exception: Where using refrigerants in quantities limited to the amounts based on the volume set forth in the *International Mechanical Code.*

❖ Refrigeration rooms also have a higher hazard level (see the commentary to Sections 1006.2.2.1 and 1006.2.2.2). The exception is intended to apply if Chapter 11 of the *International Mechanical Code*® (IMC®) does not require a separate refrigeration machinery room due to the small amount of refrigerant used (see the commentary to Section 1104 of the IMC for further explanation of machinery room requirements).

[BE] 1006.2.2.4 Group I-4 means of egress. Group I-4 facilities, rooms or spaces where care is provided for more than 10 children that are $2^1/_2$ years of age or less, shall have access to not less than two *exits* or *exit access doorways*.

❖ Rooms or spaces in Group I-4, day care occupancies are limited to a maximum of 10 infants and toddlers before two exits from a room are required.This limit is in consideration of needing a quick means of egress for children who would need to be carried or led for evacuation (children under $2^1/_2$ years of age).

There is an exception for Group I-4 facilities in IBC Section 308.5.1 that allows day care facilities with up to 100 children $2^1/_2$ years of age or less to be classified as Group E if the care rooms have direct access to the exterior. An exterior door to the outside from infant and toddler rooms can serve as the second exit to meet the requirements of this section. It is not the intent that a day care facility classified as Group E, with children $2^1/_2$ years of age or less, use the means of egress requirements for Group E for these rooms.

[BE] 1006.2.2.5 Vehicular ramps. Vehicular ramps shall not be considered as an *exit access ramp* unless pedestrian facilities are provided.

❖ A vehicle-only ramp may be considered as one of the required exit access ramps if pedestrian walkways are provided along the ramp. The low-slope ramps that are lined with parking spaces are not considered vehicle ramps. In open parking garages, according to

Section 1019.3, Item 6, the exit access stairways and ramps are not required to be enclosed since an open parking structure is designed to permit the ready ventilation of the products of combustion to the outside by exterior wall openings (see Section 406.5.2). Also, parking structures are characterized by open floor areas that allow the occupants to observe a fire condition and choose a travel path that would avoid the fire threat.

[BE] 1006.2.2.6 Groups R-3 and R-4. Where Group R-3 occupancies are permitted by Section 903.2.8 to be protected by an automatic sprinkler system installed in accordance with Section 903.3.1.3, the exit access travel distance for Group R-3 shall be not more than 125 feet (38 100 mm). Where Group R-4 occupancies are permitted by Section 903.2.8 to be protected by an automatic sprinkler system installed in accordance with Section 903.3.1.3, the exit access travel distance for Group R-4 shall be not more than 75 feet (22 860 mm).

❖ Section 1006.2 is applicable to spaces, so this section is applicable for Group R-3 and R-4 dwellings in a mixed-use building, such as two apartments above a store. In a mixed-use building where an NFPA 13D system is permitted in the fire area containing the Group R-3 or R-4 units, the exit access travel distance is limited to 125 feet (38 100 mm) for the Group R-3 units and 75 feet (22 860 mm) for the Group R-4 units. If a designer chooses to use an NFPA 13 or NFPA 13R system in the fire areas containing the Group R-3 and R-4 units, the common path of travel for both the Group R-3 and R-4 units is 125 feet (38 100 mm) (Table 1006.2.1), with the total exit access travel distance being 200 feet (60 960 mm) (Table 1017.2). If these facilities are in a separate building, the exit access travel distance inside a Group R-3 or R-4 dwelling is 200 feet (60 960 mm) (see Section 1006.3.3, Exception 4, and Table 1017.2).

[BE] 1006.3 Egress from stories or occupied roofs. The *means of egress* system serving any *story* or occupied roof shall be provided with the number of separate and distinct *exits* or access to *exits* based on the aggregate *occupant load* served in accordance with this section. Where *stairways* serve more than one story, only the occupant load of each *story* considered individually shall be used in calculating the required number of *exits* or access to *exits* serving that *story*.

❖ While Section 1006.2 deals with rooms or spaces, Section 1006.3 deals with stories (including occupied roofs). Emergency evacuation from a multistory building will typically involve stairways or ramps as the vertical element for the means of egress route. The number of required ways off the story (via exit or exit access elements) is based on the occupant loads shown in Table 1006.3.2. These stairways and ramps (Sections 1011 and 1012, respectively) must comply with the general provisions and can be exit access (Section 1019) or exits (Sections 1023 and 1027). By including "access to exits," the code is allowing for the use of open exit access stairways to serve as a means of egress off a story.

For open exit access stairways or ramps, it is important to consider where a stairway/ramp can be open (Section 1019), where that stairway/ramp is part of the required ways off the floor (Section 1006.3), and how much travel distance is allowed (Sections 1006.3.1 and 1017). Similar to access to bathrooms, the travel distance is limited both by length and number of stories.

The occupants of a mezzanine are added to the total occupant load of the room below to determine the capacity and number of ways out of the room. When calculating the capacity and number of stairways or ramps from a story, the occupant load from each story is considered separately (see Section 1005.3).

[BE] 1006.3.1 Adjacent story. The path of egress travel to an *exit* shall not pass through more than one adjacent *story*.

Exception: The path of egress travel to an *exit* shall be permitted to pass through more than one adjacent *story* in any of the following:

1. In Group R-1, R-2 or R-3 occupancies, exit access stairways and ramps connecting four stories or fewer serving and contained within an individual dwelling unit or sleeping unit or live/work unit.
2. Exit access stairways serving and contained within a Group R-3 congregate residence or a Group R-4 facility.
3. Exit access stairways and ramps in open parking garages that serve only the parking garage.
4. Exit access stairways and ramps serving open-air assembly seating complying with the exit access travel distance requirements of Section 1029.7.
5. Exit access stairways and ramps between the balcony, gallery or press box and the main assembly floor in occupancies such as theaters, places of religious worship, auditoriums and sports facilities.

❖ In Section 1006.3, "access to exits" allows for the use of open exit access stairways to serve as required ways off the story (means of egress via exit or exit access elements). For open exit access stairways or ramps, it is important to consider where a stairway/ramp can be open (Section 1019), where that stairway/ramp is part of the required ways off the floor (Section 1006.3), and how much travel distance is allowed (Sections 1006.3.1 and 1017). Similar to access to bathrooms, the travel distance is limited both by length and number of stories.

Where exit access stairways or ramps are part of that egress route, the measurement of the exit access travel distance will include travel from the most remote point on the floor, to and down the exit access stairway or ramp, and from the bottom of the stairway or ramp to an enclosure for an exit stairway or ramp, horizontal exit, or exterior exit door (see Section 1017.3) on the story above or below. Vertical travel is slower than horizontal travel, so the exit access stairway or ramp in a building with two or more exits should not be used for more than one story before an exit is reached.

The exceptions are in recognition of where travel down more than one story has been historically accepted.

Exceptions 1 and 2 basically allow travel down two or three flights of stairs within dwellings operating as a single-family apartment or residence.

Exceptions 3 and 4 are allowances for open parking garages and open-air assembly seating facilities. Occupants are permitted to travel down more than one flight of stairs since the chance of accumulation of smoke is limited given the requirements for these types of buildings—both open to the air and with limited combustible elements (see also Sections 1017.3 and 1029.7).

Exception 5 allows for multiple balcony levels in a large assembly space. This would also allow for occupants from a press box to move down more than one flight of stairs within that assembly space.

It should be noted that even though other facilities are permitted to have open exit access stairways, (see Section 1019.3, Items 4 and 5), if those stairways are part of the required means of egress, they can only be used to travel down one flight before reaching an exit.

[BE] 1006.3.2 Egress based on occupant load. Each *story* and occupied roof shall have the minimum number of separate and distinct *exits*, or access to *exits*, as specified in Table 1006.3.2. A single *exit* or access to a single *exit* shall be permitted in accordance with Section 1006.3.3. The required number of *exits*, or *exit access stairways* or *ramps* providing access to *exits*, from any story or occupied roof shall be maintained until arrival at the *exit discharge* or *public way*.

❖ This section states that every occupant on a story must have access to the required number of means of egress as specified:

- Per Table 1006.3.2—at least two means of egress per story.
- Three means of egress for stories with greater than 500 occupants and four means of egress for stories with greater than 1,000 occupants.
- Per Sections 1006.3.3 and 1006.3.3.1—limited allowance for a single means of egress from a story.

Referring to "means of egress" instead of "exits" acknowledges that direct entrances to exits on each story are not always mandatory since access to exits (i.e., exit access stairways or ramps) on some stories is permissible within certain limitations. This allows some freedom of design where, for instance, required exit stairways may not be available without passing through other tenant spaces. The intent is to allow for a balance of security concerns while providing adequate safety for emergency evacuation.

If a designer chooses to use horizontal exits instead of exit stairways or exit ramps, those specific provisions are addressed in Section 1026. For buildings built into a hillside, an exit door directly to the outside would also provide the same or better level of protection as an interior exit element. It is not the intent of this provision to prohibit horizontal exits or direct exterior exit doors as an option.

Once the number of means of egress is determined, those paths must remain available until occupants leave the building (see Commentary Figure 1006.3.2). The need for exits to be independent of each other cannot be overstated. Each occupant of each floor must be provided with the required number of exits without having to pass through one exit to gain access to another. Each exit is required to be independent of other exits to prohibit such areas from merging downstream and becoming, in effect, one exit.

[BE] TABLE 1006.3.2
MINIMUM NUMBER OF EXITS OR ACCESS TO EXITS PER STORY

OCCUPANT LOAD PER STORY	MINIMUM NUMBER OF EXITS OR ACCESS TO EXITS FROM STORY
1-500	2
501-1,000	3
More than 1,000	4

❖ Table 1006.3.2 specifies the minimum number of evacuation routes (exits or access to exits) available to each occupant of a story based on the total occupant load of that story. This is to guarantee at least one available way off the story in case of a fire emergency and to increase the likelihood that a larger number of occupants can be accommodated by the remaining ways off the story where one of the ways off is not available. While an equal distribution of width or capacity among all of the doors or stairways leading off the story is not required, a proper design would not only balance width and capacity with the occupant load distribution, but also consider a reasoned distribution of width and capacity to avoid a severe dependence on one way out.

[BE] 1006.3.3 Single exits. A single *exit* or access to a single *exit* shall be permitted from any *story* or occupied roof, where one of the following conditions exists:

1. The *occupant load*, number of *dwelling units* and *common path of egress* travel distance do not exceed the values in Table 1006.3.3(1) or 1006.3.3(2).
2. Rooms, areas and spaces complying with Section 1006.2.1 with *exits* that discharge directly to the exterior at the *level of exit discharge*, are permitted to have one *exit* or access to a single *exit*.
3. Parking garages where vehicles are mechanically parked shall be permitted to have one *exit* or access to a single *exit*.
4. Group R-3 and R-4 occupancies shall be permitted to have one *exit* or access to a single *exit*.

5. Individual single-story or multistory *dwelling units* shall be permitted to have a single *exit* or access to a single *exit* from the *dwelling unit* provided that both of the following criteria are met:
   5.1. The *dwelling unit* complies with Section 1006.2.1 as a space with one means of egress.
   5.2. Either the *exit* from the *dwelling unit* discharges directly to the exterior at the *level of exit discharge*, or the *exit access* outside the *dwelling unit*'s entrance door provides access to not less than two approved independent *exits*.

❖ The base assumption is that all stories of a building shall have access to at least two separate ways out for emergencies (see Section 1006.3.2). This section allows for stories with only one way out (means of egress via exit or exit access).

A story can have a single way out (exit or access to exits) if the design meets one of the five conditions listed.

Item 1 states what situations permit one way out by a reference Tables 1006.3.3(1) and 1006.3.3(2). If a story can meet the provisions for occupant load, number of units and exit access travel distance in Table 1006.3.3(1) or 1006.3.3(2), then that story can have one way out. See the commentary for Tables 1006.3.3(1) and 1006.3.3(2) for information on stories with a single means of egress.

Item 2 references Section 1006.2.1 for spaces with one way out. Section 1006.2.1 is intended to be applicable to rooms and spaces on a story, but not to an entire story level. One of the main concerns has been that vertical travel takes longer than horizontal travel in emergency exiting situations. However, if the space can exit directly to the exterior rather than egress into an interior corridor or an exit stairway, a higher level of safety is provided. While the term "building" limits the area addressed to that bordered by exterior walls or fire walls, a common application of Item 2 is on a tenant-by-tenant basis. For example, a single-story strip mall may not meet the provisions for a building with one means of egress, but each tenant area meets the provisions for a space with one means of egress in accordance with Section 1006.2. This tenant could exist as either a stand-alone, single-exit building or as a tenant space with one way out into an interior corridor. See also the commentary to Tables 1006.3.3(1) and 1006.3.3(2).

While not specifically stated in this section, since a mezzanine is part of the story below, a tenant with a mezzanine could use Item 2. Item 3 allows for one way out from all stories in a parking garage where the cars are mechanically parked. This is in recognition of the extremely low occupant load in this unique type of building. The single exit would be for maintenance and service personnel who could be on the different levels. Exit access travel distance would still have to meet the requirements listed in Table 1017.2. If this facility is a typical open parking garage, it could have one way out per Table 1006.3.3(2).

Group R-3 occupancies are limited to not more than two dwelling units per building. Often these units are townhouse style with direct exits at grade or one unit on top of another. Group R-3 and R-4 congregate residences typically operate as single-family homes. The Fair Housing Act (FHA) does not discriminate based

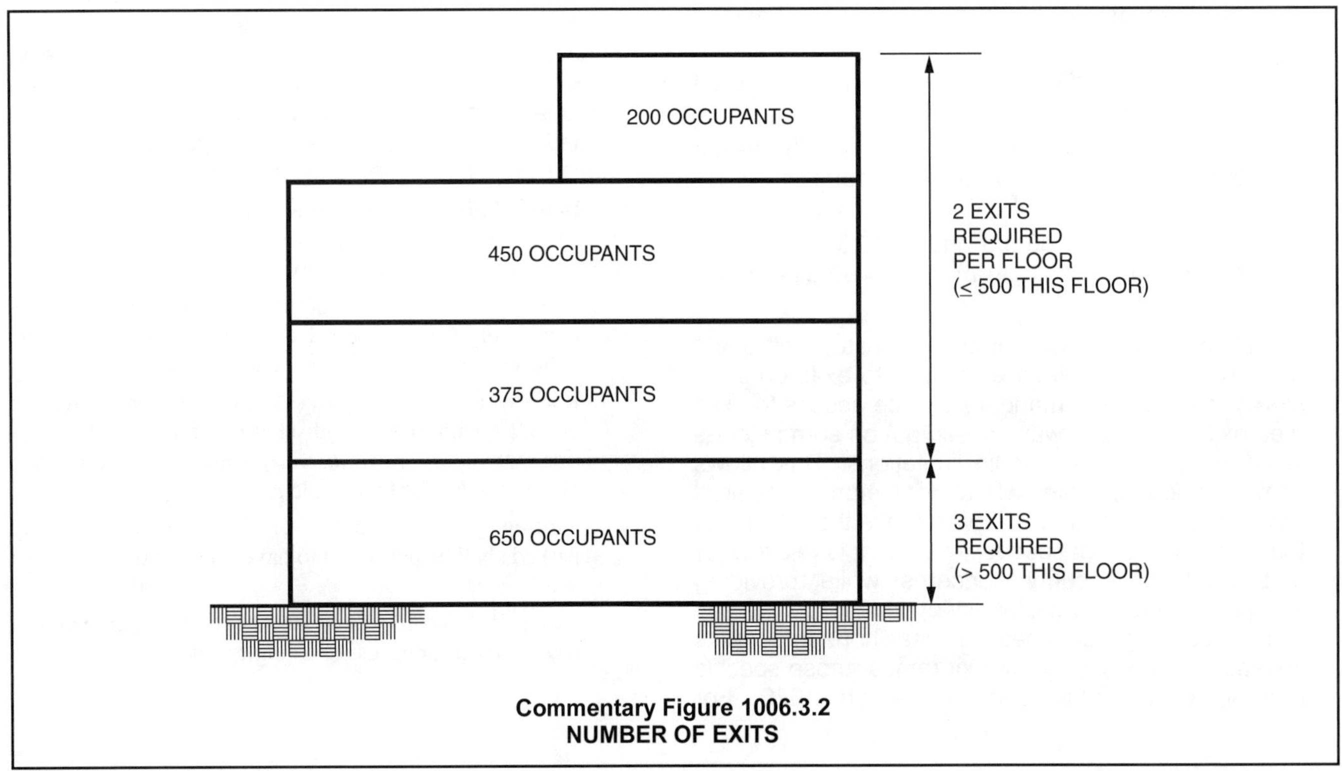

Commentary Figure 1006.3.2
NUMBER OF EXITS

on familial status (i.e., family cannot be determined by blood or marriage). Many court cases have been filed under the Fair Housing Act requiring that group homes be permitted to operate similar to a single-family home as a point of nondiscrimination. For additional information on the FHA, see the commentaries at the beginning of IBC Chapter 11 and under IBC Section 1107. In either configuration, per Item 4, each unit is only required to have one way leading out from each story in the building. In a multistory unit, any interior stairway would be considered an exit access stairway (Section 1006.3.1, Exceptions 1 and 2, and Section 1019.3, Item 2) and would be part of the exit access travel distance listed in Table 1017.2.

Item 5 is based on decades of experience within individual multistory dwelling units—typically in Group R-1 or R-2.

In a Group R-2 apartment- or townhouse-style building, if the building is sprinklered with an NFPA 13 or 13R system and the common path of travel from the most remote point on any level to the exit access door from the unit itself is 125 feet (38 100 mm) maximum (see Section 1006.2.1), that unit may have only one means of egress. Table 1006.2.1 provides for a maximum occupant load of 20, rather than the 10 occupants allowed in Table 1006.3.3(2). Therefore, this could allow apartments of up to 4,000 square feet (371.6 m^2). An exit access stairway would be permitted within the unit as part of the exit access travel distance (Section 1006.3.1, Exception 1, and Section 1019.3, Item 2). Once the occupants exit the unit itself, however, they must be outside at grade or the story level must have access to two or more means of egress for all tenants, depending on the number required for the building as a whole [see Commentary Figures 1006.3.3(1) and 1006.3.3(3)]. The common path of egress within the unit would be part of the overall exit access travel distance of 250 feet (76 200 mm) required in Table 1017.2. It is not the intent to allow this exception for apartment-style dwelling units in conjunction with the allowances for a single-exit building. The emergency escape and rescue openings addressed in Section 1030 do not count toward the required number of exits.

TABLE 1006.3.3(1). See page 10-30.

❖ Per Note b, this table addresses where a single way out can be provided from stories in Group R-2 occupancies having dwelling units only, such as apartments and condominiums. For Group R-2 occupancies with sleeping units, such as dormitories, sororities, fraternities, convents, monasteries or boarding houses, see Table 1006.3.3(2). The second row in Table 1006.3.3(1) is to clarify that R-2 buildings that are four stories or taller have to have at least two ways off each story. In addition to meeting the specified number of dwelling units per story and exit access travel distance, these buildings must be equipped

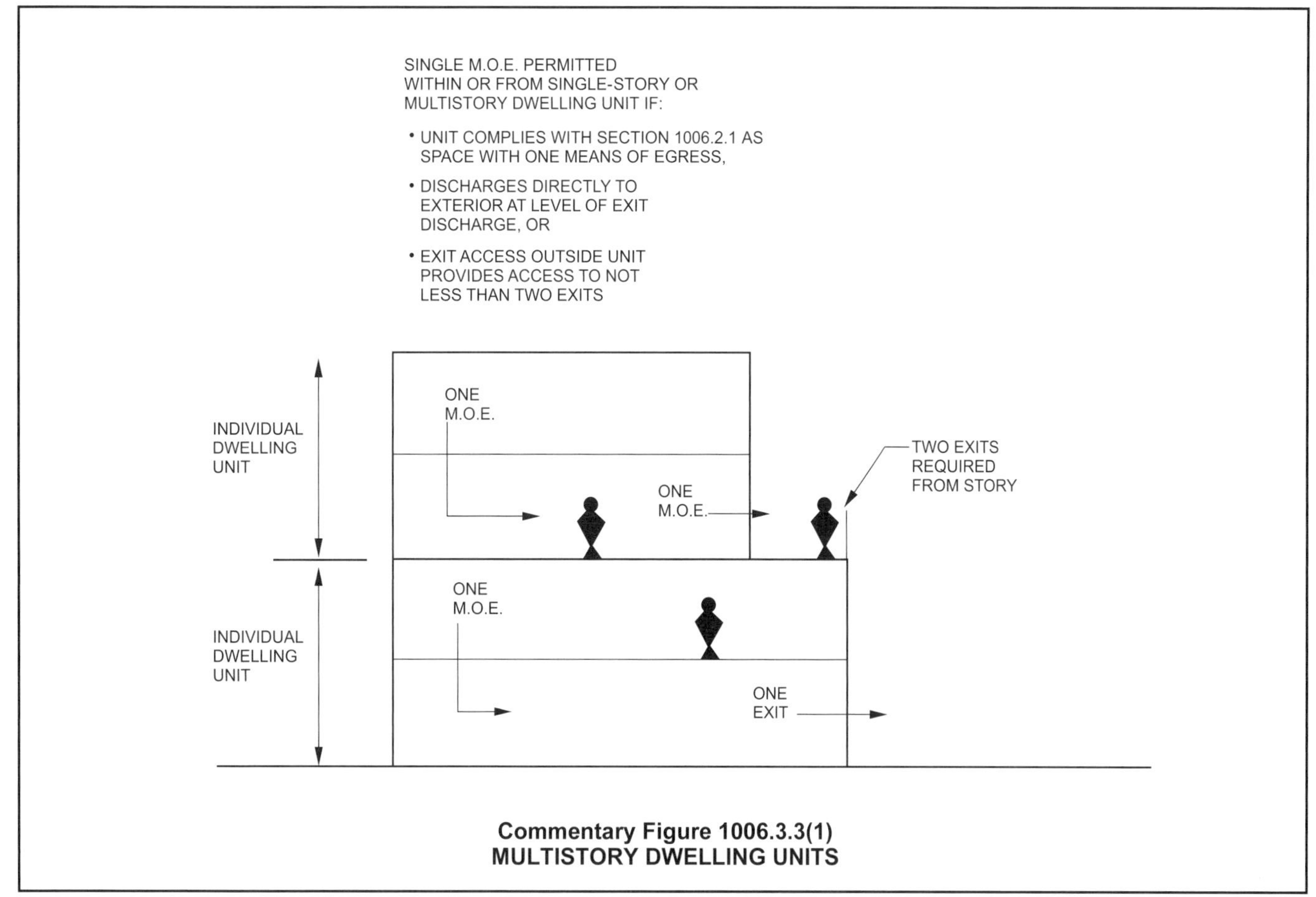

Commentary Figure 1006.3.3(1)
MULTISTORY DWELLING UNITS

throughout with an NFPA 13 or 13R sprinkler system, and an emergency escape and rescue opening must be provided in every bedroom (Note a). The exit access travel distance would be measured from the most remote point in the unit to the exit from the story or down an open exit access story to the exit on the story below (see Section 1006.3.1). This is different from the common path of egress travel distance in Section 1006.2.1 where the travel distance is measured to the door of the unit. However, in order to be able to use the one way off per story design, each unit must also meet the requirements for one way out of the individual units, so the occupant load of each of the four apartments is limited to 20 by Table 1006.2.1. See Commentary Figures 1006.3.3(2) and 1006.3.3(3) for examples of the differences. Formal committee interpretation 21-14 states that this table allows for groups of four units on a story to have access to a single exit. These units would have to be separated in accordance with IBC Section 420, but would not have to be separated by fire barriers or fire walls.

See the commentary to Table 1006.3.3(2) for additional discussion on options for stories with a single means of egress.

Table 1006,3,3(2) is not intended to work in combination with Section 1006.3.3, Item 5. That section requires a minimum of two exits from the story.

TABLE 1006.3.3(2). See page 10-31.

❖ Stories with one way out (exits or access to exits) are permitted where the configuration and occupancy meet certain characteristics so as not to present an unacceptable fire risk to the occupants. Stories that are relatively small in size have a shorter travel distance and fewer occupants; thus, having access to a single way out does not significantly compromise the safety of the occupants since they will also be alerted to and get away from the fire more quickly. It is important to note that the provisions in Section 1006.3.3 apply to individual stories. Multiple spaces or units with one way out may exist in the same building, including those cases where differing occupancies exist. Therefore, Tables 1006.3.3(1) and 1006.3.3(2) can address mixed occupancy buildings (see Section 1006.3.3.1).

Occupants of a story of limited size and configuration may have access to a single way out, provided that the building does not have more than one level below the first story above grade plane. The limitation on the number of levels above and below the first story is intended to limit the vertical travel an occupant must accomplish to reach the exit discharge.

Only one way out is required from a story where permitted by Table 1006.3.3(1) or 1006.3.3(2), regardless of the number of exits required from other stories in the building. For example, a Group B occupancy on the second story of a two-story building is only required to have one way out from the story, provided its occupant load does not exceed 29 and the maximum exit access travel distance to the exit stairway or down an exit access stairway to the exit door does not exceed 75 feet (22 860 mm). The number of exits and travel distances on the first story do not affect the determination of the second story as a story with a single way out. Other stories are also regulated independently as to number of ways out. For mixed occupancy floors or floors where tenant spaces have separate exits, see Section 1006.3.3.1.

Tables 1006.3.3(1) and 1006.3.3(2) list the characteristics a story must have to qualify for a single way out, including occupancy, maximum number of stories above grade plane, maximum occupants or dwelling units per story, and exit access travel distance. The occupant load of each story is determined in accordance with the provisions of Section 1004. The exit access travel distance is measured along the natural and unobstructed path to the exit, as described in Section 1017.3. If the occupant load or exit access travel distance is exceeded, two ways out are required from each story in the building.

The enclosure required for the exit in a two- or three-story, single-exit building is identical to any other complying exit (e.g., interior stairs, exterior stairs). Similarly, the fire-resistance rating required for opening protectives is identical to that required by Section 716. Exit access stairways could be used in two-story buildings, with or without basements, where permitted by Sections 1006.3.1 and 1019.3.

Per Note c, for Group R-2 sleeping units, such as congregate residences, fraternities, sororities, dormitories, convents or monasteries with more than 16 residents (see Section 310), use Table 1006.3.3(2). Table 1006.3.3(1) addresses dwelling units in Group R-2. Effectively, this section allows for one-story

[BE] TABLE 1006.3.3(1)
STORIES WITH ONE EXIT OR ACCESS TO ONE EXIT FOR R-2 OCCUPANCIES

STORY	OCCUPANCY	MAXIMUM NUMBER OF DWELLING UNITS	MAXIMUM COMMON PATH OF EGRESS TRAVEL DISTANCE
Basement, first, second or third story above grade plane	R-2[a, b]	4 dwelling units	125 feet
Fourth story above grade plane and higher	NP	NA	NA

For SI: 1 foot = 3048 mm.

NP = Not Permitted.

NA = Not Applicable.

a. Buildings classified as Group R-2 equipped throughout with an automatic sprinkler system in accordance with Section 903.3.1.1 or 903.3.1.2 and provided with emergency escape and rescue openings in accordance with Section 1030.

b. This table is used for R-2 occupancies consisting of dwelling units. For R-2 occupancies consisting of sleeping units, use Table 1006.3.3(2).

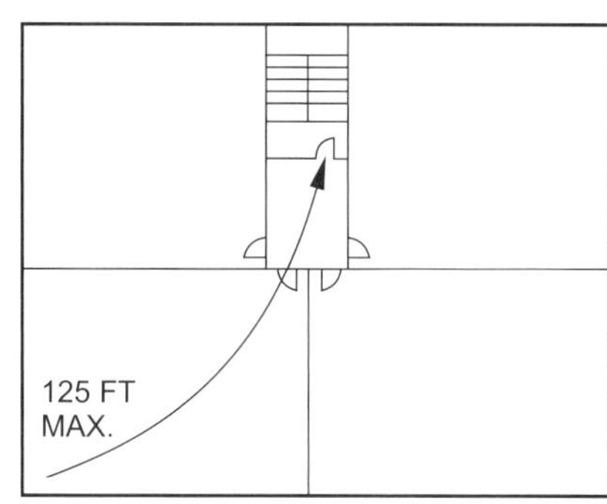

R-2 DWELLING UNITS

SECOND OR THIRD STORY
SINGLE EXIT PERMITTED

- MAXIMUM OF 4 UNITS AND 3 STORIES
- 125 FT. MAX. TRAVEL DISTANCE TO EXIT
- COMPLY WITH TABLE 1006.2.1 20 OCCUPANTS MAX.

For SI: 1 foot = 304.8 mm.

Commentary Figure 1006.3.3(2)
EXAMPLE OF SINGLE-EXIT APARTMENT BUILDING

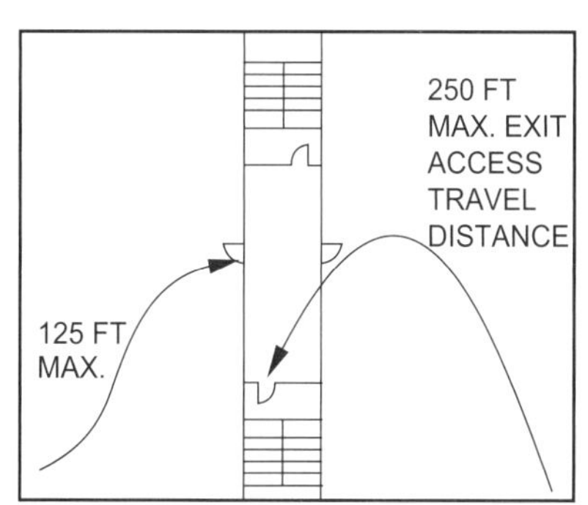

SINGLE EXIT WITHIN AND FROM UNIT

- 250 FT. MAX. EXIT ACCESS TRAVEL DISTANCE
- NO LIMIT ON NUMBER OF UNITS
- 125 FT. MAX. COMMON PATH OF TRAVEL (TO APARTMENT DOOR)
- 20 OCCUPANT MAX. PER UNIT PER TABLE 1006.2.1

For SI: 1 foot = 304.8 mm.

Commentary Figure 1006.3.3(3)
EXAMPLE OF SINGLE-EXIT APARTMENT WITHIN A TWO-EXIT BUILDING

[BE] TABLE 1006.3.3(2)
STORIES WITH ONE EXIT OR ACCESS TO ONE EXIT FOR OTHER OCCUPANCIES

STORY	OCCUPANCY	MAXIMUM OCCUPANT LOAD PER STORY	MAXIMUM COMMON PATH OF EGRESS TRAVEL DISTANCE (feet)
First story above or below grade plane	A, B[b], E F[b], M, U	49	75
	H-2, H-3	3	25
	H-4, H-5, I, R-1, R-2[a, c]	10	75
	S[b, d]	29	75
Second story above grade plane	B, F, M, S[d]	29	75
Third story above grade plane and higher	NP	NA	NA

For SI: 1 foot = 304.8 mm.
NP = Not Permitted.
NA = Not Applicable.

a. Buildings classified as Group R-2 equipped throughout with an automatic sprinkler system in accordance with Section 903.3.1.1 or 903.3.1.2 and provided with emergency escape and rescue openings in accordance with Section 1030.

b. Group B, F and S occupancies in buildings equipped throughout with an automatic sprinkler system in accordance with Section 903.3.1.1 shall have a maximum exit access travel distance of 100 feet.

c. This table is used for R-2 occupancies consisting of sleeping units. For R-2 occupancies consisting of dwelling units, use Table 1006.3.3(1).

d. The length of exit access travel distance in a Group S-2 open parking garage shall be not more than 100 feet.

Group R-2 congregate residences to have a single way out where there are 10 or fewer occupants on the first story or basement level. The exit access travel distance from the most remote part of a unit to the exit must be less than 75 feet (22 860 mm). The maximum occupant load would limit the congregate residence to 2,000 square feet (185.81 m^2) maximum. Per Note a, the congregate residence must be sprinklered throughout with an NFPA 13 or 13R system, and all bedrooms must have emergency escape and rescue openings (Section 1030.1).

Table 1006.3.3(2) allows for two-story business, factory, mercantile and storage facilities to have a single-exit stairway or exit access stairway (see Sections 1006.3.1 and 1019.3) from the second story if the space meets the maximums of 29 occupants and a 75-foot (22 860 mm) exit access travel distance. The increased travel distance in Note b is not permitted for the second story. However, there is an increase for travel distance permitted for Group S-2 open parking garages in Note d.

Table 1006.3.3(2) allows for a variety of single-story buildings, with or without basements, that meet the maximum occupant load and exit access travel distance specified. Exit access stairways from the basement would be a viable option where permitted by Sections 1006.3.1 and 1019.3.

Tables 1006.3.3(1) and 1006.3.3(2) are based on per-story criteria. These tables would also allow for mixed occupancy buildings with a different occupancy in each story, such as four apartments over a restaurant or a business over a day care, as long as occupant loads and exit access travel distances are met. Means of egress could be by an exit or exit access stairway through the story below or a separate exterior stairway from the upper level. For additional information on a mixed-use story, see Section 1006.3.3.1.

Formal code interpretation 21-14 states that this table allows for an exit configuration for multiple single-exit spaces for Groups B, M, F and S on the second story where each group meets Table 1006.3.3(2) requirements.

[BE] 1006.3.3.1 Mixed occupancies. Where one *exit*, or *exit access stairway* or *ramp* providing access to exits at other stories, is permitted to serve individual stories, mixed occupancies shall be permitted to be served by single *exits* provided that each individual occupancy complies with the applicable requirements of Table 1006.3.3(1) or 1006.3.3(2) for that occupancy. Where applicable, cumulative *occupant loads* from adjacent occupancies shall be considered to be in accordance with the provisions of Section 1004.1. In each *story* of a mixed occupancy building, the maximum number of occupants served by a single *exit* shall be such that the sum of the ratios of the calculated number of occupants of the space divided by the allowable number of occupants indicated in Table 1006.3.3(2) for each occupancy does not exceed one. Where *dwelling units* are located on a story with other occupancies, the actual number of *dwelling units* divided by four plus the ratio from the other occupancy does not exceed one.

❖ Where multiple tenants or occupancies are located on a specific story, they are to be regulated by a "unity" formula if they want to use the same way out (exit or access to exits). If they have separate ways out, they will be evaluated separately. This would allow for the second story of a mixed-use occupancy to be evaluated similarly to criteria listed in Section 1016.2, which apply where multiple spaces combine. For example, the second story of a building houses two tenants, one business and one mercantile. Each tenant would be permitted a single, but separate, exit, provided each had an occupant load of less than 30 and an exit access travel distance not exceeding 75 feet (22 860 mm) (see Commentary Figure 1006.3.3.1, Option 2). However, if the tenants wanted to share the same single exit, the combined occupant load would have to be less than 30 (see Commentary Figure 1006.3.3.1, Option 3).

Where the mixed-use story includes dwelling units, and since four dwelling units are allowed per story in a single-exit building, for the unity formula use 0.25 for one unit, 0.50 for two units and 0.75 for three units.

SECTION 1007 EXIT AND EXIT ACCESS DOORWAY CONFIGURATION

[BE] 1007.1 General. *Exits*, *exit access doorways*, and *exit access stairways* and *ramps* serving spaces, including individual building stories, shall be separated in accordance with the provisions of this section.

❖ The final exits, as well as the doors, stairways and ramps that get occupants to those exits (exit access elements), need to be unobstructed and obvious at all times for occupants to evacuate the building safely in an emergency situation. This is consistent with the requirements in Section 1010.1 that exits or exit access doors are not to be concealed by curtains, drapes, decorations or mirrors. Whether the doors from the space are exit access doors leading to a hallway or actual exit doors leading to an exit enclosure or directly to the outside, they must be located in accordance with this section.

The need for exits from a space or story to be independent of each other cannot be overstated. Each occupant of each floor must be provided with the required number of exits without having to pass through one exit to gain access to another. Each exit is required to be independent of other exits to prohibit such areas from merging downstream and becoming, in effect, one exit.

The requirement for exits to be continuous is consistent with the exit termination requirements in Section 1023.3 and the exit discharge termination

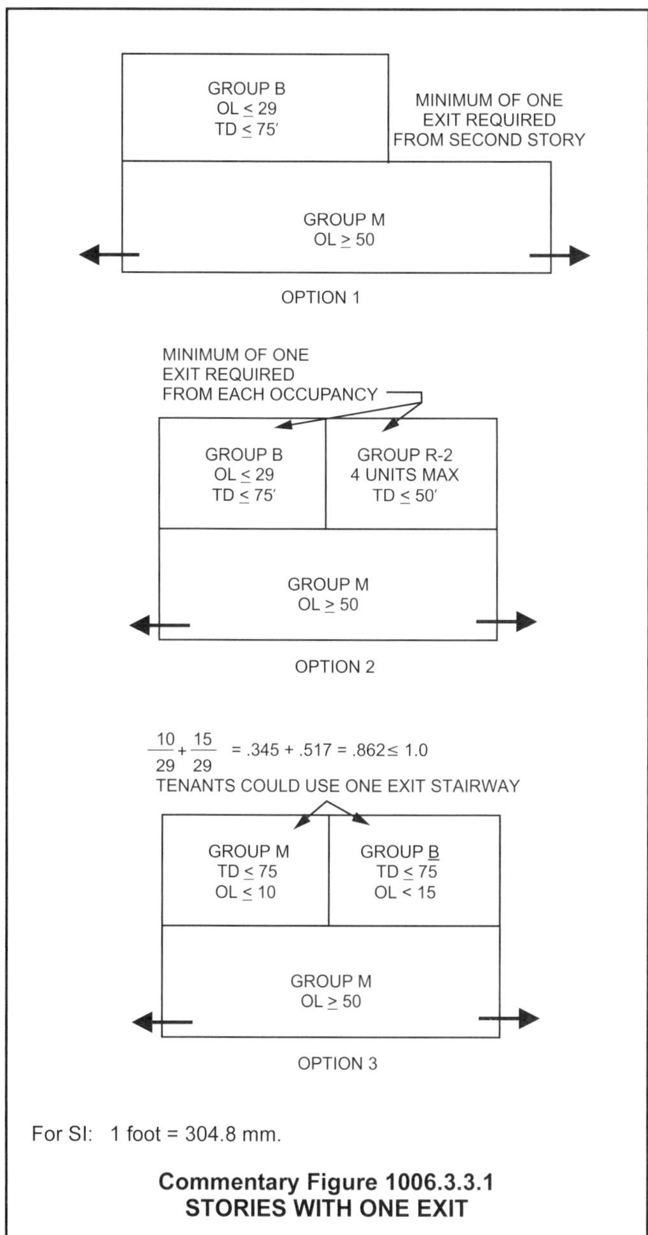

For SI: 1 foot = 304.8 mm.

Commentary Figure 1006.3.3.1
STORIES WITH ONE EXIT

requirements in Section 1024.4. The intent is to provide safety in all portions of the exit by requiring continuity of the fire protection characteristics of the enclosure for the exit stairway or ramp. Exit passageways (see Section 1024) are a continuation of an exit enclosure. This includes, but is not limited to, the fire-resistance rating of the exit enclosure walls and the opening protection rating of the doors.

Section 1028.1, Exceptions 1 and 2, allow for an alternative for direct access to the outside via an intervening lobby or vestibule. Horizontal exits (see Section 1026), while not providing direct access to the outside of the structure, do move occupants to another "building" by moving through a fire wall (see Section 1028.1, Exception 3) or into a refuge area protected by fire barriers and horizontal assemblies. Horizontal exits are commonly used in hospitals and jails for a defend-in-place type of protection.

[BE] 1007.1.1 Two exits or exit access doorways. Where two *exits*, *exit access doorways*, *exit access stairways* or *ramps*, or any combination thereof, are required from any portion of the *exit access*, they shall be placed a distance apart equal to not less than one-half of the length of the maximum overall diagonal dimension of the building or area to be served measured in a straight line between them. Interlocking or *scissor stairways* shall be counted as one exit *stairway*.

Exceptions:

1. Where *interior exit stairways* or *ramps* are interconnected by a 1-hour fire-resistance-rated corridor conforming to the requirements of Section 1020, the required *exit* separation shall be measured along the shortest direct line of travel within the *corridor*.
2. Where a building is equipped throughout with an *automatic sprinkler system* in accordance with Section 903.3.1.1 or 903.3.1.2, the separation distance shall be not less than one-third of the length of the maximum overall diagonal dimension of the area served.

❖ This section provides a method to determine, quantitatively, remoteness between exits and exit access doors based on the dimensional characteristics of the space served. This measure has been common practice for some years with significant success. Very simply, the method involves determining the maximum dimension between any two points in a story or a room (e.g., a diagonal between opposite corners in a rectangular room or story or the diameter in a circular room or story). If two doors or exits are required from the room or story (see Sections 1006.2 and 1006.3), the straight-line distance between the thresholds of the doors must be at least one-half of the maximum diagonal dimension [see Commentary Figure 1007.1.1(1)].

While technical proof is not available to substantiate this method of determining remoteness, it has been found to be realistic and practical for most building designs. Buildings with exits in a center core and occupied spaces around the perimeter are addressed in Exception 1.

If a scissor stairway is utilized, regardless of the separation of the two entrances, the scissor stairway may only be counted as one exit. Two independent stairways within the same enclosure could result in both stairways being unusable in an emergency where smoke penetrates the single enclosure (see the definition for "Scissor stairways" in Chapter 2). Interlocking stairways that occur over the same building footprint but within separate enclosures are not scissor stairways and can count as two independent exits. Due to concern about smoke migration, careful review of the construction details and verification that they meet all the provisions for fire barriers and horizontal assemblies must be made. Of special concern would be the provisions for continuity, penetrations and joints.

The entrance to the enclosures for exit stairways or ramps shall meet the same arrangement as exit and exit access doorways. The need for exits to be independent of each other cannot be overstated.

In Exception 1, a method of permitting the distance between exits to be measured along a complying corridor connecting the enclosure for the exit stairway or ramp has served to mitigate the disruption to this design concept [see Commentary Figure 1007.1.1(2)].

As reflected in Exception 2, the protection provided by an automatic sprinkler system can reduce the threat of fire buildup so that the reduction in remoteness to one-third of the diagonal dimension is not unreasonable, based on the presumption that it provides the occupants with an acceptable level of safety from fire [see Commentary Figure 1007.1.1(3)]. The automatic sprinkler system must be installed throughout the building in accordance with NFPA 13 or 13R. This reduced separation (one-third of the diagonal) may also be used when applying the requirements of Exception 1.

In applying the provisions of this section, it is important to recognize any convergence of egress paths that may exist. Commentary Figure 1007.1.1(4) illustrates an assembly room with remotely located exit access doors, but the doors from the entire space are not considered remote in accordance with this section.

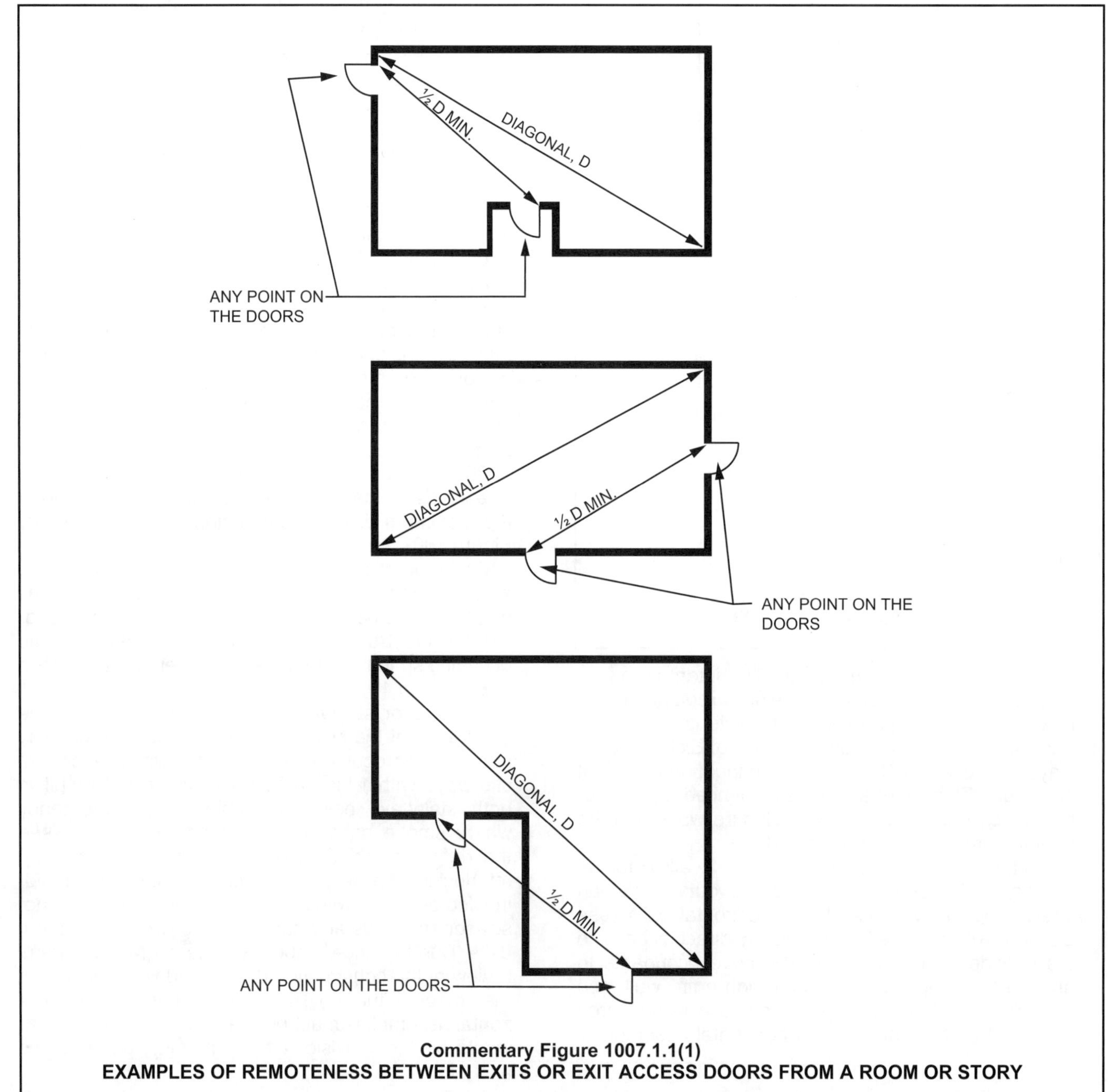

Commentary Figure 1007.1.1(1)
EXAMPLES OF REMOTENESS BETWEEN EXITS OR EXIT ACCESS DOORS FROM A ROOM OR STORY

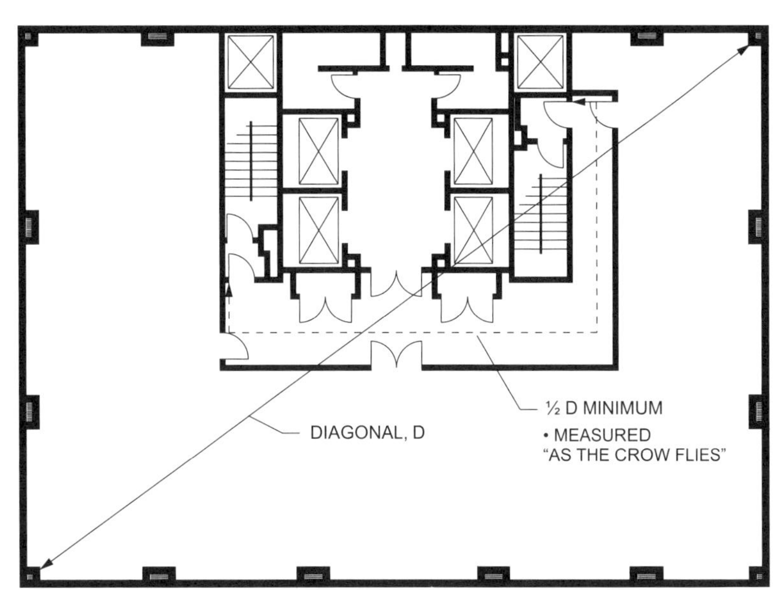

EXAMPLE:

DIAGONAL DIMENSION = 134′-0″
MIN. SEPARATION OF EXITS = 134′ ÷ 2 = 67″-0′

For SI: 1 inch = 25.4 mm, 1 foot = 304.8 mm.

Commentary Figure 1007.1.1(2)
REMOTENESS OF INTERCONNECTING BY A 1-HOUR FIRE-RESISTANCE-RATED CORRIDOR

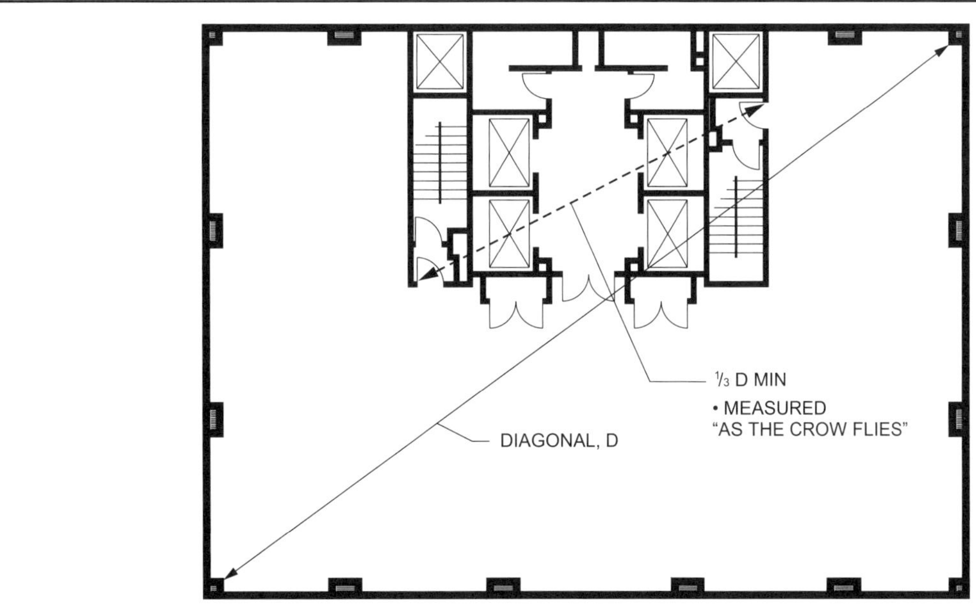

EXAMPLE:
DIAGONAL DIMENSION = 134′-0″
MIN. SEPARATION OF EXITS = 134′ ÷ 3 = 44′-8″

For SI: 1 inch = 25.4 mm, 1 foot = 304.8 mm.

Commentary Figure 1007.1.1(3)
REMOTENESS OF EXITS IN A BUILDING WITH AN AUTOMATIC SPRINKLER SYSTEM

[BE] 1007.1.1.1 Measurement point. The separation distance required in Section 1007.1.1 shall be measured in accordance with the following:

1. The separation distance to *exit* or *exit access doorways* shall be measured to any point along the width of the doorway.
2. The separation distance to *exit access stairways* shall be measured to the closest riser.
3. The separation distance to *exit access ramps* shall be measured to the start of the ramp run.

❖ Where exit access stairways are permitted to be unenclosed, the remoteness measurement for doorways shall begin at the top riser of the unenclosed stairway; this is consistent with the exit access travel distance measurement in Section 1017.3. Where an open ramp is used, the separation is measured to where the slope of the ramp starts. Where a rated enclosure is provided, distances are measured to the door of the enclosure. Historically, exit access travel distance was measured to the center of the door, ramp or stairway; however, there is an allowance for that point to be at any location along the door, stairway or ramp. The intent is to reduce subjectivity in the determination of exit/exit access configuration. The result is that a designer could literally measure to the far extreme edge of the two doorways leading out of a room to meet the separation requirements.

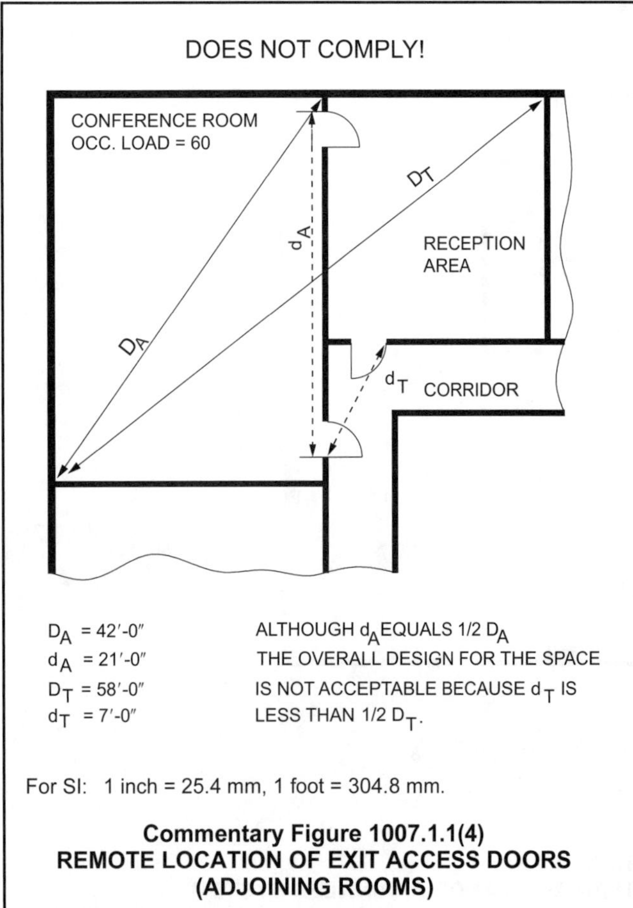

Commentary Figure 1007.1.1(4)
REMOTE LOCATION OF EXIT ACCESS DOORS (ADJOINING ROOMS)

[BE] 1007.1.2 Three or more exits or exit access doorways. Where access to three or more exits is required, not less than two exit or *exit access doorways* shall be arranged in accordance with the provisions of Section 1007.1.1. Additional required exit or *exit access doorways* shall be arranged a reasonable distance apart so that if one becomes blocked, the others will be available.

❖ Where there are three or more required exits from a story or exit access doors from a room, they are to be analyzed identically to the method described in Section 1007.1.1. Two of the exits or exit access doors must meet the remoteness test. Any additional exits or exit access doors can be located anywhere within the floor plan that meets the code requirements, including independence, accessibility, capacity and continuity.

There is no specific separation requirement provided in Section 1007.1.2 for the third exit, but the exits must be located so that one fire event will not block two exits; thus, two doors immediately adjacent would not be acceptable. The appropriate separation is subjective and would be partially dependent on the layout of the space. Using some other provisions in the code for guidance can help. Section 1005.5 states that multiple means of egress need to be sized such that the loss of any one will not reduce the capacity below 50 percent. This intent is repeated for an assembly space with more than 300 occupants. Sections 1029.2 and 1029.3 can require this space to have a main exit that accommodates one-half of the total occupant load and then require the balance of the exits (means of egress) to provide for the remaining one-half of the occupant load. The "main exit" is typically the result of a single "main entrance" for fee or ticket entry. If there is not a main exit, Sections 1029.2 and 1029.3 permit the means of egress to be "distributed around the perimeter of the building."

[BE] 1007.1.3 Remoteness of exit access stairways or ramps. Where two *exit* access *stairways* or *ramps* provide the required *means of egress* to *exits* at another story, the required separation distance shall be maintained for all portions of such *exit access stairways* or *ramps*.

❖ These provisions are intended to prohibit open stairways and ramps that meet the separation distance at the first riser or start of the ramp run from converging toward one another such that the separation distance is reduced as the occupants follow the egress path to the lower level. Exit access stairways and ramps have to maintain the separation distance until the travel to the lower floor is complete (see Commentary Figure 1007.1.3).

[BE] 1007.1.3.1 Three or more exit access stairways or ramps. Where more than two *exit access stairways* or *ramps* provide the required *means of egress*, not less than two shall be arranged in accordance with Section 1007.1.3.

❖ See the commentary to Section 1007.1.3, Remoteness of exit access stairways and ramps.

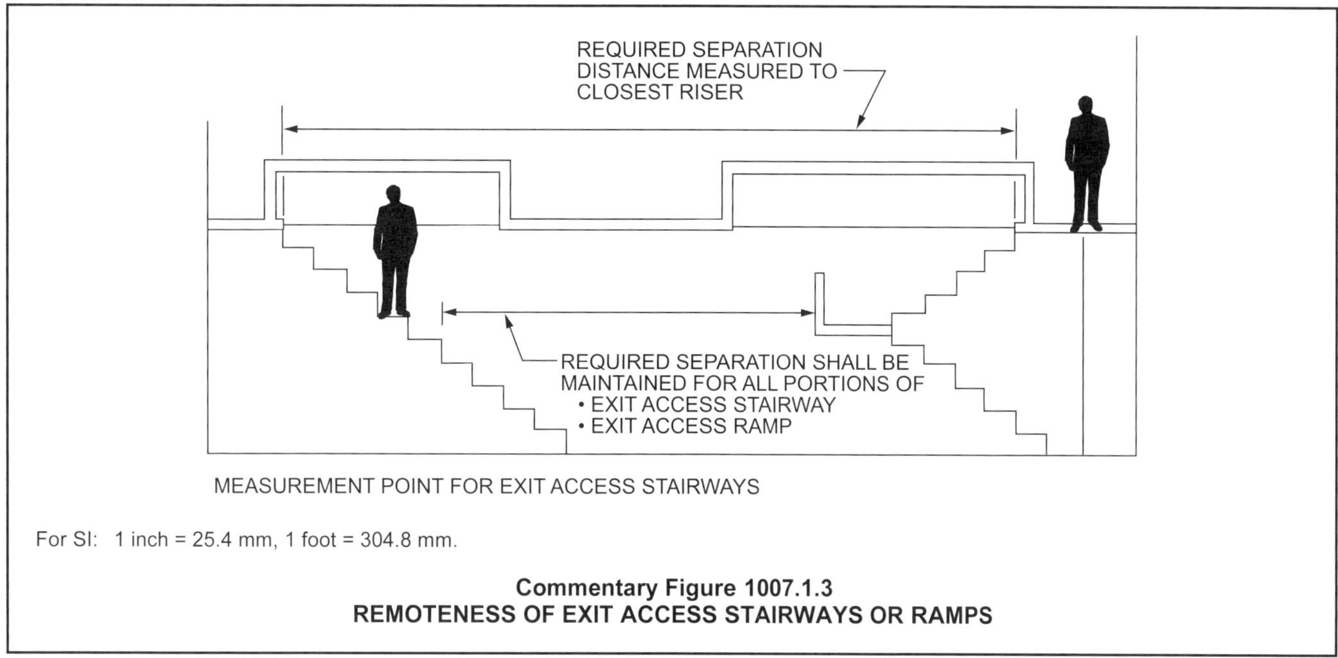

Commentary Figure 1007.1.3
REMOTENESS OF EXIT ACCESS STAIRWAYS OR RAMPS

SECTION 1008
MEANS OF EGRESS ILLUMINATION

[BE] 1008.1 Means of egress illumination. Illumination shall be provided in the *means of egress* in accordance with Section 1008.2. Under emergency power, *means of egress* illumination shall comply with Section 1008.3.

❖ This section is split into two distinct requirements: Section 1008.2 for egress lighting during typical lighting situations and Section 1008.3 for egress lighting for emergencies where the building has lost normal power.

[BE] 1008.2 Illumination required. The *means of egress* serving a room or space shall be illuminated at all times that the room or space is occupied.

Exceptions:

1. Occupancies in Group U.
2. *Aisle accessways* in Group A.
3. *Dwelling units* and *sleeping units* in Groups R-1, R-2 and R-3.
4. *Sleeping units* of Group I occupancies.

❖ All portions of the means of egress serving a space must be illuminated by artificial lighting when that space is occupied, so that the paths of exit travel are always visible and available for evacuation of the occupants during emergencies. The intent is to allow portions of a building to have the lights turned off when that portion is unoccupied.

Three of the exceptions are for occupancies where the constant illumination of the means of egress would interfere with the use of the space, such as sleeping areas or theater seating during a performance.

Bear in mind that means of egress lighting is not emergency lighting. For emergency lighting requirements, see Section 1008.3.

The high-rise provisions in Section 403 utilize the means of egress lighting and emergency lighting in this section. High-rise buildings containing Groups A, B, E, I-1, M and R-1 also require a secondary backup system of luminous egress path markings within enclosed exit stairways (Section 1025). Section 1025.5 requires the enclosed exit stairways to be illuminated for 60 minutes prior to the daily occupancy and during the entire time the building is occupied so that the self-luminous markings can charge. In a building that is always occupied, such as an assisted living facility, this would require at least some of the lights in the stairway to be on 24 hours per day.

[BE] 1008.2.1 Illumination level under normal power. The *means of egress* illumination level shall be not less than 1 footcandle (11 lux) at the walking surface.

Exception: For auditoriums, theaters, concert or opera halls and similar assembly occupancies, the illumination at the walking surface is permitted to be reduced during performances by one of the following methods provided that the required illumination is automatically restored upon activation of a premises' fire alarm system:

1. Externally illuminated walking surfaces shall be permitted to be illuminated to not less than 0.2 footcandle (2.15 lux).
2. Steps, landings and the sides of *ramps* shall be permitted to be marked with self-luminous materials in accordance with Sections 1025.2.1, 1025.2.2 and 1025.2.4 by systems *listed* in accordance with UL 1994.

❖ The intensity of lighting along the entire means of egress, including open plan spaces, aisles, corridors and passageways, exit stairways, exit doors and places of exit discharge at the walking surface or floor level, must not be less than 1 footcandle (11 lux). One footcandle (11 lux) is approximately the same lighting level as found outdoors at twilight. It has been found that even this relatively low level of lighting renders enough visibility for occupants to evacuate a building safely.

It is important to note that this lighting level is measured at the floor in order to make the floor surface visible. Levels of illumination above the floor may be higher or lower, thus allowing lights along steps to be used rather than general area lighting.

The exception addresses assembly occupancies where low light level is needed for the function of the space. It is not the intent of the exception to require a fire alarm system but to require a connection to the egress lighting where a fire alarm system is provided. There are two options for that path lighting. Per Exception 1, the level of intensity of aisle lighting in such spaces may be reduced to 0.2 footcandle (2.15 lux), but only during the time of a performance. This intensity of illumination is sufficient to distinguish the aisles and stairs leading to the egress doors and not be a source of distraction during a performance. The option in Exception 2 allows for internally illuminated luminous path stripes (see Section 1025). Since the illumination in the space between shows and the duration of the shows may not be compatible with luminous path markings that charge from a light source, this option is currently not permitted.

[BE] 1008.2.2 Group I-2. In Group I-2 occupancies where two or more *exits* are required, on the exterior landings required by Section 1010.6.1, means of egress illumination levels for the *exit discharge* shall be provided such that failure of a single lamp in a luminaire shall not reduce the illumination level on that landing to less than 1 footcandle (11 lux).

❖ Section 1008.1, by requiring the means of egress to be illuminated, would also include the exit discharge. Often, when moving to the outside of the building, the lighting from the parking lot or street lights will sufficiently light the exit discharge without additional lighting from the building itself. The transition of moving from a lighted space to the outside may be an issue at the exit door; therefore, many facilities do provide a light over the exit door on the outside. For hospitals, the fixture provided must have at least two light bulbs so that if one burns out, the other will still provide sufficient light for this transition.

While this requirement is limited to Group I-2, to reduce potential hazards at this important juncture, this could be considered best practice for other occupancies.

[BE] 1008.2.3 Exit discharge. Illumination shall be provided along the path of travel for the *exit discharge* from each *exit* to the *public way*.

Exception: Illumination shall not be required where the path of the *exit discharge* meets both of the following requirements:

1. The path of exit discharge is illuminated from the exit to a safe dispersal area complying with Section 1028.5.
2. A dispersal area shall be illuminated to a level not less than 1 footcandle (11 lux) at the walking surface.

❖ Section 1008.1, by requiring the means of egress to be illuminated, would also include the exit discharge. On large parcels and where buildings are constructed on private campuses (i.e., business parks, hospital complex, college/university), the need to provide required lighting to the public way can be significant. Often, when moving to the outside of the building, the lighting from the parking lot or street lights will sufficiently light the exit discharge without additional lighting from the building itself.

The exception allows for the option of providing a route to a safe dispersal area rather than a public way in places that do not have the typical streets around buildings, but may have large open areas. Examples would be college campuses.

[BE] 1008.3 Emergency power for illumination. The power supply for *means of egress* illumination shall normally be provided by the premises' electrical supply.

❖ The main routes for means of egress must be illuminated in times of emergency where occupants must have a lighted path of exit travel in order to evacuate the building safely. The code is very specific in the description of the areas that are required to be illuminated by the emergency, not the standby, power system (see Section 2702.2.13).

[BE] 1008.3.1 General. In the event of power supply failure in rooms and spaces that require two or more *means of egress* an emergency electrical system shall automatically illuminate all of the following areas:

1. *Aisles.*
2. *Corridors.*
3. *Exit access stairways* and *ramps.*

❖ Where two or more means of egress are required from a room or space, emergency lighting must be provided along aisles, corridors, exit access stairways and ramps. It is not the intent to require the entire space to be lit as during normal use situations addressed in Section 1008.2. However, the main egress paths out of the two exit spaces must be illuminated. This would always include the main corridor in a story with two or more required exits, and could include paths off that main corridor. For example, an aisle in an open office plan must be illuminated with emergency lighting, but not the path within individual offices that egress through the open area. Open exit access stairways from a mezzanine (as permitted by Sections 1006.2 and 1019.3) and the route from the bottom of the stairway to the exit must also be illuminated.

[BE] 1008.3.2 Buildings. In the event of power supply failure, in buildings that require two or more *means of egress*, an emergency electrical system shall automatically illuminate all of the following areas:

1. Interior *exit access stairways* and *ramps.*

2. *Interior* and *exterior exit stairways* and *ramps*.
3. *Exit passageways*.
4. Vestibules and areas on the *level of discharge* used for *exit discharge* in accordance with Section 1028.1.
5. Exterior landings as required by Section 1010.1.6 for exit doorways that lead directly to the *exit discharge*.

❖ Where two or more exits are required from a story, essential portions of the interior egress system must be illuminated. This includes:

- Exit access stairways from a story (as permitted by Sections 1006.3 and 1019.3) as well as the route from the bottom of the stairway to the exit (see Section 1008.3.1).
- All exit stairways and ramps along their entire length.
- Exit passageways (Section 1024) used in facilities with long travel distances, such as malls, or as an extension of the exit stairway enclosure.
- Means of egress systems that use exit balconies (see Section 1021) or open exterior exit stairways or ramps (see Section 1027).
- Interior exit discharge elements, such as lobbies and vestibules (see Section 1028.1), where stairways discharge into these elements instead of directly to the exterior of a building.
- Exterior landings at exit doors leading to the exit discharge. Note that only the portion of the exterior discharge that is immediately adjacent to the building exit discharge door is required to have emergency illumination and not the entire exterior discharge path to the public way.

[BE] 1008.3.3 Rooms and spaces. In the event of power supply failure, an emergency electrical system shall automatically illuminate all of the following areas:

1. Electrical equipment rooms.
2. Fire command centers.
3. Fire pump rooms.
4. Generator rooms.
5. Public restrooms with an area greater than 300 square feet (27.87 m^2).

❖ The intent of Items 1 through 4 is to have emergency lighting in areas significant for emergency responders or maintenance personnel who may be trying to locate and fix the loss of power issue for the building.

Item 5 requires an emergency light in large restrooms. Given the activity, people may need some illumination to quickly get themselves ready to be able to evacuate.

[BE] 1008.3.4 Duration. The emergency power system shall provide power for a duration of not less than 90 minutes and shall consist of storage batteries, unit equipment or an on-site generator. The installation of the emergency power system shall be in accordance with Section 2702 of the *International Building Code*.

❖ So that there will be a continuing source of electrical energy for maintaining the illumination of the means of egress when there is a loss of the main power supply, the means of egress lighting system must be connected to an emergency electrical system that consists of storage batteries, unit equipment or an on-site generator. This emergency power-generating facility must be capable of supplying electricity for at least 90 minutes, thereby giving the occupants sufficient time to leave the premises. In most cases, where the loss of the main electrical supply is attributed to a malfunction in the distribution system of the electric power company, experience has shown that such power outages do not usually last as long as 90 minutes.

IFC requirements for emergency power for emergency egress lighting and exit signage in existing buildings only require a 60-minute time duration. This is not a conflict, but rather recognition of the loss of battery storage capability over a length of time.

[BE] 1008.3.5 Illumination level under emergency power. Emergency lighting facilities shall be arranged to provide initial illumination that is not less than an average of 1 footcandle (11 lux) and a minimum at any point of 0.1 footcandle (1 lux) measured along the path of egress at floor level. Illumination levels shall be permitted to decline to 0.6 footcandle (6 lux) average and a minimum at any point of 0.06 footcandle (0.6 lux) at the end of the emergency lighting time duration. A maximum-to-minimum illumination uniformity ratio of 40 to 1 shall not be exceeded. In Group I-2 occupancies, failure of a single lamp in a luminaire shall not reduce the illumination level to less than 0.2 foot-candle (2.2 lux).

❖ This section provides the criteria of the illumination levels of the emergency lighting system. The initial average level for the main egress paths is the same as for the overall means of egress illumination in Section 1008.2.1. The reduction of illumination recognizes the performance characteristics over time of some types of power supplies, such as batteries. The minimum levels are sufficient for the occupants to egress from the building. In addition, the emergency lighting system is a secondary system that is spaced along the main egress routes. It will not provide the same level of general lighting over the route as what can be provided by the building lighting system.

The maximum-to-minimum illumination uniformity ratio of 40 to 1 means that the variation in the illumination levels is not to exceed that number. For example, a minimum of 0.06 footcandle (0.6 lux) would establish a maximum illumination of 2.4 footcandles (24 lux) in an adjacent area. This is to establish a variation limit such that the means of egress can be seen as a person walks from bright to darker areas along the egress path.

Group I-2 nursing homes and hospitals typically use a defend-in-place strategy for patients and residents who require assistance from a staff trained in the fire safety and evacuation plans. Given the possible critical nature of some of the patients and the need to move some people with life-sustaining equipment, there is an additional requirement that the lighting in the main corridors and along the exit path will always have some redundancy in the fixtures providing that illumination. This could be done with either two bulb fixtures, or locating emergency lighting fixtures close enough that if one burned out, light from fixtures on each side would overlap enough to not result in a dark spot.

SECTION 1009 ACCESSIBLE MEANS OF EGRESS

[BE] 1009.1 Accessible means of egress required. *Accessible means of egress* shall comply with this section. Accessible spaces shall be provided with not less than one *accessible means of egress*. Where more than one *means of egress* is required by Section 1006.2 or 1006.3 from any *accessible* space, each accessible portion of the space shall be served by not less than two *accessible means of egress*.

Exceptions:

1. One *accessible means of egress* is required from an accessible *mezzanine* level in accordance with Section 1009.3, 1009.4 or 1009.5.
2. In assembly areas with ramped *aisles* or stepped *aisles*, one *accessible means of egress* is permitted where the *common path of egress travel* is *accessible* and meets the requirements in Section 1029.8.

❖ The Access Board has revised and updated its accessibility guidelines for buildings and facilities covered by the Americans with Disabilities Act (ADA) of 1990 and the Architectural Barriers Act (ABA) of 1968. The final ADA/ABA Guidelines, published by the Access Board in July 2004, serve as the basis for the minimum standards when adopted by other federal agencies responsible for issuing enforceable standards. The plan is to eventually use this new document in place of the Uniform Federal Accessibility Standards (UFAS) and ADAAG. The US Department of Justice officially adopted the new federal requirements on September 15, 2010. The name is the *2010 ADA Standards for Accessible Design,* otherwise known as the *2010 ADA Standards*. The *2010 ADA Standards*, Section 207/F207, references the 2000 edition of the IBC with 2001 Supplement, as well as the 2003 edition of the IBC, for accessible means of egress requirements. The International Code Council® (ICC®) is very proud to be recognized for its work regarding accessible means of egress in this manner. Refer to the Access Board website (www.access-board.gov) for more specific information and the current status of this adoption process. Based on the date of the publication and the adoption process, later editions of the IBC are not specifically referenced; however, none of the later editions reduced the accessible means of egress requirements found in the referenced IBC editions, so the newer editions provide for equivalent or better accessibility.

The accessible means of egress locations may not be near the accessible route used for ingress into the building (see IBC Sections 1104 and 1105). For example, a two-story building requires one accessible route to connect all accessible spaces within the building. The accessible route to the second level is typically by an elevator. During a fire emergency, persons with mobility impairments on the second level should move to the exit stairways for assisted rescue, not back the way they came in via the elevator. Signage at the elevator will direct occupants to an exit stairway.

This section establishes the minimum requirements for means of egress facilities serving all spaces that are required to be accessible to people with physical disabilities. Previously, attention was focused on response to the civil-rights-based issue of providing adequate access for people with physical disabilities into and throughout buildings. Concerns about life safety and evacuation of people with mobility impairments were frequently cited as reasons for not embracing widespread building accessibility, in the best interests of the disabled community.

The provisions for accessible means of egress are predominantly, though not exclusively, intended to address the safety of persons with a mobility impairment. These requirements reflect the balanced philosophy that accessible means of egress are to be provided for occupants who have gained access into the building but are incapable of independently utilizing the typical means of egress facilities, such as the exit stairways. By making such provisions, the code now addresses means of egress for all building occupants, with and without physical disabilities.

Any space that is not required by the code to be accessible in accordance with Chapter 11 is not required to be provided with accessible means of egress. This may include an entire story, a portion of a story, a mezzanine or an individual room. For example, a mechanical penthouse is not required to be accessible in accordance with Section 1103.2.9; therefore, the mechanical penthouse is not required to have an accessible means of egress.

In new construction and additions, at least two accessible means of egress are required. For example, in buildings, stories or spaces required by Section 1006.3.1 to have three or more exits or exit access doors, a minimum of two accessible means of egress is required. The accessibility requirements are based on the required means of egress from both individual spaces and the building as a whole. Therefore, facilities with multiple large assembly rooms, such as banquet halls or multiplex theaters where the second exit from the space is often a door directly to the outside, may require additional accessible means of egress from the building because of space requirements.

While there are no dispersement requirements specific to accessible means of egress or travel distance limitations where there is not an area of refuge requirement (see Sections 1009.3, 1009.4 and 1009.6), the code requires all exits to be distinct, separate and independent. The main intent is that a person with mobility impairments will always have options. If not all exits are accessible, possible entrapment should be a consideration in determining which exits are to be made accessible. In most buildings, the upper floors will already have an accessible route to all stairways. On the first floor, if the issue is accessible exit discharge, see Section 1009.7.

An accessible means of egress is required to provide a continuous path of travel to a public way. This principle is consistent with the general requirements for all means of egress, as reflected in Section 1003.1 and in the definition of "Means of egress" in Chapter 2. This section also emphasizes the intent that accessible means of egress must be available to a person with a mobility impairment, such as a person using a wheelchair, scooter or walker. Some mobility impairments do not allow for self-evacuation along a stairway; therefore, utilization of the exit and exit discharge may require assistance. This assistance is typically provided by the fire department or other trained personnel, either along the exit stairways or, in buildings five stories or taller, with the elevator system or a combination of both (see commentary, Section 1009.2.1). The safety and fire evacuation plans (see Sections 404 and 1002.2) require planning for all occupants of a building. It is required that accessible routes, areas of refuge and exterior areas of rescue assistance are indicated on these plans. These plans must be approved by the local fire official and reviewed annually.

While not stated in this section, existing buildings undergoing alterations are not required to be provided with accessible means of egress as part of that alteration (see IEBC Section 305.6). In many cases, meeting the requirements for accessible means of egress, especially the 48-inch (1219 mm) clear stair width required in nonsprinklered buildings, would be considered technically infeasible. However, if an accessible means of egress was part of the original construction, it must be maintained in accordance with IEBC Section 305.2.

The exceptions address special situations where accessible means of egress requirements need special consideration. Note that these are exceptions for accessible means of egress, not exceptions for accessible entrance requirements (see IBC Section 1105).

Exception 1 is a special consideration for mezzanines. The size of mezzanines is limited to a portion of the space below (see Section 505). Most are open to the space below; thus, with the same atmosphere and line of sight, fire recognition is quicker than in a two-story situation. If the elevator used for ingress has not gone into fire department recall, that system could be used for self-evacuation. There are three different scenarios:

1. If the mezzanine is exempted from accessibility, such as a mechanical mezzanine (see Section 1103.2.9), or small enough not to be required to be accessed by an accessible route (see IBC Section 1104.4, Exception 1), no accessible means of egress is required.
2. If a mezzanine is required to be accessed by an accessible route (see IBC Section 1104.4) and meets the provisions for spaces with one means of egress (see Section 1006.2), the exit access stairway must meet the provisions of Section 1009.3. Per the exception to Section 1009.3.1, this can be an open exit access stairway. Per Section 1009.3.3, Exception 1, in a nonsprinklered building, a designer would have the option of either an area of refuge or two-way communication at the elevator. Per Section 1009.3.3, Exception 2, in sprinklered buildings, an area of refuge would not be required.
3. If a mezzanine is required to be accessed by an accessible route (see Section 1104.4) and is required to have two means of egress, at least one of the means of egress stairways must meet the provisions of Section 1009.3. Per the exception to Section 1009.3.1, this can be an open exit access stairway. Per Section 1009.3.3, Exception 1, in a nonsprinklered building, a designer would have the option of either an area of refuge or two-way communication at the elevator. Per Section 1009.3.3, Exception 2, in sprinklered buildings, an area of refuge would not be required. Practically speaking, in a sprinklered building, both stairways from the mezzanine will meet the provisions of Section 1009.3.

While in Scenarios 2 and 3 it is optional to have the elevator meet the requirements of Section 1009.4, the provisions for standby power at elevators are based on fire department assisted rescue. This is an expensive option that would likely never be used during a fire event given the limited elevation change. Where platform lifts can be used in new construction (see Section 1109.8), they are so limited that it is not likely that they will provide an accessible route to a mezzanine. If the platform lift serves as part of the route to the space, Section 1009.5 allows for platform lifts to serve as part of the accessible route for accessible means of egress where they have standby power.

Exception 2 is in consideration of the practical difficulties of providing accessible routes in assembly areas with sloped floors and stepped aisles. Rooms with more than 50 persons are required to have two means of egress; therefore, each accessible seating location is required to have access to two accessible means of egress. Depending on the slope of the seating arrangement, providing an accessible route to both distinct exits can be difficult to achieve, especially in small theaters. A maximum egress travel distance of 30 feet (9144 mm) for ambulatory persons moving from the last seat in dead-end aisles or from box-type seating arrangements to where they have access to a choice of means of egress routes has been established in Section 1029.8. In accordance with Exception 2, persons using wheelchair seating spaces have the same maximum 30-foot (9144 mm) egress travel distance from the accessible seating locations to a cross aisle or to an adjacent corridor or space where two choices for accessible means of egress are provided. Note that there are increases in egress travel distance for smoke-protected and outdoor open-air assembly seating. For additional information, see Section 1029.8.

[BE] 1009.2 Continuity and components. Each required *accessible means of egress* shall be continuous to a *public way* and shall consist of one or more of the following components:

1. *Accessible routes* complying with Section 1104 of the *International Building Code.*
2. *Interior exit stairways* complying with Sections 1009.3 and 1023.
3. *Exit access stairways* complying with Sections 1009.3 and 1019.3 or 1019.4.
4. *Exterior exit stairways* complying with Sections 1009.3 and 1027 and serving levels other than the *level of exit discharge*.
5. Elevators complying with Section 1009.4.
6. Platform lifts complying with Section 1009.5.
7. *Horizontal exits* complying with Section 1026.
8. *Ramps* complying with Section 1012.
9. *Areas of refuge* complying with Section 1009.6.
10. Exterior areas for assisted rescue complying with Section 1009.7 serving *exits* at the *level of exit discharge*.

❖ There are many mobility impairments that can limit or negate a person's ability to walk up and down stairs. The taller the building, the higher the percentage of the population that will be affected. For example, an elderly person or a person with a broken foot may be able to get down a couple of flights, but not from an upper floor in a high-rise. Therefore, the taller the building, the higher the percentage of people who may need assistance in evacuation, and the higher the demand for accessible means of egress.

This section identifies the various building features that can serve as elements of an accessible means of egress. Accessible routes are readily recognizable as to how they can provide accessible means of egress; however, some nontraditional principles have been established for the total concept of accessible means of egress. This is evident in that stairways and elevators are also identified as elements that can be part of an accessible means of egress. For example, elevators are generally not available for egress during a fire, while stairways are not independently usable by a person using a wheelchair. The concept of accessible means of egress includes the idea that evacuating people with a mobility impairment may require the assistance of others. In some situations, provisions are also included for creating an area of refuge or exterior areas of rescue assistance wherein people can safely await either further instructions or evacuation assistance. Larger refuge areas can also be established by utilizing horizontal exits. All of these elements can be arranged in the manner prescribed in this section to provide accessible means of egress.

In Item 10, it is important to note that exterior areas for assisted rescue are intended to be used only at the level of exit discharge (see commentary in Chapter 2 for the defined term, "Level of exit discharge"). Exterior exit stairways from other levels are addressed by Item 4.

This section requires the accessible means of egress to have an accessible route along the path for exit access, exit and exit discharge. Stairways that lead from the level of exit discharge to grade are considered part of the exit discharge. Ideally, an accessible route would be available to a public way to allow for self-evacuation; however, where the exit discharge is not accessible, the options are an interior area of refuge complying with Section 1009.6 or an exterior area of assisted rescue in accordance with Section 1009.7.

[BE] 1009.2.1 Elevators required. In buildings where a required *accessible floor* is four or more *stories* above or below a *level of exit discharge*, not less than one required *accessible means of egress* shall be an elevator complying with Section 1009.4.

Exceptions:

1. In buildings equipped throughout with an *automatic sprinkler system* installed in accordance with Section 903.3.1.1 or 903.3.1.2, the elevator shall not be required on floors provided with a *horizontal exit* and located at or above the *levels of exit discharge*.
2. In buildings equipped throughout with an *automatic sprinkler system* installed in accordance with Section 903.3.1.1 or 903.3.1.2, the elevator shall not be required on floors provided with a *ramp* conforming to the provisions of Section 1012.

❖ Elevators are the most common and convenient means of providing access to the upper floors in multistory buildings. As such, elevators represent a prime candidate for accessible means of egress from such buildings, especially in light of the difficulties involved in carrying a person up or down a stairway for multiple levels. The primary consideration for elevators as an accessible means of egress is that the elevator will be available and protected during a fire event to allow for fire department assisted rescue. Typically, it is not the intent that people use the elevator for self-evacuation due to the hazards associated with smoke in the elevator shaft or the elevator taking people to the floor with a direct fire hazard. There are some new technological advances for fire service access elevators and occupant evacuation elevators that are discussed in IBC Sections 403, 3007 and 3008.

This section addresses where an elevator must serve as part of an accessible means of egress. See Section 1104 for where elevators are required for the accessible route into a building. By referencing Section 1009.4, both an area of refuge and a standby source of power for the elevator are required. The standby power requirement establishes a higher degree of reliability that the elevator will be available and usable by reducing the likelihood of power loss to the elevator caused by fire or other conditions of power failure.

The code defines "Exit discharge, level of" as the story at the point at which an exit terminates. In buildings having four or more stories above or below the level of exit discharge, it is unreasonable to rely solely on exit stairways for all of the required accessible means of egress. This is the point at which complete reliance on assisted evacuation down the stairs will not be effective or adequate because of the limited availability of either experienced personnel who are trained to carry people safely (e.g., fire fighters) or the availability of special devices (i.e., self-braking stairway descent equipment or evacuation chairs). In this case, the code requires that at least one elevator, serving all floors of the building, is to serve as one of the required accessible means of egress. This should not represent a hardship, since elevators are typically provided in such buildings for the convenience of the occupants.

On a flat site, buildings with four or more stories above a level of exit discharge would typically be a five-story building. The level of exit discharge is the entire first story level (not merely the plane or level of the first floor); therefore, the fifth floor is the fourth story above the level of exit discharge. In a building with multiple basements, a story four stories below the level of exit discharge would be the fourth basement level. The actual vertical distance is the same from the fifth floor above grade down to discharge, as it is from the fourth floor below grade up to discharge. The verbiage is such that a building built on a sloped site can take into consideration that people may be exiting the building from different levels on different sides of the building (see Commentary Figure 1009.2.1).

Exception 1 establishes that accessible egress elevator service to floor levels at or above the level of exit discharge is not necessary under specified conditions. The conditions are that the building is equipped throughout with an automatic sprinkler system in accordance with NFPA 13 or 13R (see Section 903.3.1.1 or 903.3.1.2) and that floors not serviced by an accessible egress elevator are provided with a horizontal exit. The presence of an automatic sprinkler system significantly reduces the potential fire hazard and provides for increased evacuation time. The combination of automatic sprinklers and a horizontal exit provides adequate protection for the occupants despite their distance to the level of exit discharge. This exception does not apply to floor levels below the level of exit discharge, since such levels are typically below grade and do not have the added advantage of exterior openings that are available for fire-fighting or rescue purposes. This option is most often utilized where a defend-in-place approach to occupant protection is utilized, such as in a hospital, nursing home or jail. Keep in mind that the horizontal exit (see Section 1026) creates large refuge areas that have separation requirements and capacity requirements that exceed area of refuge requirements.

Exception 2 specifies that a building sprinklered throughout in accordance with NFPA 13 or 13R (see Section 903.3.1.1 or 903.3.1.2), with ramp access to each level, such as in a sports stadium, is not required to also have an elevator for accessible means of egress. The reasoning behind this is that the issue of carrying people down stairways does not occur because the ramps may be utilized instead.

[BE] 1009.3 Stairways. In order to be considered part of an *accessible means of egress*, a *stairway* between *stories* shall comply with Sections 1009.3.1 through 1009.3.3.

❖ This section addresses stairways between floor levels or to a mezzanine level (see the exception to Section 1009.3.1). Stairways (exit or exit access) between floor levels, while not part of an accessible route, can serve as part of the accessible means of egress where they are used as part of an assisted evacuation route.

Note that this section is for interior and exterior exit stairways as addressed in Sections 1023 and 1027 and exit access stairways as addressed in Section 1019. The same stairway that serves the ambulatory population between floor levels can also serve as part of the accessible means of egress. Therefore, exit access stairways between stories or to a mezzanine can be considered part of an accessible means of egress, but exit access steps within the same level, such as steps in a corridor or room leading to an exit or exit access doorway, cannot. Stairways that lead from the level of exit discharge (see Chapter 2, "Exit discharge, level of") to grade are considered part of the exit discharge. Where the exit discharge is not accessible, the options are an interior area of refuge complying with Section 1009.6 or an exterior area for assisted rescue in accordance with Section 1009.7. Do not use the provisions in this section.

[BE] 1009.3.1 Exit access stairways. *Exit access stairways* that connect levels in the same *story* are not permitted as part of an accessible *means of egress.*

Exception: *Exit access stairways* providing *means of egress* from mezzanines are permitted as part of an *accessible means of egress.*

❖ This section indicates that steps that connect raised or lowered areas in the same story are not permitted to be part of an accessible means of egress. People with mobility impairments cannot be asked to wait at the top of steps that may be anywhere in the building; they must be able to get to the stairways where the fire department will be coming into the building.

In the building code, a mezzanine is considered part of the room below, with a required height of at least 7′-0″ (2134 mm) underneath (Section 505.2). For purposes of accessible means of egress, this exception allows for this exit access stairway to be considered the same as a stairway leading from the second floor.

[BE] 1009.3.2 Stairway width. *Stairways* shall have a clear width of 48 inches (1219 mm) minimum between *handrails.*

Exceptions:

1. The clear width of 48 inches (1219 mm) between handrails is not required in buildings equipped throughout with an *automatic sprinkler* system installed in accordance with Section 903.3.1.1 or 903.3.1.2.
2. The clear width of 48 inches (1219 mm) between *handrails* is not required for *stairways* accessed from a refuge area in conjunction with a *horizontal exit.*

❖ The dimension of 48 inches (1219 mm) clear width between handrails is sufficient to enable two persons to carry a person in a basket carry or for a fireman's carry.

Exceptions for sprinklered buildings are in recognition of the increased safety and evacuation times that are afforded in a sprinklered occupancy. The expec-

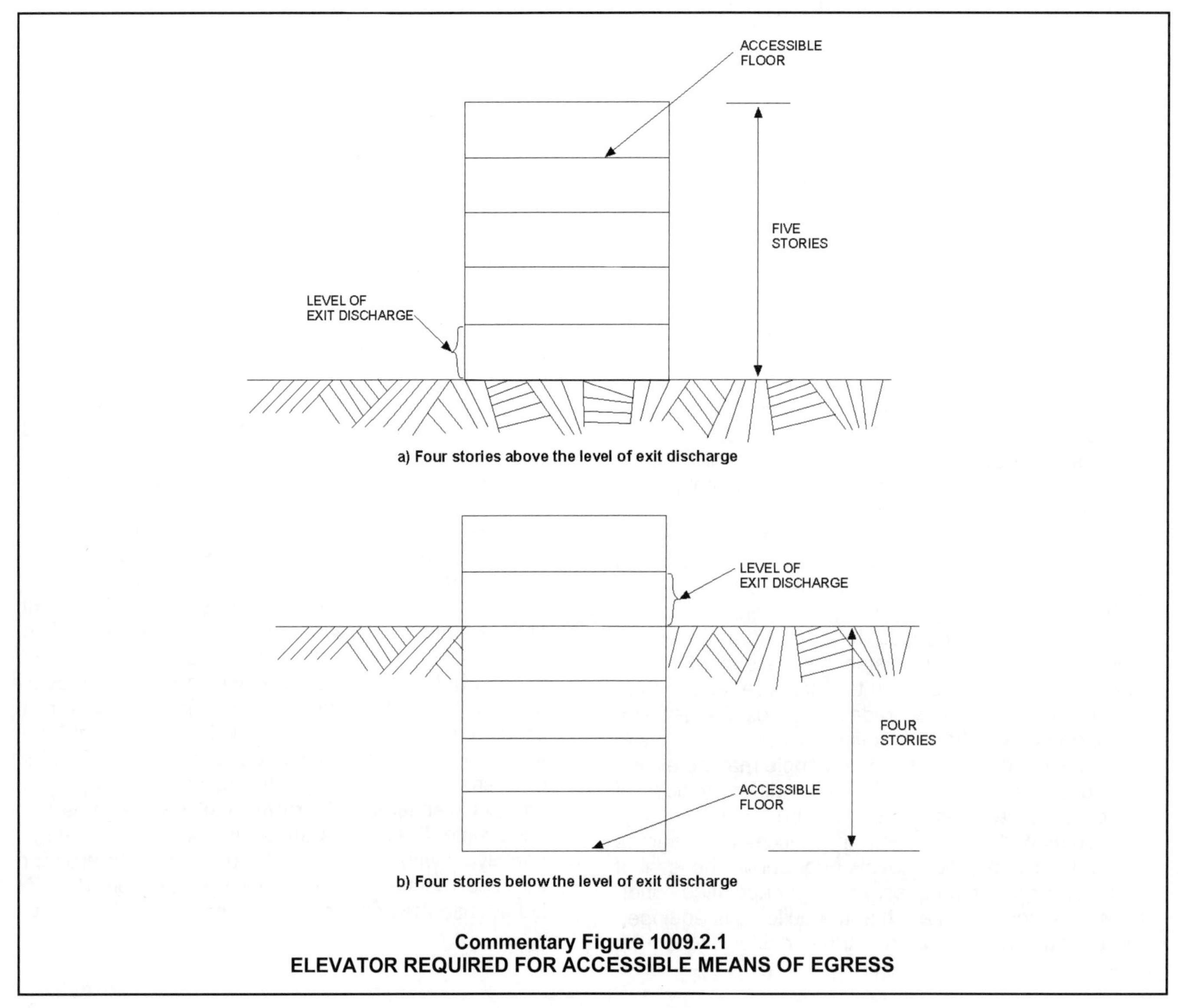

Commentary Figure 1009.2.1
ELEVATOR REQUIRED FOR ACCESSIBLE MEANS OF EGRESS

tation is that a supervised system will reduce the threat of fire by reliably controlling and confining the fire to the immediate area of origin. There is also additional safety afforded by sprinkler system requirements for automatic notification when the system is activated. This has been substantiated by a study of accessible means of egress conducted for the General Services Administration (GSA). A report issued by the National Institute of Standards and Technology (NIST), NIST IR 4770, *Staging Areas for Persons with Mobility Limitations*, concluded that the operation of a properly designed sprinkler system eliminates the life threat to all building occupants, regardless of their individual physical abilities, and is a superior form of protection as compared to areas of refuge. It was deemed that the ability of a properly designed and operational automatic sprinkler system to control a fire at its point of origin and to limit production of toxic products to a level that is not life-threatening to all occupants of the building, including persons with disabilities, eliminates the need for areas of refuge.

Exception 1 allows the stairway width to go back to the base requirements in Section 1011.2 in buildings sprinklered in accordance with NFPA 13 or 13R for both unenclosed and enclosed exit and exit access stairways (see Sections 1011, 1019, 1022 and 1027). Section 1009.3.2, Exception 1, is often used in conjunction with Section 1009.3.3, Exception 2. With the sprinkler system in place, there is more opportunity for the fire department to bring in evacuation chairs or possibly bring people to the elevator for evacuation; thus, the extra width for carrying someone down the stairway is not needed. This is safer for both emergency responders and evacuees.

Exception 2 allows the stairway width to go back to the base requirements in Section 1011.2 where the stairway is within the refuge area created by a horizontal exit [see Commentary Figure 1009.3.3(3)]. This exception considers that the extra exiting time will permit the egress down the stairway to be more deliberate. Horizontal exits are often used in hospitals, nursing homes or jails where the defense scenario is defend-in-place rather than evacuation. Section 1009.3.2, Exception 2, can be used in conjunction with Section 1009.3.3, Exception 6.

[BE] 1009.3.3 Area of refuge. Stairways shall either incorporate an *area of refuge* within an enlarged floor-level landing or shall be accessed from an *area of refuge* complying with Section 1009.6.

Exceptions:

1. *Areas of refuge* are not required at *exit access stairways* where two-way communication is provided at the elevator landing in accordance with Section 1009.8.
2. *Areas of refuge* are not required at *stairways* in buildings equipped throughout with an *automatic sprinkler system* installed in accordance with Section 903.3.1.1 or 903.3.1.2.
3. *Areas of refuge* are not required at *stairways* serving *open parking garages*.
4. *Areas of refuge* are not required for *smoke-protected* or *open-air assembly seating* areas complying with Sections 1029.6.2 and 1029.6.3.
5. *Areas of refuge* are not required at *stairways* in Group R-2 occupancies.
6. *Areas of refuge* are not required for *stairways* accessed from a refuge area in conjunction with a *horizontal exit*.

❖ The enclosed exit stairway, in combination with an area of refuge, can provide for safety from fire in one of two ways. One approach is for the fire-resistance-rated stairway enclosure to afford the necessary safety. To accomplish this, the landing within the stairway enclosure must be able to contain a wheelchair. The concept is that the person in the wheelchair will remain on the stairway landing for a period of time awaiting further instructions or evacuation assistance; therefore, the stairway landing must be able to accommodate the wheelchair without obstructing the use of the stairway by other egressing occupants. An enlarged, story-level landing is required within the stairway enclosure and must be of sufficient size to accommodate the required number of wheelchairs [see Section 1009.6 and Commentary Figure 1009.3.3(1)].

The other approach is to utilize an enclosed exit stairway that is accessed from an area of refuge complying with Section 1009.6. Under this approach, the stairway is made safe by virtue of its access being in an area that is separated and protected from the point of fire origin. An area of refuge can be created by constructing a vestibule adjacent and with direct access to the stair enclosure [see Section 1009.6 and Commentary Figure 1009.3.3(2)]. This is similar in theory to the approach of an enlarged landing within the stairway enclosure. Again, the general means of egress path must be available past the wheelchair spaces. Where areas of refuge are required, see Section 1009.6 for configuration, size, construction and two-way communication requirements.

It is very important to note that an exception for the area of refuge in Section 1009.3.3 or 1009.4.2 is not an exception for the accessible means of egress. The accessible route must be available to the stairway or elevator so that people with mobility impairments and emergency responders can meet up as soon as possible.

In a nonsprinklered building, Exception 1 would allow for two-way communication at the elevator as an alternative to providing an area of refuge at the top of the open exit access stairway, such as on a mezzanine. At a stairway without walls, there is not a good location or a practical way to require an area of refuge. In a sprinklered building, the activation of the sprinklers notifies the emergency responders. In a nonsprinklered building, the two-way communication at the elevator is a way for occupants to communicate.

Exception 2 is in recognition of the increased safety and evacuation times that are afforded in a sprinklered occupancy (see the commentary to Section 1009.3.2). Section 1009.3.3, Exception 2, is often used in conjunction with Section 1009.3.2, Exception 1. Exception 2 exempts the area of refuge for all exit access stairways and exit stairways, interior and exterior (see Sections 1011, 1019, 1023 and 1027), where the building is sprinklered throughout with an NFPA 13 or 13R system.

Exceptions 3 and 4 are for structures where the natural ventilation of the products of combustion will be afforded by the exterior openings or smoke protection required of such structures (see Sections 909 and 1029.6.2 and IBC Section 406.3). The most immediate hazard for occupants in a fire incident is exposure to smoke and fumes. Floor areas in open parking structures communicate sufficiently with the outdoors such that the need for protection from smoke is not necessary; therefore, open parking garages are exempted from the requirements for an area of refuge (see also the exception to Section 1009.6.4). Because of this level of natural ventilation, parking garage exit stairways are not required to be enclosed (see Section 1019.3, Item 6). The logic for open-air assembly seating (e.g. exterior sports facilities) and smoke-protected seating is the same: if there is no accumulation of smoke, there is no need for areas of refuge, even where a sprinkler system is not included (see Section 1019.3, Item 7).

Exception 5 is in recognition of the dwelling unit separation and fire-resistance-rated corridors in Group R-2 facilities (see Section 1020 and IBC Section 420). Effectively, each dwelling unit can serve as a protected area. Since the current text requires all Group R structures to be sprinklered (see Section 903.2.8), Section 1009.3.2, Exception 1, and Section 1009.3.3, Exception 2, could also be utilized.

Section 1009.3.2, Exception 2, can be used in conjunction with Section 1009.3.3, Exception 6. In the case of a horizontal exit [see Commentary Figure 1009.3.3(3)], each floor area on either side of the exit is considered a refuge area (see commentary, Section 1026.1) by virtue of the construction and separation requirements for horizontal exits. The discharge area is always assumed to be the nonfire side and thereby protected from fire. Therefore, per Exception 6, stairways within this refuge area are not required to have areas of refuge.

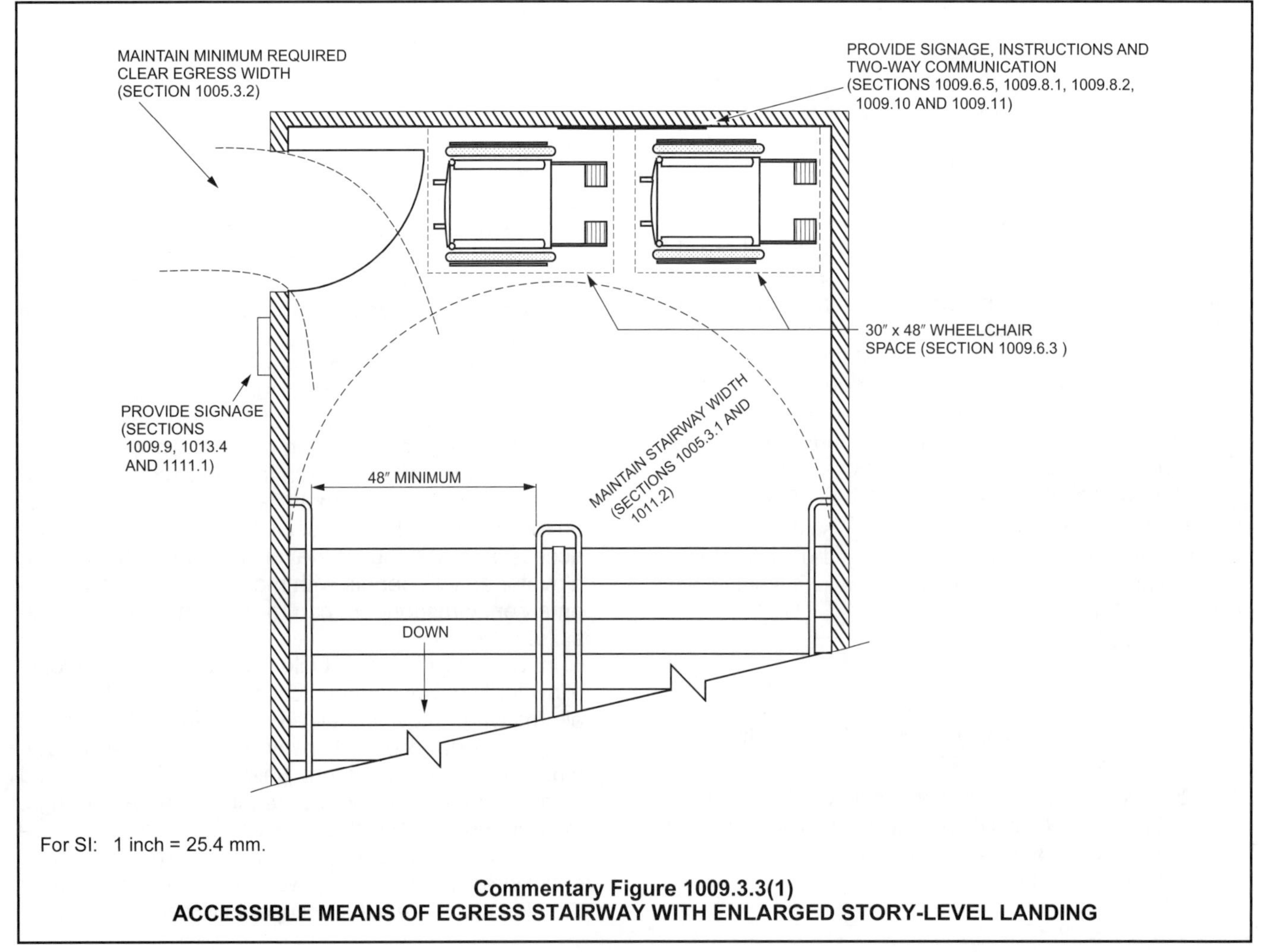

Commentary Figure 1009.3.3(1)
ACCESSIBLE MEANS OF EGRESS STAIRWAY WITH ENLARGED STORY-LEVEL LANDING

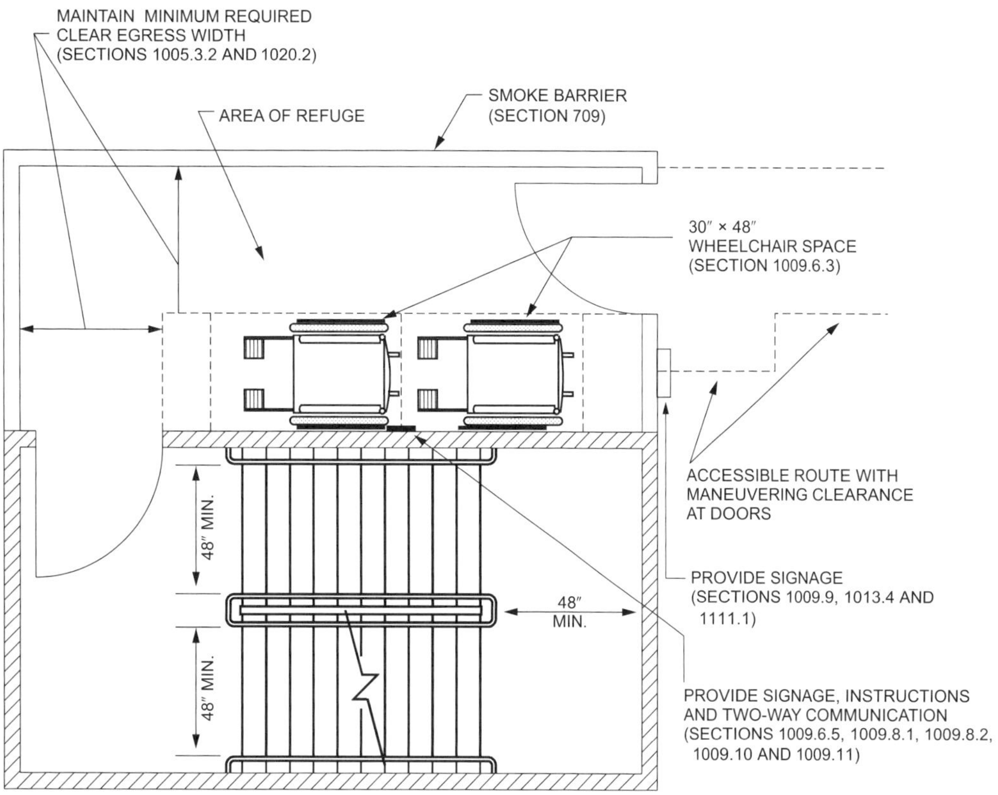

MAINTAIN MINIMUM REQUIRED CLEAR EGRESS WIDTH (SECTIONS 1005.3.2 AND 1020.2)
AREA OF REFUGE
SMOKE BARRIER (SECTION 709)
30″ × 48″ WHEELCHAIR SPACE (SECTION 1009.6.3)
ACCESSIBLE ROUTE WITH MANEUVERING CLEARANCE AT DOORS
48″ MIN.
48″ MIN.
48″ MIN.
PROVIDE SIGNAGE (SECTIONS 1009.9, 1013.4 AND 1111.1)
PROVIDE SIGNAGE, INSTRUCTIONS AND TWO-WAY COMMUNICATION (SECTIONS 1009.6.5, 1009.8.1, 1009.8.2, 1009.10 AND 1009.11)

For SI: 1 inch = 25.4 mm.

Commentary Figure 1009.3.3(2)
ACCESSIBLE MEANS OF EGRESS STAIRWAY ACCESSED FROM AN AREA OF REFUGE

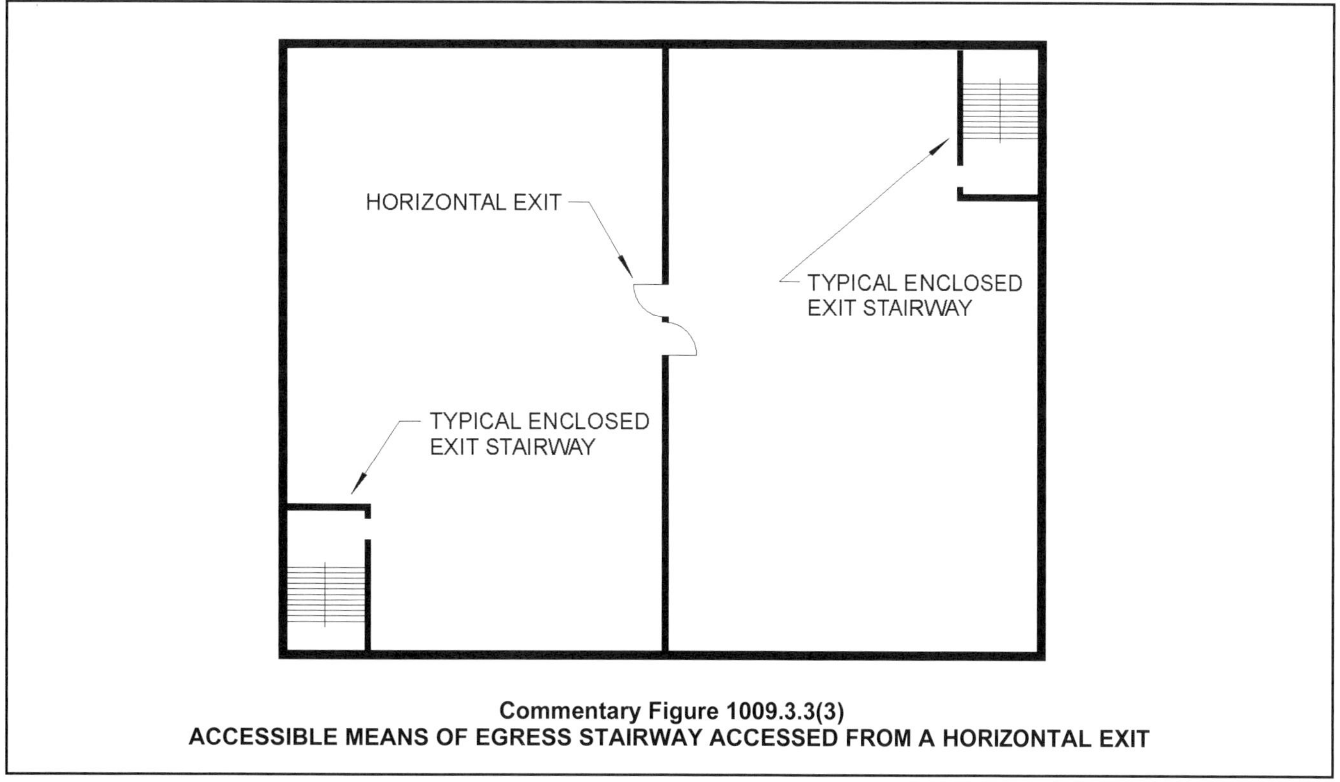

HORIZONTAL EXIT
TYPICAL ENCLOSED EXIT STAIRWAY
TYPICAL ENCLOSED EXIT STAIRWAY

Commentary Figure 1009.3.3(3)
ACCESSIBLE MEANS OF EGRESS STAIRWAY ACCESSED FROM A HORIZONTAL EXIT

[BE] 1009.4 Elevators. In order to be considered part of an accessible *means of egress*, an elevator shall comply with Sections 1009.4.1 and 1009.4.2.

❖ Section 1009.2.1 provides criteria for determining where elevators are required to serve as one of the accessible means of egress. This section includes the criteria for the elevator itself. Elevators are the most common and convenient means of providing access to upper and lower floors in multistory buildings. However, since a person would not know where the fire was in a building, the use of the elevator for emergency evacuation during a fire is always with fire department assistance. As such, elevators represent a prime candidate for accessible means of egress from such buildings, especially in light of the difficulties involved in carrying a person in a wheelchair up or down a stairway. The primary consideration for elevators as an accessible means of egress is that the elevator will be available and protected during a fire event. See Sections 403, 3007 and 3008 for new provisions in high-rise buildings for fire service access elevators and occupant evacuation elevators.

This section addresses the use of an elevator as part of an accessible means of egress by requiring both a backup source of power for the elevator (Section 1009.4.1) and access to the elevator from an area of refuge (Section 1009.4.2). For situations where elevators are required to be part of one of the accessible means of egress, see Section 1009.2.1. Note that an elevator lobby that is off a fire-resistance-rated corridor must also comply with IBC Section 713.14 and IBC Chapter 30.

[BE] 1009.4.1 Standby power. The elevator shall meet the emergency operation and signaling device requirements of Section 2.27 of ASME A17.1/CSA B44. Standby power shall be provided in accordance with Chapter 27 and Section 3003 of the *International Building Code*.

❖ In order for an elevator to be reliably available for fire department assisted rescue, standby power is required in case the regular power is interrupted. The elevator must also be equipped with the fire department recall and emergency operation controls specified in the elevator safety standard, ASME A17.1. Additionally, the reference to Chapter 27 and Section 3003 of the IBC clarifies that the elevator will comply with the emergency operation features that relate to operating an elevator under fire conditions (see commentary, IBC Sections 2702.2.2 and 3003).

[BE] 1009.4.2 Area of refuge. The elevator shall be accessed from an *area of refuge* complying with Section 1009.6.

Exceptions:

1. *Areas of refuge* are not required at the elevator in *open parking garages*.
2. *Areas of refuge* are not required in buildings and facilities equipped throughout with an *automatic sprinkler system* installed in accordance with Section 903.3.1.1 or 903.3.1.2.
3. *Areas of refuge* are not required at elevators not required to be located in a shaft in accordance with Section 712 of the *International Building Code*.
4. *Areas of refuge* are not required at elevators serving *smoke protected or open-air assembly seating* areas complying with Sections 1029.6.2 and 1029.6.3.
5. *Areas of refuge* are not required for elevators accessed from a refuge area in conjunction with a *horizontal exit*.

❖ Requiring access from an area of refuge affords the same degree of fire safety as described for stairways (see commentary, Section 1009.3.3). Where areas of refuge are required, see Section 1009.6 for configuration, size, construction and two-way communication requirements. Elevators on an accessible route are also required to meet the accessibility provisions of ICC A117.1 (see commentary, IBC Sections 1109.7 and 3001.3).

It is important to note that an exception for the area of refuge in Section 1009.3.3 or 1009.4.2 is not an exception for the accessible means of egress. The accessible route must be available to the stairway or elevator so that emergency responders and people with mobility impairments can meet up as soon as possible.

Exception 2 is for areas of refuge at all elevators where the building is sprinklered throughout with an NFPA 13 or 13R system. Again, this is not an exception for the accessible route to the exit, just the area of refuge at the elevator with standby power. Exception 2 is in recognition of the increased safety and evacuation times that are afforded in a sprinklered occupancy. The expectation is that a supervised system will reduce the threat of fire by reliably controlling and confining the fire to the immediate area of origin. There is also additional safety afforded by sprinkler system requirements for automatic notification when the system is activated. This has been substantiated by a study of accessible means of egress conducted for the GSA. NIST IR 4770 concluded that the operation of a properly designed sprinkler system eliminates the life threat to all building occupants, regardless of their individual physical abilities, and is a superior form of protection as compared to areas of refuge. It was deemed that the ability of a properly designed and operational automatic sprinkler system to control a fire at its point of origin and to limit production of toxic products to a level that is not life threatening to all occupants of the building, including persons with disabilities, eliminates the need for areas of refuge.

If a level in an open parking garage contains accessible parking spaces or is part of the route to and from those spaces, that level is required to have accessible means of egress. Exception 1 is in recognition of the natural ventilation of the products of combustion that will be afforded by the exterior openings required of open parking structures (see IBC Section

406.5.2). The most immediate hazard for occupants in a fire incident is exposure to smoke and fumes. Floor areas in open parking structures are sufficiently exposed to the outdoors; thus, the need for protection from smoke is not necessary. Therefore, open parking garages are exempt from the requirements for an area of refuge to access an elevator that is utilized as part of the accessible means of egress. The same idea holds true for smoke-protected and open-air assembly seating areas, in accordance with Exception 4. The protection offered by the smoke control system or being outside allows for adequate evacuation time before there is danger from smoke and fume accumulation.

Exception 3 allows elevators not required to be enclosed (see Section 712) to not have an area of refuge. If there is no shaft enclosure around the elevator, construction of a smoke-tight compartment immediately in front of the elevator doors would be very difficult. Typically, this would be elevators in atriums or in parking garages. Again, the nature of locations adjacent to atriums or open ramps in parking garages would minimize the chances of smoke accumulation at the elevators.

In the case of a horizontal exit [see Commentary Figure 1009.3.3(3)], each floor area on either side of the exit is considered a refuge area (see commentary, Section 1026.1) by virtue of the construction and separation requirements for horizontal exits. The discharge area is always assumed to be the nonfire side and thereby protected from fire. Therefore, per Exception 5, any elevator within this refuge area is not required to have areas of refuge.

[BE] 1009.5 Platform lifts. Platform lifts shall be permitted to serve as part of an *accessible means of egress* where allowed as part of a required *accessible route* in Section 1109.8 of the *International Building Code* except for Item 10. Standby power for the platform lift shall be provided in accordance with Chapter 27 of the *International Building Code.*

❖ Previously, there have been concerns about whether a platform lift will be reliably available at all times. However, ASME A18.1, the standard for platform lifts, no longer requires key operation. It is important to note that platform lifts are not prohibited by the code. They simply cannot be counted as a required accessible means of egress in locations other than where they are allowed as part of the accessible route into a space (see commentary, IBC Section 1109.8). Where platform lifts are utilized as part of an accessible means of egress, they must come equipped with standby power. Per ASME A18.1, the standby power needs to be sufficient to run the platform lift for at least five round-trips. Note that platform lifts cannot be used to meet accessible means of egress requirements for a situation that utilizes IBC Section 1109.8, Item 10. Accessible means of egress must be provided at other locations.

IBC Section 1109.8, Item 10, recognizes that existing site constraints may make installation of a ramp or elevator infeasible. An example would be existing public sidewalks, easements and public ways in downtown urban areas where the street and sidewalk follow grade and the building's floor is level, resulting in steps up or down at entrances. The concern for allowing a lift as part of the accessible means of egress is due to requiring standby power for only five cycles. If a platform lift was utilized to provide entry for a building with a large number of occupants who may use mobility devices, such as a hospital, there might not be sufficient time or power for everyone to evacuate safely.

In existing buildings undergoing alterations, platform lifts are allowed as part of an accessible route into a building (see commentary, IEBC Section 305.8.3) at any location as long as they are compliant with ASME A18.1. Note that accessible means of egress are not required in existing buildings undergoing an alteration or a change of occupancy (see IEBC Section 305.6, Exception 2).

[BE] 1009.6 Areas of refuge. Every required *area of refuge* shall be accessible from the space it serves by an *accessible means of egress.*

❖ Areas of refuge, where provided, are an important component of fire safety and evacuation plans for buildings. These areas must be included in the plans required by Sections 404 and 1002.2.

An area of refuge is of no value as part of an accessible means of egress if it is not accessible. The code states an obvious but essential requirement: the path that leads to an area of refuge must qualify as an accessible means of egress. This provision is required so that there will be an accessible route leading from every accessible space to each required area of refuge.

While stairways and elevators that are part of the accessible means of egress from upper and lower floors have exceptions for an area of refuge, if an area of refuge is chosen as the option at the level of exit discharge, there are no exceptions (see Commentary Figure 1009.6).

[BE] 1009.6.1 Travel distance. The maximum travel distance from any accessible space to an *area of refuge* shall not exceed the *exit access* travel distance permitted for the occupancy in accordance with Section 1017.1.

❖ For consistency in principle with the general means of egress design concepts, the code also limits the exit access travel distance to the area of refuge. The limitation is the same distance as specified in Section 1017.2 for maximum exit access travel distance. This equates the maximum travel distance required to reach an exit with the maximum distance required to reach an area of refuge. It should be noted that an area of refuge is not necessarily an exit in the classic sense. For example, where the area of refuge is an enlarged, story-level landing within an exit stairway, the area of refuge is within the exit and the maximum travel distance for both the conventional exit and the accessible area of refuge is measured to the same point (the entrance to the exit stairway). If the area of refuge is a vestibule immediately adjacent to an enclosed exit stairway, the maximum travel distance for the required accessible means of egress is measured to the entrance of the area of refuge and, for the travel distance to the exit, to the entrance of the exit stairway (see Commentary Figure 1009.6). In the case of accessible means of egress with an elevator, the maximum travel distance may end up being measured along two different paths, with the only consistency between the conventional means of egress and the accessible means of egress being the maximum travel distance (see Commentary Figure 1009.6). The travel distance within an area of refuge is not directly regulated, but will be limited by the general provisions for maximum exit access travel distance, which are always applicable.

In summary, the code takes a reasonably consistent approach for both conventional and accessible means of egress by limiting the distance one must travel to reach a safe area from which further egress to a public way is available.

Where areas of refuge are exempted (Sections 1009.3.3 and 1009.4.2), the general exit requirements in Chapter 10 are assumed to address number of exits, travel distance and separation.

[BE] 1009.6.2 Stairway or elevator access. Every required *area of refuge* shall have direct access to a *stairway* complying with Sections 1009.3 and 1023 or an elevator complying with Section 1009.4.

❖ To ensure that there is continuity in an accessible means of egress, the code requires that every area of refuge have direct access to either an exit stairway (see Section 1009.3) or an elevator (see Section 1009.4). This, again, may be viewed as stating the obvious, but it is necessary so that the egress layout does not involve entering an area of refuge and then having to leave that protected area before gaining access to a stairway or elevator. Once an occupant reaches the safety of an area of refuge, that level of protection must be continuous until the vertical transportation element (the stairway or elevator) is reached.

If one chooses to comply with accessible means of egress requirements by providing an accessible elevator with an area of refuge in the form of an elevator lobby, the elevator shaft and the lobby are required to be constructed in accordance with IBC Section 713.14 and IBC Chapter 30. The requirements provide additional assurance that the elevator will not be rendered unavailable because of smoke movement into the elevator shaft. If the elevator is in a refuge area that is formed by the use of a horizontal exit (i.e., fire walls or fire barriers in accordance with Section 1026.2) or smoke compartments formed by smoke barriers (see IBC Sections 407.5 and 408.6), it is presumed that the refuge area is relatively free from smoke; therefore, the extra protection of IBC Section 713.14 and IBC Chapter 30 may not be needed.

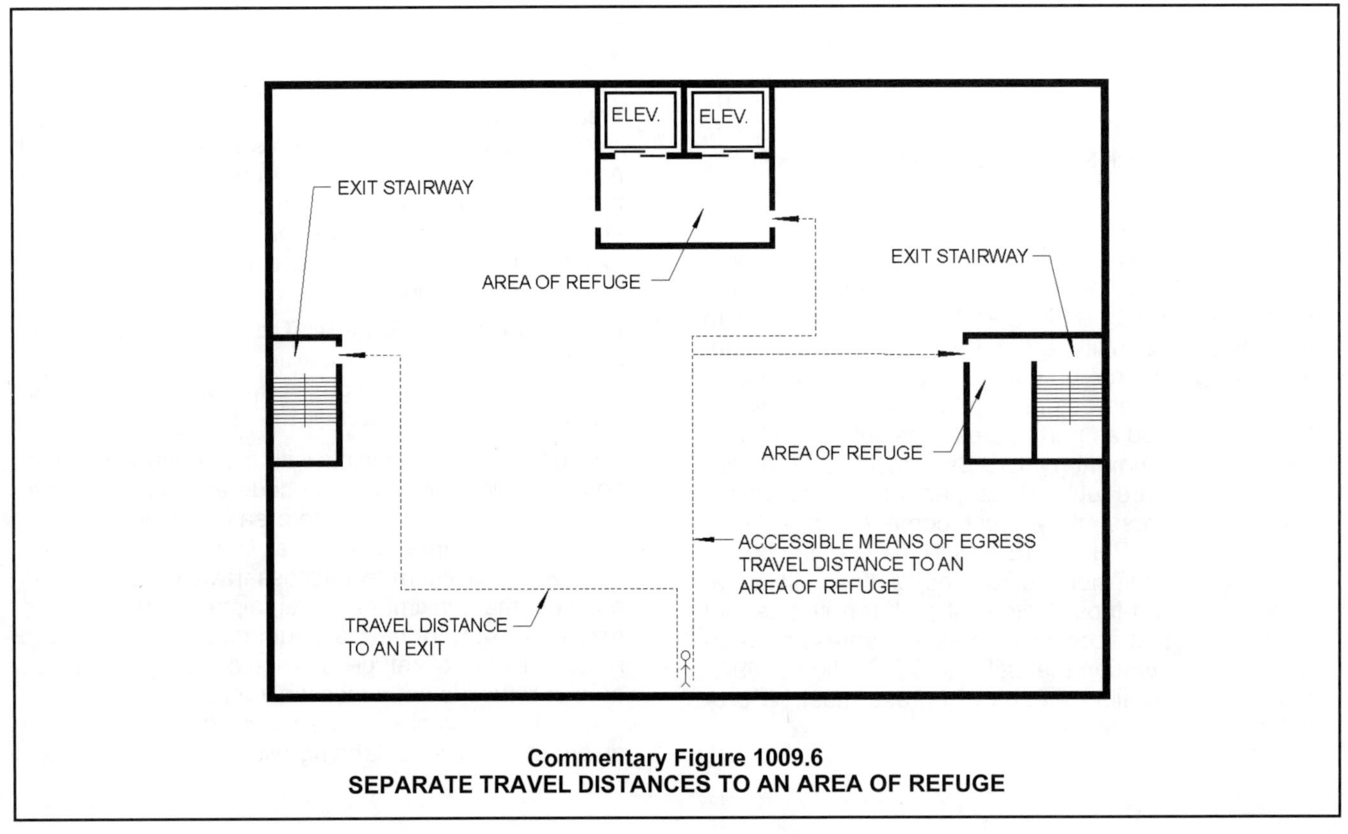

Commentary Figure 1009.6
SEPARATE TRAVEL DISTANCES TO AN AREA OF REFUGE

[BE] 1009.6.3 Size. Each *area of refuge* shall be sized to accommodate one wheelchair space of 30 inches by 48 inches (762 mm by 1219 mm) for each 200 occupants or portion thereof, based on the *occupant load* of the *area of refuge* and areas served by the *area of refuge*. Such wheelchair spaces shall not reduce the *means of egress* minimum width or required capacity. Access to any of the required wheelchair spaces in an *area of refuge* shall not be obstructed by more than one adjoining wheelchair space.

❖ The number of wheelchair spaces that are required to be provided in an area of refuge is intended to represent broadly the expected population of the average building. As one point of measurement, a 1977 survey conducted by the National Center for Health Statistics indicated that one in 333 civilian, noninstitutionalized persons uses a wheelchair. The 1990 ADA currently utilizes the criterion of one space for every 200 occupants, based on the space served by the area of refuge. Given the variations and difficulties involved in accurately predicting a representative ratio for application to all occupancies, it was concluded that requiring one space for every 200 occupants, based on the area of refuge itself plus the areas served by the area of refuge, represents a reasonable criterion. Very few buildings would ever require more than four wheelchair spaces on a floor, since nearly all buildings with an occupant load greater than 400 per floor would be sprinklered and using Exception 2 in Section 1009.3.3.

Arrangement of the required wheelchair spaces is critical so as not to interfere with the means of egress for ambulatory occupants (see Section 1011.6). Since the design concept is that wheelchair occupants will move to the area of refuge and await further instructions or evacuation assistance, the spaces must be located so as not to reduce the required means of egress width of the stairway, door, corridor or other egress path through the exterior area of rescue.

In order to provide for orderly maneuvering of wheelchairs, this section states that access to any of the required wheelchair spaces cannot be obstructed by more than one adjoining wheelchair space. For example, this precludes an arrangement that three or more wheelchairs could be stacked down a dead-end corridor. This also effectively limits the difficulty any given wheelchair occupant would have in reaching or leaving a given wheelchair space, as well as providing easier access to all wheelchair spaces by persons providing evacuation assistance [see Commentary Figures 1009.3.3(1) and 1009.3.3(2)].

[BE] 1009.6.4 Separation. Each *area of refuge* shall be separated from the remainder of the story by a *smoke barrier* complying with Section 709 of the *International Building Code* or a *horizontal* exit complying with Section 1026. Each *area of refuge* shall be designed to minimize the intrusion of smoke.

Exceptions:

1. *Areas of refuge* located within an enclosure for *interior exit stairways* complying with Section 1023.
2. *Areas of refuge* in outdoor facilities where *exit access* is essentially open to the outside.

❖ The minimum standard for construction of an area of refuge is a smoke barrier, in accordance with IBC Section 709. This establishes a minimum degree of performance by means of a 1-hour fire-resistance rating, including opening protectives and a minimum degree of performance against the intrusion of smoke into an enclosed area of refuge, as specified in IBC Sections 709.4 and 709.5. By the nature of the connection to the stair enclosure or elevator shaft, the normal smoke barrier requirement for extension from exterior wall to exterior wall is replaced by connection to the shaft enclosure.

An alternative is to provide a refuge area created by a horizontal exit complying with Section 1026. Horizontal exits are formed by fire walls or fire barriers with a minimum fire-resistance rating of 2 hours. The horizontal exit separation must extend vertically through all levels of the building, unless floor assemblies have a fire-resistance rating of not less than 2 hours with no unprotected openings (see Section 1026.2). The other provisions for horizontal exits for additional egress elements, opening protection and capacity must also be complied with.

This section does not require an area of refuge within an exit stairway to be designed to prevent the intrusion of smoke. This was based on a study of areas of refuge conducted by the NIST for the GSA, which concluded that a story-level landing within a fire-resistance-rated exit stairway would provide a satisfactory staging area for evacuation assistance (see Exception 1).

Exception 2 is in recognition that, despite not being a sprinklered venue, where the entire facility is protected from smoke and fumes by the nature of being open to the outside, a separation for areas of refuge is not required.

[BE] 1009.6.5 Two-way communication. *Areas of refuge* shall be provided with a two-way communication system complying with Sections 1009.8.1 and 1009.8.2.

❖ If a building includes areas of refuge at stairways or elevators, each area of refuge must include a two-way communication system. If the building uses one of the exceptions for areas of refuge, Section 1009.8 would still require a two-way communication system at the elevator. This way anyone needing assistance can communicate with a person at a constantly attended location to request evacuation assistance. This system is an important part of the fire safety and evacuation plans required by Sections 404 and 1002.2. See Sections 1009.8.1 and 1009.8.2 for specific requirements for this system.

[BE] 1009.7 Exterior areas for assisted rescue. Exterior areas for assisted rescue shall be accessed by an *accessible route* from the area served.

Where the *exit discharge* does not include an *accessible route* from an *exit* located on the *level of exit discharge* to a *public way*, an exterior area of assisted rescue shall be provided on the exterior landing in accordance with Sections 1009.7.1 through 1009.7.4.

❖ Section 1009.2 requires the accessible means of egress to have an accessible route along the path for exit access, exit and exit discharge. Stairways that lead from the level of exit discharge (see Chapter 2, "Exit discharge, level of") to grade are considered part of the exit discharge. Where the exit discharge is not accessible, the options are an interior area of refuge complying with Section 1009.6 or an exterior area for assisted rescue in accordance with Section 1009.7. If the area of refuge option is chosen, there are not exceptions for sprinklered buildings.

The provisions for stairways in Section 1009.3 are not applicable for steps in the exit discharge. If this is an exterior exit stairway (i.e., more than one story of vertical travel), the provisions in Section 1009.3 would be applicable instead of the criteria in this section.

Exterior areas for assisted rescue are intended to be open-air locations for persons with physical disabilities to wait for assisted rescue. There must be an interior or exterior accessible route along the path of travel for access to this location. This allows a person unable to negotiate the exit discharge to get to a location where they can be quickly discovered by the fire department or other emergency responders.

In most situations, interior areas of refuge are not a positive alternative. Tenants tend to use such areas as convenient storage areas. Where persons with mobility impairments can wait for assisted rescue outside of the building, they are effectively protected from interior smoke and fumes—the deadliest of the fire hazards. Being immediately visible at an exit should also result in a shorter period of time before assisted rescue is achieved.

Exterior areas for assisted rescue, where provided, are an important component of the fire safety and evacuation plans for buildings. These areas must be included in the plans required by Sections 404 and 1002.2.

The option under Section 1009.7 is commonly used only at the level of exit discharge for the second exit at the back of a building or tenant space. This will be either a single-story building or the first level of a multistory building where the secondary exit discharge is not accessible due to changes in elevation around the perimeter. See the following examples.

Example 1:

A strip mall would have an accessible entrance to each tenant in the front (IBC Section 1105.1.6). Many have service entrances or loading bays across the back, so the second exit door leads to steps. Installing a ramp for accessible exit discharge could: create a prohibitively large structure due to the elevation change, block access to the loading docks, cause damage to maneuvering trucks, or be impossible because of space restrictions in a narrow alley.

Example 2:

An office building has a second exit that leads to a concrete stoop. If the exit discharge is sloped, uneven or blocked by snow, this is just as impassible for a person using a wheelchair as a series of steps. Providing a sidewalk all the way to the front of the building may not be practical because of adjacent buildings or because someone could be traveling adjacent to a burning building.

Sections 1009.7.1 through 1009.7.4 provide criteria for a safe place to wait temporarily for assistance. These address size, separation/protection, openness and any steps leading from the exterior area for assisted rescue.

[BE] 1009.7.1 Size. Each exterior area for assisted rescue shall be sized to accommodate wheelchair spaces in accordance with Section 1009.6.3.

❖ The exterior area for assisted rescue must have an enlarged landing area with space for at least one wheelchair for every 200 occupants that will be using that exit. The wheelchair spaces must be located so that they do not obstruct the general means of egress. If these spaces are confined by walls, guards or edges, they must also meet the alcove provisions in ICC A117.1 so that persons using wheelchairs can maneuver into the space (see Commentary Figure 1009.7.1).

[BE] 1009.7.2 Separation. *Exterior walls* separating the exterior area of assisted rescue from the interior of the building shall have a minimum fire-resistance rating of 1 hour, rated for exposure to fire from the inside. The fire-resistance-rated *exterior wall* construction shall extend horizontally not less than 10 feet (3048 mm) beyond the landing on either side of the landing or equivalent fire-resistance-rated construction is permitted to extend out perpendicular to the *exterior wall* not less than 4 feet (1220 mm) on the side of the landing. The fire-resistance-rated construction shall extend vertically from the ground to a point not less than 10 feet (3048 mm) above the floor level of the area for assisted rescue or to the roof line, whichever is lower. Openings within such fire-resistance-rated *exterior walls* shall be protected in accordance with Section 716 of the *International Building Code*.

Exception: The fire-resistance rating and opening protectives are not required in the exterior wall where the building is equipped throughout with an *automatic sprinkler system* installed in accordance with Section 903.3.1.1 or 903.3.1.2.

❖ The protection provided by an exterior area for assisted rescue would be equivalent to that required for an interior area of refuge. Note that there is no exception for the exterior area of assisted rescue for buildings that contain sprinkler systems, just the separations requirements. The separation requirements are similar to exterior exit stairways, rated walls and protected openings for 10 feet (3048 mm) above, below and to the sides of the landing (see Sections 1023.7 and 1027.6). The exceptions for exterior exit stairway protection in Section 1027.6 would not be applicable where the area includes an exterior area for assisted rescue (see Commentary Figure 1009.7.2).

The current separation requirements address typical rear exit situations. Other locations may require alternative protection measures to "shield" an exterior area for assisted rescue. The principle of "wing" walls (as used at a fire wall extension) suggests an alternative to $^{3}/_{4}$-hour opening protectives at dock doors adjacent to an exterior area for assisted rescue.

Note that providing a rescue location 10 feet (3048 mm) away from an exterior wall does not serve as a viable alternative to a fire-resistance-rated exterior wall. Persons waiting for assistance must have a minimum level of shielding from a fire in the building. An alternative for access to a public way is a safe dispersal area in accordance with Section 1028.5, which sets a minimum distance of 50 feet (15 240 mm).

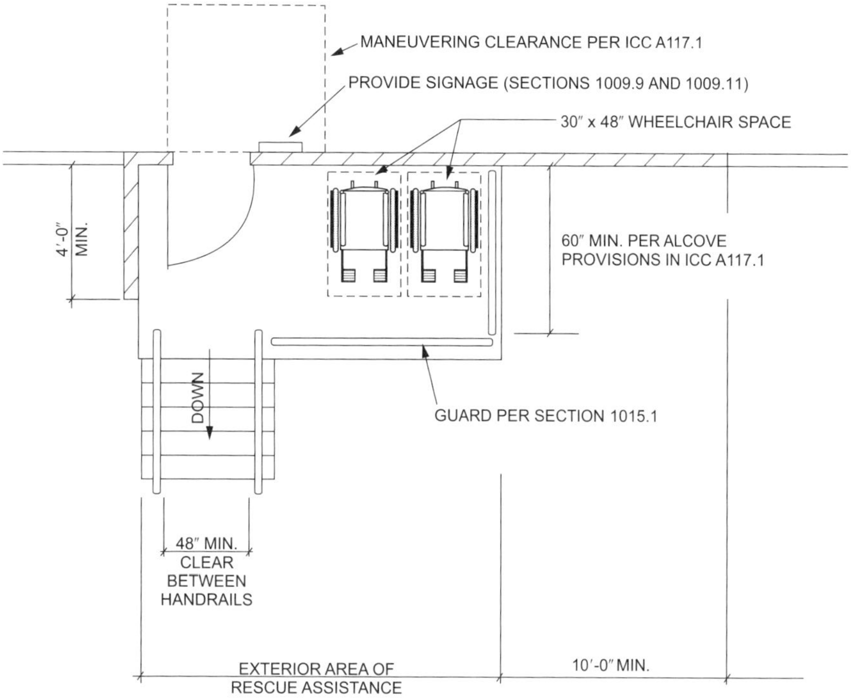

For SI: 1 inch = 25.4 mm, 1 foot = 304.8 mm.

Commentary Figure 1009.7.1
EXTERIOR AREA OF RESCUE ASSISTANCE—PLAN VIEW

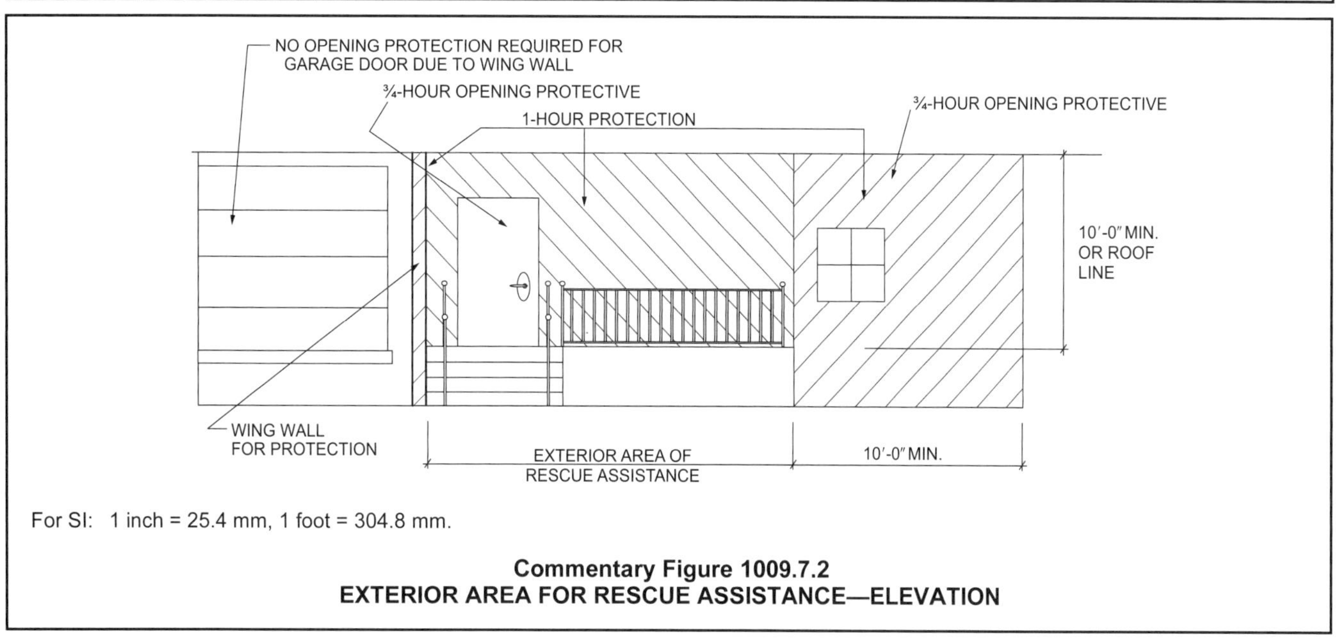

For SI: 1 inch = 25.4 mm, 1 foot = 304.8 mm.

Commentary Figure 1009.7.2
EXTERIOR AREA FOR RESCUE ASSISTANCE—ELEVATION

A common situation is for the path of egress travel from the first floor to move through the bottom level of an enclosed exit stairway. If there are steps outside the exit door of the stairway, there is no accessible path for exit discharge. Where approved by the code official (see Section 104.11), the stairway enclosure could be considered equivalent to a protected exterior wall. It is assumed that the fire is in the building somewhere, not in the stairway. A person with a mobility impairment could be provided with a place to wait—either inside the stairway enclosure or outside the building with the stairway enclosure as the separation between them and the fire—as an alternative to Section 1009.7.2. The exterior wall of an interior exit stairway can be nonrated where permitted by Section 1023.7.

The exception for the wall rating and opening protectives is in recognition of the increased safety and evacuation times that are afforded in a sprinklered occupancy (see the commentary to Section 1009.3.2). This is not an exception for the accessible means of egress or the exterior area for assisted rescue. Occupants must be able to get to this area to connect with the emergency responders as quickly as possible.

[BE] 1009.7.3 Openness. The exterior area for assisted rescue shall be open to the outside air. The sides other than the separation walls shall be not less than 50 percent open, and the open area shall be distributed so as to minimize the accumulation of smoke or toxic gases.

❖ The openness criteria for exterior areas of assisted rescue are similar to the requirements for exterior balconies. The purpose is to ensure that a person at an exterior area for rescue assistance is not in danger from smoke and fumes. The criteria are to address the situation where the rescue area is open to outside air, but a combination of roof overhangs and perimeter walls or guards could still trap enough smoke that the safety of the occupants would be jeopardized.

[BE] 1009.7.4 Stairways. *Stairways* that are part of the *means of egress* for the exterior area for assisted rescue shall provide a minimum clear width of 48 inches (1220 mm) between *handrails*.

Exception: The minimum clear width of 48 inches (1220 mm) between *handrails* is not required at *stairways* serving buildings equipped throughout with an *automatic sprinkler system* installed in accordance with Section 903.3.1.1 or 903.3.1.2.

❖ Any steps that lead from an exterior area for assisted rescue to grade must have a clear width of 48 inches (1219 mm) between handrails. The additional width is to permit adequate room to assist a mobility-impaired person down the steps and to a safe location.

If the building is sprinklered, the exception allows for the stairway to utilize the minimum widths required in Section 1011.2. This is consistent with Section 1009.3.2, Exceptions 1 and 2.

[BE] 1009.8 Two-way communication. A two-way communication system complying with Sections 1009.8.1 and 1009.8.2 shall be provided at the landing serving each elevator or bank of elevators on each accessible floor that is one or more stories above or below the *level of exit discharge*.

Exceptions:

1. Two-way communication systems are not required at the landing serving each elevator or bank of elevators where the two-way communication system is provided within *areas of refuge* in accordance with Section 1009.6.5.
2. Two-way communication systems are not required on floors provided with *ramps* conforming to the provisions of Section 1012.
3. Two-way communication systems are not required at the landings serving only service elevators that are not designated as part of the *accessible means of egress* or serve as part of the required *accessible route* into a facility.
4. Two-way communication systems are not required at the landings serving only freight elevators.
5. Two-way communication systems are not required at the landing serving a private residence elevator.
6. Two-way communication systems are not required in Group I-2 or I-3 facilities.

❖ In multistory buildings, unless provided in areas of refuge, a two-way communication system must be located at the elevator landing of each accessible floor level other than the level of exit discharge. The system is intended to offer a means of communication to individuals with mobility impairment, either permanent or temporary, who need assistance during an emergency situation. Such a system can be useful not only in the event of a fire, but also in the case of a natural or technological disaster by providing emergency responders with the location of individuals who will require assistance in being evacuated from floor levels above or below the discharge level. The ability of emergency responders to quickly locate persons needing assistance is an important part of the fire safety and evacuation plan. The two-way communication system is a critical element in that plan.

Exception 1 exempts the requirement for locating two-way communication systems at elevator landings where the building is provided with complying areas of refuge. Since areas of refuge are required by Section 1009.6.5 to be equipped with two-way communication systems, there is limited need to provide such additional systems at the elevator landings. However, where multistory buildings are not provided with areas of refuge, such as is the case with most sprinklered buildings, the installation of two-way communication systems at the elevator landings is important to those individuals unable to negotiate egress stairways during an emergency. As a result, both sprinklered and nonsprinklered multistory buildings will be provided with the means for two-way communication at all accessible floor levels other than the level of exit discharge.

Exception 2 applies to floor levels that utilize ramps as vertical accessible means of egress elements. Where complying ramps are available for independent evacuation, such as occurs in a sports stadium, the two-way communication system is not required at elevator landings.

Because persons at an exterior area for rescue assistance provided at ground level (i.e., level of exit discharge) are immediately visible and such locations are at high risk for vandalism, two-way communication systems are not required at exterior areas for assisted rescue.

If the option of horizontal exits is utilized, the code does not currently address whether a two-way communication system should be provided within a refuge area that does not contain an elevator. Since the horizontal exit is not typically recognizable by a person not familiar with the building plan, the most logical location for the two-way communication system, if provided, would seem to be adjacent to the exit stairway that is located within the refuge area.

Exceptions 3, 4 and 5 address types of elevators where two-way communication systems are not required. The two-way communication system is intended for anyone to be able to communicate with emergency responders. If it is located in the lobby of the public elevator, a system at a back service elevator would be redundant and not easy for most occupants to find. A freight elevator cannot be part of an accessible route, so again, this is not the elevator that occupants would typically use. The ASME A17.1 limits the use of private residence elevators to those within or serving individual dwelling units. If a person lives in a unit with an elevator, it is not unreasonable to expect them to address any communication needs that may arise by carrying a portable or cell phone with them.

Group I-2 and I-3 facilities use a defend-in-place scenario where staff is trained to protect in place or relocate everyone in the building—patients and guests—to smoke compartments where they will be protected from smoke and fumes. Therefore, in these facilities, two-way communication systems are not required at the elevators (Exception 6).

[BE] 1009.8.1 System requirements. Two-way communication systems shall provide communication between each required location and the fire command center or a central control point location *approved* by the fire department. Where the central control point is not a constantly attended location, a two-way communication system shall have a timed automatic telephone dial-out capability to a monitoring location or 9-1-1. The two-way communication system shall include both audible and visible signals.

❖ Use of an elevator, stair enclosure or other area of refuge as part of an accessible means of egress requires a person to wait for evacuation assistance or relevant instructions. The two-way communication system allows this person to inform emergency personnel of his or her location and to receive additional instructions or assistance as needed.

The arrangement and design of the two-way communication system is specified in Section 1009.8.1. In addition to the required locations specified in Section 1009.6.5 for areas of refuge or Section 1009.8 for elevator landings, a two-way communication device is also required to be located in a high-rise building's fire command center or at a central control point whose location is approved by the fire department (see Section 907.2.12.2 and IBC Section 403.4.4). "Central control point" is not a defined term. However, given the intent and function of the two-way communication system, a central control point is a location where an individual answers the call for assistance and either provides or requests aid for a person who needs help. A suitable central control point is often not available in low-rise buildings or in a high-rise building where the central control point may not be manned on a 24-hour basis. In order that a caller may reach an appropriate emergency contact, the fire department must approve the configuration of the system. A central control point could be the lobby of a building constantly staffed by a security officer, an alarm company, a public safety answering point such as a 9-1-1 center or a central supervising station in a Group I-1 occupancy. There could be a combination solution, such as a system configured to automatically call 9-1-1 when the central control point within the building is not manned. The two-way communication system provides visual signals for the hearing impaired and audible signals to assist the vision impaired.

[BE] 1009.8.2 Directions. Directions for the use of the two-way communication system, instructions for summoning assistance via the two-way communication system and written identification of the location shall be posted adjacent to the two-way communication system. Signage shall comply with the ICC A117.1 requirements for visual characters.

❖ Guidance to the users of a two-way communication system is also specified. Operating instructions for the two-way communication system must be posted and the instructions are to include a means of identifying the physical location of the communication device. If a signal from a two-way communication system terminates to a public safety answering point, such as a fire department communication center, current 9-1-1 telephone technology only reports the address of the location of the emergency—it does not report the specific floor or area of the address reporting the emergency. The "identification of the location" posted adjacent to the two-way communication system should ensure that most discrete location information can be provided to the central control point. This will aid emergency responders, especially in high-rise buildings or corporate campuses with multiple multistory structures. The signage is not required to be raised letters or braille, but is required to meet the style, size and contrast requirements for visual signage in ICC A117.1.

[BE] 1009.9 Signage. Signage indicating special accessibility provisions shall be provided as shown:

1. Each door providing access to an *area of refuge* from an adjacent floor area shall be identified by a sign stating: AREA OF REFUGE.
2. Each door providing access to an exterior area for assisted rescue shall be identified by a sign stating: EXTERIOR AREA FOR ASSISTED RESCUE.

Signage shall comply with the ICC A117.1 requirements for visual characters and include the International Symbol of Accessibility. Where exit sign illumination is required by Section 1013.3, the signs shall be illuminated. Additionally, visual characters, raised character and braille signage complying with ICC A117.1 shall be located at each door to an *area of refuge* and exterior area for assisted rescue in accordance with Section 1013.4.

❖ Signage enables an occupant to become aware of an area of refuge and/or the exterior area for rescue assistance. The assistance areas must provide signage on or above the door stating either "AREA OF REFUGE" or "EXTERIOR AREA FOR ASSISTED RESCUE" and includes the International Symbol of Accessibility. The approach that the code takes for identification of the area of refuge is comparable to the general provisions for identification of exits, including the requirement for lighted signage. Raised letters and braille stating "EXIT" are also required adjacent to the door for the benefit of persons with a visual impairment.

The current text does not clearly indicate how to identify a refuge area formed by a horizontal exit. In hospitals and jails, where this option is typically utilized, the location of the horizontal exits must be part of the staff training for the fire safety and evacuation plans.

[BE] 1009.10 Directional signage. Directional signage indicating the location of all other means of egress and which of those are *accessible means of egress* shall be provided at the following:

1. At *exits* serving a required accessible space but not providing an *approved accessible means of egress.*
2. At elevator landings.
3. Within *areas of refuge*.

❖ The additional signage required by this section is intended to advise persons of the locations of all means of egress and which of those also serve as accessible means of egress. Since not all of the exits will necessarily be accessible means of egress, it is appropriate to provide this information at exit stairways and, particularly, at all elevators, regardless of whether they are part of an accessible means of egress. Directional signage is not required to meet raised character or braille signage requirements. Depending on the facility, this could be as simple as a basic block plan of the main corridors and stairways in the building in relation to the elevator.

[BE] 1009.11 Instructions. In *areas of refuge* and exterior areas for assisted rescue, instructions on the use of the area under emergency conditions shall be posted. Signage shall comply with the ICC A117.1 requirements for visual characters. The instructions shall include all of the following:

1. Persons able to use the *exit stairway* do so as soon as possible, unless they are assisting others.
2. Information on planned availability of assistance in the use of *stairs* or supervised operation of elevators and how to summon such assistance.
3. Directions for use of the two-way communication system where provided.

❖ The instructions provided at the exterior area for rescue assistance and the areas of refuge will differ. The required instructions on the proper use of the area of refuge and the two-way communication system provide a greater likelihood that the two-way communication system will accomplish its intended function and occupants will behave as expected. A two-way communication system will not be of much value if a person in that area does not know how to operate it. Also, since the area of refuge is required by Section 1009.9 to be identified as such, ambulatory occupants may mistakenly conclude that they should remain in that area. The instructions remind ambulatory occupants that they should continue to egress as soon as possible.

For an exterior area for assisted rescue at grade level, a two-way communication system is not required, so this portion of the instructions is not needed. However, instructions for any ambulatory persons to move to the exit discharge are still required, as well as information on how assistance will be provided at this location.

Since each building's means of egress and fire safety and evacuation plans are unique, specific requirements for verbiage are not indicated, but will depend on the situation. The signage is not required to be raised letters or braille, but is required to meet the style, size and contrast requirements for visual signage in ICC A117.1.

SECTION 1010
DOORS, GATES AND TURNSTILES

[BE] 1010.1 Doors. *Means of egress* doors shall meet the requirements of this section. Doors serving a *means of egress* system shall meet the requirements of this section and Section 1022.2. Doors provided for egress purposes in numbers greater than required by this code shall meet the requirements of this section.

Means of egress doors shall be readily distinguishable from the adjacent construction and finishes such that the doors are easily recognizable as doors. Mirrors or similar reflecting materials shall not be used on *means of egress* doors. *Means of egress* doors shall not be concealed by curtains, drapes, decorations or similar materials.

❖ The general requirements for doors are in this section and the following subsections. The reference to Section 1022.2 is intended to emphasize that exterior exit doors must lead to a route that will allow a path to a public street or alley (see definition for "Public way"). A door that is intended to be used for egress purposes, even though that door may not be required by the code, is also required to meet the requirements of this section. An example may be an assembly occupancy where four doors would be required to meet the required capacity of the occupant load. But assume the designer elects to provide six doors for aesthetic reasons or occupant convenience. All six doors must comply with the requirements of this section.

Doors need to be easily recognizable for immediate use in an emergency condition. Thus, the code specifies that doors are not to be hidden in such a manner that a person would have trouble seeing where to egress.

[BE] 1010.1.1 Size of doors. The required capacity of each door opening shall be sufficient for the *occupant load* thereof and shall provide a minimum clear opening width of 32 inches (813 mm). The clear opening width of doorways with swinging doors shall be measured between the face of the door and the stop, with the door open 90 degrees (1.57 rad). Where this section requires a minimum clear opening width of 32 inches (813 mm) and a door opening includes two door leaves without a mullion, one leaf shall provide a minimum clear opening width of 32 inches (813 mm). In Group I-2, doors serving as *means of egress* doors where used for the movement of beds shall provide a minimum clear opening width of $41^1/_2$ inches (1054 mm). The maximum width of a swinging door leaf shall be 48 inches (1219 mm) nominal. The minimum clear opening height of doors shall be not less than 80 inches (2032 mm).

Exceptions:

1. In Group R-2 and R-3 *dwelling and sleeping units* that are not required to be an Accessible unit, Type A unit or Type B unit, the minimum and maximum width shall not apply to door openings that are not part of the required *means of egress*.
2. Group I-3 door openings to resident *sleeping units* that are not required to be an Accessible unit shall have a minimum clear opening width of 28 inches (711 mm).
3. Door openings to storage closets less than 10 square feet (0.93 m^2) in area shall not be limited by the minimum clear opening width.
4. The width of door leaves in revolving doors that comply with Section 1010.1.4.1 shall not be limited.
5. The maximum width of door leaves in *power-operated doors* that comply with Section 1010.1.4.2 shall not be limited
6. Door openings within a *dwelling unit* or *sleeping unit* shall have a minimum clear opening height of 78 inches (1981 mm).
7. In *dwelling* and *sleeping units* that are not required to be Accessible, Type A or Type B units, exterior door openings, other than the required *exit* door, shall have a minimum clear opening height of 76 inches (1930 mm).
8. In Groups I-1, R-2, R-3 and R-4, in *dwelling* and *sleeping units* that are not required to be Accessible, Type A or Type B units, the minimum clear opening widths shall not apply to interior egress doors.
9. Door openings required to be *accessible* within Type B units intended for user passage shall have a minimum clear opening width of 31.75 inches (806 mm).
10. Doors to walk-in freezers and coolers less than 1,000 square feet (93 m^2) in area shall have a maximum width of 60 inches (1524 mm) nominal.
11. The minimum clear opening width shall not apply to doors for nonaccessible shower or sauna compartments.
12. The minimum clear opening width shall not apply to the doors for nonaccessible toilet stalls.

❖ The size of a door opening determines its capacity as a component of egress and its ability to fulfill its function in normal use. A door opening must meet certain minimum criteria as to its width and height in order to be used safely and to provide accessibility to people with physical disabilities. Doorways that are not part of the means of egress are not limited in size by this section. However, doors that are used for egress purposes, including additional doors over and above the number of means of egress required by the code, are required to meet the requirements of this section unless one of the exceptions applies.

The minimum clear opening width of an egress doorway for occupant capacity is based on the portion of the occupant load (see Section 1004.1) intended to utilize the doorway for egress purposes, multiplied by the egress width per occupant from Section 1005.1. The capacity of a 32-inch (813 mm) clear opening width door is 32/0.2 = 160 occupants. The 0.15-inch (3.81 mm) allowance for capacity is permitted in sprinklered buildings (32/0.15 = 213 occupants). The clear opening width of a swinging door is the horizontal dimension measured between the face of the door and the door stops where the door is in the 90-degree (1.57 rad) position [see Commentary Figure 1010.1.1(1)].

Using the face of the door as the measurement point (to the door stop) is consistent with the provisions of ICC A117.1 and the ADAAG Review Advisory Committee. Further, this measurement is not intended to prohibit door hardware projections into the required clear width, such as latching or panic hardware [see the commentary to Section 1010.1.1.1 and Commentary Figure 1010.1.1(2) for further discussion on the specific projections allowed in the required clear width]. For nonswinging means of egress doors, such as a sliding door, the clear opening width is to be measured from the face of the door jambs.

The minimum clear opening width in a doorway of 32 inches (813 mm) is to allow passage of a wheelchair as well as persons utilizing walking devices or other support apparatus. Similarly, because of the difficulties that a person with physical disabilities would have in opening a pair of doors simultaneously, the 32-inch (813 mm) minimum must be provided by a single door leaf.

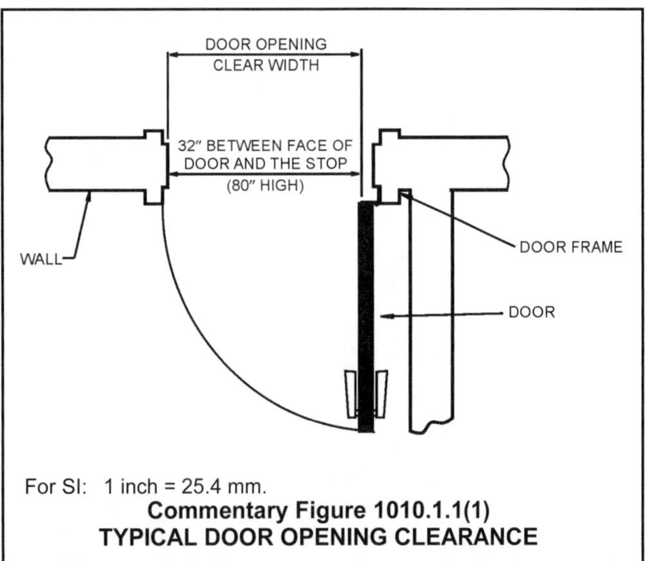

For SI: 1 inch = 25.4 mm.

**Commentary Figure 1010.1.1(1)
TYPICAL DOOR OPENING CLEARANCE**

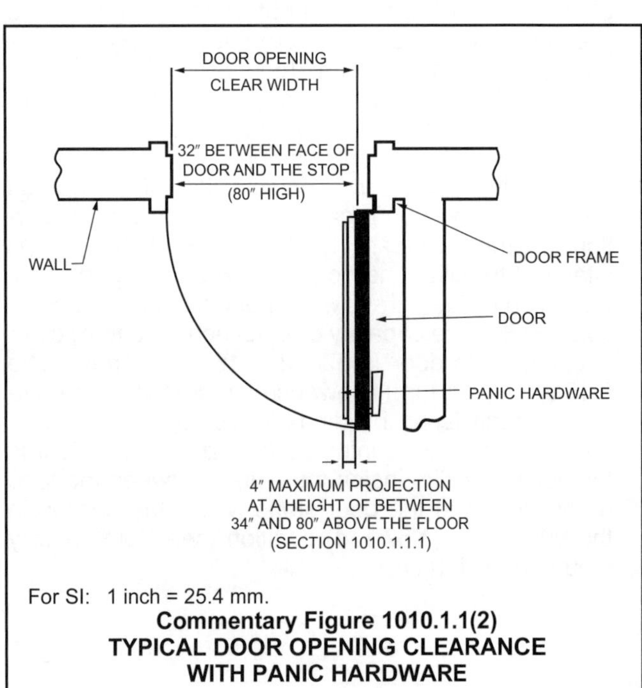

For SI: 1 inch = 25.4 mm.

**Commentary Figure 1010.1.1(2)
TYPICAL DOOR OPENING CLEARANCE
WITH PANIC HARDWARE**

Note that in some cases, with standard door construction and hardware, a 36-inch-wide (914 mm) door is the narrowest door that can be used while still providing the minimum clear opening width of 32 inches (813 mm). A standard 34-inch-wide (864 mm) door might have less than a 32-inch (813 mm) clear opening width, depending on the thickness of the opposing doorstop, the door thickness and the type of hinge. The building designer must verify that the swinging door specified will provide the required clear width.

A minimum clear opening width of $41^1/_2$ inches (1054 mm) is required for doors in any portion of Group I-2 occupancies where patients may need to be moved in beds. This is especially important for evacuating patients from one smoke compartment to another in the event of a fire.

The maximum width for a means of egress door leaf in a swinging door is 48 inches (1219 mm) because larger doors are difficult to handle and are of sizes that typically are not fire tested. The maximum width only applies to swinging doors and not to horizontal sliding doors.

Minimum heights at door openings are required to provide clear headroom for the users. A minimum clear opening height of 80 inches (2032 mm) has been empirically derived as sufficient for most users. Note that this is the minimum height of the opening, not the minimum height of the door. The exception in Sections 1003.3.1 and 1010.1.1.1 allows for door closers and doorstops to be as low as 78 inches (1981 mm).

Exception 1 is very limited in scope and is primarily intended to permit decorative-type doors, e.g., café doors, in Group R-2, R-3 and R-4 dwelling units that are not required to be accessible. This exception addresses spaces that are provided with two or more doors where only one means of egress is required. These nonrequired doors are exempted from the minimum and maximum dimensions.

Exception 2 permits the continued use of door openings to resident sleeping units (cells) in jails (Group I-3) to be a minimum of 28 inches (711 mm), according to current practices. Only the cells required to be Accessible cells would have to have door openings with a 32-inch (813 mm) minimum clear opening width.

Exception 3 is for all occupancies. This exception permits door openings to storage closets less than 10 square feet (0.9 m^2) in area to be less than 32 inches (813 mm). This provision is intended to include those closets that can be reached in an arm's length and thus do not require full passage into the closet to be functional.

Exception 4 permits the door leaves in a revolving door assembly to comply with Section 1010.1.4.1, which provides for adequate egress width where the revolving door is collapsed into a breakout position.

Exception 5 allows for power-operated doors to be of any size since an individual would not have to move them manually. The accessible route provisions would allow for two automatic doors working simultaneously to meet the width for an accessible route.

Exception 6 permits a door opening within a dwelling or sleeping unit to be a minimum of 78 inches (1981 mm) in clear height. This is deemed acceptable because of the familiarity persons in a dwelling or sleeping unit usually have with the egress system and the lack of adverse injury statistics relating to such openings. Note that this exception does not apply to exterior doors of a townhouse or the main entrance doors leading to the hallway in hotels or apartment buildings. However, exterior doors could use the limited exception for doorstops and closers in Sections 1003.3.1 and 1010.1.1.1.

Exception 7 permits exterior doorways to a dwelling or sleeping unit, except for the required exit door, to be a minimum of 76 inches (1930 mm) in clear height. Accordingly, the required exterior exit door to a dwelling or sleeping unit must be 80 inches (2032 mm) in height, but other exterior doors are allowed to be a height of only 76 inches (1930 mm). This provision allows for the continued use of 76-inch-high (1930 mm) sliding patio doors and swinging doors sized to replace such doors. Doors within accessible units cannot use this exception.

Exception 8 allows interior means of egress doors within dwelling or sleeping units (Groups I-1, R-2, R-3 and R-4) to have a clear opening width less than 32 inches (813 mm). If the dwelling or sleeping unit is required to be an Accessible unit, this exception is not applicable. ICC A117.1 requires door openings within Accessible and Type A units to be a minimum 32 inches (813 mm) clear opening width and doors within Type B units to be a minimum $31^3/_4$ inches (806 mm) clear opening width. This exception is not applicable to transient lodging (Group R-1). The requirement is for all doorways within a Group R-1 unit to be sized wide enough for persons using mobility devices such as walkers or crutches to move through entrance doors to the units and all doors to rooms in the unit (e.g., bathroom doors). Because of the social interaction and visitation that often occur in lodging facilities, a door opening sized for accessibility (e.g., wheelchairs, walkers, canes, crutches) is deemed necessary to allow people with disabilities to visit a friend's, colleague's or relative's unit. In addition, wider doors provide an additional benefit to all persons handling luggage and bulky items, or for the situation when an Accessible unit is not available. This requirement for Group R-1 occupancies is consistent with the *2010 ADA Standards*.

Exception 9 addresses the clear width of doors within a Type B dwelling or sleeping unit. The $31^3/_4$-inch (806 mm) dimension effectively allows for 34-inch (864 mm) doors to be used inside the unit. Again, note that the exterior door to garden-style apartments or the main door to the hallway for units in an apartment building is not covered by this exception. ICC A117.1 requires exterior doors of Type B dwelling units to provide a 32-inch (813 mm) clear opening width. Refer to Chapter 11 for additional information related to Type B dwelling and sleeping units.

Exception 10 allows for doors on walk-in freezers and coolers that would allow for the use of small carts to move supplies in and out. Such doors would still have to meet the force requirements in Section 1010.1.3.

Exceptions 11 and 12 address bathrooms with multiple showers, saunas, steam rooms, or toilet stalls or showers, saunas, and steam rooms within hotel rooms or dwelling units that are not required to be accessible. These exceptions allow for continued use of typical sizes for sliding doors on showers and partition doors on 30-inch (762 mm) wide stalls.

[BE] 1010.1.1.1 Projections into clear width. There shall not be projections into the required clear opening width lower than 34 inches (864 mm) above the floor or ground. Projections into the clear opening width between 34 inches (864 mm) and 80 inches (2032 mm) above the floor or ground shall not exceed 4 inches (102 mm).

Exception: Door closers and door stops shall be permitted to be 78 inches (1980 mm) minimum above the floor.

❖ This section of the code provides specific allowances for projection into the required clear widths of the openings provided by the means of egress doors. These allowances directly correspond with the method of measuring the required clear width of door openings as specified in Section 1010.1.1. A reasonable range of projections for door hardware and trim has been established by these requirements. The use of the means of egress door by a person using a wheelchair will not be significantly impacted by small projections located in inconspicuous areas. The key to these allowances is location. Projections are allowed at a height between 34 inches (864 mm) and 80 inches (2032 mm). Below the 34-inch (864 mm) height, the code does not permit any projections since they would decrease the available width for wheelchair operation. The full 32-inch (813 mm) width must be provided at this location. At 34 inches (864 mm) and higher, projections of up to and including 4 inches (102 mm) are permitted. The 4-inch (102 mm) projection is consistent with the allowances of Section 1003.3.3. This section permits door hardware, such as panic hardware, to extend into the clear width while maintaining accessibility for persons with physical disabilities [see Commentary Figure 1010.1.1(2)].

Allowance must be made for door closers and stops since their design and function necessitates placement within the door opening. The minimum allowable headroom clearance for door closers and stops is 78 inches (1981 mm) [see Commentary Figure 1003.3.1(1)]. The 2-inch (51 mm) projection into the doorway height is reasonable since these devices are normally mounted away from the center of the door opening, thus minimizing the potential for contact with a person moving through the opening. This is consistent with the exception in Section 1003.3.1. Other items that are mounted at the top of the door opening, such as an electromagnetic lock on a door or a pair of doors, would still require an 80-inch (2032 mm) minimum headroom.

While this section deals with door hardware projections within the clear door opening width, door hardware projections into the required width of corridors, aisles, exit passageways and exit discharge are addressed in Section 1005.7.1.

[BE] 1010.1.2 Door swing. Egress doors shall be of the pivoted or side-hinged swinging type.

Exceptions:

1. Private garages, office areas, factory and storage areas with an *occupant load* of 10 or less.
2. Group I-3 occupancies used as a place of detention.
3. Critical or intensive care patient rooms within suites of health care facilities.
4. Doors within or serving a single *dwelling unit* in Groups R-2 and R-3.
5. In other than Group H occupancies, revolving doors complying with Section 1010.1.4.1.
6. In other than Group H occupancies, special purpose horizontal sliding, accordion or folding door assemblies complying with Section 1010.1.4.3.
7. Power-operated doors in accordance with Section 1010.1.4.2.
8. Doors serving a bathroom within an individual *sleeping unit* in Group R-1.
9. In other than Group H occupancies, manually operated horizontal sliding doors are permitted in a *means of egress* from spaces with an *occupant load* of 10 or less.

❖ Generally, egress doors are required to be side swinging. The swinging hardware can be either a hinge or a pivot. The method of operation for side-swinging doors should be familiar to all occupants. Door designs with pivots are permitted by this section since the door action itself is similar to that of a side-hinged swinging door.

The code has several conditions where it allows egress doors that are not side-hinged swinging types.

Examples of the doors permitted in Exception 1 are overhead garage doors and horizontal sliding doors. Exception 1 allows doors other than the swinging type for the listed uses where the number of occupants is very low.

Exception 2 allows for the sliding-type doors that are commonly used in prisons and jails.

Exception 3 allows for sliding doors between nursing areas and patient rooms in critical care and intensive care suites. Patients are not typically moving around on their own in these areas, visitors are extremely limited, the glass doors allow a better view for nurse supervision and the sliding option allows for equipment locations to be unaffected by door swing.

Exception 4 allows for sliding-type doors or pocket-type doors within or serving individual units in a non-transient residential occupancy (Groups R-2, R-3 and R-4). Residents are typically familiar with the door operation. The use of sliding doors on the interior of dwelling units is permitted by the Fair Housing Accessibility Guidelines (FHAG) and by ICC A117.1 for Accessible, Type A and Type B units.

Exception 5 allows for revolving doors that meet the requirements of Section 1010.1.4.1. Revolving doors are not permitted for egress from high-hazard spaces.

Exception 6 allows for special-purpose horizontal sliding, accordion or folding doors that meet the requirements of Section 1010.1.4.3 to be used in the means of egress. The doors addressed by Section 1010.4.3 are commonly in the open position (hidden in their enclosure). In the event of fire or smoke, where these doors are installed in the means of egress, Section 1010.1.4.3 requires the doors to be power operated but also capable of being operated manually to the required minimum egress width. This exception is intended to allow wide span openings to be used in a means of egress.

Exception 7 allows for power-operated doors that meet the requirements of Section 1010.1.4.2. This is to enhance the movement of the general population as well as people with mobility impairments to areas of safety without obstructions, since the specified doors afford simple operation by persons for both typical and emergency operation.

Exception 8 allows for pocket doors between the bathroom and living or sleeping space within hotel rooms. Since the bathroom is often placed immediately inside the entrance to the room, a side-swinging door could be an obstruction. Familiarity with these types of doors and minimal occupant loads makes this situation acceptable.

For horizontal sliding doors, Exception 9 partially overlaps the allowances in Exception 1 by matching the 10 or less occupant load, but extends the use to all other groups except for high hazard. For example, some emergency rooms or clinics use glazed horizontal sliding doors to divide patient care rooms, providing for increased privacy and infection control while still allowing visual supervision. Another example would be a pocket door used for access to a bathroom within a private office. Yet another example is the use of a manually operated sliding door to an office or a small conference room (with an occupant load of 10 or less). The allowance for such a manually operated horizontal sliding door provides greater design flexibility and efficiency, while at the same time maintaining an acceptable level of safety.

[BE] 1010.1.2.1 Direction of swing. Pivot or side-hinged swinging doors shall swing in the direction of egress travel where serving a room or area containing an occupant load of 50 or more persons or a Group H occupancy.

❖ A side-hinged door must swing in the direction of egress travel where the calculated occupant load of the room or area is 50 or more. As such, a room with two doors and an occupant load of 99 would require both doors to swing in the direction of egress travel, even though each door has a calculated occupant usage of less than 50. At this level of occupant load, the possibility exists that, in an emergency situation, a compact line of people could form at a closed door that swings in a direction opposite the egress flow. This could delay or eliminate the first person's ability to open the door inward with the rest of the queue behind the person.

In a Group H occupancy, the threat of rapid fire buildup, or worse, is such that any delay in egress caused by door swing may jeopardize the opportunity for all occupants to evacuate the premises. For this reason, all egress doors in Group H occupancies are to swing in the direction of egress.

[BE] 1010.1.3 Door opening force. The force for pushing or pulling open interior swinging egress doors, other than fire doors, shall not exceed 5 pounds (22 N). These forces do not apply to the force required to retract latch bolts or disengage other devices that hold the door in a closed position. For other swinging doors, as well as sliding and folding doors, the door latch shall release when subjected to a 15-pound (67 N) force. The door shall be set in motion when subjected to a 30-pound (133 N) force. The door shall swing to a full-open position when subjected to a 15-pound (67 N) force.

❖ The ability of all potential users to be physically capable of opening an egress door is a function of the forces required to open the door. The 5-pound (22 N) maximum force for pushing and pulling interior swinging doors without closers that are part of the means of egress inside a building is based on that which has been deemed appropriate for people with a physical limitation due to size, age or disability. The operating force is permitted to be higher for all exterior doors, interior swinging doors that are not part of the means of egress, doors that are part of the means of egress but also serve as opening protectives in fire-resistance-rated walls (i.e., fire doors), sliding doors and folding doors. This recognizes that doors with closers, particularly fire doors, require greater operating forces in order to close fully in an emergency where combustion gases may be exerting pressure on the door assembly. Similarly, exterior doors are exempted because air pressure differentials and strong winds may prevent doors from fully closing automatically. Requirements for power-operated doors are in Section 1010.1.4.2.

The opening force is different than the force to retract bolts or operate other types of door hardware. A maximum force of 15 pounds (67 N) is required for operating the latching mechanism. Once unlatched, a maximum force of 30 pounds (133 N) is applied to the latch side of the leaf to start the door in motion by overcoming its stationary inertia. Once in motion, it must not take more than 15 pounds (67 N) of force to keep the door in motion until it reaches its full open position and the required clear width is available. To conform to this requirement on a continual basis, door closers must be adjusted periodically and door fits must also be checked and adjusted where necessary.

[BE] 1010.1.3.1 Location of applied forces. Forces shall be applied to the latch side of the door.

❖ See the commentary for door opening forces in Section 1010.1.3.

[BE] 1010.1.4 Special doors. Special doors and security grilles shall comply with the requirements of Sections 1010.1.4.1 through 1010.1.4.5.

❖ This section simply defines the scope of the code requirements for special doors such as revolving doors; power-operated doors; special purpose horizontal sliding, accordion or folding doors; lockdown arrangements in educational facilities; and security grilles.

[BE] 1010.1.4.1 Revolving doors. Revolving doors shall comply with the following:

1. Revolving doors shall comply with BHMA A156.27 and shall be installed in accordance with the manufacturer's instructions.
2. Each revolving door shall be capable of *breakout* in accordance with BHMA A156.27 and shall provide an aggregate width of not less than 36 inches (914 mm).
3. A revolving door shall not be located within 10 feet (3048 mm) of the foot or top of *stairways* or escalators. A dispersal area shall be provided between the *stairways* or escalators and the revolving doors.
4. The revolutions per minute (rpm) for a revolving door shall not exceed the maximum rpm as specified in BHMA A156.27. Manual revolving doors shall comply with Table 1010.1.4.1(1). Automatic or power-operated revolving doors shall comply with Table 1010.1.4.1(2).
5. An emergency stop switch shall be provided near each entry point of power or automatic operated revolving doors within 48 inches (1220 mm) of the door and between 24 inches (610 mm) and 48 inches (1220 mm) above the floor. The activation area of the emergency

stop switch button shall be not less than 1 inch (25 mm) in diameter and shall be red.

6. Each revolving door shall have a side-hinged swinging door that complies with Section 1010.1 in the same wall and within 10 feet (3048 mm) of the revolving door.
7. Revolving doors shall not be part of an *accessible route* required by Section 1009 of this code and Chapter 11 of the *International Building Code*.

❖ Revolving doors must comply with all seven provisions.

Item 1: BHMA A156.27 is the revolving door industry standard and includes numerous safety-related requirements for revolving doors. For example, BHMA A156.27 requires manually operated revolving doors to contain governors to limit the rotational speed of the door. For automatic, or power-operated, revolving doors, BHMA A156.27 includes requirements for numerous sensors and switches and complex motor controls to safely operate the door.

Item 2: One of the causes contributing to the loss of lives in the 1942 Cocoanut Grove fire in Boston was that the revolving doors at the club's entrance could not collapse (break out) for emergency egress and there was not an alternative means of egress adjacent to the revolving doors. Thus, in the panic of the fire, the door became jammed and the club's occupants were trapped.

As a result of this fire experience, all revolving doors, including those for air structures, now are required to be equipped with a breakout feature. A breakout operation is where all leaves collapse parallel to each other and to the direction of egress [see Commentary Figure 1010.1.4.1(1)]. A breakout operation creates two openings of approximately equal width. The sum of the widths is not to be less than 36 inches (914 mm) so that a stream of pedestrians may use each side of the opening. BHMA A156.27 includes explicit breakout requirements for the wide range of sizes and configurations of manual and automatic revolving doors.

Commentary Figure 1010.1.4.1(1)
REVOLVING DOORS IN BREAKOUT POSITION

Item 3: If a stairway or escalator delivers users to a landing in front of a revolving door at a greater rate than the capacity of the door, a compact line of people will develop. Lines of people formed on a stairway or escalator create an unsafe situation since stairways and escalators are not intended to be used as standing space for persons who may be waiting to use the revolving doors. Therefore, to avoid congestion at a revolving door that under normal operation has a maximum delivery capacity of users, a dispersal area is required between the stairways or escalators and the revolving doors to allow for the queuing of people as they enter the door. Accordingly, to create a dispersal area for users of a revolving door, the door is not to be placed closer than 10 feet (3048 mm) from the foot or top of a stairway or escalator.

Item 4: Door speeds also directly relate to the capacity of a revolving door, which is calculated by multiplying the number of leaves (wings) by the revolutions per minute (rpm). For example, if you have a four-leaf door (four-bay door) moving at 10 rpm, the door will allow 40 people to move in either direction in 1 minute. The larger revolving doors are designed to allow more than one person in each bay, and this should be taken into account when calculating the capacity of a revolving door.

Item 5: An emergency stop switch near each entry point of automatic or power-operated revolving doors provides a method to stop the door's operation.

Item 6: In case a revolving door malfunctions or becomes obstructed, the adjacent area is to be equipped with a conventional side-hinged door to provide users with an immediate alternative way to exit a building. The side-hinged door is intended to be used as a relief device for people lined up to use the revolving door or for those who desire to avoid the revolving door because of a physical disability or other reason. It also can be used when the revolving door is obstructed or out of service. The swinging door is to be immediately adjacent to the revolving door so that its availability is obvious [see Commentary Figure 1010.1.4.1(2)]. A single swinging door can be located between side-by-side revolving doors in order to comply with this provision.

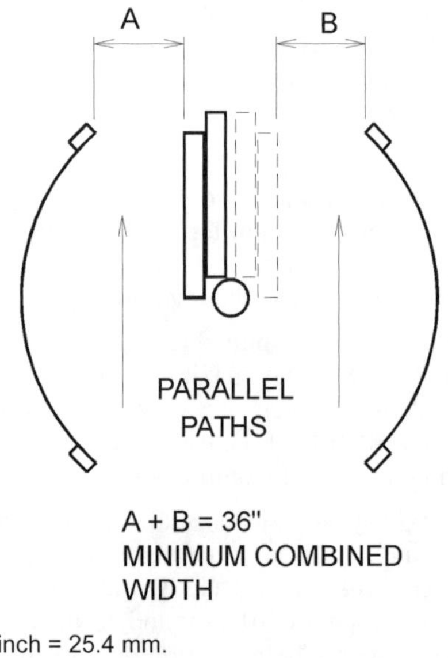

Item 7: While some revolving doors may be considered part of a means of egress, they cannot be con-

sidered part of a required accessible route for either ingress or egress. This requirement is consistent with ICC A117.1, which also prohibits revolving gates and turnstiles along the only accessible route. The side-swinging door required by Item 6 can serve as the accessible exit or entrance required by Sections 1009 and 1105.

A route through a hinged or sliding door differs remarkably from that provided through a revolving door. For a revolving door, the route includes a turn into the doorway, an arcing path of travel as the door revolves, followed by a change of direction when leaving the door. Factors that may cause difficulty for anyone with mobility impairments could involve the overall doorway diameter, the number of leaves and their relative angle, and the configuration of the return walls surrounding the revolving door. Additionally, the speed of the door movement if motorized, or the force required for movement if not motorized, would be a concern for anyone who needed to keep both hands on their device to move forward (e.g., walker or wheelchair).

Automatic revolving doors, if large enough, may be usable by many people who use wheelchairs. However, the intent of this section is that these types of doors not be the only means of passage at an entrance or exit. An alternative door in full compliance with this section is considered necessary because some people with disabilities may be uncertain of the usability, or may not have enough strength or speed to use them. Although manufacturers have developed safety criteria, certain questions remain, such as the appropriate maximum and minimum speeds that would work for persons trying to maneuver a wheelchair through a revolving door.

Revolving doors range from smaller, manually operated revolving door systems to automatic (power-operated) revolving doors of small (8-foot) to large (24-foot) diameter. Three configurations of revolving doors are illustrated in Commentary Figures 1010.1.4.1(3) through 1010.1.4.1(5).

[BE] TABLE 1010.1.4.1(1)
MAXIMUM DOOR SPEED MANUAL REVOLVING DOORS

REVOLVING DOOR MAXIMUM NOMINAL DIAMETER (FT-IN)	MAXIMUM ALLOWABLE REVOLVING DOOR SPEED (RPM)
6-0	12
7-0	11
8-0	10
9-0	9
10-0	8

For SI: 1 inch = 25.4 mm, 1 foot = 304.8 mm.

❖ See the commentary for Section 1010.1.4.1 and Table 1010.1.4.1(2).

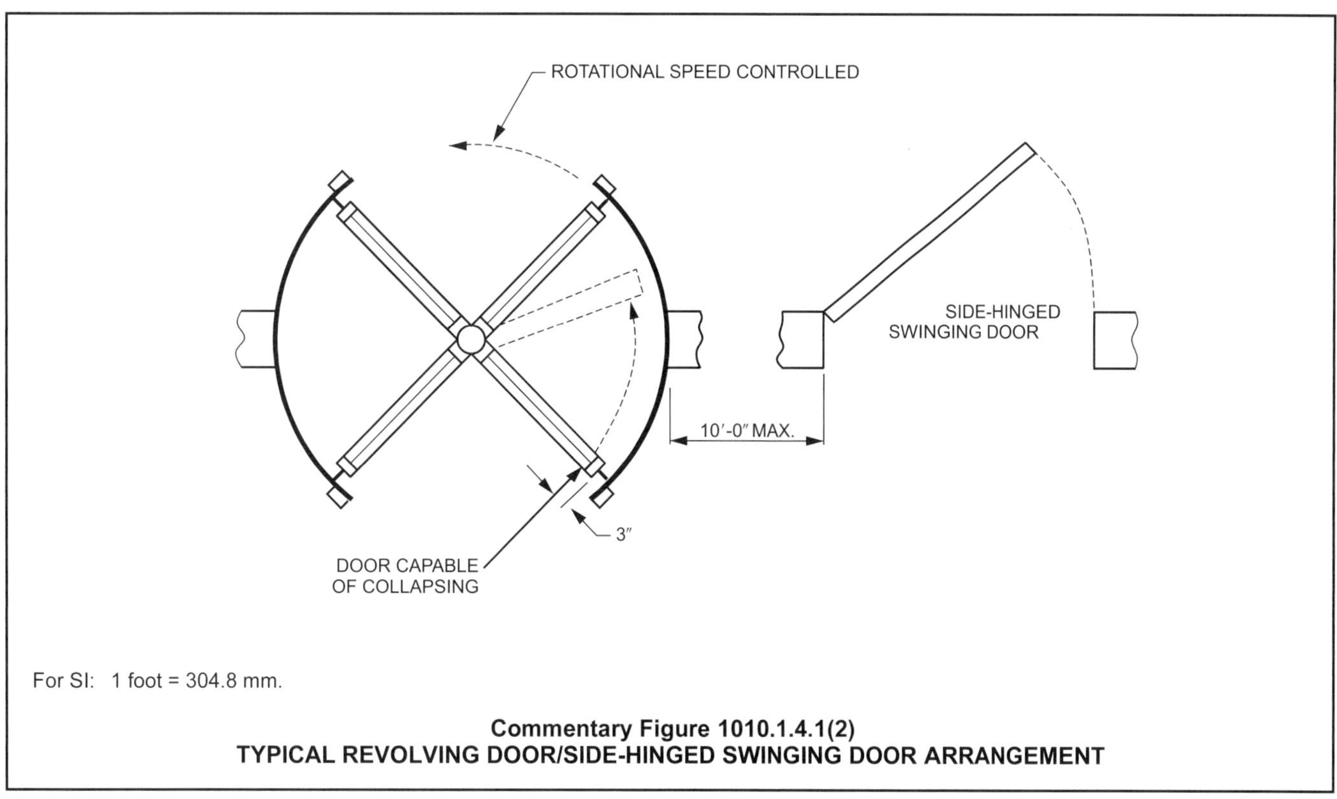

For SI: 1 foot = 304.8 mm.

Commentary Figure 1010.1.4.1(2)
TYPICAL REVOLVING DOOR/SIDE-HINGED SWINGING DOOR ARRANGEMENT

[BE] TABLE 1010.1.4.1(2)
MAXIMUM DOOR SPEED AUTOMATIC OR POWER-OPERATED REVOLVING DOORS

REVOLVING DOOR MAXIMUM NOMINAL DIAMETER (FT-IN)	MAXIMUM ALLOWABLE REVOLVING DOOR SPEED (RPM)
8-0	7.2
9-0	6.4
10-0	5.7
11-0	5.2
12-0	4.8
12-6	4.6
14-0	4.1
16-0	3.6
17-0	3.4
18-0	3.2
20-0	2.9
24-0	2.4

For SI: 1 inch = 25.4 mm, 1 foot = 304.8 mm.

❖ Door speeds also directly relate to the capacity of a revolving door, which is calculated for smaller revolving doors by multiplying the number of leaves (wings) by the revolutions per minute (rpm). For example, if you have an 8-foot diameter four-leaf door (four-bay door) moving at 10 rpm, the door will allow 40 people to move in either direction in 1 minute. Larger revolving doors may be designed to allow for more than one person in each bay as the door rotates, which should be taken into account when determining maximum egress capacity of the revolving door.

Commentary Figure 1010.1.4.1(3)
EXAMPLE OF MANUAL REVOLVING DOOR (7-FOOT DIAMETER)

Commentary Figure 1010.1.4.1(4)
EXAMPLE OF AUTOMATIC REVOLVING DOOR (8-FOOT DIAMETER)

Commentary Figure 1010.1.4.1(5)
EXAMPLE OF AUTOMATIC REVOLVING DOOR (20-FOOT DIAMETER)

[BE] 1010.1.4.1.1 Egress component. A revolving door used as a component of a *means of egress* shall comply with Section 1010.1.4.1 and the following three conditions:

1. Revolving doors shall not be given credit for more than 50 percent of the minimum width or required capacity.
2. Each revolving door shall be credited with a capacity based on not more than a 50-person *occupant load.*

3. Each revolving door shall provide for egress in accordance with BHMA A156.27 with a *breakout* force of not more than 130 pounds (578 N).

❖ A revolving door can be incorporated, to a very limited extent, in a means of egress. Compliance with these three additional conditions is required.

Condition 1 limits the exit capacity that revolving doors can provide in a building. This is so that 50 percent of the capacity has conventional egress components and is not dependent on mechanical devices or fail-safe mechanisms.

Condition 2 limits the capacity of any one revolving door for the same reasons as stated in Condition 1. Each revolving door is therefore limited to a 50-person capacity.

Condition 3 limits the breakout force to 130 pounds (578 N), as opposed to the 180-pound (801 N) value listed in Section 1010.1.4.1.2. Revolving doors used as means of egress are not permitted to have the breakout force exceed 130 pounds (578 N) under any circumstances.

[BE] 1010.1.4.1.2 Other than egress component. A revolving door used as other than a component of a *means of egress* shall comply with Section 1010.1.4.1. The *breakout* force of a revolving door not used as a component of a *means of egress* shall not be more than 180 pounds (801 N).

Exception: A *breakout* force in excess of 180 pounds (801 N) is permitted if the breakout force is reduced to not more than 130 pounds (578 N) when not less than one of the following conditions is satisfied:

1. There is a power failure or power is removed to the device holding the door wings in position.
2. There is an actuation of the *automatic sprinkler system* where such system is provided.
3. There is an actuation of a smoke detection system that is installed in accordance with Section 907 to provide coverage in areas within the building that are within 75 feet (22 860 mm) of the revolving doors.
4. There is an actuation of a manual control switch, in an *approved* location and clearly identified, that reduces the *breakout* force to not more than 130 pounds (578 N).

❖ This section addresses revolving doors that are not used to serve any portion of the occupant egress capacity. For example, where adjacent side-hinged doors have more than the required egress capacity, the revolving door would not be part of the required means of egress.

The maximum breakout force of 180 pounds (801 N), applied within 3 inches (76 mm) of the outer edge of a wing, is based on industry standards to accommodate normal use conditions and other forces that may act on the leaves, such as wind or air pressure. An exception for revolving doors that are not a component of a required means of egress allows the breakout force to exceed 180 pounds (801 N) in normal operating conditions provided that a force of not more than 130 pounds (578 N) is required wherever any one of the listed conditions is satisfied.

[BE] 1010.1.4.2 Power-operated doors. Where *means of egress* doors are operated or assisted by power, the design shall be such that in the event of power failure, the door is capable of being opened manually to permit *means of egress* travel or closed where necessary to safeguard *means of egress*. The forces required to open these doors manually shall not exceed those specified in Section 1010.1.3, except that the force to set the door in motion shall not exceed 50 pounds (220 N). The door shall be capable of opening from any position to the full width of the opening in which such door is installed when a force is applied to the door on the side from which egress is made. Power-operated swinging doors, power-operated sliding doors and power-operated folding doors shall comply with BHMA A156.10. Power-assisted swinging doors and low energy *power-operated* swinging *doors* shall comply with BHMA A156.19. Low-energy *power-operated* sliding *doors* and low-energy power-operated folding doors shall comply with BHMA A156.38.

Exceptions:

1. Occupancies in Group I-3.
2. Special-purpose horizontal sliding, accordion or folding doors complying with Section 1010.1.4.3.
3. For a biparting door in the emergency *breakout* mode, a door leaf located within a multiple-leaf opening shall be exempt from the minimum 32-inch (813 mm) single-leaf requirement of Section 1010.1.1, provided that a minimum 32-inch (813 mm) clear opening is provided when the two biparting leaves meeting in the center are broken out.

❖ For convenience purposes, power-operated doors are intended to facilitate the normal nonemergency flow of persons through a doorway. Where a power-operated or power-assisted door is also required to be an egress door, the door must conform to the requirements of this section. The essential characteristic is that the door is to be manually openable from any position to its full open position at any time, with or without a power failure or a failure of a door mechanism. Hence, both swinging and horizontal sliding doors that comply with this section may be used, provided the door can be operated manually from any position as a swinging door and that the minimum required clear width for egress capacity is not less than 32 inches (813 mm). Note that the opening forces of Section 1010.1.3 are applicable, except that the 30-pound (133 N) force needed to set the door in motion is increased to 50 pounds (220 N) as an operational tolerance in the design of the power-operated door.

Definitions for the different types of power-operated doors help clarify which standard (BHMA A156.10, BHMA A156.19 or BMHA A156.38) is applicable to which type of power-operated door (see Chapter 2 for the definitions for "Low-energy power-operated door," "Power-assisted door" and "Power-operated door").

Power-operated doors are required to comply with BHMA A156.10. These doors open automatically when approached by a person or upon an action by a person, close automatically and include provisions such as presence sensors to prevent entrapment. Low-energy power-operated doors are required to comply with BHMA A156.19 or A156.38, depending on whether they are swinging, sliding or folding. These doors open automatically upon an action by a person such as pressing a push plate or waving a hand in front of a sensor. Additionally, these doors close automatically and operate with decreased forces and decreased speeds (compared to power-operated doors). Least common are power-assisted doors, which are required to comply with BHMA A156.19. These doors are swinging doors that open by reduced pushing or pulling force on the door-operating hardware, close automatically after the pushing or pulling force is released, and function with decreased forces.

In accordance with Exception 1, power-operated doors in detention and correctional occupancies (Group I-3) are not required to be manually operable by the occupants (inmates) for security reasons, but otherwise are required to conform to Section 408.

Exception 2 states that power-operated, special purpose horizontal sliding, accordion or folding doors that meet the requirements of Section 1010.1.4.3 are not required to meet the requirements of Section 1010.1.4.2. This is consistent with the option offered in Section 1010.1.2 by Exception 7.

Exception 3 allows an individual leaf of a biparting door to be less than 32 inches (813 mm) wide, provided 32 inches (813 mm) of clear space is available where the two center biparting leaves are broken out as part of the emergency breakaway feature.

[BE] 1010.1.4.3 Special-purpose horizontal sliding, accordion or folding doors. In other than Group H occupancies, special-purpose horizontal sliding, accordion, or folding door assemblies permitted to be a component of a *means of egress* in accordance with Exception 6 to Section 1010.1.2 shall comply with all of the following criteria:

1. The doors shall be power operated and shall be capable of being operated manually in the event of power failure.
2. The doors shall be openable by a simple method from both sides without special knowledge or effort.
3. The force required to operate the door shall not exceed 30 pounds (133 N) to set the door in motion and 15 pounds (67 N) to close the door or open it to the minimum required width.
4. The door shall be openable with a force not to exceed 15 pounds (67 N) when a force of 250 pounds (1100 N) is applied perpendicular to the door adjacent to the operating device.
5. The door assembly shall comply with the applicable *fire protection rating* and, where rated, shall be self-closing or automatic closing by smoke detection in accordance with Section 716.2.6.6 of the *International Building Code*, shall be installed in accordance with NFPA 80 and shall comply with Section 716 of the *International Building Code*.
6. The door assembly shall have an integrated standby power supply.
7. The door assembly power supply shall be electrically supervised.
8. The door shall open to the minimum required width within 10 seconds after activation of the operating device.

❖ Special purpose horizontal sliding, accordion or folding doors are permitted in the means of egress, in other than Group H rooms or areas, under the conditions set forth in this section. Special purpose horizontal sliding, accordion or folding doors are not permitted to be used in Group H occupancies because of the potential for delaying or impeding egress from those areas and the additional risk to occupants in hazardous occupancies. Note that this section regulates doors that are part of the means of egress to meet a set of requirements different than Section 1010.1.4.2 (e.g., a power-operated horizontal sliding door that does not have breakout capabilities to allow the door panels to swing if power is lost). The doors addressed by Section 1010.1.4.3 are commonly in the normally open position (hidden in their enclosure).

All eight of the criteria listed in this section must be met for a special purpose horizontal sliding, accordion or folding door since there is a concern that it must be able to be easily opened to the minimum required width under all conditions.

Additionally, the door must be openable even if a force of 250 pounds (1100 N) is being applied perpendicular to it, as may occur if a group of people were pushing on it.

Since the doors are manually operable, they need not automatically open or close during a loss of power; however, a standby power supply must be provided. The primary power supply must be supervised so that an alarm is received at a constantly attended location (such as a security desk) on the loss of primary power. If the doors are also serving as opening protective (i.e., fire doors), they must be automatic closing or self-closing in accordance with IBC Section 716.

Since the maximum swinging door leaf width limitations of Section 1010.1.1 do not apply, a maximum opening time of 10 seconds is permitted. It should be noted, however, that the door need not open fully within the 10 seconds; rather, it must open to the minimum required width. For example, if the door is protecting an opening that is 10 feet (3048 mm) wide, but the minimum required width of the opening is 32 inches (813 mm) (as determined by Section 1010.1.1), the door need only open 32 inches (813 mm) within the 10-second criterion. In fact, the door may have controls such that the automatic opening feature only opens the door to a width of 32 inches (813 mm). If additional width is required, it can be accomplished by manual means and, possibly, by an additional activation of the operating device.

[BE] 1010.1.4.4 Locking arrangements in educational occupancies. In Group E and Group B educational occupancies, egress doors from classrooms, offices and other occupied rooms shall be permitted to be provided with locking arrangements designed to keep intruders from entering the room, where all of the following conditions are met:

1. The door shall be capable of being unlocked from outside the room with a key or other approved means.
2. The door shall be openable from within the room in accordance with Section 1010.1.9.
3. Modifications shall not be made to listed *panic hardware*, fire door hardware or door closers.

❖ Many schools are developing a variety of lockdown plans to protect the children and staff in the school from possible intruders. Plans can vary from an emergency outside the building where the school building is locked down but classes continue as normal to an emergency inside the building where students and faculty lock exterior doors and interior classroom doors immediately—and several levels in between. Consistent with previous editions of the code, this new section in the 2018 does not require locks on doors to classrooms, offices and other occupied rooms. But if systems are provided for occupants to lock doors to prevent access to these rooms, the system chosen must comply with these provisions.

It may be appropriate to recognize that for decades schools have installed locks on classroom doors, office doors, and doors to other occupiable rooms that comply with all the requirements of this section. Traditionally, the classroom door was unlocked from the corridor side with a key by the teacher at the beginning of the school day. At the end of the school day, the classroom door was locked from the corridor side with a key by the teacher. The custodians and administrators had master keys for authorized access to the rooms. Traditionally, to help prevent mischief in the classroom, the classroom door was not lockable from inside the classroom, resulting in the need during a lockdown situation to open the door and lock the door from the corridor side of the door.

In response to acts of violence in schools, door locks lockable from inside the classroom (and lockable/unlockable from outside the room) have been installed in the vast majority of recently constructed schools.

Section 404 provides criteria for lockdown plans. Part of that plan is to identify security measures that could adversely affect egress for the occupants and movement of emergency responders. Plans also have to include information on what doors will be secured along with a description of the locking systems. The intent is to allow for a system that will allow a staff person to lock a classroom from the inside but still allow for authorized personnel and emergency responders to open the room from the outside in order to be able to assist and evacuate occupants. The requirements of Section 1010.1.4.4 prohibit the use of locking devices that do not comply with the longstanding requirements in Section 1010.1.9 and its subsections. The requirements of Section 1010.1.4.4 also prohibit the use of devices that are not unlockable from outside the room by a key or other approved means.

Item 1 is intended to make sure that authorized personnel and emergency responders can get into the rooms from the outside. Examples of unlocking from outside the room could be a key to operate a lock cylinder, a magnetic card to swipe in a magnetic card reader, or knowledge of a specific code for keypad operations. The requirement that the door is unlockable from outside the room is important in helping prevent using the door locks in unintended ways.

By referencing Section 1010.1.9 in Item 2, the system would still have to be openable from the inside with one releasing operation to unlatch the door, so a separate deadbolt would not be permitted. Section 1010.1.9 also requires hardware to be operable without tight grasping, tight pinching or twisting of the wrist, where required by IBC Chapter 11 to meet the accessibility standards, and to allow the door to be unlatched for egress without a key or special knowledge or effort.

Item 3 is to prevent modification of listed panic hardware, fire exit hardware or door closers to maintain these important features for opening protectives. Item 3 is also a reminder of the requirements of the IBC in Section 716.1 that states: "Opening protectives required by other sections of this code shall comply with the provisions of this section and shall be installed in accordance with NFPA 80." NFPA 80 has explicit requirements regarding fire-rated door assemblies.

Section 1010.1.4.4.1 allows for a remote locking system. Some school districts may desire to install locks on classroom doors that can all be locked remotely, enabling a quick building-wide lockdown. The remote operation of locks is permitted providing all the requirements of Section 1010.1.4.4 are met, and the remote operation of locks does not interfere with any of the required functional requirements.

[BE] 1010.1.4.4.1 Remote operation of locks. Remote operation of locks complying with Section 1010.1.4.4. shall be permitted.

❖ See the commentary to Section 1010.1.4.4.

[BE] 1010.1.4.5 Security grilles. In Groups B, F, M and S, horizontal sliding or vertical security grilles are permitted at the main *exit* and shall be openable from the inside without the use of a key or special knowledge or effort during periods that the space is occupied. The grilles shall remain secured in the full-open position during the period of occupancy by the general public. Where two or more *means of egress* are required, not more than one-half of the *exits* or *exit access doorways* shall be equipped with horizontal sliding or vertical security grilles.

❖ This section functions as an exception to several sections, including Sections 1010.1.2 and 1010.1.9.4, and permits the use of these security grilles under conditions that are similar to those found in Section 402 for covered mall buildings. These security grilles will be open when the space is occupied and will, therefore, not obstruct any egress path. Since the building may be partially used (e.g., team practice in a football stadium) when not fully occupied, not more than one-half of the exits from the building can be through security grilles.

[BE] 1010.1.5 Floor elevation. There shall be a floor or landing on each side of a door. Such floor or landing shall be at the same elevation on each side of the door. Landings shall be level except for exterior landings, which are permitted to have a slope not to exceed 0.25 unit vertical in 12 units horizontal (2-percent slope).

Exceptions:

1. Doors serving individual *dwelling units* in Groups R-2 and R-3 where the following apply:
   1.1. A door is permitted to open at the top step of an interior *flight* of *stairs*, provided that the door does not swing over the top step.
   1.2. Screen doors and storm doors are permitted to swing over *stairs* or landings.
2. Exterior doors as provided for in Section 1003.5, Exception 1, and Section 1022.2, which are not on an *accessible route*.
3. In Group R-3 occupancies not required to be *Accessible units, Type A units* or *Type B units*, the landing at an exterior doorway shall be not more than $7^3/_4$ inches (197 mm) below the top of the threshold, provided the door, other than an exterior storm or screen door, does not swing over the landing.
4. Variations in elevation due to differences in finish materials, but not more than $^1/_2$ inch (12.7 mm).
5. Exterior decks, patios or balconies that are part of Type B *dwelling units*, have impervious surfaces and that are not more than 4 inches (102 mm) below the finished floor level of the adjacent interior space of the dwelling unit.
6. Doors serving equipment spaces not required to be accessible in accordance with Section 1103.2.9 of the *International Building Code* and serving an *occupant load* of five or less shall be permitted to have a landing on one side to be not more than 7 inches (178 mm) above or below the landing on the egress side of the door.

❖ Changes in floor surface elevation at a door, however small, often are slip or trip hazards. This is because persons passing through a door, including those who may have some mobility impairments, usually do not expect changes in floor surface elevation or are not able to recognize them because of the intervening door leaf. Under emergency conditions, a fall in a doorway could result not only in injury to the falling occupant but also interruption of orderly egress by other occupants. The exterior landing is allowed to slope to drain.

The size of this landing is set by Section 1010.1.6. In accordance with Exception 4, the floor surface elevation of the landing is to be at the same elevation plus or minus $^1/_2$ inch (12.7 mm) (see Commentary Figure 1010.1.5).

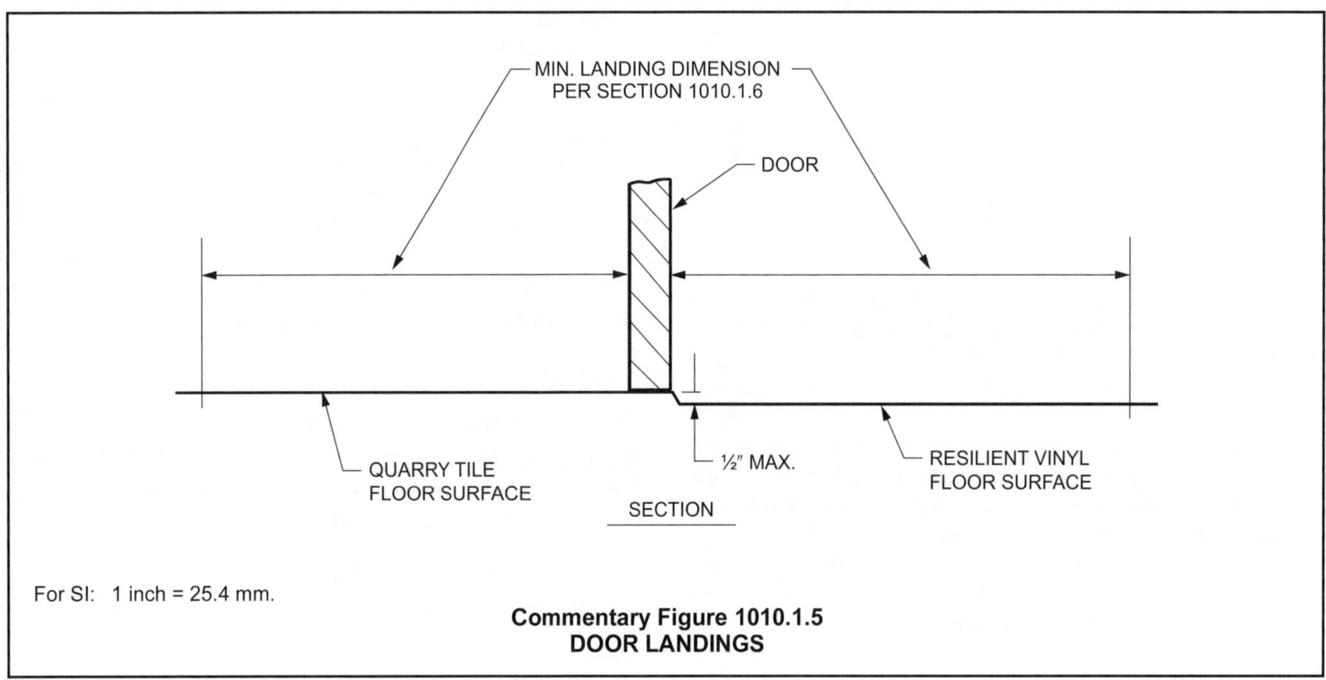

Commentary Figure 1010.1.5
DOOR LANDINGS

Note that some of the exceptions indicate which direction the door swings to allow the exceptions while others do not limit the door swing direction.

Exception 1, which applies to nontransient residential occupancies, recognizes that occupants are familiar with the stair and landing arrangements. In Exception 1.1, an interior stairway can start immediately at the door, provided the door leaf does not swing over the stairway. Exception 1.2 clarifies that a screen door or storm door would not be considered the main door prohibited from swinging over the stairway by Exception 1.1.

Exception 2 references two other locations. Section 1003.5, Exception 1, permits a 7-inch (178 mm) change in elevation at exterior doors in Groups F, H, R-2, R-3, S and U if they are not on an accessible route. The door could swing in either direction for this exception and may actually be required to swing out in accordance with Section 1010.1.2. A reference to Section 1022.2 does not address a change in elevation but does address exterior exit doors.

In accordance with Exception 3, for a residential unit, the step-down is limited to $7^3/_4$ inches (197 mm) measured from the top of the threshold rather than the interior floor surface. This is consistent with Section 1010.1.7, Exception 1. In addition, the exterior door cannot swing over the exterior landing. A screen door or storm door could swing over the exterior landing.

Exception 4 addresses a change in floor finish material (see Commentary Figure 1010.1.5).

In accordance with Exception 5, Type B dwelling or sleeping units are not required to have level landings on both sides of some of the exterior doors. Please note that this exception is not applicable for the primary entrance door to the unit (see Section 1105.1.7). Exterior doors that open out onto an exterior deck, patio or balcony are allowed a 4-inch (102 mm) step-down. Type B units are established by Chapter 11 for residential occupancies containing four or more dwelling or sleeping units. In order to use this exception, the exterior decks, patios or balconies must be of solid and impervious construction, such as concrete or wood. A 4-inch (102 mm) step from inside the unit down to the exterior surface is allowed for weather purposes. This allowance is consistent with the provisions of ICC A117.1 and Fair Housing Accessibility Guidelines (FHAG).

While Exception 2 would allow for exterior doors of Group F or S to have a step-down, it would not have this same allowance for small equipment spaces within a building as found in Exception 6. Sometimes these rooms have a step-down to allow for spills within the space to not leak out under the door. This space is not required to be accessible (Section 1103.2.9) and the space is only accessed by maintenance and service personnel, so a step-down would not be a barrier.

[BE] 1010.1.6 Landings at doors. Landings shall have a width not less than the width of the *stairway* or the door, whichever is greater. Doors in the fully open position shall not reduce a required dimension by more than 7 inches (178 mm). Where a landing serves an *occupant load* of 50 or more, doors in any position shall not reduce the landing to less than one-half its required width. Landings shall have a length measured in the direction of travel of not less than 44 inches (1118 mm).

Exception: Landing length in the direction of travel in Groups R-3 and U and within individual units of Group R-2 need not exceed 36 inches (914 mm).

❖ Door landings are at either side of the door. Landings can overlap floor surfaces within a room or corridor, overlap an exterior porch or balcony, or share the landings for stairways. The 7-inch (178 mm) encroachment and one-half required width limitations are consistent with Section 1005.7 for door encroachment. Section 1005.7 deals with egress width and capacity and is referenced for aisles (see Section 1018.1), corridors (see Section 1020.3), exit passageways (see Section 1024.2) and egress courts (see Section 1028.4.1).

This section also is intended to address landings at the entrance door to enclosed stairways (also see Section 1011.6 for stairway landings). The width of a landing at a door in a stairway is to be not less than the width of the stairway or the door, whichever is greater [see Commentary Figure 1011.6(4) for an example of these provisions].

No matter what size the door or stair landing is, door landings are to have the floor elevation requirements of Section 1010.1.5 extending at least 44 inches (1118 mm) in the direction of egress travel.

The reduction in landing length from 44 inches (1118 mm) minimum to 36 inches (914 mm) minimum for certain residential occupancies allowed by the exception is in recognition of their low occupant load.

[BE] 1010.1.7 Thresholds. Thresholds at doorways shall not exceed $^3/_4$ inch (19.1 mm) in height above the finished floor or landing for sliding doors serving *dwelling units* or $^1/_2$ inch (12.7 mm) above the finished floor or landing for other doors. Raised thresholds and floor level changes greater than $^1/_4$ inch (6.4 mm) at doorways shall be beveled with a slope not greater than one unit vertical in two units horizontal (50-percent slope).

Exceptions:

1. In occupancy Group R-2 or R-3, threshold heights for sliding and side-hinged exterior doors shall be permitted to be up to $7^3/_4$ inches (197 mm) in height if all of the following apply:
   - 1.1. The door is not part of the required *means of egress*.
   - 1.2. The door is not part of an *accessible route* as required by Chapter 11 of the *International Building Code*.

1.3. The door is not part of an accessible unit, Type A unit or Type B unit.

2. In Type B units, where Exception 5 to Section 1010.1.5 permits a 4-inch (102 mm) elevation change at the door, the threshold height on the exterior side of the door shall not exceed $4^{3}/_{4}$ inches (120 mm) in height above the exterior deck, patio or balcony for sliding doors or $4^{1}/_{2}$ inches (114 mm) above the exterior deck, patio or balcony for other doors.

❖ A threshold is a potential tripping hazard and a barrier to accessibility by people with mobility impairments. For these reasons, thresholds for all doorways, except exterior sliding doors serving dwelling units, are to be a maximum of $^{1}/_{2}$ inch (12.7 mm) high. Exterior sliding doors serving dwelling units, however, are permitted to be $^{3}/_{4}$ inch (19.1 mm) high because of practical design considerations, concern for deterioration of the doorway because of snow and ice buildup and lack of adequate drainage in severe climates. Raised threshold and floor level changes at doorways without beveled edge treatment [see Commentary Figure 1010.1.7(1)] are limited to $^{1}/_{4}$ inch (6.4 mm) high vertically.

Commentary Figures 1010.1.7(2), 1010.1.7(3) and 1010.1.7(4) illustrate configurations where the change in elevation is between $^{1}/_{4}$ inch (6.4 mm) and $^{1}/_{2}$ inch (12.7 mm). The slope of required beveled edges cannot exceed 1 unit vertical in 2 units horizontal (1:2 or 50-percent slope) but lesser slopes are fully compliant. This kind of threshold treatment provides for minimum obstructions for wheelchair users and limits the trip hazard for those with other mobility disabilities.

Exception 1 permits a $7^{3}/_{4}$-inch (197 mm) threshold at both sliding and side-hinged exterior doors in Group R-2 and R-3 buildings. However, this door cannot be part of the required means of egress out of a building, cannot be part of a required accessible route required into a building or unit (see IBC Sections 1104 and 1105) and cannot serve an Accessible, Type A or Type B unit. The result is that this exception would be permitted at the "back door," stoop or patio in single-family homes (see Section 1103.2.3) or upper floor balconies within individual apartments in buildings without elevators (see Section 1107). This terminology is consistent with the $7^{3}/_{4}$-inch (197 mm) step-down in Section 1010.1.5, Exception 3; however, this exception is to the threshold requirements, not the landing elevations.

Exception 2 is for doors where a 4-inch (102 mm) step down is permitted in Type B dwelling units between the interior finished floor surface and the exterior surface of exterior decks, patios and balconies (Section 1010.1.5, Exception 5). This section would permit the height of the threshold itself to exceed $^{1}/_{2}$ or $^{3}/_{4}$ inch (12.7 or 19.1 mm) in height, as long as the resultant profile from the interior floor to the exterior surface is maintained.

The threshold itself can be higher than $^{1}/_{2}$ or $^{3}/_{4}$ inch (12.7 or 19.1 mm) measured from the outside. The additional height, however, is contained within the 4-inch (102 mm) step-down. The height of the threshold is limited to $^{1}/_{2}$ or $^{3}/_{4}$ inch (12.7 or 19.1 mm) above the interior floor and the total height must not be more than $4^{1}/_{2}$ or $4^{3}/_{4}$ inches (114.3 or 120.7 mm) above the exterior surface, depending on the type of door. If the threshold is greater than $^{1}/_{4}$ inch (6.4 mm) above the interior floor, it is to be beveled. See Commentary Figure 1010.1.7(5).

¼" MAX.
6.4 mm

For SI: 1 inch = 25.4 mm.

Commentary Figure 1010.1.7(1)
VERTICAL CHANGES IN LEVEL

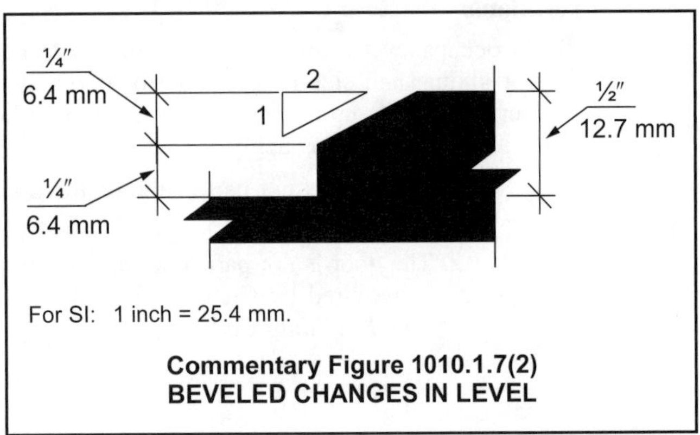

For SI: 1 inch = 25.4 mm.

Commentary Figure 1010.1.7(2)
BEVELED CHANGES IN LEVEL

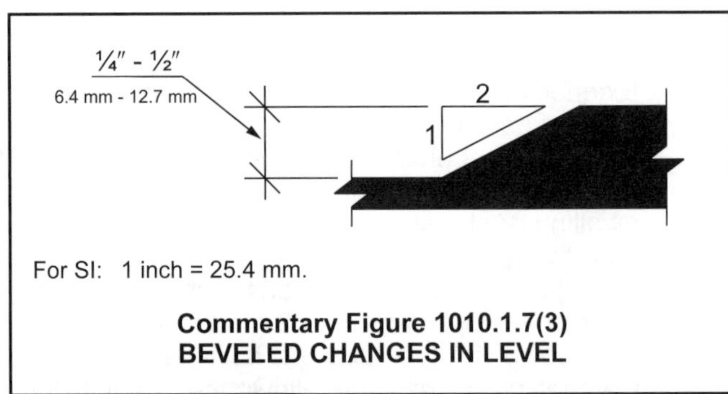

For SI: 1 inch = 25.4 mm.

Commentary Figure 1010.1.7(3)
BEVELED CHANGES IN LEVEL

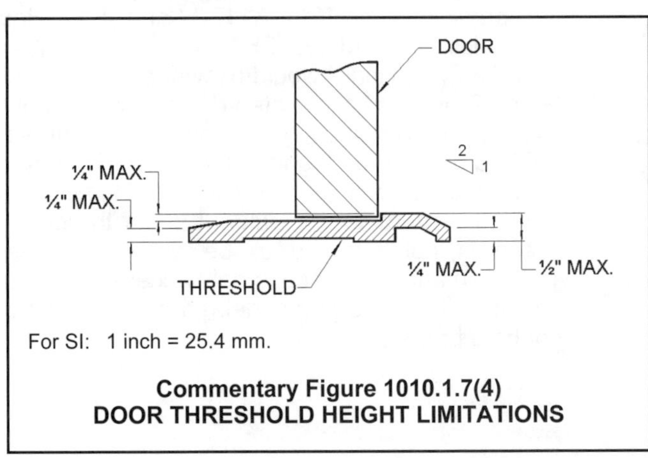

For SI: 1 inch = 25.4 mm.

Commentary Figure 1010.1.7(4)
DOOR THRESHOLD HEIGHT LIMITATIONS

[BE] 1010.1.8 Door arrangement. Space between two doors in a series shall be 48 inches (1219 mm) minimum plus the width of a door swinging into the space. Doors in a series shall swing either in the same direction or away from the space between the doors.

Exceptions:

1. The minimum distance between horizontal sliding power-operated doors in a series shall be 48 inches (1219 mm).
2. Storm and screen doors serving individual *dwelling units* in Groups R-2 and R-3 need not be spaced 48 inches (1219 mm) from the other door.
3. Doors within individual *dwelling units* in Groups R-2 and R-3 other than within Type A dwelling units.

❖ Door arrangement is required to be such that an occupant's use of a means of egress door is not hampered by the operation of a preceding door located in the same line of travel so that the occupant flow can be smooth through the openings. Successive doors in a single egress path (i.e., in a series) can cause such interference. The 4-foot (1219 mm) clear distance between doors when the first door is open at 90 degrees allows an occupant, including a person using a wheelchair, to move past one door and its swing before beginning the operation of the next door [see Commentary Figure 1010.1.8(1)]. Note that where doors in a series are not arranged in a straight line, the intent of the code is to provide sufficient space to enable occupants to negotiate the second door without being encumbered by the first door's swing arc. To facilitate accessibility, the space between doors should provide sufficient clear space for a wheelchair [30 inches by 48 inches (762 mm by 1219 mm)] beyond the arc of the door swing [see Commentary Figure 1010.1.8(2)]. Additionally, the approach and access provisions of ICC A117.1 must be considered for all doors along an accessible route.

Exception 1 permits horizontal sliding power-operated doors (see Section 1010.1.4.2) to be designed with a lesser distance between them in a series arrangement because they are customarily designed to open simultaneously or in sequence such that movement through them is unhampered.

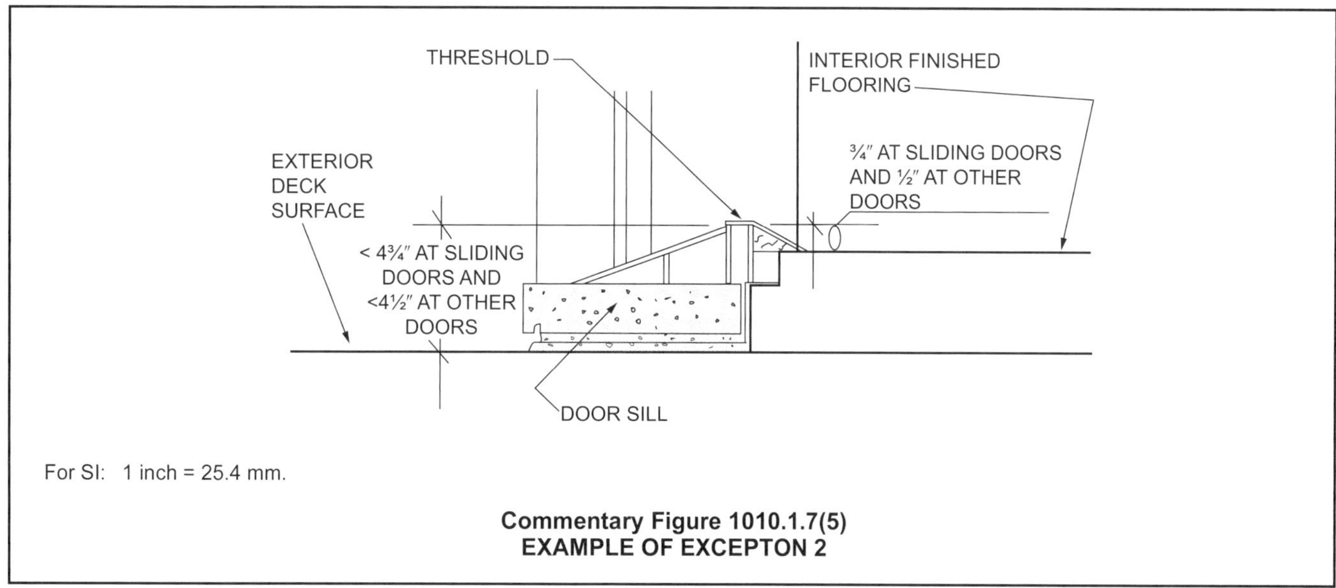

For SI: 1 inch = 25.4 mm.

Commentary Figure 1010.1.7(5)
EXAMPLE OF EXCEPTON 2

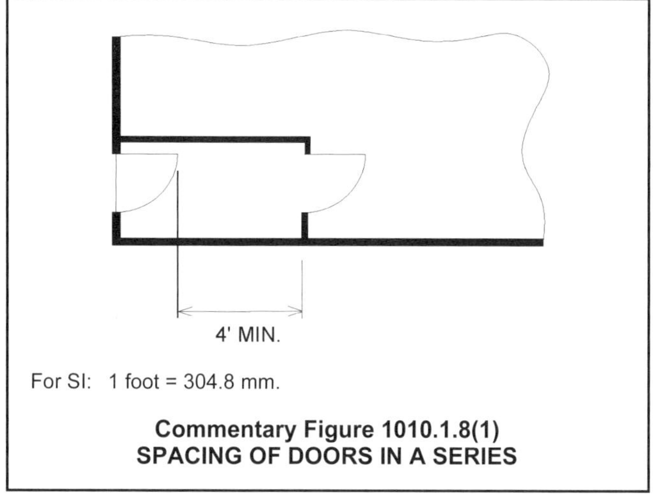

For SI: 1 foot = 304.8 mm.

Commentary Figure 1010.1.8(1)
SPACING OF DOORS IN A SERIES

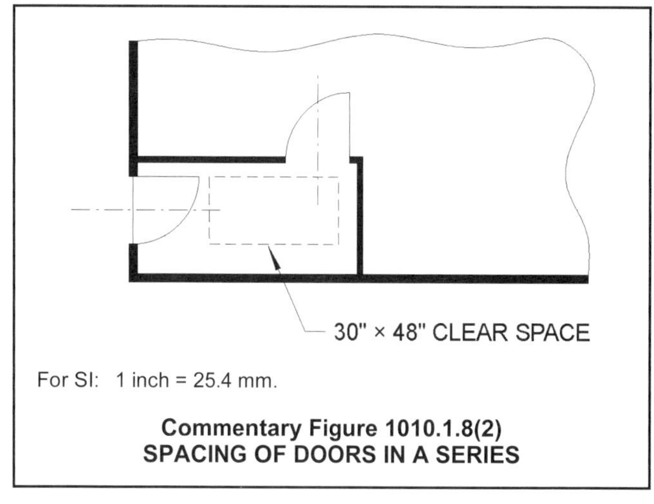

For SI: 1 inch = 25.4 mm.

Commentary Figure 1010.1.8(2)
SPACING OF DOORS IN A SERIES

Exception 2 addresses storm and screen doors on residential dwelling units in that storm and screen doors need not be spaced at 48 inches (1219 mm) since it would be impractical, and they do not operate the same as doors in a series. Storm and screen doors in these applications would need to meet all other requirements of the code but are exempt from the specific requirements of doors in series.

Exception 3 addresses doors within dwelling units of Group R-2 or R-3 that are not Type A dwelling units (see Section 1107) in that these doors are also permitted to have a lesser distance between doors because the accessibility provisions do not apply. There are requirements in Chapter 10 of the ICC A117.1 for door arrangements within Accessible and Type A dwelling and sleeping units.

[BE] 1010.1.9 Door operations. Except as specifically permitted by this section, egress doors shall be readily openable from the egress side without the use of a key or special knowledge or effort.

❖ A door is required to be easily and quickly openable from the egress side without requiring a key, special knowledge or effort—except where permitted by this section. However, under certain circumstances, locks and latches can intentionally inhibit or delay the use of a door for egress and thus interfere with or prevent the egress of occupants at the time of a fire. While the security of property is important, the life safety of occupants is essential. Where security and life safety objectives conflict, alternative measures, such as those permitted by each of the exceptions in Section 1010.1.9.4, may be applicable.

Egress doors are permitted to be locked to prevent entry, but must be capable of being unlocked and readily openable from the side from which egress is to be made. The outside of a door can be key locked as long as the inside—the side from which egress is to be made—can be unlocked without the use of tools, keys or special knowledge or effort. For example, an unlocking operation that is integral with an unlatching operation is acceptable.

Examples of special knowledge would be a combination lock or an unlocking device or deadbolt in an unknown, unexpected or hidden location. Special effort would dictate the need for unusual and unexpected physical ability to unlock or make the door fully available for egress, or the need for two actions to be conducted simultaneously to release the latch.

Where a pair of egress door leaves is installed, with or without a center mullion, the general requirement is that each leaf must be provided with its own releasing or unlatching device so as to be readily openable. Door arrangements or devices that depend on the release of one door before the other can be opened are not to be used except as permitted by Section 1010.1.9.5. This includes the use of manual flush bolts where allowed by Section 1010.1.9.5 and automatic flush bolts where allowed by Section 1010.1.9.4, Item 3.

[BE] 1010.1.9.1 Hardware. Door handles, pulls, latches, locks and other operating devices on doors required to be accessible by Chapter 11 of the *International Building Code* shall not require tight grasping, tight pinching or twisting of the wrist to operate.

❖ Any doors that are located along an accessible route for ingress or egress must have door hardware that is easy to operate by a person with limited mobility or dexterity. This would include all elements of the door hardware used in typical door operation, such as door levers, locks, security chains, and so on. This requirement is also an advantage for persons with arthritis in their hands. Items such as small, full-twist thumb turns or smooth circular knobs are examples of hardware that is not acceptable. There are many types of latching or locking devices that can be operated without tight grasping, tight pinching, or twisting of the wrist that would comply with the requirements of this section.

Some people with disabilities are unable to grasp objects with their hands or twist their wrists. Such people are unable to operate, or have great difficulty operating, door hardware other than lever-operated mechanisms, push-type mechanisms and U-shaped door pulls. Door hardware that can be operated with a closed fist or a loose grip accommodates the greatest range of users. Hardware operated by simultaneous hand and finger movement requires greater dexterity and coordination and should be avoided for doors along an accessible route (see Commentary Figure 1010.1.9.1).

Commentary Figure 1010.1.9.1
DOOR HARDWARE

[BE] 1010.1.9.2 Hardware height. Door handles, pulls, latches, locks and other operating devices shall be installed 34 inches (864 mm) minimum and 48 inches (1219 mm) maximum above the finished floor. Locks used only for security purposes and not used for normal operation are permitted at any height.

> **Exception:** Access doors or gates in barrier walls and fences protecting pools, spas and hot tubs shall be permitted to have operable parts of the latch release on self-latching devices at 54 inches (1370 mm) maximum above the finished floor or ground, provided that the self-latching devices are not also self-locking devices operated by means of a key, electronic opener or integral combination lock.

❖ The requirements in this section place the door hardware at a level that is usable by most people, including a person using a wheelchair. Security locks can be placed at any height. An example would be an unframed glass front door of a tenant space in a mall that has the lock near the floor level. The lock is only used when the store is not open for business. Such locks are not required for the normal operation of the door.

The exception permits a special allowance for security latches at pools, spas and hot tubs. The concern is that the 48-inch (1219 mm) maximum height would place the security latch within reach of children. The 54-inch (1372 mm) maximum height is intended to override the maximum 48-inch (1219 mm) reach range in ICC A117.1. This compromise addresses concerns for children's safety and still maintains accessibility to a reasonable level. Based on the last phrase in the exception, if the gate hardware also had a locking function and a key or other similar device would be needed to unlock the hardware to allow unlatching the latch, then the exception to allow the hardware to be 54 inches (1372 mm) above the floor is not applicable. This is because the secure nature of the hardware would provide the level of security needed to prevent access by children, and the hardware would be installed in the 34-inch to 48-inch (864 mm to 1219 mm) range. Explained differently: If the gate to the pool requires a key, then access into the pool would be restricted by availability of the key that would unlock the gate. If the gate to the pool has a latch only and no lock controlling access, then placing the latch hardware at 54 inches (1372 mm) above the floor decreases access to the pool by small children. Thus, if the gate hardware has a locking function and a key would be needed to unlock the gate, then there would not be a reason to require, or allow, the hardware to be 54 inches (1372 mm) above the floor. Access to the pool would be limited to those with a key. A reference to this exception is found in Section 1109.13, Exception 7, for the accessibility requirements for operable parts. This is consistent with the *2010 ADA Standards* and ANSI/NSPI-8 1996, *Model Barrier Code for Residential Swimming Pools, Spas and Hot Tubs.*

[BE] 1010.1.9.3 Monitored or recorded egress. Where electrical systems that monitor or record egress activity are incorporated, the locking system shall comply with Section 1010.1.9.7, 1010.1.9.8, 1010.1.9.9, 1010.1.9.10 or 1010.1.9.11, or shall be readily openable from the egress side without the use of a key or special knowledge or effort.

❖ This section allows for security systems that monitor people entering and leaving yet still allow for the locking systems to provide ready egress. This section is not applicable if a system monitors only those going into a space and the monitoring system has no effect on egress.

Monitored or recorded egress is where a device requiring some type of authorization or credential is used to monitor who is coming in or leaving a secured area. The active device could be a card reader, keypad, iris scan, fingerprint scan, and so on. A monitored egress device could be utilized in conjunction with any of the five "special locking arrangements," provided the functions of that specific locking arrangement are retained and maintained. For example, a monitored egress system may be installed where doors are readily openable, as required in Section 1010.1.9 where egress would always be available to the occupant, but an alarm might sound if someone did not have authorization to be in the area or did not present the correct credential upon exiting.

Examples of the systems being used in conjunction with a special locking arrangement would be a keypad installed adjacent to an electromagnetically locked egress door, a card reader installed adjacent to a delayed egress door, or a keypad installed in the approach area of a sensor release door. One example of a situation where this might be used is in an airport where staff uses key cards to move in and out of exit doors along the passenger terminal. The card key releases the delayed egress lock so that the alarm will not sound and the door will open immediately. The delayed egress lock would work in the traditional manner of alarm and release for someone who did not have that card key.

[BE] 1010.1.9.4 Locks and latches. Locks and latches shall be permitted to prevent operation of doors where any of the following exist:

1. Places of detention or restraint.
2. In buildings in occupancy Group A having an *occupant load* of 300 or less, Groups B, F, M and S, and in places of religious worship, the main door or doors are permitted to be equipped with key-operated locking devices from the egress side provided:
    - 2.1. The locking device is readily distinguishable as locked.
    - 2.2. A readily visible durable sign is posted on the egress side on or adjacent to the door stating: THIS DOOR TO REMAIN UNLOCKED WHEN THIS SPACE IS OCCUPIED. The sign shall be in letters 1 inch (25 mm) high on a contrasting background.
    - 2.3. The use of the key-operated locking device is revokable by the *fire code official* for due cause.
3. Where egress doors are used in pairs, *approved* automatic flush bolts shall be permitted to be used, provided that the door leaf having the automatic flush bolts does not have a doorknob or surface-mounted hardware.
4. Doors from individual *dwelling* or *sleeping units* of Group R occupancies having an *occupant load* of 10 or less are permitted to be equipped with a night latch, dead bolt or security chain, provided such devices are openable from the inside without the use of a key or tool.
5. Fire doors after the minimum elevated temperature has disabled the unlatching mechanism in accordance with *listed* fire door test procedures.

6. Doors serving roofs not intended to be occupied shall be permitted to be locked, preventing entry to the building from the roof.

❖ Where security and life safety objectives conflict, alternative measures, such as those permitted by each of the listed situations, may be applicable.

Item 1 is needed for jails and prisons (Occupancy Group I-3). Item 1 is also needed for locations where someone must be kept inside for their own safety, such as dementia wards, psychiatric wards and other uses of Occupancy Groups I-1 and I-2. Controlled egress locking systems of 1010.1.9.7 or delayed egress locking systems of 1010.1.9.8 may be permitted in these applications.

Item 2 permits a locking device, such as a double-cylinder dead bolt, on the main entrance door to a building or space. It must be immediately apparent that these doors are locked. For example, such locking devices may have an integral indicator that automatically reflects the "locked" or "unlocked" status of the device. In addition, a sign must be provided that clearly states that the door is to be unlocked when the building or space is occupied. The sign on or adjacent to the door not only reminds employees to unlock the door, but also advises the public that an unacceptable arrangement exists if one finds the door locked. Ideally, the individual who encounters the locked door will notify management and possibly the building official. Note that the use of the key-operated locking device is revocable by the building official. The locking arrangement is not permitted on any door other than the main exit and, therefore, the employees, security and cleaning crews will have access to other exits without requiring the use of a key. This allowance is not limited just to multiple-exit buildings but also to small buildings with one exit. This option is an alternative to the panic hardware required by Section 1010.1.10.

In Item 3, an automatic flush bolt is one that is internal to the inactive leaf of a pair of doors. When the active leaf is opened, the bolt is automatically retracted. When the active leaf is closed, a small knuckle is pressed into the inactive leaf by the active leaf, extending the flush bolt(s) in the head or sill of the inactive leaf (see Commentary Figure 1010.1.9.4).

Automatic flush bolts on one leaf of a pair of egress doors are acceptable, provided the leaf with the automatic flush bolts is not equipped with a doorknob or other hardware that would imply to the user that the door leaf is unlatched independently of the companion leaf.

Item 4 addresses the need for security in residential dwelling and sleeping units such as hotel rooms, apartments, dormitory rooms or townhouses. The occupants are familiar with the operation of the indicated devices, which are intended to be relatively simple to operate without the use of a key or tool. Note that this item only applies to the door leading from individual dwelling or sleeping units in a building. This item would not be applicable for doors locked as part of a security system in a multiple-unit building.

Item 5 is in recognition of required test procedures (UL 10B or UL 10C) for listed fire doors, which include the disabling of the locking mechanism when a fire door is exposed to the elevated temperatures of

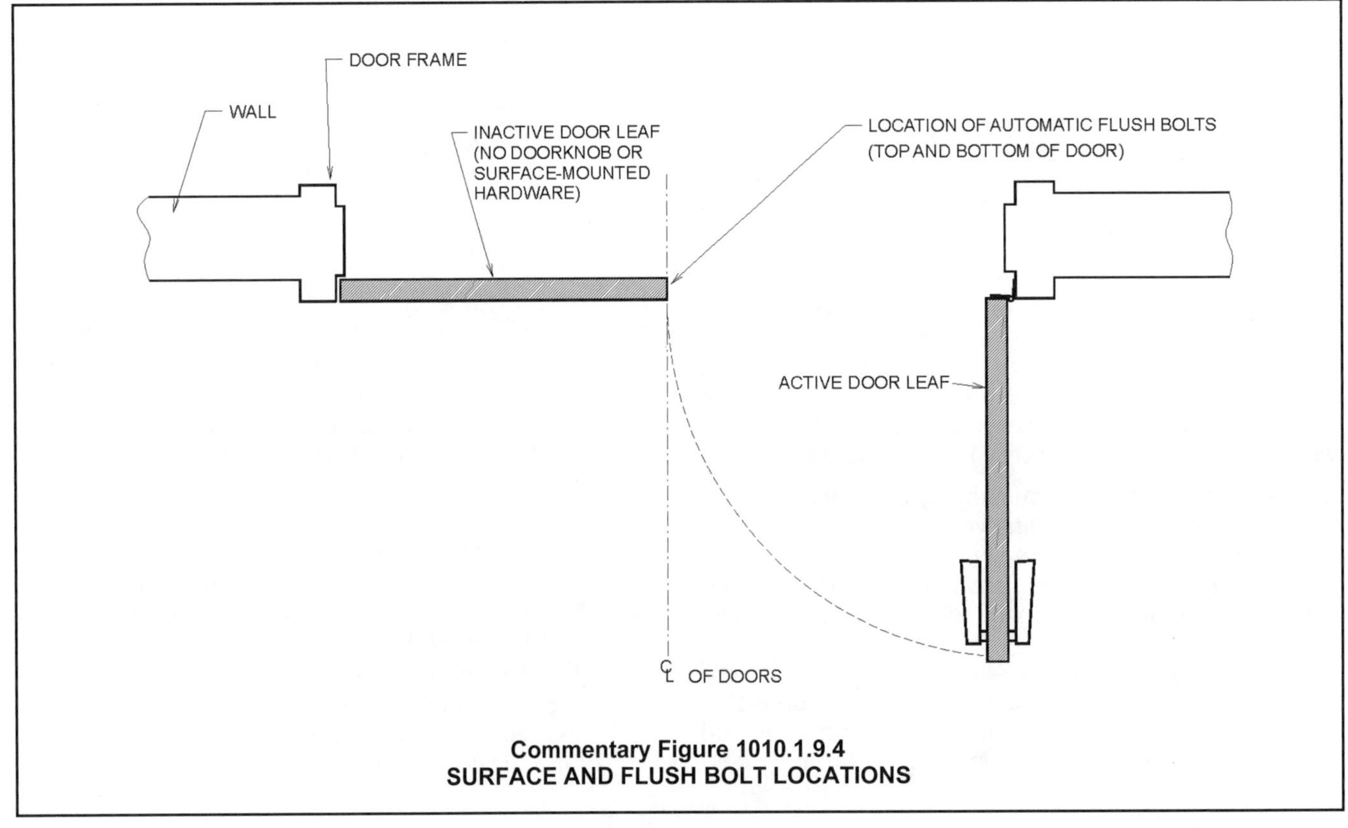

Commentary Figure 1010.1.9.4
SURFACE AND FLUSH BOLT LOCATIONS

a fire such as the auxiliary fire pin that is often required for fire exit hardware installed without the bottom latch.

Item 6 addresses a security concern about people gaining access into a building from unoccupied roofs. Getting back into the building should not be an issue for personnel that went onto the roof to repair equipment because they would have keys to get out onto the roof for work.

[BE] 1010.1.9.5 Bolt locks. Manually operated flush bolts or surface bolts are not permitted.

Exceptions:

1. On doors not required for egress in individual *dwelling units* or *sleeping units*.
2. Where a pair of doors serves a storage or equipment room, manually operated edge- or surface-mounted bolts are permitted on the inactive leaf.
3. Where a pair of doors serves an *occupant load* of less than 50 persons in a Group B, F or S occupancy, manually operated edge- or surface-mounted bolts are permitted on the inactive leaf. The inactive leaf shall not contain doorknobs, panic bars or similar operating hardware.
4. Where a pair of doors serves a Group B, F or S occupancy, manually operated edge- or surface-mounted bolts are permitted on the inactive leaf provided that such inactive leaf is not needed to meet egress capacity requirements and the building is equipped throughout with an *automatic sprinkler system* in accordance with Section 903.3.1.1. The inactive leaf shall not contain doorknobs, panic bars or similar operating hardware.
5. Where a pair of doors serves patient care rooms in Group I-2 occupancies, self-latching edge- or surface-mounted bolts are permitted on the inactive leaf provided that the inactive leaf is not needed to meet egress capacity requirements and the inactive leaf shall not contain doorknobs, panic bars or similar operating hardware.

❖ This section is applicable to doors that are required to be for means of egress purposes or are identified as a means of egress, such as by an exit sign or other indicator. Doors intended for convenience or building operations, as well as the second leaf in a doorway that is provided for a purpose other than means of egress, should be arranged or identified so as not to be mistaken as a means of egress. The use of manually operated flush bolts or surface bolts on means of egress doors have traditionally been prohibited because of the inability of users to quickly identify and operate such devices under emergency conditions.

This section prohibits installation of manually operated flush and surface bolts except in limited situations. The exceptions allowing the use of such hardware are intended to expand the use of manually operated edge- or surface-mounted bolts under specified conditions while maintaining an appropriate degree of safety for the building occupants. Flush and surface bolts represent locking devices that may be difficult to operate because of their location and operation (see Commentary Figure 1010.1.9.5).

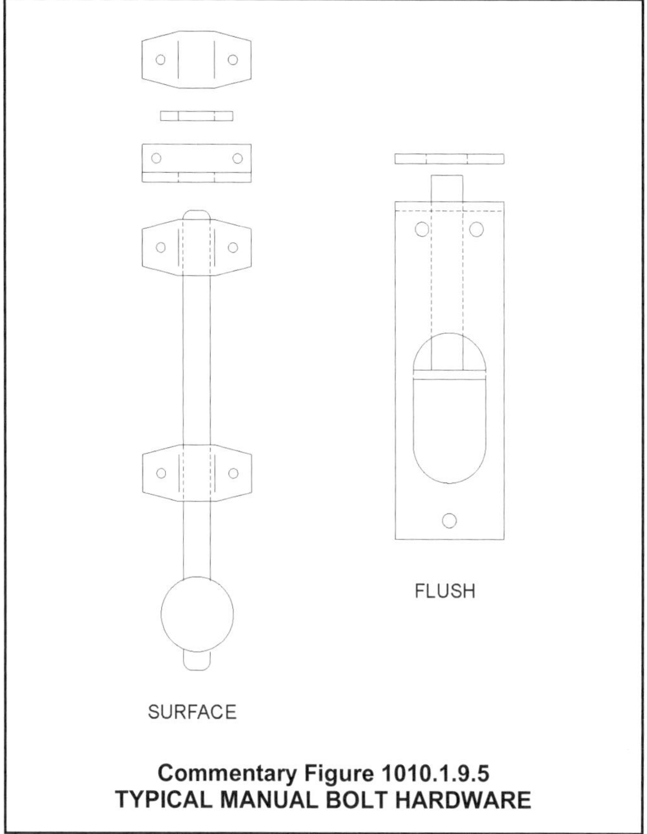

Commentary Figure 1010.1.9.5
TYPICAL MANUAL BOLT HARDWARE

Where edge-mounted or surface-mounted manually operated bolts are installed on the inactive leaf of a pair of doors, per the exceptions that follow, the manually operated bolts must have no effect on the egress operation of the active leaf.

Exception 1 allows manual flush bolts and surface bolts at some doors within an individual dwelling or sleeping unit. Even then, such bolts may only be used on doors not required for egress (see Section 1010.1.9.4, Item 4, for security of doors from individual dwelling and sleeping units).

Exception 2 provides for edge-mounted or surface-mounted bolts on the inactive leaf of a pair of doors from storage or equipment areas. Double doors are often provided to allow for the easy removal or replacement of large pieces of equipment or bulk movement of goods.

Exceptions 3 and 4 offer two options for limited doors in Group B, F and S occupancies. Again, the wider door opening is sometimes needed for the movement of equipment. Automatic flush bolts and removable center posts can be easily damaged and difficult to maintain in areas of frequent door usage. Revisions to the requirements for door hardware on such pairs of doors will increase building functionality while maintaining a very high degree of occupant safety.

In Exception 3, the number of occupants within the space must be less than 50, the active leaf must meet means of egress requirements and the inactive leaf must not have any operating hardware so that it could be mistaken for an egress door.

In accordance with Exception 4, if the Group B, F or S occupancy is sprinklered throughout with an NFPA 13 system, the room served by the pair of doors can have any occupant load if the inactive leaf is not required for egress capacity and has no operating hardware.

Exception 5 is in recognition of the need to move equipment into and out of some patient sleeping and treatment rooms in hospital and nursing home environments. Again, the inactive leaf must not be needed for means of egress or have any operating hardware. This is consistent with Section 407.4.1.1, which allows for staff to operate patient sleeping and treatment room doors during emergency events. The doors would still have to meet smoke barrier opening protective requirements. The clear width requirement of $41^1/_2$ inches (1054 mm) in Section 1010.1.1 would still have to be met with the active door leaf. Constant-latching flush bolts, a type of automatic flush bolts, are commonly used for this application.

[BE] 1010.1.9.6 Unlatching. The unlatching of any door or leaf shall not require more than one operation.

Exceptions:

1. Places of detention or restraint.
2. Where manually operated bolt locks are permitted by Section 1010.1.9.5.
3. Doors with automatic flush bolts as permitted by Section 1010.1.9.4, Item 3.
4. Doors from individual *dwelling units* and *sleeping units* of Group R occupancies as permitted by Section 1010.1.9.4, Item 4.

❖ The code prohibits the use of locks or latching devices that require more than one operation on any door required or used for egress, which could be a safety hazard in an emergency situation. The exceptions address locations where multiple locks or latching devices that require more than one operation are acceptable. See the referenced sections for additional commentary.

[BE] 1010.1.9.6.1 Closet doors. Closet doors that latch in the closed position shall be openable from inside the closet.

❖ This provision is intended to address possible entrapment concerns in closets. If a closet door has a door latch, the closet door must be openable from both inside and outside. This will ensure that someone cannot get stuck inside a closet by accident. If a closet does not latch, no interior hardware is required.

[BE] 1010.1.9.7 Controlled egress doors in Groups I-1 and I-2. Electric locking systems, including electro-mechanical locking systems and electromagnetic locking systems, shall be permitted to be locked in the means of egress in Group I-1 or I-2 occupancies where the clinical needs of persons receiving care require their containment. Controlled egress doors shall be permitted in such occupancies where the building is equipped throughout with an *automatic sprinkler system* in accordance with Section 903.3.1.1 or an approved automatic smoke or heat detection system installed in accordance with Section 907, provided that the doors are installed and operate in accordance with all of the following:

1. The door locks shall unlock on actuation of the *automatic sprinkler system* or automatic fire detection system.
2. The door locks shall unlock on loss of power controlling the lock or lock mechanism.
3. The door locking system shall be installed to have the capability of being unlocked by a switch located at the fire command center, a nursing station or other approved location. The switch shall directly break power to the lock.
4. A building occupant shall not be required to pass through more than one door equipped with a controlled egress locking system before entering an exit.
5. The procedures for unlocking the doors shall be described and approved as part of the emergency planning and preparedness required by Chapter 4.
6. All clinical staff shall have the keys, codes or other means necessary to operate the locking systems.
7. Emergency lighting shall be provided at the door.
8. The door locking system units shall be *listed* in accordance with UL 294.

Exceptions:

1. Items 1 through 4 shall not apply to doors to areas occupied by persons who, because of clinical needs, require restraint or containment as part of the function of a psychiatric treatment area.
2. Items 1 through 4 shall not apply to doors to areas where a *listed* egress control system is utilized to reduce the risk of child abduction from nursery and obstetric areas of a Group I-2 hospital.

❖ These provisions are intended to address the special safety needs for wards, units or areas in assisted living facilities, nursing homes and hospitals where egress may need to be controlled for the safety of the occupants or where specialized protective measures are needed for patients. “Controlled egress” means that the ability of occupants, such as patients or residents, to leave a space is controlled by others, such as staff. The areas where controlled egress may be permitted include psychiatric areas, dementia units, Alzheimer’s units, maternity units and newborn nurseries. Code officials may also permit these provisions in other areas such as emergency departments or pediatric areas where the safety and security of the occupants are of primary concern. In all situations, there must be a balance between maintaining a safe and secure environment and providing for emergency egress.

The requirements of this section apply to locking systems controlling egress. The functions of a controlled ingress locking system are not addressed in the codes and are unrelated as long as egress is provided as required or permitted by this section and other applicable provisions of the code.

IBC Section 907.6 requires a fire alarm system to be installed in accordance with the requirements of that section and NFPA 72. NFPA 72 includes specific requirements for unlocking doors in the direction of egress that are consistent with the requirements in this section for controlled egress locking systems. Additionally, NFPA 72 includes specific requirements and guidance for backup power where the backup power is used to keep these doors in a locked condition in the direction of egress.

Items 1 through 3 address where the controlled egress locks would be required to automatically unlock, allowing unrestricted egress.

Item 4 requires that no occupant shall have to pass through more than one controlled egress lock before entering an exit.

Item 5 requires the procedures for unlocking the doors to be described, approved by the code official, and included in the emergency planning and preparedness required by Chapter 4.

Item 6 requires clinical staff to have the means necessary to operate the controlled egress locking system, such as keys, codes, and so on (see Section 1010.1.9.3).

Item 7 requires emergency lighting at the controlled egress door to ensure visibility for egress during a possible power outage.

Item 8 requires the units of the controlled egress locking system to be listed according to UL 294. UL 294, *Standard for Access Control System Units,* applies to construction, performance and operation of systems that control passage through a door and the electrical, electronic or mechanical units of these systems.

Exception 1 allows for the automatic unlocking requirements to be omitted for doors in a psychiatric treatment area in hospitals or nursing homes due to additional safety concerns for the residents.

Exception 2 allows for automatic unlocking requirements to be omitted where a listed egress control system is installed for the specific purpose of reducing child abductions from nursery and obstetric areas of hospitals.

[BE] 1010.1.9.8 Delayed egress. Delayed egress locking systems, shall be permitted to be installed on doors serving the following occupancies in buildings that are equipped throughout with an *automatic sprinkler system* in accordance with Section 903.3.1.1 or an *approved* automatic smoke or heat detection system installed in accordance with Section 907:

1. Group B, F, I, M, R, S and U occupancies.
2. Group E classrooms with an occupant load of less than 50.

   Exception: Delayed egress locking systems shall be permitted to be installed on exit or exit access doors, other than the main exit or exit access door, serving a courtroom in buildings equipped throughout with an *automatic sprinkler system* in accordance with Section 903.3.1.1.

❖ These provisions are intended to address special needs where there are concerns about internal security. Delays in egress, as allowed in this section by Item 1 for Groups B, F, I, M, R, S and U occupancies, are not considered detrimental to occupant evacuation. These provisions also address special needs for security or where occupants may need to be protected from harm because of their own actions. For example, residents or patients in some Group I-1 or Group I-2 occupancies may present a danger to themselves where elopement from the building exposes them to traffic, weather and other environmental hazards.

Item 2 addresses the needs of small educational occupancies to help prevent wandering/elopement, especially for the very young and for special needs students. Delayed egress locks would not be permitted on doors from spaces such as multipurpose rooms, auditoriums, gymnasiums or similar spaces associated with Group E occupancies. The limit of less than 50 occupants would be coordinated with the requirements for panic hardware in Group E occupancies in Section 1010.1.10.

Delayed egress locks are not permitted in Group H because of the potential for rapid fire buildup in such areas.

Per the exception, delayed egress locks are permitted in limited situations in Group A-3 courtrooms, but they would not be permitted in other Group A occupancies, including other Group A-3 areas of a courthouse. A courthouse is a unique building type that is designed with three separate and distinct circulation systems—one for the public, one for the judiciary/security staff, and one for in-custody inmates. The three circulation systems are segregated and only meet in a single location, the courtrooms. The public enter the courtroom from the public corridor; the judges and court staff enter from the rear, secure staff corridor; and the prisoners enter from the holding area at the side. Most of the time, these groups are kept separate for security reasons. Where a courtroom has an occupant load of 50 of more, a minimum of two means of egress are required, and the doors of the means of egress would be required to have panic hardware. Standard courtroom design provides unobstructed egress for the public out the back of the courtroom with enough egress capacity to handle the entire occupant load of the courtroom. Doors leading to the prisoner interface are locked and fail secure (see Section 1010.1.9.4, Exception 1).

Industry practice has been to utilize the exit at the front of the courtroom as the second means of egress. To maintain the security separation of occupants, it is industry practice to equip this second means of egress with a delayed egress device that prevents any unauthorized person from gaining access to the secure staff areas without notice. This is not considered detrimental to egress. A courtroom is a controlled environment. A bailiff is located within the courtroom when occupied by the public and/or prisoners. The bailiff, along with other court personnel, is equipped with a security access card that can override the delayed egress locks (Section 1010.1.9.3). If the bailiff is dealing with a security issue, the delayed egress system would operate normally and allow egress. In the event of a fire, the activation of the automatic sprinkler system or the automatic fire detection system deactivates the delay of the delayed egress system (see Section 1010.1.9.8.1, Item 1), allowing immediate egress, with the door functioning for egress just like a door without a delayed egress system. It is common to install mechanical latching or locking hardware on a door in unison with the delayed egress door locking system to increase security and prevent access (ingress). Panic hardware would be required in Group A, E, and H occupancies where required by Section 1010.1.10.

[BE] 1010.1.9.8.1 Delayed egress locking system. The delayed egress locking system shall be installed and operated in accordance with all of the following:

1. The delay electronics of the delayed egress locking system shall deactivate upon actuation of the *automatic sprinkler system* or automatic fire detection system, allowing immediate, free egress.
2. The delay electronics of the delayed egress locking system shall deactivate upon loss of power controlling the lock or lock mechanism, allowing immediate free egress.
3. The delayed egress locking system shall have the capability of being deactivated at the fire command center and other approved locations.
4. An attempt to egress shall initiate an irreversible process that shall allow such egress in not more than 15 seconds when a physical effort to exit is applied to the egress side door hardware for not more than 3 seconds. Initiation of the irreversible process shall activate an audible signal in the vicinity of the door. Once the delay electronics have been deactivated, rearming the delay electronics shall be by manual means only.

   Exception: Where *approved*, a delay of not more than 30 seconds is permitted on a delayed egress door.
5. The egress path from any point shall not pass through more than one delayed egress locking system.

   Exceptions:

   1. In Group I-2 or I-3 occupancies, the egress path from any point in the building shall pass through not more than two delayed egress locking systems provided that the combined delay does not exceed 30 seconds.
   2. In Group I-1 or I-4 occupancies, the egress path from any point in the building shall pass through not more than two delayed egress locking systems provided that the combined delay does not exceed 30 seconds and the building is equipped throughout with an *automatic sprinkler system* in accordance with Section 903.3.1.1.
6. A sign shall be provided on the door and shall be located above and within 12 inches (305 mm) of the door exit hardware:

   6.1. For doors that swing in the direction of egress, the sign shall read: PUSH UNTIL ALARM SOUNDS. DOOR CAN BE OPENED IN 15 [30] SECONDS.

   6.2. For doors that swing in the opposite direction of egress, the sign shall read: PULL UNTIL ALARM SOUNDS. DOOR CAN BE OPENED IN 15 [30] SECONDS.

   6.3 The sign shall comply with the visual character requirements in ICC A117.1.

   Exception: Where *approved*, in Group I occupancies, the installation of a sign is not required where care recipients who, because of clinical needs, require restraint or containment as part of the function of the treatment area.
7. Emergency lighting shall be provided on the egress side of the door.
8. The delayed egress locking system units shall be *listed* in accordance with UL 294.

❖ The requirements of this section apply to locking systems that delay egress. This locking system is called delayed egress because of Item 4, which permits a fixed amount of time to pass prior to allowing egress.

The functions of a controlled ingress locking system are unrelated and are not addressed as long as egress is provided as required or permitted by this section and other applicable provisions of the code.

IBC Section 907.6 requires a fire alarm system to be installed in accordance with the requirements of that section and NFPA 72. NFPA 72 includes specific requirements for unlocking doors in the direction of egress that are consistent with the requirements in this section for delayed egress locking systems. Additionally, NFPA 72 includes specific requirements and guidance for backup power where the backup power is used to keep these doors in a locked condition in the direction of egress.

Because of the egress delay caused by the system on the egress door, the building must be provided throughout with compensating fire protection features to promptly warn occupants of a fire condition. All listed conditions must be met in order to permit use of a delayed egress locking system.

Item 1 interconnects the locking system with an automatic sprinkler system in accordance with NFPA 13 or, alternatively, an automatic fire detection system in accordance with Section 907, which is required to be installed throughout the building. Such systems are to provide occupants with early warning of a fire event, and thus additional time for egress. Note that actuation of the automatic sprinkler system or actuation of the automatic fire detection system must eliminate the delay of the delayed egress locking system so the door immediately allows egress (without delay).

Item 2 specifies the delay is to be eliminated on loss of power. Since the operation of the delayed egress locking system is dependent on electrical power, in the event of electrical power loss to the lock or locking mechanism, the doors must immediately allow egress (without delay).

Item 3 specifies that the delay in the delayed egress locking system is capable of being eliminated by a signal sent from the fire command center or other approved locations. Personnel at the fire command center location would normally be the first alerted to an emergency event and would be expected to take appropriate action to allow immediate egress at all doors equipped with delayed egress locking systems. Other locations may be alternates to back up the fire command center. Item 3 facilitates remotely eliminating the delay in the delayed egress locking system in the event of a fire or in the event of other nonfire emergencies.

Item 4 specifies the operational characteristics of the delayed egress locking system. The delay timer of the system and the audible signal (alarm) at the door may be configured one of two ways. In some occupancies, the delay timer is initiated and the alarm sounds immediately upon an attempt to open the door by pushing on the panic bar or causing a slight movement of the door. In other occupancies, to prevent nuisance alarms from inadvertent bumps or accidental contact, the initiation of the delay timer and sounding of the alarm may be deferred by up to 3 seconds, requiring the occupant to attempt to operate the door hardware for up to, but not more than, 3 seconds.

Once the delay timer starts, the door is required to be openable from the egress side in not more than 15 seconds (or not more than 30 seconds where approved by the code official, per the exception). At the end of the delay, the door's locking system is required to allow the door to be opened by the occupant operating the egress door hardware (i.e., pushing on the panic bar), allowing egress. The unlocking cycle is irreversible; once it is started, it does not stop. Once the door is openable from the egress side at the end of the delay, it remains openable, allowing immediate egress until someone comes to the door and manually rearms the delay. The first user to the door may face a delay, but after that, other users would be able to exit immediately. Automatically rearming the delayed egress locking system from a remote location such as a central control station or security office is not permitted.

The exception to Item 4 permits the code official to increase the time delay prior to allowing egress beyond 15 seconds, but not in excess of 30 seconds. This exception is more often granted for the safety and security of occupants (e.g., to reduce or prevent elopement of patients) than for loss prevention.

Item 5 limits the egress path to not more than one door with a delayed egress locking system. However, the two exceptions to Item 5 allow not more than two doors with delayed egress locking systems in Group I with the delay of the two systems to be not more than 30 seconds total.

Having multiple doors can help with preventing resident elopement and yet the overall delay does not exceed the previously accepted time period. An example of where the two-door arrangement may be helpful is a multistory facility where both the door from the story and the door from the building could each be equipped with a delayed egress system.

Item 6 requires a sign to inform occupants how to operate the delayed egress locking system and when that door will become available for egress. An undesirable consequence of the door not unlocking immediately may be the user assuming it will never be available for egress and then proceeding to another exit door. In some occupancies, delayed egress locking systems may be utilized on doors not required to swing in the direction of egress travel. Options 6.1 and 6.2 allow for signs appropriate for the swing of the door. The required sign is typically supplied with the delayed egress locking system. The reference to ICC A117.1 visual requirements would not require raised letters or braille, but would require readable text with good finish and contrast. The exception in Item 6 allows the sign to be omitted if the clinical needs of occupants require restraint or containment, as these patients may be capable of reading and following the sign's instructions and then potentially putting themselves in harm's way. Based on the level of staff training within these facilities and the need to protect patients by preventing elopement, and given that these systems are required to interconnect with the sprinkler or fire detection systems and unlock upon loss of power, it was determined that eliminating the sign in these facilities is reasonable.

Item 7 requires emergency lighting on the egress side of the door so that the user can read the sign required by Item 6.

Item 8 requires the units of the delayed egress locking system to be listed according to UL 294. UL 294, *Standard for Access Control System Units*, applies to construction, performance and operation of systems that control passage through a door and the electrical, electronic or mechanical units of these systems.

[BE] 1010.1.9.9 Sensor release of electrically locked egress doors. Sensor release of electric locking systems shall be permitted on doors located in a the *means of egress* in any occupancy except Group H where installed and operated in accordance with all of the following criteria:

1. The sensor shall be installed on the egress side, arranged to detect an occupant approaching the doors and shall cause the electric locking system to unlock.
2. The electric locks shall be arranged to unlock by a signal from or loss of power to the sensor.
3. Loss of power to the lock or locking system shall automatically unlock the electric locks.
4. The doors shall be arranged to unlock from a manual unlocking device located 40 inches to 48 inches (1016 mm to 1219 mm) vertically above the floor and within 5 feet (1524 mm) of the secured doors. Ready access shall be provided to the manual unlocking device and the device shall be clearly identified by a sign that reads "PUSH TO EXIT." When operated, the manual unlocking device shall result in direct interruption of power to the electric lock—independent of other electronics—and the electric lock shall remain unlocked for not less than 30 seconds.
5. Activation of the building fire alarm system, where provided, shall automatically unlock the electric lock, and the electric lock shall remain unlocked until the fire alarm system has been reset.
6. Activation of the building *automatic sprinkler system* or fire detection system, where provided, shall automatically unlock the electric lock. The electric lock shall remain unlocked until the fire alarm system has been reset.
7. The door locking system units shall be listed in accordance with UL 294.

❖ This section is intended to provide consistent requirements where an electrically locked door is unlocked by activating devices mounted somewhere other than on the door itself. The unlocking activation is designed to be from a passive action by the occupant (e.g., walking to the door triggering a sensor), but the system includes a required nearby manual unlocking device (such as a push button) as a secondary electrical lock release device.

This section permits means of egress doors and entrance doors to tenant spaces in other than Group H occupancies to be electrically secured (locked) to control ingress while maintaining the doors as a means of egress. Typically these systems are used in high-security areas where a record of who has entered and left a space is desired. Or this system may be used where there is a concern for elopement or child abduction (Group I-1, I-2 or I-4). In areas where additional security may be a concern, a door hardware system may include an unlocking device, such as a keypad, card reader, eye scanner, thumbprint scanner or other credential device (see Section 1010.1.9.3).

For buildings with fire alarm systems, NFPA 72 includes specific requirements for unlocking doors in the direction of egress, which are consistent with the requirements in this section. Additionally, NFPA 72 includes specific requirements and guidance for where the backup power is used to keep these doors in a locked condition.

The requirements of this section apply to locking systems with a sensor release. The functions of a controlled ingress locking system are not addressed and are unrelated as long as egress is provided as required.

Items 1 through 6 provide operational criteria to ensure egress during normal and emergency situations.

Item 1 requires that such doors be provided with an occupant sensor on the egress side of the door. This sensor is required to automatically release the electric lock as an occupant approaches from the egress side or when there is a loss of power to the sensor (Item 2). This provision is written as performance based, where any means of sensor design can be utilized to cause the doors to unlock, allowing immediate egress. This section does not indicate at what distance the sensor should be set to operate. The sensor may be set to detect an approaching occupant in time to unlock the electric lock prior to the occupant reaching the door. In other applications, the sensor may be set to require the occupant to be closer to the door prior to unlocking.

Item 3 states that if there is a loss of power to the electric lock or to the locking system, the electric lock on the door must unlock. These doors are commonly secured with fail-safe devices that prioritize life safety over security (such as electromagnetic locks or fail-safe power bolts), so the electric locks on these doors will automatically unlock when power to the electric locking device or locking system is interrupted. In some instances, the locking system controller may be powered from a different source than the electric locking device itself. A loss of power to the locking system controller must cause the electric locking device on the egress door to automatically unlock (regardless of whether power remains applied to the locking device).

Item 4 requires that there be a manual unlocking device (push button) within 5 feet (1524 mm) of the door, mounted unobstructed 40 inches to 48 inches (1016 mm to 1219 mm) above the floor, with a clearly identifiable sign that says "PUSH TO EXIT." When operated, the manual unlocking device is to directly interrupt, independent of other electronics, the power to the electric lock and cause the doors to remain unlocked for a minimum of 30 seconds. The 30-second minimum is to allow adequate time for an individual to operate the manual unlocking device and then to egress through the door.

Items 5 and 6 require the building fire alarm system, automatic fire detection system or sprinkler system, if provided, to interface with and automatically unlock the door's electric locking system upon activation. The electric locks on the doors are to remain unlocked until the system is reset, ensuring egress is not impeded by the electric locking system.

Item 7 requires the units of the locking system to be listed according to UL 294. UL 294, *Standard for Access Control System Units*, applies to construction, performance and operation of systems that control passage through a door and the electric, electronic, or mechanical units of these systems.

To summarize, it is important to keep in mind that an egress door equipped with a sensor release system must always allow egress, whether power is present or not. The egress door must be fail-safe when power is removed from any part of the sensor release system so that the egress door is capable of being opened. People must be kept from being involuntarily locked inside buildings.

[BE] 1010.1.9.10 Door hardware release of electrically locked egress doors. Door hardware release of electric locking systems shall be permitted on doors in the *means of egress* in any occupancy except Group H where installed and operated in accordance with all of the following:

1. The door hardware that is affixed to the door leaf has an obvious method of operation that is readily operated under all lighting conditions.
2. The door hardware is capable of being operated with one hand and shall comply with Section 1010.1.9.6.
3. Operation of the door hardware directly interrupts the power to the electric lock and unlocks the door immediately.
4. Loss of power to the electric locking system automatically unlocks the door.
5. Where *panic* or *fire exit hardware* is required by Section 1010.1.10, operation of the *panic* or *fire exit hardware* also releases the electric lock.
6. The locking system units shall be *listed* in accordance with UL 294.

❖ This section is intended to provide consistent requirements where an electrically locked system, such as an electromagnetic lock, is released by door-mounted hardware such as a panic bar, lockset/latchset or touch-sense bar, all of which would be equipped with an integral switch that, when actuated by opening the door, causes the electric lock to release, allowing immediate egress. In other than Group H, doors in the means of egress are permitted to be locked with an electric locking system where equipped with door hardware that incorporates a built-in switch, provided all the specified conditions are met. Additionally, doors to tenant spaces other than Group H may be equipped with electric locks, provided all of the specified conditions are met. The use of this type of locking system may provide for a greater degree of security, preventing or controlling access or ingress, than that afforded by a door with mechanical locking devices alone. The allowance for electrically locked egress doors is limited to low- and moderate-hazard occupancies where security may be a concern.

It may be important to note other "shall be permitted" locking arrangements in the code that also use electric locks as part of their system: controlled egress locking systems (Section 1010.1.9.7), delayed egress locking systems (Section 1010.1.9.8), and sensor release of electrically locked egress doors (Section 1010.1.9.9).

The requirements of this section apply to electric locking systems that unlock upon hardware activation. The functions of a controlled ingress locking system are not addressed in the codes and are unrelated as long as egress is provided as required or permitted by this section and other applicable provisions of the code.

In areas where additional security may be a concern, a door hardware system may include an unlocking device, such as a keypad, card reader, eye scanner, thumbprint scanner or other credential device (see Section 1010.1.9.3).

When the occupant prepares to egress through the door, the method of operating the door hardware must be obvious, even under poor lighting conditions. The operation shall be accomplished through the use of a single motion and meet the general requirement that the door be readily openable without the use of special knowledge or effort. The release of the electric lock on the door must occur immediately on the operation of the door hardware by interrupting the power supply to the electric lock. This requirement is the same regardless of the type of door hardware: panic hardware, fire exit hardware, a latchset/lockset or a touch-sense bar. As an additional safeguard, the loss of power to the locking system is required to automatically release the electric lock on the door.

A properly designed and installed electric locking system complying with the requirements of this section of the IBC may not be obvious to the occupants, as the door unlatches/unlocks (electrically and mechanically), allowing egress through the normal operation of the door hardware (panic or fire exit hardware, latchset/lockset, or touch-sense bar). Considering these performance requirements, this section of the IBC does not include a requirement that the electromagnetic lock be unlocked (released) upon activation of the building fire alarm system. Also, this section of the IBC does not limit the number of doors in the means of egress that may be equipped with these electric locking systems.

The units of the electric locking system are required to be listed in accordance with UL 294. UL 294, *Standard for Access Control System Units*, applies to construction, performance and operation of systems that control passage through a door and the electrical, electronic or mechanical units of these systems. Where these special provisions are utilized, the requirements of Section 1010.1.10 regarding panic hardware remain applicable. In Group A and E occupancies having occupant loads of 50 or more, the door hardware must also comply with the requirements for panic hardware.

[BE] 1010.1.9.11 Locking arrangements in buildings within correctional facilities. In buildings within correctional and detention facilities, doors in *means of egress* serving rooms or spaces occupied by persons whose movements are controlled for security reasons shall be permitted to be locked where equipped with egress control devices that shall unlock manually and by not less than one of the following means:

1. Activation of an *automatic sprinkler system* installed in accordance with Section 903.3.1.1.
2. Activation of an *approved* manual fire alarm box.
3. A signal from a constantly attended location.

❖ Correctional facilities can include a variety of uses where detainees may be gathered for eating, recreational activities, education, technical training, job training, and so on. Correctional facilities can also contain types of support services, such as a store, storage areas or hospital area. Security is still a concern within these areas. This provision allows the correctional facility to maintain security for all areas. Most commonly, the doors would be opened by staff from a central control point under Item 3, but Items 1 and 2 allow for other alternatives in lower security facilities.

[BE] 1010.1.9.12 Stairway doors. Interior *stairway means of egress* doors shall be openable from both sides without the use of a key or special knowledge or effort.

Exceptions:

1. *Stairway* discharge doors shall be openable from the egress side and shall only be locked from the opposite side.
2. This section shall not apply to doors arranged in accordance with Section 403.5.3 of the *International Building Code*.
3. *Stairway* exit doors are permitted to be locked from the side opposite the egress side, provided that they are openable from the egress side and capable of being unlocked simultaneously without unlatching upon a signal from the *fire command center*, if present, or a signal by emergency personnel from a single location inside the main entrance to the building.
4. *Stairway* exit doors shall be openable from the egress side and shall only be locked from the opposite side in Group B, F, M and S occupancies where the only interior access to the tenant space is from a single *exit stairway* where permitted in Section 1006.3.3.
5. *Stairway* exit doors shall be openable from the egress side and shall only be locked from the opposite side in Group R-2 occupancies where the only interior access to the *dwelling unit* is from a single exit stairway where permitted in Section 1006.3.3.

❖ Based on adverse fire experience where occupants have become trapped in smoke-filled stairway enclosures, stairway doors generally must be arranged to permit reentry into the building without the use of any tools, keys or special knowledge or effort. For security reasons, this restriction does not apply to the discharge door from the stairway enclosure to the outside or into an exit passageway (Exception 1). Section 403 for high-rise buildings permits locking doors from the stairway side, provided the doors are capable of being unlocked from a fire command station and there is a communications system within the stairway enclosure that allows contact with the fire command station (Exception 2).

Exception 3, for security reasons, allows the stairway exit door(s) to be locked, preventing ingress from the exit discharge side of the door. In addition, to allow quick entrance for fire fighters and emergency responders, a means of simultaneously unlocking all of the doors by emergency personnel must be provided. This provision further requires that the stairway doors be unlocked without unlatching. Stairway doors will typically be fire door assemblies, and their continued latching is necessary to maintain the integrity of the fire-resistive separation for the exit enclosure. The remote unlocking signal shall be initiated from the fire command center, if provided, or a single point of signal initiation at an approved location inside the building's main entrance.

Exceptions 4 and 5 allow for stairways in single-exit buildings to have doorways that lead to multiple tenants and dwelling units. For security reasons, those doors can remain locked from the stairway side so no one can enter another tenant space or dwelling unit from the exit stairway.

[BE] 1010.1.10 Panic and fire exit hardware. Swinging doors serving a Group H occupancy and swinging doors serving rooms or spaces with an *occupant load* of 50 or more in a Group A or E occupancy shall not be provided with a latch or lock other than *panic hardware* or *fire exit hardware*.

Exceptions:

1. A main *exit* of a Group A occupancy shall be permitted to have locking devices in accordance with Section 1010.1.9.4, Item 2.
2. Doors provided with *panic hardware* or *fire exit hardware* and serving a Group A or E occupancy shall be permitted to be electrically locked in accordance with Section 1010.1.9.9 or 1010.1.9.10.

Electrical rooms with equipment rated 1,200 amperes or more and over 6 feet (1829 mm) wide, and that contain overcurrent devices, switching devices or control devices with exit or exit access doors, shall be equipped with *panic hardware* or *fire exit hardware*. The doors shall swing in the direction of egress travel.

❖ Swinging doors that are part of a means of egress from the locations listed in this section shall not be provided with a latch or lock other than panic hardware or fire exit hardware unless one of the two exceptions is met. Fire exit hardware is essentially panic hardware that has been tested and listed for use on fire-rated doors. Also see the commentaries to Chapter 2 definitions for "Fire exit hardware" or "Panic hardware" and Sections 1010.1.10.1 and 1010.1.10.2.

For all Group H occupancies, regardless of the occupant load, if latching (or locking) hardware is installed, it must be panic hardware or fire exit hardware because of the physical hazards of these spaces.

For all doors that provide means of egress for assembly and educational occupancies (Groups A and E) with an occupant load of 50 or more, if latching (or locking) hardware is installed, it must be panic hardware or fire exit hardware. This would include large assembly spaces in mixed-use buildings. These uses are characterized by higher occupant load densities. Whereas doors from an assembly or educational room with an occupant load of less than 50 do not require panic hardware or fire exit hardware, a door that provides means of egress for two or more such rooms would require panic hardware or fire exit hardware where the combination of spaces has a total occupant load of 50 or more.

See the exception to Section 1010.1.9.8 for a special allowance for delayed egress locks on some of the doors in courtrooms. This specific requirement would override the general requirement for panic hardware in all Group A.

Exception 1 clarifies that the provisions for key-operated locking hardware at the main exit in Group A occupancies are permitted instead of panic hardware at those specific locations. (For the Group A exception, see the commentary to Section 1010.1.9.4, Item 2.)

Exception 2 resolves a potential conflict between Section 1010.1.9.9 and Section 1010.1.9.10. Section 1010.1.9.9 allows sensor release of electrically locked egress doors, so panic hardware would not be required. Section 1010.1.9.10, Item 5, allows electric locks to be installed in addition to panic or fire exit hardware as long as the operation of the panic or fire exit hardware releases the electric lock.

Certain electrical rooms are required to have panic hardware. Refer to IBC Chapter 27 and *NFPA 70: National Electrical Code®* (NEC) for specific requirements for where panic hardware or fire exit hardware is required. This requirement is applicable only where multiple conditions are present. The type of room regulated creates a potentially hazardous environment. In the event of an electrical accident, the more immediate egress provided by the panic hardware is desirable.

[BE] 1010.1.10.1 Installation. Where *panic* or *fire exit hardware* is installed, it shall comply with the following:

1. *Panic hardware* shall be *listed* in accordance with UL 305.
2. *Fire exit hardware* shall be *listed* in accordance with UL 10C and UL 305.
3. The actuating portion of the releasing device shall extend not less than one-half of the door leaf width.
4. The maximum unlatching force shall not exceed 15 pounds (67 N).

❖ As its name implies, panic hardware is special unlatching and unlocking hardware that is intended to simplify the unlatching and unlocking operation to a single force of not more than 15 pounds (67 N), applied in the direction of egress [see Commentary Figures 1010.1.10.1(1) and (2)]. In a panic situation with a rush of persons trying to utilize a door, devices such as doorknobs or thumb turns may cause sufficient delay so as to create a crush at the door and prevent or slow the opening operation.

The locational specifications for the activating panel or bar are based on ready availability and access to the unlatching device. Note that the section requires the width of the actuating portion of the panic hardware or fire exit hardware to measure at least one-half the width of the door leaf. For example, on a 3′-0″ door (nominal 36 inches wide), the activating portion of the panic or fire hardware would measure at least 18 inches (457 mm). Panic and fire exit hardware must be listed. UL 305, *Standard for Panic Hardware*, includes construction and performance requirements dealing with endurance, emergency operation, elevated ambient exposure and low-temperature impact tests to ensure that the panic device operates properly (for panic hardware on a balanced door, see Section 1010.1.10.2). The activation device must be mounted between 34 inches and 48 inches (864 mm and 1219 mm) above the floor in accordance with Section 1010.1.9.2. Section 1010.1.1.1 allows the panic hardware to extend the full width of the door as long as it does not protrude more than 4 inches (102 mm) into the door's required minimum clear width.

Standard panic hardware or "listed panic hardware" is not approved for use on fire door assemblies. Panic hardware and fire exit hardware can be similar in appearance. Fire exit hardware can be installed on a door that is not a fire door.

Where a fire door, such as to an exit stairway, is required to be equipped with panic hardware, the hardware must accomplish the dual objectives of panic hardware and continuity of the enclosure in which it is located—thus the reference to UL 10C, *Standard for Positive Pressure Fire Tests of Door Assemblies*. In this case, fire exit hardware that meets both objectives and requirements is to be provided, since panic hardware is not tested for use on fire doors. There are standard test procedures designed to evaluate the performance of panic and fire exit hardware from the panic standpoint as well as from a fire protection standpoint. "Fire door assembly" is defined as any combination of a fire door, frame, hardware and other accessories that together provide a specific degree of fire and smoke

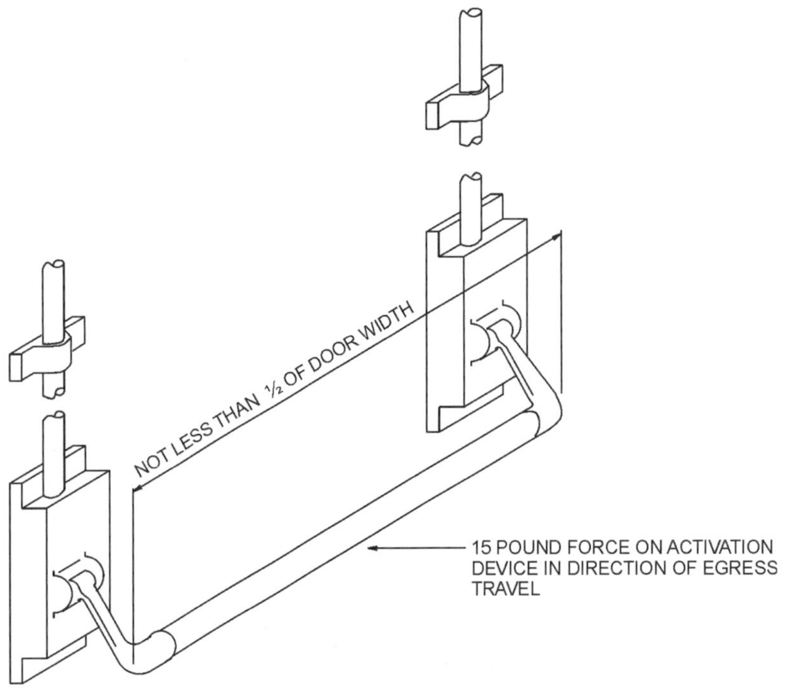

For SI: 1 pound = 4.4 N.

Commentary Figure 1010.1.10.1(1)
EXAMPLES OF TYPICAL PANIC HARDWARE

Commentary Figure 1010.1.10.1(2)
EXAMPLES OF TYPICAL PANIC HARDWARE

barrier protection to the opening in a fire wall, fire barrier, fire partition, smoke barrier or exterior wall required to have a fire-resistance rating.

Fire doors must close and positively latch in order to protect exit stairways, corridors and other areas of the building from the spread of smoke and fire. Additionally, fire doors are required to self-close and automatically latch after each use. Positive latching of fire doors is not related to the locking of the door and should never be confused with locking or security issues.

The requirement for positive latching means that mechanical dogging devices are not permitted on fire exit hardware. A dogging device is an option on the hardware that allows for the panic hardware to be mechanically locked in the fully depressed position. A dogging device mechanically defeats the latching feature of panic hardware, preventing the door from positively latching when in the closed position. The dogging device is typically manually activated by inserting a small wrench or tool through a hole adjacent to the activation bar. Dogging capability is often provided on exterior doors that are intended as building entrances. Electric latch retraction or electric dogging may be used on fire exit hardware if the latch automatically projects upon activation of the fire alarm.

Fire exit hardware must be labeled. Typical locations are on either end of the hardware. Information on the label must include the words “listed” and “fire exit hardware” and indicate a control or serial number. The label on the fire door itself should indicate that it is a fire door suitable for use with fire exit hardware.

[BE] 1010.1.10.2 Balanced doors. If *balanced doors* are used and *panic hardware* is required, the *panic hardware* shall be the push-pad type and the pad shall not extend more than one-half the width of the door measured from the latch side.

❖ The provisions for balanced doors ensure that the occupants push only on the latch side of the door since the hinge side of a balanced door pivots “against” the direction of egress (see the commentary for the definition of “Balanced door” in Chapter 2).

[BE] 1010.2 Gates. Gates serving the *means of egress* system shall comply with the requirements of this section. Gates used as a component in a *means of egress* shall conform to the applicable requirements for doors.

Exception: Horizontal sliding or swinging gates exceeding the 4-foot (1219 mm) maximum leaf width limitation are permitted in fences and walls surrounding a stadium.

❖ This section specifies that all requirements for doors also apply to gates, except that gates surrounding a stadium are allowed to exceed 4 feet (1219 mm) in width. Usually a large gate is required to adequately serve a stadium crowd for egress purposes.

[BE] 1010.2.1 Stadiums. *Panic hardware* is not required on gates surrounding stadiums where such gates are under constant immediate supervision while the public is present, and where safe dispersal areas based on 3 square feet (0.28 m^2) per occupant are located between the fence and enclosed space. Such required safe dispersal areas shall not be located less than 50 feet (15 240 mm) from the enclosed space. See Section 1028.5 for *means of egress* from safe dispersal areas.

❖ Panic hardware is impractical for large gates that surround stadiums. Normally, these gates are opened and closed by the stadium's grounds crew, which is constantly in attendance during the use of such gates. The safe dispersal area requirement provides for the safety of the crowd if for some reason the gate is not open. The safe dispersal area is to be between the stadium enclosure and the surrounding fence, and the area to be occupied is not to be closer than 50 feet (15 240 mm) to the stadium enclosure.

See the commentary for Section 1028.5 for access to a safe dispersal area where access to a public way is not available.

[BE] 1010.3 Turnstiles and similar devices. Turnstiles or similar devices that restrict travel to one direction shall not be placed so as to obstruct any required *means of egress*, except where permitted in accordance with Sections 1010.3.1, 1010.3.2 and 1010.3.3.

❖ This section provides for a limited use of three different types of turnstiles to serve as a means of egress component. The limitations in Section 1010.3.1 have historically been applied to the three-arm, rotating, waist-high turnstiles previously common at entrances to sports venues and subway stations. Section 1010.3.2 is applicable to the newer style of security access turnstiles that more closely resemble sliding or swinging gates. These devices can vary in height and sophistication to address building security concerns. Typically, these security devices are located at building entrances and elevator lobbies. Section 1010.3.3 addresses turnstiles that are tall enough that they more closely resemble revolving doors. Some types of security access turnstiles would also be considered high turnstiles.

[BE] 1010.3.1 Capacity. Each turnstile or similar device shall be credited with a capacity based on not more than a 50-person *occupant* load where all of the following provisions are met:

1. Each device shall turn free in the direction of egress travel when primary power is lost and on the manual release by an employee in the area.
2. Such devices are not given credit for more than 50 percent of the required egress capacity or width.
3. Each device is not more than 39 inches (991 mm) high.
4. Each device has not less than $16^1/_2$ inches (419 mm) clear width at and below a height of 39 inches (991 mm) and not less than 22 inches (559 mm) clear width at heights above 39 inches (991 mm).

❖ Historically, these limitations have been applied to the three-arm, rotating, waste-high turnstiles previously common at the entrances to sports venues and subway stations (see Commentary Figure 1010.3.1).

Commentary Figure 1010.3.1
EXAMPLES OF THREE 3-ARM, ROTATING TURNSTILES AND ONE SIDE-SWINGING TURNSTILE

This section limits each turnstile to a maximum egress capacity of 50 persons. The turnstile must comply with all four listed items to be considered as serving any part of the occupant load for means of egress. The turnstiles must rotate freely both when there is a loss of power and when they are manually released. Note that the 50-person limit applies to each individual turnstile. These provisions are similar to the revolving door provisions in Section 1010.1.4.1.

[BE] 1010.3.1.1 Clear width. Where located as part of an *accessible route*, turnstiles shall have not less than 36 inches (914 mm) clear width at and below a height of 34 inches (864 mm), not less than 32 inches (813 mm) clear width between 34 inches (864 mm) and 80 inches (2032 mm) and shall consist of a mechanism other than a revolving device.

❖ Where turnstiles are located along an accessible route, the route for persons using mobility devices must include something other than a revolving device, such as a swinging gate. A common example would be the turnstiles for automatic ticket taking, such as at the entrance to a mass transit platform.

[BE] 1010.3.2 Security access turnstiles. Security access turnstiles that inhibit travel in the direction of egress utilizing a physical barrier shall be permitted to be considered as a component of the *means of egress*, provided that all of the following criteria are met:

1. The building is protected throughout by an approved, supervised *automatic sprinkler system* in accordance with Section 903.3.1.1.
2. Each security access turnstile lane configuration has a minimum clear passage width of 22 inches (559 mm).
3. Any security access turnstile lane configuration providing a clear passage width of less than 32 inches (810 mm) shall be credited with a maximum egress capacity of 50 persons.
4. Any security access turnstile lane configuration providing a clear passage width of 32 inches (810 mm) or more shall be credited with a maximum egress capacity as calculated in accordance with Section 1005.
5. Each secured physical barrier shall automatically retract or swing to an unobstructed open position in the direction of egress, under each of the following conditions:
   - 5.1. Upon loss of power to the turnstile or any part of the access control system that secures the physical barrier.
   - 5.2. Upon actuation of a clearly identified manual release device with ready access that results in direct interruption of power to each secured physical barrier, after which such barriers remain in the open position for not less than 30 seconds. The manual release device shall be positioned at one of the following locations:
     - 5.2.1. On the egress side of each security access turnstile lane.
     - 5.2.2. At an approved location where it can be actuated by an employee assigned to the area at all times that the building is occupied.
   - 5.3. Upon actuation of the building fire alarm system, if provided, after which the physical barrier remains in the open position until the fire alarm system is manually reset.

     Exception: Actuation of a manual fire alarm box.
   - 5.4. Upon actuation of the building automatic sprinkler or fire detection system, after which the physical barrier remains in the open position until the fire alarm system is manually reset.

❖ Manufacturers of turnstile devices have expanded into the security access control market and currently have products that have physical barrier leaves that restrict access into and out of buildings. These devices can vary in height and sophistication to address building security concerns but may not meet safety requirements related to the means of egress. Typically, these turnstile devices are located at building entrances and elevator lobbies (see Commentary Figure 1010.3.2).

The requirements intend to provide guidance on evaluating these new modern turnstiles. Turnstiles on the market can be as narrow as 22 inches (559 mm). For turnstiles that are less than 32 inches (813 mm), there are additional capacity issues that need to be considered. The fail-safe provisions for overriding the turnstile access restrictions are derived from existing code provisions (e.g., delayed egress locks and forces to open doors).

Commentary Figure 1010.3.2
EXAMPLE OF SECURITY ACCESS TURNSTILES

[BE] 1010.3.3 High turnstile. Turnstiles more than 39 inches (991 mm) high shall meet the requirements for revolving doors or the requirements of Section 1010.3.2 for security access turnstiles.

❖ Where a turnstile is higher than 39 inches (991 mm), the restriction to egress is much like a revolving door. Thus, the egress limitations for revolving doors in Section 1010.1.4.1 apply to this type of turnstile [see Commentary Figure 1010.3.3(1)]. There is also the additional option of meeting the criteria for security access turnstiles in Section 1010.3.2 [see Commentary Figure 1010.3.3(2)]. If a high turnstile does not meet the requirements for doors or turnstiles that are egress components, it is not to be included as serving a portion of the means of egress. It would be necessary to provide doors for egress in these areas. High turnstiles that operate similar to revolving doors may not be part of an accessible route for ingress or egress.

[BE] 1010.3.4 Additional door. Where serving an *occupant load* greater than 300, each turnstile that is not portable shall have a side-hinged swinging door that conforms to Section 1010.1 within 50 feet (15 240 mm).

Exception: A side-hinged swinging door is not required at security access turnstiles that comply with Section 1010.3.2.

❖ This section addresses a common egress condition for sports arenas where a number of turnstiles are installed for ticket taking. Portable turnstiles are moved from the egress path for proper exiting capacity. Permanent turnstiles are not considered as providing any of the required egress capacity where serving an occupant load greater than 300, no matter how many turnstiles are installed. Doors are required to provide occupants with a path of egress other than through turnstiles. The doors are to be located within 50 feet (15 240 mm) of the turnstiles.

The exception allows for the option to provide security access turnstiles that more closely resemble the operation of doors or gates [see Commentary Figures 1010.3.2 and 1010.3.3(2)]. The operation of these types allows for free egress, so an extra door is not needed.

Commentary Figure 1010.3.3(1)
EXAMPLE OF HIGH TURNSTILE THAT OPERATES SIMILAR TO A REVOLVING DOOR

Commentary Figure 1010.3.3(2)
EXAMPLE OF HIGH TURNSTILE THAT OPERATES AS A SECURITY ACCESS TURNSTILE

SECTION 1011 STAIRWAYS

[BE] 1011.1 General. *Stairways* serving occupied portions of a building shall comply with the requirements of Sections 1011.2 through 1011.13. *Alternating tread devices* shall comply with Section 1011.14. Ships ladders shall comply with Section 1011.15. Ladders shall comply with Section 1011.16.

Exception: Within rooms or spaces used for assembly purposes, stepped *aisles* shall comply with Section 1029.

❖ It is important for stairway safety that all stairways meet the provisions in this section. This would include all elevation changes using stairways: everything from one riser to multiple flights and landings between stories (see the definitions for "Stair" and "Stairway" in Chapter 2). These provisions will be applicable for interior exit access stairways, interior exit stairways and exterior exit stairways, as well as any steps along the paths for exit access or exit discharge. It is intended that this section be applicable to required stairways as well as what can be called "convenience" stairways.

It is important to understand the terminology. Exit stairways are stairways that provide a protected path of egress travel between the exit access and the exit discharge. Interior exit stairways are required to be enclosed in accordance with Section 1023. Exterior exit stairways are protected by the exterior wall of the building and must comply with Section 1027. Exit access stairways are typically unenclosed interior stairways and comply with Section 1019 where they provide access between stories. Exit access travel distance stops at an exit stairway enclosure, but includes any travel down an exit access stairway. Stairways that are outside and provide a route from the level of exit discharge to grade are considered part of the exit discharge. See the commentary in Chapter 2 for the defined term "Exit discharge, level of."

Sections 1011.2 through 1011.13 provide criteria for the typical stairway. Special provisions are provided for curved stairways (Section 1011.9), spiral stairways (Section 1011.10), and stairways to the roof for fire department access and for elevator equipment service (Sections 1011.12 and 1011.12.1).

Items that provide vertical access similar to stairways are also addressed in this section: alternating tread devices (Section 1011.14), ships ladders (Section 1011.15) and ladders (Section 1011.16). These devices are only permitted to provide access to very limited spaces.

The exception indicates that stepped aisles (previously called aisle stairs) are addressed in Section 1029. Having this exception at the beginning of the stairway section negates the need for repeated exceptions throughout the stairway provisions. While both stairways and stepped aisles are a series of treads and risers, how occupants move on and off and configurations are very different. Occupants leave and join stepped aisles along the entire run, while occupants only enter stairways at the top and bottom. Stepped aisles have center handrails with breaks to allow for access into seating, while most stairways have handrails on both sides. Stepped aisles can be nonuniform in some locations to allow for parabolic seating bowls, while uniform tread and riser configurations are required for stairways. Section 1029 should be used for stepped aisles between and immediately adjacent to seating or where the steps are a direct continuation of the stepped aisles and lead to a level cross aisle or floor. Section 1011 is used for stairways that lead from the balcony, concourse or cross aisle to a floor level above or below the seating areas (see Sections 1011.5.2, 1011.5.4 and 1011.6).

[BE] 1011.2 Width and capacity. The required capacity of *stairways* shall be determined as specified in Section 1005.1, but the minimum width shall be not less than 44 inches (1118 mm). See Section 1009.3 for *accessible means of egress stairways*.

Exceptions:

1. *Stairways* serving an *occupant load* of less than 50 shall have a width of not less than 36 inches (914 mm).
2. *Spiral stairways* as provided for in Section 1011.10.
3. Where an incline platform lift or *stairway* chairlift is installed on *stairways* serving occupancies in Group R-3, or within *dwelling units* in occupancies in Group R-2, a clear passage width not less than 20 inches (508 mm) shall be provided. Where the seat and platform can be folded when not in use, the distance shall be measured from the folded position.

❖ To provide adequate space for occupants traveling in opposite directions and to permit the intended full egress capacity to be developed, minimum dimensions are dictated for means of egress stairways. A minimum width of 44 inches (1118 mm) is required for stairway construction to permit two columns of users to travel in the same or opposite directions. The reference to Section 1005.1 is for the determination of stairway width based on the occupant load it will serve (i.e, capacity). The larger of the two widths is to be used.

Exception 1 recognizes that relatively small occupant loads of less than 50 permit a staggered file of users where traveling in the same direction. Where traveling in opposite directions, one column of users must stop their ascent (or descent) to permit the opposite column to continue. Again, considering the relatively small occupant loads, any disruption of orderly flow will be infrequent and brief. The use of this exception is limited to buildings where the entire occupant load of each upper story and/or basement is less than 50.

Exception 2 permits a spiral stairway to have a minimum width of 26 inches (660 mm), where it conforms to Section 1011.10, on the basis that the configuration of a spiral stairway will allow nothing other than single-file travel.

Exception 3 addresses the use of incline platform lifts or stairway chairlifts for individual dwelling units. For clarification on the types of lifts, see the commentary to Section 1109.8. Both types of lifts may be installed to aid persons with mobility impairments in their homes. The code and ASME A18.1 allow for a reduction in the width of the stair to a minimum of 20 inches (508 mm) of clear passageway to be maintained on a stairway where a lift is located. If a portion of the lift, such as a platform or seat, can be folded, the minimum clear dimension is to be measured from the folded position. If the lift cannot be folded, then the 20 inches (508 mm) is measured from the fixed position. The track for these lifts typically extends 9 inches to 12 inches (229 mm to 305 mm) from the wall, making the 20-inch (508 mm) clear measurement actually 24 inches to 27 inches (610 mm to 686 mm) from the edge of the track.

The code does not have any specific provisions for where incline platform lifts are utilized along stairways in locations other than within dwelling units. Section 1109.8 limits the use of platform lifts in new construction to mainly areas with minimal occupant loads or where elevators and ramps are impracticable. IEBC Section 305.8.3 allows for platform lifts anywhere in existing buildings in order to gain accessibility for persons with mobility impairments. When in the closed and off position, platform lifts should not block the clear width required for the stairway or use of the handrails. The industry is currently working on different options to address the concern that the lift may be in operation during an event that requires evacuation.

[BE] 1011.3 Headroom. *Stairways* shall have a headroom clearance of not less than 80 inches (2032 mm) measured vertically from a line connecting the edge of the *nosings*. Such headroom shall be continuous above the *stairway* to the point where the line intersects the landing below, one tread depth beyond the bottom riser. The minimum clearance shall be maintained the full width of the *stairway* and landing.

Exceptions:

1. *Spiral stairways* complying with Section 1011.10 are permitted a 78-inch (1981 mm) headroom clearance.
2. In Group R-3 occupancies; within *dwelling units* in Group R-2 occupancies; and in Group U occupancies that are accessory to a Group R-3 occupancy or accessory to individual *dwelling units* in Group R-2 occupancies; where the *nosings* of treads at the side of a *flight* extend under the edge of a floor opening through which the *stair* passes, the floor opening shall be allowed to project horizontally into the required headroom not more than $4^3/_4$ inches (121 mm).

❖ This headroom requirement is necessary to avoid an obstruction to orderly flow and to provide visibility to the users so that the desired path of travel can be planned and negotiated. Height is a vertical measurement above every point along the stairway stepping and walking surfaces, with minimum height measured vertically from the tread nosing or from the surface of a landing or platform up to the ceiling [see Commentary Figure 1011.3(1)].

Sections 1003.2 and 1207.2 require a minimum ceiling height of 7 feet 6 inches (2286 mm) within a room. A bulkhead or doorway at the bottom of the stairway would be allowed to meet the minimum headroom height of 80 inches (2032 mm), as permitted in Section 1003.3.

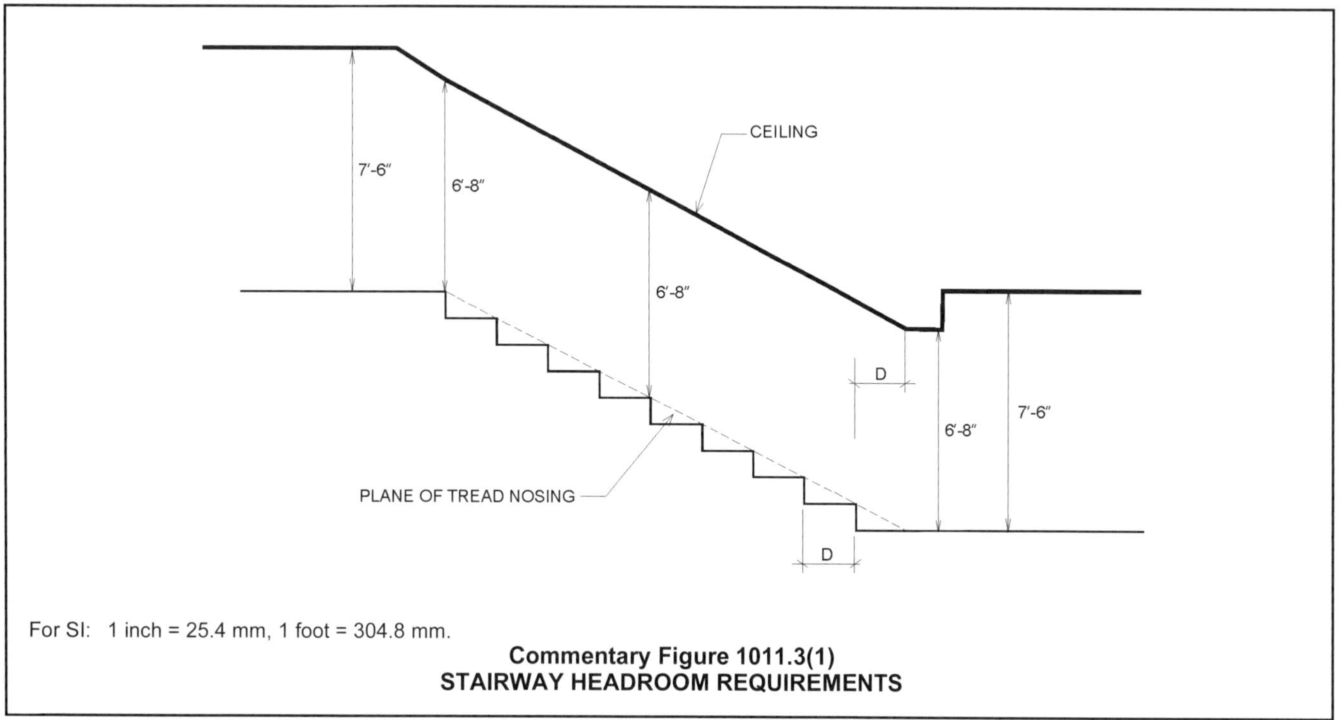

Commentary Figure 1011.3(1)
STAIRWAY HEADROOM REQUIREMENTS

Exception 1, allowing for a clear headroom of 6 feet 6 inches (1981 mm) for spiral stairs, correlates with the provisions of Section 1011.10.

Exception 2 recognizes a common method of stairwell construction in which the stringer on the open side of a stair is supported by the same floor joists or wall that supports the edge of the opening through which the stairway passes to the floor above, thus resulting in the stairway being wider at the lower portion than at the top portion. In this case, headroom is not required for a distance of up to $4^3/_4$ inches (121 mm) measured horizontally from the edge of the opening above to the handrail or guard system, which limits the clear width on the lower open sides of the stairway. The $4^3/_4$-inch (121 mm) maximum is derived from the finished width of a typical 2 by 4 supporting wall and is not critical to obstructing orderly flow or visibility in the desired path of travel [see Commentary Figure 1011.3(2)].

[BE] 1011.4 Walkline. The walkline across *winder* treads shall be concentric to the direction of travel through the turn and located 12 inches (305 mm) from the side where the *winders* are narrower. The 12-inch (305 mm) dimension shall be measured from the widest point of the clear *stair* width at the walking surface of the *winder*. Where *winders* are adjacent within the *flight*, the point of the widest clear *stair* width of the adjacent *winders* shall be used.

❖ This requirement is essential for smooth, consistent travel on stairs that turn with winder treads. It provides a standard location for the regulation of the uniform tread depth of winders. Because of the wide range of anthropometrics of stairway users, there is no one line that all persons will travel on stairs; however, the code recognizes a standard location of a walkline is essential to design and enforcement. Each footfall of the user through the turn can be associated with an arc to describe the path traveled. As a user ascends or descends the flight, the turning at each step should be consistent through the turn. The walkline is established concentric to, or having the same center (approximately parallel) as, the arc of travel of the user. The tread depth dimension at the walkline is one of two tread depths across the width of the stair at which winder tread depth is regulated, cited in Section 1011.5.2. The second is the minimum tread depth. Regulation at these two points controls the angularity of the turn and the configuration of the flight. In order to establish consistently shaped winders, tread depths must always be measured concentric to the arc of travel. The walkline is unique as the only line or path of travel where winder tread depth is controlled by the same minimum tread depth as rectangular treads. However, Exception 2 of Section 1011.5.4 recognizes that winder tread depth need not be compared to rectangular tread depths for dimensional uniformity in the same flight because the location of the walkline is chosen for the purpose of providing a standard and cannot be specific to the variety of actual paths followed by all users. This specific line location is determined by measuring along each nosing edge 12 inches (305 mm) from the extreme of the clear width of the stair at the surface of the winder tread or the limit of where the foot might be placed in use of the stair. If adjacent winders are present, the point of the widest clear stair width at the

Commentary Figure 1011.3(2)
EXAMPLE OF SECTION 1011.3, EXCEPTION 2

surface of the tread in the group of adjacent consecutive winders is used to provide the reference from which the 12-inch (305 mm) dimension will be measured along each nosing. The tread depth may be determined by measuring between adjacent nosings at these determined intersections of the nosings with the walkline. It is important to note that the clear stair width is only that portion of the stair width that is clear for passage. Portions of the stair beyond the clear width are not consequential to use of the stair, consistent travel or location of the walkline.

[BE] 1011.5 Stair treads and risers. *Stair* treads and risers shall comply with Sections 1011.5.1 through 1011.5.5.3.

❖ The provisions for treads and risers contribute to the efficient use of the stairway, facilitating smooth and consistent travel. This section provides dimensional ranges and tolerances for the component elements to allow the flexibility required to design and construct a stair or a flight of stairs that are elements of a stairway. The allowed proportion of maximum riser height and minimum tread depth provide for a maximum angle of ascent but there is no maximum tread depth to consider with the minimum riser height that would define a minimum angle for a stairway. Nor is the proportion of riser height to tread depth compared with the limitations of the length of the user's stride on stairways, which is significantly foreshortened from the user's stride on the level. For this reason, care should be taken where incorporating larger tread depths and controlling the point at which a tread might be wide enough to require more than one step to cross, which can vary significantly where considering ascent and descent movement patterns. Especially in areas where all segments of the public might use the stairs, those persons requiring two smaller sequential steps to cross the tread would progress at significantly different rates than those who might be able to stretch or jump, which could lead to dangerous complications, especially in egress. Of equal significance is the use of shorter risers without increasing tread depth, resulting in a proportion that could cause overstepping. However, by controlling the minimum depth of rectangular treads and the minimum depth and angularity of winder treads, these components can dictate the configuration of the plan for a flight of stairs to provide for smooth and consistent travel.

Section 1011.5.1 provides for consistent identification of the surfaces that are to be measured. This is as critical to the users' experience throughout the built environment as it is to determining all the dimensions in this section, as they must relate to each other and the ultimate design and construction of a safe stairway.

The remaining sections address the uniformity and essential attributes of the tread and riser. Of particular note is the nosing, or leading edge, of the tread. The nosing shape and projection affect the determination of the tread depth and riser height and are regulated for all steps throughout the stairway, including the nosings at landings, to provide for smooth and consistent travel. Furthermore, the line connecting the nosings is used to determine handrail height, guard height and headroom, making consistent nosings integral to every element of the stairway design, construction and regulation.

[BE] 1011.5.1 Dimension reference surfaces. For the purpose of this section, all dimensions are exclusive of carpets, rugs or runners.

❖ Carpets, rugs and runners, like furniture, are frequently changed by the occupants and are not regulated by the code. For this reason, it is essential that the riser height and tread depth be regulated exclusive of these transitory surfaces to provide an enforceable standard. This practice minimizes possible variation due to the removal of nonpermanent carpeting throughout the life of a structure and provides a standard enforcement methodology that will provide consistency across the built environment for all users. Where owners or occupants add carpeting, rugs or runners, they need to add it to all tread and landing surfaces in the stairway. It is important that the tread and landing surfaces are consistent and comply with the code prior to the addition of carpet. This methodology of enforcement makes it unnecessary to reconstruct floor and stair elevations in the stairway where nonpermanent carpet surfaces that do not require a building permit are changed and eliminates the resulting variations in the built environment that would not comply with the tolerance in Section 1011.5.4 (see Commentary Figure 1011.5.1).

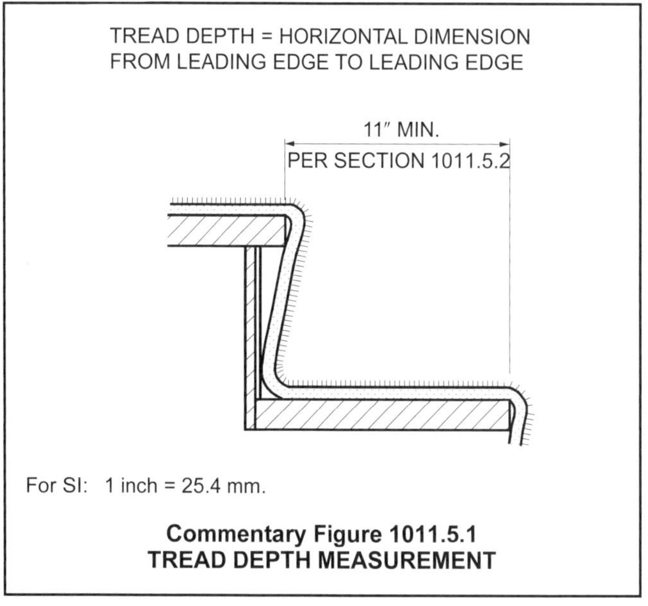

Commentary Figure 1011.5.1
TREAD DEPTH MEASUREMENT

[BE] 1011.5.2 Riser height and tread depth. *Stair* riser heights shall be 7 inches (178 mm) maximum and 4 inches (102 mm) minimum. The riser height shall be measured vertically between the *nosings* of adjacent treads. Rectangular tread depths shall be 11 inches (279 mm) minimum measured horizontally between the vertical planes of the foremost projection of adjacent treads and at a right angle to the tread's *nosing*. *Winder* treads shall have a minimum tread depth of 11 inches (279 mm) between the vertical planes of the foremost projection of adjacent treads at the intersections with the walkline and a minimum tread depth of 10 inches (254 mm) within the clear width of the *stair*.

Exceptions:

1. *Spiral stairways* in accordance with Section 1011.10.
2. *Stairways* connecting stepped *aisles* to cross aisles or concourses shall be permitted to use the riser/tread dimension in Section 1029.14.2.
3. In Group R-3 occupancies; within *dwelling units* in Group R-2 occupancies; and in Group U occupancies that are accessory to a Group R-3 occupancy or accessory to individual *dwelling units* in Group R-2 occupancies; the maximum riser height shall be $7^3/_4$ inches (197 mm); the minimum tread depth shall be 10 inches (254 mm); the minimum *winder* tread depth at the walkline shall be 10 inches (254 mm); and the minimum *winder* tread depth shall be 6 inches (152 mm). A *nosing* projection not less than $^3/_4$ inch (19.1 mm) but not more than $1^1/_4$ inches (32 mm) shall be provided on *stairways* with solid risers where the tread depth is less than 11 inches (279 mm).
4. See Section 503.1 of the *International Existing Building Code* for the replacement of existing *stairways*.
5. In Group I-3 facilities, *stairways* providing access to guard towers, observation stations and control rooms, not more than 250 square feet (23 m^2) in area, shall be permitted to have a maximum riser height of 8 inches (203 mm) and a minimum tread depth of 9 inches (229 mm).

❖ The riser height—the vertical dimension from tread surface to tread surface or tread surface to landing surface—is typically limited to not more than 7 inches (178 mm) or less than 4 inches (102 mm). The minimum tread depth—the horizontal distance from the leading edge (nosing) of one tread to the leading edge (nosing) of the next adjacent tread or landing—is typically limited to not less than 11 inches (279 mm) (see Commentary Figure 1011.5.2). The minimum tread depth of 11 inches (279 mm) is intended to accommodate the largest shoe size found in 95 percent of the adult population, allowing for an appropriate overhang of the foot beyond the tread nosing while descending a stairway. Tread depths under 11 inches (279 mm) could cause a larger overhang (depending on the size of the foot) and could force users with larger feet to increase the angle of their foot to the line of travel while descending a stairway. Based on the probability of adequate foot placement, the rate of misstep with various step sizes, and consideration for the user's comfort and energy expenditure, it was agreed that the 11-inch (279 mm) minimum tread depth and maximum 7-inch (178 mm) riser height resulted in the reasonable proportion of riser height and tread depth for stairway construction. A minimum riser height of 4 inches (102 mm) is considered to allow the visual identification of the presence of the riser in ascent or descent.

The precise location of rectangular tread depth and riser measurements is to be perpendicular to the

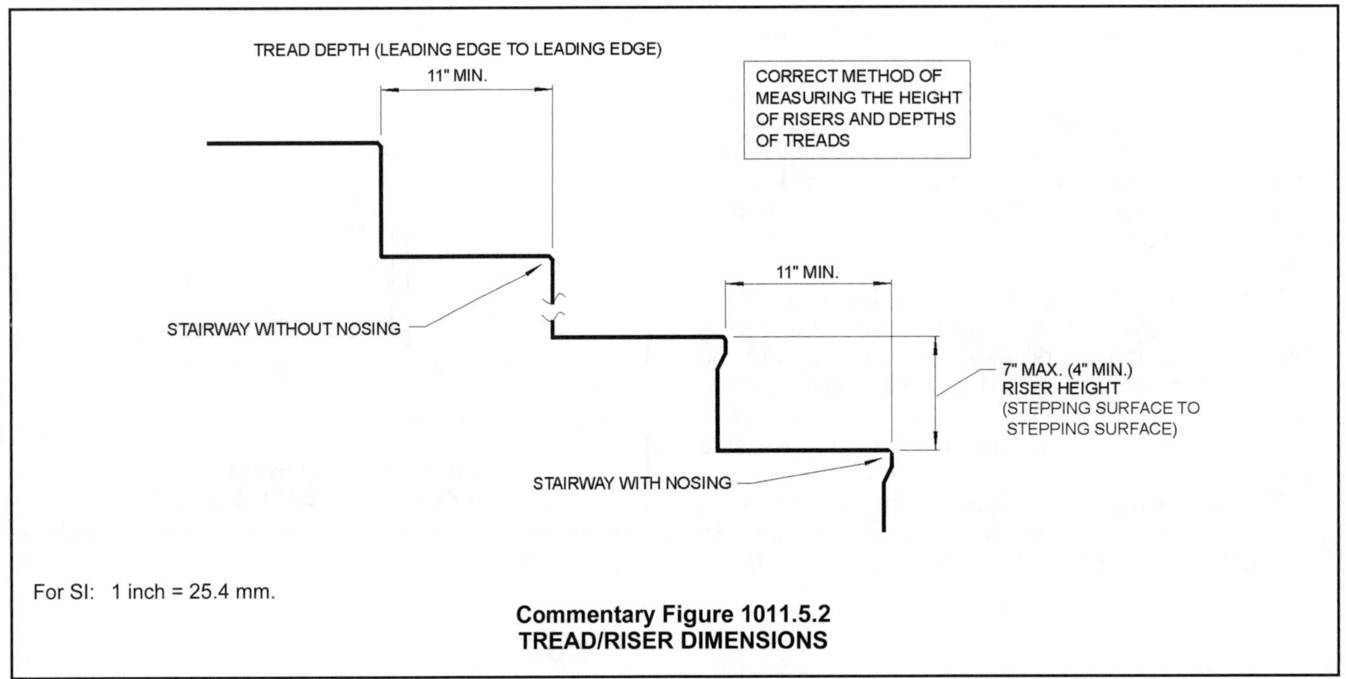

For SI: 1 inch = 25.4 mm.

Commentary Figure 1011.5.2
TREAD/RISER DIMENSIONS

tread's nosing or leading edge. This is to duplicate the user's anticipated foot placement in traveling the stairway.

The size for a winder tread is also considered for proper foot placement along the walkline (see Commentary Figure 1011.9 and the commentary for Section 1011.4). The dimensional requirements are consistent with the straight tread.

The exceptions apply only to the extent of the text of each exception. For example, the entire text of Section 1011.5.2 is set aside for spiral stairways conforming to Section 1011.10 (see Exception 1). However, Exception 3 allows a different maximum riser and minimum tread under limited conditions, but retains the minimum riser height and measurement method of Section 1011.5.2.

Exception 1 is for spiral staircases, a unique type of stairway. Section 1011.5.2 is not applicable to this stair type because of construction issues and limited applications. For a discussion on spiral staircases, see Section 1011.10.

Exception 2 provides a practical exception where assembly facilities are designed for viewing. See Section 1029.14.2 for assembly stepped aisles. This exception is limited to where stairways are a direct continuation of the path of travel from the level cross aisle to the stepped aisles. It is not permitted for other stairways within the assembly space.

Exception 3 allows revisions to the maximum 7 inches/11 inches (178 mm/279 mm) riser/tread requirements for Group R-3 occupancies and any associated utility (such as barns, connected garages or detached garages) and within individual units of Group R-2 and their associated utility areas (such as attached garages). This change is allowed because of the low occupant load and the high degree of occupant familiarity with the stairways. Where this exception is applied for stairways that have solid risers, each tread is required to have a nosing projection with a minimum dimension of $^3/_4$ inch (19.1 mm) and maximum dimension of $1^1/_4$ inches (32 mm) where the tread depth is less than 11 inches (279 mm). Nosing projections are created where the nosing of the tread above extends beyond the trailing edge of the tread below or where a solid riser is angled under the tread above and connected to the trailing edge of the tread below. Nosing projections are not required for residential stairs with open risers and 10-inch (254 mm) treads. A nosing projection provides a greater stepping surface for those ascending the stairway. For users descending the stairway, the nosing projection allows the toe of the foot to be placed farther away from the riser above, providing the necessary clearance for the heel of the foot as it swings down in an arc to its position on the tread (see Commentary Figure 1011.5.3).

Exception 4 allows for the replacement of existing stairways. Where a change of occupancy would require compliance with current standards, this exception allows for a stairway that may be steeper than that permitted, provided it does not constitute a hazard (see IEBC Section 503.1).

In spaces of not more than 250 square feet (23 m^2) in correctional facilities (Group I-3), Exception 5 allows for steeper stairs with a maximum riser height of 8 inches (203 mm) and a minimum tread depth of 9 inches (229 mm) because of the minimal occupant load and the familiarity of the users with the stairway. Although not stated in this exception, utilizing a nosing projection to provide effective tread depth is a good design practice [see Exception 3 regarding tread depths less than 11 inches (279 mm)].

[BE] 1011.5.3 Winder treads. *Winder* treads are not permitted in *means of egress stairways* except within a *dwelling unit*.

Exceptions:

1. Curved *stairways* in accordance with Section 1011.9.
2. *Spiral stairways* in accordance with Section 1011.10.

❖ The intent of this section is to coordinate the general provisions for stairway tread and riser dimensions in Section 1011.5.2 with the provisions for winder treads permitted in curved and spiral stairways (see Sections 1011.9 and 1011.10). Winders are permitted in means of egress stairways within dwelling units where occupant loads are small and occupants have increased familiarity (see Commentary Figure 1011.5.3 and Section 1011.5.2, Exception 3). This is consistent with provisions in the *International Residential Code*® (IRC®).

Winders are used to change the direction of a flight by introducing a consistent incremental turn associated with each tread. The risk of injury in the use of stairways constructed with winders is considered to be greater than for stairways constructed as straight

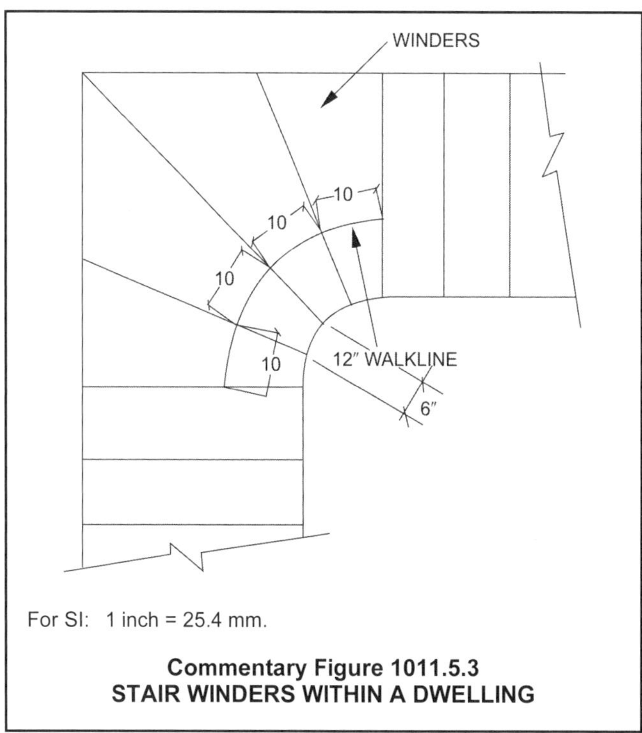

For SI: 1 inch = 25.4 mm.

Commentary Figure 1011.5.3
STAIR WINDERS WITHIN A DWELLING

runs because users may be restricted by the presence of other users, limiting visual clues or influencing the rate of travel. Additional user attention in the turn and the aid of the turn in arresting falls (similar to turns at landings) is also understood to negate this.

The employment of winders in stairway construction may necessitate the change of the user's gait in both ascent and descent where the tread depth of the winder is not equal to the tread depth of any rectangular treads in the same flight. For example, a person descending a straight flight of stairs will develop a particular gait conforming to the proportion of the riser height and tread depth that will be consistent throughout the flight. However, in a flight that includes winders and rectangular treads, the user must accommodate a change in the proportion of the riser height and tread depth as determined by the path of travel chosen. Visual clues are important to the users' instinctive responses to alter the path of travel, the length of stride, or a combination of both that may result in nonconcentric movement. To ensure users of the visual clues necessary to alter their gait and limit the need to alter the path of travel in conditions of higher occupant loading, flights with winders must meet the specific safety provisions listed for curved or spiral stairways unless they are within a dwelling unit.

[BE] 1011.5.4 Dimensional uniformity. *Stair* treads and risers shall be of uniform size and shape. The tolerance between the largest and smallest riser height or between the largest and smallest tread depth shall not exceed $^3/_8$ inch (9.5 mm) in any *flight* of *stairs*. The greatest *winder* tread depth at the walkline within any *flight* of *stairs* shall not exceed the smallest by more than $^3/_8$ inch (9.5 mm).

Exceptions:

1. *Stairways* connecting stepped *aisles* to cross *aisles* or concourses shall be permitted to comply with the dimensional nonuniformity in Section 1029.14.2.
2. Consistently shaped *winders*, complying with Section 1011.5, differing from rectangular treads in the same *flight* of *stairs*.
3. Nonuniform riser dimension complying with Section 1011.5.4.1.

❖ Dimensional uniformity in the design and construction of stairways contributes to safe stairway use. When ascending or descending a stair, users establish a gait based on the instinctive expectation or "feel" that each step taken will be at the same height and will land in approximately the same position on the tread as the previous steps in the pattern. A change in tread or riser dimensions in a stairway flight in excess of the allowed dimensional tolerance can break the rhythm and cause a misstep, stumbling or physical strain that may result in a fall or serious injury. Therefore, this section limits the dimensional variations to a tolerance of $^3/_8$ inch (9.5 mm) between the largest and smallest riser or tread dimension in a flight of stairs. A "flight of stairs" is defined as a run of stairs between landings.

For special conditions of construction and as a practical matter, this section allows some greater variations in stairway tread and riser dimensions than the general limitations specified previously.

Exception 1 provides a practical exception where assembly facilities are designed for viewing. See Sections 1029.14 through 1029.14.2.4 for assembly stepped aisles. This exception is limited to where stairways are a direct continuation of the path of travel from the level cross aisle to the stepped aisles. It is not permitted for other stairways within the assembly space.

Exception 2 addresses winder treads, which must be consistent along the walkline (see Commentary Figure 1011.5.4) when compared to other winder treads in the same flight but are not required to meet the tolerance when compared to the uniform dimension of rectangular treads in the same flight.

Exception 3 is in recognition of the situation where a stairway meets a surface that slopes up or down perpendicular to the stairway. See the commentary to Section 1105.4.1.

[BE] 1011.5.4.1 Nonuniform height risers. Where the bottom or top riser adjoins a sloping *public way*, walkway or driveway having an established grade and serving as a landing, the bottom or top riser is permitted to be reduced along the slope to less than 4 inches (102 mm) in height, with the variation in height of the bottom or top riser not to exceed one unit vertical in 12 units horizontal (8-percent slope) of stair width. The nosings or leading edges of treads at such nonuniform height risers shall have a distinctive marking stripe, different from any other *nosing* marking provided on the *stair flight*. The distinctive marking stripe shall be visible in descent of the *stair* and shall have a slip-resistant surface. Marking stripes shall have a width of not less than 1 inch (25 mm) but not more than 2 inches (51 mm).

❖ This section addresses the situation where the bottom riser of a flight of stairs meets a sloped landing, such as a public way, walk or driveway (see Commentary Figure 1011.5.4.1). Because the sidewalk landing is sloped, stepping off the bottom tread on one side will result in a higher riser than stepping off the bottom tread on the other side. This is permitted provided the bottom riser is marked so that someone using the stairs will be aware of the hazard of a nonuniform riser.

[BE] 1011.5.5 Nosing and riser profile. *Nosings* shall have a curvature or bevel of not less than $^1/_{16}$ inch (1.6 mm) but not more than $^9/_{16}$ inch (14.3 mm) from the foremost projection of the tread. Risers shall be solid and vertical or sloped under the tread above from the underside of the *nosing* above at an angle not more than 30 degrees (0.52 rad) from the vertical.

❖ The profiles of treads and risers contribute to stairway safety. The radius or bevel of the nosing eases the otherwise square edge of the tread and prevents irregular chipping and wear that can become a maintenance issue and seriously affect the safe use of the stair. The minimum curvature or bevel of $^1/_{16}$ inch (1.6 mm) eliminates a sharp square edge that would

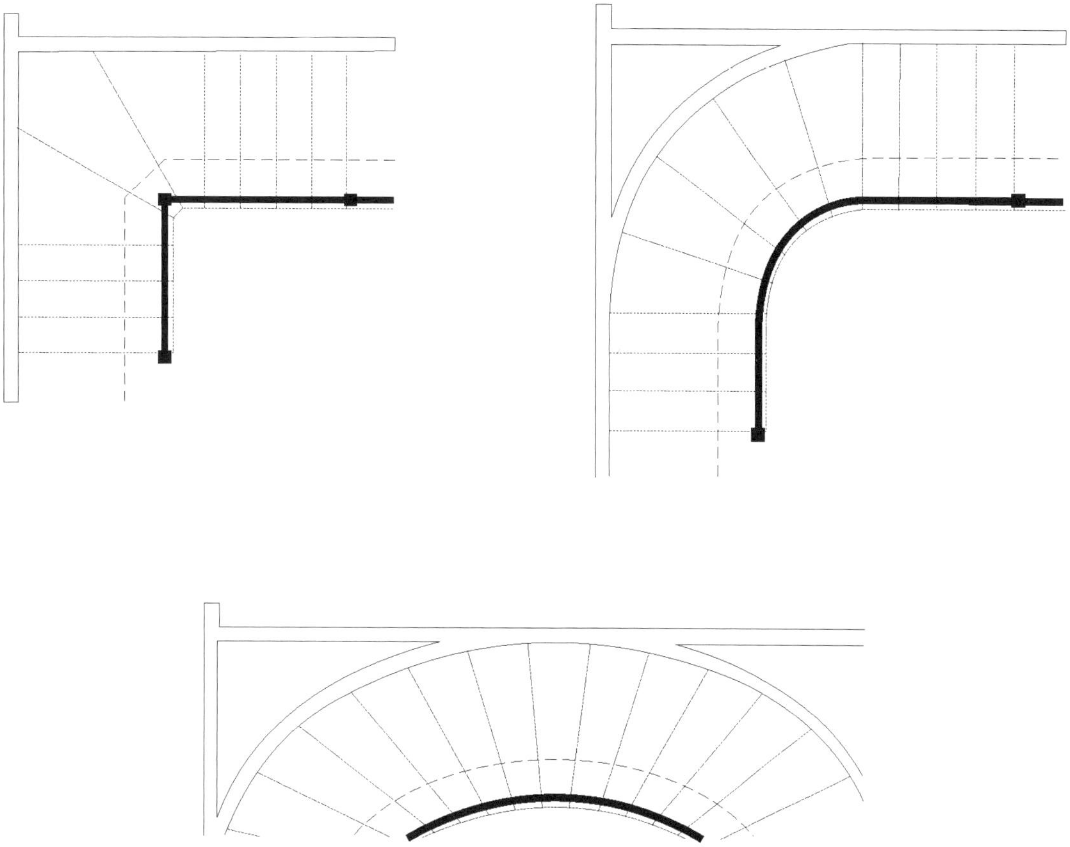

Commentary Figure 1011.5.4
CONSISTENTLY SHAPED WINDERS

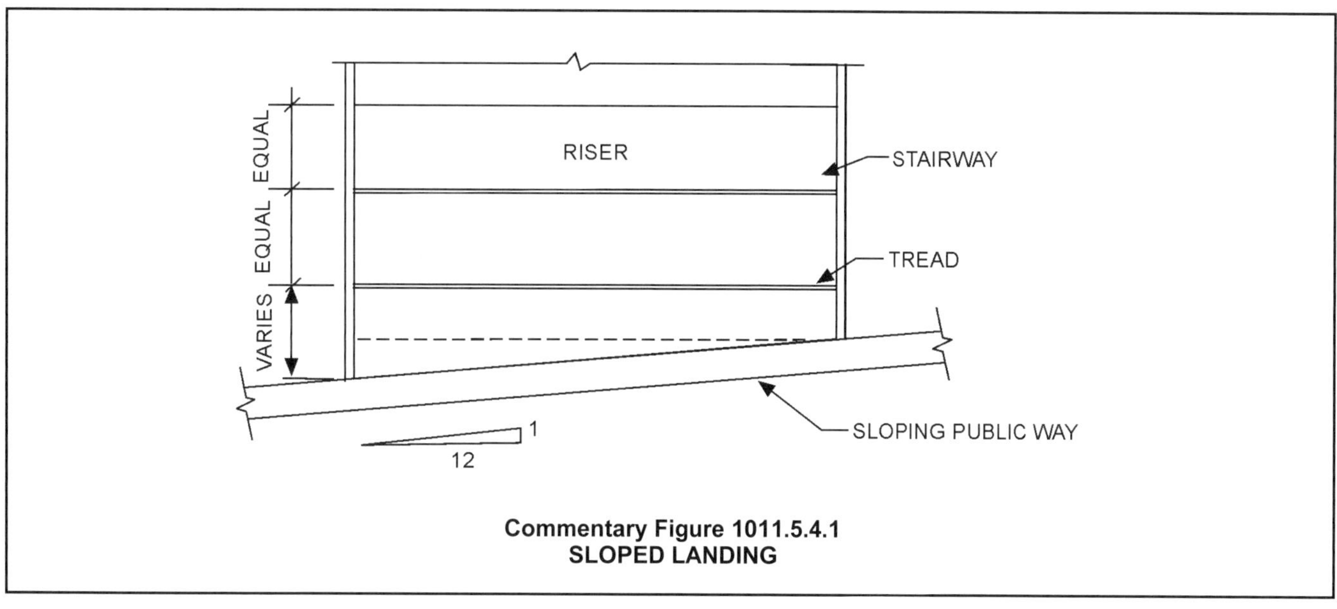

Commentary Figure 1011.5.4.1
SLOPED LANDING

cause greater injury in falls and provides a certain contrast from the other surfaces of the stair for easier visual location of the start of the tread surface. The $^{9}/_{16}$-inch (14.3 mm) limit of beveling and maximum radius of curvature at the leading edge of the tread is intended to allow descending foot placement on a surface that does not pitch the foot forward or allow the ball of the foot to slide off the treads and ascending foot placement to slide onto the tread without catching on a square edge. This section also states that risers shall be solid; however, Section 1011.5.5.3 specifically states exceptions to this requirement that are to be applied. The sloping of risers allows the step profile to have a nosing projection without a lip that might cause a foot to catch when dragged up the face of the riser. Such designs are subject to the maximum nosing projection stated in Section 1011.5.5.1 that must be considered when choosing the angle to slope the riser.

[BE] 1011.5.5.1 Nosing projection size. The leading edge (*nosings*) of treads shall project not more than $1^{1}/_{4}$ inches (32 mm) beyond the tread below.

❖ A nosing projection allows the descending foot to be placed farther forward on the tread and the heel to then clear the nosing of the tread above as it swings down in an arc, landing on a tread that is effectively deeper than if no nosing projection is used. Nosing projections are so common in stair design that they are usually only noticed by users where they are absent since the lack of nose projection can affect one's gait. Treads with vertical risers are allowed with or without a nosing projection. A nosing projection may also be accommodated by slanting the riser under the tread above. The nosing projection is limited to $1^{1}/_{4}$ inch (32 mm) maximum. Treads designed with rounding or bevel on the underside would reduce the chance that a user's toe might catch while ascending the stairway (see Commentary Figure 1011.5.5.1).

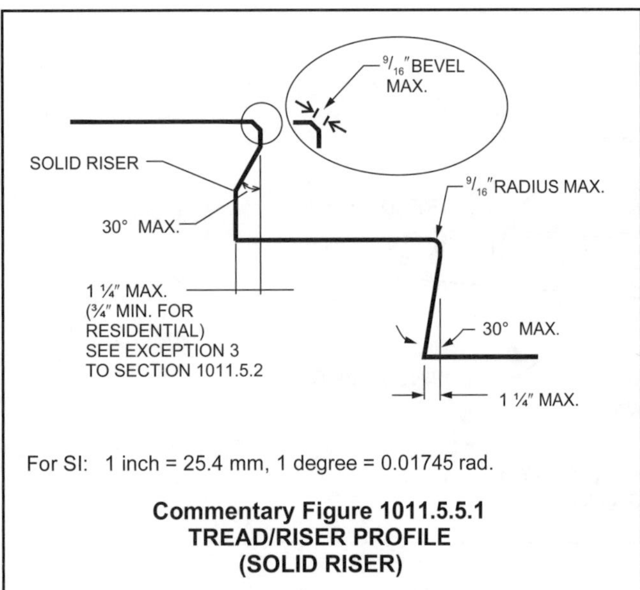

For SI: 1 inch = 25.4 mm, 1 degree = 0.01745 rad.

Commentary Figure 1011.5.5.1
TREAD/RISER PROFILE
(SOLID RISER)

[BE] 1011.5.5.2 Nosing projection uniformity. *Nosing* projections of the leading edges shall be of uniform size, including the projections of the *nosing's* leading edge of the floor at the top of a *flight*.

❖ See the commentary to Section 1011.5.5.1.

[BE] 1011.5.5.3 Solid risers. Risers shall be solid.

Exceptions:

1. Solid risers are not required for *stairways* that are not required to comply with Section 1009.3, provided that the opening between treads does not permit the passage of a sphere with a diameter of 4 inches (102 mm).
2. Solid risers are not required for occupancies in Group I-3 or in Group F, H and S occupancies other than areas accessible to the public. The size of the opening in the riser is not restricted.
3. Solid risers are not required for *spiral stairways* constructed in accordance with Section 1011.10.

❖ The code does not address where a riser could contain openings and still be considered solid. However, the intent is so that someone would not catch their toe as they moved up the stairway (see the commentary for nosing projections in Section 1011.5.5). It is not the intent to prohibit risers made of grills or other designs where a toe would not catch. Grill stairways are often used in exterior locations to allow for the passage of snow or rain to decrease the chance of accumulation and possible slips and falls.

Exception 1 allows the use of open risers on all stairways that are not part of an accessible means of egress. Where the riser is allowed to be open, the opening is limited to be consistent with the requirements for guards (see Commentary Figure 1011.5.5.3). While not required, the second option shown in Commentary Figure 1011.5.5.3 would limit the possibility of a toe catch as someone moved up the stairways and would be a safer design. The code does not reference ICC A117.1 for stairways because stairways are not part of an accessible route; however, the code and standard provide opening limita-

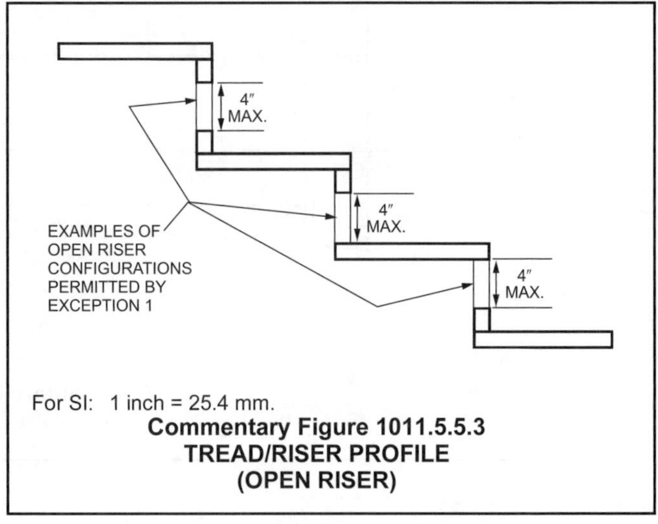

For SI: 1 inch = 25.4 mm.

Commentary Figure 1011.5.5.3
TREAD/RISER PROFILE
(OPEN RISER)

tions in tread surfaces. Section 1011.7.1 states that tread surface openings shall be of a size that does not permit the passage of a $^1/_2$-inch-diameter (12.7 mm) sphere.

Exception 2 recognizes that open risers are commonly used for stairs in occupancies such as detention facilities, storage, industrial and high-hazard areas for practical reasons. In detention facilities, open risers provide a greater degree of security and supervision because people cannot effectively conceal themselves behind the stairs. Factories, high-hazard buildings and storage facilities have areas where workers may need the open risers to decrease the chance of spillage, water or snow accumulating on the stairs. See Section 1011.7.1 for permitted openings in the treads.

Exception 3 recognizes open risers as necessary for adequate foot placement in spiral stairways. The 4-inch (102 mm) opening limitations of Exception 1 are not applicable to spiral stairways.

[BE] 1011.6 Stairway landings. There shall be a floor or landing at the top and bottom of each *stairway*. The width of landings, measured perpendicularly to the direction of travel, shall be not less than the width of *stairways* served. Every landing shall have a minimum depth, measured parallel to the direction of travel, equal to the width of the *stairway* or 48 inches (1219 mm), whichever is less Doors opening onto a landing shall not reduce the landing to less than one-half the required width. When fully open, the door shall not project more than 7 inches (178 mm) into a landing. Where *wheelchair* spaces are required on the *stairway* landing in accordance with Section 1009.6.3, the *wheelchair* space shall not be located in the required width of the landing and doors shall not swing over the *wheelchair* spaces.

Exception: Where *stairways* connect stepped *aisles* to cross *aisles* or concourses, *stairway* landings are not required at the transition between *stairways* and stepped *aisles* constructed in accordance with Section 1029.

❖ A level portion of a stairway provides users with a place to rest in their ascent or descent, to enter a stairway and to adjust their gait before continuing. Landings also break up the run of a stairway, especially at a turn, to aid in the arrest of falls that may occur (see Section 1011.8).

The minimum size (width and depth) of all landings in a stairway is determined by the actual width of the stairway. If Section 1011.2 requires a stairway to have a width of at least 44 inches (1118 mm) and the stairway is constructed with that minimum width, then all landings serving that stairway must be at least 44 inches (1118 mm) wide and 44 inches (1118 mm) deep [see Commentary Figure 1011.6(1)]. If a stairway is constructed wider than required, landings must increase accordingly so as to not create a bottleneck situation in egress travel. However, where a stairway is configured so that it has a straight run, the depth of the landing between flights in the direction of travel is not required to exceed 48 inches (1219 mm) even though the actual width of the stair may exceed 48 inches (1219 mm) [see Commentary Figure 1011.6(2)].

It is not the intent of this section to require that a stairway landing be shaped as a square or rectangle. A landing turning the stairway 90 degrees (1.57 rad) or more with a curved or segmented outside periphery would be permitted, as long as the landing provides an area described by an arc with a radius equal to the actual stairway width [see Commentary Figure 1011.6(3)]. In this case, the space necessary for means of egress will be available.

The last portion of the requirement limits the extent to which doors that swing onto landings may interfere or encroach upon the required landing space. This limits the arc of the door swing on a landing, so that the effect on the means of egress is minimized [see Commentary Figure 1011.6(4)]. This is consistent with a door opening into an exit access corridor in Section 1005.7. For safety reasons and to ensure the means of egress is continually available for everyone, where an area of refuge/wheelchair space must be located on a landing, the wheelchair spaces must not

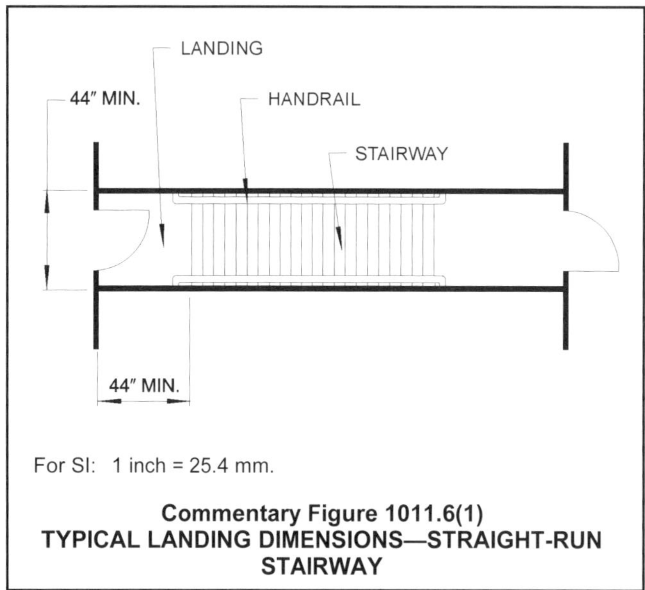

For SI: 1 inch = 25.4 mm.

Commentary Figure 1011.6(1)
TYPICAL LANDING DIMENSIONS—STRAIGHT-RUN STAIRWAY

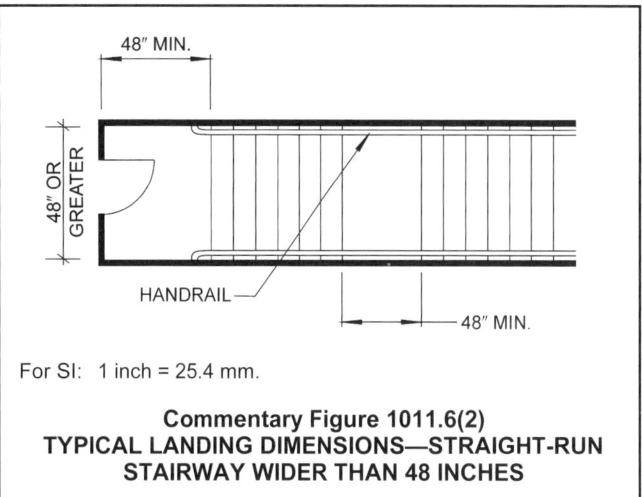

For SI: 1 inch = 25.4 mm.

Commentary Figure 1011.6(2)
TYPICAL LANDING DIMENSIONS—STRAIGHT-RUN STAIRWAY WIDER THAN 48 INCHES

be within the required landing width and the entrance door to the stair enclosure may not swing over the wheelchair spaces [see Commentary Figure 1009.3.3(1)].

The exception provides a practical exception where assembly facilities are designed for viewing. See Section 1029.14 for assembly stepped aisle walking surfaces. This exception is limited to where stairways are a direct continuation of the path of travel from the level cross aisle to the stepped aisles. It is not permitted for other stairways within the assembly space.

[BE] 1011.7 Stairway construction. *Stairways* shall be built of materials consistent with the types permitted for the type of construction of the building, except that wood *handrails* shall be permitted for all types of construction.

❖ In keeping with the different levels of fire protection provided by each of the five basic types of construction designated in Chapter 6, the materials used for stairway construction must meet the appropriate combustibility/noncombustibility requirements indicated in Section 602 for the particular type of construction of the building in which the stairway is located. This is required regardless of whether the stairway is part of the required means of egress. Any structure supporting the stairway and the stairway enclosure must be fire-resistance rated consistent with the construction

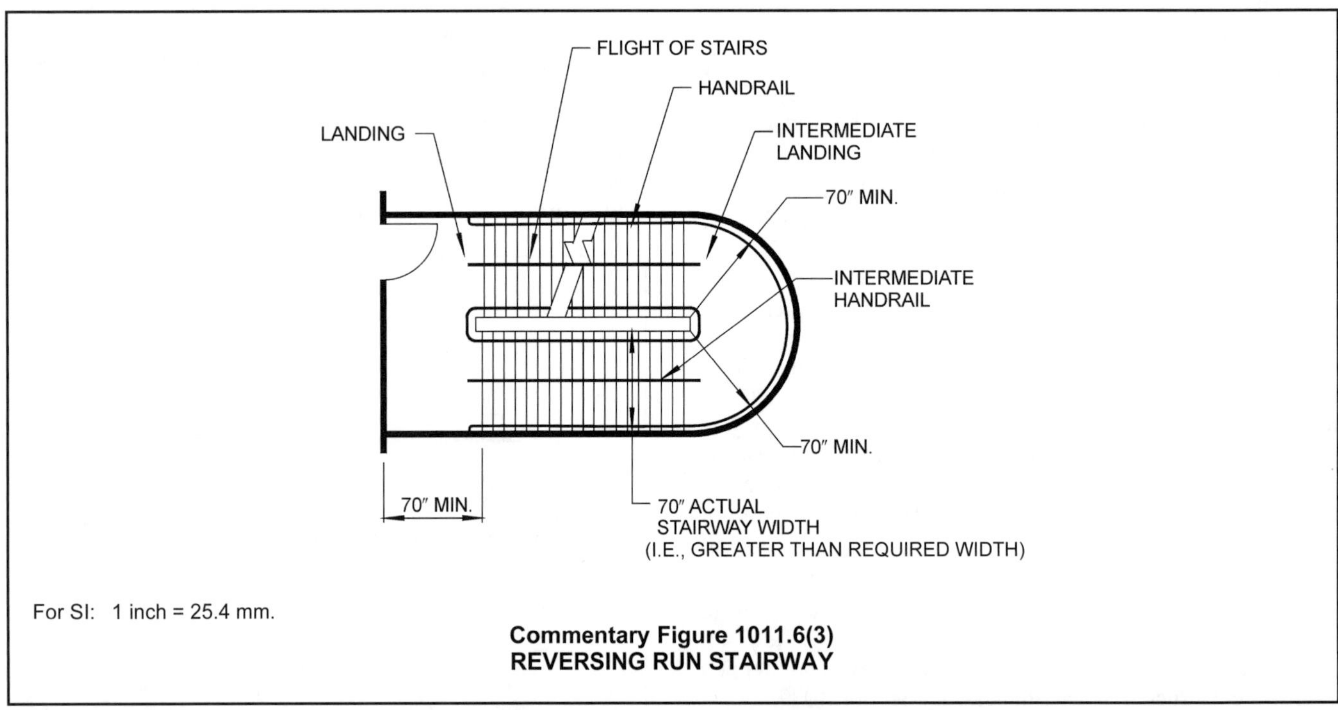

For SI: 1 inch = 25.4 mm.

Commentary Figure 1011.6(3)
REVERSING RUN STAIRWAY

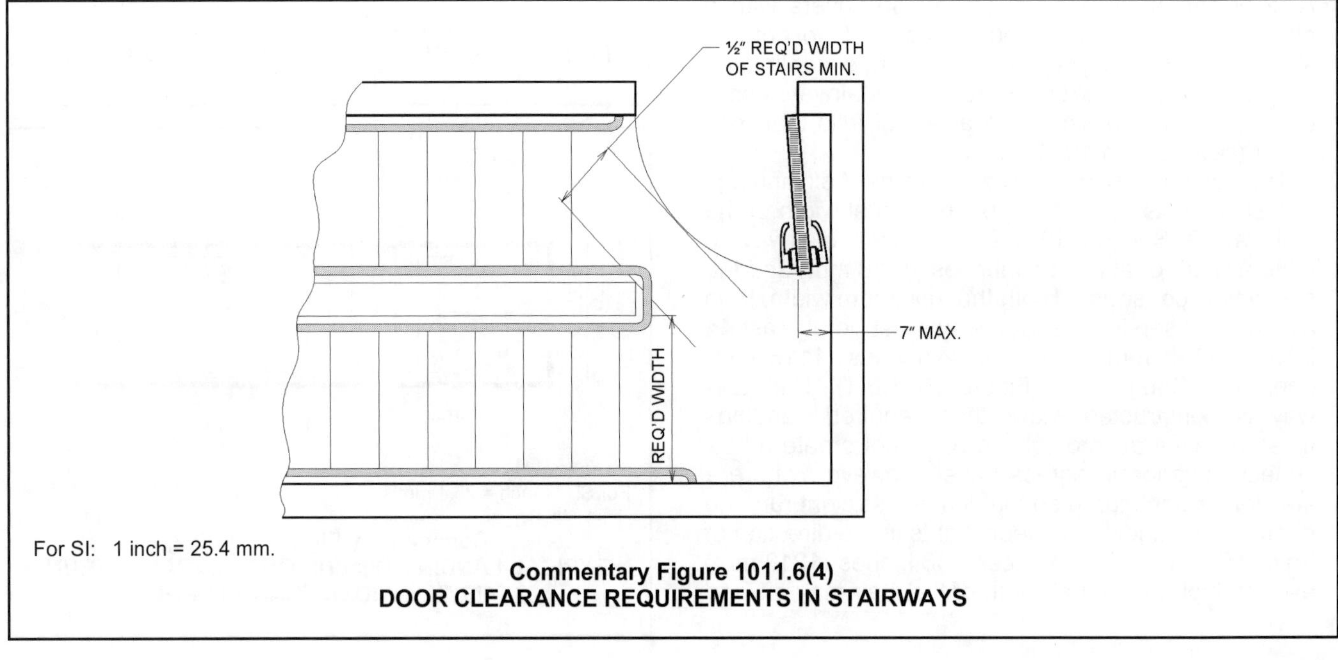

For SI: 1 inch = 25.4 mm.

Commentary Figure 1011.6(4)
DOOR CLEARANCE REQUIREMENTS IN STAIRWAYS

type; however, the stairway components inside the enclosure need only comply with the material limits for the type of construction.

If desired, wood handrails may be used on the basis that the fuel load contributed by this combustible component of stairway construction is insignificant and will not pose a fire hazard.

[BE] 1011.7.1 Stairway walking surface. The walking surface of treads and landings of a *stairway* shall not be sloped steeper than one unit vertical in 48 units horizontal (2-percent slope) in any direction. *Stairway* treads and landings shall have a solid surface. Finish floor surfaces shall be securely attached.

Exceptions:

1. Openings in stair walking surfaces shall be a size that does not permit the passage of $^1/_2$-inch-diameter (12.7 mm) sphere. Elongated openings shall be placed so that the long dimension is perpendicular to the direction of travel.
2. In Group F, H and S occupancies, other than areas of parking structures accessible to the public, openings in treads and landings shall not be prohibited provided that a sphere with a diameter of $1^1/_8$ inches (29 mm) cannot pass through the opening.

❖ It is the intent of this section that both landing and stair treads be solid and level with firmly attached surface materials; however, the 1:48 slope should be adequate to allow for drainage to limit the chance for an accumulation of water where someone might slip.

The exceptions permit the use of open grate-type material or slotted grill for stairway treads and landings in two different situations.

Exception 1 allows for up to a $^1/_2$-inch-diameter (12.7 mm) opening on stairway treads in public areas and serving any use (see Commentary Figure 1011.7.1). This is very beneficial on exterior stairways where snow, ice or water may accumulate. The $^1/_2$-inch-diameter (12.7 mm) limitation is based on the size of a crutch or cane tip and is consistent with ICC A117.1 and federal accessibility requirements. The opening limitation is also small enough that most shoe heels will not get stuck. If a slotted grill pattern is used, the slots must run side to side on the stairway tread, not nosing to back.

Commentary Figure 1011.7.1
OPEN TREAD IN ACCORDANCE WITH EXCEPTION 1

Exception 2 is applicable in factory, industrial, storage and high-hazard occupancies. This provision is intended to apply primarily to stairs that provide access to areas not required to be accessible, such as pits, catwalks, tanks, equipment platforms, roofs or mezzanines. Walking surfaces with limited-size openings are typically used because open grate-type material is less susceptible to accumulation of dirt, debris or moisture, as well as being more resistant to corrosion. Most commercially available grate material is manufactured with a maximum nominal 1-inch (25 mm) opening; therefore, the limitation that the openings not allow the passage of a sphere of $1^1/_8$-inch (29 mm) diameter allows the use of most material as well as accounts for manufacturing tolerances.

The allowances for openings in risers is addressed in Section 1011.5.5.3.

[BE] 1011.7.2 Outdoor conditions. Outdoor *stairways* and outdoor approaches to *stairways* shall be designed so that water will not accumulate on walking surfaces.

❖ Outdoor stairways and approaches to stairways are to be constructed with a slope that complies with Section 1011.7.1 or are required to be protected such that walking surfaces do not accumulate water. While not specifically stated, any interior locations, such as near a pool, should also have the stair designed to limit the accumulation of water in order to maintain slip resistance (see Section 1003.4).

Where exterior stairways are used in moderate or severe climates, there may also be a concern to protect the stairway from accumulations of snow and ice to provide a safe path of egress travel at all times. Maintenance of the means of egress requires an unobstructed path to allow for full instant use in case of a fire or emergency (see Section 1031.3). Typical methods for protecting these egress elements include roof overhangs or canopies; heated slabs; grated treads and landings; or, where approved by the building official, a reliable snow removal maintenance program.

[BE] 1011.7.3 Enclosures under interior stairways. The walls and soffits within enclosed usable spaces under enclosed and unenclosed *stairways* shall be protected by 1-hour fire-resistance- rated construction or the *fire-resistance rating* of the *stairway* enclosure, whichever is greater. Access to the enclosed space shall not be directly from within the *stairway* enclosure.

Exception: Spaces under *stairways* serving and contained within a single residential *dwelling unit* in Group R-2 or

R-3 shall be permitted to be protected on the enclosed side with $^{1}/_{2}$-inch (12.7 mm) gypsum board.

❖ This section addresses the fire hazard of storage under an interior stairway, whether it is an exit access stairway or exit stairway. The stairway must be protected from a storage area under it, even if the stairway is not required to be enclosed. The section also requires that the storage area not open into a stairway enclosure. This limits the potential of a fire that starts in the storage area from affecting the means of egress. The exception provides specific criteria for separation for storage areas under an interior stairway for the indicated residential occupancies.

[BE] 1011.7.4 Enclosures under exterior stairways. There shall not be enclosed usable space under *exterior exit stairways* unless the space is completely enclosed in 1-hour fire-resistance-rated construction. The open space under *exterior stairways* shall not be used for any purpose.

❖ If the space under an exterior stairway is to be used, such as for storage, the area below the stairway must be separated from the stairway with walls and a ceiling with a fire-resistance rating of at least 1 hour. If the space under the exterior stairway is open, it must remain free and clear. A fire occurring in this space would jeopardize the use of the stairway for exiting during an emergency.

[BE] 1011.8 Vertical rise. A *flight* of *stairs* shall not have a vertical rise greater than 12 feet (3658 mm) between floor levels or landings.

> **Exception:** *Spiral stairways* used as a *means of egress* from technical production areas.

❖ Between landings and platforms, the vertical rise is to be measured from one landing walking surface to another (see Commentary Figure 1011.8). The limited height provides a reasonable interval for users with physical limitations to rest on a level surface and also serves to alleviate potential negative psychological effects of long and uninterrupted stairway flights.

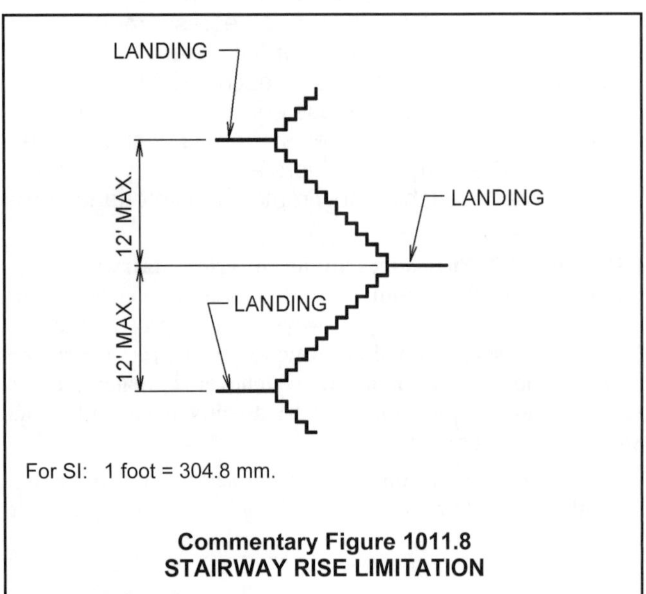

For SI: 1 foot = 304.8 mm.

Commentary Figure 1011.8
STAIRWAY RISE LIMITATION

The exception allows for spiral stairways that only serve technical production areas to eliminate intermediate landings, regardless of height. These stairways typically have limited use and serve areas such as catwalks or lighting booths in stadiums and theaters. In addition, there is the technical difficulty of maintaining proper headroom in a spiral stairway with an intermediate landing.

[BE] 1011.9 Curved stairways. Curved *stairways* with *winder* treads shall have treads and risers in accordance with Section 1011.5 and the smallest radius shall be not less than twice the minimum width or required capacity of the *stairway*.

> **Exception:** The radius restriction shall not apply to curved *stairways* in Group R-3 and within individual *dwelling units* in Group R-2.

❖ Curved stairway construction consists of a series of winder treads that form a stairway configuration. Options are many, including circular, S-shaped, oval, elliptical, hourglass, and so on. The commentary to Section 1011.5.3 regarding the possible event of non-concentric movement on stairways with winders also applies to curved stairways. This type of stairway is allowed to be used as a component of a means of egress where tread and riser dimensions meet the requirements of Section 1011.5. This section also requires that the smallest radius must be equal to or greater than twice the required width (see Section 1011.2) of the stairway to limit the degree of turning, thereby expediting egress from higher occupancies (see Commentary Figure 1011.9).

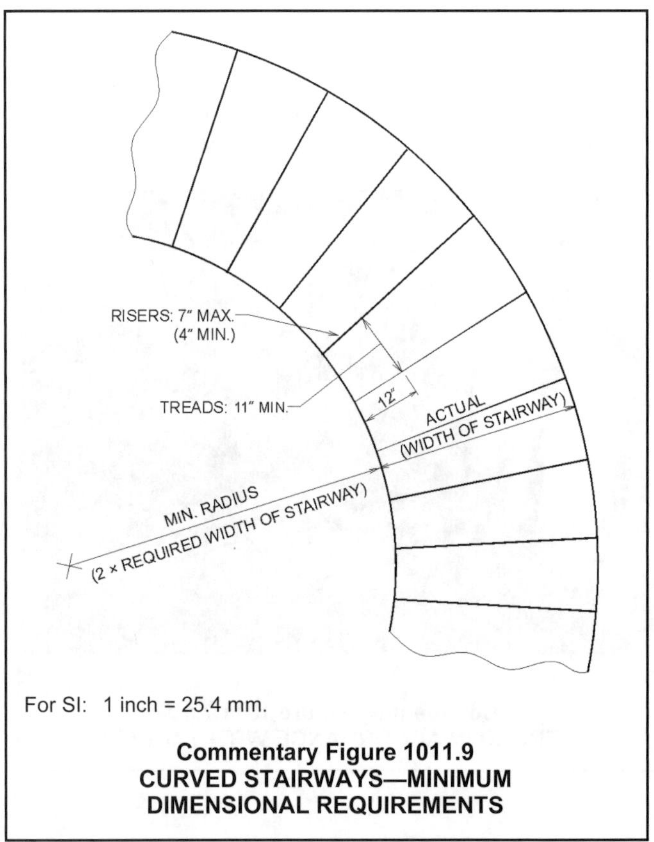

For SI: 1 inch = 25.4 mm.

Commentary Figure 1011.9
CURVED STAIRWAYS—MINIMUM DIMENSIONAL REQUIREMENTS

The exception for residential units eliminates the minimum radius requirement where the occupants are familiar with the extent of the turning of the stair through the curve.

[BE] 1011.10 Spiral stairways. *Spiral stairways* are permitted to be used as a component in the *means of egress* only within *dwelling units* or from a space not more than 250 square feet (23 m^2) in area and serving not more than five occupants, or from technical production areas in accordance with Section 410.5 of the *International Building Code*.

A *spiral stairway* shall have a $6^3/_4$-inch (171 mm) minimum clear tread depth at a point 12 inches (305 mm) from the narrow edge. The risers shall be sufficient to provide a headroom of 78 inches (1981 mm) minimum, but riser height shall not be more than $9^1/_2$ inches (241 mm). The minimum *stairway* clear width at and below the *handrail* shall be 26 inches (660 mm).

❖ Spiral stairways can be used within individual dwelling units, from small spaces in other occupancies and from technical production areas in spaces such as theaters. Spiral stairways are permitted to provide access between the levels within a live/work unit (see Section 419.3.2).

Spiral stairways are generally constructed with a fixed center pole that serves as either the primary or the only means of support from which pie-shaped treads radiate to form a winding stairway. The term "spiral" in the geometrical sense describes a curve that diminishes in radius and relates to the form of the stair as viewed in perspective from above or below; however, "spiral" does not describe the actual geometry of the stairway. The unique turning of spiral stairs allows the center pole to act as the guard at the inside of the stair, and the typically narrow width requires users to choose a walkline along the outer perimeter near the only required handrail. On spiral stairways of larger widths where two users can pass and restrict access to the single handrail, the provision of a handrail at both sides should be considered.

The commentary to Section 1011.5.3 regarding the possible event of nonconcentric movement on stairways with winders also applies to spiral stairways. The nature of stairway construction is such that it does not serve well when used in emergencies that require immediate evacuation, nor does a spiral stairway configuration permit the handling of a large occupant load in an efficient and safe manner. Furthermore, it is impossible for fire service personnel to use a spiral stairway at the same time and in a direction opposite that being used by occupants to exit the premises, possibly causing a serious delay in fire-fighting operations. Therefore, this section allows only very limited use of spiral stairways where used as part of a required means of egress. Spiral stairways may be used in any occupancy as long as such stairways are not a component of a required means of egress.

Spiral stairways are required to have dimensional uniformity. The stairway must have a clear width of at least 26 inches (660 mm) at and below the handrail. The depth of the treads must not be less than $6^3/_4$ inches (171 mm) measured at a point that is 12 inches (305 mm) out from the narrow edge (see Commentary Figure 1011.10). Riser heights are required to be the same throughout the stairway, but are not to exceed $9^1/_2$ inches (241 mm). Minimum headroom of 6 feet 6 inches (1981 mm) is required.

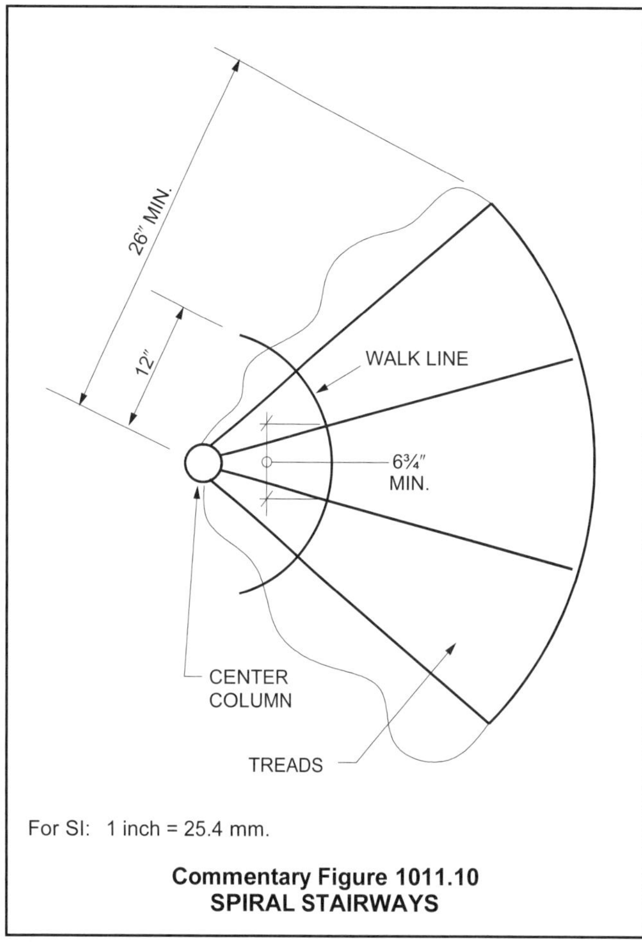

For SI: 1 inch = 25.4 mm.

Commentary Figure 1011.10
SPIRAL STAIRWAYS

[BE] 1011.11 Handrails. *Flights of stairways* shall have *handrails* on each side and shall comply with Section 1014. Where glass is used to provide the *handrail*, the *handrail* shall comply with Section 2407 of the *International Building Code*.

Exceptions:

1. *Flights of stairways* within *dwelling units*, and *flights of spiral stairways* are permitted to have a *handrail* on one side only.
2. Decks, patios and walkways that have a single change in elevation where the landing depth on each side of the change of elevation is greater than what is required for a landing do not require *handrails*.

3. In Group R-3 occupancies, a change in elevation consisting of a single riser at an entrance or egress door does not require *handrails*.
4. Changes in room elevations of three or fewer risers within *dwelling units* and *sleeping units* in Group R-2 and R-3 do not require *handrails*.

❖ Handrails are required along each side of a flight of stairs; however, handrails are not required along stairway landings. Handrail continuity and extensions that will overlap the landings are addressed in Sections 1014.4 and 1014.6.

Handrails have four recognized functions in stairway use. First, they serve to guide persons in ascent and descent along the path of egress travel, especially important for those with low vision and in cases of fire where vision might be obscured by smoke. Second, they provide a tool for the user to exert stabilizing forces longitudinally (along the length of the rail), vertically and, most importantly, transversely (perpendicular) to the rail as the body transfers weight from side to side with each leg swing of the unique gait used on stairs. Third, they provide for pulling when arms are used to augment legs in ascent of steeper angles or where such climbing strategies result in more efficient use of the strengths of the user. Fourth, they are a tool that can be utilized to help in the arrest of a fall. In these capacities, handrails serve to aid in the use of the stairway and are required on both sides of stairways to allow passing users unencumbered access to a handrail, in compliance with Section 1014. Finally, where glass is the material used to provide the handrail, it must comply with Section 2407.

Note that if the handrail extension is at a location that could be considered a protruding object, the handrail must return to the post at a height of less than 27 inches (686 mm) above the floor. Handrails along the stair flights are not considered protruding objects.

The exceptions state conditions where handrails are required on only one side or are not needed at all. By the nature of their construction, spiral stairways can have only a single handrail (see Exception 1). In accordance with Exceptions 1 and 4, all stairways within dwelling units can have a handrail on one side only, and stairs with three or fewer risers are not required to have any handrails. Since "Stair" is defined as one or more risers, Exceptions 2 and 3 are necessary. Exception 3 exempts the single step at the front or back door of a Group R-3 dwelling unit (i.e., townhouse). Decks, patios and walkways often move down with the grade. Where there are single steps, either off a patio or deck to grade, or along the surface, a handrail is not required (Exception 2, see Commentary Figure 1011.11). Many of these exceptions dealing with residential units are consistent with the IRC.

For guard requirements at stairways, see Section 1011.13.

Commentary Figure 1011.11
EXAMPLE OF SECTION 1011.11, EXCEPTION 2

[BE] 1011.12 Stairway to roof. In buildings four or more stories above grade plane, one *stairway* shall extend to the roof surface, unless the roof has a slope steeper than four units vertical in 12 units horizontal (33-percent slope).

Exception: Other than where required by Section 1011.12.1, in buildings without an occupied roof, access to the roof from the top story shall be permitted to be by an *alternating tread device*, a ships ladder or a permanent ladder.

❖ Because of safety considerations, roofs used for habitable purposes such as roof gardens, observation decks, sporting facilities (including jogging or walking tracks and tennis courts) or similar uses must be provided with conventional stairways that will serve as required means of egress. Access by ladders or an alternating tread device for such uses is not permitted.

In buildings four or more stories high, roofs that are not used for habitable purposes must be provided with ready access by conventional stairways or by an alternating tread device (see Section 1011.14). If this stair is also to provide access to an elevator penthouse on the roof, see additional requirements in Section 1011.12.1. Two reasons for this are access for roof or rooftop equipment repair and fire department access during a fire event. Sloping roofs with a rise greater than 4 inches (102 mm) for every 12 inches (305 mm) in horizontal measurement (4:12) are exempt from the requirements of this section because of the steepness of the construction and the inherent dangers to life safety.

While it is not specifically required that roof access be through an exit stairway enclosure, since part of the intent is for fire department access to the roof, it is strongly advised. Section 1023.9 requires signage at the level of exit discharge indicating whether the stairway has roof access.

[BE] 1011.12.1 Stairway to elevator equipment. Roofs and penthouses containing elevator equipment that must be accessed for maintenance are required to be accessed by a *stairway*.

❖ The requirement for a stair to the roof for maintaining elevator equipment correlates the code with ASME A17.1/CSA B44, *Safety Code for Elevators and Escalators*. This referenced standard (see Section 3001.3) has required stairs and a door to access elevator equipment since 1955. More specifically, Section 2.7.3.2.1 of ASME A17.1/CSA B44 states the following: "a stairway with a swinging door and platform at the top level, conforming to 2.7.3.3, shall be provided from the top floor of the building to the roof level. Hatch covers, as a means of access to the roofs, shall not be permitted." Alternating tread devices or ladders are not permitted as an alternative to the stairway for access to the elevator penthouse. This provision is more specific; therefore, while not prohibiting using the same stairway for access to the roof and the elevator penthouse (see Sections 1011.12 and 1011.12.2), access to that elevator penthouse must be via a stairway with door access, not an alternating tread device and hatch.

[BE] 1011.12.2 Roof access. Where a *stairway* is provided to a roof, access to the roof shall be provided through a penthouse complying with Section 1510.2 of the *International Building Code*.

Exception: In buildings without an occupied roof, access to the roof shall be permitted to be a roof hatch or trap door not less than 16 square feet (1.5 m^2) in area and having a minimum dimension of 2 feet (610 mm).

❖ The purpose of the penthouse or stairway bulkhead requirement in this section is to protect the walking surface of the stairway to the roof. The exception provides for situations where roof access is only needed for service or maintenance purposes, and where the access may be permitted by alternatives such as alternating tread devices, ships ladders or ladders.

[BE] 1011.13 Guards. *Guards* shall be provided along *stairways* and landings where required by Section 1015 and shall be constructed in accordance with Section 1015. Where the roof hatch opening providing the required access is located within 10 feet (3049 mm) of the roof edge, such roof access or roof edge shall be protected by *guards* installed in accordance with Section 1015.

❖ Section 1015.2 requires guards along stairways and landings where the edges of the walking surfaces are 30 inches (762 mm) or more above the floor below. Except where permitted by Section 1015.3, the top of the guard cannot also serve as the handrail. The handrail must be located inside the guard because of the differences in height requirements.

While guards are required at the edge of a normally occupied roof by Section 1015, there is also a safety concern for roof areas that need to be accessed by service personnel, inspectors and emergency responders. This requirement for guards provides a minimum measure of safety where the roof access is close to the roof edge. This is consistent with the requirements for mechanical equipment in Sections 1015.6 and 1015.7.

[BE] 1011.14 Alternating tread devices. *Alternating tread devices* are limited to an element of a *means of egress* in buildings of Groups F, H and S from a *mezzanine* not more than 250 square feet (23 m^2) in area and that serves not more than five occupants; in buildings of Group I-3 from a guard tower, observation station or control room not more than 250 square feet (23 m^2) in area and for access to unoccupied roofs. *Alternating tread devices* used as a *means of egress* shall not have a rise greater than 20 feet (6096 mm) between floor levels or landings.

❖ This type of device is constructed in such a way that each tread alternates with each adjacent tread so that the device consists of a system of right-footed and left-footed treads (see Commentary Figure 1011.14).

The use of center stringer construction, half-treads and an incline that is considerably steeper than allowed for ordinary stairway construction makes the alternating tread device unique. However, because of its structural feature, only single-file use of the device (between handrails) is possible, thus preventing the occupants from passing one another. The pace of occupant travel is set by the slowest user, a condition that could become critical in an emergency situation. Furthermore, it is impossible for fire service personnel to use an alternating tread device at the same time and in a direction opposite that being used by occupants to exit the premises, possibly causing a serious delay in fire-fighting operations. For these reasons, this section greatly restricts the use of alternating tread devices as a means of egress. Alternating tread devices may be used in any occupancy as long as such stairways are not a component of a required means of egress.

Alternating tread devices are considered a modest improvement to ladder construction and, therefore, can be used as an unoccupied roof access in accordance with the requirements of Section 1011.12.

Alternating tread devices are permitted 20 feet (6096 mm) between landings given their limited application and low occupant loads. In addition, it is recognized that a vertical rise higher than the typical stairway is needed for these steeper devices, which are used where space is often too restrictive for a regular stairway.

[BE] 1011.14.1 Handrails of alternating tread devices. *Handrails* shall be provided on both sides of *alternating tread devices* and shall comply with Section 1014.

❖ For the safety of occupants, this section references the dimensional requirements for handrail locations to be used in conjunction with the special construction features of alternating tread devices provided in Section 1011.14. Because of the steepness of these devices, handrails on both sides are essential for safe functional use and additional clearances are required so that hand movement will not be encumbered by obstructions. Section 1015.3, Exception 5, permits the handrails along alternating tread devices to also serve as guards.

[BE] 1011.14.2 Treads of alternating tread devices. *Alternating tread devices* shall have a minimum tread depth of 5 inches (127 mm), a minimum projected tread depth of $8^1/_2$ inches (216 mm), a minimum tread width of 7 inches (178 mm) and a maximum riser height of $9^1/_2$ inches (241 mm). The tread depth shall be measured horizontally between the vertical planes of the foremost projections of adjacent treads. The riser height shall be measured vertically between the leading edges of adjacent treads. The riser height and tread depth provided shall result in an angle of ascent from the horizontal of between 50 and 70 degrees (0.87 and 1.22 rad). The initial tread of the device shall begin at the same elevation as the platform, landing or floor surface.

Exception: *Alternating tread devices* used as an element of a *means of egress* in buildings from a *mezzanine* area not more than 250 square feet (23 m^2) in area that serves not more than five occupants shall have a minimum tread depth of 3 inches (76 mm) with a minimum projected tread depth of $10^1/_2$ inches (267 mm). The rise to the next alternating tread surface shall not exceed 8 inches (203 mm).

❖ Alternating tread devices are required to have tread depths of at least 5 inches (127 mm). Tread projections are not to be less than $3^1/_2$ inches (89 mm) where measured from tread nosing to tread nosing [next adjacent tread to the left or right to provide a minimum projected tread depth of $8^1/_2$ inches (216 mm)] (see Commentary Figure 1011.14).

The risers are to be not more than $9^1/_2$ inches (241 mm) where measured from tread to alternating tread (next adjacent tread to the left or right). The rise between treads on the same side would be 19 inches (483 mm) maximum. Applying these limiting dimensions results in a device with a very steep incline that

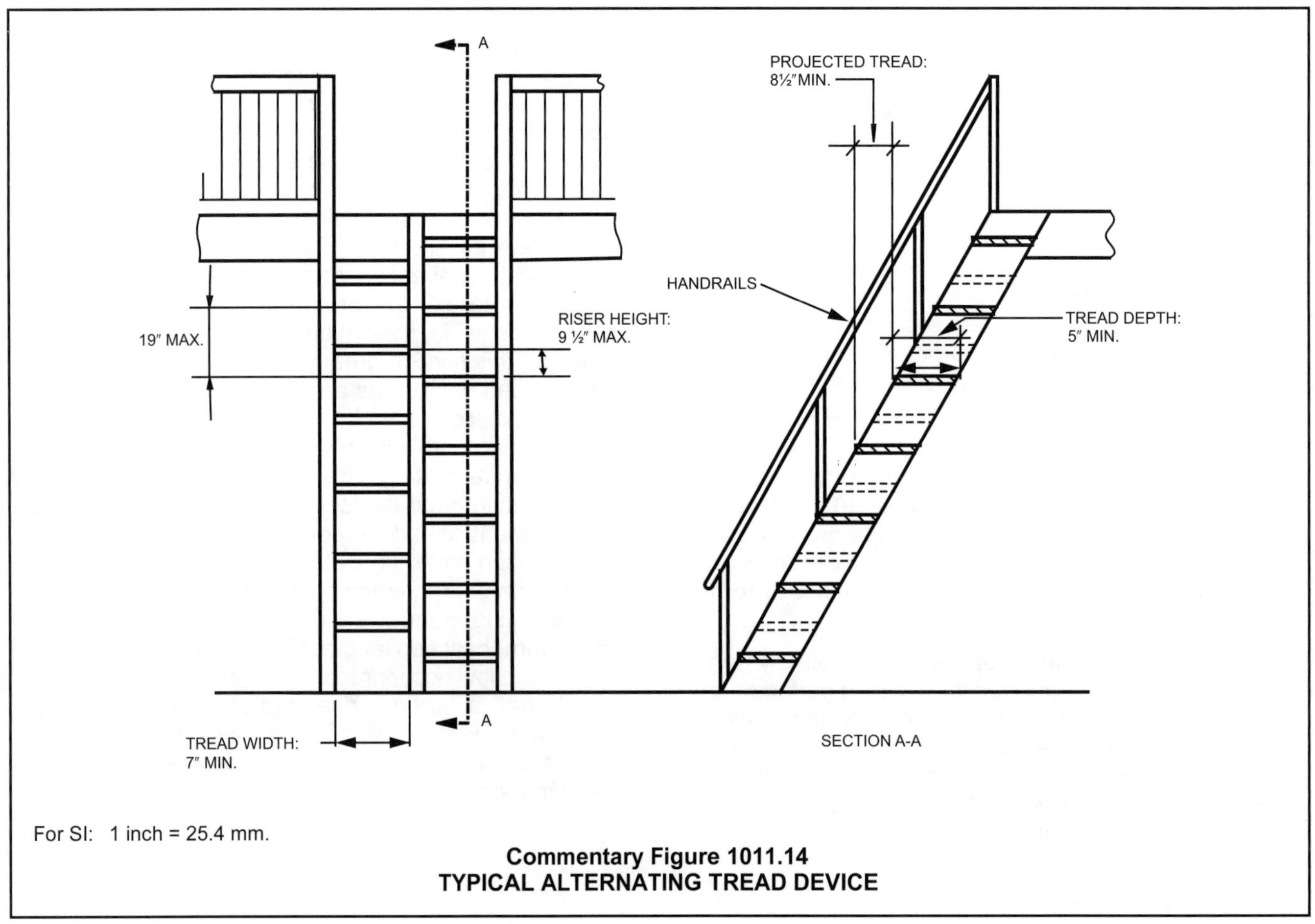

For SI: 1 inch = 25.4 mm.

Commentary Figure 1011.14
TYPICAL ALTERNATING TREAD DEVICE

is common to ladders; however, because the device may be walked facing down in descent, it is considered a type of stairway in the code.

Tread widths are required to be a minimum of 7 inches (178 mm) or more. With a center support, the total width will be more than 15 inches (381 mm). Although no maximum width of the tread is stated, the device must be of a width to provide for functional use of both handrails at the same time in ascent and descent. For this same reason, handrail heights for alternating tread devices are modified from those stairways in Section 1014.2.

Just using the dimensions could result in an alternating tread device with an angle greater than 75 degrees (1.3 rad). In any case, the overall angle of the device must be between 50 and 70 degrees (0.87 and 1.22 rad).

For alternating tread devices used as a means of egress from small-area mezzanines as prescribed in the exception, the treads must project at least $7^1/_2$ inches (191 mm) as compared to the $3^1/_2$ inches (89 mm) stated earlier; treads are to be at least 3 inches (76 mm) in depth [compared to 5 inches (127 mm)] and risers are not to exceed 8 inches (203 mm) in height [compared to $9^1/_2$ inches (241 mm)].

[BE] 1011.15 Ships ladders. Ships ladders are permitted to be used in Group I-3 as a component of a *means of egress* to and from control rooms or elevated facility observation stations not more than 250 square feet (23 m^2) with not more than three occupants and for access to unoccupied roofs. The minimum clear width at and below the *handrails* shall be 20 inches (508 mm).

❖ Ships ladders can be used in correctional facilities for access to small control rooms, observation stations and unoccupied roofs. Where approved by the code official, ships ladders could be used for access to unoccupied roofs in other occupancies. Ships ladders are of similar gradient or pitch to alternating tread devices; however, the treads span the full width like that of a ladder rather than being staggered to either side (see Commentary Figure 1011.15).

[BE] 1011.15.1 Handrails of ships ladders. *Handrails* shall be provided on both sides of ships ladders.

❖ Handrails are needed on both sides to assist in ascent and descent and in the absence of a maximum width. Section 1015.3, Exception 5, permits the handrails along ships ladders to also serve as guards.

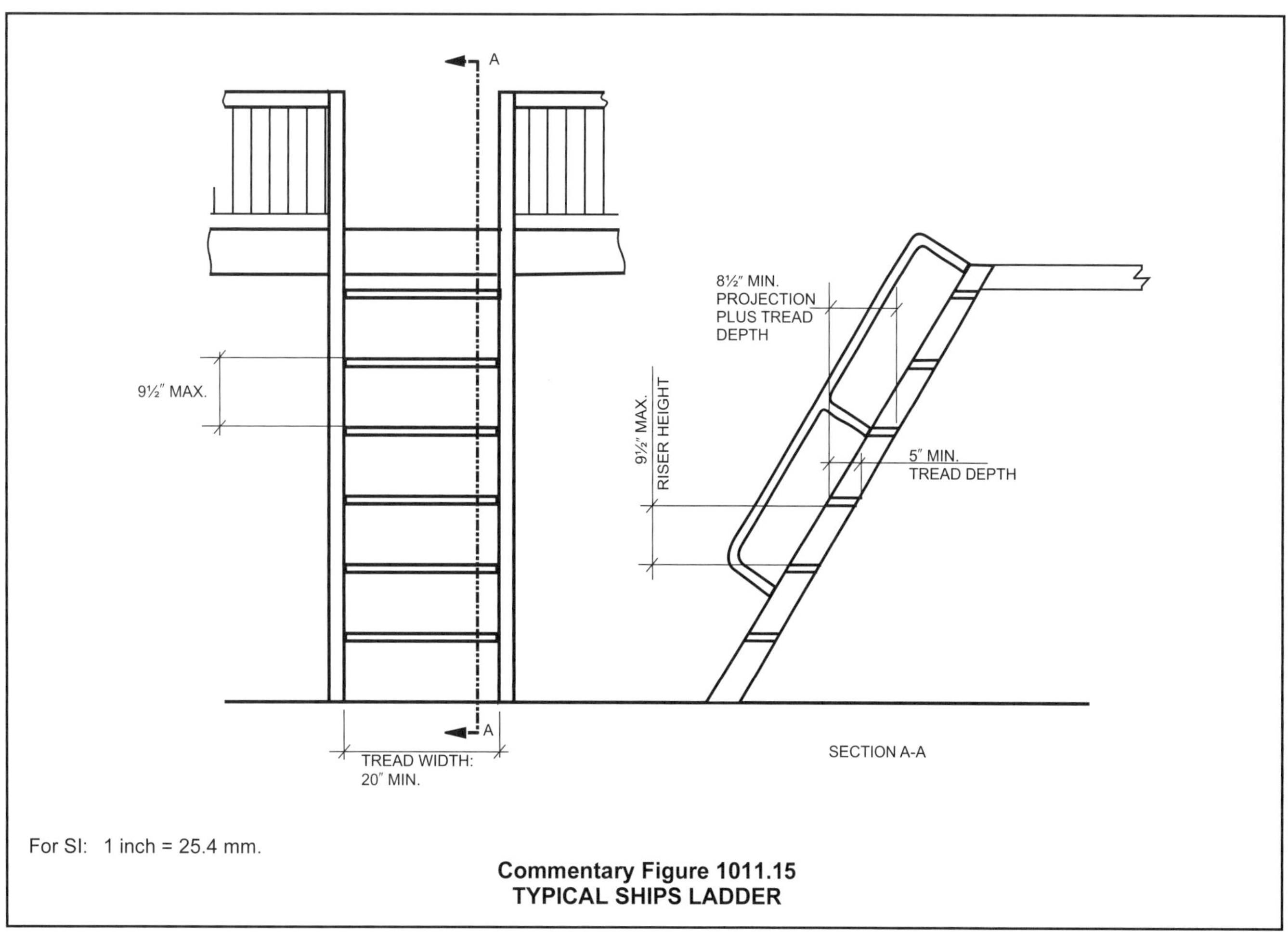

Commentary Figure 1011.15
TYPICAL SHIPS LADDER

[BE] 1011.15.2 Treads of ships ladders. Ships ladders shall have a minimum tread depth of 5 inches (127 mm). The tread shall be projected such that the total of the tread depth plus the *nosing* projection is not less than $8^1/_2$ inches (216 mm). The maximum riser height shall be $9^1/_2$ inches (241 mm).

❖ See Commentary Figure 1011.15 for an example of this configuration.

[BE] 1011.16 Ladders. Permanent ladders shall not serve as a part of the *means of egress* from occupied spaces within a building. Permanent ladders shall be constructed in accordance with Section 306.5 of the *International Mechanical Code*. Permanent ladders shall be permitted to provide access to the following areas:

1. Spaces frequented only by personnel for maintenance, repair or monitoring of equipment.
2. Nonoccupiable spaces accessed only by catwalks, crawl spaces, freight elevators or very narrow passageways.
3. Raised areas used primarily for purposes of security, life safety or fire safety including, but not limited to, observation galleries, prison guard towers, fire towers or lifeguard stands.
4. Elevated levels in Group U not open to the general public.
5. Nonoccupied roofs that are not required to have *stairway* access in accordance with Section 1011.12.1.
6. Where permitted to access equipment and appliances in accordance with Section 306.5 of the *International Mechanical Code*.

❖ Permanent ladders are permitted as a means of ingress and egress to very limited spaces. Typically, these spaces are not considered occupied and, as such, are not required to have a means of egress. While the term "technical production areas" is not used in this section, Section 410.5.3.4, Item 6, allows ladders to be used to access technical production areas. Item 6 of this section references the IMC for where ladders can be used to access mechanical equipment that is located in an elevated space or in a room. The details and construction requirements for a permanent ladder are also found in that section. This will help ensure that permanent ladders are safe and usable, while providing consistency for both the designer and the building official.

SECTION 1012
RAMPS

[BE] 1012.1 Scope. The provisions of this section shall apply to ramps used as a component of a *means of egress*.

Exceptions:

1. Ramped *aisles* within assembly rooms or spaces shall comply with the provisions in Section 1029.
2. Curb *ramps* shall comply with ICC A117.1.
3. Vehicle *ramps* in parking garages for pedestrian *exit access* shall not be required to comply with Sections 1012.3 through 1012.10 where they are not an *accessible route* serving accessible parking spaces, other required accessible elements or part of an *accessible means of egress*.

❖ Ramps provide an alternative method of vertical means of access to or egress from a building. Ramps are required for access to building areas for persons who are mobility impaired (see IBC Chapter 11) and for small changes in floor elevations that are a safety hazard in themselves (see Section 1003.5). All ramps intended for pedestrian usage, whether required or otherwise provided, must comply with the requirements of this section. The code considers any walking surface that has a slope steeper than 1 unit vertical in 20 units horizontal (5-percent slope) to be a ramp (see the definition for "Ramp" in Chapter 2).

As with stairways, it is important to understand the terminology. Exit ramps are ramps that provide a protected path of travel between the exit access and the exit discharge. Interior exit ramps are required to be enclosed in accordance with Section 1023. Exterior exit ramps are protected by the exterior wall of the building and must comply with Section 1027. Exit access ramps are typically unenclosed interior ramps and comply with Section 1019 where they provide access between stories. Exit access travel distance stops at an exit ramp enclosure, but includes any travel down an exit access ramp. Ramps that are outside and provide a route from the level of exit discharge to grade are considered part of the exit discharge. See the commentary in Chapter 2 for the defined term, "Exit discharge, level of."

Exception 1 indicates that ramped aisles are addressed in Section 1029. Having this exception at the beginning of the ramp section negates the need for repeated exceptions throughout the ramp provisions. While ramps and ramped aisles may look similar, configurations and how occupants move on and off those walking surfaces are very different. Occupants leave and join ramped aisles along the entire run, while occupants enter the ramp only at the top and bottom. Ramped aisles may have no or only one handrail in order to allow for access to the seats, while most ramps have handrails on both sides. Ramped aisles can have steeper slopes to allow for seating bowls to address line of sight. Section 1029 should be used for ramped aisles between and immediately adjacent to seating or where the ramps are a direct continuation of the ramped aisles and lead to a level cross aisle or floor. Section 1012 is used for ramps that lead from the balcony, concourse or cross aisle to a floor level above or below the seating areas.

Exception 2 references specific curb cut requirements found in Section 406 of ICC A117.1. It is important to realize there are different provisions for curb ramps and ramps. For example, a curb ramp can have a rise of any height and not require handrails. Ramps require handrails where the rise is more than 6 inches.

Exception 3 addresses parking garages. An accessible route is required to and from any accessible parking space, and all ramp provisions must be followed. However, ramps that provide access to and from nonaccessible spaces in the remainder of the parking garage need only comply with the provisions for slope and guard requirements. This permits nonaccessible portions of garages to be constructed as a continuous slope. Ramps that are strictly for vehicles, such as jump ramps, are not required to meet any of the ramp provisions.

[BE] 1012.2 Slope. *Ramps* used as part of a *means of egress* shall have a running slope not steeper than one unit vertical in 12 units horizontal (8-percent slope). The slope of other pedestrian *ramps* shall not be steeper than one unit vertical in eight units horizontal (12.5-percent slope).

❖ Maximum slope is limited to facilitate the ease of ascent and to control the descent of persons with or without a mobility impairment. The maximum slope of a ramp in the direction of travel is limited to 1 unit vertical in 12 units horizontal (1:12) (see Commentary Figure 1012.2). Ramps in existing buildings may be permitted to have a steeper slope at small changes in elevation (see IEBC Section 305.8.5). An example of a ramp that is not part of a means of egress, and therefore is allowed to be a maximum slope of 1:8, is a loading dock or delivery ramp where the ramp is not part of any required exit discharge.

[BE] 1012.3 Cross slope. The slope measured perpendicular to the direction of travel of a *ramp* shall not be steeper than one unit vertical in 48 units horizontal (2-percent slope).

❖ The limitation of 1 unit vertical in 48 units horizontal on the slope across the direction of travel is to prevent a severe cross slope that would pitch a user to one side (see Commentary Figure 1012.2).

[BE] 1012.4 Vertical rise. The rise for any *ramp* run shall be 30 inches (762 mm) maximum.

❖ Because pushing a wheelchair up a ramp requires a great deal of energy, landings must be situated so that a person can rest after each 30-inch (762 mm) elevation change (see Commentary Figure 1012.2).

[BE] 1012.5 Minimum dimensions. The minimum dimensions of *means of egress ramps* shall comply with Sections 1012.5.1 through 1012.5.3.

❖ These minimum dimension requirements allow the ramp to function as a means of egress and an accessible route.

[BE] 1012.5.1 Width and capacity. The minimum width and required capacity of a *means of egress ramp* shall be not less than that required for *corridors* by Section 1020.2. The clear width of a *ramp* between *handrails*, if provided, or other permissible projections shall be 36 inches (914 mm) minimum.

❖ The requirements for the width of a means of egress ramp is based on the required minimum width [typically 36 inches (914 mm)] and the capacity based on

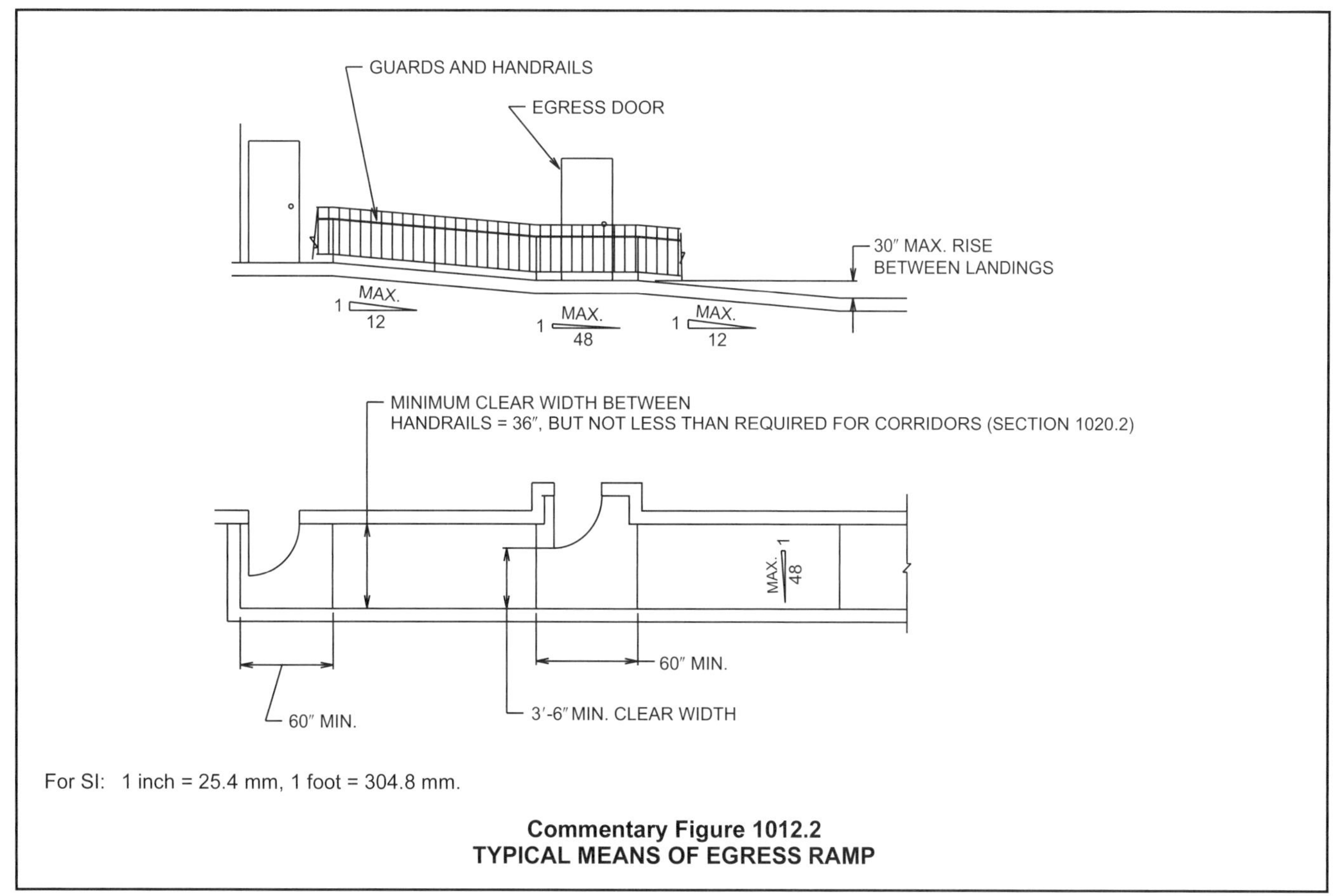

Commentary Figure 1012.2
TYPICAL MEANS OF EGRESS RAMP

the occupant load to be served (see Section 1005.3.2). Note that the clear width of 36 inches (914 mm) is required between the handrails and any other obstructions (e.g., handrail supports, curbs) for proper clearance for a person in a wheelchair. This is different from stairways where handrails are permitted to project into the required width. The 36-inch (914 mm) minimum clear width between handrails is consistent with ICC A117.1 and the federal *2010 ADA Standards*.

[BE] 1012.5.2 Headroom. The minimum headroom in all parts of the *means of egress ramp* shall be not less than 80 inches (2032 mm) above the finished floor of the ramp run and any intermediate landings. The minimum clearance shall be maintained for the full width of the ramp and landing.

❖ The requirement for headroom on any part of an egress ramp is identical to the requirement of a conventional (nonspiral) stairway (see Section 1011.3). General headroom heights along the means of egress are addressed in Section 1003.2.

[BE] 1012.5.3 Restrictions. *Means of egress ramps* shall not reduce in width in the direction of egress travel. Projections into the required *ramp* and landing width are prohibited. Doors opening onto a landing shall not reduce the clear width to less than 42 inches (1067 mm).

❖ The purpose of not allowing ramps to reduce in width in the direction of egress travel is to prevent a restriction that would interfere with the flow of occupants out of a facility. This would include ramp landings in accordance with Section 1012.6.2. Handrails are the only exception in accordance with Sections 1012.5.1 and 1014.8.

Doors that open onto a ramp landing, including those at the top and bottom landings, must not reduce the clear width to less than 42 inches (1067 mm). This is a more restrictive provision than for corridors that would permit the reduction to one-half the required width (see Section 1005.7). Since one of the purposes of a ramp is to accommodate persons with physical disabilities, it must provide the additional clear width for access by those confined to wheelchairs without the interference or potential blockage caused by the swing of a door (see Commentary Figures 1012.2 and 1012.5.3).

[BE] 1012.6 Landings. *Ramps* shall have landings at the bottom and top of each *ramp*, points of turning, entrance, *exits* and at doors. Landings shall comply with Sections 1012.6.1 through 1012.6.5.

❖ Landings must be provided to allow users of a ramp to rest on a level floor surface and to adjust to the change in floor surface pitch.

Landings are required at the top and bottom of each ramp run (see Commentary Figure 1012.6). In addition, Section 1012.4 requires a landing every 30 inches (762 mm) of vertical rise of the ramp. The requirements for landings allow those occupants of the structure the ability to negotiate all changes in direction, and prepare themselves to either ascend or descend the ramp and to rest. If there is a door at the top or the bottom of the ramp, there are additional requirements in Section 1012.5.3 for door swing over the landing and Section 405 of ICC A117.1 for maneuvering space and turning space at the door.

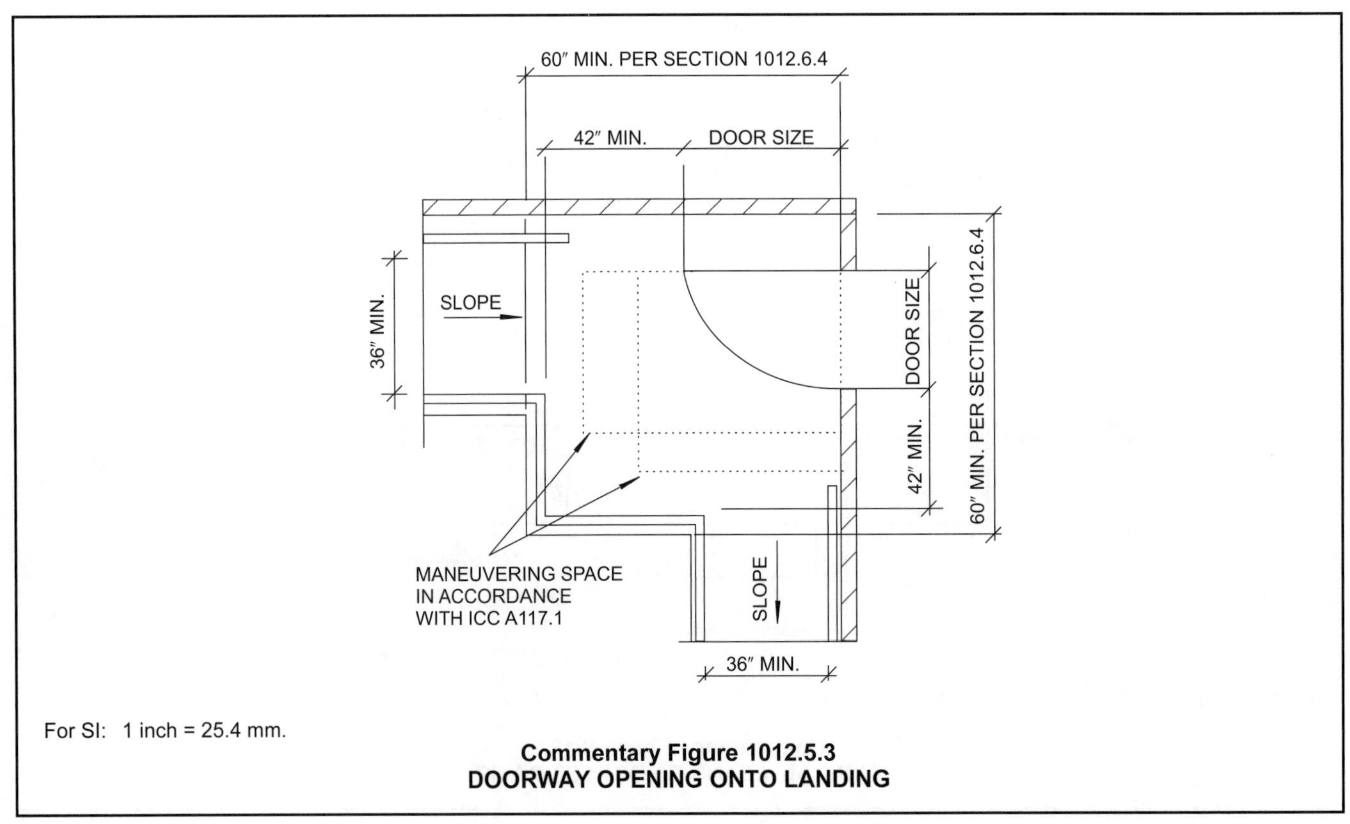

Commentary Figure 1012.5.3
DOORWAY OPENING ONTO LANDING

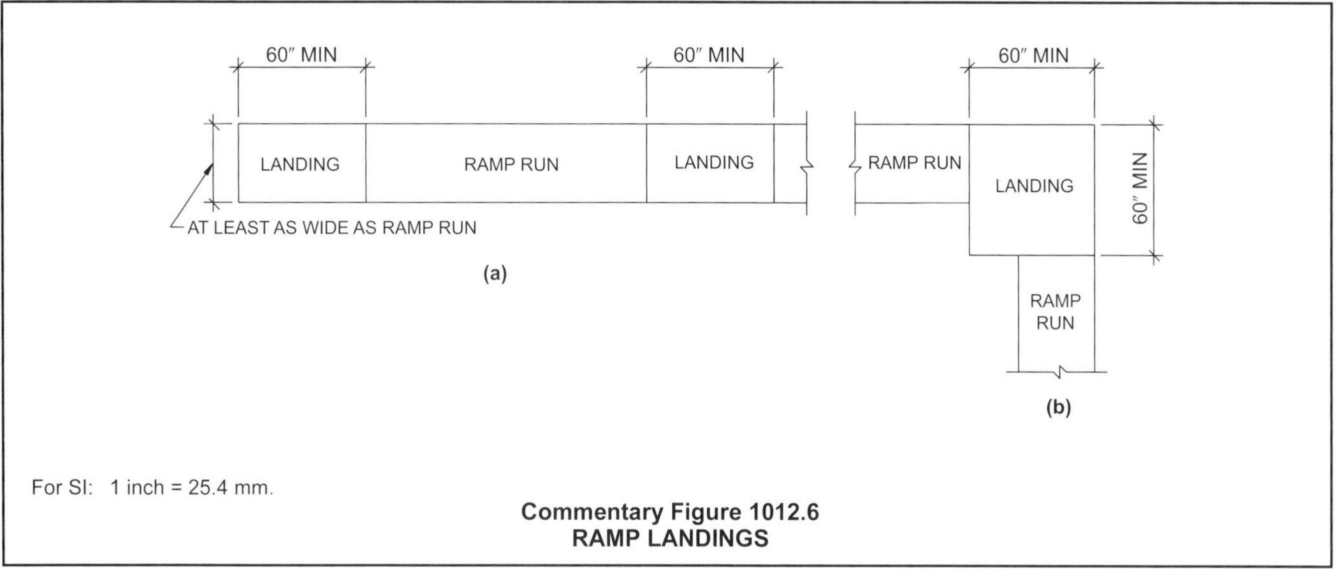

For SI: 1 inch = 25.4 mm.

Commentary Figure 1012.6
RAMP LANDINGS

[BE] 1012.6.1 Slope. Landings shall have a slope not steeper than one unit vertical in 48 units horizontal (2-percent slope) in any direction. Changes in level are not permitted.

❖ Landings must be almost flat. This allows persons confined to a wheelchair to come to a complete stop without having to activate the brake or hold themselves stationary at the landing. The maximum slope or cross slope of the landing in any direction is 1:48 (see Commentary Figure 1012.2). This minimum slope is to allow for drainage to limit the accumulation of water on the landing surface.

[BE] 1012.6.2 Width. The landing width shall be not less than the width of the widest *ramp* run adjoining the landing.

❖ The width of all landings must be consistently as wide as the widths of the ramp runs leading to them. Means of egress ramps cannot be reduced in width in the direction of egress travel. This is also applicable to the landings connecting the ramp runs (see Commentary Figure 1012.6).

[BE] 1012.6.3 Length. The landing length shall be 60 inches (1525 mm) minimum.

Exceptions:

1. In Group R-2 and R-3 individual *dwelling* and *sleeping units* that are not required to be Accessible units, Type A units or Type B units in accordance with Section 1107 of the *International Building Code*, landings are permitted to be 36 inches (914 mm) minimum.
2. Where the *ramp* is not a part of an *accessible route*, the length of the landing shall not be required to be more than 48 inches (1220 mm) in the direction of travel.

❖ The landings for ramps must be at least 60 inches (1524 mm) long (see Commentary Figure 1012.6). This allows persons confined to wheelchairs a sufficient distance to stop and rest along with any persons who may be assisting them. This requirement is directly applicable to straight-run ramps that may require an intermediate landing at every 30 inches (762 mm) of vertical rise (see Commentary Figure 1012.2). If the landing is also to be used to negotiate a change in the ramp's direction, Section 1012.6.4 is applicable. If a door overlaps the landing, Section 1012.5.3 is applicable.

The exceptions provide for smaller landings in dwelling and sleeping units and other locations where the ramp is not part of an accessible route. Exception 1 is consistent with the IRC. Exception 2 would be applicable in areas such as service ramps and ramps serving assembly seating areas that do not contain any wheelchair spaces.

[BE] 1012.6.4 Change in direction. Where changes in direction of travel occur at landings provided between *ramp* runs, the landing shall be 60 inches by 60 inches (1524 mm by 1524 mm) minimum.

Exception: In Group R-2 and R-3 individual *dwelling* or *sleeping units* that are not required to be Accessible units, Type A units or Type B units in accordance with Section 1107 of the *International Building Code*, landings are permitted to be 36 inches by 36 inches (914 mm by 914 mm) minimum.

❖ Where a change in direction is made in the ramp at a landing, the landing must be a square of at least 60 inches (1524 mm). This allows the person confined to a wheelchair enough room to move off the sloped surface and then negotiate the turn with minimal effort. The length of the landing may need to exceed 60 inches (1524 mm) to match the widths of the two ramp runs. In any case, the landing would still need to be 60 inches (1524 mm) wide (see Commentary Figures 1012.5.3 and 1012.6). If a door overlaps the landing, Section 1012.5.3 is applicable. It is not the intent of this provision to prohibit curved ramps. As long as the cross slope meets the limitations in Section 1012.3, a curved ramp is permitted.

The exception provides for smaller landings in dwelling and sleeping units where the ramp is not part of an accessible route. This is consistent with requirements in the IRC.

[BE] 1012.6.5 Doorways. Where doorways are located adjacent to a *ramp* landing, maneuvering clearances required by ICC A117.1 are permitted to overlap the required landing area.

❖ This section specifies that the area required for maneuvering to open the door and the area of the landing are allowed to overlap. It is not necessary to provide the sum of the two area requirements (see Commentary Figure 1012.5.3). The idea is that someone coming up or down the sloped surface would be able to move onto the landing and not be stopped on the sloped surface by someone opening the door. Requirements for maneuvering space and turning space at the top and bottom of ramps are found in Section 405 of ICC A117.1. ICC A117.1 requires a turning space at the top or bottom landing of a ramp where the door may be locked. This allows people to turn around to travel back along the ramp.

[BE] 1012.7 Ramp construction. *Ramps* shall be built of materials consistent with the types permitted for the type of construction of the building, except that wood *handrails* shall be permitted for all types of construction.

❖ Material requirements for the type of construction as required by Section 602 for floors are also the material requirements for ramp construction.

[BE] 1012.7.1 Ramp surface. The surface of *ramps* shall be of slip-resistant materials that are securely attached.

❖ As the pace of exit travel becomes hurried during emergency situations, the probability of slipping on smooth or slick floor surfaces increases. To minimize the hazard, all floor surfaces in the means of egress are required to be slip resistant. The use of hard floor materials with highly polished, glazed, glossy or finely finished surfaces should be avoided. This is consistent with Section 1003.4.

Field testing and uniform enforcement of the concept of slip resistance is not practical. One method used to establish slip resistance is that the static coefficient of friction between leather [Type 1 (Vegetable Tanned) of Federal Specification KK-L-165C] and the floor surface is greater than 0.5. Laboratory test procedures such as ASTM D2047 can determine the static coefficient of resistance. Bulletin No. 4 entitled “Surfaces” issued by the US Access Board (ATBCB) contains further information regarding slip resistance.

[BE] 1012.7.2 Outdoor conditions. Outdoor *ramps* and outdoor approaches to *ramps* shall be designed so that water will not accumulate on walking surfaces.

❖ Outdoor ramps, landings and the approaches to the ramp must be sloped so that surfaces do not accumulate water so as to provide a safe path of egress travel at all times. While not specifically stated, any interior locations, such as near a pool, should also have the ramps designed to limit the accumulation of water in order to maintain slip resistance (see Sections 1003.4 and 1012.7.1).

Where exterior ramps are used in moderate or severe climates, there may also be a concern to protect the ramp from accumulations of snow and ice to provide a safe path of egress travel at all times, including in inclement weather. Maintenance of the means of egress in the IFC requires an unobstructed path to allow for full instant use in case of a fire or emergency (see Section 1031.3). Typical methods for protecting these egress elements include roof overhangs or canopies, heated slabs and, when approved by the building official, a reliable snow removal maintenance program.

[BE] 1012.8 Handrails. *Ramps* with a rise greater than 6 inches (152 mm) shall have *handrails* on both sides. *Handrails* shall comply with Section 1014.

❖ To aid in the use of a ramp, handrails are to be provided. Handrails are intended to provide the user with a graspable surface for guidance and support. All ramps with a vertical rise greater than 6 inches (152 mm) between landings are to be provided with handrails on both sides [see Commentary Figures 1012.8(1) and 1014.2]. General strength requirements for handrails are found in Section 1014 with a reference to IBC Section 1607.8. Note that if the handrail extension is at a location that could be considered a protruding object, the handrail extension must return to the post at a height of less than 27 inches (686 mm) above the floor. Handrails along the ramp runs are not considered protruding objects.

Depending on the configuration of the ramp and the adjacent walking surface, ramps may require a combination of handrails, edge protection and guards. See Commentary Figures 1012.8(1), 1012.8(2), 1012.8(3) and 1012.8(4) for illustrations of some alternatives.

[BE] 1012.9 Guards. *Guards* shall be provided where required by Section 1015 and shall be constructed in accordance with Section 1015.

❖ To protect the user from falls to surfaces below, guards are to be provided where the sides of a ramp or landing are more than 30 inches (762 mm) above the adjacent grade. Guards are to be constructed in accordance with Section 1015, including the minimum height of 42 inches (1067 mm) [see Commentary Figure 1012.8(4)]. Except where permitted by Section 1015.3, the top of the guard cannot serve as the handrail.

Depending on the configuration of the ramp and the adjacent walking surface, ramps may require a combination of handrails, edge protection and guards. See Commentary Figures 1012.8(1), 1012.8(2), 1012.8(3) and 1012.8(4) for illustrations of some alternatives.

[BE] 1012.10 Edge protection. Edge protection complying with Section 1012.10.1 or 1012.10.2 shall be provided on each side of *ramp* runs and at each side of *ramp* landings.

Exceptions:

1. Edge protection is not required on *ramps* that are not required to have *handrails*, provided that they have flared sides that comply with the ICC A117.1 curb *ramp* provisions.
2. Edge protection is not required on the sides of *ramp* landings serving an adjoining *ramp* run or *stairway*.
3. Edge protection is not required on the sides of *ramp* landings having a vertical dropoff of not more than $^1/_2$ inch (12.7 mm) within 10 inches (254 mm) horizontally of the required landing area.

❖ This section of the code now addresses the comprehensive requirements for edge protection for all ramps. It must be noted that edge protection is not the same as the requirements for guards. The presence of a guard does not necessarily provide adequate edge protection, and the presence of adequate edge protection does not satisfy the requirements for a guard. Edge protection is necessary to prevent the wheels of a wheelchair from leaving the ramp surface or becoming lodged between the edge of the ramp and any adjacent construction. For example, a ramp may be located relatively adjacent to the exterior wall of a building. However, between the ramp edge and the exterior wall, there is a strip of earth for landscape purposes. Without adequate edge protection, persons confined to wheelchairs could possibly have their wheels run off the side of the ramp into the landscape, causing them to tip. These requirements are consistent with Section 405 of ICC A117.1 and those in the federal *2010 ADA Standards.*

Exception 1 allows a ramp to have minimal edge protection as long as its vertical rise is 6 inches (152 mm) or less. The exception is predicated on the ramp not needing any handrails, which is established by the provisions of Section 1012.8. Such a ramp would only need flared sides or returned curbs. Edge protection without handrails or guards could be a tripping hazard for ambulatory persons. For specific details of these types of edge protection, the provisions of Section 406 of ICC A117.1 for curb ramps must be followed.

Exception 2 reiterates that edge protection is not literally required entirely around a ramp landing. Obviously, edge protection is not required along that portion of the landing that directly adjoins a ramp run; it is only required along edges of the landing with a dropoff (other than steps of ramp runs).

Exception 3 states that edge protection is not required for those sides of a ramp landing directly adjacent to the ground surface that gently slopes away from the edge of the landing. If the grade adjacent to the ramp landing slopes no more than $^1/_2$:10 (which equates to 1:20) away from the landing, additional edge protection is not required. Such a gradual slope would not be detrimental to persons confined to wheelchairs as they negotiate the ramp landing. Note that this exception is limited to landings, not the ramp surface itself. The ramp must meet the edge protection in Section 1012.10.1 or 1012.10.2.

Depending on the configuration of the ramp and the adjacent walking surface, ramps may require a combination of handrails, edge protection and guards. See Commentary Figures 1012.8(1), 1012.8(2), 1012.8(3) and 1012.8(4) for illustrations of some alternatives.

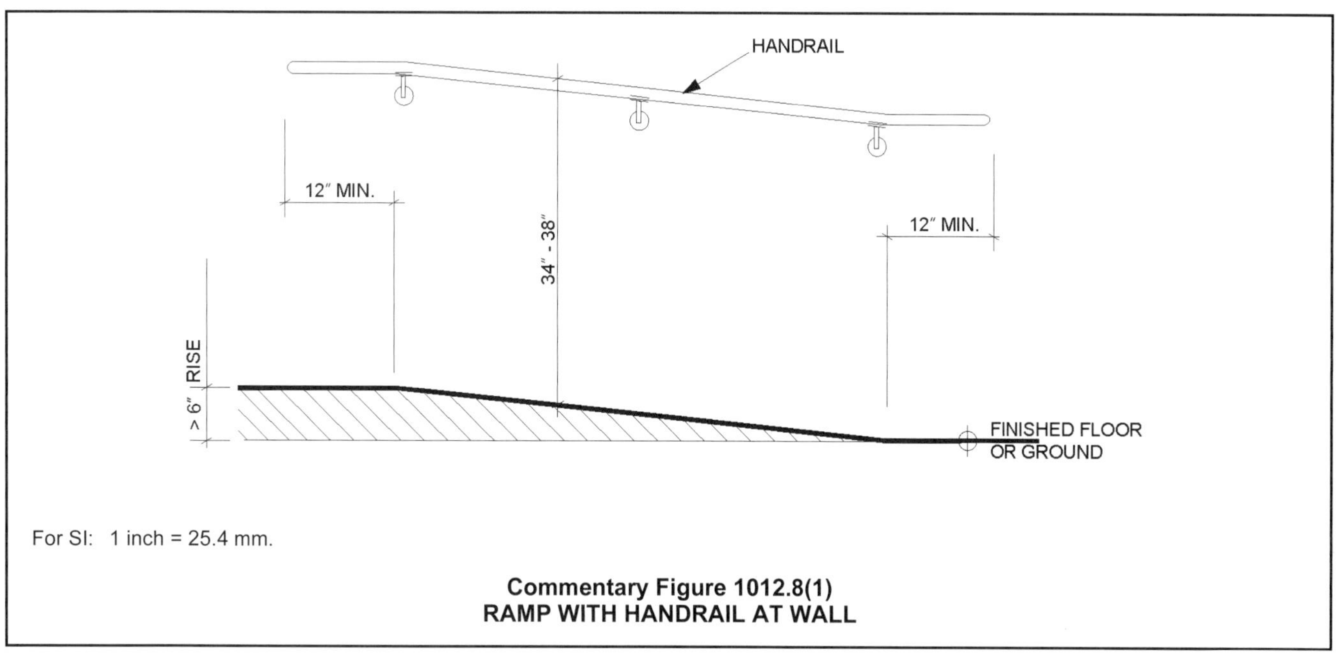

Commentary Figure 1012.8(1)
RAMP WITH HANDRAIL AT WALL

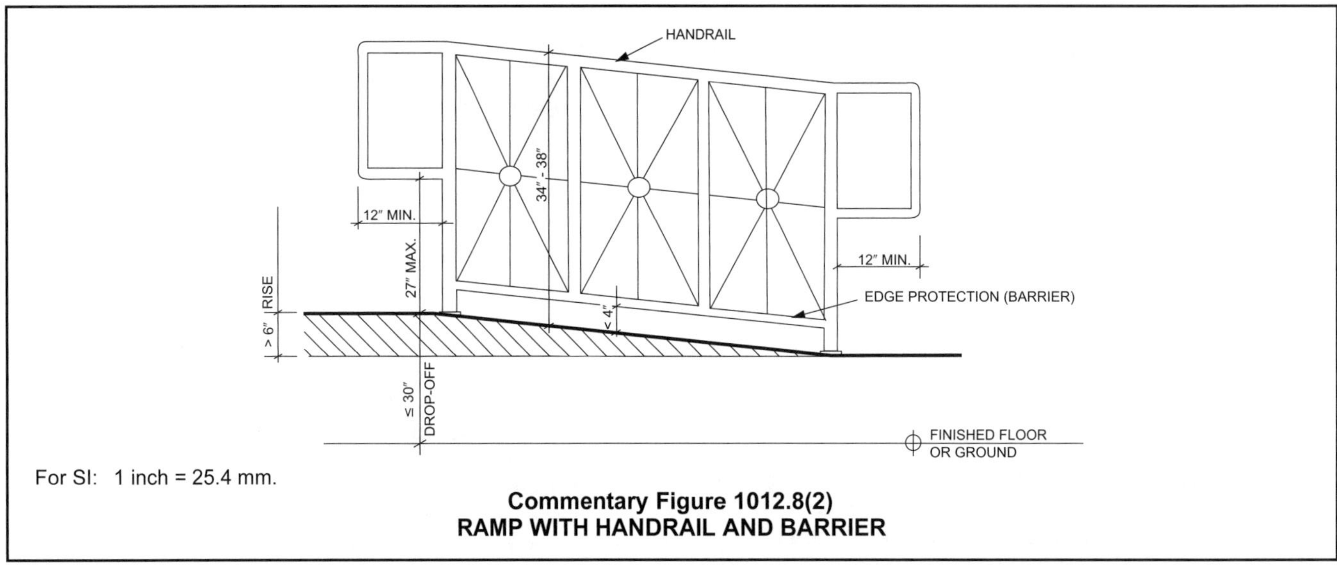

For SI: 1 inch = 25.4 mm.

Commentary Figure 1012.8(2)
RAMP WITH HANDRAIL AND BARRIER

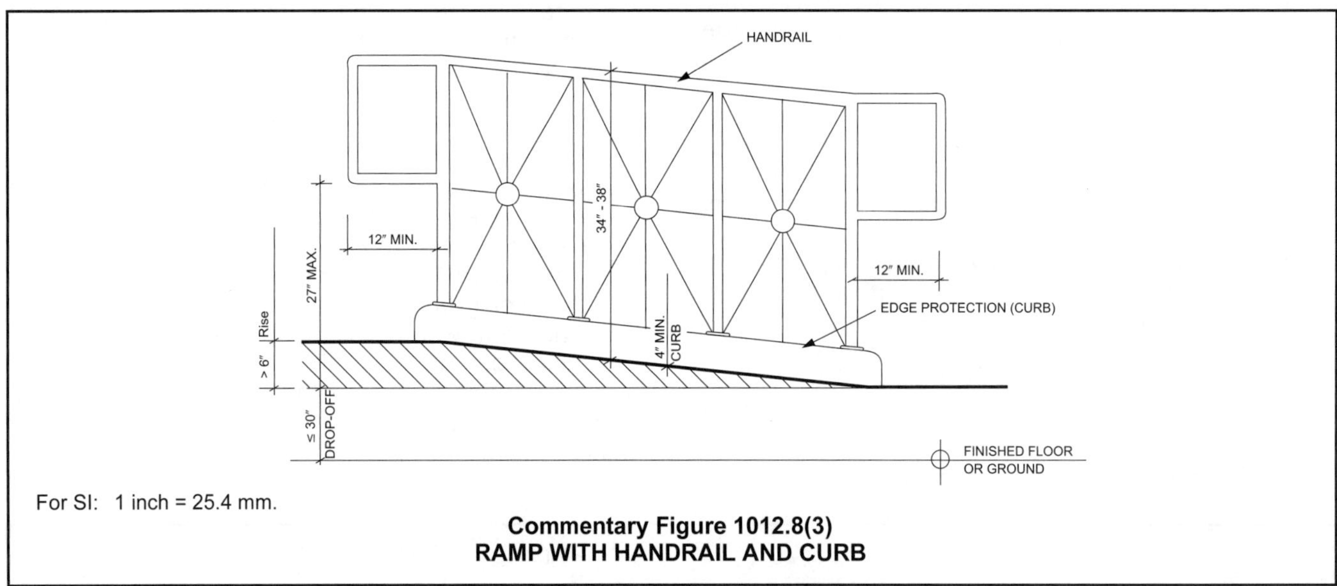

For SI: 1 inch = 25.4 mm.

Commentary Figure 1012.8(3)
RAMP WITH HANDRAIL AND CURB

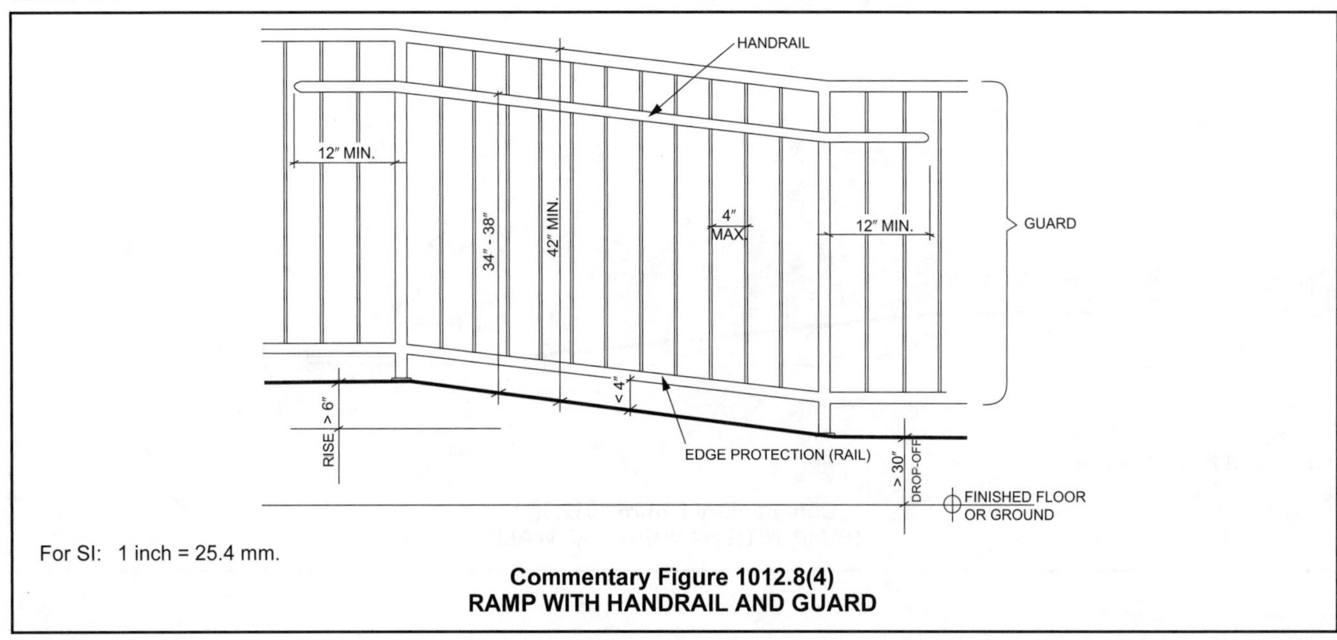

For SI: 1 inch = 25.4 mm.

Commentary Figure 1012.8(4)
RAMP WITH HANDRAIL AND GUARD

[BE] 1012.10.1 Curb, rail, wall or barrier. A curb, rail, wall or barrier shall be provided to serve as edge protection. A curb shall be not less than 4 inches (102 mm) in height. Barriers shall be constructed so that the barrier prevents the passage of a 4-inch-diameter (102 mm) sphere, where any portion of the sphere is within 4 inches (102 mm) of the floor or ground surface.

❖ Edge protection for ramps and ramp landings may be achieved with a built-up curb or other barrier, such as a rail, wall or guard. The barrier must be located near the surface of the ramp and landing such that a 4-inch-diameter (102 mm) sphere cannot pass through any openings. An example of an effective barrier would be the bottom rail of a guard system. If the bottom rail is located less than 4 inches (102 mm) above the ramp and landing surface, edge protection has been provided. If a curb option is used, the curb must be a minimum of 4 inches (102 mm) high. The curb or barrier prevents the wheel of a wheelchair from running off the edge of the surface and provides people with visual disabilities a toe stop at the edge of the walking surface (see Commentary Figure 1012.10.1).

[BE] 1012.10.2 Extended floor or ground surface. The floor or ground surface of the *ramp* run or landing shall extend 12 inches (305 mm) minimum beyond the inside face of a *handrail* complying with Section 1014.

❖ An alternative to providing some type of barrier at the edge of the ramp (see Section 1012.10.1) is to make the ramp surface wider than the handrails provided at either side. The combination of the wider surface and the handrail barrier would assist in preventing a wheelchair or crutch tip from moving very far off the ramp during a temporary slip (see Commentary Figure 1012.10.1).

SECTION 1013 EXIT SIGNS

[BE] 1013.1 Where required. *Exits* and *exit access* doors shall be marked by an *approved* exit sign readily visible from any direction of egress travel. The path of egress travel to *exits* and within *exits* shall be marked by readily visible exit signs to clearly indicate the direction of egress travel in cases where the *exit* or the path of egress travel is not immediately visible to the occupants. Intervening *means of egress* doors within *exits* shall be marked by exit signs. Exit sign placement shall be such that any point in an *exit access corridor* or *exit passageway* is within 100 feet (30 480 mm) or the *listed* viewing distance of the sign, whichever is less, from the nearest visible exit sign.

Exceptions:

1. Exit signs are not required in rooms or areas that require only one *exit* or *exit access*.
2. Main exterior *exit* doors or gates that are obviously and clearly identifiable as *exits* need not have *exit* signs where *approved* by the *fire code official*.
3. Exit signs are not required in occupancies in Group U and individual *sleeping units* or *dwelling units* in Group R-1, R-2 or R-3.
4. Exit signs are not required in dayrooms, sleeping rooms or dormitories in occupancies in Group I-3.
5. In occupancies in Groups A-4 and A-5, exit signs are not required on the seating side of vomitories or openings into seating areas where exit signs are provided in the concourse that are readily apparent from the vomitories. Egress lighting is provided to identify each vomitory or opening within the seating area in an emergency.

❖ Where an occupancy has two or more required exits or exit accesses, the means of egress must be provided with illuminated signs that readily identify the location of, and indicate the path of travel to, the exits. The signs must be illuminated with letters reading "Exit." The illumination may be internal or external to the sign. The signs should be visible from all directions in the exit access route. In cases where the signs are not visible to the occupants because of turns in the corridor or for other reasons, additional illuminated signs must be provided indicating the direction of egress to an exit. Exit signs must be located so that, where required, the nearest one is within 100 feet (30 480 mm) of the sign's listed viewing distance. UL 924 permits exit signs to be listed with a viewing distance of less than 100 feet (30 480 mm) (see Section 1013.5). Where a sign is listed for a

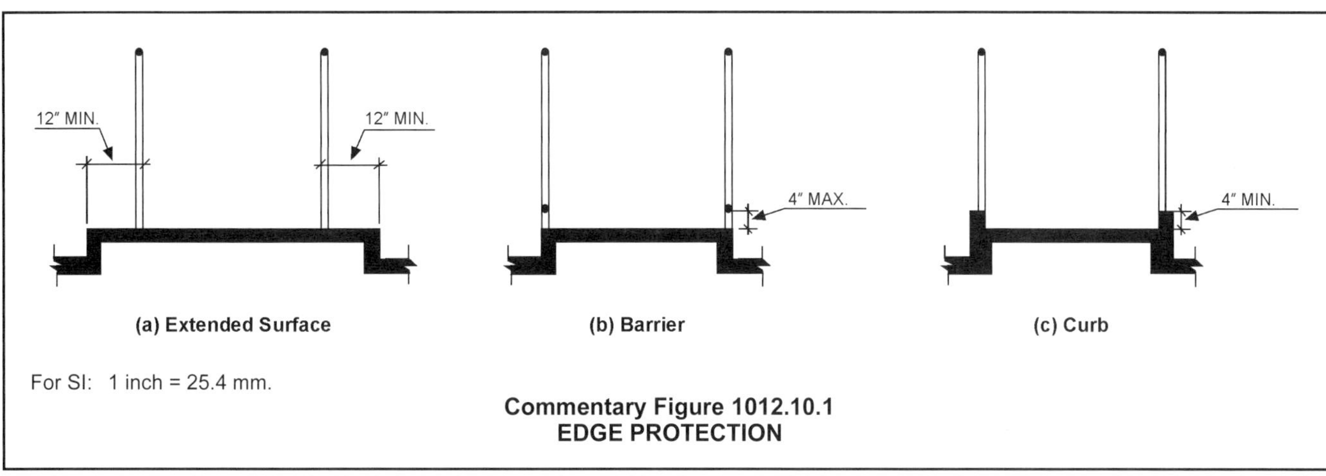

Commentary Figure 1012.10.1 EDGE PROTECTION

viewing distance of less than 100 feet (30 480 mm), the label on the sign will indicate the appropriate viewing distance. If such a sign is used, the spacing of the signs should be based on the listed viewing distance.

Typically, once an occupant enters an exit enclosure, exit signs are no longer needed; however, in buildings with more complicated egress layouts, it is possible that the direction for egress travel within the exit is not immediately apparent. For example, exit passageways can be part of the path of exit travel at the level of exit discharge or transfer floors. Evacuees may hesitate or be confused where the vertical travel becomes horizontal travel, which may result in a delay in evacuation. In these situations, exit signs may be needed within the exit enclosure (see Commentary Figure 1013.1).

The exceptions identify conditions where exit signs are not necessary since they would not increase the safety of the egress path.

For Exceptions 1 and 3, the assumption is that the occupants are familiar enough with the space to know the way out and/or the exits are obvious. Also, in most cases, the way out is the same as the way in.

In accordance with Exception 2, where the main exterior door through which occupants enter the building is obviously an exit, exit signs are not required. For example, a two-story Group B building has a main employee/customer entrance. The entrance consists of a storefront arrangement with glass doors and sidelights. The entrance is centrally located within the building. These main exterior exit doors can be quickly observed as being an exit and would not need to be marked with an exit sign.

In accordance with Exception 4, exit signs are not required in detainee living and sleeping room areas of Group I-3 buildings. In cases of emergency, occupants in Group I-3 are escorted by staff to the exits and to safety. Exit sign materials can also be potential weapons where accessible to the detainees.

In the Group A-4 and A-5 occupancies described in Exception 5, the egress path is obvious and thus exit signs are not needed. Additionally, because of the configuration of the vomitories, the exit signs are not readily visible to persons immediately adjacent to or above the vomitory.

[BE] 1013.2 Low-level exit signs in Group R-1. Where exit signs are required in Group R-1 occupancies by Section 1013.1, additional low-level exit signs shall be provided in all areas serving guestrooms in Group R-1 occupancies and shall comply with Section 1013.5.

The bottom of the sign shall be not less than 10 inches (254 mm) nor more than 18 inches (455 mm) above the floor level. The sign shall be flush mounted to the door or wall. Where mounted on the wall, the edge of the sign shall be within 4 inches (102 mm) of the door frame on the latch side.

❖ Because people may be sleeping and because most residents are transient (and thus unfamiliar with the space) in hotels (i.e., Group R-1), low-level exit signs must be provided for emergency exit routes from guestrooms. When smoke at the ceiling obscures the exit signs required by Section 1013.1, these signs will serve as backup identification of the exit door. By the

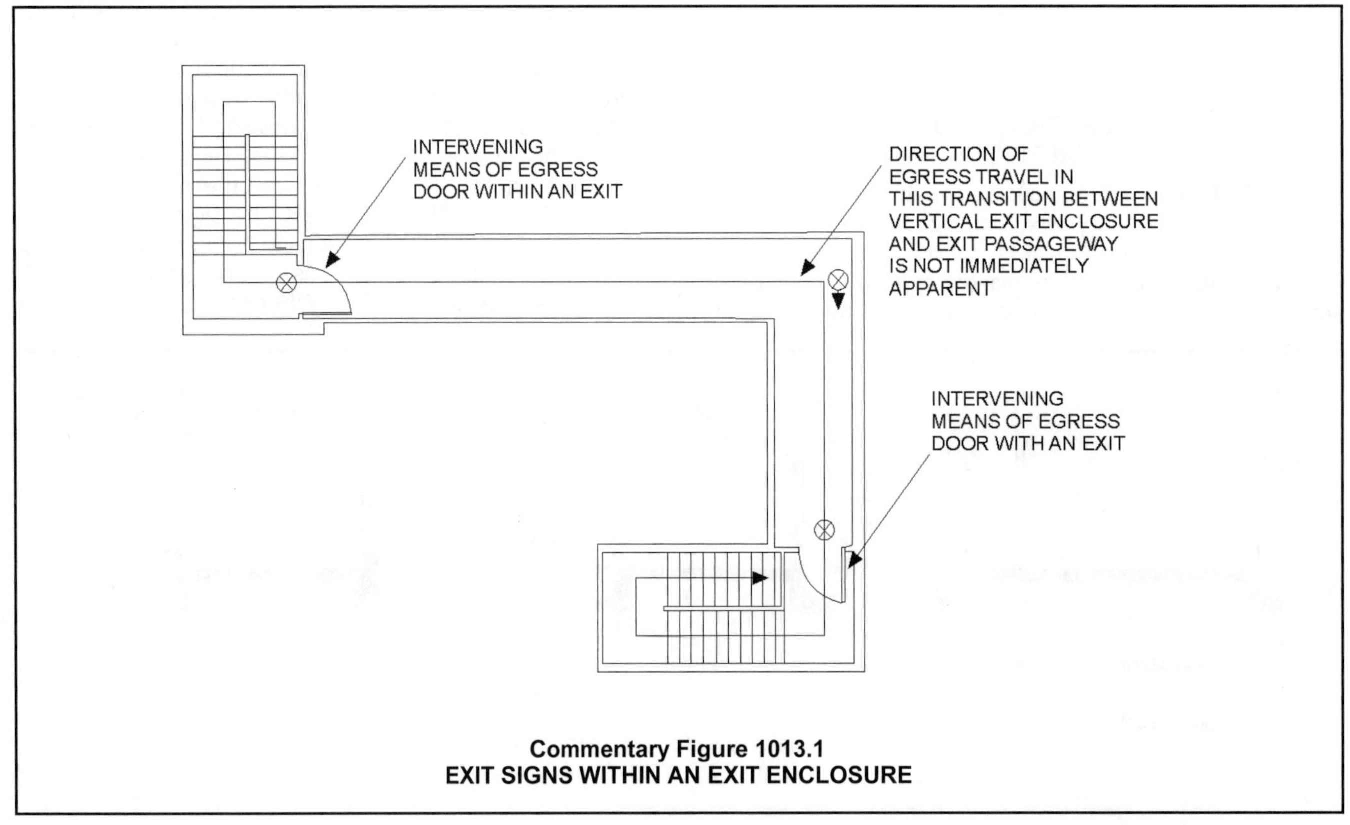

Commentary Figure 1013.1
EXIT SIGNS WITHIN AN EXIT ENCLOSURE

reference to Section 1013.5, these signs must be internally illuminated and listed and labeled in accordance with UL 924. It is not the intent of this section to require low-level exit signs in the guestrooms. The low-level exit signs are required only in areas where Section 1013.1 requires exit signs and only leading from the guestroom area, not throughout the entire hotel.

The exit signs must be mounted on the exit door itself or to the side of the exit door on the latch side. The height of the bottom of the exit sign will allow for exit signs not to conflict with accessible route requirements. ICC A117.1 requires doors on an accessible route to have a smooth surface for the bottom 10 inches (254 mm) so that someone could use the footplates on their wheelchair to assist in opening the door.

The requirements do not indicate what low-level signage is appropriate for exit signs that provide direction rather than at the exit. It is also not clear on how an exit sign on a door will be visible from down the corridor if the door is perpendicular to the direction of the hallway.

[BE] 1013.3 Illumination. Exit signs shall be internally or externally illuminated.

Exception: Tactile signs required by Section 1013.4 need not be provided with illumination.

❖ This section simply provides the scope for illumination of regulated exit signs. Exit signs must be illuminated so that they are readily apparent in situations where the lights may be off or the building has lost power. Exit signs with raised letters and braille are specifically addressed in Section 1013.4.

[BE] 1013.4 Raised character and braille exit signs. A sign stating EXIT in visual characters, raised characters and braille and complying with ICC A117.1 shall be provided adjacent to each door to an *area of refuge,* providing direct access to a stairway, an exterior area for assisted rescue, an *exit stairway* or *ramp*, an *exit passageway* and the *exit discharge*.

❖ The purpose of this sign is to serve as way finding for a person with vision impairments. This is in addition to the exit signs required by Section 1013.1.

"Tactile" is defined as "used for the sense of touch;" therefore, signage that has either raised letters or braille is considered tactile. For exit signage, visual, raised letters and braille are required. ICC A117.1 includes requirements for the sign and the correct placement. Typically, the sign is placed at about 4 feet 6 inches (1375 mm) above the floor and on the wall at the latch side of the door. While not required to be illuminated by these provisions, illumination would be advantageous for a person with partial sight. High contrast is important (see Commentary Figure 1013.4).

This signage is needed to indicate which doors are serving as exits for those persons with visual impairments. Signs are needed on the required exit doors in the building, including:

- At doors leading to an interior or exterior exit stairway or ramp.
- At doors leading to an exit passageway.
- Within the exit enclosures leading to the outside or to an exit passageway.
- At exit doors that lead directly to the outside.

While an area of refuge may be located within an enclosure for an exit stairway, Section 1009.3 also allows the area of refuge to be located immediately outside of the enclosure for the exit stairway. In this situation, exit signage with visual, raised letters and braille would be required both at the door leading into the area of refuge and the door leading to the exit stairway. Exterior areas for assisted rescue are typically located immediately outside of an exit door (see Section 1009.7).

This is not intended to preclude the signage from including additional information as long as "Exit" is first. For example, labeling the door to the exit enclosure as "Exit Stairway" would indicate to the visually impaired person that once they moved through the door, they would be dealing with vertical travel. This could be considered an additional safety feature. This section is also referenced in Section 1111.3. For additional way-finding signage inside the stairway enclosure, see Section 1023.9.

[BE] 1013.5 Internally illuminated exit signs. Electrically powered, *self-luminous* and *photoluminescent exit* signs shall be *listed* and labeled in accordance with UL 924 and shall be installed in accordance with the manufacturer's instructions and Section 1203. Exit signs shall be illuminated at all times.

❖ All exit signage must be listed and labeled as indicated in UL 924, *Standard for Emergency Lighting*

Commentary Figure 1013.4
EXAMPLE OF EXIT SIGNAGE WITH VISUAL AND RAISED CHARACTERS WITH BRAILLE

and Power Equipment. Listed exit signs are required by UL 924 to meet the same graphics, illumination and power sources defined in Sections 1013.6.1 through 1013.6.3 for externally illuminated signs. Internal illumination may be electrically powered or be of a self-luminous or photoluminescent product. Electrically powered would include LED, incandescent, fluorescent and electroluminescent types of signs. If a sign is photoluminescent, the "charging" source must be continually available (see the definitions in Chapter 2 for "Photoluminescent" and "Self-luminous"). Exit signs must be illuminated at all times, including when the building may not be fully occupied. If a fire occurs late at night, there may be cleaning crews or persons working overtime in the building who will need to be able to find the exits. The reference to Chapter 27 is so the signs will be equipped with a connection to an emergency power supply.

[BE] 1013.6 Externally illuminated exit signs. Externally illuminated exit signs shall comply with Sections 1013.6.1 through 1013.6.3.

❖ Externally illuminated exit signage must meet the graphic, illumination and emergency power requirements in the referenced sections. The requirements are the same as for internally illuminated signage.

[BE] 1013.6.1 Graphics. Every exit sign and directional exit sign shall have plainly legible letters not less than 6 inches (152 mm) high with the principal strokes of the letters not less than $^3/_4$ inch (19.1 mm) wide. The word "EXIT" shall have letters having a width not less than 2 inches (51 mm) wide, except the letter "I," and the minimum spacing between letters shall be not less than $^3/_8$ inch (9.5 mm). Signs larger than the minimum established in this section shall have letter widths, strokes and spacing in proportion to their height.

The word "EXIT" shall be in high contrast with the background and shall be clearly discernible when the means of exit sign illumination is or is not energized. If a chevron directional indicator is provided as part of the exit sign, the construction shall be such that the direction of the chevron directional indicator cannot be readily changed.

❖ Every exit sign and directional sign located in the exit access or exit route is required to have a color contrast vivid enough to make the signs readily visible, even where not illuminated. Letters must be at least 6 inches (152 mm) high and their stroke not less than $^3/_4$ inch (19.1 mm) wide (see Commentary Figure 1013.6.1). The sizing of the letters is predicated on the readability of the wording from a distance of 100 feet (30 480 mm).

While red letters are common for exit signs, sometimes green on black is used in auditorium areas with low-lighting levels, such as theaters, because that color combination tends not to distract the audience's attention. It is more important that the exit sign be readily visible with respect to the background.

Exit signs may be larger than the minimum size specified; however, the standardized proportion of the letters must be maintained. Externally illuminated signage that is smaller could use the requirements in UL 924 for guidance; however, sign spacing would need to be adjusted, and alternative approval would be through the building official having jurisdiction.

A "chevron directional indicator" is the same as a directional arrow. The language is intended to be consistent with UL 924.

[BE] 1013.6.2 Exit sign illumination. The face of an exit sign illuminated from an external source shall have an intensity of not less than 5 footcandles (54 lux).

❖ Every exit sign and directional sign must be continuously illuminated to provide a light intensity at the illuminated surface of at least 5 footcandles (54 lux). It is not a requirement that the exit signs be internally illuminated. An external illumination source with the power capabilities specified by Section 1013.6.3 is acceptable.

[BE] 1013.6.3 Power source. Exit signs shall be illuminated at all times. To ensure continued illumination for a duration of not less than 90 minutes in case of primary power loss, the sign illumination means shall be connected to an emergency power system provided from storage batteries, unit equipment or an on-site generator. The installation of the emergency power system shall be in accordance with Section 604. Group I-2, Condition 2 exit sign illumination shall not be provided by unit equipment batteries only.

> **Exception:** *Approved* exit sign illumination types that provide continuous illumination independent of external power sources for a duration of not less than 90 minutes, in case of primary power loss, are not required to be connected to an emergency electrical system.

❖ Exit signs must be illuminated on a continuous basis so that when a fire emergency occurs, occupants will be able to identify the locations of the exits. The reliability of the power sources supplying the electrical energy required for maintaining the illumination of exit signs is important. When power interruptions occur,

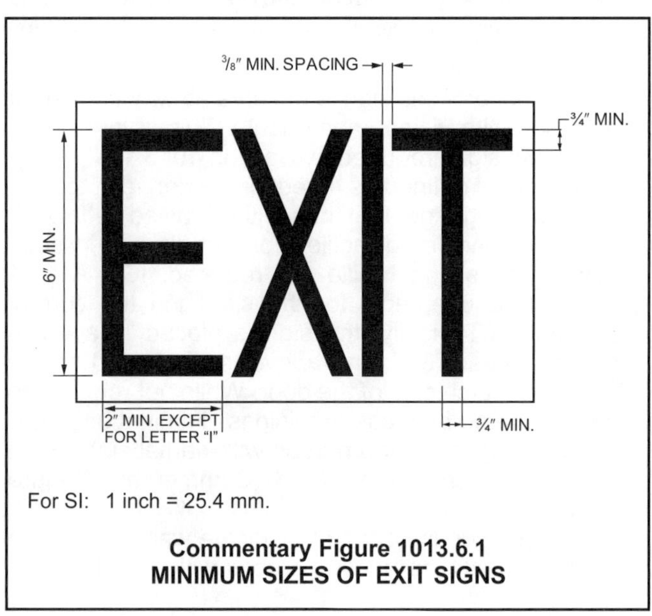

For SI: 1 inch = 25.4 mm.

Commentary Figure 1013.6.1
MINIMUM SIZES OF EXIT SIGNS

exit sign illumination must be obtained from an emergency power system. This does not imply that the sign must be internally illuminated. Whatever illumination system is used, whether internal or external, it must be connected to a system designed to pick up the power load required by the exit signs after loss of the normal power supply. The last sentence is a more restrictive requirement for hospitals. Hospitals cannot rely only on equipment batteries for the illumination of their exit signs. Typically, hospitals connect illumination of their exit signage to the emergency on-site generator.

Per the exception, where self-luminous signs are used, connection to the emergency electrical supply system is not required. A trickle-charge battery to illuminate the exit sign is another option.

IFC requirements for emergency power for emergency egress lighting and exit signage in existing buildings only requires a 60-minute time duration. This is not a conflict, but rather recognition of the loss of battery storage capability over a length of time.

SECTION 1014 HANDRAILS

[BE] 1014.1 Where required. *Handrails* serving *flights of stairways*, *ramps*, stepped *aisles* and ramped *aisles* shall be adequate in strength and attachment in accordance with Section 1607.8 of the *International Building Code*. *Handrails* required for *flights of stairways* by Section 1011.11 shall comply with Sections 1014.2 through 1014.9. *Handrails* required for *ramps* by Section 1012.8 shall comply with Sections 1014.2 through 1014.8. *Handrails* for stepped *aisles* and ramped *aisles* required by Section 1029.16 shall comply with Sections 1014.2 through 1014.8.

❖ Handrails are required at stairways and ramps. In all situations, they must be designed in accordance with the structural requirements in IBC Section 1607.8. There are, however, distinct differences in how handrail requirements are applied in stairways, ramps, stepped aisles and ramped aisles. The specific section references allow for this consideration. Where and how many handrails for stairways and ramps are specified in Sections 1003.5, 1011.11 and 1012.8. Where handrails are required in assembly seating for stepped aisles and ramped aisles is specified in Section 1029.14.

Stairways and their handrails are not part of an accessible route and are not subject to the stairway technical requirements in ICC A117.1. Standards are referenced only to the extent specified by the code (see Section 102.4).

Handrails are also very distinct from guards, even though they are sometimes incorrectly called "guardrails." The handrail is the element that is grasped during vertical travel for guidance, stabilization, pulling and as an aid in arresting a possible fall. Guards are located near the side of an elevated walking surface to minimize the possibility of a fall to a lower level and are discussed in Section 1015. However, in residential applications, in some locations in assembly seating, and along alternating tread devices and ships ladders, the top rail of a guard may also serve as a handrail (see Section 1015.3, Exceptions 3–6 and Section 1029.16).

[BE] 1014.2 Height. *Handrail* height, measured above *stair* tread *nosings*, or finish surface of *ramp* slope, shall be uniform, not less than 34 inches (864 mm) and not more than 38 inches (965 mm). *Handrail* height of *alternating tread devices* and ships ladders, measured above tread *nosings*, shall be uniform, not less than 30 inches (762 mm) and not more than 34 inches (864 mm).

Exceptions:

1. Where handrail fittings or bendings are used to provide continuous transition between *flights*, the fittings or bendings shall be permitted to exceed the maximum height.
2. In Group R-3 occupancies; within *dwelling units* in Group R-2 occupancies; and in Group U occupancies that are associated with a Group R-3 occupancy or associated with individual *dwelling units* in Group R-2 occupancies; where handrail fittings or bendings are used to provide continuous transition between *flights*, transition at *winder* treads, transition from *handrail* to *guard*, or where used at the start of a *flight*, the *handrail* height at the fittings or bendings shall be permitted to exceed the maximum height.
3. *Handrails* on top of a *guard* where permitted along stepped *aisles* and ramped *aisles* in accordance with Section 1029.16.

❖ It has been demonstrated that for safe use, the height of handrails must not be less than 34 inches (864 mm) nor more than 38 inches (965 mm) above the leading edge of stairway treads, landings or other walking surfaces (see Commentary Figure 1014.2). This requirement is applicable for all uses, including handrails within a dwelling unit.

The fundamental stairway requirements are not appropriate for alternating tread devices and ships ladders since they differ significantly from other types of stairways. The permitted range for handrail height for alternating tread devices and ships ladders allows for a lower height above the tread nosings. The minimum required height is reduced from 34 inches (864 mm) to 30 inches (762 mm), with a maximum permitted height of 34 inches (864 mm). The special features of an alternating tread device or ships ladder result in differences of handrail use, such as different arm posture, the hand gripping the handrail near a higher part of the body and the use of handrails under the arms for stabilization when descending. Therefore, a lower handrail height is more appropriate.

Exceptions 1 and 2 allow for the use of common fittings and bendings to provide for continuous transition of the handrail at specified turns and pitch changes in the stairway where the fitting or bending might exceed the maximum handrail height. In some cases, there is no reference for the height when the fitting or handrail might extend beyond the nosings at the intersection of adjoining flights. Exception 1 applies to all stairways between flights. This typically occurs at the center handrail at the landings on a dogleg or switchback stairway configuration. Although handrails are not required on the landing, the code requirement for handrail extensions or for handrail continuity often creates the need for some type of transition, especially at turns (see also Section 1014.6). This exception would allow for an easing or gooseneck riser over the landing to be used for a smooth transition of the handrail. The use of the new exceptions may permit a more gradual variation in the height even though it will allow for portions of the handrail to exceed the normal 38-inch (965 mm) maximum height. The belief is that handrail continuity is more important than staying within the height limitation.

Exception 2 applies to dwelling units with the intent to allow transition elements at common locations, such as the start of the flight, at winder treads or from handrail to guard at landings. Combined with the guard height reduction in Section 1015.3, Exception 1, the end result may be fewer transition pieces. This is consistent with provisions in the IRC.

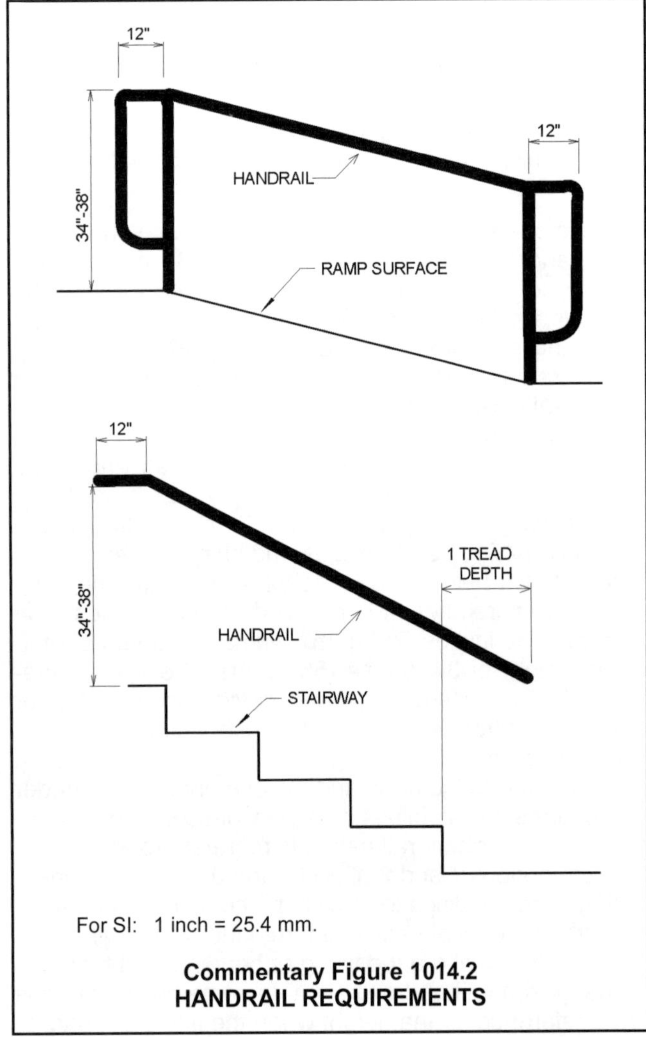

Commentary Figure 1014.2
HANDRAIL REQUIREMENTS

Exception 3 is in recognition of the special allowances for the top rail of a guard to serve as a handrail in limited situations in an assembly seating area. See Section 1029.16 for specifics.

[BE] 1014.3 Handrail graspability. Required *handrails* shall comply with Section 1014.3.1 or shall provide equivalent graspability.

> **Exception:** In Group R-3 occupancies; within *dwelling units* in Group R-2 occupancies; and in Group U occupancies that are accessory to a Group R-3 occupancy or accessory to individual *dwelling units* in Group R-2 occupancies; *handrails* shall be Type I in accordance with Section 1014.3.1, Type II in accordance with Section 1014.3.2 or shall provide equivalent graspability.

❖ The abilities to grasp a handrail firmly and slide a hand along the rail's gripping surface without meeting obstructions are important factors in the safe use of stairways and ramps. These properties are largely functions of the shape of the handrail. Handrails for stairways and ramps must meet the specifications of Section 1014.3.1 or be determined to have grasping properties and attributes equivalent to profiles allowed in Section 1014.3.1. Such determinations of equivalence are an allowed option made by local building officials based on the profile presented and the building official's evaluation of its properties. A complete evaluation will consider the four basic functions of a handrail: guidance, stabilization, pulling and aid in arresting a fall. The determination is best made by comparative use on stairs or ramps of properly mounted samples. Handrails that meet neither Type I nor Type II characteristics may be considered to have equivalent graspability. Complete evaluation will also consider the mounting of the handrail and understanding the interference of handrail mounts on the gripping surfaces of smaller profiles. For a discussion of this, see Section 1014.4.

The exception allows for an alternative Type II handrail within residential units and their associated structures. A handrail on common stairways within an apartment building or on the steps to the front door of a townhouse could not use this exception unless approved by the building official as being equivalent to Type I. The residential allowance is consistent with the IRC.

[BE] 1014.3.1 Type I. *Handrails* with a circular cross section shall have an outside diameter of not less than $1^1/_4$ inches (32 mm) and not greater than 2 inches (51 mm). Where the *handrail* is not circular, it shall have a perimeter dimension of not less than 4 inches (102 mm) and not greater than $6^1/_4$ inches (160 mm) with a maximum cross-sectional dimension of $2^1/_4$ inches (57 mm) and minimum cross-sectional dimension of 1 inch (25 mm). Edges shall have a minimum radius of 0.01 inch (0.25 mm).

❖ Handrails have traditionally been regulated as either circular or noncircular rails. The noncircular rails have previously been limited to a maximum perimeter dimension of $6^1/_4$ inches (160 mm), with other limitations addressing minimum perimeter and minimum and maximum cross-sectional dimensions. These handrail shapes are now referred to as Type I handrails.

Type I handrails include circular cross sections with an outside diameter of at least $1^1/_4$ inches (32 mm) but not greater than 2 inches (51 mm). This limits the perimeter of the cross section such that the gripping surface incorporates the bottom of the rail. A handrail with either a very narrow or a large cross section is not graspable in a power grip by all able-bodied users and certainly not by those with hand-strength or flexibility deficiencies. A power grip typically accesses the bottom surface of the handrail, such as around a bar. A pinching grip is not as effective when there is a need to arrest a fall. An example of a pinching grip would be where a 2x4 stud on edge was used as a handrail. This would not comply with graspability concerns.

Noncircular Type I cross sections must meet the alternative noncircular criteria in this section, and the bottom of the rail must be considered part of the suitable gripping surface. Of note is that this criteria now includes a minimum cross section of 1 inch (25 mm) to provide for designs that reduce the interference of fingers and an opposing thumb that occurs when small objects are tightly grasped. Edges must be slightly rounded and not sharp. An example is shown in Commentary Figure 1014.3.1.

Ramp requirements in ICC A117.1 are referenced as part of the accessible route requirements in IBC Chapter 11. Current handrail provisions are largely coordinated with the Type I handrail requirements in this section. Section 103 of ICC A117.1 would also permit alternative handrail shapes if they provide equivalent or better graspability.

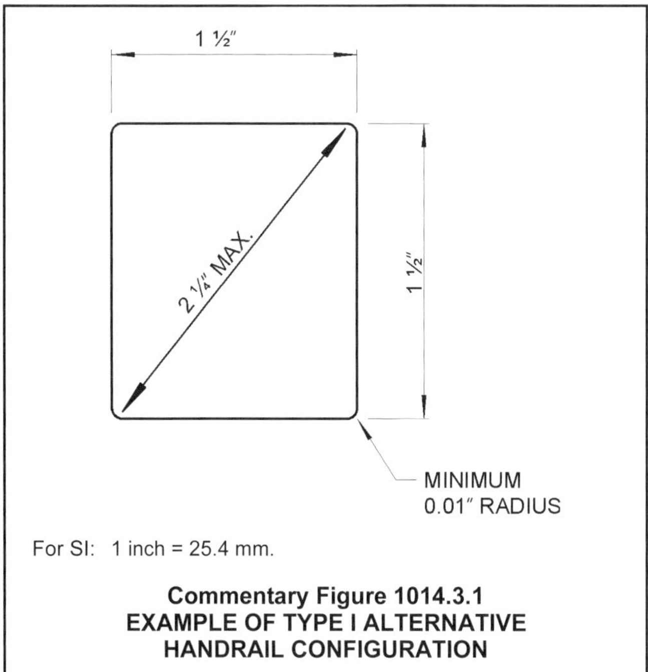

Commentary Figure 1014.3.1
EXAMPLE OF TYPE I ALTERNATIVE HANDRAIL CONFIGURATION

[BE] 1014.3.2 Type II. *Handrails* with a perimeter greater than $6^1/_4$ inches (160 mm) shall provide a graspable finger recess area on both sides of the profile. The finger recess shall begin within a distance of $^3/_4$ inch (19 mm) measured vertically from the tallest portion of the profile and achieve a depth of not less than $^5/_{16}$ inch (8 mm) within $^7/_8$ inch (22 mm) below the widest portion of the profile. This required depth shall continue for not less than $^3/_8$ inch (10 mm) to a level that is not less than $1^3/_4$ inches (45 mm) below the tallest portion of the profile. The width of the *handrail* above the recess shall be not less than $1^1/_4$ inches (32 mm) to not greater than $2^3/_4$ inches (70 mm). Edges shall have a minimum radius of 0.01 inch (0.25 mm).

❖ Handrail profiles having a perimeter dimension greater than $6^1/_4$ inches (160 mm), identified as Type II handrails, are acceptable within dwelling units and their associated structures when complying with all of the specific dimensional requirements.

Research has shown that Type II handrails have graspability that is essentially equal to or greater than the graspability of handrails meeting the long-accepted and codified shape and size now defined as Type I.

The key features of the graspability of Type II handrails are graspable finger recesses on both sides of the handrail. These recesses allow users to firmly grip a properly proportioned grasping surface on the top of the handrail, ensuring that the user can tightly retain a power-span grip on the handrail for all forces that are associated with attempts to arrest a fall.

This class of handrails incorporates a grip surface with controlled recesses for the purchase of the fingers and opposing thumb. These handrail shapes allow the use of power-span grips that need not encompass the bottom surfaces of the rail, allowing the design of taller cross sections that can eliminate the interference of mountings and provide a completely uninterrupted gripping surface for the user. The limits of the position and depth of the required recesses represent the minimum standard. Optimizing the design within the parameters with larger recesses and complete finger clearance from mountings will enhance the performance of these profiles. Although this standard allows design flexibility, it is important to follow the specifications accurately to comply. Each drawing in Commentary Figure 1014.3.2 illustrates the requirements of each sentence for clarity.

[BE] 1014.4 Continuity. *Handrail* gripping surfaces shall be continuous, without interruption by newel posts or other obstructions.

Exceptions:

1. *Handrails* within *dwelling units* are permitted to be interrupted by a newel post at a turn or landing.
2. Within a *dwelling unit*, the use of a volute, turnout, starting easing or starting newel is allowed over the lowest tread.
3. Handrail brackets or balusters attached to the bottom surface of the *handrail* that do not project horizon-

tally beyond the sides of the *handrail* within $1^1/_2$ inches (38 mm) of the bottom of the *handrail* shall not be considered obstructions. For each $^1/_2$ inch (12.7 mm) of additional *handrail* perimeter dimension above 4 inches (102 mm), the vertical clearance dimension of $1^1/_2$ inches (38 mm) shall be permitted to be reduced by $^1/_8$ inch (3.2 mm).

4. Where *handrails* are provided along walking surfaces with slopes not steeper than 1:20, the bottoms of the handrail gripping surfaces shall be permitted to be obstructed along their entire length where they are integral to crash rails or bumper guards.

5. *Handrails* serving stepped *aisles* or ramped *aisles* are permitted to be discontinuous in accordance with Section 1029.16.1.

❖ Handrails must be usable for their entire length without requiring the users to release their grasp. Typically, when using the handrail while traveling the means of egress, an individual's arm is extended to lead the body with the hand forming a loose grip on the top and sides of the rail. If handrails are to be of service to users, they must be uninterrupted and continuous. Oversize newels, changes in the guard system or excessive supports at the bottom of small perimeter handrails can cause interruption of the handrail, requiring the occupants to release their grip [see Commentary Figure 1014.4(1)]. Exception 1 allows the interruption of the handrail by a newel post at the intersection of two handrail sections at a turn within a flight or at a landing in dwelling units; however, this exception is not applicable to curved or spiral stairs. Exception 2 provides for familiar and historical handrail details, often combined with guards, that have been used for decades in dwelling units without substantiated detriment to the safety of the occupants. Exception 3 provides specifications for the attachment of brackets and balusters to the bottom of handrails to provide for minimum finger clearance such that they will not be considered obstructions. This method of handrail support limits interruptions of the grip surfaces at the bottom of smaller perimeter shapes that otherwise would deter or impede the user's ability to attain a stabilizing grip essential to safe stairway use. Larger handrail sizes permit shorter brackets since geometrically the finger clearance is still maintained [see Commentary Figure 1014.4(2)]. For example, a Type II handrail may elevate the fingertips completely above the supports, allowing the rail to be mounted by other means that do not obstruct where providing the clearances specified. Exception 4 allows for products that serve dual purposes, such as the bumper guard/handrail found in hospitals and nursing homes along corridors, to have a continuous bottom support. Since these are only permitted on slopes that are less than what is defined as a ramp, the handrails are more for assistance in mobility or balance rather than to arrest a fall.

Exception 5 references provisions for stepped and ramped aisles in assembly seating. Discontinuous handrails are permitted to allow for access to seats. Such discontinuous handrails must still extend the full run of the aisle stairs or ramp. See Section 1029.16.1.

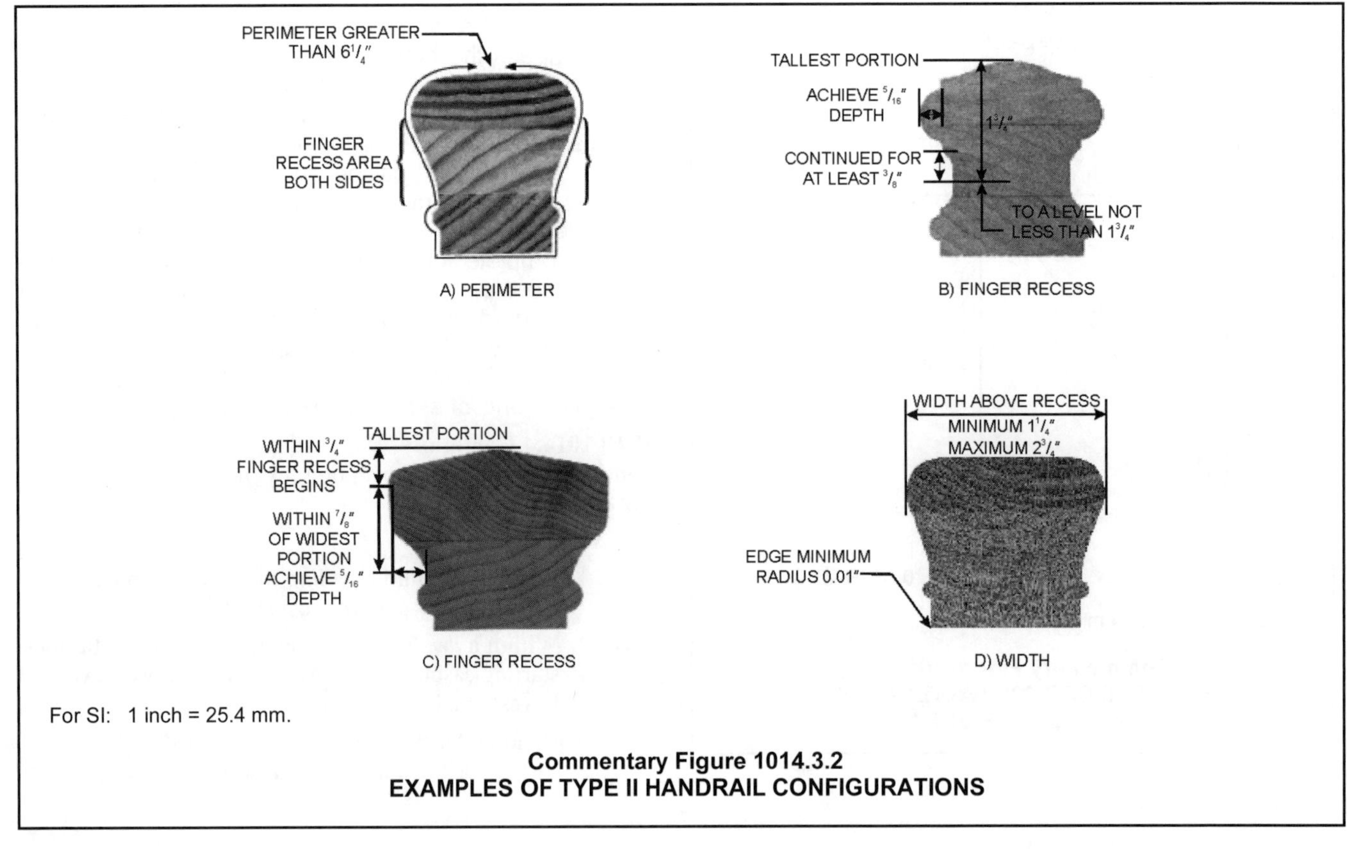

Commentary Figure 1014.3.2
EXAMPLES OF TYPE II HANDRAIL CONFIGURATIONS

[BE] 1014.5 Fittings. *Handrails* shall not rotate within their fittings.

❖ Fittings are those component pieces of a continuous handrail that are shaped or bent and attached to the longer sections of straight or curved handrail to provide for transition at changes in pitch or direction or to provide for termination of a continuous handrail. Fittings and handrails must be securely joined to ensure a stable handrail that does not allow any portion to rotate when grasped.

[BE] 1014.6 Handrail extensions. *Handrails* shall return to a wall, *guard* or the walking surface or shall be continuous to the *handrail* of an adjacent *flight* of *stairs* or *ramp* run. Where *handrails* are not continuous between *flights* the *handrails* shall extend horizontally not less than 12 inches (305 mm) beyond the top riser and continue to slope for the depth of one tread beyond the bottom riser. At *ramps* where *handrails* are not continuous between runs, the *handrails* shall extend horizontally above the landing 12 inches (305 mm) minimum beyond the top and bottom of *ramp* runs. The extensions of

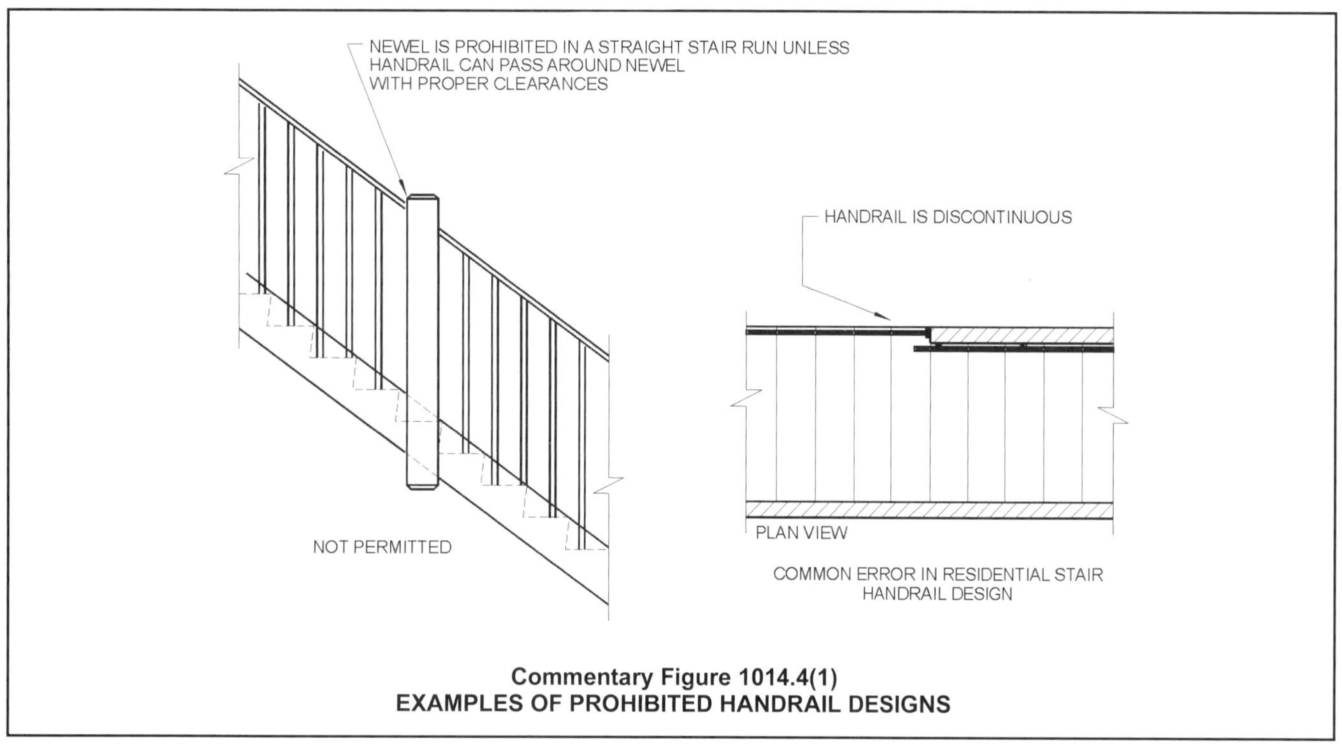

Commentary Figure 1014.4(1)
EXAMPLES OF PROHIBITED HANDRAIL DESIGNS

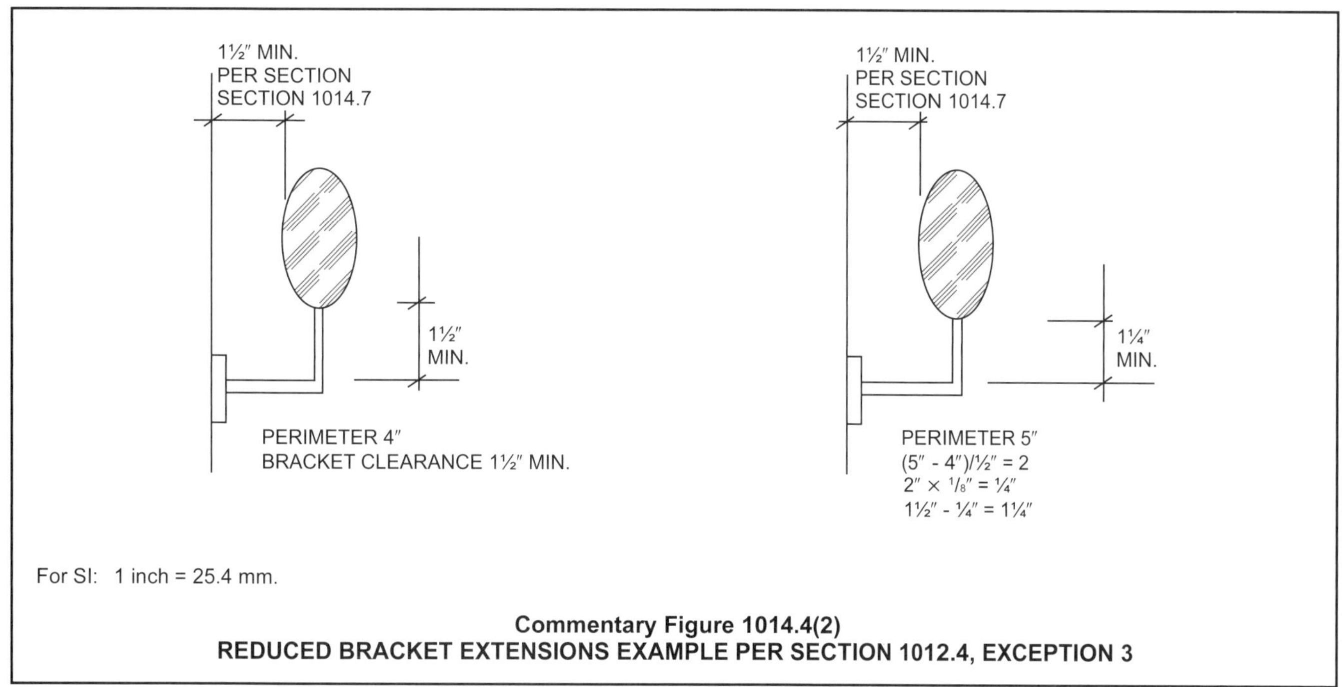

For SI: 1 inch = 25.4 mm.

Commentary Figure 1014.4(2)
REDUCED BRACKET EXTENSIONS EXAMPLE PER SECTION 1012.4, EXCEPTION 3

handrails shall be in the same direction of the *flights* of *stairs* at *stairways* and the *ramp* runs at *ramps*.

Exceptions:

1. *Handrails* within a *dwelling unit* that is not required to be accessible need extend only from the top riser to the bottom riser.
2. *Handrails* serving *aisles* in rooms or spaces used for assembly purposes are permitted to comply with the *handrail* extensions in accordance with Section 1029.16.
3. *Handrails* for *alternating tread devices* and ships ladders are permitted to terminate at a location vertically above the top and bottom risers. *Handrails* for *alternating tread devices* are not required to be continuous between *flights* or to extend beyond the top or bottom risers.

❖ The purpose of return requirements at handrail ends is to prevent a person from catching an article of clothing or satchel straps, or from being injured by falling on the extended end of a handrail.

The length that a handrail extends beyond the top and bottom of a stairway, ramp or intermediate landing where handrails are not continuous to another stair flight or ramp run is an important factor for the safety of the users. An occupant must be able to securely grasp a handrail beyond the last riser of a stairway or the last sloped segment of a ramp. Handrail terminations that bend around a corner do not provide this stability; therefore, the handrail must extend in the direction of the stair flight or ramp run. The handrail extensions are not required where a user could keep his or her hand on the handrail, such as the continuous handrail at the landing of a switchback stairway or ramp (see Section 1014.2, Exception 1).

For stairways, handrails must be extended 12 inches (305 mm) horizontally beyond the top riser and sloped a distance of one tread depth beyond the bottom riser. For ramps, handrails must be extended 12 inches (305 mm) horizontally beyond the last sloped ramp segment at both the top and bottom locations. These handrail extensions are not only required at the top and bottom on both sides of stairways and ramps, but also at other places where handrails are not continuous, such as landings and platforms. These requirements are intended to reflect the current provisions of ICC A117.1 (see Commentary Figure 1014.2) and the *2010 ADA Standards*. Note that if the handrail extension is at a location that could be considered a protruding object, the handrail must return to the post at a height of less than 27 inches (686 mm) above the floor (see Sections 1003.3.2 and 1003.3.3).

In accordance with Exception 1, handrail extensions are not required where a dwelling unit is not required to meet any level of accessibility (i.e., Accessible unit, Type A unit or Type B unit). Handrail extensions are permitted to end at a newel post or turnaround.

Exception 2 provides for handrails along ramped or stepped aisles in assembly seating configurations, such as in sports facilities, theaters and lecture halls. It is necessary to limit handrail extensions in assembly aisles so that circulation in cross aisles that run perpendicular to the stepped or sloped aisles is not compromised.

Exception 3 allows for the unique construction considerations for alternating tread devices and ships ladders. Again, usage of these devices is very limited. Since alternative tread devices and ships ladders are typically utilized as a safer alternative to a vertical ladder, they are often located in tight spaces where traditional-type stairs cannot be used or are not required. With a much steeper angle than traditional stairs and differing usage, handrail extensions and continuity provisions are not practical.

[BE] 1014.7 Clearance. Clear space between a *handrail* and a wall or other surface shall be not less than $1^1/_2$ inches (38 mm). A *handrail* and a wall or other surface adjacent to the *handrail* shall be free of any sharp or abrasive elements.

❖ A clear space is needed between a handrail and the wall or other surface to allow the user to slide his or her hand along the rail with fingers in the gripping position without contacting the wall surface, which could have an abrasive texture. In climates where persons may be expected to be wearing heavy gloves during the winter, an open design with greater clearance would be desirable at an exterior stairway, or a stairway directly inside the entrance to a building. [See Commentary Figures 1014.4(2) and 1014.8(2) for illustrations of handrail clearance.]

[BE] 1014.8 Projections. On *ramps* and on ramped *aisles* that are part of an *accessible route*, the clear width between *handrails* shall be 36 inches (914 mm) minimum. Projections into the required width of *aisles*, *stairways* and *ramps* at each side shall not exceed $4^1/_2$ inches (114 mm) at or below the *handrail* height. Projections into the required width shall not be limited above the minimum headroom height required in Section 1011.3. Projections due to intermediate *handrails* shall not constitute a reduction in the egress width. Where a pair of intermediate *handrails* are provided within the *stairway* width without a walking surface between the pair of intermediate *handrails* and the distance between the pair of intermediate *handrails* is greater than 6 inches (152 mm), the available egress width shall be reduced by the distance between the closest edges of each such intermediate pair of *handrails* that is greater than 6 inches (152 mm).

❖ Handrails may not project more than $4^1/_2$ inches (114 mm) into the required width of a stairway, so that the clear width of the passage will not be seriously reduced [see Commentary Figure 1014.8(1)]. This is consistent with Section 1003.3.3. This projection may exist below the handrail height as well [see Commentary Figure 1014.8(2)]. The projection can be greater on stairways or ramps exceeding minimum width requirements.

The requirement for some stairways to have intermediate handrails (Section 1014.9) could result in a single or double handrail down the center of the flight of stairs. Since these stairways are 60 inches (1525 mm) or wider, a center handrail would typically not be an obstruction and, therefore, would not reduce the capacity of the stairway. Schools and large assembly spaces commonly put in center handrails to aid in the flow up and down the stairs during peak usage times. If the center handrail is a double rail with a spacing of more than 6 inches (152 mm), the width of the stairway may need to be adjusted to compensate for the loss of available width.

[BE] 1014.9 Intermediate handrails. *Stairways* shall have intermediate *handrails* located in such a manner that all portions of the *stairway* minimum width or required capacity are within 30 inches (762 mm) of a *handrail*. On monumental *stairs*, *handrails* shall be located along the most direct path of egress travel.

❖ In order to always be available to the user of the stairway, the maximum horizontal distance to a handrail from within the width required must not exceed 30 inches (762 mm). People tend to walk close to handrails, and if intermediate handrails are not provided for very wide stairways, the center portion of such stairways will normally receive less use. More importantly, in emergencies, the center portions of wide stairways with handrails would enhance egress travel rather than delay it by overcrowding at the sides with the handrails. This would especially be true under panic conditions where the use of wide interior stairways could become particularly hazardous.

The distance to the handrail applies to the "required" width of the stairway. If a stairway is greater than 60 inches (1524 mm) in width, but only 60 inches (1524 mm) total width is required based on occupant load (see Section 1005.3.1), intermediate handrails are not required. Adequate safety is pro-

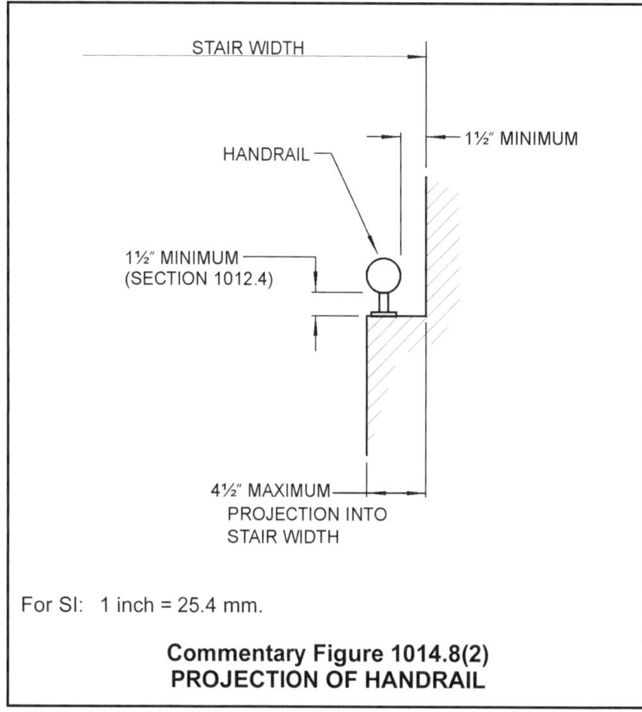

For SI: 1 inch = 25.4 mm.

Commentary Figure 1014.8(2)
PROJECTION OF HANDRAIL

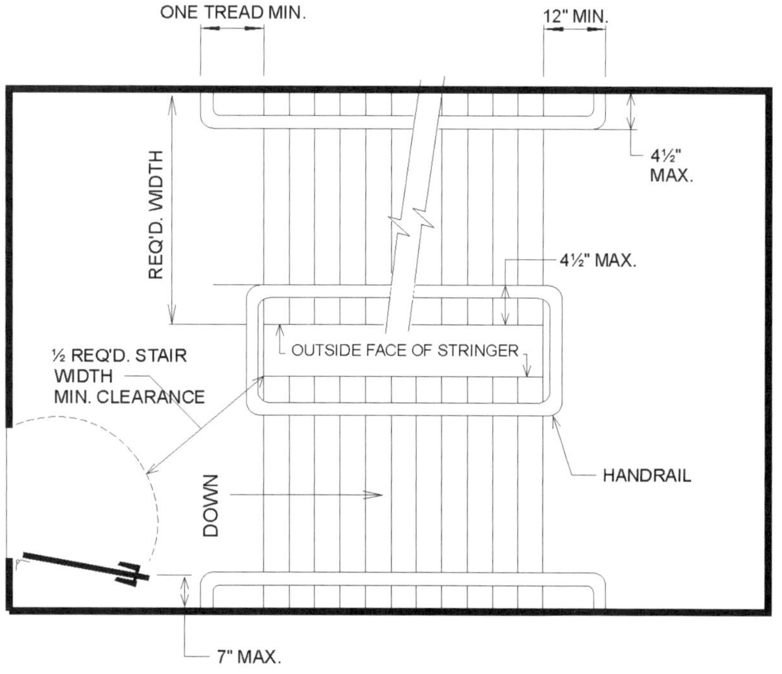

For SI: 1 inch = 25.4 mm.

Commentary Figure 1014.8(1)
TYPICAL HANDRAIL ARRANGEMENT

vided since every user is within 30 inches (762 mm) of a handrail.

Monumental stairways are typically provided for architectural effect and may or may not be considered required egress stairs. The criteria for monumental egress stairways deal with the very wide stairway in relation to the required width. While handrails on both sides of the stairway may be sufficient to accommodate the required width, the handrails may not be near the stream of traffic or even apparent to the user. In this case, the handrails are to be placed in a location more reflective of the egress path (see Commentary Figure 1014.9).

SECTION 1015 GUARDS

[BE] 1015.1 General. *Guards* shall comply with the provisions of Section 1015.2 through 1015.7. Operable windows with sills located more than 72 inches (1829 mm) above finished grade or other surface below shall comply with Section 1015.8.

❖ Guards required along dropoffs must comply with the provisions for height, strength and opening limitations. Special provisions are provided for unique locations, such as screened-in porches, around mechanical equipment on platforms or roofs and at hatch openings.

Where there are operable windows on upper floors, there is a concern over the possibility of a child falling; thus, the placement of this requirement is in the guard section. Such windows must comply with Section 1015.8.

[BE] 1015.2 Where required. *Guards* shall be located along open-sided walking surfaces, including *mezzanines*, equipment platforms, *aisles*, *stairs*, *ramps* and landings that are located more than 30 inches (762 mm) measured vertically to the floor or grade below at any point within 36 inches (914 mm) horizontally to the edge of the open side. *Guards* shall be adequate in strength and attachment in accordance with Section 1607.8 of the *International Building Code*.

Exception: *Guards* are not required for the following locations:

1. On the loading side of loading docks or piers.
2. On the audience side of stages and raised platforms, including *stairs* leading up to the stage and raised platforms.
3. On raised stage and platform floor areas, such as runways, *ramps* and side stages used for entertainment or presentations.
4. At vertical openings in the performance area of stages and platforms.
5. At elevated walking surfaces appurtenant to stages and platforms for access to and utilization of special lighting or equipment.
6. Along vehicle service pits not accessible to the public.
7. In assembly seating areas at cross aisles in accordance with Section 1029.17.2.

❖ Where one or more sides of a walking surface are open to the floor level or grade below, a guard system must be provided to minimize the possibility of occupants accidentally falling to the surface below. A guard is required only where the difference in eleva-

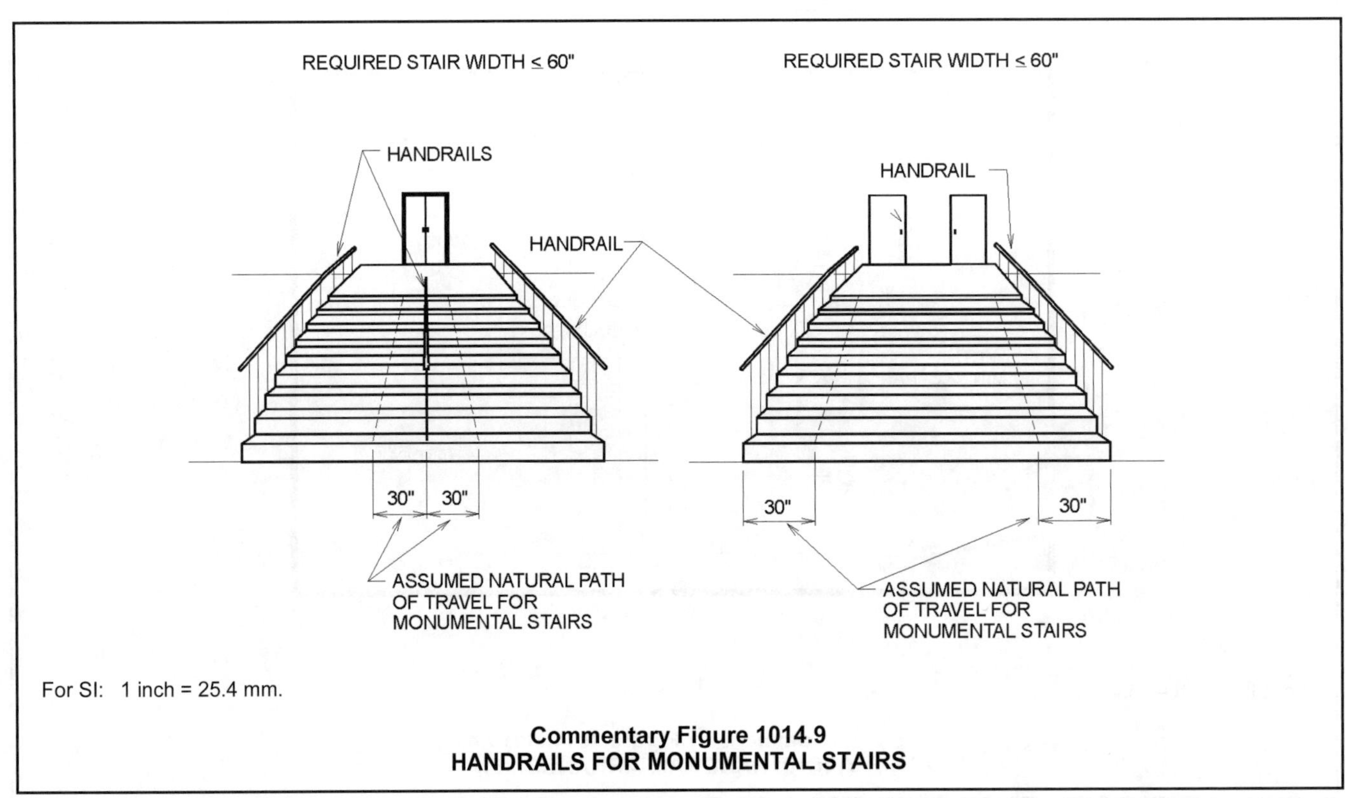

For SI: 1 inch = 25.4 mm.

Commentary Figure 1014.9 HANDRAILS FOR MONUMENTAL STAIRS

tion between the higher walking surface and the surface below is greater than 30 inches (762 mm). Where the ground slopes away from the edge, the vertical distance from the walking surface to the grade or floor below must also be more than 30 inches (762 mm) on the lowest point within a 36-inch (914 mm) radius measured horizontally from the edge of the open-sided walking surface (see Commentary Figure 1015.2).

The loads for guard design are addressed in IBC Section 1607 and are typically 50 plf (0.73 kN/m) along the top with a 200-pound (0.89 kN) concentrated force. If glazing is used as part of a guard system, or windows are located adjacent to stairways or ramps, the guard must also comply with Section 1015.2.1 (see Section 1015.2.1 and IBC Sections 1607.8 and 2407).

Most of the exceptions identify situations where guards are not practical, such as along loading docks, stages and their approaches, and vehicle service pits. Exception 7 references assembly spaces where a lower guard is permitted or the alternative of seat backs where the dropoff is adjacent to a cross aisle.

42″ PER SECTION 1015.3
GUARD
36″
30″
>30″
36″

For SI: 1 inch = 25.4 mm.

Commentary Figure 1015.2
DROP-OFF MEASUREMENTS AND GUARD HEIGHT

[BE] 1015.2.1 Glazing. Where glass is used to provide a *guard* or as a portion of the *guard* system, the *guard* shall comply with Section 2407 of the *International Building Code*. Where the glazing provided does not meet the strength and attachment requirements of Section 1607.8 of the *International Building Code*, complying *guards* shall be located along glazed sides of open-sided walking surfaces.

❖ Glazing in guards may be infill or structural. The loads for guard design in Section 1015.2, which references IBC Section 1607, are typically 50 plf (0.73 kN/m) along the top with a 200-pound (0.89 kN) concentrated force. Two different situations are addressed with glazing: where glazing is installed in a guard on the side of a stairway, ramp or landing; or where a stairway, ramp or landing is immediately adjacent to a window where the glazing has not been designed to resist the forces from a fall (see IBC Sections 1607.8 and 2407 and Commentary Figure 1015.2.1).

Commentary Figure 1015.2.1
GUARD SYSTEM WITH GLAZING

[BE] 1015.3 Height. Required *guards* shall be not less than 42 inches (1067 mm) high, measured vertically as follows:

1. From the adjacent walking surfaces.
2. On *stairways* and stepped *aisles*, from the line connecting the leading edges of the tread *nosings*.
3. On *ramps* and ramped *aisles*, from the *ramp* surface at the *guard*.

Exceptions:

1. For occupancies in Group R-3 not more than three stories above grade in height and within individual *dwelling units* in occupancies in Group R-2 not more than three stories above grade in height with separate *means of egress*, required *guards* shall be not less than 36 inches (914 mm) in height measured vertically above the adjacent walking surfaces.
2. For occupancies in Group R-3, and within individual *dwelling units* in occupancies in Group R-2, *guards* on the open sides of *stairs* shall have a height not less than 34 inches (864 mm) measured vertically from a line connecting the leading edges of the treads.
3. For occupancies in Group R-3, and within individual *dwelling units* in occupancies in Group R-2, where the top of the *guard* serves as a *handrail* on the open sides of *stairs*, the top of the *guard* shall be not less than 34 inches (864 mm) and not more than 38 inches (965 mm) measured vertically from a line connecting the leading edges of the treads.
4. The *guard* height in assembly seating areas shall comply with Section 1029.17 as applicable.
5. Along *alternating tread devices* and ships ladders, *guards* where the top rail serves as a *handrail* shall have height not less than 30 inches (762 mm) and not more than 34 inches (864 mm), measured vertically from the leading edge of the device tread *nosing*.
6. In Group F occupancies where *exit access stairways* serve fewer than three stories and such *stairways* are not open to the public, and where the top of the *guard* also serves as a *handrail*, the top of the *guard* shall be not less than 34 inches (864 mm) and not more than 38 inches (965 mm) measured vertically from a line connecting the leading edges of the treads.

❖ Guards must not be less than 42 inches (1067 mm) in height as measured vertically from the top of the guard down to the sloped line connecting the leading edge of the tread along stairways or stepped aisles or to an adjacent walking surface for floors, ramps and ramped aisles [see Commentary Figures 1012.8(4), 1015.2, and 1015.4(1) and (2)]. Experience has shown that 42 inches (1067 mm) or more provides adequate height to minimize accidental falls in occupancies where crowding is more likely to occur. This puts the top of the guard above the center of gravity of the average adult. The height requirement is not intended to consider such items as planters or loose furniture next to the dropoff as walking surfaces. Because of safety concerns, the designer often chooses to install a barrier where there is a dropoff of less than 30 inches (762 mm). Decorative barriers may be utilized to support handrails or serve as part of the edge protection along a ramp. Where nonrequired guards/barriers are provided, provisions for guard height, openings and strength may be used for design, but are not required. It is common practice to follow the strength provisions, but not always the opening or height provisions, for nonrequired guards.

Exception 1 is coordination between the IRC and Group R-2 and R-3 units that are three stories or less. Within dwelling units, the incidence of the exposure to crowds and to egress from higher occupancy spaces is extremely limited; thus, a minimum guard height of 36 inches (914 mm) is appropriate (see Commentary Figure 1015.3). Where the minimum guard height requirement is 42 inches (1067 mm), and both a guard and handrail are required, the handrail cannot be the top of the guard but must be placed along the inside face of the guard unless specifically permitted in Exceptions 2 through 6.

Exceptions 2 and 3 are for nontransient residential occupancies and only address guard heights along the stairways, not at other dropoffs such as balconies or second-floor landings. For Group R-2, these guard height exceptions are only permitted for stairways within individual dwelling units, not common stairways within the building. The handrail provisions allow some

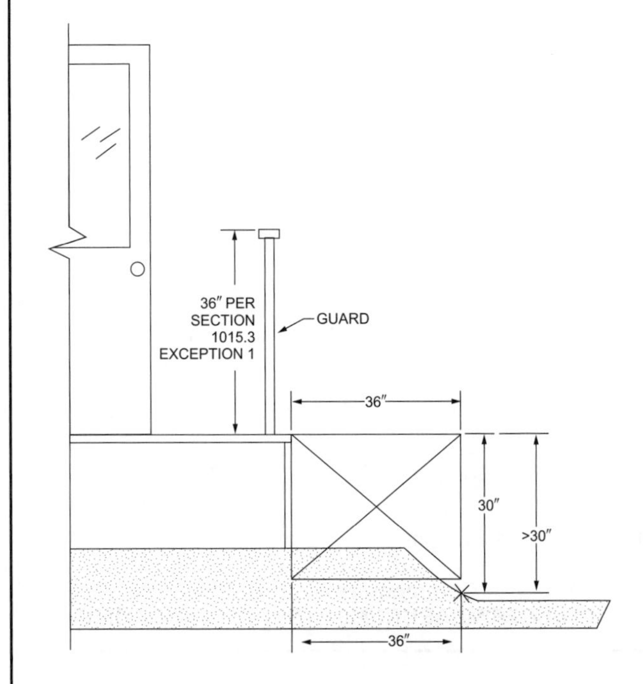

For SI: 1 inch = 25.4 mm.

Commentary Figure 1015.3
DROPOFF MEASUREMENTS AND GUARD HEIGHTS FOR TWO- AND THREE-STORY GROUPS R-2 AND R-3

residential stairways to have only one handrail (see Section 1011.11). Exceptions 2 and 3 allow for a reduced guard height where the guard is also used as a handrail and where it just serves the purpose of a guard along a stairway. The reduced allowable guard height along stairways is consistent with current construction practice. Unless a dwelling could comply with Exception 1, the guard height along other dropoffs would have to be 42 inches (1067 mm) measured from the floor.

Exception 4 references the lower guards permitted at limited locations where a line of sight for assembly spaces is part of the consideration. There are also allowances in Section 1029.16 that would allow for the top of the guard to serve as a handrail.

Exception 5 permits a reduction in guard height based on the limited use and unique design considerations for alternating tread devices and ships ladders (see Sections 1011.14 and 1011.15).

Exception 6 is for nonpublic areas of factory buildings that are three stories or less. Guards along open exit access stairways can be lower and have the top rail serve as a guard. Literally enclosed exit stairways within the same building would have to have the higher guards with handrails inside the guard.

[BE] 1015.4 Opening limitations. Required *guards* shall not have openings that allow passage of a sphere 4 inches (102 mm) in diameter from the walking surface to the required *guard* height.

Exceptions:

1. From a height of 36 inches (914 mm) to 42 inches (1067 mm), *guards* shall not have openings that allow passage of a sphere $4^3/_8$ inches (111 mm) in diameter.
2. The triangular openings at the open sides of a *stair*, formed by the riser, tread and bottom rail shall not allow passage of a sphere 6 inches (152 mm) in diameter.
3. At elevated walking surfaces for access to and use of electrical, mechanical or plumbing systems or equipment, *guards* shall not have openings that allow passage of a sphere 21 inches (533 mm) in diameter.
4. In areas that are not open to the public within occupancies in Group I-3, F, H or S, and for *alternating tread devices* and ships ladders, *guards* shall not have openings that allow passage of a sphere 21 inches (533 mm) in diameter.
5. In assembly seating areas, *guards* required at the end of *aisles* in accordance with Section 1029.17.4 shall not have openings that allow passage of a sphere 4 inches (102 mm) in diameter up to a height of 26 inches (660 mm). From a height of 26 inches (660 mm) to 42 inches (1067 mm) above the adjacent walking surfaces, *guards* shall not have openings that allow passage of a sphere 8 inches (203 mm) in diameter.
6. Within individual *dwelling units* and *sleeping units* in Group R-2 and R-3 occupancies, *guards* on the open sides of *stairs* shall not have openings that allow passage of a sphere $4^3/_8$ (111 mm) inches in diameter.

❖ The opening limitations in a guard are based on anthropometric research that indicates children in the 99th percentile who have developed to the point of being able to crawl will have chest depth and head size of at least $4^3/_4$ inches (121 mm). Both the 4-inch (102 mm) and the $4^3/_8$-inch (111 mm) sphere rules are intended to provide an additional margin of safety. Note that the opening limitations are stated as preventing the passage of a sphere, requiring the openings to be smaller than the dimensions stated.

Exception 1 allows the $4^3/_8$-inch (111 mm) opening limitation at heights where falling through the guard is not a risk for children of early development who cannot access the opening [i.e., above 36 inches (914 mm) in height] [see Commentary Figure 1015.4(1)].

Exception 2 allows a 6-inch (152 mm) opening limitation at openings formed by the riser, tread and bottom rail of guards at the open side of a stairway. The geometry of these openings is such that the entire body cannot pass through the triangular opening, and further limiting such openings is impractical, given a sloped bottom member in the guard, without intersecting the tread nosings [see Commentary Figure 1015.4(1)].

Exceptions 3 and 4 address areas where the presence of small children is unlikely and often prohibited. Guards along walkways leading to electrical, mechanical and plumbing systems or equipment and in occupancies in Groups I-3, F, H and S may be constructed in such a way that a sphere 21 inches (533 mm) in diameter will not pass through any of the openings [see Commentary Figure 1015.4(2)]. This requirement allows the use of one horizontal intermediate member with the standard top-of-guard height of 42 inches (1067 mm).

Exception 5, for the guard infill near the top of the aisle guard in assembly seating areas, is provided to reduce sightline problems in limited locations (see Section 1029.17.3).

Exception 6 recognizes a standard construction practice within residential units. In practicality, this allows a stairway with the 7-inch riser height/11-inch tread depth (178 mm riser height/279 mm tread depth) step geometry to have two common $1^1/_4$-inch (32 mm) balusters per stair tread instead of three. Where the $7^3/_4$-inch riser height/10-inch tread depth (197 mm riser height/254 mm tread depth) step geometry (see Section 1011.5.2, Exception 3) is utilized, the two balusters would meet the 4-inch (102 mm) opening limitation and most profiled or turned balusters would meet the $4^3/_8$-inch (111 mm) sphere rule.

The provisions of guards are to minimize accidental falls through or over a guard. Opening limitations do not prohibit the use of horizontal members or ornamentation infill as guard components. Research has shown that no practical design for guard infill, including solid panels, can prevent climbing, but good design practices can greatly reduce the opportunity for small children to "climb" the guard [see Commentary Figure 1015.4(3)]. In this example, the handrail stops a child from climbing the guard.

[BE] 1015.5 Screen porches. Porches and decks that are enclosed with insect screening shall be provided with *guards* where the walking surface is located more than 30 inches (762 mm) above the floor or grade below.

❖ Insect screening located on the open sides of porches and decks does not provide an adequate barrier to reasonably protect an occupant from falling to the surface below. Guards are required on the open sides of porches and decks where the floor is located more than 30 inches (762 mm) above the surface below. The guards must comply with all of the provisions of Section 1015.

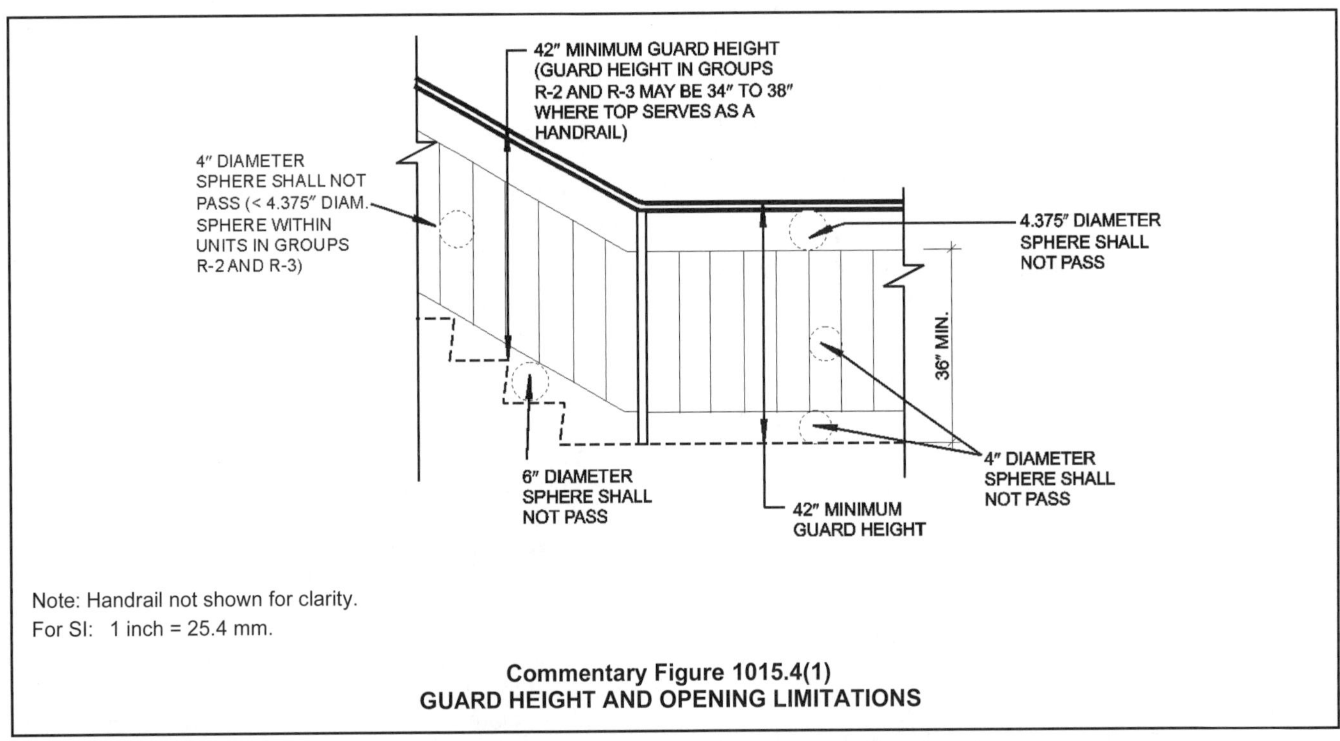

Note: Handrail not shown for clarity.
For SI: 1 inch = 25.4 mm.

Commentary Figure 1015.4(1)
GUARD HEIGHT AND OPENING LIMITATIONS

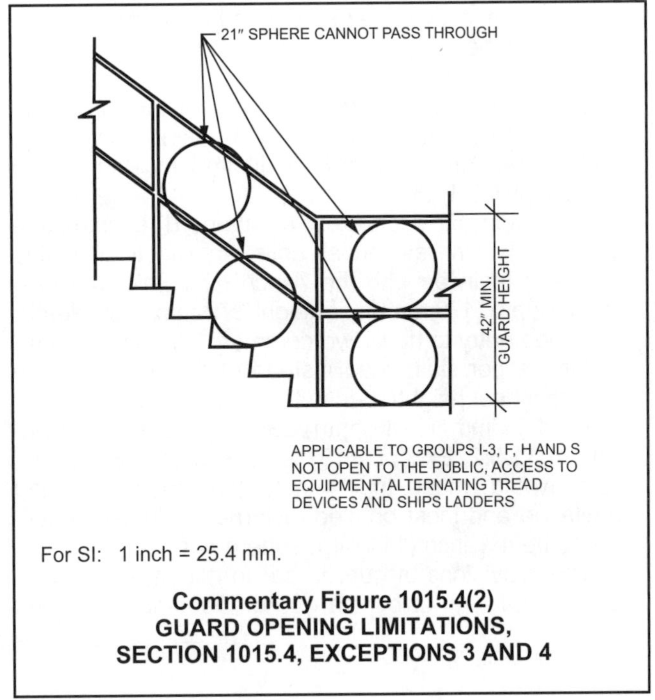

For SI: 1 inch = 25.4 mm.

Commentary Figure 1015.4(2)
GUARD OPENING LIMITATIONS, SECTION 1015.4, EXCEPTIONS 3 AND 4

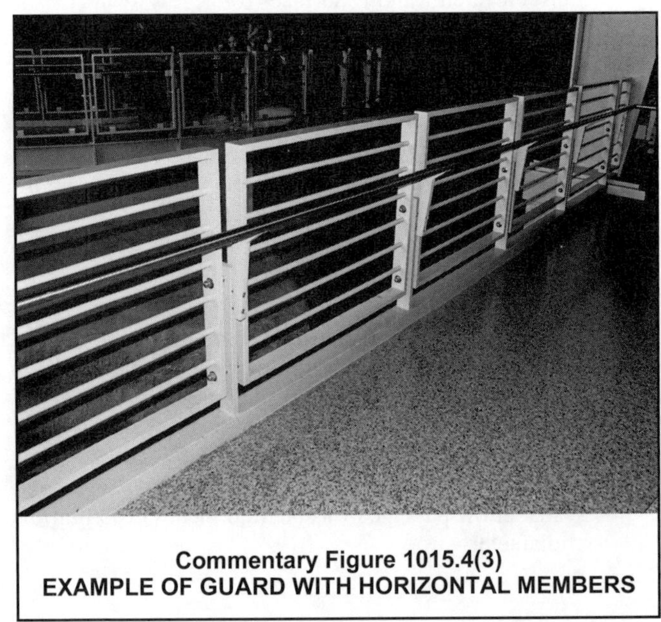

Commentary Figure 1015.4(3)
EXAMPLE OF GUARD WITH HORIZONTAL MEMBERS

[BE] 1015.6 Mechanical equipment, systems and devices. *Guards* shall be provided where various components that require service are located within 10 feet (3048 mm) of a roof edge or open side of a walking surface and such edge or open side is located more than 30 inches (762 mm) above the floor, roof or grade below. The *guard* shall extend not less than 30 inches (762 mm) beyond each end of such components. The *guard* shall be constructed so as to prevent the passage of a sphere 21 inches (533 mm) in diameter.

> **Exception:** *Guards* are not required where personal fall arrest anchorage connector devices that comply with ANSI/ASSE Z 359.1 are installed.

❖ The purpose of this requirement is to protect workers from falls off roofs or from open-sided walking surfaces when doing maintenance work on equipment. The guard opening is allowed to be up to 21 inches (533 mm) since children are not likely to be in such areas. Either the equipment should be located so that it is more than 10 feet (3048 mm) from the roof edge, or a guard or raised parapet must be provided to prevent falls. The guard also has to extend at least 30 inches (762 mm) in all directions past the corners of the equipment (see Commentary Figure 1015.7).

The exception is an alternative to guards—a personal fall arrest system with anchorage points, more commonly called tie-down points, for restraining harnesses. The code does not specify who has to provide the equipment that fits the maintenance crew and attaches to the system. This system is more commonly used on sloped roofs, while guards are more often used on flat roofs.

[BE] 1015.7 Roof access. *Guards* shall be provided where the roof hatch opening is located within 10 feet (3048 mm) of a roof edge or open side of a walking surface and such edge or open side is located more than 30 inches (762 mm) above the floor, roof or grade below. The *guard* shall be constructed so as to prevent the passage of a sphere 21 inches (533 mm) in diameter.

> **Exception:** *Guards* are not required where personal fall arrest anchorage connector devices that comply with ANSI/ASSE Z 359.1 are installed.

❖ The code already requires guards around equipment on the roof; this section is intended to provide the same level of safety at the hatch opening service personnel use to access the roof (see Commentary Figure 1015.7 and the commentary to Section 1015.6). While not specifically indicated for roof hatches, Section 1015.6 requires the guard to extend at least 30 inches (762 mm) past the corners of the equipment.

[BE] 1015.8 Window openings. Windows in Group R-2 and R-3 buildings including *dwelling units*, where the top of the sill of an operable window opening is located less than 36 inches above the finished floor and more than 72 inches (1829 mm) above the finished grade or other surface below on the exterior of the building, shall comply with one of the following:

1. Operable windows where the top of the sill of the opening is located more than 75 feet (22 860 mm) above the finished grade or other surface below and that are provided with window fall prevention devices that comply with ASTM F2006.

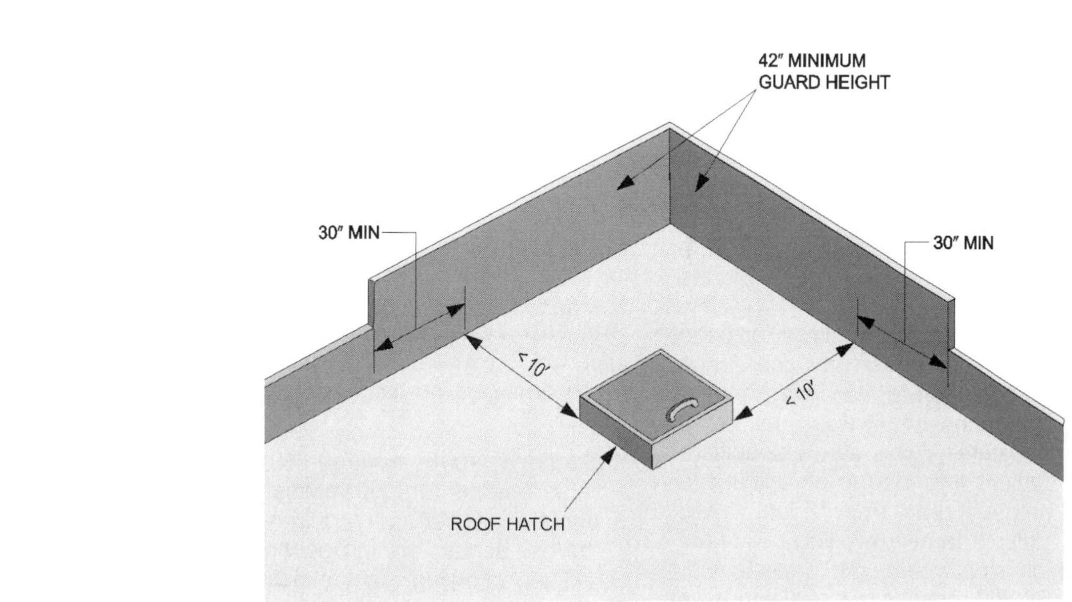

For SI: 1 inch = 25.4 mm, 1 foot = 304.8 mm.

Commentary Figure 1015.7
PROTECTION AT ROOF-HATCH OPENING

2. Operable windows where the openings will not allow a 4-inch-diameter (102 mm) sphere to pass through the opening when the window is in its largest opened position.
3. Operable windows where the openings are provided with window fall prevention devices that comply with ASTM F2090.
4. Operable windows that are provided with window opening control devices that comply with Section 1015.8.1.

❖ The window limitations specified here are intended for Group R-2 and R-3 units. These facilities have the highest potential for infants and toddlers being present for an extended period of time. The requirement is intended to provide a level of protection to children and to help limit the chances of them falling through window openings. In most cases, these provisions are not applicable to first-floor windows. Typically, the 72 inches (1829 mm) to finished grade would make these provisions applicable for windows starting at the second floor. For windows in bedrooms that may also be required to serve as emergency escape and rescue openings, see Section 1030.

There are basically five options offered:

One option is to locate the window so that any opening is at least 36 inches (915 mm) above the floor. By raising the lowest operable portion of a window to 36 inches (915 mm) or more, the sill height is above the center of gravity of smaller children. Note that Section R312.2.1 of the IRC requires a minimum sill height of 24 inches (610 mm). The National Ornamental & Miscellaneous Metals Association (NOMMA) commissioned a paper on child safety related to falls. The report indicates that the standing center of gravity of children aged 2 to 3.5 years is 24.1 inches (612 mm) [50th percentile is 22.2 inches (564 mm)] and of children aged 3.5 to 4.5 years is 25.2 inches (640 mm) [50th percentile is 23.6 inches (599 mm)]. The 36-inch (915 mm) sill height was chosen to reduce the ability of a child to climb onto the sill, enabling the fall through the opening. Windows that are also to serve as emergency escape windows must also comply with Section 1030.3 sill height requirements for 44 inches (1118 mm) maximum.

The second option offered (Item 1) allows for fixed fall-prevention devices to be installed in accordance with ASTM F2006. The limitation for window sills over 75 feet (22 860 mm) is for consistency with Section 1.3 of ASTM F2006, which states: "This safety specification applies only to devices intended to be applied to windows installed at height of more than 75 feet above the ground level in multiple family dwelling buildings. This safety specification is not intended to apply to windows below 75 feet (22 860 mm) because all windows below 75 feet (22 860 mm) that are operable could be used as a possible secondary means of escape." Since these devices will always prevent the opening of the window, they cannot be used for windows that are required to also serve as emergency escape openings.

A third option (Item 2) would be for windows with an opening lower than 36 inches (915 mm) to limit the opening to 4 inches (102 mm) maximum. This opening size is consistent with the guard opening provisions (see Section 1015.4). Many awning or hopper-type casement windows have control arms that limit the opening width.

ASTM F2090 includes window fall prevention devices (Item 3) and window opening control devices (Item 4) (see Section 1015.8.1). Window fall prevention devices (such as a window guard) must be removable from the interior of the building so the window can be used for emergency escape. Window opening control devices allow the window to be opened beyond 4 inches (102 mm) so that a window can be used for emergency escape. This standard is specifically written for window openings within 75 feet (22 860 mm) of grade and specifically allows for windows to be used for emergency escape and rescue. Both the code and the IRC reference ASTM F2090, *Standard Specification for Window Fall Prevention Devices with Emergency Escape (Egress) Release Mechanisms*. This standard was updated in 2008 to address window opening control devices. Opening control devices allow for normal operation to result in a 4-inch (102 mm) maximum opening (Section 1015.8 and Section R312.2.2 of the IRC). This control device can be released from the inside to allow the window to be fully opened in order to comply with the emergency escape provisions in both the code (Section 1030.2) and the IRC (Section R310.1.1).

Criteria have also been added to the IEBC to address window opening controls in existing buildings.

[BE] 1015.8.1 Window opening control devices. Window opening control devices shall comply with ASTM F2090. The window opening control device, after operation to release the control device allowing the window to fully open, shall not reduce the minimum net clear opening area of the window unit to less than the area required by Section 1030.2.

❖ See the commentary to Section 1015.8.

SECTION 1016
EXIT ACCESS

[BE] 1016.1 General. The *exit access* shall comply with the applicable provisions of Sections 1003 through 1015. *Exit access* arrangement shall comply with Sections 1016 through 1021.

❖ Sections 1016 through 1021 include the design requirements for exit access and exit access components. The general requirements that also apply to the exit access are in Sections 1003 through 1015.

The following sections are included under exit access:

- Section 1016 deals with egress through intervening spaces, as well as travel and separation of the common path of travel to the exit.

- Section 1017 lists the total exit access travel distance from an occupied space to an exit. This distance includes the common path of egress travel addressed in Sections 1006.2.1 and 1006.3.2.
- Section 1018 takes a look at requirements for aisles and aisle accessways for occupancies other than assembly spaces. Aisle and aisle accessways in spaces used for assembly purposes are specifically addressed in Section 1029.
- Section 1019 provides criteria for where an open stairway between floors can serve as a required exit access stairway.
- Section 1020 deals with another type of confined part of the exit access path: corridors.
- Section 1021 addresses egress balconies, where the path of travel to the exterior exit stairway is partially open to the exterior.

[BE] 1016.2 Egress through intervening spaces. Egress through intervening spaces shall comply with this section.

1. Exit access through an enclosed elevator lobby is permitted. Access to not less than one of the required *exits* shall be provided without travel through the enclosed elevator lobbies required by Section 3006 of the *International Building Code*. Where the path of *exit access* travel passes through an enclosed elevator lobby the level of protection required for the enclosed elevator lobby is not required to be extended to the *exit* unless direct access to an *exit* is required by other sections of this code.
2. Egress from a room or space shall not pass through adjoining or intervening rooms or areas, except where such adjoining rooms or areas and the area served are accessory to one or the other, are not a Group H occupancy and provide a discernible path of egress travel to an *exit*.

   Exception: *Means of egress* are not prohibited through adjoining or intervening rooms or spaces in a Group H, S or F occupancy where the adjoining or intervening rooms or spaces are the same or a lesser hazard occupancy group.
3. An *exit access* shall not pass through a room that can be locked to prevent egress.
4. *Means of egress* from *dwelling units* or sleeping areas shall not lead through other sleeping areas, toilet rooms or bathrooms.
5. Egress shall not pass through kitchens, storage rooms, closets or spaces used for similar purposes.

   Exceptions:

   1. *Means of egress* are not prohibited through a kitchen area serving adjoining rooms constituting part of the same *dwelling unit* or *sleeping unit.*
   2. *Means of egress* are not prohibited through stockrooms in Group M occupancies where all of the following are met:

      2.1. The stock is of the same hazard classification as that found in the main retail area.

      2.2. Not more than 50 percent of the *exit access* is through the stockroom.

      2.3. The stockroom is not subject to locking from the egress side.

      2.4. There is a demarcated, minimum 44-inch-wide (1118 mm) *aisle* defined by full- or partial-height fixed walls or similar construction that will maintain the required width and lead directly from the retail area to the *exit* without obstructions.

❖ This section allows adjoining spaces to be considered a part of the room or space from which egress originates, provided that there are reasonable assurances that the continuous egress path will always be available. The code does not limit the number of intervening or adjoining rooms through which egress can be made, provided that all other code requirements (e.g., travel distance, number of doorways) are met. For example, an exit access route may be laid out such that an occupant leaves a room or space, passes through an adjoining space, enters an exit access corridor, passes through another room and, finally, into an exit [see Commentary Figure 1016.2(2)].

The intent of Item 1 is to correlate the provision for corridor continuity (Section 1020.6) and elevator lobbies. This is especially important since elevator lobbies for fire service access elevators require direct connection to a stairway. Therefore, occupants may need to egress through an elevator lobby to get to the exit stairway. In a two-exit building, only one exit can be through an elevator lobby, but at the same time, the elevator lobby will not be considered an intervening room [see Commentary Figure 1020.6(3)]. This also clarifies that protection requirements for corridors would not be necessary in addition to protection requirements for elevator lobbies.

The intent of Item 2 is not that the accessory space be limited to the 10-percent area in Section 508.2.3, but that the spaces be interrelated so that doors between the spaces are not at risk of being blocked or locked. For example, a conference room and managers' offices could exit through the executive assistant's office to reach the exit access corridor; or several office spaces could exit through a common reception/lobby area. Requiring occupants to egress from an area and pass through an adjoining Group H area that can be characterized by rapid fire buildup places them in an unreasonable risk situation [see Commentary Figure 1016.2(1)]; therefore, this illustrated egress path would be prohibited. As an exception to Item 2, in facilities that may contain a Group H area, buildings of Group H, S or F can exit through adjoining rooms or spaces that have the same or lesser hazard. For example, a person exiting from a Group H storage room (see Section 415) could egress either through a similar Group H storage area or through the factory to get to an exit, but the person in the factory could not egress through the Group H storage rooms to get to the outside.

As expressed in Item 3, a common code enforcement problem is a locked door in the egress path. Twenty-five workers perished in September 1991 when they were trapped inside the Imperial Foods processing plant in Hamlet, North Carolina, in part because of locked exit doors. As long as the egress door is readily openable in the direction of egress travel without the use of keys, special knowledge or effort (see Section 1010.1.9.6), the occupants can move unimpeded away from a fire emergency. Relying on an egress path through an adjacent dwelling unit being available at all times is not a reasonable expectation. Egress through an adjacent business tenant space can be unreasonable given the security and privacy measures the adjacent tenant may take to secure such a space. However, egress through a reception area that serves a suite of offices of the same tenant is clearly accessible and is permitted.

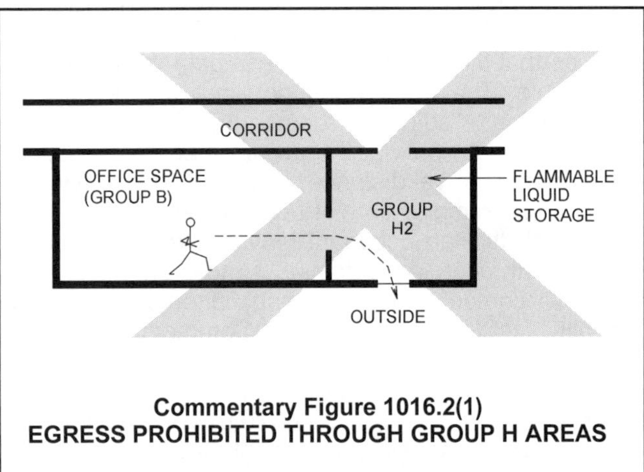

Commentary Figure 1016.2(1)
EGRESS PROHIBITED THROUGH GROUP H AREAS

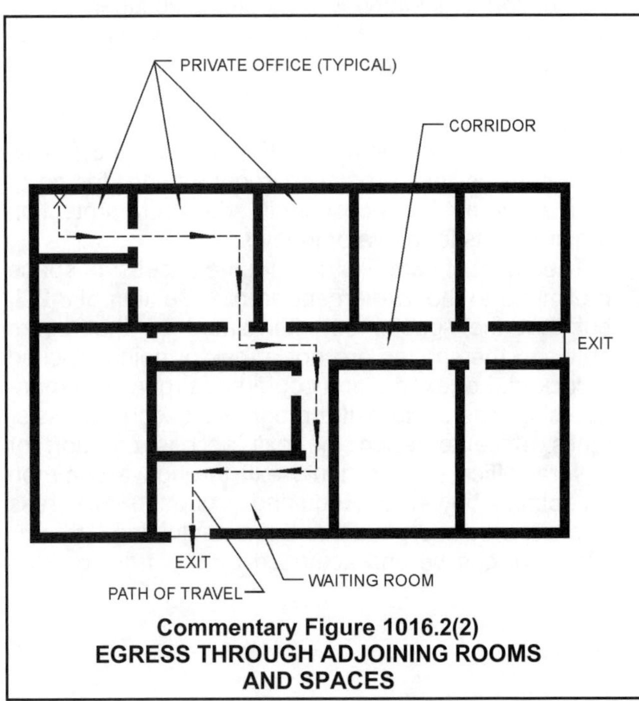

Commentary Figure 1016.2(2)
EGRESS THROUGH ADJOINING ROOMS AND SPACES

Item 4 addresses concerns along the path of egress travel within individual dwelling or sleeping units. The concern once again is possible locking devices. Egress for one bedroom should not be through another bedroom or bathroom.

The concern in Item 5 is that kitchens, storage rooms and similar spaces may be subject to locking or blockage of the exit access path. This is not a general provision for all Group S occupancies; therefore, it is not the intent of this provision to address the situation of egress for offices through an associated warehouse space. Item 5, Exception 1, does not apply this same prohibition to areas within dwelling or sleeping units. However, for other spaces, a customer means of egress should not be through the working portions of a commercial kitchen in a restaurant or the stock storage area of a storage room in a mercantile occupancy. A dedicated path must be established through such space. The four items listed in Item 5, Exception 2, are intended to provide measurable criteria to increase the likelihood that the path of exit access travel would always be available and identifiable through the stockroom of a store. It is not acceptable to just mark the path on the floor. Whatever defines the route must permanently establish the egress path in a manner that maintains the minimum required unobstructed width.

[BE] 1016.2.1 Multiple tenants. Where more than one tenant occupies any one floor of a building or structure, each tenant space, *dwelling unit* and *sleeping unit* shall be provided with access to the required *exits* without passing through adjacent tenant spaces, *dwelling units* and *sleeping units*.

> **Exception:** The *means of egress* from a smaller tenant space shall not be prohibited from passing through a larger adjoining tenant space where such rooms or spaces of the smaller tenant occupy less than 10 percent of the area of the larger tenant space through which they pass; are the same or similar occupancy group; a discernable path of egress travel to an *exit* is provided; and the *means of egress* into the adjoining space is not subject to locking from the egress side. A required *means of egress* serving the larger tenant space shall not pass through the smaller tenant space or spaces.

❖ Where a floor is occupied by multiple tenants, each tenant must be provided with full and direct access to the required exits serving that floor without passing through another tenant space. Tenants typically lock the doors to their spaces for privacy and security.

Should an egress door that is shared by both tenants be locked, occupants in one of the spaces could be trapped and unable to reach a secondary exit. Therefore, an egress layout where occupants from one tenant space travel through another tenant space to gain access to one of the required exits from that floor is prohibited.

This limitation is so that occupants from all tenant spaces will have unrestricted access to the required egress elements while maintaining the security and privacy of the individual tenants. This limitation is based on one of the fundamental principles of egress: to provide a means of egress where all components are capable of being used by occupants without keys, tools, special knowledge or special effort (see Section 1010.1.9.6).

A common practice is to have a bank or small restaurant located within a large grocery store or department store. These can be separate tenants. In these situations, the small tenants are not open when the main store is closed. The intent of the exception is to allow those small tenants to egress through the large tenant. Since there may be times when the larger tenant is open and the smaller tenant is closed (e.g., bank holidays), the larger tenant cannot exit through the smaller tenant.

SECTION 1017
EXIT ACCESS TRAVEL DISTANCE

[BE] 1017.1 General. Travel distance within the *exit access* portion of the *means of egress* system shall be in accordance with this section.

❖ "Exit access" is defined as "that portion of a means of egress system that leads from any occupied portion of a building or structure to an exit" (see the commentary for the definition in Chapter 2). Exit access includes rooms, spaces, aisles and corridors that an occupant would travel along to get to an exit. This can also include stairways and ramps between levels.

Doors and doorways along this route are exit access doorways, but may sometimes be called "exit doors." True exits for this exit access travel can be:

1. An exterior exit door at grade.
2. The door to an enclosure for an interior exit stairway, ramp or exit passageway.
3. The exit door leading to an exterior stairway or ramp.
4. A door leading through a horizontal exit.

When considering open exit access stairways or ramps, it is important to determine where a stairway/ramp can be open (Section 1019), where that stairway/ramp is part of the required ways off a story (Section 1006.3), and egress travel distance (Sections 1006.3.1 and 1017). Similar to access to bathrooms, the travel distance is both by length and number of stories. How exit access travel distance is measured is one of the key differences between interior exit access stairways/ramps (see Section 1017.3.1) and interior exit stairways/ramps (see Section 1017.3).

It is important to understand the relationship between the common path of egress travel limitations (Sections 1006.2.1 and 1006.3.2) and the exit access travel distance limitations of this section. Measurements start at the same location, the most remote location in any occupied space. Both are measured in the exit access portion of the means of egress system. The common path of egress travel is measured to the point where the occupant has two distinct paths of travel, which will lead to two distinct exits. Travel distance is measured all the way until the exit is reached. The common path of egress travel measurement can end within a space or at a corridor where a single means of egress space (Section 1006.2.1) has its door to a corridor that provides access to two exits.

[BE] 1017.2 Limitations. *Exit access* travel distance shall not exceed the values given in Table 1017.2.

❖ The table includes the travel distance measurements for buildings with or without sprinkler systems. "Not Permitted" is in support of the Chapter 9 requirements for all Group I and H occupancies to be sprinklered. While the other occupancies may also be required to be sprinklered, the exit access travel distance is indicated for existing buildings.

TABLE 1017.2 See page 10-134.

❖ This table reflects the maximum distance a person is allowed to travel from any point in a building floor area to the nearest exit along a natural and unobstructed path. While quantitative determinations or formulas are not available to substantiate the tabular distances, empirical factors are utilized to make relative judgments as to reasonable limitations. Such considerations include the nature and fitness of the occupants; the typical configuration within the space; and the level of fire hazard with respect to the specific uses of the facilities, including fire spread and the potential intensity of a fire. The inclusion of an automatic sprinkler system throughout the building can serve to control, confine or possibly eliminate the fire threat to the occupants so an increased travel distance is permitted. Increased travel distances are permitted where an automatic sprinkler system is installed in accordance with NFPA 13 or 13R.

When measuring travel distance, it is important to consider the natural path of exit access travel [see Commentary Figure 1017.3(1)]. In many cases, the actual layout of furnishings and equipment is not known or is not identified on the plans submitted with the permit application. In such instances, it may be necessary to measure travel distance using the legs of a right triangle instead of the hypotenuse [see Commentary Figure 1017.3(2)]. Since most people tend to migrate to more open spaces while egressing, measurement of the natural path of exit access travel

[BE] TABLE 1017.2
EXIT ACCESS TRAVEL DISTANCE[a]

OCCUPANCY	WITHOUT SPRINKLER SYSTEM (feet)	WITH SPRINKLER SYSTEM (feet)
A, E, F-1, M, R, S-1	200	250[b, e]
I-1	Not Permitted	250[b]
B	200	300[c]
F-2, S-2, U	300	400[c]
H-1	Not Permitted	75[d]
H-2	Not Permitted	100[d]
H-3	Not Permitted	150[d]
H-4	Not Permitted	175[d]
H-5	Not Permitted	200[c]
I-2, I-3	Not Permitted	200[c]
I-4	150	200[c]

For SI: 1 foot = 304.8 mm.

a. See the following sections for modifications to exit access travel distance requirements:

Section 402.8 of the *International Building Code*: For the distance limitation in malls.

Section 404.9 of the *International Building Code*: For the distance limitation through an atrium space.

Section 407.4 of the *International Building Code*: For the distance limitation in Group I-2.

Sections 408.6.1 and 408.8.1 of the *International Building Code*: For the distance limitations in Group I-3.

Section 411.3 of the *International Building Code*: For the distance limitation in special amusement buildings.

Section 412.6 of the *International Building Code*: For the distance limitations in aircraft manufacturing facilities.

Section 1006.2.2.2: For the distance limitation in refrigeration machinery rooms.

Section 1006.2.2.3: For the distance limitation in refrigerated rooms and spaces.

Section 1006.3.3: For buildings with one exit.

Section 1017.2.2: For increased distance limitation in Groups F-1 and S-1.

Section 1029.7: For increased limitation in assembly seating.

Section 3103.4 of the *International Building Code*: For temporary structures.

Section 3104.9 of the *International Building Code*: For pedestrian walkways.

b. Buildings equipped throughout with an automatic sprinkler system in accordance with Section 903.3.1.1 or 903.3.1.2. See Section 903 for occupancies where automatic sprinkler systems are permitted in accordance with Section 903.3.1.2.

c. Buildings equipped throughout with an automatic sprinkler system in accordance with Section 903.3.1.1.

d. Group H occupancies equipped throughout with an automatic sprinkler system in accordance with Section 903.2.5.1.

e. Group R-3 and R-4 buildings equipped throughout with an automatic sprinkler system in accordance with Section 903.3.1.3. See Section 903.2.8 for occupancies where automatic sprinkler systems are permitted in accordance with Section 903.3.1.3.

typically excludes floor areas within 1 foot (305 mm) of walls, corners, columns and other permanent construction. Where the travel path includes passage through a doorway, the natural route is generally measured through the centerline of door openings.

The common path of egress travel addressed in Sections 1006.2.1 and 1006.3.2 is part of the overall exit access travel distance, with both starting at the same point. Common path of egress travel stops where the occupant has a choice of at least two exits, and overall egress travel distance stops where an occupant gets to the closest exit.

Note a is a reference to other travel distance limitations in the code. The travel distance for Group I-4 in a nonsprinklered building is in recognition of the exceptions in Section 903.2.6.

Notes b and c are simply references to the allowed types of sprinkler system—NFPA 13 or 13R. Some exit access travel distance increases are based on the type of sprinkler system provided. Note e treats Groups R-3 and R-4 that have an NFPA 13D sprinkler system the same as a building without a sprinkler system with regard to exit access travel distance.

Note d addresses the sprinkler requirements in Group H. Group H occupancies are only required to be sprinklered within Group H and not throughout the building; therefore, Note d distinguishes this requirement from Notes b and c. The travel distance is the same if the path is through Group H or leaves Group H and continues through a nonsprinklered occupancy (see Section 1016.2, Item 2.)

[BE] 1017.2.1 Exterior egress balcony increase. *Exit access* travel distances specified in Table 1017.2 shall be increased up to an additional 100 feet (30 480 mm) provided that the last portion of the *exit access* leading to the *exit* occurs on an exterior egress balcony constructed in accordance with Section 1021. The length of such balcony shall be not less than the amount of the increase taken.

❖ This section allows an additional travel distance on exterior egress balconies since smoke disperses rapidly. Note that the length of the increase is not to be more than the length of the exterior balcony. For example, if the length of the balcony is 75 feet (22 860 mm), the additional travel distance is limited to 75 feet (22 860 mm). In order for the increase to apply, the exterior balcony must be located at the end of the path of egress travel and not in some other portion of the egress path.

[BE] 1017.2.2 Groups F-1 and S-1 increase. The maximum *exit access* travel distance shall be 400 feet (122 m) in Group F-1 or S-1 occupancies where all of the following conditions are met:

1. The portion of the building classified as Group F-1 or S-1 is limited to one story in height.
2. The minimum height from the finished floor to the bottom of the ceiling or roof slab or deck is 24 feet (7315 mm).
3. The building is equipped throughout with an *automatic sprinkler system* in accordance with Section 903.3.1.1.

❖ This section provides the criteria for an increased exit access travel distance of 400 feet in Group F-1 and S-1 occupancies where three criteria are met: the S-1/F-1 area is one story, has a ceiling height of at least 24 feet, and is sprinklered.

The travel distance increase is only applicable to portions of the building that are one story in height.

This is not intended to preclude a building with a one-story storage warehouse or factory area and a two-story office or a mezzanine from also utilizing this section. The section is written so that the one-story limitation is only applicable to the area where the 400-foot travel distance is utilized.

The 24 feet of clearance is based on the "Fire Modeling Analysis Report" by Aon Fire Protection Engineering. The ceiling height is used to provide a volume for the smoke to accumulate during the fire and provide time for egress, much like the concept used for smoke-protected seating. Control mode sprinklers were utilized in the fire modeling to demonstrate the more conservative approach.

The building is required to sprinklered in accordance with NFPA 13 requirements. While not required, ESFR or specialty sprinklers would be more effective.

[BE] 1017.3 Measurement. *Exit access* travel distance shall be measured from the most remote point of each room, area or space along the natural and unobstructed path of horizontal and vertical egress travel to the entrance to an *exit.*

Exception: In open parking garages, *exit access* travel distance is permitted to be measured to the closest riser of an *exit access stairway* or the closest slope of an *exit access ramp*.

❖ The length of exit access travel, as measured from the most remote point within a structure to an exit, is limited to restrict the amount of time that the occupant is exposed to a potential fire condition [see Commentary Figure 1017.3(1)]. The route must be assumed to be the natural path of travel without obstruction. This commonly results in a rectilinear path similar to what can be experienced in most occupancies, such as a schoolroom or an office with rows of desks [see Commentary Figure 1017.3(2)]. The "arc" method, using

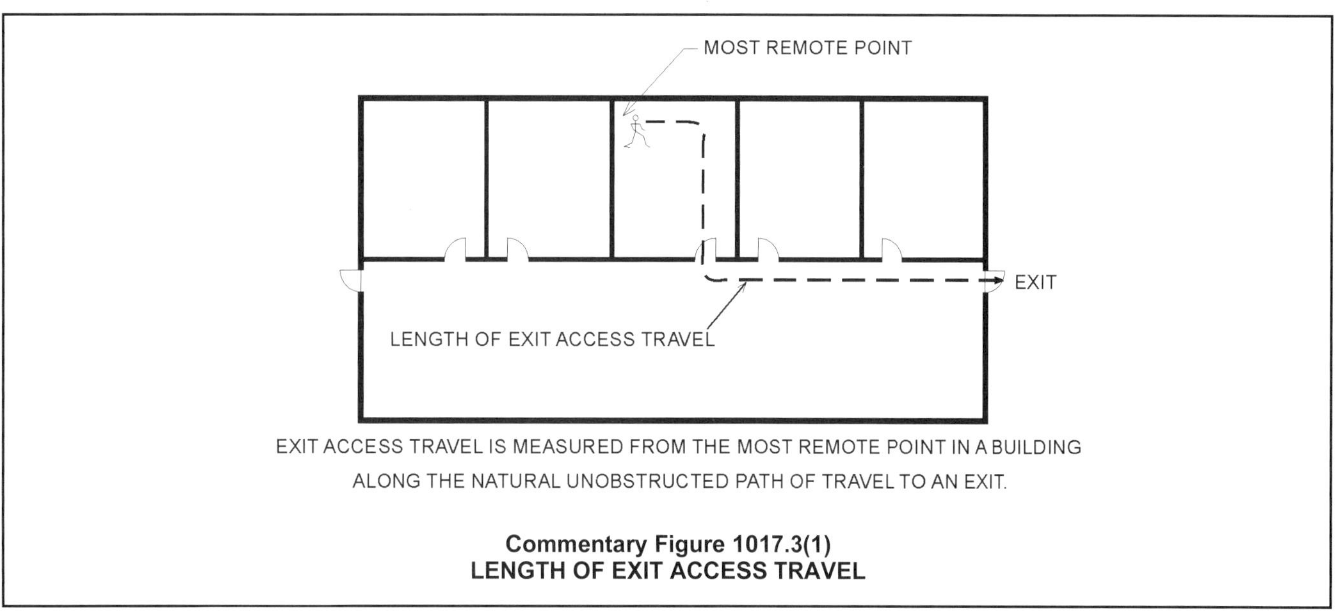

Commentary Figure 1017.3(1)
LENGTH OF EXIT ACCESS TRAVEL

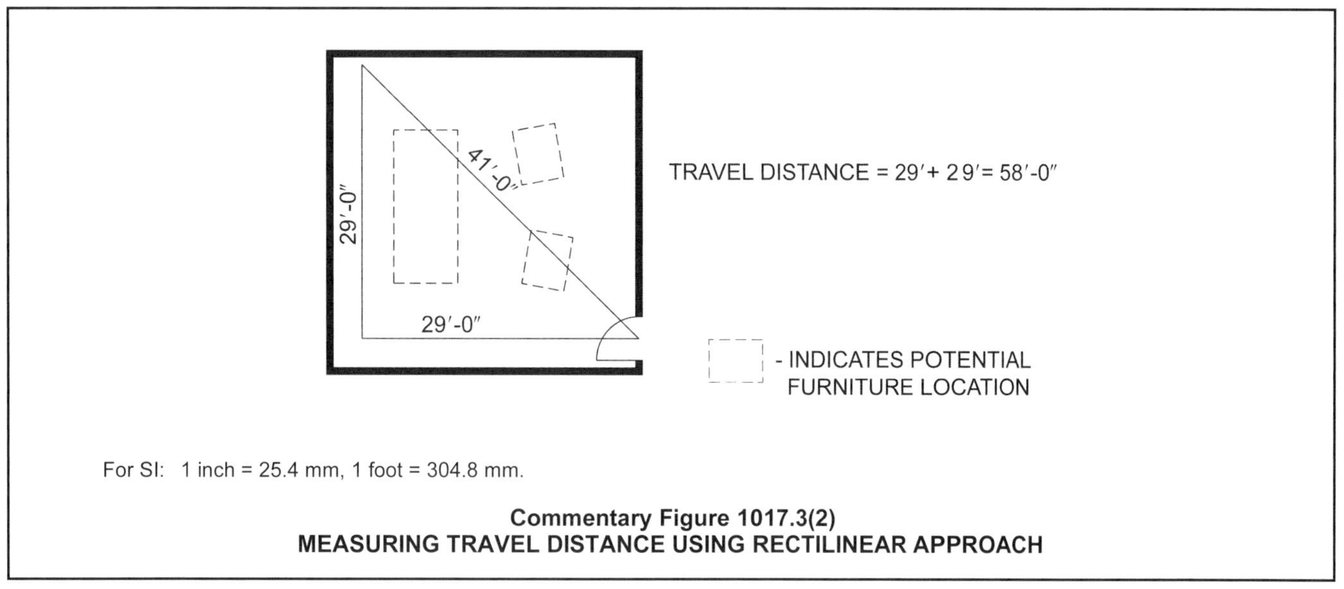

Commentary Figure 1017.3(2)
MEASURING TRAVEL DISTANCE USING RECTILINEAR APPROACH

an "as the crow flies" linear measurement, must be used with caution, as it seldom represents typical floor design and room layout and, in most cases, would not be the natural, unobstructed path.

The travel distance is measured from every occupiable point on a floor to the closest exit. While each occupant may be required to have access to a second or third exit, the travel distance limitation is only applicable to the distance to the nearest exit. In effect, this means that the distance an occupant must travel to the second or third exit is not regulated.

For exit access travel distances that include vertical elements, such as stairways or ramps, see Section 1017.3.1. For outdoor assembly seating, see Section 1029.7.

The exception provides for a travel distance terminating at the top of an open exit access stairway in an open parking structure (see Section 1006.3, Exception 3, and Section 1019.3, Exception 6). This is appropriate in view of the low hazard and minimal possible smoke accumulation in these facilities. While Section 1006.3.1 does say that an open exit access stairway can only be used for one story, travel distance typically does include the exit access stairway. With this exception for travel distance, the intent is to allow open parking garages to have open exit access stairways all the way down and out of the building. The number of means of egress requirements are met where the exit access travel distance requirement is met on each floor. There is a similar allowance for open-air assembly seating in Section 1029.7.

The travel distances within an exit enclosure (e.g., enclosed interior exit stairway or ramp or exit passageway) and in the exit discharge portion of the means of egress are also not regulated. Section 1006.3.3 permits certain buildings to be provided with a single exit. In instances where there is a single exit, travel distances less than those permitted in Table 1017.2 apply [see Tables 1006.3.3(1) and 1006.3.3(2)].

[BE] 1017.3.1 Exit access stairways and ramps. Travel distance on *exit access stairways* or *ramps* shall be included in the *exit access* travel distance measurement. The measurement along *stairways* shall be made on a plane parallel and tangent to the *stair* tread *nosings* in the center of the *stair* and landings. The measurement along *ramps* shall be made on the walking surface in the center of the *ramp* and landings.

❖ When considering open exit access stairways or ramps, it is important to determine where a stairway/ramp can be open (Section 1019), where that stairway/ramp is part of the required ways off a story (Section 1006.3), and egress travel distance (Sections 1006.3.1 and 1017). Similar to access to bathrooms, the travel distance is both by length and number of stories.

The number of ways off a story or out of a space is addressed in Section 1006.3. Saying "means of egress" instead of "exits" acknowledges that direct entrances to exits on each story are not always mandatory since access to exits (i.e., exit access stairways or ramps) on some stories is permissible within certain limitations. This allows some freedom of design where, for instance, required exit stairways may not be available without passing through other tenant spaces. The intent is to allow for a balance of security concerns, providing adequate safety for emergency evacuation.

Travel distance is measured along the exit access path. An example of exit access stairways would be unenclosed exit access stairways from a mezzanine level, open exit access stairways from a second floor (see Section 1019.3, Exception 1), or steps along the path of travel in a split floor-level situation. An example of an open exit access ramp would be a ramp between levels, such as to a stage or platform, or ramps leading from the upper levels in an open parking garage (see Section 1006.3.1, Exception 3, and Section 1019.3, Exception 6). Where an open exit access stairway is used to meet the required number of ways off the story (see Section 1006.3), the travel distance would also include travel down the open stairway or ramp and to an enclosed exit stairway or ramp, a horizontal exit or an exit door to the outside. If the open exit access is not required for egress (such as a supplemental stairway), this section is not applicable.

Section 1006.3.1 also sets an additional limit on the travel of one story. So if you have an open exit access stairway that is permitted by Section 1019.3 to extend more than one story, you can only rely on that stairway to count as a required means of egress from one floor to the next. Section 1006.3.1 does have exceptions for where the exit access travel distance can be more than one story. An example of this would be an open exit stairway within an individual dwelling unit (see Section 1006.3.1, Exception 1, and Section 1019.3, Exception 2) or an open exit stairway from a balcony or press box (see Section 1006.3.1, Exception 5, and Section 1019.3, Exception 8).

For an open parking garage, the exception in Section 1017.3 allows for the exit access travel distance to be measured to the top of the ramp or stairway rather than down the ramp or stairway and to the exit (see Section 1006.3.1, Exception 3, and Section 1019.3, Exception 6). Section 1029.7, Exception 2, has a similar allowance for open air assembly seating.

SECTION 1018
AISLES

[BE] 1018.1 General. *Aisles* and *aisle accessways* serving as a portion of the *exit access* in the *means of egress* system shall comply with the requirements of this section. *Aisles* or *aisle accessways* shall be provided from all occupied portions of the *exit access* that contain seats, tables, furnishings, displays and similar fixtures or equipment. The minimum width or required capacity of *aisles* shall be unobstructed.

Exception: Encroachments complying with Section 1005.7.

❖ This section addresses aisles and aisle accessways, primarily in occupancies other than assembly seating areas. Current provisions address aisles in all uses, but only address aisle accessways for assembly spaces and mercantile.

"Aisle accessway" is defined in Chapter 2 as "that portion of an exit access that leads to an aisle." The term "Aisle" is defined in Chapter 2 as "an unenclosed exit access component that defines and provides a path of egress travel." Given the many possible configurations of fixtures and furniture, both permanent and movable, the determination of where aisle accessways stop and aisles begin is often subject to interpretation. The concepts are the same as rooms and corridors, but without the hard delineations.

Typically, the aisle accessways lead to the aisles, which in turn lead to the exits. Since the aisle serves as a path for means of egress similar to a corridor, the requirements for obstructing and protruding objects in the aisle are the same (see Section 1005.7).

A cross reference to Section 1005.7 in the exceptions for width in aisles (see Section 1018.1), corridors (see Section 1020.3), exit passageways (see Section 1024.2) and exit courts (see Section 1028.4.1) reinforces the fact that encroachment limits are generally applicable for these types of confined routes.

[BE] 1018.2 Aisles in assembly spaces. *Aisles and aisle accessways* serving a room or space used for assembly purposes shall comply with Section 1029.

❖ The provisions for aisles and aisle accessways in spaces with assembly seating, such as restaurants, theaters and sports arenas, are unique. See Section 1029 for criteria.

[BE] 1018.3 Aisles in Groups B and M. In Group B and M occupancies, the minimum clear *aisle* width shall be determined by Section 1005.1 for the *occupant load* served, but shall be not less than that required for *corridors* by Section 1020.2.

Exception: Nonpublic *aisles* serving less than 50 people and not required to be accessible by Chapter 11 of the *International Building Code* need not exceed 28 inches (711 mm) in width.

❖ This requirement establishes aisle-width criteria for Group B and M occupancies based on the occupant load served by the aisle. While not providing as confined a path as corridors, the displays or equipment would limit the choice of paths, so the minimum width is the same as corridors (see Section 1020.2). The reference to Section 1005.1 would trigger a requirement for aisles wider than 44 inches (1118 mm) where the anticipated occupant load of that aisle is greater than 220 (44 inches/0.2 = 220 occupants for nonsprinklered buildings and 44 inches/0.15 = 293 occupants in sprinklered buildings). Where an aisle allows for access to exits in two directions, the occupant load could be split, similar to corridors. The exception addresses aisles that may be found in an archival file room or stock storage racks.

For mercantile, if fixtures are permanent, such as in a typical grocery store or office cubicles in a business, the aisle provisions would be applicable throughout. In a situation where there were groups of displays separated by aisles, the area within the displays may be considered aisle accessways (see Section 1018.4).

[BE] 1018.4 Aisle accessways in Group M. An *aisle accessway* shall be provided on not less than one side of each element within the *merchandise pad*. The minimum clear width for an *aisle accessway* not required to be accessible shall be 30 inches (762 mm). The required clear width of the *aisle accessway* shall be measured perpendicular to the elements and merchandise within the *merchandise pad*. The 30-inch (762 mm) minimum clear width shall be maintained to provide a path to an adjacent *aisle* or *aisle accessway*. The *common path of egress travel* shall not exceed 30 feet (9144 mm) from any point in the *merchandise pad*.

Exception: For areas serving not more than 50 occupants, the *common path of egress travel* shall not exceed 75 feet (22 860 mm).

❖ The definition for "Merchandise pad" can be found in Chapter 2. The idea is that a merchandise pad contains movable displays and aisle accessways. A surrounding aisle or permanent walls or displays would define the extent of the merchandise pad. Large department stores will have numerous merchandise pads (see Commentary Figure 1018.4). In accordance with Section 105.2, Item 13, movable cases, counters and partitions not over 5 feet 9 inches (1753 mm) in height do not require a building permit to move, add or alter, so a merchandise pad can be reconfigured many times as seasonal projects change, such as moving from a swimsuit display to a coat display. Every element within a merchandise pad must adjoin a minimum 30-inch-wide (762 mm) aisle accessway on at least one side. Travel within a merchandise pad is limited, with a maximum common path of egress travel of 30 feet (9144 mm). The common path of egress travel limitation is extended to 75 feet (22 m) in those areas serving a maximum occupant load of 50. Similar to a room, the common path of egress travel is the distance to get from the farthest point inside the merchandise pad to an aisle where there is a choice of two ways to move to an exit.

Commentary Figure 1018.4
AISLES AND AISLE ACCESSWAYS IN MERCANTILE

[BE] 1018.5 Aisles in other than assembly spaces and Groups B and M. In other than rooms or spaces used for assembly purposes and Group B and M occupancies, the minimum clear *aisle* capacity shall be determined by Section 1005.1 for the *occupant load* served, but the width shall be not less than that required for *corridors* by Section 1020.2.

> **Exception:** Nonpublic *aisles* serving less than 50 people and not required to be accessible by Chapter 11 of the *International Building Code* need not exceed 28 inches (711 mm) in width.

❖ Aisles can occur in other occupancies where there is a confined path of travel to the exit access or exit door leading from a space.

While not providing as confined a path as corridors, the displays or equipment would limit the choice of paths, so the minimum width is the same as corridors (see Section 1020.2). The reference to Section 1005.1 would trigger a requirement for aisles wider than 44 inches (1118 mm) where the anticipated occupant load of that aisle is greater than 220 (44 inches/0.2 = 220 occupants for nonsprinklered buildings and 44 inches/0.15 = 293 occupants in sprinklered buildings). Where an aisle allows for access to exits in two directions, the occupant load could be split to determine minimum width/capacity, similar to corridors. The exception addresses aisles that may be found in an archival file room or stock storage racks.

SECTION 1019
EXIT ACCESS STAIRWAYS AND RAMPS

[BE] 1019.1 General. *Exit access stairways* and *ramps* serving as an *exit access* component in a *means of egress* system shall comply with the requirements of this section. The number of stories connected by *exit access stairways* and *ramps* shall include *basements*, but not *mezzanines*.

❖ This is a general scoping section for open stairways and ramps. All open stairways or ramps are part of exit access. When considering open exit access stairways or ramps, it is important to determine where a stairway/ramp can be open (Section 1019), where that stairway/ramp is part of the required ways off a story (Section 1006.3), and egress travel distance (Sections 1006.3.1 and 1017). Similar to access to bathrooms, the travel distance is both by length and number of stories.

Exit access stairways can be between levels or between stories. Section 1019.2 addresses steps and ramps between levels on the same floor, including mezzanines. Mezzanines are considered part of the room below and not a separate story. Section 1019.3 addresses stairways and ramps between stories. Where the open stairway or ramp is part of a required way out (means of egress via exits or access to exits), the exit access travel distance would include the path along the open stairway or ramp. Exit stairways are addressed in Sections 1023 and 1027. To ensure safe travel along these vertical elements, all stairways and ramps are required to comply with Sections 1011 and 1012, respectively.

[BE] 1019.2 All occupancies. *Exit access stairways* and *ramps* that serve floor levels within a single story are not required to be enclosed.

❖ Exit access stairways and ramps between levels on the same story and between a story and an associated mezzanine are always permitted to be open unless they are part of a fire-resistance-rated corridor (see Section 1020.6).

[BE] 1019.3 Occupancies other than Groups I-2 and I-3. In other than Group I-2 and I-3 occupancies, floor openings containing *exit access stairways* or *ramps* that do not comply with one of the conditions listed in this section shall be enclosed with a shaft enclosure constructed in accordance with Section 713 of the *International Building Code*.

1. *Exit access stairways* and *ramps* that serve, or atmospherically communicate between, only two stories. Such interconnected stories shall not be open to other stories.
2. In Group R-1, R-2 or R-3 occupancies, *exit access stairways* and *ramps* connecting four stories or less serving and contained within an individual *dwelling unit* or *sleeping unit* or live/work unit.
3. *Exit access stairways* serving and contained within a Group R-3 congregate residence or a Group R-4 facility are not required to be enclosed.
4. *Exit access stairways* and *ramps* in buildings equipped throughout with an *automatic sprinkler system* in accordance with Section 903.3.1.1, where the area of the vertical opening between stories does not exceed

twice the horizontal projected area of the *stairway* or *ramp*, and the opening is protected by a draft curtain and closely spaced sprinklers in accordance with NFPA 13. In other than Group B and M occupancies, this provision is limited to openings that do not connect more than four stories.

5. *Exit access stairways* and *ramps* within an atrium complying with the provisions of Section 404 of the *International Building Code*.
6. *Exit access stairways* and *ramps* in *open parking garages* that serve only the parking garage.
7. *Exit access stairways* and *ramps* serving smoke-protected or open-air assembly seating complying with the *exit access* travel distance requirements of Section 1029.7.
8. *Exit access stairways* and *ramps* between the balcony, gallery or press box and the main assembly floor in occupancies such as theaters, *places of religious worship*, auditoriums and sports facilities.

❖ This section includes conditions that permit unprotected floor openings for exit access stairways and ramps. Groups I-2 and I-3 use smoke compartments as part of their defend-in-place strategies; as such, they are addressed separately in Section 1019.4.

The allowances listed are for interior exit access stairways and ramps that are between stories. Exit access stairways and ramps between elevation changes on the same story or serving mezzanines do not serve different stories; therefore, the enclosure requirements in this section are not applicable (see Section 1017.2). For simplicity in the commentary to Sections 1019.3 and 1019.4, where interior exit access stairways are mentioned, let it be understood that the same rules apply to interior exit access ramps.

The primary difference between interior exit access stairways and interior exit stairways is how exit access travel distance is measured (see Section 1017.3). Where a designer chooses to use an exit access stairway, the exit access travel distance includes travel along the slope of the exit access stairway, similar to stairways leading from an open mezzanine or steps at a change in level on a floor.

The base requirement is that exit access stairways between floors are permitted and protected in a similar manner as floor openings (see IBC Sections 712 and 713). A stairway penetrates the floor/ceiling assemblies between levels, creating a vertical opening or shaft. In cases of fire, a vertical opening may act as a chimney, causing smoke, hot gases and light-burning products to flow upward (buoyant force). If an opening is unprotected, these products of combustion will be forced by positive pressure differentials to spread horizontally into building spaces. There are exceptions for shaft protection around openings in IBC Section 712.1 or exit access stairways as permitted in this section in Items 1 through 8 (see also IBC Section 712.1.12).

Exit access stairways are not required to discharge directly to the exterior as are interior exit stairways (see Section 1023.3). Instead, exit access stairways are part of the route that leads to the exit (i.e., exterior exit door, horizontal exit, enclosed interior exit stairway or ramp, exterior exit stairway or ramp). See the commentary to IBC Sections 712 and 713 for a discussion of other differences in protection permitted for the enclosure of exit access stairways versus exit stairways.

It is important to remember that while exit access stairways may be open for multiple floors, Section 1006.3.1 states "The path of egress travel to an exit shall not pass through more than one adjacent story." However, if there are provisions in the exceptions in Sections 1006.3.1 and items in Section 1019.3, the exit access path could be all the way down the open exit access stairway for multiple levels (Items 2, 3, 6, 7 and 8).

Item 1 allows an open exit access stairway where the opening is only between two stories. There cannot be any other unprotected openings that connect to other stories since this could create a staggered stack effect for the movement of smoke between multiple stories. In two-story buildings, this would allow for open stairways between the basement and ground level or between the first and second stories. Another example would be an open exit access stairway between the fifth and sixth stories of a building, provided there were no other unprotected openings between the fourth and fifth stories or the sixth and seventh stories. This is consistent with IBC Section 712.1.9 for openings between two stories.

In Item 2, for residential occupancies, exit access stairways within a single-family home or townhouse are not required to be enclosed because of the small occupant load and resident familiarity with the space. Examples of "within an individual dwelling unit or sleeping unit" would be a two-story hotel suite or a multistory apartment unit. See Section 1006.3.3, Items 2 and 5, for the allowance for these to be single-exit stories. Live/work units call for the egress to be designed for the "function served," and vertical openings are not required to be enclosed (IBC Sections 419.3 and 419.4); therefore, it is appropriate to allow open exit access stairways to serve the dwelling portion of the live/work unit. Note that IBC Section 712.1.2 limits any vertical opening within dwelling units, including stairways, to four stories or less.

Item 3 refers to Group R-3 and R4 congregate residences. A congregate residence would not be considered an individual dwelling unit, so Item 2 would not be applicable; however, these small facilities operate similarly to a single-family home. Thus, they have an allowance for open exit access stairways for the same reasons as dwelling units in Item 2. See Section 1006.3.3, Item 4, which allows a single exit in Group R-3 and R-4 congregate residences. These congregate residences are limited to 16 occupants who are capable of self-preservation (IBC Sections

308.2.3, 310.4 and 310.5). If a facility offers medical care, it would be classified as Group I-2, and it needs to comply with Section 1019.4.

Item 4 discusses buildings sprinklered throughout with an NFPA 13 system. The size of the opening is limited to twice the size of the stairway footprint. The opening must be protected with a draft curtain and closely spaced sprinklers (see Commentary Figure 1019.3). This allows for such an opening to extend the entire height of the building. For groups other than business and mercantile, there is the additional limitation of a maximum of four stories. However, to serve as one of the required ways off the floor (means of egress via access to exits), the exit access stairway must still meet the exit access travel distance (see Section 1017.3.1) and cannot be used for more than one story (see Section 1006.3.1) before occupants have access to exits. This item is similar to what is permitted for escalators (see IBC Sections 712.1.3 and 712.1.3.1). The power-operated automatic shutter permitted in IBC Section 712.1.3.2 would not be an option for exit access stairways since the stairways must be available for exit access travel.

Item 5 allows for exit access stairways to travel down through an atrium. Atriums often penetrate more than two stories. Atriums must meet the provisions in IBC Section 404 for sprinklers, fire alarms, smoke control, enclosure, limitations on flame spread and smoke development of interior finishes, and the reduction in the normal exit access travel distance. Where the stairway serves as a required way off the floor (means of egress via exit access), in no case can the exit access travel distance through the atrium, including travel along the stairway, be greater than 200 feet (60 960 mm) (see IBC Section 404.9.3) or more than one story (see Section 1006.3.1). See also the commentary for Section 1023.2, Exception 2.

In Item 6, exit access stairways located in open parking structures are exempt from the enclosure requirements because of the ease of accessibility by the fire services, the natural ventilation of such structures, the low level of fire hazard, the small number of people using the structure at any one time and the excellent fire record of such structures. The exception to Section 1017.3 permits the exit access travel distance to be measured to the top step of the exit access stairway in open parking garages. In essence, open parking garages using this item can have open stairways for the full height of the building. By the travel distance being met at the top of the stairway, the means of egress requirements have been met, and there are no travel distance limits on the stairway.

In Item 7, stairways in outdoor facilities (i.e., Group A-5) in which the means of egress is essentially open to the outside need not be enclosed because of the ability to vent the fire to the outside. This item is coordinated with the requirements for open-air assembly seating as regulated by Section 1028.7, which allows unlimited travel distance in noncombustible construction and 400 feet in combustible construction. This same allowance is permitted for indoor seating that is smoke protected.

Item 8 addresses the unique situation for multiple-tier indoor assembly seating areas. Since press boxes, galleries and balconies all have the same atmosphere and fire recognition ability as the rest of the seating, the stairways serving these spaces are protected by the same system as the seating (e.g., open to the interior volume and smoke protected; open to the outside); therefore, it is logical to treat the access to these spaces the same as the seating bowl. Open exit access stairways can serve the press box, gallery and balconies where those stairways move the occupants directly from the press box, gallery and balconies into the seating bowl. See Section 1029 for specific criteria.

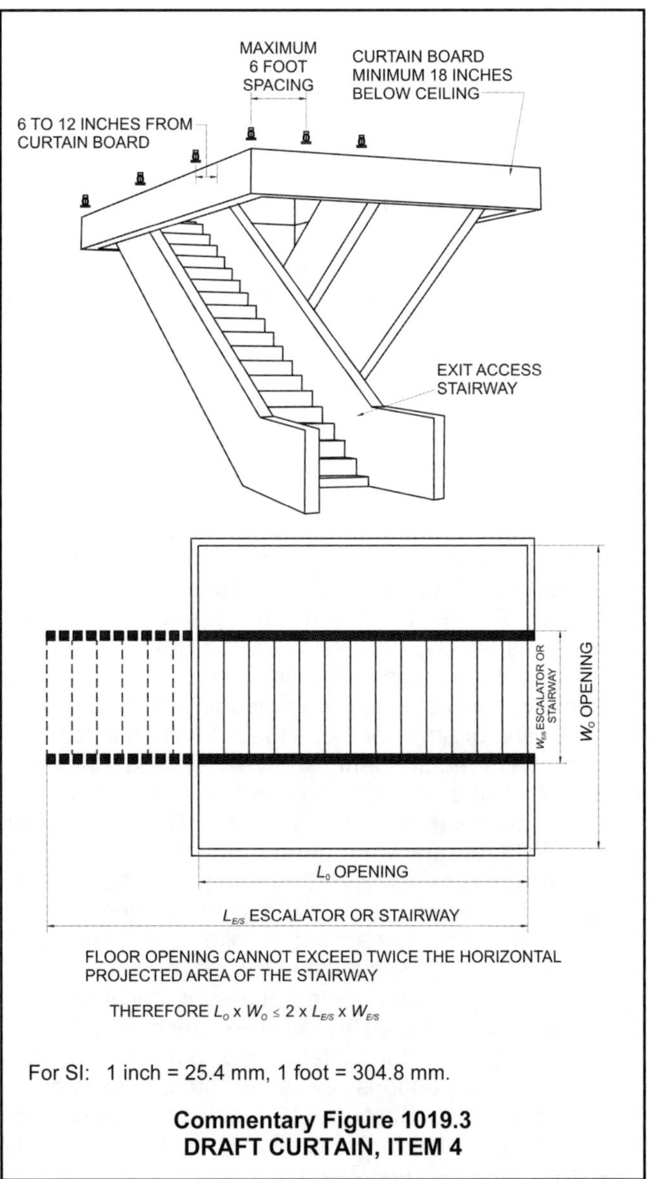

Commentary Figure 1019.3
DRAFT CURTAIN, ITEM 4

[BE] 1019.4 Group I-2 and I-3 occupancies. In Group I-2 and I-3 occupancies, floor openings between stories containing *exit access stairways* or *ramps* are required to be enclosed with a shaft enclosure constructed in accordance with Section 713 of the *International Building Code*.

> **Exception:** In Group I-3 occupancies, *exit access stairways* or *ramps* constructed in accordance with Section 408 of the *International Building Code* are not required to be enclosed.

❖ Groups I-2 and I-3 use smoke compartments as part of their defend-in-place strategies; as such, they are addressed separately in this section. Any openings in the floors must be protected the same as a shaft.

The exception allows for observation and security needs in detention facilities, and exit access stairways within a housing unit to not be required to be enclosed (see IBC Section 408.5.1). Section 1023.2 also includes a limited exception for enclosure of exit stairways within jails per IBC Section 408.3.8.

SECTION 1020 CORRIDORS

[BE] 1020.1 Construction. *Corridors* shall be fire-resistance rated in accordance with Table 1020.1. The *corridor* walls required to be fire-resistance rated shall comply with Section 708 of the *International Building Code* for fire partitions.

Exceptions:

1. A fire-resistance rating is not required for *corridors* in an occupancy in Group E where each room that is used for instruction has not less than one door opening directly to the exterior and rooms for assembly purposes have not less than one-half of the required *means of egress* doors opening directly to the exterior. Exterior doors specified in this exception are required to be at ground level.
2. A fire-resistance rating is not required for *corridors* contained within a *dwelling unit* or *sleeping unit* in an occupancy in Groups I-1 and R.
3. A fire-resistance rating is not required for *corridors* in *open parking garages*.
4. A fire-resistance rating is not required for *corridors* in an occupancy in Group B that is a space requiring only a single *means of egress* complying with Section 1006.2.
5. *Corridors* adjacent to the *exterior walls* of buildings shall be permitted to have unprotected openings on unrated *exterior walls* where unrated walls are permitted by Table 602 of the *International Building Code* and unprotected openings are permitted by Table 705.8 of the *International Building Code*.

❖ This section is not intended to require corridors. Once corridors are provided and occupants are limited to a confined path of travel, then these provisions apply.

The purpose of corridor enclosures is to provide fire protection to occupants as they travel the confined path, perhaps unaware of a fire buildup in an adjacent floor area. The base protection is a fire partition having a 1-hour fire-resistance rating (see Table 1020.1). The table allows a reduction or elimination of the fire-resistance rating, depending on the occupant load and the presence of an NFPA 13 or 13R automatic sprinkler system throughout the building.

IBC Section 708 addresses the continuity of fire partitions serving as corridor walls. In addition to allowing the fire partitions to terminate at the underside of a fire-resistance-rated floor/ceiling or roof/ceiling assembly, the supporting construction need not have the same fire-resistance rating in buildings of Types IIB, IIIB and VB construction as specified in IBC Section 708. If such walls were required to be supported by fire-resistance-rated construction, the use of these construction types would be severely restricted where the corridors are required to have a fire-resistance rating. IBC Section 407.3 requires that corridor walls in Group I-2 occupancies that are required to have a fire-resistance rating must be continuous to the underside of the floor or roof deck above or at a smoke-limiting ceiling membrane. Continuity is required because of the defend-in-place protection strategy utilized in such buildings. Requirements for corridor construction within Group I-3 occupancies are found in IBC Section 408.8. Dwelling unit separation in Groups I-1, R-1, R-2 and R-3 is found in IBC Sections 420.2 and 420.3. Ambulatory care facilities have special requirements in Section 422.2 where some of the patients can be incapable of self-preservation. For additional requirements for an elevator lobby that is adjacent to or part of a corridor, see the commentaries to Sections 713.14, 1020.6 and 3006.

Exception 1 indicates a fire-resistance rating is not required for corridors in Group E where any room that is used for instruction or assembly purposes is adjacent to the corridor and has a door directly to the outside. The need for a fire-resistance-rated corridor is eliminated because these rooms are provided with an alternative egress path as a result of the exterior exits. This option is typically utilized in nonsprinklered buildings, such as day care facilities, since a sprinkler system would also allow for unrated corridors in Group E (see Table 1020.1). Grade schools and high schools have security concerns that sometimes make the outdoor exit for every classroom not a preferred option.

In accordance with Exception 2, a fire-resistance rating for a corridor contained within a single dwelling unit (e.g., apartment, townhouse) or sleeping unit (e.g., hotel guestroom, assistive living suite) is not required for practical reasons. It is unreasonable to expect fire doors and the associated hardware and closing devices to be within dwellings and similar occupancies.

Given the relatively smoke-free environment of open parking structures, Exception 3 does not require rated corridors in these types of facilities.

If an office suite is small enough that only one means of egress is required from the suite, Exception 4 indicates that a rated corridor would not be required in that area. The main corridor that connects these suites to the exits would be evaluated in accordance with Table 1020.1.

Exception 5 addresses where the exterior wall of a building is also the wall of a corridor. The exterior wall is not required to be rated by the corridor provisions where there is a sufficient fire separation distance for the exterior wall to be able to have unprotected openings. This is similar to the exterior wall for an enclosed interior exit stairway. The fire is assumed to be inside the building, so that is where the protection is required.

**[BE] TABLE 1020.1
CORRIDOR FIRE-RESISTANCE RATING**

OCCUPANCY	OCCUPANT LOAD SERVED BY CORRIDOR	REQUIRED FIRE-RESISTANCE RATING (hours)	
		Without sprinkler system	With sprinkler system[c]
H-1, H-2, H-3	All	Not Permitted	1
H-4, H-5	Greater than 30	Not Permitted	1
A, B, E, F, M, S, U	Greater than 30	1	0
R	Greater than 10	Not Permitted	0.5[c]/1[d]
I-2[a]	All	Not Permitted	0
I-1, I-3	All	Not Permitted	1[b]
I-4	All	1	0

a. For requirements for occupancies in Group I-2, see Sections 407.2 and 407.3 of the *International Building Code*.

b. For a reduction in the fire-resistance rating for occupancies in Group I-3, see Section 408.8 of the *International Building Code*.

c. Buildings equipped throughout with an automatic sprinkler system in accordance with Section 903.3.1.1 or 903.3.1.2 where allowed.

d. Group R-3 and R-4 buildings equipped throughout with an automatic sprinkler system in accordance with Section 903.3.1.3. See Section 903.2.8 for occupancies where automatic sprinkler systems are permitted in accordance with Section 903.3.1.3.

❖ The required fire-resistance ratings of corridors serving adjacent spaces are provided in Table 1020.1. The fire-resistance rating is based on the group classification (considering characteristics such as occupant mobility, density and familiarity with the building as well as the fire hazard associated with the classification), the total occupant load served by the corridor and the presence of an automatic sprinkler system.

Where the corridor serves a limited number of people (second column in Table 1020.1), the fire-resistance rating is eliminated because of the limited size of the facility and the likelihood that the occupants would become aware of a fire buildup in sufficient time to exit the structure safely. The total occupant load that the corridor serves is used to determine the requirement for a rated corridor enclosure. The number of occupants served is the total occupants that will move into the corridor to egress. Corridors serving a total occupant load equal to or less than that indicated in the second column of Table 1020.1 are not required to be enclosed with fire-resistance-rated construction. For example, a corridor serving an occupant load of 30 or less in an unsprinklered Group B occupancy is not required to be enclosed with fire-resistance-rated construction. This example is illustrated in Commentary Figure 1020.1.

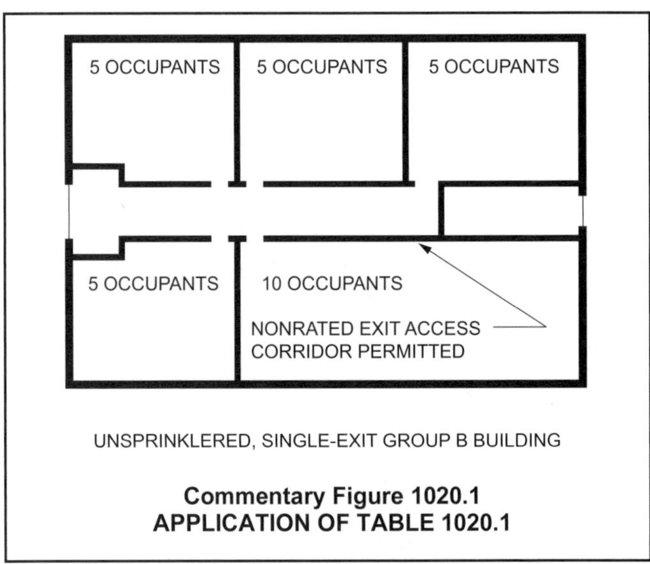

**Commentary Figure 1020.1
APPLICATION OF TABLE 1020.1**

The purpose of corridor enclosures is to provide fire protection to occupants as they travel the confined path, perhaps unaware of a fire buildup in an adjacent floor area. The base protection is a fire partition having a 1-hour fire-resistance rating. The table allows a reduction or elimination of the fire-resistance rating, depending on the occupant load and the presence of an NFPA 13 or 13R automatic sprinkler system throughout the building.

A common mistake is assuming a building is sprinklered throughout and utilizing the corridor rating reductions, where in fact certain requirements in NFPA 13 would not qualify the building as sprinklered throughout. For example, a health club installs a sprinkler system, but chooses to eliminate the sprinklers over the swimming pool in accordance with the exception in IBC Section 507.4. Any corridors within the building that serve greater than 30 occupants must be rated because the building would not be considered sprinklered throughout in accordance with NFPA 13 requirements.

Note that because of the hazardous nature of occupancies in Groups H-1, H-2 and H-3, fire-resistance-rated corridors are required under all conditions. Regardless of the presence of a fire sprinkler system, a 1-hour-rated corridor enclosure is required in high-hazard occupancies with detonation, deflagration, accelerated burning, readily supported combustion or physical hazards. Group H-4 and H-5 occupancies that contain semiconductor fabrication materials or operations constituting a health hazard do not pose the same relative fire or explosion hazard as Group H-1, H-2 or H-3 materials. As such, in Group H-4 or H-5, where the corridor serves a total occupant load of 30 or less, a fire-resistance-rated enclosure is not required. The "not permitted" in the third column is in coordination with Section 903.2.5, which requires all Group H buildings to be fully sprinklered.

The code acknowledges that an automatic sprinkler system can serve to control or eliminate fire development that could threaten the exit access corridor. Most occupancies where sleeping rooms are not present (Groups A, B, E, F, M, S and U) are permitted to have nonfire-resistance-rated corridors if a sprinkler system is installed throughout the building in accordance with NFPA 13.

In residential facilities, within individual dwelling units or sleeping units, Section 1020.1, Exception 2, would exempt the corridors within the units from being rated. Therefore, the table is applicable to the corridors outside of the units. The response time to a fire might be delayed because the residents could be sleeping. With this additional safety concern, the requirements for common corridors are more restrictive than for nonresidential occupancies. If a corridor serves multiple dwelling or sleeping units and the total number of occupants is more than 10, it is required to be rated for 1 hour where the building uses an NFPA 13D sprinkler system. If the building is sprinklered throughout with either an NFPA 13 or 13R system, then the rating of the corridor may be reduced to $^1/_2$ hour. This information is reflected in Notes c and d of the table.

While all Group I facilities are supervised environments, the level of supervision in Group I-2 occupancies would permit assisted evacuation by staff in an emergency; therefore, corridors are not required to be rated. Corridors in Group I-2 occupancies are also regulated by Sections 407.2 and 407.3 (Note a). Because of the lower staff/resident ratio in Group I-1 and the limitation of free egress in Group I-3, corridors must have a 1-hour fire-resistance rating [see IBC Section 408.8 for a reduction in the fire-resistance rating for Group I-3 (Note b)]. The "not permitted" in the third column is in coordination with Section 903.2.6, which requires all Group I buildings to be fully sprinklered. The rated corridor in buildings without sprinkler systems in Group I-4 is in recognition of the exceptions in Section 903.2.6.

[BE] 1020.1.1 Hoistway opening protection. Elevator hoistway openings shall be protected in accordance with Section 3006.2.1 of the *International Building Code*.

❖ There are three things to consider simultaneously—corridors, vertical shafts and elevator lobby requirements.

In a rated corridor, the opening protectives for fire partitions have to have a fire-resistance rating of 20 minutes and smoke and draft control [see Section 1020.2 and IBC Section 708.6 and Table 716.1(2)]. At the elevator/vertical shafts, openings have to meet the shaft opening protectives for fire barriers in IBC Sections 713.7 and 716.2.1.2.

IBC Section 3006.2.1 states that where a hoistway opens onto a corridor that is required to be rated, that elevator opening may have additional protection required by IBC Section 3006.3. IBC Section 3006.3 would allow for a lobby enclosed by fire partitions or smoke partitions (Items 1 and 2), smoke and draft control doors at the elevator opening (Item 3), or pressurizing the elevator shaft (Item 4).

Note that IBC Section 3006.2 would not require hoistway opening protection in a low-rise building [occupied floors 75 feet (22 860 mm) or less above fire department vehicle access] with an NFPA 13 or NFPA 13R sprinkler system or an unsprinklered building that is three stories or less. IBC Section 3006.2 exempts protection of the hoistway opening on the level of exit discharge where the building has an NFPA 13 sprinkler system.

The following is a list of where opening protectives for fire partitions (Section 1020) and vertical shafts (IBC Section 713) as well as hoistway protection (IBC Section 3006) would apply.

- Unsprinklered buildings:
  - Rated corridors in Group A, B, E, F, I-4, M, S and U occupancies
  - Hoistways connecting more than three stories
- Sprinklered buildings
  - Rated corridors in Groups H, I-1, I-3, R-1 and R-2
  - Hoistways in high-rise buildings (buildings with occupied floors greater than 75 feet (22 860 mm) above fire department vehicle access)

Protection options for elevator lobbies (IBC Section 3006) are the same as the protection requirements for elevators using rated corridors, nonrated corridors and no corridors.

See the commentary for Section 1020.6 for options on how criteria can be met with the combination of requirements for elevator/vertical shaft opening protectives (IBC Sections 713 and 716) (i.e., elevators not covered by IBC Section 3006) and fire partition opening protectives (IBC Sections 708 and 716) for rated corridors.

In buildings with nonrated corridors or no corridors that also fall below the thresholds for elevator lobbies in IBC Section 3006.2, only the elevator/vertical shaft provisions would apply.

[BE] 1020.2 Width and capacity. The required capacity of *corridors* shall be determined as specified in Section 1005.1, but the minimum width shall be not less than that specified in Table 1020.2.

Exception: In Group I-2 occupancies, *corridors* are not required to have a clear width of 96 inches (2438 mm) in areas where there will not be stretcher or bed movement for access to care or as part of the defend-in-place strategy.

❖ The corridor widths specified in Table 1020.2 are long-established minimums originally derived from human dimensions, practical concerns, occupant loads and psychological considerations. Additional corridor capacity, where necessary for large crowds, is determined in accordance with Section 1005.

The number of occupants using a corridor for egress establishes the required capacity of a corridor, as well as for any specific portion of a multiple-leg corridor system. Portions of a corridor system may differ in width for a variety of reasons not related to code minimums. The designer and building official are expected to verify that corridor widths and corridor fire-resistance ratings are in accordance with Sections 1005 and 1020, whichever is more restrictive.

The required capacity of a corridor is based on the total occupant load of the rooms and spaces served by the corridor as determined by Section 1004. Where a corridor is served by two exits in opposite directions, the corridor capacity is split to determine the minimum required width of those exits (i.e., exit door, exit stairway) at each end of the corridor (see Section 1005.3.2). The total occupant load served by a corridor is not split when establishing the corridor fire-resistance rating (see Section 1020.1) or when determining minimum widths.

The exception addresses an item in Table 1020.2 that requires a 96-inch-wide (2438 mm) corridor in Group I-2 facilities. While this is required in the area of patient sleeping rooms and patient care areas, there are a large number of areas in a hospital that will not be for the movement of beds, either for patient care or for the hospital's defend-in-place strategies. For example, a hospital may have office or therapy areas where patients are brought in walking on their own or using wheelchairs. Many nursing homes do not move patients in beds at all. The exception is intended to clarify that the 96-inch (2438 mm) corridor width is not a minimum for all corridors throughout a hospital or nursing home, but only in certain areas.

[BE] TABLE 1020.2
MINIMUM CORRIDOR WIDTH

OCCUPANCY	MINIMUM WIDTH (inches)
Any facility not listed below	44
Access to and utilization of mechanical, plumbing or electrical systems or equipment	24
With an occupant load of less than 50	36
Within a dwelling unit	36
In Group E with a corridor having a occupant load of 100 or more	72
In corridors and areas serving stretcher traffic in ambulatory care facilities	72
Group I-2 in areas where required for bed movement	96

For SI: 1 inch = 25.4 mm.

❖ The widths of passageways, aisles and corridors are functional elements of building construction that allow the occupants to circulate freely and comfortably throughout the floor area under nonemergency conditions. Under emergency situations, the egress paths must provide the needed width to accommodate the number of occupants that must utilize the corridor for egress.

Where the occupant load of the space exceeds 49, the minimum width of the passageway, aisle or corridor serving that space is required to be at least 44 inches (1118 mm) to permit two unimpeded parallel columns of users to travel in opposite directions. Where the total occupant load served by a corridor is 49 or less, a minimum width of 36 inches (914 mm) is permitted. Users are expected to encounter some intermittent travel interference from fellow users, but the lower occupant load makes those occasions infrequent and tolerable. The 36-inch (914 mm) minimum width is also required within a dwelling unit.

Passageways that lead to building equipment and systems must be at least 24 inches (610 mm) in width to provide a means to access and service the equipment when needed. Because of the frequency of servicing intervals and the limited number of occupants in these normally unoccupied areas, a reduced width is warranted. The minimum width criteria apply to many common situations, such as stage lighting and special-effects catwalks; catwalks leading to heating and cooling equipment; as well as passageways providing access to boilers, furnaces, transformers, pumps, piping and other equipment.

Except for small buildings, Group E occupancies are required to have minimum 72-inch-wide (1829 mm) corridors where the corridors serve educational areas. This width is needed not only for proper functional use, but also because of the edge effect caused by student lockers and other boundary attractions and objects. Service and other corridors outside of educational areas, such as an administrative area, would be regulated consistent with their use. Note that Section 1020.3 would not allow wall lockers to overlap the required corridor width.

In Group I-2 occupancies, where the corridor is utilized during a fire emergency for moving patients confined to beds, it is required to be at least 96 inches (2438 mm) in clear width. This width requirement is applicable to all areas where there are patient sleeping rooms, and may also be required in some of the treatment room areas where in-house patients will be brought in on beds or rolling stretchers. This minimum width allows two rolling beds or stretchers to pass in a corridor and permits the movement of a bed/stretcher into the corridor through a room door. In Group I-2 and ambulatory care center areas where the movement of beds is not anticipated, such as administrative and some outpatient areas of a hospital or clinic, the corridor would not be required to be 96 inches (2438 mm) wide. Most nursing homes do not move residents in beds. The minimum width would be determined by one of the appropriate applicable criteria. For outpatient medical care where the patient may be incapable of self-preservation, such as some outpatient surgery areas or dialysis treatment areas, the 72-inch-wide (1829 mm) corridor is required. In addition to Group B ambulatory care facilities, this could be applicable for Group I surgical areas, areas such as MRI suites or dialysis centers, or emergency rooms.

[BE] 1020.3 Obstruction. The minimum width or required capacity of *corridors* shall be unobstructed.

Exception: Encroachments complying with Section 1005.7.

❖ It is important to maintain required corridor width so that the path of travel to an exit is continually available and unobstructed. Because corridors tend to be lined with user passage doors, there are allowances under Section 1005.7. In no case may a door block more than 50 percent of the required corridor width. In addition, when fully open, the doors must not protrude more than 7 inches (178 mm) into the required width. Where doors swing out into the corridor, options would be to move doors back into alcoves or to provide corridors wider than the required width. The alcoves would have to be deep enough to also meet the 7-inch (118 mm) maximum protrusion when doors are open, or at least 29 inches (737 mm) deep. For an example of the wider corridor: a standard door is 36 inches (914 mm) wide, and the typical minimum corridor width is 44 inches (1118 mm). By adding the door leaf and half the required corridor width (36 + 22 = 58), a designer could provide a corridor width of 58 inches (1473 mm) and not have any issues with encroachment of doors. This is consistent with the provisions in aisles, corridors, stairways, ramps, exit passageways and exit discharge courts.

A cross reference to Section 1005.7 in the exceptions for width in aisles (see Section 1018.1), corridors (see Section 1020.3), exit passageways (see Section 1024.2) and exit courts (see Section 1028.4.1) reinforces the fact that the protrusion limits are generally applicable for these types of confined routes.

[BE] 1020.4 Dead ends. Where more than one *exit* or exit access doorway is required, the *exit access* shall be arranged such that dead-end *corridors* do not exceed 20 feet (6096 mm) in length.

Exceptions:

1. In Group I-3, Condition 2, 3 or 4 occupancies, the dead end in a *corridor* shall not exceed 50 feet (15 240 mm).
2. In occupancies in Groups B, E, F, I-1, M, R-1, R-2, S and U, where the building is equipped throughout with an *automatic sprinkler system* in accordance with Section 903.3.1.1, the length of the dead-end *corridors* shall not exceed 50 feet (15 240 mm).
3. A dead-end *corridor* shall not be limited in length where the length of the dead-end *corridor* is less than 2.5 times the least width of the dead-end *corridor*.

❖ The requirements of this section apply where a space is required to have more than one means of egress according to Section 1006.2. Dead-end requirements are not applicable to single exit spaces, only common paths of travel.

Dead ends in corridors and passageways can seriously increase the time needed for an occupant, especially if unfamiliar with the space, to locate the exits. More importantly, dead ends will allow a single fire event to eliminate access to all of the exits by trapping the occupants in the dead-end area. A dead end exists wherever a user of the corridor or passageway has only one direction to travel to reach any building exit [see Commentary Figure 1020.4(1)]. While a preferred building layout would be one without dead ends, a maximum dead-end length of 20 feet (6096 mm) is permitted and is to be measured from the extreme point in the dead end to the point where occupants have a choice of two directions to separate exits. Having to go back only 20 feet (6096 mm) after coming to a dead end is not such a significant distance as to cause a serious delay in reaching an exit during an emergency situation.

A dead end results whether or not egress elements open into it. A dead end is a hazard for occupants who enter the area from adjacent spaces, travel past an exit into a dead end or enter a dead end with the mistaken assumption that an exit is directly accessible from the dead end.

Note that Section 402.8.6 deals with dead-end distances in covered malls and assumes that, with a sufficiently wide mall in relation to its length, alternative paths of travel will be available in the mall itself for reaching an exit (i.e., the common mall area is not to be construed as a corridor).

Under special conditions, exceptions to the 20-foot (6096 mm) dead-end limitation apply.

Exception 1 is permitted based on the considerations of the functional needs of Group I-3, Condition 2, 3 or 4, occupancies; the requirements for smoke compartmentalization in IBC Section 408.6; and the requirement for automatic sprinkler protection of the facility in Section 903.2.6.

Exception 2 recognizes the fire protection benefits and performance history of automatic fire sprinkler systems. While the degree of hazard in Group B, E, F, M, S and U occupancies does not initially require an automatic fire suppression system, the length of a dead-end corridor or passageway is permitted to be extended to 50 feet (15 240 mm) where an automatic fire sprinkler system, in accordance with NFPA 13, is provided throughout the building. This exception is also permitted in Group I-1, R-1 and R-2 occupancies, but only where they use an NFPA 13 system, not an NFPA 13R system. In addition, these provisions are consistent with those in the IEBC and IFC in the regulation of dead-end corridors in existing buildings undergoing alterations. Dead-end provisions are not applicable in single-exit spaces; therefore, dead-end provisions are not applicable in Group R-3 and R-4 occupancies.

Exception 3 addresses the condition presented by "cul-de-sac" elevator lobbies directly accessible from exit access corridors. In such an elevator lobby, lengths of 20 to 30 feet (6096 to 9144 mm) are common for three- or four-car elevator banks. Typically, the width of this elevator lobby is such that the possibility of confusion with a path of egress is minimized. Where the length/width ratio of a dead-end corridor is less than 2.5:1, the dead end becomes so wide that it is less likely to be perceived as a corridor leading to an exit. For example, based on the 2.5:1 ratio limitation, a 25-foot-long (7620 mm) dead end over 10 feet (3048 mm) in width would not be considered a dead-end corridor [see Commentary Figure 1020.4(2)]. For additional elevator lobby requirements, see the commentaries to IBC Section 3006.

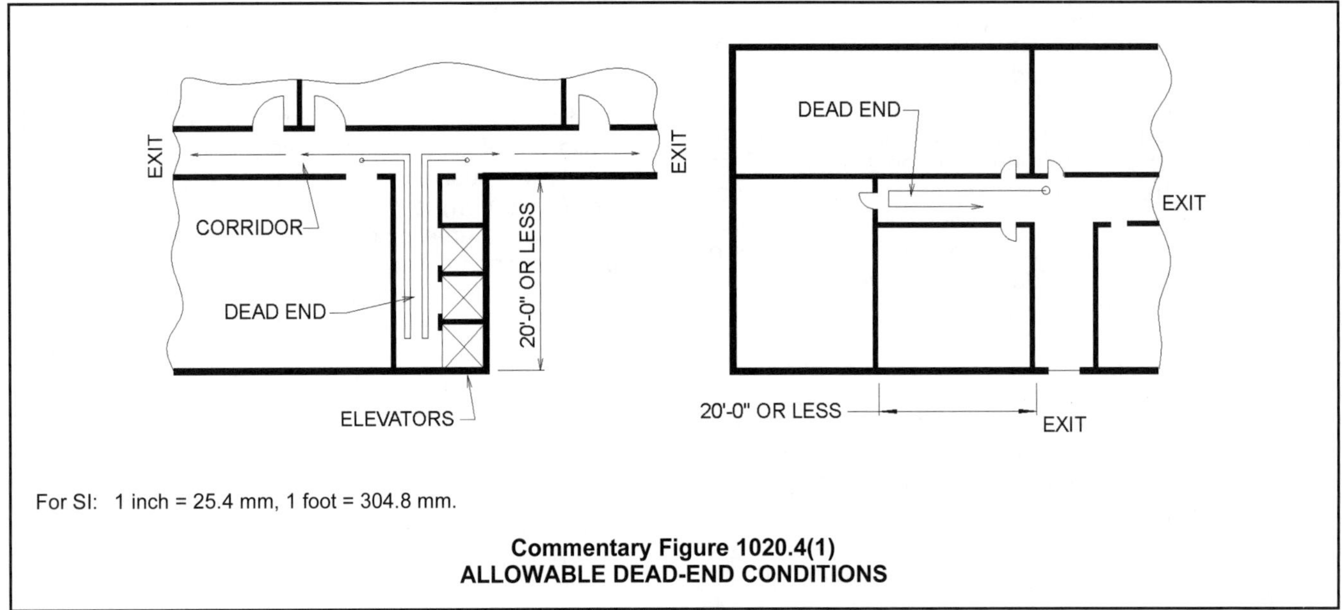

For SI: 1 inch = 25.4 mm, 1 foot = 304.8 mm.

Commentary Figure 1020.4(1)
ALLOWABLE DEAD-END CONDITIONS

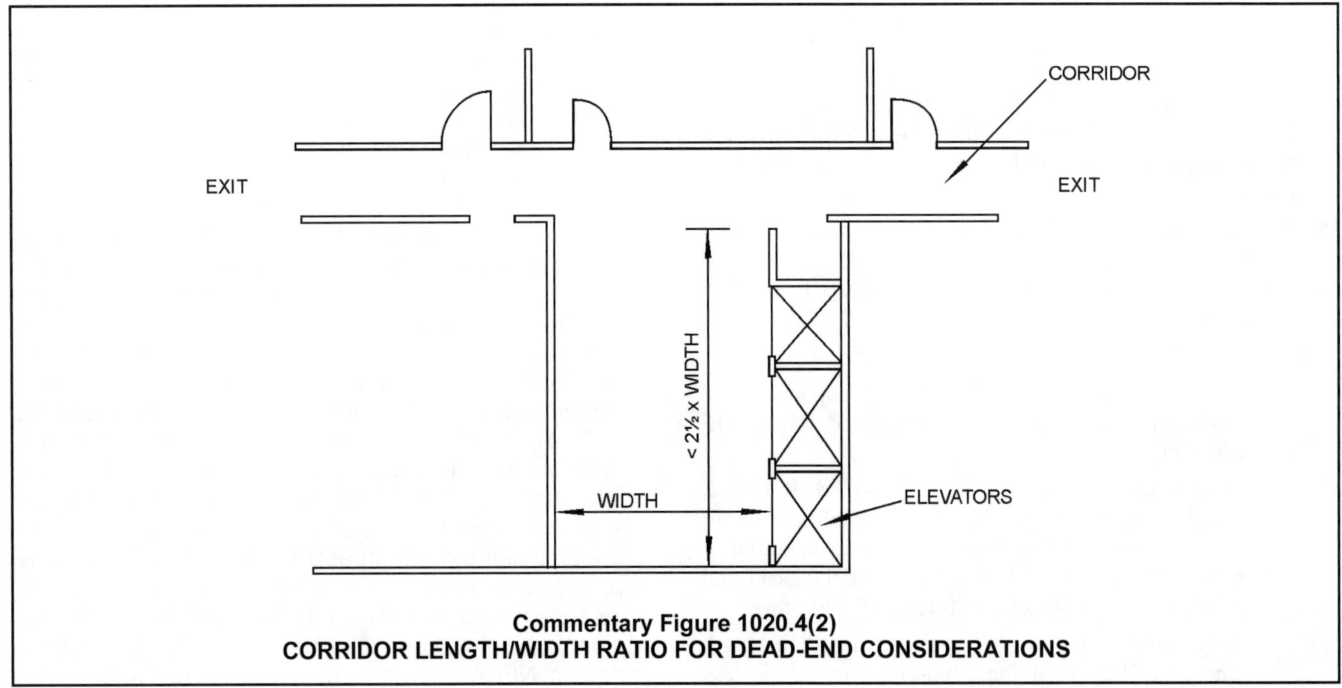

Commentary Figure 1020.4(2)
CORRIDOR LENGTH/WIDTH RATIO FOR DEAD-END CONSIDERATIONS

[BE] 1020.5 Air movement in corridors. *Corridors* shall not serve as supply, return, exhaust, relief or ventilation air ducts.

Exceptions:

1. Use of a *corridor* as a source of makeup air for exhaust systems in rooms that open directly onto such *corridors*, including toilet rooms, bathrooms, dressing rooms, smoking lounges and janitor closets, shall be permitted, provided that each such *corridor* is directly supplied with outdoor air at a rate greater than the rate of makeup air taken from the *corridor*.
2. Where located within a *dwelling unit*, the use of *corridors* for conveying return air shall not be prohibited.
3. Where located within tenant spaces of 1,000 square feet (93 m^2) or less in area, utilization of *corridors* for conveying return air is permitted.
4. Incidental air movement from pressurized rooms within health care facilities, provided that the *corridor* is not the primary source of supply or return to the room.

❖ Two of the most critical elements of the means of egress are the required exit stairways and corridors. Exit stairways serve as protected areas in the building that provide occupants with safe passage to the level of exit discharge. Since required exits and corridors are critical elements in the means of egress, the potential spread of smoke and fire into these spaces must be minimized. The scope of this section is corridors. For requirements for the exits, see Section 1022.

The use of these corridors as part of the air distribution system could render those egress elements unusable. The intent is to have positive pressure in the corridors. Therefore, any air movement condition that could introduce smoke into these vital egress elements is prohibited. It is not the intent of this section to prohibit the air movement necessary for ventilation and space conditioning of corridors, but rather to prevent those spaces from serving as conduits for the distribution of air to, or the collection of air from, adjacent spaces. This restriction also extends to door transoms and door grilles that would allow the spread of smoke into a corridor. This limitation is not, however, intended to restrict slight pressure differences across corridor doors, such as a negative pressure differential maintained in kitchens to prevent odor migration into dining rooms. Note that air distribution via ducted systems located in or above corridors is acceptable since the corridor itself would not be functioning as a duct.

The four exceptions to this section identify conditions where a corridor can be utilized as part of the air distribution system. The exceptions apply only to exit access corridors, not to exit passageways.

Exception 1 addresses the common practice of using air from the corridor as makeup air for small exhaust fans in adjacent rooms. Where the corridor is supplied directly with outdoor air at a rate equal to or greater than the makeup air rate, negative pressure will not be created in the corridor with respect to the adjoining rooms and smoke would generally not be drawn into the corridor.

Regarding Exception 2, it is common practice to locate return air openings in the corridors of dwelling units and draw return air from adjoining spaces through the corridor. Such use of dwelling unit corridors for conveying return air is not considered to be a significant hazard and is permitted. Individual dwelling units are permitted to have unprotected openings between floors. Corridors within dwelling units that serve small occupant loads are short in length and are not required to be fire-resistance rated. For these reasons, the use of the corridor or the space above a corridor ceiling for conveying return air does not constitute an unacceptable hazard.

Exception 3 permits corridors located in small tenant spaces to be used for conveying return air based on the relatively low occupant load and the relatively short length of the corridor. These conditions do not pose a significant hazard. In the event of an emergency, the occupants of the space would tend to simply retrace their steps to the entrance.

Health care facilities require direct pressurization control of certain rooms to provide a clean and sterile environment for patients. For example, operating rooms and pharmacies are required to have positive air pressure in the room, resulting in a general air movement out of the room. This ensures that airborne contaminants do not infect a sterile procedure or supplies. Pressurization is achieved by supplying air at a greater or lesser rate than the return air. Exception 4 recognizes the need of infection control and clarifies that the corridor should not be the primary source of supply return. There should be supply and return air in the room.

[BE] 1020.5.1 Corridor ceiling. Use of the space between the *corridor* ceiling and the floor or roof structure above as a return air plenum is permitted for one or more of the following conditions:

1. The *corridor* is not required to be of fire-resistance-rated construction.
2. The *corridor* is separated from the plenum by fire-resistance-rated construction.
3. The air-handling system serving the *corridor* is shut down upon activation of the air-handling unit smoke detectors required by the *International Mechanical Code*.
4. The air-handling system serving the *corridor* is shut down upon detection of sprinkler water flow where the building is equipped throughout with an *automatic sprinkler system*.

5. The space between the *corridor* ceiling and the floor or roof structure above the *corridor* is used as a component of an *approved* engineered smoke control system.

❖ This section identifies five different conditions where the space above the corridor ceiling is permitted to serve as a return air plenum. Since a return air plenum operates at a negative pressure with respect to the corridor, any smoke and gases within the plenum should be contained within that space. Conversely, a supply plenum operates at a positive pressure with respect to the corridor, thus increasing the likelihood that smoke and gases will infiltrate the corridor enclosure. Where any one of the five conditions is present, the use of the corridor ceiling space as a return air plenum is permitted. This is consistent with IMC Section 601.2.1.

Where the corridor is permitted to be constructed without a fire-resistance rating (see Section 1020.1), Item 1 permits the space above the ceiling to be utilized as a return air plenum without requiring it to be separated from the corridor with fire-resistance-rated construction.

Item 2 is only applicable to corridors that are required to be enclosed with fire-resistance-rated construction. Compliance with this item requires the plenum to be separated from the corridor by fire-resistance-rated construction equivalent to the rating of the corridor enclosure itself. Therefore, the ceiling membrane itself must provide the fire-resistance rating required of the corridor enclosure. IBC Section 708.4, Exception 3, is an example of this method of construction.

Items 3 and 4 recognize that the hazard associated with smoke spread through a plenum is minimized if the air movement is stopped.

It is not uncommon for an above-ceiling plenum to be utilized as part of the smoke removal system. This practice is permitted by Item 5. Because of the way these systems are designed, the higher equipment ratings and the power supply provisions, this is considered acceptable.

[BE] 1020.6 Corridor continuity. Fire-resistance-rated *corridors* shall be continuous from the point of entry to an *exit*, and shall not be interrupted by intervening rooms. Where the path of egress travel within a fire-resistance-rated *corridor* to the *exit* includes travel along unenclosed *exit access stairways* or *ramps*, the fire-resistance-rating shall be continuous for the length of the *stairway* or *ramp* and for the length of the connecting *corridor* on the adjacent floor leading to the *exit*.

Exceptions:

1. Foyers, lobbies or reception rooms constructed as required for *corridors* shall not be construed as intervening rooms.
2. Enclosed elevator lobbies as permitted by Item 1 of Section 1016.2 shall not be construed as intervening rooms.

❖ This section requires that where fire protection is offered by a corridor, it is to be continuous from the point of entry into the corridor to one exit. This is to protect occupants from the accumulation of smoke or fire exposure and to allow for sufficient time to evacuate the building. Where a corridor is served by two or more exits, only one of the exits is required to be accessed directly from the corridor. Other exits may be accessed through intervening spaces in accordance with Section 1016.2, provided that there is an opening protective at the end of the corridor to separate the rated corridor from the intervening rooms. This ensures that occupants will always have a protected path to an exit while still allowing a reasonable degree of design freedom [see Commentary Figure 1020.6(1)]. Access to one of the exits can be through an elevator lobby (see Commentary Figure 1020.6(3)].

Where a level is permitted to have unenclosed exit access stairways in accordance with Section 1019.3, the corridor protection is required to continue down the exit access stairway to an enclosure for an interior exit stairway or to an exit door leading to the outside. Since the exit access stairway effectively becomes part of the corridor, doors would not be required at the top and bottom of the open exit access stairway as they are when entering enclosures for exit stairways.

Exception 1 allows a foyer, lobby or reception room to be located on the path of egress from a corridor or as part of the fire-resistance-rated corridor, provided the room has the same fire-resistance-rated walls and doors as required for the corridor. The use of this provision should be viewed as limiting the types of uses that may occur within the protected corridor. Occupied spaces within the corridor should have very limited uses and hazards. Foyers and lobbies are included in this exception based on the low fire hazard of the contents in such rooms [see Commentary Figure 1020.6(2)].

Another consideration is corridor continuity at an elevator opening. Where an elevator opens into a corridor that is required to be of fire-resistance-rated construction, the opening between the elevator shaft and the corridor must be protected to meet not only the shaft's fire protection rating but also the additional smoke and draft protection requirements necessary to limit the spread of smoke into the corridor (see IBC Sections 716.2.2.1 and 716.2.2.1.1). Because elevator hoistway doors do not typically comply as doors with a 20-minute fire-protection rating with smoke- and draft-control assemblies, they would not be able to open directly into a rated corridor. The provisions in IBC Section 3006 that waive the requirements for an elevator lobby (see the commentary to Section 1020.1.1) do not waive the corridor opening protection requirements. Therefore, to maintain the integrity of the corridor, the elevator hoistway shaft doors opening into such rated corridors will need to be separated from the corridor by one of the following methods of protection:

1. A lobby needs to be provided with the appropriate walls and doors [see Commentary Figure

1020.6(4) and IBC Section 3006.3, Items 1 and 2] to separate the lobby from the corridor.

2. Additional doors must be provided at the hoistway [see Commentary Figure 1020.6(5) and IBC Section 3006.3, Item 3] that will protect shaft openings the same as required for corridor doors.

3. An elevator shaft door that meets both the fire protection rating and the smoke and draft protection requirements for corridor doors in IBC Sections 716.2.2.1 and 716.2.2.1.1 and the appropriate fire protection rating for shafts [see IBC Table 716.1(2)] must be provided.

4. The corridor must be separated from the lobby [see Commentary Figure 1020.6(6) and IBC Section 3006.3, Items 1 and 2]. Per Exception 2 of Section 1020.6, a fourth option is permitted for corridor continuity since the elevator lobby is also not considered an intervening room. Section 1016.2, Item 1, states that at least one end of a fire-resistance-rated corridor must lead directly to an exit without going through an elevator lobby. Alternatively, the second means of egress serving the corridor can be an elevator lobby with direct access to an exit [see Commentary Figure 1020.6(3)].

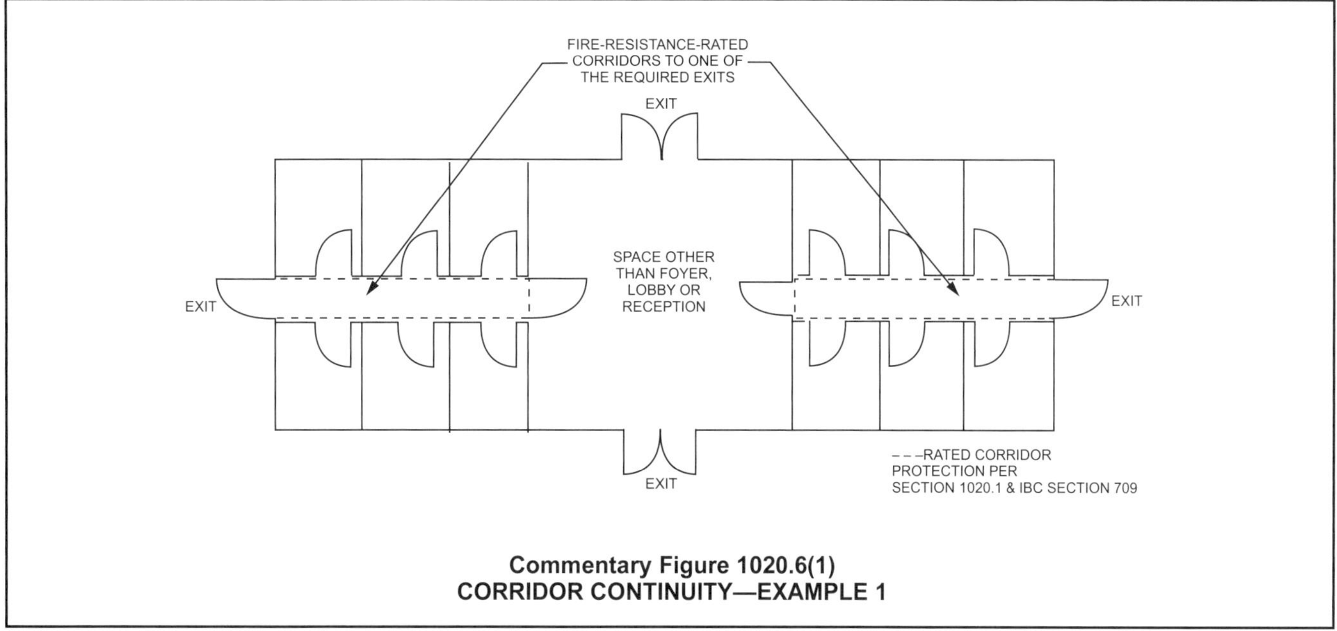

Commentary Figure 1020.6(1)
CORRIDOR CONTINUITY—EXAMPLE 1

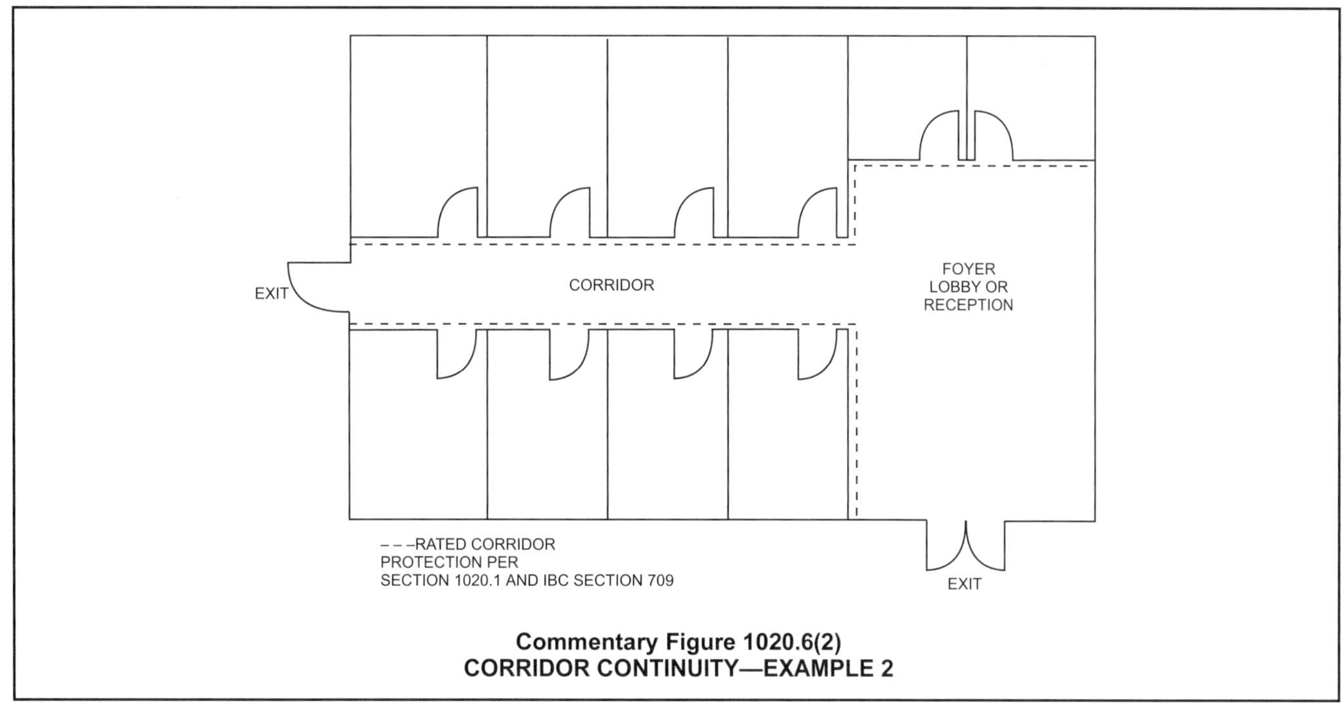

Commentary Figure 1020.6(2)
CORRIDOR CONTINUITY—EXAMPLE 2

5. The elevator hoistway can be pressurized so that smoke will not move up the shaft (see IBC Section 3006.3, Item 4). While not specifically stated that the fire partition opening protectives are not required, this would be equivalent to providing protection via alternative means.

While many elevator hoistway/vertical shaft doors are tested and labeled for the 1-hour or $1^1/_2$-hour fire-resistance rating (see IBC Section 716.2.1), very few, if any, of the doors typically sold in the United States will also meet the smoke and draft requirements (see IBC Section 716.2.2.1.1) that would allow them to open directly into a fire-resistance-rated corridor. Because of this, Items 1, 2 and 4 will be the general methods for protecting such openings.

For additional explanation of the requirements for elevator lobbies that are adjacent to rated corridors, see IBC Section 3006. For requirements for exit enclosures, see Section 1023.

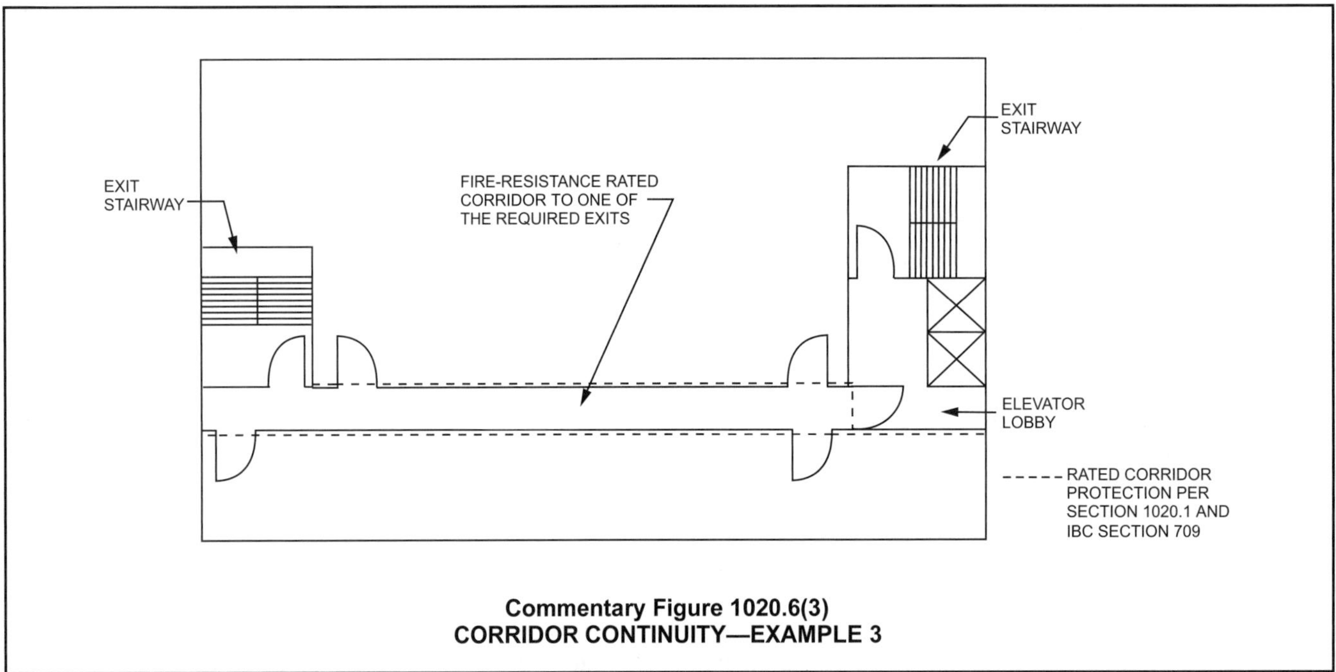

Commentary Figure 1020.6(3)
CORRIDOR CONTINUITY—EXAMPLE 3

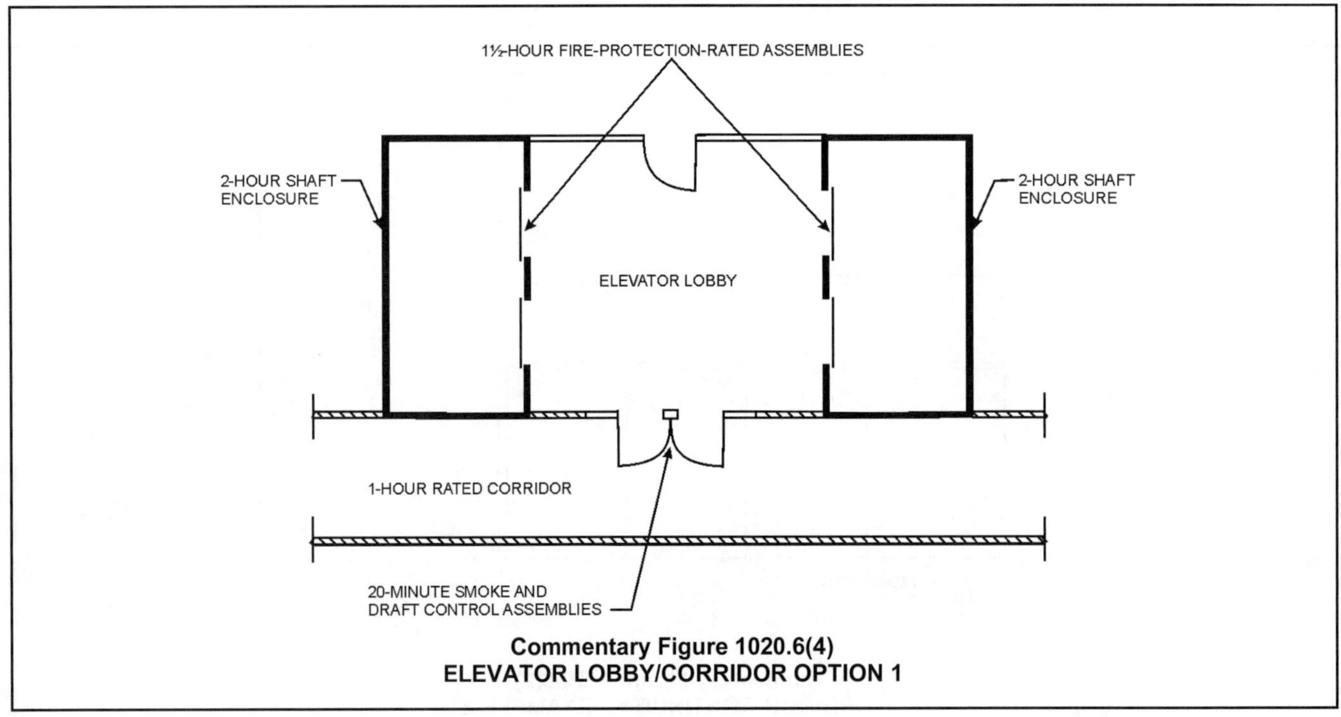

Commentary Figure 1020.6(4)
ELEVATOR LOBBY/CORRIDOR OPTION 1

SECTION 1021
EGRESS BALCONIES

[BE] 1021.1 General. Balconies used for egress purposes shall conform to the same requirements as *corridors* for minimum width, required capacity, headroom, dead ends and projections.

❖ This section regulates balconies that are used as an exit access element. Requirements are the same as exit access corridors, except for the enclosure.

Where exterior egress balconies are used in moderate or severe climates, there may also be a concern to protect the egress balcony from accumulations of snow and ice to provide a safe path of egress travel at all times, including winter. Maintenance of the means of egress requires an unobstructed path to allow for full instant use in case of a fire or emergency. Typical methods for protecting these egress elements include roof overhangs or

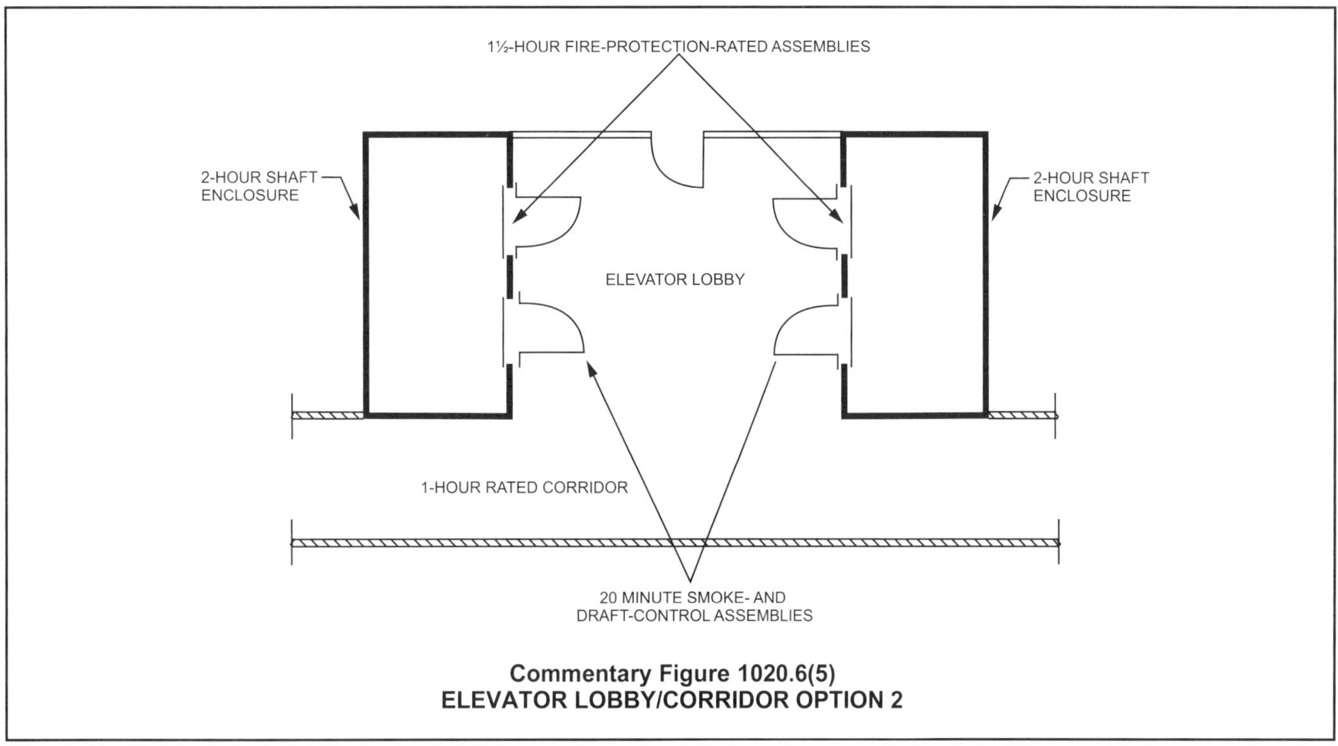

Commentary Figure 1020.6(5)
ELEVATOR LOBBY/CORRIDOR OPTION 2

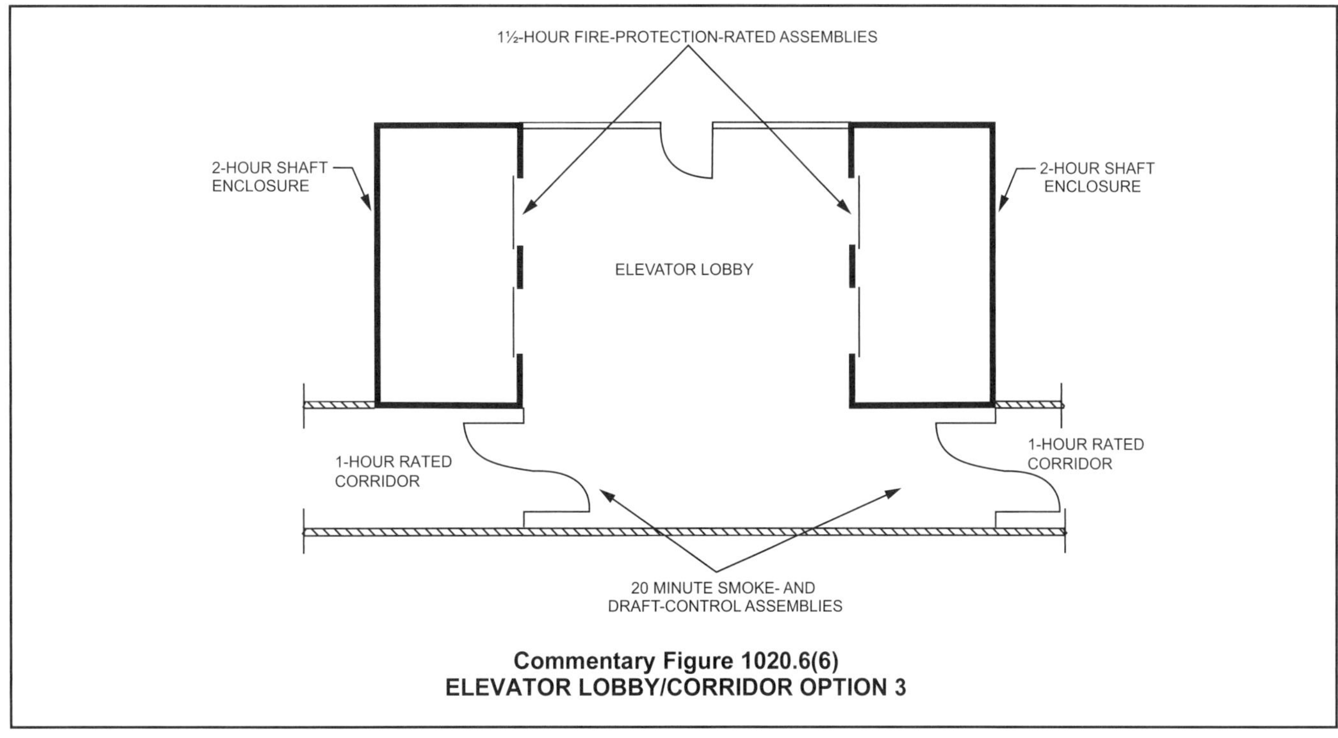

Commentary Figure 1020.6(6)
ELEVATOR LOBBY/CORRIDOR OPTION 3

canopies, a heated slab and, where approved by the building official, a reliable snow removal maintenance program.

[BE] 1021.2 Wall separation. Exterior egress balconies shall be separated from the interior of the building by walls and opening protectives as required for *corridors*.

Exception: Separation is not required where the exterior egress balcony is served by not less than two *stairways* and a dead-end travel condition does not require travel past an unprotected opening to reach a *stairway*.

❖ An exterior exit access balcony has a valuable attribute in that the products of combustion may be freely vented to the open air. In the event of a fire in an adjacent space, the products of combustion would not be expected to build up in the balcony area as would commonly occur in an interior corridor. However, there is still a concern for the egress of occupants who must use the balcony for exit access, and, consequently, may have to pass the room or space where the fire is located. Therefore, an exterior exit access balcony is required to be separated from interior spaces by fire partitions, as is required for interior corridors. The other provisions of Section 1020 relative to dead ends and opening protectives also apply.

If there are no dead-end conditions that require travel past an unprotected opening and the balcony is provided with at least two stairways, then the wall separating the balcony from the interior spaces need not have a fire-resistance rating (see Commentary Figure 1021.2). Such an arrangement reduces the probability that occupants will need to pass the area with the fire to gain access to an exit.

[BE] 1021.3 Openness. The long side of an egress balcony shall be not less than 50 percent open, and the open area above the guards shall be so distributed as to minimize the accumulation of smoke or toxic gases.

❖ This section provides an opening requirement that is intended to preclude the rapid buildup of smoke and toxic gases. A minimum of one side of the exterior balcony is required to have a minimum open exterior area of 50 percent of the side area of the balcony. The side openings are to be uniformly distributed along the length of the balcony.

[BE] 1021.4 Location. Exterior egress balconies shall have a minimum fire separation distance of 10 feet (3048 mm) measured at right angles from the exterior edge of the egress balcony to the following:

1. Adjacent *lot lines*.
2. Other portions of the building.
3. Other buildings on the same lot unless the adjacent building *exterior walls* and openings are protected in accordance with Section 705 of the *International Building Code* based on fire separation distance.

For the purposes of this section, other portions of the building shall be treated as separate buildings.

❖ The location requirements for exterior egress balconies given by this section protect the users of the egress balcony from the effects of a fire in another building on the same lot or an adjacent lot. The separation distance reduces the exposure to heat and smoke. If the egress balcony is closer than specified, then the adjacent buildings' exterior walls and openings are to be protected in accordance with IBC Section 705 so that the users of the egress balcony are protected. The reason for the required distance to a lot line is to provide for a future building that could be built on the adjacent lot. While buildings on the same lot can be considered one building for height and area limitations (see Section 503.1.2), they must be separated by a minimum of 10 feet (3048 mm) if there is a path for exit discharge between them. The purpose of the last sentence is to clarify that an egress balcony needs a minimum 10-foot separation where a building wraps around on itself, such as a U-shaped building. It is not intended that the distance be measured to the imaginary lot line between buildings on the same lot.

Requirements are the same for exterior exit stairways and ramps. For an illustration of how exterior egress balconies and exterior exit stairways work together, see Commentary Figure 1027.5.

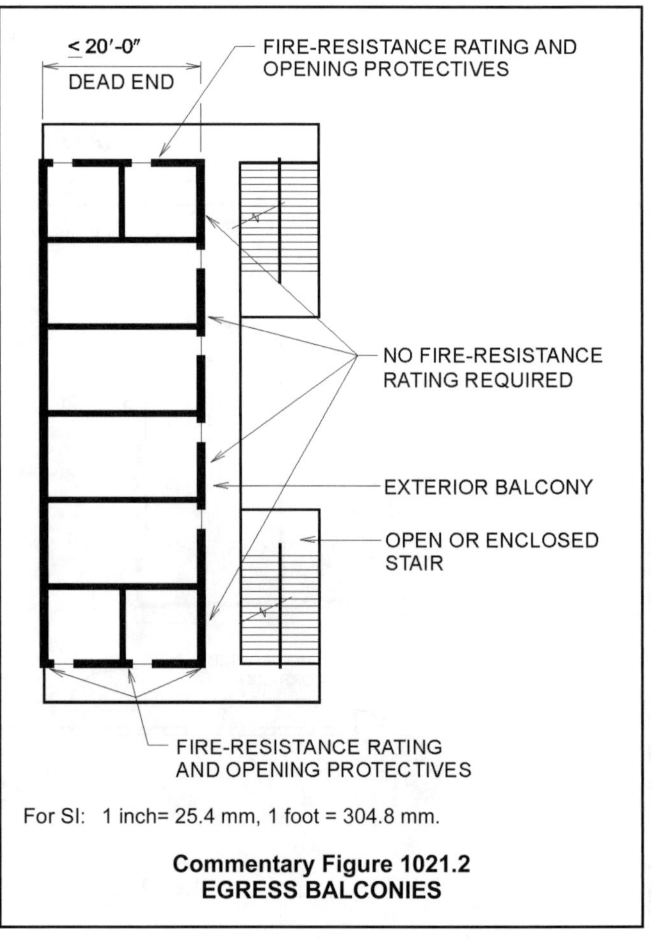

For SI: 1 inch= 25.4 mm, 1 foot = 304.8 mm.

Commentary Figure 1021.2
EGRESS BALCONIES

SECTION 1022
EXITS

[BE] 1022.1 General. *Exits* shall comply with Sections 1022 through 1027 and the applicable requirements of Sections 1003 through 1015. An *exit* shall not be used for any purpose that interferes with its function as a *means of egress*. Once a given level of *exit* protection is achieved, such level of protection shall not be reduced until arrival at the *exit discharge*. *Exits* shall be continuous from the point of entry into the *exit* to the *exit discharge*.

❖ This group of sections is applicable to the "exit" portion of the three-part means of egress system. Sections 1003 through 1015 are also applicable to exits. The following sections are covered in this group:

- Section 1022 provides general requirements for exterior exit doorways.
- Section 1023 provides criteria for interior exit stairways and ramps.
- Section 1024 covers horizontal portions of the exit and exit passageways.
- Section 1025 is referenced by the high-rise provisions in IBC Section 403. This section addresses a backup system for means of egress lighting (see Section 1008). "Glow-in-the-dark" stripes identify steps, handrails, obstructions and doorways within the enclosure for interior exit stairways.
- Section 1026 discusses the option of horizontal exits. Horizontal exits are used in buildings where travel to the exit stairways are too far, so the building is subdivided to meet travel distance requirements. This type of system is sometimes used in combination with smoke barriers and refuge areas for buildings such as hospitals and jails where building evacuation is not always the best option.
- Section 1027 provides criteria for stairways or ramps that are primarily open to the exterior, thus reducing the chance of accumulation of smoke or fumes.

The use of required exterior exit doors, exit stairways, exit passageways and horizontal exits for any purpose other than exiting is prohibited because it might interfere with use as an exit. This is not intended to prohibit a door or stairway being used as part of normal circulation patterns, such as the exit doors also serving as entrances, or using the stairway to move between floors when there is not an emergency. However, these spaces must not include furniture, storage or work space. For example, the use of an exit stairway landing for storage, vending machines, copy machines, displays or any purpose other than for exiting is not permitted. Such a situation could not only lead to obstruction of the path of exit travel, thereby creating a hazard to life safety, but if the contents consist of combustible materials, then the use of the stairway as a means of egress could be jeopardized by fire or smoke in the exit enclosure.

It is recognized that standpipe risers are provided within the stair enclosure and that vertical electrical conduit may be necessary for power or lighting. However, such risers must be located so as not to interfere with the required clear width of the exit. For example, a standpipe riser located in the corner of a stairway will not reduce the required clear radius of the landing. This also applies where the stairway landing is used as an area of refuge. The spaces for wheelchairs must not obstruct the general path of egress travel [see Commentary Figures 1009.3.3(1) and 1009.3.3(2)]. Electrical conduit and mechanical equipment are permitted where necessary to serve the exit enclosure.

In existing buildings, sometimes the only viable option for providing access into the space is a platform lift. These platform lifts can be located within the enclosure for the exit (see IEBC Section 305.8.3). Regulations in ASME A18.1 would limit the potential for any concerns for platform lifts being a fuel load in an exit stairway. However, the platform lift must be located so that it is not an obstruction to the exit pathway. Typically, this is reviewed when the platform lift is in the off and folded position.

Sections 1022 through 1027 apply to all exits but do not apply to elements of the means of egress that are not actually exits, such as exit access stairways, ramps, corridors and passageways, or elements of the exit discharge. Once an exit is entered, that same level of protection must be available until the occupants leave the building at the level of exit discharge. For exit discharge options for the enclosure, other than a door leading directly to the outside, see the requirements for exit passageways in Section 1024 or the options permitting usage of a lobby or vestibule in the exceptions to Section 1028.1.

[BE] 1022.2 Exterior exit doors. Buildings or structures used for human occupancy shall have not less than one exterior door that meets the requirements of Section 1010.1.1.

❖ The purpose of this section is to specify that at least one exterior exit door is required to meet the door size requirements in Section 1010.1.1. It is not the intent of this section to specify the number of exit doors required, which is addressed in Section 1006.

[BE] 1022.2.1 Detailed requirements. Exterior exit doors shall comply with the applicable requirements of Section 1010.1.

❖ The purpose of this section is simply to provide a cross reference from the exit section to all of the detailed requirements for doors that are included in Section 1010.1 and all of its subsections. For example, the requirements for door operation on exterior exit doors are dictated by Section 1010.1.9.

[BE] 1022.2.2 Arrangement. Exterior exit doors shall lead directly to the *exit discharge* or the *public way*.

❖ The exterior exit door is to be the entry point of the exit discharge or lead directly to the public way. When a person reaches the exterior exit door, he or she is directly outside, where smoke and toxic gases are not a health hazard. Additionally, this section will keep exterior doors at other locations, such as to an egress balcony, from being viewed as an exit element.

SECTION 1023 INTERIOR EXIT STAIRWAYS AND RAMPS

[BE] 1023.1 General. *Interior exit stairways* and *ramps* serving as an *exit* component in a *means of egress* system shall comply with the requirements of this section. *Interior exit stairways* and *ramps* shall be enclosed and lead directly to the exterior of the building or shall be extended to the exterior of the building with an *exit passageway* conforming to the requirements of Section 1024, except as permitted in Section 1028.1. An *interior exit* stairway or *ramp* shall not be used for any purpose other than as a *means of egress* and a circulation path.

❖ The first sentence is a general reference to the rest of the section. Sections 1023.2 through 1023.7 deal with the construction of the walls and ceiling that enclose the exit stairway or exit ramp. Sections 1023.8 through 1023.10 deal with information required in the enclosure for safe exiting. Section 1023.11 provides criteria for stairways in high-rise or underground buildings where a smokeproof enclosure and pressurization of the stair tower are required (see IBC Sections 403.5.4 and 405.7.2).

Most exit stairways or ramps have an exterior door at the level of exit discharge that leads directly to the outside. From this doorway, there must be a path for exit discharge that leads to the public way; however, there are other options. Exit passageways are considered an extension of the exit enclosure. The stairway enclosure discharges into the exit passageway, which in turn leads to the outside of the building. There are limited allowances for the exit enclosure to discharge through a lobby or vestibule (see Section 1028.1, Exceptions 1 and 2). A stairway enclosure could also discharge through a horizontal exit (see Section 1028.1, Exception 3). The termination requirements are the same as stated in Section 1023.3.

It is important that an exit stairway or ramp not be used for any purpose other than normal circulation and as a means of egress. For example, there is a tendency to use stairway landings for storage purposes. Such a situation obstructs the path of exit travel and if the stored contents consist of combustible materials, the use of the exit stairway as part of the path for a means of egress may be jeopardized, creating a hazard to life safety. It is not the intent of these provisions to prohibit an exit stairway from being used as part of the normal building circulation system. If the tenants or building owner have security concerns that would prompt them to wish to limit stairway access, consult Section 1010.1.9.12.

It is not the intent of this provision to exclude inclined platform lifts in the enclosure for the stairway; however, it is important that when not in operation, they do not block access to the exit stairway or handrails. The referenced technical standard, ASME A18.1, basically requires noncombustible elements so there is not a fire load issue associated with the lifts. Platform lifts are an important option for providing accessibility in a building. Section 1109.8 limits the use of platform lifts in new construction to mainly areas with minimal occupant loads or where elevators and ramps are impracticable. Platform lifts can be part of an accessible means of egress in limited situations (Section 1009.5). IEBC Section 305.8.3 allows for platform lifts anywhere in existing buildings in order to gain accessibility for persons with mobility impairments. The industry is currently working on different options to address the concern that the lift may be in operation during an event that requires evacuation.

[BE] 1023.2 Construction. Enclosures for *interior exit stairways* and *ramps* shall be constructed as *fire barriers* in accordance with Section 707 of the *International Building Code* or *horizontal assemblies* constructed in accordance with Section 711 of the *International Building Code*, or both. *Interior exit stairway* and *ramp* enclosures shall have a *fire-resistance rating* of not less than 2 hours where connecting four stories or more and not less than 1 hour where connecting less than four stories. The number of stories connected by the *interior exit stairways* or *ramps* shall include any *basements*, but not any *mezzanines*. *Interior exit stairways* and *ramps* shall have a fire-resistance rating not less than the floor assembly penetrated, but need not exceed 2 hours.

Exceptions:

1. *Interior exit stairways* and *ramps* in Group I-3 occupancies in accordance with the provisions of Section 408.3.8 of the *International Building Code*.
2. *Interior exit stairways* within an atrium enclosed in accordance with Section 404.6 of the *International Building Code*.

❖ This section requires that all interior exit stairways or ramps are to be enclosed with rated walls (i.e., fire barriers) and floor/ceiling assemblies (i.e., horizontal assemblies). The fire-resistance rating required depends on the number of connected stories and the required fire-resistance rating of the penetrated floors. The minimum fire-resistance rating of an enclosure for an exit stairway or ramp is at least 1 hour. The fire-resistance rating of the enclosure must be increased to 2 hours if the stairway or ramp connects four or more stories or if it penetrates a floor system with a fire-resistance rating of 2 hours or more (see IBC Table 602 for Type I construction). Note that the criteria are based on the number of stories connected by the stairway or ramp and not the height of the building. Therefore, a building that has three stories located entirely above grade plane and a basement would require an enclosure with a 2-hour fire-resistance rating if the stairway or ramp connects all four stories. Where the floor construction penetrated by the enclosure has a fire-resistance rating, the enclosure must have the same minimum rating. For example, an enclosure that penetrates a 2-hour floor assembly must have a minimum fire-resistance rating of 2 hours, regardless of the number of stories the enclosure connects. The fire-resistance rating of an enclosure need never exceed 2 hours. If the floor assembly penetrated requires a minimum 3-hour fire-resistance rating, the enclosure rating is only required to be 2-hour fire-resistance rated. All linear voids at joints between fire-resistance-rated wall and floor/ceiling assemblies and where an enclosure would intersect with an exterior wall must be filled so that the integrity of the enclosure is maintained (see IBC Section 715). The fire-resistance-rated requirements for enclosures for exit stairways and ramps are consistent with those for shaft enclosures and enclosures for exit access stairways and ramps.

The enclosure is needed because an exit stairway or ramp penetrates the floor/ceiling assemblies between levels, creating a vertical opening or shaft. In cases of fire, a vertical opening may act as a chimney, causing smoke, hot gases and light-burning products to flow upward (buoyant force). If an opening is unprotected, these products of combustion will be forced by positive pressure differentials to spread horizontally into building spaces. There are exceptions for shaft protection around stairways and ramps that are not part of a required means of egress in IBC Section 712 or exit access stairways as permitted in Section 1019.3.

The enclosure of interior stairways or ramps with construction having a fire-resistance rating is intended to prevent the spread of fire from floor to floor. Another important purpose is to provide a safe path of travel for the building occupants and to serve as a protected means of access to the fire floor by fire department personnel. For this reason, Sections 1023.4 through 1023.6 limit the penetrations and openings permitted in the enclosure for an exit stairway or ramp.

For travel distance measurements at the exit stairways, see the commentary to Section 1017.3. While not specifically mentioned as an exception, Section 1027 for exterior exit stairways is considered to provide an equivalent level of protection to enclosed interior stairways.

Per Exception 1, because of security needs in detention facilities, one of the exit stairways is permitted to be glazed in a manner similar to atrium enclosures. Specific limitations and requirements are discussed in IBC Section 408.3.8. Exit access stairways within housing units are addressed in Section 1019.4 and IBC Section 408.5.1.

Exception 2 is in consideration of an increased level of safety in an atrium. IBC Section 404 for atriums requires the space to be enclosed by a 1-hour passive enclosure and also protected by various active systems including fire suppression and smoke control features. The natural configuration of an atrium affords building occupants immediate views of the entire egress to the bottom of the atrium. If either of these exceptions are used for the exterior protection of an exit stairway, the other provisions for exit stairways would still be applicable, including not moving through one exit to get to another exit, not being used for any purpose other than circulation or exiting, not having doors except for those needed for exit access, appropriately installing standpipes in the enclosure, and so on. This would prohibit the typical hotel atrium with doors opening into the atrium and the hotel reception and lobby areas on the first floor from using this exception and considering the stairway an exit.

[BE] 1023.3 Termination. *Interior exit stairways* and *ramps* shall terminate at an *exit discharge* or a *public way*.

> **Exception:** A combination of *interior exit stairways*, *interior exit ramps* and *exit* passageways, constructed in accordance with Sections 1023.2, 1023.3.1 and 1024, respectively, and forming a continuous protected enclosure, shall be permitted to extend an *interior exit stairway* or *ramp* to the *exit discharge* or a *public way*.

❖ This section is intended to provide safety in all portions of the exit by requiring continuity of the fire protection characteristics of the enclosure for the exit stairway. Exit passageways (see Section 1024) are a continuation of the enclosure for the exit stairway. This would include, but not be limited to, the fire-resistance rating of the exit enclosure walls and the opening protection rating of the doors. While an exit passageway is most commonly found on the level of exit discharge as a means to connect a stairway enclosure to the exterior, in buildings that step back in footprint as they rise, the stairways may not be totally vertical shafts, but move out as they move down to keep the required separation distance. Exit passageways can be at any level to connect the stair towers. There are special exit signage considerations for this particular issue in Section 1013.1 (see Commentary Figure 1013.1).

Section 1028.1 allows an alternative for direct access to the outside via an intervening lobby or vestibule.

Horizontal exits (see Section 1026), while not providing direct access to the outside of the structure, do move occupants to another "building" through a fire wall or into a refuge area protected by fire barriers and horizontal assemblies (see Sections 1026 and 1028.1, Exception 3). Horizontal exits are commonly used in hospitals and jails for a defend-in-place type of protection or in large buildings where travel distance is an issue.

[BE] 1023.3.1 Extension. Where *interior exit stairways* and *ramps* are extended to an *exit discharge* or a *public way* by an *exit passageway*, the *interior exit stairway* and *ramp* shall be separated from the *exit passageway* by a *fire barrier* constructed in accordance with Section 707 of the *International*

Building Code or a *horizontal assembly* constructed in accordance with Section 711 of the *International Building Code*, or both. The *fire-resistance rating* shall be not less than that required for the *interior exit stairway* and *ramp*. A *fire door* assembly complying with Section 716 of the *International Building Code* shall be installed in the *fire barrier* to provide a *means of egress* from the *interior exit stairway* and *ramp* to the *exit passageway*. Openings in the *fire barrier* other than the *fire door* assembly are prohibited. Penetrations of the *fire barrier* are prohibited.

Exceptions:

1. Penetrations of the *fire barrier* in accordance with Section 1023.5 shall be permitted.
2. Separation between an *interior exit stairway* or *ramp* and the *exit passageway* extension shall not be required where there are no openings into the *exit passageway* extension.
3. Separation between an *interior exit stairway* or *ramp* and the *exit passageway* extension shall not be required where the *interior exit stairway* and the *exit passageway* extension are pressurized in accordance with Section 909.20.5 of the *International Building Code*.

❖ Once a person enters the enclosure surrounding an exit stairway, that same level of protection should be provided to them until they can leave the building. Where an enclosure for an exit stairway connects to an exit passageway, either at the ground level or at an intermediate transition floor, the exit passageway must provide the same level of protection as the enclosure for the exit stairway, including fire resistance of the walls, floor, ceiling and supporting construction and protection of any openings. At the junction between the enclosure for the exit stairway and the exit passageway, there must be both a rated fire barrier and a fire door. This has the additional benefit of preventing any smoke that may migrate into the exit passageway from also moving up the exit stairway or ramp. Permitted penetrations for the exit passageway are the same as those limitations set for the enclosure for the exit stairway. See Sections 1013.1 and 1025 for egress markings and signage within these types of spaces. Where an exit stairway is constructed as a smokeproof enclosure or a pressurized stairway, see Section 1023.9.1.

Exception 1—The penetrations for the exit passageway are allowed to be the same as permitted for the stairway enclosure.

Exception 2—The purpose in having a fire door at this interface in the existing requirement is to prevent smoke from a possible open door or other penetration in the passageway from traveling up the exit enclosure. This is prevented if there are no openings or penetrations in the exit passageway. Then the exit passageway is a horizontal offset of the exit enclosure and does not present the same hazard. Egress can proceed faster if there are no intermediate doors contained at the enclosure transitions.

Exception 3—Similar to the intent of Exception 2, where an interior exit stairway and an associated exit passageway are pressurized, a door between the two could be an issue for dependable operation of that system. The pressurization will keep smoke out of the stairway, so from the smoke movement perspective, no door is required between the stairway and the exit passageway.

[BE] 1023.4 Openings. *Interior exit stairway* and *ramp* opening protectives shall be in accordance with the requirements of Section 716 of the *International Building Code*.

Openings in *interior exit stairways* and *ramps* other than unprotected exterior openings shall be limited to those required for *exit access* to the enclosure from normally occupied spaces and for egress from the enclosure.

Elevators shall not open into *interior exit stairways* and *ramps*.

❖ In order for fire doors to be effective, they must be in the closed position; therefore, the preferred arrangement is to install self-closing doors. Recognizing that operational practices often require doors to be open for an extended period of time, automatic-closing doors are permitted as long as this opening will not pose a threat to occupant safety and the doors will be self-latching. Automatic-closing devices enable the opening to be protected during a fire condition. The basic requirement for closing devices and specific requirements for automatic-closing and self-closing devices are given in NFPA 80. Automatic-closing doors that are provided at protected openings in exits are also required to close on the actuation of smoke detectors or loss of power to the smoke detectors (see IBC Section 716.2.6.6).

The only openings that are permitted in fire-resistance-rated enclosures for exit stairways or ramps are doors that lead from normally occupied spaces into the enclosure and doors leading out of the enclosure to the outside. This restriction on openings essentially prohibits the use of windows in an exit enclosure except for those exterior windows or doors that are not exposed to any hazards. This requirement is not intended to prohibit windows or other openings in the exterior walls of the exit enclosure. The verbiage "unprotected exterior openings" includes windows or doors not required to be protected by either IBC Section 705.8 or 1023.7. The only exception would be window assemblies that have been tested as wall assemblies in accordance with ASTM E119 or UL 263. The objective of this provision is to minimize the possibility of fire spreading into an enclosure and endangering the occupants or even preventing the use of the exit at a time when it is most needed. The limitation on openings applies regardless of the fire protection rating of the opening protective. The limitation on openings from normally occupied areas is intended to reduce the probability of a fire occurring in an unoccupied area, such as a storage closet, which has an opening into the stairway, thereby possibly resulting in fire spread into the stairway. Other spaces that are not normally occupied include, but are not limited to, toilet rooms, electrical/mechanical equipment rooms and janitorial closets. For connection between the vertical exit enclosure and an exit passageway, see Section 1023.3.1.

Elevators may not open into exit enclosures. The difficulty is having elevator doors that can meet the opening protectives for a fire barrier, but still operate effectively as elevator doors. For additional information on elevator lobbies and doors, see the commentary for Section 1020.6 and IBC Sections 713.14 and 3006.

These opening limitations are very similar to those required for an exit passageway (see Section 1024.5).

[BE] 1023.5 Penetrations. Penetrations into or through *interior exit stairways* and *ramps* are prohibited except for the following:

1. Equipment and ductwork necessary for independent ventilation or pressurization.
2. *Fire protection systems.*
3. Security systems.
4. Two-way communication systems.
5. Electrical raceway for fire department communication systems.
6. Electrical raceway serving the interior *exit stairway* and *ramp* and terminating at a steel box not exceeding 16 square inches (0.010 m^2).

Such penetrations shall be protected in accordance with Section 714 of the *International Building Code*. There shall not be penetrations or communication openings, whether protected or not, between adjacent *interior exit stairways* and *ramps*.

Exception: Membrane penetrations shall be permitted on the outside of the *interior exit stairway* and *ramp*. Such penetrations shall be protected in accordance with Section 714.4.2 of the *International Building Code*.

❖ This section specifically lists the items that are allowed to penetrate the walls and ceiling of the enclosure for the exit stairway. This is consistent for all types of enclosures for exits, including interior exit stairways or interior exit ramps and exit passageways (see Section 1024.6). In general, only portions of the building service systems that serve the enclosure are allowed to penetrate the enclosure. As indicated in the commentary to Section 1023.12, standpipe systems are commonly located in the exit stair enclosures. If two exit enclosures are adjacent to one another, there must be no penetrations between them, thereby limiting the chances of smoke being in both stairwells.

IBC Section 714 addresses through penetrations and membrane penetrations for fire-resistance-rated walls and floor/ceiling assemblies. The intent is to maintain the integrity of the enclosure for the exit access stairway. This section and Section 1023.6 are meant to work together. Penetrations in exterior walls are addressed in Section 1023.7.

The exception allows for such items as electrical boxes, exit signs or fire alarm pull stations to be installed on the outside of the enclosure, provided that the boxes are installed so that the required fire-resistance rating is not reduced (see IBC Section 714.4.2).

[BE] 1023.6 Ventilation. Equipment and ductwork for *interior exit stairway* and *ramp* ventilation as permitted by Section 1023.5 shall comply with one of the following items:

1. Such equipment and ductwork shall be located exterior to the building and shall be directly connected to the *interior exit stairway* and *ramp* by ductwork enclosed in construction as required for shafts.
2. Where such equipment and ductwork is located within the *interior exit stairway* and *ramp*, the intake air shall be taken directly from the outdoors and the exhaust air shall be discharged directly to the outdoors, or such air shall be conveyed through ducts enclosed in construction as required for shafts.
3. Where located within the building, such equipment and ductwork shall be separated from the remainder of the building, including other mechanical equipment, with construction as required for shafts.

In each case, openings into the fire-resistance-rated construction shall be limited to those needed for maintenance and operation and shall be protected by opening protectives in accordance with Section 716 of the *International Building Code* for shaft enclosures.

The *interior exit stairway* and *ramp* ventilation systems shall be independent of other building ventilation systems.

❖ The purpose of the requirements for ventilation system equipment and ductwork is to maintain the fire resistance of the enclosure for the exit stairway. The ventilation system serving the enclosure is to be independent of other building systems to prevent smoke in the enclosure from traveling to other areas of the building. This section and Section 1023.5 are meant to work together. Where ductwork penetrates the outside wall, if it is not required to be rated by Section 1023.7, then the duct does not require a fire and smoke damper. If the ductwork serving the shaft does penetrate a rated wall or rated floor/ceiling assembly, a fire and smoke damper would be required by IBC Section 717.5.3. Openings required for access to the ventilation system for maintenance and operation shall be protected in accordance with IBC Section 716.

[BE] 1023.7 Interior exit stairway and ramp exterior walls. *Exterior walls* of the *interior exit stairway* or *ramp* shall comply with the requirements of Section 705 of the *International Building Code* for *exterior walls*. Where nonrated walls or unprotected openings enclose the exterior of the *stairway* or *ramps* and the walls or openings are exposed by other parts of the building at an angle of less than 180 degrees (3.14 rad), the building *exterior walls* within 10 feet (3048 mm) horizontally of a nonrated wall or unprotected opening shall have a *fire-resistance rating* of not less than 1 hour. Openings within such *exterior walls* shall be protected by opening protectives having a *fire protection rating* of not less than $^3/_4$ hour. This construction shall extend vertically from the ground to a point 10 feet (3048 mm) above the topmost landing of the *stairway* or *ramp*, or to the roof line, whichever is lower.

❖ This section does not require exterior walls of an enclosure for an exit stairway or ramp to have the same fire-resistance rating as the interior walls. IBC Table 602 and IBC Section 705 establish where exterior walls are required to be rated and openings limited due to adjacent buildings or lot lines. This exposure is different from exterior load-bearing walls that are required to be rated because of the type of construction per Table 601. What is unique to exterior walls at exit stairways is the need to stop fires from burning through an exterior wall adjacent to the enclosure, which may then jeopardize the occupant's ability to continue to use that exit stairway. Essentially, there are two alternatives where an exposure hazard exists:

1. Provide protection to the stairway by having a fire-resistance rating on its exterior wall.
2. Provide a fire-resistance rating to the walls adjacent to the stairway.

The ratings apply for a distance of 10 feet (3048 mm) measured horizontally and vertically from the stairway enclosure where those walls are at an angle of less than 180 degrees (3.14 rad) from the exterior wall portion of the enclosure (see Condition 1 in Commentary Figure 1023.7). Where the adjacent exterior wall is protected in lieu of the stairway enclosure wall, the protection is to extend from the ground to a level of 10 feet (3048 mm) above the highest landing of the stairway. However, the protection is not required to extend beyond the normal roof line of the building.

The 180-degree (3.14 rad) angle criterion is based on the scenario where the exterior wall of the stair enclosure is in the same plane and flush with the exterior wall of the building (see Conditions 2 and 3 in Commentary Figure 1023.7). In this scenario, heat or fire would need to travel 180 degrees (3.14 rad) in order to impinge on the stair. Based on studies of existing buildings, this 180-degree (3.14 rad) spread of fire does not appear to be a problem. This criterion is only applicable where the angle between the walls is 180 degrees (3.14 rad) or less.

As fire exposure on the exterior is different than can be expected on the interior, the fire-resistance rating of the exterior wall is not required to exceed 1 hour, regardless of whether it is the stairway enclosure wall or the adjacent exterior wall, unless the exterior wall is required by other sections of the code to have a higher fire-resistance rating (see IBC Tables 601 and 602). The fire protection rating on any openings in the exterior wall of a stairway enclosure or adjacent exterior wall within 180 degrees (3.14 rad) is to be a minimum of $^3/_4$ hour.

In a situation where upper levels are smaller than lower levels, an interior stairway can end up having an exterior wall where it moves above the roof of the lower levels. In this situation, the question is the rating requirements for the exterior wall of the stairway over the roof. Therefore, the exterior wall of the stairway must meet the vertical opening provisions in IBC Section 705.8.6.

[BE] 1023.8 Discharge identification. An *interior exit stairway* and *ramp* shall not continue below its *level of exit discharge* unless an *approved* barrier is provided at the *level of exit discharge* to prevent persons from unintentionally continuing into levels below. Directional exit signs shall be provided as specified in Section 1013.

❖ So that building occupants using an exit stairway during an emergency situation will be prevented from going past the level of exit discharge, the run of the stairway is to be interrupted by a partition, door, gate or other approved means. These devices help users of the stairway to recognize when they have reached the point that is the level of exit discharge.

The code does not specify the type of material or construction of the barrier used to identify the level of exit discharge. The key issues to be considered in the selection and approval of the type of barrier to be used are:

1. Whether the barrier provides a visible and physical means of alerting occupants who are exiting under emergency conditions that they have reached the level of exit discharge.
2. Whether the barrier is constructed of materials that are permitted by the construction type of the building.

In an emergency situation, some occupants are likely to come in contact with the barrier during exiting before realizing that they are at the level of exit discharge. Therefore, the barrier should be constructed in a manner that is substantial enough to withstand the anticipated physical contact, such as pushing or shoving. It would be reasonable, as a minimum, to design the barrier to withstand the structural load requirements of IBC Section 1607.5 for interior walls and partitions. The barrier could be opaque (such as gypsum wallboard and stud framing) or not (such as a wire grid-type material).

The use of signage only or relatively insubstantial barriers, such as ropes or chains strung across the opening, is typically not sufficient to prevent occupants from attempting to continue past the level of exit discharge during an emergency.

Commentary Figure 1023.8 is an example of one method of discharge identification.

Exit signs, including raised letters and braille, are to be provided for occupant guidance at the door leading to the way out [i.e., exit discharge either directly to the exterior or via an exit passageway, lobby or vestibule (see Section 1013.4). In situations where there may be transfer levels with exit passageways or unusual stairway configurations, visual directional exit signage may also be required within the enclosure (see Commentary Figure 1013.1).

INTERIOR

FIRE-RESISTANCE-RATED STAIR ENCLOSURE

CONDITION #1

EXTERIOR

<180°

FIRE-RESISTANCE-RATED WALL WITH OPENING PROTECTIVES WITHIN 10' OF STAIR

10' 0"

NONFIRE-RESISTANCE-RATED WALLS OR UNPROTECTED OPENINGS

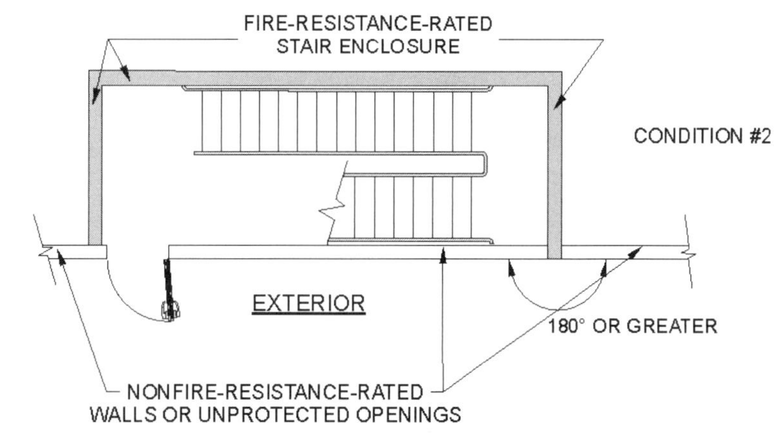

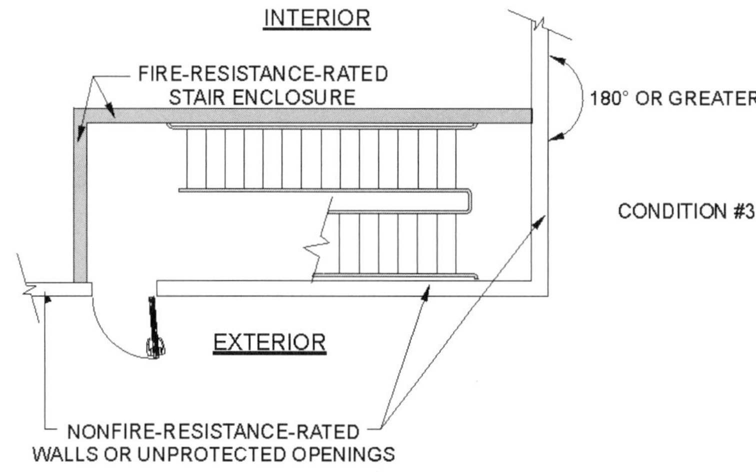

For SI: 1 foot = 304.8 mm, 1 degree = 0.01745 rad.

Commentary Figure 1023.7
EXAMPLES OF EXTERIOR WALL PROTECTION AT INTERIOR EXIT STAIRWAYS

[BE] 1023.9 Stairway identification signs. A sign shall be provided at each floor landing in an *interior exit stairway* and *ramp* connecting more than three stories designating the floor level, the terminus of the top and bottom of the *interior exit stairway* and *ramp* and the identification of the *stairway* or *ramp*. The signage shall state the story of, and the direction to, the *exit discharge* and the availability of roof access from the *interior exit stairway* and *ramp* for the fire department. The sign shall be located 5 feet (1524 mm) above the floor landing in a position that is readily visible when the doors are in the open and closed positions. In addition to the *stairway* identification sign, a floor-level sign in visual characters, raised characters and braille complying with ICC A117.1 shall be located at each floor-level landing adjacent to the door leading from the *interior exit stairway* and *ramp* into the *corridor* to identify the floor level.

❖ This section discusses two distinct sign requirements that have totally different purposes.

Signs are to be placed at each floor landing in all exit stairways connecting more than three stories. Each sign is to be placed in an obvious location for someone to see it when they enter the stairway. The required height of the bottom of the sign at 5 feet (1524 mm) is so the sign is at about eye level, but would be visible above the heads of people if there is a crowd on the stairway. The purpose is for both occupants and emergency responders entering the stairway to have the information they need. Information on the signs should include:

- Which level the user is currently on—this information is the largest item on the sign (see Section 1023.9.1, Item 3).
- Which floor is the level of exit discharge and in which direction—this could be an arrow and information such as "Exit at Level 1."
- Which stairway the user is in—designations typically are something like "North Stair" or "Stair A."
- The extent of the stairway—such as "Basement to 5th floor."
- If there is roof access directly from the stairway enclosure—this is for emergency responders in case they need to get onto the roof to vent the fire (for where roof access is required, see Section 1011.12).

To aid people with vision impairments who are moving within the stairway, the floor designation must also be available in a separate sign with visual and raised letters and braille adjacent to each door on the latch side. The intent is to let persons with vision impairments be able to determine what floor they are on without leaving the stairway enclosure. The reference to ICC A117.1 would require these signs to have the braille below the visual/raised letters. The height of the sign would have the bottom of the braille and the raised letter at between 48 inches (1220 mm) and 60 inches (1525 mm) above the floor. The space for someone to stand and touch the sign is an 18-inch (455 mm) minimum square and must be located outside of the swing of the door. The number indicating the floor designation for the visual and raised letter sign has to be between $^5/_8$ inch (16 mm) and 2 inches (51 mm) in height (see ICC A117.1, Section 703).

Commentary Figure 1023.8
EXAMPLE OF A STAIRWAY BARRIER AT THE LEVEL OF EXIT DISCHARGE

Signs with visual and raised letters and braille indicating the door leading to the exterior and exit signage at each door leading into the exit enclosure is covered in Section 1013.4.

[BE] 1023.9.1 Signage requirements. *Stairway* identification signs shall comply with all of the following requirements:

1. The signs shall be a minimum size of 18 inches (457 mm) by 12 inches (305 mm).
2. The letters designating the identification of the *interior exit stairway* and *ramp* shall be not less than $1^1/_2$ inches (38 mm) in height.
3. The number designating the floor level shall be not less than 5 inches (127 mm) in height and located in the center of the sign.
4. Other lettering and numbers shall be not less than 1 inch (25 mm) in height.
5. Characters and their background shall have a nonglare finish. Characters shall contrast with their background, with either light characters on a dark background or dark characters on a light background.
6. Where signs required by Section 1023.9 are installed in the *interior exit stairways* and *ramps* of buildings subject to Section 1025, the signs shall be made of the same materials as required by Section 1025.4.

❖ The requirements for stairway identification signage will provide for a consistent approach. The intent is to make signs visible and immediately recognizable to occupants and emergency responders upon entering the stairway (see Commentary Figure 1023.9.1).

Commentary Figure 1023.9.1
STAIRWAY IDENTIFICATION SIGN

Per Section 1023.9, this sign should have the bottom of the sign at 5 feet (1524 mm) above the floor so it is at about eye level and can be seen above the heads of people using the stairway. The high contrast (dark on light) and nonglare finish are to increase the readability of the sign in low lighting, including when the stairway is only lit with emergency lighting. The floor designation is the largest item on the sign [5 inches (127 mm) minimum], followed by the stairway identification [$1^1/_2$ inches (38 mm)] so that this information is immediately apparent. Other requirements in Section 1023.9 are letters large enough to be readable from a distance. One-inch letters are viewable by most people from a distance of about 10 feet (3050 mm). It is recommended that information be in all capitals and the style of letters be conventional in form—not italic, oblique, script or highly decorative. In addition, if the building is a high-rise and luminous egress path markings are required (see Section 1025.1), the stairway identification signage must also be self-luminous or photoluminescent. In order to also meet the contrast requirements in Item 5, typically the sign will have dark letters on a glow-in-the-dark background.

These signs are not required to be raised letters or braille. The raised letters and braille are intentionally on a different sign in a different location (see Section 1023.9).

[BE] 1023.10 Elevator lobby identification signs. At landings in *interior exit stairways* where two or more doors lead to the floor level, any door with direct access to an enclosed elevator lobby shall be identified by signage located on the door or directly adjacent to the door stating "Elevator Lobby." Signage shall be in accordance with Section 1023.9.1, Items 4, 5 and 6.

❖ This section is mainly related to fire service access elevators required in IBC Section 403.6.1 for a building with an occupied floor more than 120 feet (36 576 mm) above the street. The elevator lobby is required to have direct access to an exit stairway (IBC Section 3007.6.1). In addition, that same exit enclosure has to have access to the floor without going back through the elevator lobby (see IBC Section 3007.9.1). This leads to two doors at each floor landing. Elevator lobby signs identify the correct door through which fire fighters should access the floor so that lobby smoke protection is maintained. See the commentary to Section 1023.9.1 for information on Items 4, 5 and 6.

Since typically the fire service access elevators will use the same lobby as the occupant evacuation elevators (where provided per Section 403.6.2), this signage would effectively be required for the doors in the stairway enclosure that lead to occupant evacuation elevator lobbies as well.

While these signs are required to be adjacent to the door leading to the lobby, these signs are not required to be raised letters and braille. These signs are information for emergency responders.

[BE] 1023.11 Smokeproof enclosures. Where required by Section 403.5.4, 405.7.2 or 412.2.2.1 of the *International Building Code*, *interior exit stairways* and *ramps* shall be *smokeproof enclosures* in accordance with Section 909.20 of the *International Building Code*.

❖ While smokeproof enclosures and pressurized stairways for exiting can, at the designer's option, be used in buildings of any occupancy, height or area, this section specifically requires smokeproof enclosures or pressurized stairways to be provided where any of three conditions occur.

The first condition requires all exit stairways in high-rise buildings [i.e., buildings with floor levels higher than 75 feet (22 860 mm) above the level of exit discharge (see IBC Section 403.5.4)] to be smokeproof enclosures or pressurized stairways. The reason for this provision is that in very tall buildings, often during fire emergencies, total and immediate evacuation of the occupants cannot be readily accomplished. In such situations, exit stairways become places of safety for the occupants and must be adequately protected with smokeproof enclosures or pressurization to provide a safe egress environment. In order to provide this safe environment, the enclosure must be constructed to resist the migration of smoke caused by the "stack effect." Stack effect occurs in tall enclosures such as chimneys, where a fluid such as smoke, which is less dense than the ambient air, is introduced into the enclosure. The smoke will rise because of the effects of buoyancy and will induce additional flow into the enclosure through openings of any size at the lower levels.

The second condition applies to underground buildings [i.e., where an occupiable floor level is located more than 30 feet (9144 mm) below the level of exit discharge (see IBC Section 405.7.2)]. Stairways serving those levels are also required to be protected by smokeproof enclosures or pressurization because underground portions of a building present unique problems in providing not only for life safety but also access for fire-fighting purposes. The choice of a 30-foot (9144 mm) threshold for this requirement is intended to provide a reasonable limitation on vertical travel distance before the requirement applies.

The third condition is for air traffic control towers (see IBC Section 412.2.2.1). So that air traffic controllers can have a 360 degree view of the airport, there is an exception for stairway enclosures to extend to the roof; however, the stairway is required to be within a smokeproof enclosure.

Detailed system requirements for a smokeproof enclosure or pressurization are in IBC Section 909.20. Note that IBC Sections 403 and 405 each have exceptions for specific building types that are not to be regulated by those sections. Likewise, the requirements of this section do not apply to buildings identified in those exceptions.

[BE] 1023.11.1 Termination and extension. A *smokeproof enclosure* shall terminate at an *exit discharge* or a *public way*. The *smokeproof enclosure* shall be permitted to be extended by an *exit passageway* in accordance with Section 1023.3. The *exit passageway* shall be without openings other than the *fire door assembly* required by Section 1023.3.1 and those necessary for egress from the *exit passageway*. The *exit passageway* shall be separated from the remainder of the building by 2-hour *fire barriers* constructed in accordance with Section 707 of the *International Building Code* or *horizontal assemblies* constructed in accordance with Section 711 of the *International Building Code*, or both.

Exceptions:

1. Openings in the *exit passageway* serving a *smokeproof enclosure* are permitted where the *exit passageway* is protected and pressurized in the same manner as the *smokeproof enclosure*, and openings are protected as required for access from other floors.
2. The *fire barrier* separating the *smokeproof enclosure* from the *exit passageway* is not required, provided that the *exit passageway* is protected and pressurized in the same manner as the *smokeproof enclosure*.
3. A *smokeproof enclosure* shall be permitted to egress through areas on the *level of exit discharge* or vestibules as permitted by Section 1028.

❖ The walls forming the smokeproof enclosure, which includes the stairway shaft and the vestibules, must be fire barriers having a fire-resistance rating of at least 2 hours. This level of fire endurance is specified because exit stairways in high-rise buildings, underground buildings or air traffic control towers serve as principal components of the egress system and as the source of fire service access to the fire floor. This supersedes any allowed reduction of enclosure rating, even if the stairway in an underground building from the level that is more than 30 feet (9144 mm) below exit discharge connects three stories or less. A pressurized stairway is a special case of a smokeproof enclosure; therefore, the requirements would be the same.

The first exception applies to openings in the exit passageway that are permitted, provided the exit passageway is protected and pressurized. If the exit stairway enclosure is connected to an exit passageway, Exception 2 allows the elimination of a door between, since this would interfere with the pressurization of the stairway and passageway as a combined exit system (see also Section 1023.3.1, Exception 3). In accordance with Exception 3, 50 percent of the stairways in smokeproof enclosures or pressurized stairways can use the exit discharge exceptions in Section 1028 to egress through a lobby or vestibule.

[BE] 1023.11.2 Enclosure access. Access to the *stairway* or *ramp* within a *smokeproof enclosure* shall be by way of a vestibule or an open exterior balcony.

> **Exception:** Access is not required by way of a vestibule or exterior balcony for *stairways* and *ramps* using the pressurization alternative complying with Section 909.20.5 of the *International Building Code*.

❖ See Commentary Figures 1023.11.2(1) and 1023.11.2(2) for illustrations of access to smokeproof stairway or ramp by way of a vestibule or an exterior balcony. The purpose of this requirement is to keep the enclosure clear of smoke. Where a pressurized stairway is used, these elements are not necessary.

[BE] 1023.12 Standpipes. Standpipes and standpipe hose connections shall be provided where required by Sections 905.3 and 905.4.

❖ Standpipes are required in interior exit stairways and ramps (Section 1023.12), in exit passageways (Section 1024.8) and on each side of horizontal exits (Section 1026.5) in many types of buildings, such as buildings that are four stories or taller, underground buildings, malls or buildings with heliports or rooftop gardens. This section does not require standpipes, but is intended as a pointer to remind designers that a standpipe may be required by Sections 905.3 and 905.4. Therefore, the enclosures must be designed to have space for these items without obstructing the path of travel in those enclosures.

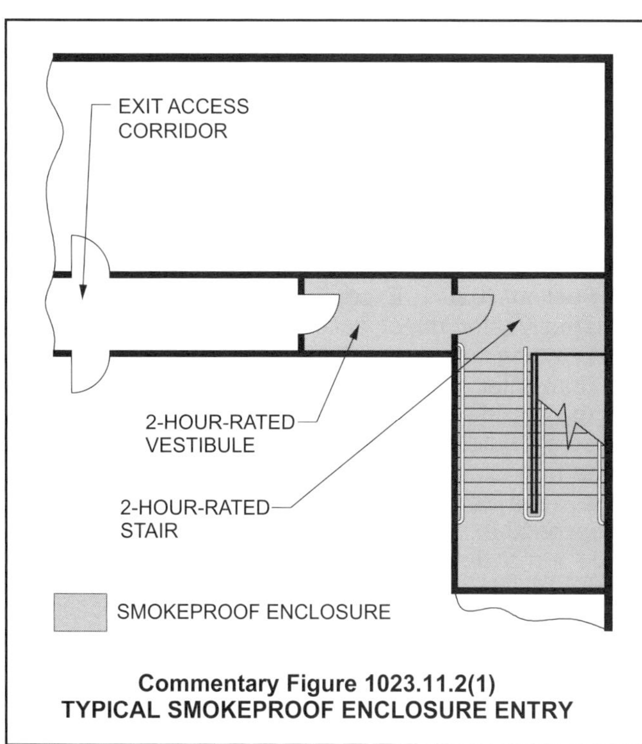

Commentary Figure 1023.11.2(1)
TYPICAL SMOKEPROOF ENCLOSURE ENTRY

SECTION 1024
EXIT PASSAGEWAYS

[BE] 1024.1 Exit passageways. *Exit passageways* serving as an exit component in a *means of egress* system shall comply with the requirements of this section. An *exit passageway* shall not be used for any purpose other than as a *means of egress* and a circulation path.

❖ This section provides acceptable methods of continuing the protected path of travel for building occupants. The building designer or owner is given different options for achieving this protected path of travel. See Commentary Figure 1024.1 for an illustration of an exit passageway arrangement. In the case of office buildings or similar structures, the exit stairways are often located at the central core or in line with the centrally located exit access corridors. Exit passageways may be used to connect the exit stair to the exterior exit door or to connect enclosures for exit stairways that are not vertically continuous. Such an arrangement provides great flexibility in the design use of the building. Without an exit passageway at the grade floor or the level of exit discharge, the occupants of the upper floors or basement levels would have to leave the safety of the exit stairway to travel to the exterior doors. Such a reduction of protection is not acceptable (see Section 1028 for exit discharge alternatives).

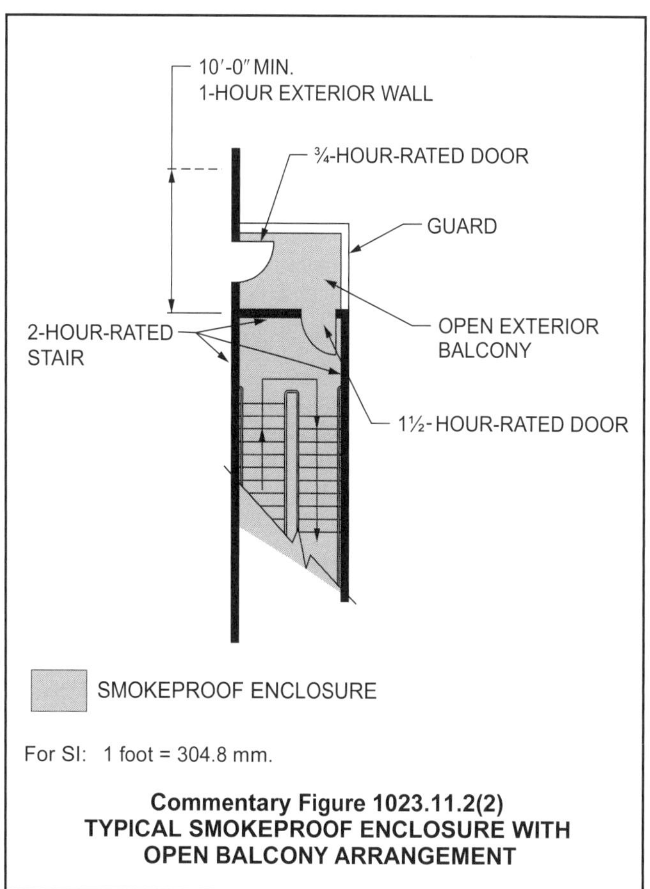

Commentary Figure 1023.11.2(2)
TYPICAL SMOKEPROOF ENCLOSURE WITH OPEN BALCONY ARRANGEMENT

Exit passageways may also be used on their own in locations not connected with an enclosure for an exit stairway. The exit passageway is often used as a protected horizontal exit path, such as in a mall or unlimited area building. Sometimes on large floor plans, an exit passageway may be used to extend an exit into areas that would not otherwise be able to meet the travel distance requirements. Like exit stairways, there is no travel distance limitation within an exit passageway.

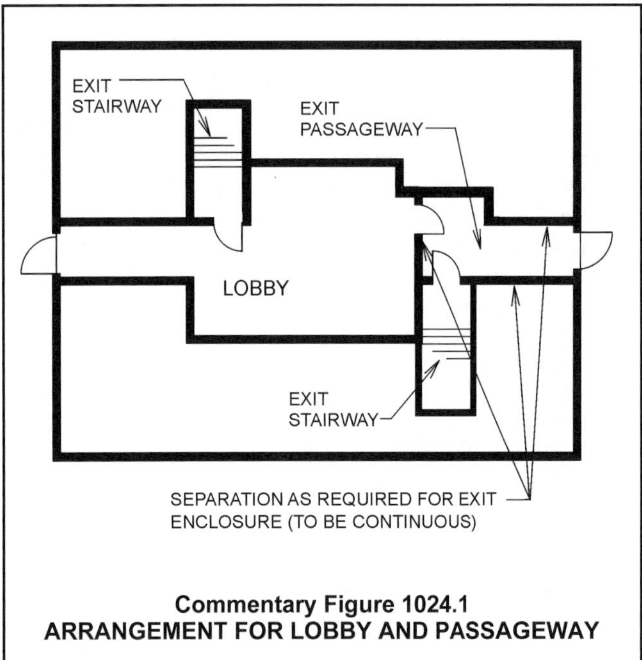

Commentary Figure 1024.1
ARRANGEMENT FOR LOBBY AND PASSAGEWAY

[BE] 1024.2 Width and capacity. The required capacity of *exit passageways* shall be determined as specified in Section 1005.1 but the minimum width shall be not less than 44 inches (1118 mm), except that *exit passageways* serving an *occupant load* of less than 50 shall be not less than 36 inches (914 mm) in width. The minimum width or required capacity of *exit passageways* shall be unobstructed.

Exception: Encroachments complying with Section 1005.7.

❖ The width of an exit passageway is to be determined in accordance with Section 1005.1, based on the number of occupants served in the same manner as for corridors. The greater of the minimum required width or the width determined based on occupancy is to be used. In situations where the exit passageway also serves as an exit access corridor for the first floor, the corridor width must comply with the stricter requirement.

A cross reference to Section 1005.7 in the exceptions for encroachments in the required width in aisles (see Section 1018.1), corridors (see Section 1020.3), exit passageways (see Section 1024.2) and exit courts (see Section 1028.4.1) reinforces the fact that the protrusion limits provision is generally applicable for these types of confined routes.

[BE] 1024.3 Construction. *Exit passageway* enclosures shall have walls, floors and ceilings of not less than a 1-hour *fire-resistance rating*, and not less than that required for any connecting *interior exit stairway* or *ramp*. *Exit passageways* shall be constructed as *fire barriers* in accordance with Section 707 of the *International Building Code* or *horizontal assemblies* constructed in accordance with Section 711 of the *International Building Code*, or both.

❖ The entire exit passageway enclosure is to be fire-resistance rated as specified. The floors and ceilings are required to be rated in addition to the walls. Where used separately, a minimum 1-hour fire-resistance rating is required. Where extending an enclosure for an exit stairway, the rating must not be less than the enclosure for the exit stairway so that the degree of protection is kept at the same level. Remember that if the exit passageway extends over a lower level, such as a basement, all supporting construction is to have the same fire-resistance rating as the elements supported in accordance with the continuity requirements for fire barriers and horizontal assemblies (see IBC Sections 707.5 and 711.2.2). The continuity requirements would also be a concern for the rated ceiling of the exit passageway. An alternative for the ceiling of the exit passageway could be a top-of-shaft enclosure (see IBC Section 713.12).

[BE] 1024.4 Termination. *Exit passageways* on the *level of exit discharge* shall terminate at an *exit discharge*. *Exit passageways* on other levels shall terminate at an *exit*.

❖ This is consistent with the exit continuity and enclosure requirements in Section 1023.3. Section 1023.3 has an exception that allows for combinations of interior exit stairways and ramps with the exit passageway. The intent of this section is to provide safety in all portions of the exit by requiring continuity of the fire protection characteristics of the enclosure for the exit stairway in combination with an exit passageway. This would include, but not be limited to, the fire-resistance rating of the enclosure walls for the exit stairways and the opening protection rating of the doors. Where an exit passageway is supported by the structure, the supporting construction must be fire-resistance rated equal to the walls and floors of the passageway being supported.

Section 1028.1, Exceptions 1 and 2, allow for an alternative for direct access to the outside via an intervening lobby or vestibule.

Horizontal exits, while not providing direct access to the outside of the structure, do move occupants to another "building" through a fire wall or into a refuge area protected by fire barriers and horizontal assemblies (see Sections 1026 and 1028.1, Exception 3). Horizontal exits are commonly used in hospitals and jails for a defend-in-place type of protection or in large buildings to meet exit access travel distance requirements.

An exit passageway may be used to move between vertical enclosures for exit stairways. This may occur where a building is shaped like a wedding cake, so the stairway towers move outward as the building gets larger toward grade level. If this situation happens, it is very important to let occupants know how to proceed. See Section 1013.1 for exit signage requirements within exit passageways.

[BE] 1024.5 Openings. *Exit passageway* opening protectives shall be in accordance with the requirements of Section 716 of the *International Building Code*.

Except as permitted in Section 402.8.7 of the *International Building Code*, openings in *exit passageways* other than unprotected exterior openings shall be limited to those necessary for *exit access* to the *exit passageway* from normally occupied spaces and for egress from the *exit passageway*.

Where an *interior exit stairway* or *ramp* is extended to an *exit discharge* or a *public way* by an *exit passageway*, the *exit passageway* shall comply with Section 1023.3.1.

Elevators shall not open into an *exit passageway*.

❖ In order for fire doors to be effective, they must be in the closed position; therefore, the preferred arrangement is to install self-closing doors. Recognizing that operational practices often require doors to be open for an extended period of time, automatic-closing doors are permitted as long as this opening will not pose a threat to occupant safety and the doors will be self-latching. Automatic-closing devices enable the opening to be protected during a fire condition. The basic requirement for closing devices and specific requirements for automatic-closing and self-closing devices are given in NFPA 80. Automatic-closing doors that protect openings into exits are also required to close on the actuation of smoke detectors or loss of power to the smoke detectors (see IBC Section 716.2.6.6).

The requirements for exit passageways are very similar to those required for enclosures for interior exit stairways (see Section 1023.4). The only openings that are permitted in fire-resistance-rated exit passageways are doors that lead from normally occupied spaces, from the enclosure for the exit stairway and to the outside. This restriction on openings essentially prohibits the use of windows or doors in an exit passageway except for those exterior windows or doors that are not exposed to any hazards. This requirement is not intended to prohibit windows or other openings in the exterior walls of the exit enclosure. The verbiage "unprotected exterior openings" includes windows or doors not required to be protected by either Section 705.8 or 1023.7. The only exception would be window assemblies that have been tested as wall assemblies in accordance with ASTM E119 and UL 263. The objective of this provision is to minimize the possibility of fire spreading into an exit passageway and endangering the occupants or even preventing the use of the exit at a time when it is most needed. The limitation on openings applies regardless of the fire protection rating of the opening protective. The limitation on openings from normally occupied areas is intended to reduce the probability of a fire occurring in an unoccupied area, such as a storage closet, that has an opening into the exit passageway, thereby resulting in smoke spreading into the exit passageway. Other spaces that are not normally occupied include, but are not limited to, toilet rooms, electrical/mechanical equipment rooms and janitorial closets. Note that exit passageways prohibit elevators from opening directly into a passageway. There are some exceptions for these unoccupied spaces in exit passageways in covered malls (see IBC Section 402.8.7).

The third paragraph addresses where the vertical enclosure for an exit stairway or ramp transitions to the exit passageway. While the exit passageway is an extension of the protection offered by the vertical exit, there must still be a door (i.e., opening protective) between the bottom of the stairway or ramp enclosure and the exit passageway. This is to prevent any smoke that may migrate into the exit passageway from also moving up the exit stairway or ramp. This door is not required if the exit stairway and exit passageway are protected by pressurization (see Section 1023.3.1, Exception 3, and Section 1023.11.1, Exception 2).

Elevators may not open into exit passageways. The difficulty is having elevator doors that can meet the opening protectives for a fire barrier, but still operate effectively. For additional information on elevator lobbies and doors, see the commentary to Section 1020.6 and IBC Sections 713.14 and 3006.

These opening limitations are very similar to those required for an exit enclosure (see Section 1023.4).

[BE] 1024.6 Penetrations. Penetrations into or through an *exit passageway* are prohibited except for the following:

1. Equipment and ductwork necessary for independent pressurization.
2. Fire protection systems.
3. Security systems.
4. Two-way communication systems.
5. Electrical raceway for fire department communication.
6. Electrical raceway serving the *exit passageway* and terminating at a steel box not exceeding 16 square inches (0.010 m^2).

Such penetrations shall be protected in accordance with Section 714 of the *International Building Code*. There shall not be penetrations or communicating openings, whether protected or not, between adjacent *exit passageways*.

Exception: Membrane penetrations shall be permitted on the outside of the *exit passageway*. Such penetrations shall be protected in accordance with Section 714.4.2 of the *International Building Code*.

❖ This section specifically lists the items that are allowed to penetrate the walls and ceiling of the enclosure for exit passageways. This is consistent for all types of enclosures for exits, including interior exit stairways or interior exit ramps and exit passageways (see Section 1023.5). In general, only portions of the building service systems that serve the enclosure are allowed to penetrate the enclosure. As indicated in the commentary to Section 1024.8, standpipe systems may be required to be located in the exit passageway.

IBC Section 714 addresses through penetrations and membrane penetrations for fire-resistance-rated walls and floor/ceiling assemblies. The intent is to maintain the integrity of the enclosure for the exit passageway. This section and Section 1024.7 are meant to work together. This requirement is not intended to prohibit penetrations in the exterior walls of the exit passageway that is not required to be rated (see Section 1024.5).

The exception allows for such items as electrical boxes, exit signs or fire alarm pull stations to be installed on the outside of the enclosure, provided that the boxes are installed so that the required fire-resistance rating is not reduced (see IBC Section 714.4.2).

[BE] 1024.7 Ventilation. Equipment and ductwork for *exit passageway* ventilation as permitted by Section 1024.6 shall comply with one of the following:

1. The equipment and ductwork shall be located exterior to the building and shall be directly connected to the *exit passageway* by ductwork enclosed in construction as required for shafts.
2. Where the equipment and ductwork is located within the *exit passageway*, the intake air shall be taken directly from the outdoors and the exhaust air shall be discharged directly to the outdoors, or the air shall be conveyed through ducts enclosed in construction as required for shafts.
3. Where located within the building, the equipment and ductwork shall be separated from the remainder of the building, including other mechanical equipment, with construction as required for shafts.

In each case, openings into the fire-resistance-rated construction shall be limited to those needed for maintenance and operation and shall be protected by opening protectives in accordance with Section 716 of the *International Building Code* for shaft enclosures.

Exit passageway ventilation systems shall be independent of other building ventilation systems.

❖ As a continuation of an exit stairway enclosure, an exit passageway has the same considerations for protection. While an exit passageway may look like a regular hallway, it is important that it be maintained as free of smoke as the exit stairway. If the ductwork serving the exit passageway penetrates a rated wall or floor/ceiling assembly, a fire and smoke damper is required by IBC Section 717.5.3. See the commentary to Section 1023.6.

[BE] 1024.8 Standpipes. Standpipes and standpipe hose connections shall be provided where required by Sections 905.3 and 905.4.

❖ Standpipes are required in interior exit stairways and ramps (Section 1023.12), in exit passageways (Section 1024.8) and on each side of horizontal exits (Section 1026.5) in many types of buildings, such as buildings that are four stories or taller, underground buildings, malls or buildings with heliports or rooftop gardens. This section does not require standpipes, but is intended as a pointer to remind designers that a standpipe may be required by Sections 905.3 and 905.4. Therefore, the enclosures must be designed to have space for these items without obstructing the path of travel in those enclosures.

SECTION 1025 LUMINOUS EGRESS PATH MARKINGS

[BE] 1025.1 General. *Approved* luminous egress path markings delineating the exit path shall be provided in high-rise buildings of Group A, B, E, I-1, M or R-1 occupancies in accordance with this section.

Exception: Luminous egress path markings shall not be required on the *level of exit discharge* in lobbies that serve as part of the exit path in accordance with Section 1028.1, Exception 1.

❖ Improved safety for individuals negotiating stairs during egress of a high-rise building is provided by improving the visibility of stair treads and handrails under emergency conditions. A second source of emergency power for exit illumination, exit signs and stairway pressurization systems in smokeproof enclosures is currently mandated for high-rise buildings. In the event of an emergency that disconnects utility power, the emergency power source should engage, causing the stairway to be illuminated and kept smoke free by the pressurization system. Unfortunately, such systems can fail under demand conditions. The provisions of Section 1025 add another level of safety to the egress path by requiring the installation of photoluminescent or self-illuminating marking systems that do not require electrical power and its associated wiring and circuits for high-rise buildings containing assembly, business, education, assisted living, mercantile and hotels. Hospitals, nursing homes and jails often have emergency lighting on generators, and they use a defend-in-place scenario. Apartments and dormitories are also not included in this requirement given the familiarity of the occupants with the building.

This additional means of ensuring that occupants can safely egress a building via exit stairways is available even if the emergency power supply and system fail to operate. The groups indicated have a high anticipated occupant load or occupants may not be familiar with the space. Note that the provisions require these markings only within the enclosure for the exit stairway, exit ramp and the exit passageway used for enclosure continuation. The markings are not required before reaching the exit (i.e., exit access) or after leaving the exit (i.e., exit discharge).

The exception indicates that if the exit stairway enclosure discharges through the lobby (see Section 1028.1, Exception 1), the egress markings would not be required outside the stairway enclosure for the portion from the stairway enclosure to the door leading to the outside. If the exit stairway discharges through an exit passageway, the exit path markings must continue to the door leading to the outside. The current text is silent regarding the options of vestibules and horizontal exits, but since Sections 1025.1 through 1025.5 only address within the enclosure for the exit, and not the exit discharge, exit path markings in the vestibule or after the horizontal exit are not required.

[BE] 1025.2 Markings within exit components. Egress path markings shall be provided in *interior exit stairways*, *interior exit ramps* and *exit passageways*, in accordance with Sections 1025.2.1 through 1025.2.6.

❖ Luminous egress path markings are required inside the enclosure for exit stairways or ramps for all floors. If the stairway connects to an exit passageway as part of the travel down to the level of exit discharge or on the level of exit discharge, the path markings must also be continued in the exit passageway.

The subsections include marking the tread nosings, the surrounding edges of landings and any exit passageways, handrails and protruding objects within the protected enclosure.

All exit path markings are required to be solid and continuous stripes. A key requirement for marking systems is that their design must be uniform. The placement and dimensions of markings must be consistent along the entire exit stairway. By specifying a standard marking dimension, the requirements will provide consistent and standard application in the design and enforcement of exit path markings and ensure that markings are visible during dark conditions. Markings installed on stair steps, perimeter demarcation lines and handrails must have a minimum width of 1 inch (25 mm). For stair steps and perimeter demarcation lines, their maximum width cannot exceed 2 inches (51 mm). The provisions for stair steps, perimeter demarcation lines and handrails allow the width of the marking to be reduced to less than 1 inch (25 mm) where marking stripes are listed in accordance with UL 1994.

[BE] 1025.2.1 Steps. A solid and continuous stripe shall be applied to the horizontal leading edge of each step and shall extend for the full length of the step. Outlining stripes shall have a minimum horizontal width of 1 inch (25 mm) and a maximum width of 2 inches (51 mm). The leading edge of the stripe shall be placed not more than $^1/_2$ inch (12.7 mm) from the leading edge of the step and the stripe shall not overlap the leading edge of the step by not more than $^1/_2$ inch (12.7 mm) down the vertical face of the step.

> **Exception:** The minimum width of 1 inch (25 mm) shall not apply to outlining stripes listed in accordance with UL 1994.

❖ Luminous stripes are required the full width of the stairway on all tread nosings and along the leading edge of stair landings. These demarcation lines serve to identify the transition from the stair steps to the landing, which is important in minimizing the risk of a fall inside a stairway enclosure that is not illuminated. In order to clearly identify the leading edge of a step, the front edge of the stripe must be within $^1/_2$ inch (13 mm), plus or minus, of the leading edge of the tread (see Commentary Figure 1025.2.1).

The code does not specify any minimum slip-resistance requirements for luminous products installed on walking surfaces. However, Section 1003.4 requires all walking surfaces for means of egress to be slip resistant. Persons with vision impairments often rely on high-contrast elements to delineate changes in elevation such as that required in Sections 1011.5.4 and 1029.14.2.2. In medium light conditions, the luminous materials may be hard to discern. Luminous materials installed adjacent to dark contrasting materials may help with both situations.

For stair steps, perimeter demarcation lines, handrails and obstacles, the exception allows the width of the marking to be reduced to less than 1 inch (25 mm) where marking stripes are listed in accordance with UL 1994.

[BE] 1025.2.2 Landings. The leading edge of landings shall be marked with a stripe consistent with the dimensional requirements for steps.

❖ The edge of the landing at the top of the steps must be marked in the same manner as the tread nosing

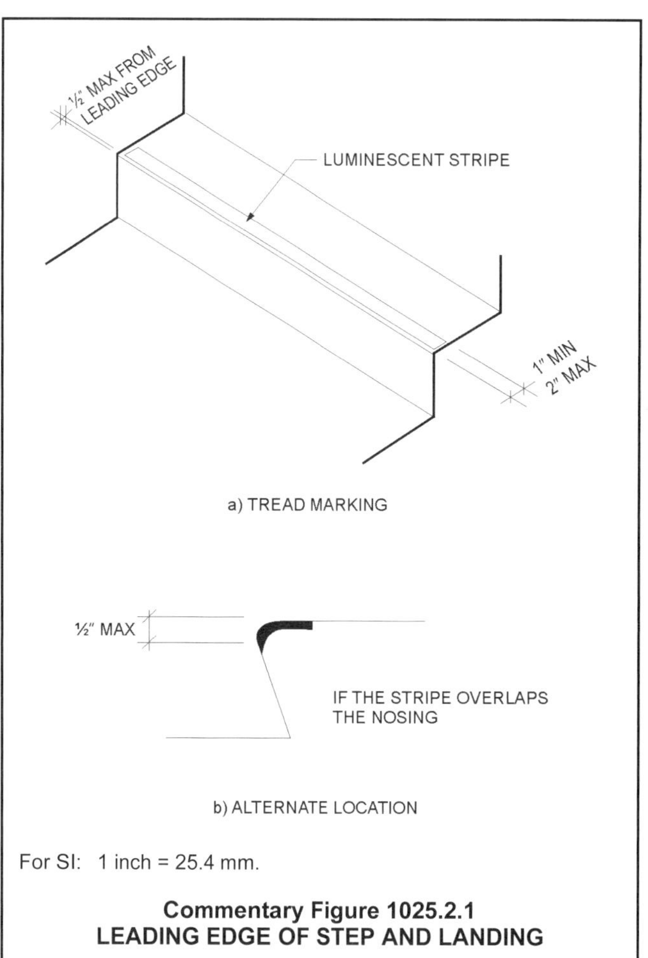

For SI: 1 inch = 25.4 mm.

Commentary Figure 1025.2.1
LEADING EDGE OF STEP AND LANDING

so that a person can tell where the steps start. See the commentary to Section 1025.2.1 and Commentary Figure 1025.2.1.

[BE] 1025.2.3 Handrails. *Handrails* and handrail extensions shall be marked with a solid and continuous stripe having a minimum width of 1 inch (25 mm). The stripe shall be placed on the top surface of the *handrail* for the entire length of the *handrail*, including extensions and newel post caps. Where *handrails* or handrail extensions bend or turn corners, the stripe shall not have a gap of more than 4 inches (102 mm).

Exception: The minimum width of 1 inch (25 mm) shall not apply to outlining stripes *listed* in accordance with UL 1994.

❖ The handrail must have a glow-in-the-dark stripe down the entire length. The 1-inch (25 mm) minimum width stripe must be on the top of the handrail so it can charge and maximize its visibility in the dark. Bends or turns may result in a break in the marking, which must not be more than 4 inches (102 mm) (see Commentary Figure 1025.2.3).

For stair steps, perimeter demarcation lines, handrails and obstacles, the exception allows the width of the marking to be reduced to less than 1 inch (25 mm) where marking stripes are listed in accordance with UL 1994.

[BE] 1025.2.4 Perimeter demarcation lines. Stair landings and other floor areas within *interior exit stairways*, *interior exit ramps* and *exit passageways*, with the exception of the sides of steps, shall be provided with solid and continuous demarcation lines on the floor or on the walls or a combination of both. The stripes shall be 1 to 2 inches (25 mm to 51 mm) wide with interruptions not exceeding 4 inches (102 mm).

Exception: The minimum width of 1 inch (25 mm) shall not apply to outlining stripes *listed* in accordance with UL 1994.

❖ In addition to the leading edge of the landing, the landing itself must have a luminous stripe all the way around the edge. If the enclosure includes any type of exit passageway, that corridor must also have a perimeter stripe. The stripe can be on the floor or on the wall at baseboard height (see Sections 1025.2.4.1 and 1025.2.4.2).

For stair steps, perimeter demarcation lines, handrails and obstacles, the exception allows the width of the marking to be reduced to less than 1 inch (25 mm) where marking stripes are listed in accordance with UL 1994.

[BE] 1025.2.4.1 Floor-mounted demarcation lines. Perimeter demarcation lines shall be placed within 4 inches (102 mm) of the wall and shall extend to within 2 inches (51 mm) of the markings on the leading edge of landings. The demarcation lines shall continue across the floor in front of all doors.

Exception: Demarcation lines shall not extend in front of *exit discharge* doors that lead out of an *exit* and through which occupants must travel to complete the exit path.

❖ Luminous stripes shall extend all the way around any stair landings. This section specifies the option of stripes on the floor (see Commentary Figure 1025.2.4.1). On a typical landing, the stripe will extend across the front of the door, indicating to someone moving down the stairway that they should continue (see Commentary Figure 1025.2.4.3). At the level of exit discharge, the occupant has a different visual cue. The exception states that the line should not extend in front of the door leading to the exterior (see Commentary Figure 1025.2.6). This should allow people to understand which door they need to move through to get to safety.

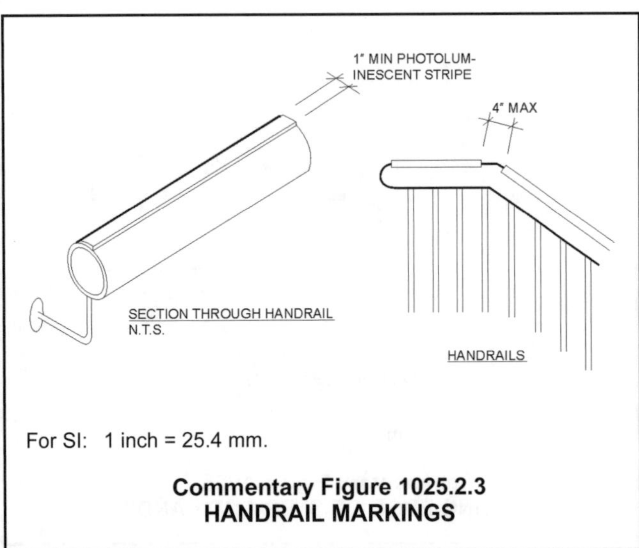

For SI: 1 inch = 25.4 mm.

**Commentary Figure 1025.2.3
HANDRAIL MARKINGS**

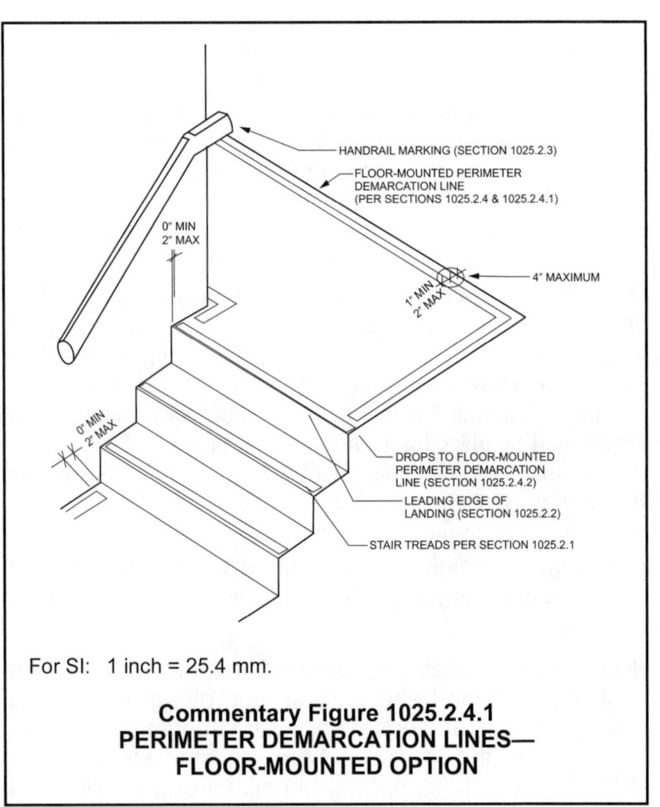

For SI: 1 inch = 25.4 mm.

**Commentary Figure 1025.2.4.1
PERIMETER DEMARCATION LINES—
FLOOR-MOUNTED OPTION**

[BE] 1025.2.4.2 Wall-mounted demarcation lines. Perimeter demarcation lines shall be placed on the wall with the bottom edge of the stripe not more than 4 inches (102 mm) above the finished floor. At the top or bottom of the *stairs*, demarcation lines shall drop vertically to the floor within 2 inches (51 mm) of the step or landing edge. Demarcation lines on walls shall transition vertically to the floor and then extend across the floor where a line on the floor is the only practical method of outlining the path. Where the wall line is broken by a door, demarcation lines on walls shall continue across the face of the door or transition to the floor and extend across the floor in front of such door.

Exception: Demarcation lines shall not extend in front of *exit discharge* doors that lead out of an *exit* and through which occupants must travel to complete the exit path.

❖ Luminous stripes that surround the stairway landings can be on the floor or on the wall. This section specifies the option of stripes on the wall (see Commentary Figure 1025.2.4.2). See the commentary to Sections 1025.2.4 and 1025.2.4.1.

The exception is effectively a reference to Section 1025.2.6.

[BE] 1025.2.4.3 Transition. Where a wall-mounted demarcation line transitions to a floor-mounted demarcation line, or vice-versa, the wall-mounted demarcation line shall drop vertically to the floor to meet a complimentary extension of the floor-mounted demarcation line, thus forming a continuous marking.

❖ While the luminous perimeter stripes on a landing can be on either the wall or the floor, where they transition from one to another, the lines should appear continuous. See Section 1025.2.4.2 for special requirements for where the wall perimeter marking transitions to the floor stripe indicating the leading edge of the landing.

Where perimeter lines cross a door frame, the lines can transition or stay on the same plain (see Commentary Figure 1025.2.4.3).

[BE] 1025.2.5 Obstacles. Obstacles at or below 6 feet 6 inches (1981 mm) in height and projecting more than 4 inches (102 mm) into the egress path shall be outlined with markings not less than 1 inch (25 mm) in width comprised of a pattern of alternating equal bands, of luminous material and black, with the alternating bands not more than 2 inches (51 mm) thick and angled at 45 degrees (0.79 rad). Obstacles shall include, but are not limited to, standpipes, hose cabinets, wall projections, and restricted height areas. However, such markings shall not conceal any required information or indicators including but not limited to instructions to occupants for the use of standpipes.

Exception: The minimum width of 1 inch (25 mm) shall not apply to markings *listed* in accordance with UL 1994.

❖ Any obstacles within the stairway must be marked with a dashed line of diagonal slashes (see Commentary Figure 1025.2.5). The markings of obstacles are

For SI: 1 inch = 25.4 mm.

Commentary Figure 1025.2.4.2
PERIMETER DEMARCATION LINES—WALL-MOUNTED OPTION

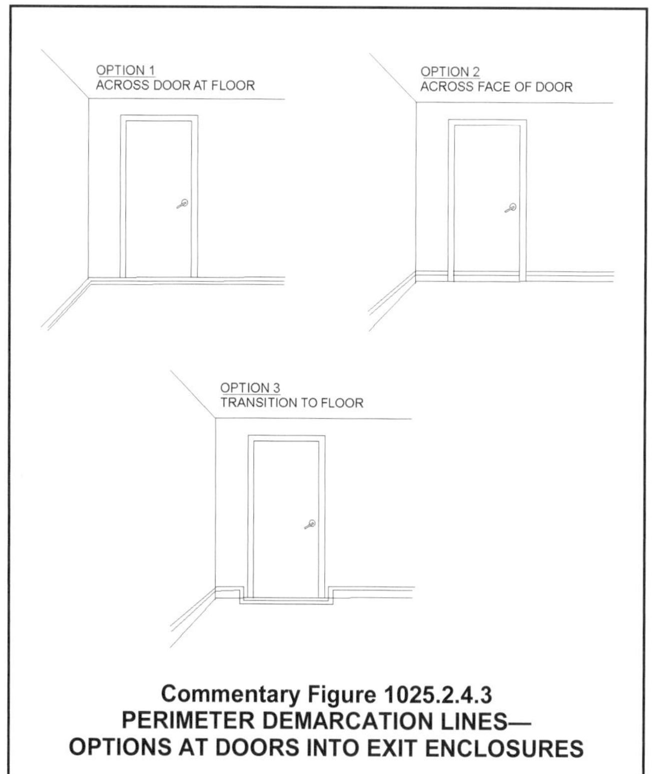

Commentary Figure 1025.2.4.3
PERIMETER DEMARCATION LINES—OPTIONS AT DOORS INTO EXIT ENCLOSURES

consistent with the intent of protruding object provisions in Section 1003.3. However, there is a difference in the height—6 feet 6 inches (1981 mm) instead of 6 feet 8 inches (2032 mm). Items permitted within the enclosures for exit stairways are limited by Sections 1023.2 and 1023.5.

For stair steps, perimeter demarcation lines, handrails and obstacles, the exception allows the width of the marking to be reduced to less than 1 inch (25 mm) where marking stripes are listed in accordance with UL 1994.

[BE] 1025.2.6 Doors within the exit path. Doors through which occupants must pass in order to complete the exit path shall be provided with markings complying with Sections 1025.2.6.1 through 1025.2.6.3.

❖ Doors within an enclosure for an exit stairway can:

- Lead directly to the exterior.
- Pass through a horizontal exit (Section 1028.1, Exception 3).
- Lead to an exit passageway, lobby or vestibule on the level of exit discharge (Section 1028.1, Exceptions 1 and 2).
- Lead to an exit passageway on a transition level.

Doors at these locations should be marked as indicated in the following three subsections. Combined with the landing markings not extending across the bottom of such doors, this will provide several visual cues to indicate which door to continue through to get out of the building (see Commentary Figure 1025.2.6).

The NIST egress study of the World Trade Center indicated that transition floors can cause delays in egress because people hesitate where it is unclear about which way they should continue. Effectively marking these doors in four different ways will decrease that hazard. Which doors to mark is consistent with the exit sign requirements within exit enclosures in Section 1013.1.

[BE] 1025.2.6.1 Emergency exit symbol. The doors shall be identified by a low-location luminous emergency exit symbol complying with NFPA 170. The exit symbol shall be not less than 4 inches (102 mm) in height and shall be mounted on the door, centered horizontally, with the top of the symbol not higher than 18 inches (457 mm) above the finished floor.

❖ The door shall include a low luminous level exit symbol within 18 inches (457 mm) of the floor. For an example of the emergency exit symbol, see Commentary Figure 1025.2.6.1. The sign on the door can be just this symbol or it can also contain additional information such as a directional arrow or "EXIT."

[BE] 1025.2.6.2 Door hardware markings. Door hardware shall be marked with not less than 16 square inches (10 323 mm^2) of luminous material. This marking shall be located behind, immediately adjacent to, or on the door handle or escutcheon. Where a panic bar is installed, such material shall be not less than 1 inch (25 mm) wide for the entire length of the actuating bar or touchpad.

❖ Door hardware locations must be clearly visible. If a panic bar is used, a luminous stripe with a minimum width of 1 inch (25 mm) should be provided down the entire length of the activation bar/paddle [see Commentary Figure 1025.2.6, Example 1]. If lever hard-

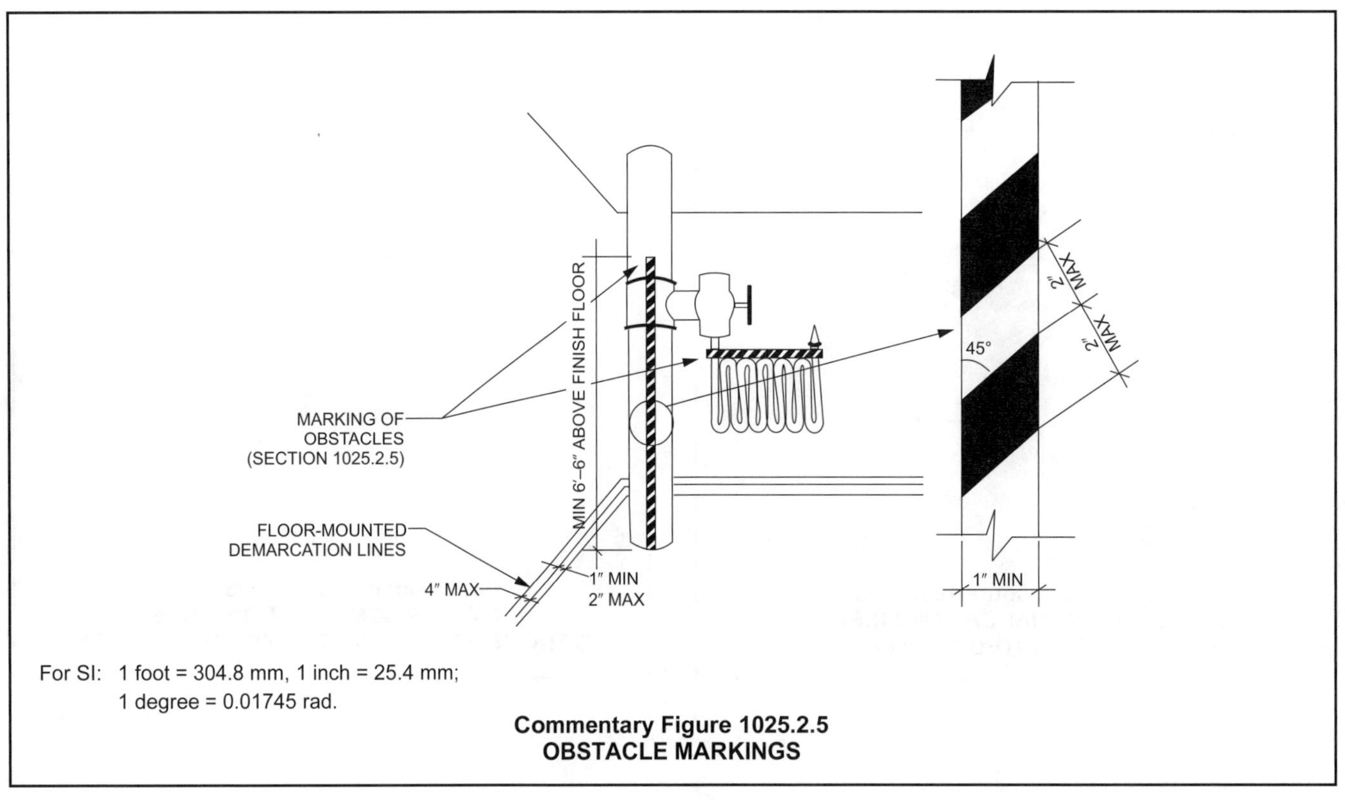

Commentary Figure 1025.2.5
OBSTACLE MARKINGS

ware is used, a donut, square or rectangle with a minimum area of 16 square inches (10 323 mm^2) should be provided behind the hardware [see Commentary Figure 1025.2.6, Example 2]. There is also the option of marking the door handle itself, but it would be difficult to get 16 square inches (10 323 mm^2) of visible surface area. Plus, over time, a finish on the hardware has a greater chance of wearing off with normal use. The language allows the designer the freedom to decide (with wear and hardware options) which configuration would give the best results.

[BE] 1025.2.6.3 Door frame markings. The top and sides of the door frame shall be marked with a solid and continuous 1-inch- to 2-inch-wide (25 mm to 51 mm) stripe. Where the door molding does not provide sufficient flat surface on

For SI: 1 inch = 25.4 mm.

Commentary Figure 1025.2.6.1
EMERGENCY EXIT SYMBOL

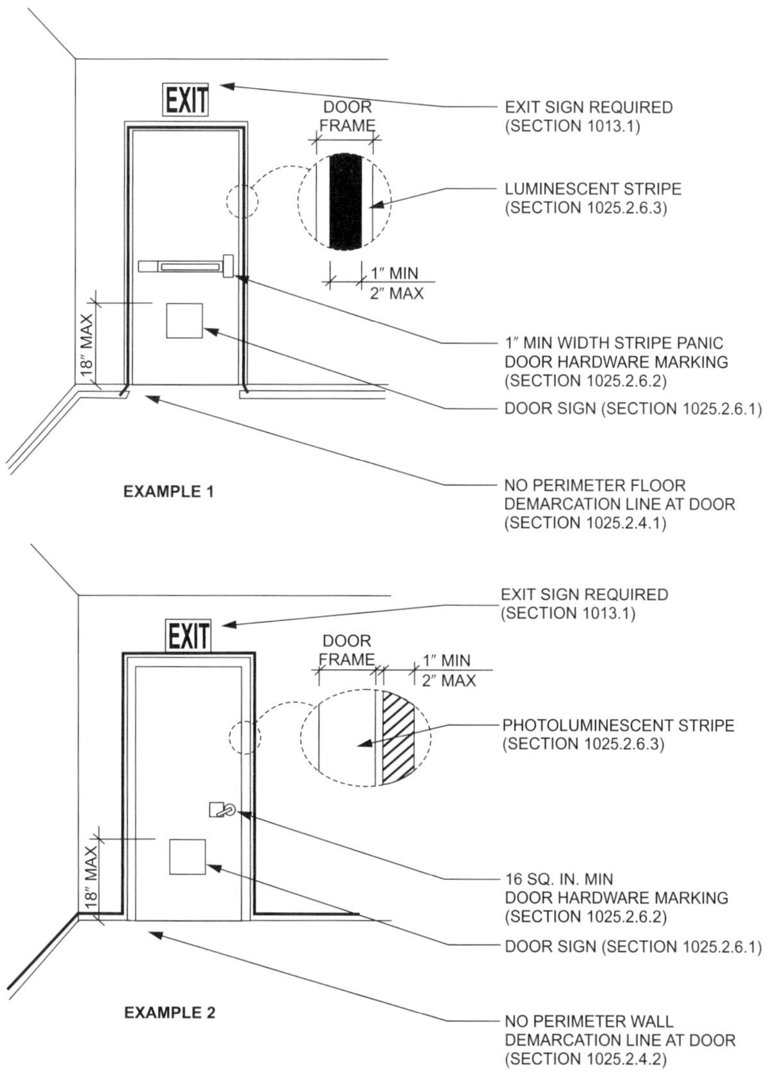

EXAMPLE 1

EXIT SIGN REQUIRED (SECTION 1013.1)

DOOR FRAME

LUMINESCENT STRIPE (SECTION 1025.2.6.3)

1" MIN 2" MAX

18" MAX

1" MIN WIDTH STRIPE PANIC DOOR HARDWARE MARKING (SECTION 1025.2.6.2)

DOOR SIGN (SECTION 1025.2.6.1)

NO PERIMETER FLOOR DEMARCATION LINE AT DOOR (SECTION 1025.2.4.1)

EXAMPLE 2

EXIT SIGN REQUIRED (SECTION 1013.1)

DOOR FRAME

1" MIN 2" MAX

PHOTOLUMINESCENT STRIPE (SECTION 1025.2.6.3)

18" MAX

16 SQ. IN. MIN DOOR HARDWARE MARKING (SECTION 1025.2.6.2)

DOOR SIGN (SECTION 1025.2.6.1)

NO PERIMETER WALL DEMARCATION LINE AT DOOR (SECTION 1025.2.4.2)

For SI: 1 inch = 25.4 mm,
1 square inch = 645.16 mm.

Commentary Figure 1025.2.6
EXIT DOOR TO EXTERIOR EXAMPLES

which to locate the stripe, the stripe shall be permitted to be located on the wall surrounding the frame.

❖ Doors must be marked along the sides and top with stripes similar to those provided on the stair nosing. Door frames come in a variety of shapes. If there is not space on the door for the marking stripe, the stripe can be around the perimeter of the door [see Commentary Figure 1025.2.6, Examples 1 and 2].

[BE] 1025.3 Uniformity. Placement and dimensions of markings shall be consistent and uniform throughout the same enclosure.

❖ All exit path markings are required to be solid and have continuous stripes. A key requirement for marking systems is that their design must be uniform. The placement and dimensions of markings must be consistent for the path of travel along the exit stairway. By specifying a standard marking dimension, the requirements will provide consistent and standard application in the design and enforcement of exit path markings and ensure that markings are visible during dark conditions. Markings installed on stair steps, perimeter demarcation lines and handrails must have a minimum width of 1 inch (25 mm). For stair steps and perimeter demarcation lines, their maximum width cannot exceed 2 inches (51 mm). The provisions for stair steps, perimeter demarcation lines, handrails and obstructions allow the width of the marking to be reduced to less than 1 inch (25 mm) where marking stripes are listed in accordance with UL 1994.

[BE] 1025.4 Self-luminous and photoluminescent. Luminous egress path markings shall be permitted to be made of any material, including paint, provided that an electrical charge is not required to maintain the required luminance. Such materials shall include, but not be limited to, *self-luminous* materials and *photoluminescent* materials. Materials shall comply with either of the following standards:

1. UL 1994.
2. ASTM E2072, except that the charging source shall be 1 footcandle (11 lux) of fluorescent illumination for 60 minutes, and the minimum luminance shall be 30 milicandelas per square meter at 10 minutes and 5 milicandelas per square meter after 90 minutes.

❖ Products utilized to meet the requirements for luminous egress path markings in high-rise buildings, special amusement buildings (see IBC Section 411.6.1) or exit signs (see Section 1013.5) may be photoluminescent or self-luminous (see definitions in Chapter 2). An example of photoluminescent material is paint or tape that is charged by exposure to light. When the lights are turned off, the product will "glow" in the dark. Self-luminous products do not need an outside light source to charge them like photoluminescent materials do.

A variety of materials can comply with the referenced standards for egress path markings (UL 1994 and ASTM E2072) and for signs (UL 924).

ASTM E2072 allows the use of paints and coatings, which can be useful because it avoids a potential tripping hazard, especially in locations where the surface substrate may not be even. The luminescence of the selected marking system must provide an illumination of 1 footcandle (11 lux) for 60 minutes, which is consistent with the requirement in Section 1008.2.1 for the illumination of walking surfaces. Section 1008.3.4 requires the emergency lighting system to have power for 90 minutes; however, because of normal battery considerations, only a 60-minute duration is required in existing buildings.

[BE] 1025.5 Illumination. Where *photoluminescent* exit path markings are installed, they shall be provided with not less than 1 footcandle (11 lux) of illumination for not less than 60 minutes prior to periods when the building is occupied and continuously during the building occupancy.

❖ Analogous to rechargeable batteries, many photoluminescent egress path markings require exposure to light to perform properly. Thus, photoluminescent egress path markings must be exposed to a minimum 1 footcandle (11 lux) of light energy at the walking surface for at least 60 minutes prior to the building being occupied. The charging rate for photoluminescent egress path markings is based on the wattage of lamps used to provide egress path illumination. Therefore, it is important to verify that the specified lamps have sufficient wattage to meet the specified time period. This requirement may be a concern for buildings developed with the IECC or trying for LEED certification.

Note that this requirement does not apply to self-luminous materials since these materials operate independently of an external power source. See the definitions for "Photoluminescent" and "Self-luminous" in Chapter 2.

SECTION 1026 HORIZONTAL EXITS

[BE] 1026.1 Horizontal exits. *Horizontal exits* serving as an *exit* in a *means of egress* system shall comply with the requirements of this section. A *horizontal exit* shall not serve as the only *exit* from a portion of a building, and where two or more *exits* are required, not more than one-half of the total number of *exits* or total *exit* minimum width or required capacity shall be *horizontal exits*.

Exceptions:

1. *Horizontal exits* are permitted to comprise two-thirds of the required *exits* from any building or floor area for occupancies in Group I-2.
2. *Horizontal exits* are permitted to comprise 100 percent of the *exits* required for occupancies in Group I-3. Not less than 6 square feet (0.6 m^2) of accessible space per occupant shall be provided on each side of the *horizontal exit* for the total number of people in adjoining compartments.

❖ Horizontal exits can provide up to 50 percent of the exits from a given area of a building. The percentage is higher for Group I-2 and I-3 occupancies where the evacuation strategy is defend-in-place rather than direct egress (see Commentary Figure 1026.1 for a typical horizontal exit arrangement). However, a horizontal exit cannot serve as the only exit from a single exit space. Section 1026.4 allows for some areas to have all the exits from a space to be horizontal exits under specific conditions. A horizontal exit can be designed for either one-way or two-way operation, depending on the exiting needs of each side of the wall providing the horizontal exit.

A horizontal exit may be an element of a means of egress where in compliance with the requirements of this section. The actual horizontal exit is the protected door opening in a wall, or the open-air balcony or bridge that separates two areas of a building. A horizontal exit is often used in hospitals and in prisons where it is not feasible or desirable that all occupants exit the facility (see Chapter 2 for the definition of "Horizontal exit").

Horizontal exits and their associated "refuge areas" are considered to provide the same or higher level of protection as an "area of refuge" for people who cannot use the egress system. Sections 1009.3 and 1009.4 allow for a horizontal exit or an area of refuge as alternatives. See these sections for exceptions for buildings with sprinkler systems and/or where the path of travel has protection from the accumulation of smoke (i.e., open parking garages, open-air assembly seating, smoke-protected assembly seating).

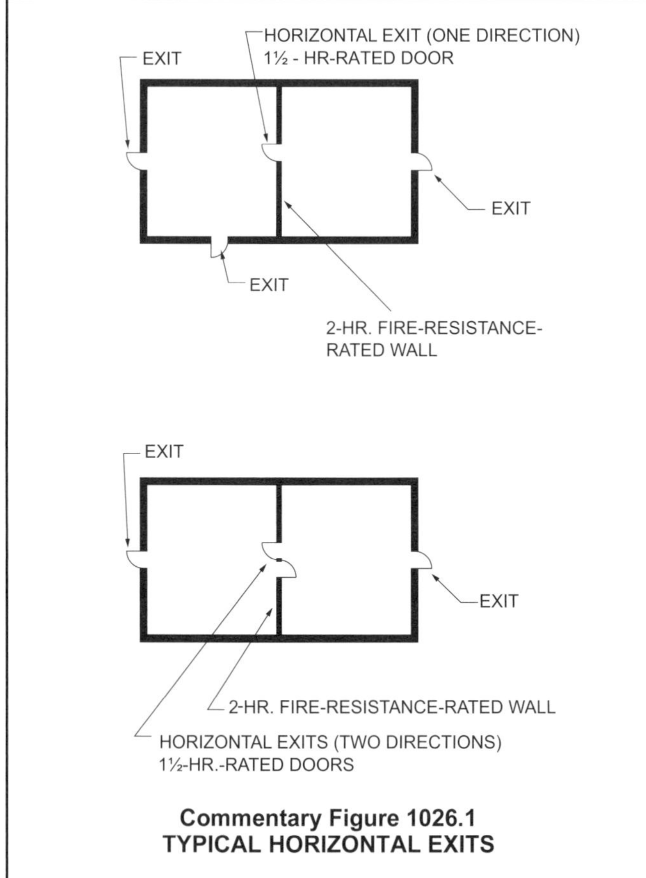

Commentary Figure 1026.1
TYPICAL HORIZONTAL EXITS

[BE] 1026.2 Separation. The separation between buildings or refuge areas connected by a *horizontal exit* shall be provided by a *fire wall* complying with Section 706 of the *International Building Code*; or by a *fire barrier* complying with Section 707 of the *International Building Code* or a *horizontal assembly* complying with Section 711 of the *International Building Code,* or both. The minimum *fire-resistance rating* of the separation shall be 2 hours. Opening protectives in *horizontal exits* shall also comply with Section 716 of the *International Building Code*. Duct and air transfer openings in a *fire wall* or *fire barrier* that serves as a *horizontal exit* shall also comply with Section 717 of the *International Building Code*. The *horizontal exit* separation shall extend vertically through all levels of the building unless floor assemblies have a *fire-resistance rating* of not less than 2 hours and do not have unprotected openings.

Exception: A *fire-resistance rating* is not required at *horizontal exits* between a building area and an above-grade pedestrian walkway constructed in accordance with Section 3104 of the *International Building Code*, provided that the distance between connected buildings is more than 20 feet (6096 mm).

Horizontal exits constructed as *fire barriers* shall be continuous from *exterior wall* to *exterior wall* so as to divide completely the floor served by the *horizontal exit.*

❖ The basic concept of a horizontal exit is that during a fire emergency, the occupants of a floor will transfer from one fire area to another. Separation between areas of a building can be accomplished by a fire wall (see IBC Section 706), a fire barrier (see IBC Section 707), horizontal assemblies (see IBC Section 711) or a combination thereof, with a fire-resistance rating not less than 2 hours. Any fire shutters or fire doors must have an opening protective of not less than $1^1/_2$ hours [see IBC Table 716.1(2)]. Ducts and air transfer openings must comply with IBC Section 717.

In buildings of Groups I-2 and I-3, it may also be desirable (while not mandatory) for the horizontal exit to serve as a smoke barrier. In such cases, the wall containing the horizontal exit must also comply with the requirements for a smoke barrier (see IBC Section 709).

In order to decrease the amount of smoke able to migrate around the edges of a horizontal exit, the horizontal exit must extend from at least the floor to the deck above (i.e., fire barrier), as well as across the floor level from one side of the building to another. Moving up from story to story, there are two choices. One option is that the horizontal exit can extend vertically through all levels of the building (i.e., fire wall or fire barriers). The second option is to utilize fire barriers that are not aligned vertically (i.e., a combination of fire barriers and horizontal assemblies), but then the floor must have a 2-hour fire-resistance rating and no unprotected openings are permitted between any two refuge areas. The supporting construction would also have to be a minimum of 2 hours.

The exception permits a pedestrian walkway or sky bridge to act as a horizontal exit where buildings are at least 20 feet (6096 mm) apart.

[BE] 1026.3 Opening protectives. *Fire doors* in *horizontal exits* shall be self-closing or automatic-closing when activated by a *smoke detector* in accordance with Section 716.2.6.6 of the *International Building Code*. Doors, where located in a cross-corridor condition, shall be automatic-closing by activation of a *smoke detector* installed in accordance with Section 716.2.6.6 of the *International Building Code*.

❖ For the safety of occupants using a horizontal exit, it is important for the doors to be fire doors that are self-closing or automatic-closing by activation of a smoke detector. Smoke detectors that initiate automatic-closing should be located at both sides of the doors. Any openings in the fire barriers or fire walls used as horizontal exits must be protected in coordination with the rating of the wall. There is a reference to IBC Section 716 for opening protectives.

[BE] 1026.4 Refuge area. The refuge area of a *horizontal exit* shall be a space occupied by the same tenant or a public area and each such refuge area shall be adequate to accommodate the original *occupant load* of the refuge area plus the *occupant load* anticipated from the adjoining compartment. The anticipated *occupant load* from the adjoining compartment shall be based on the capacity of the *horizontal exit* doors entering the refuge area, or the total occupant load of the adjoining compartment, whichever is less.

❖ The building area on the discharge side of a horizontal exit must serve as a refuge area for the occupants of both sides of the floor areas connected by the horizontal exit. Therefore, adequate space must be available on each side of the wall to hold the full occupant load of that side, plus the number of occupants from the other side that may be required to use the horizontal exit. Explaining the anticipated occupant load is easiest with an example. If one side of the horizontal exit contained an assembly space with 750 occupants, three exits would be required. If one of the exits through the horizontal exit was a double door, that double exit door would have a capacity of 320 (64 inches/0.2 = 320 occupants). Therefore, the refuge area must be sized for the occupant load in the space, plus the 320 people who might come through the horizontal exit. This is a higher number than would be anticipated if the occupant load of the assembly space was divided equally between the three exits, but it is also not the entire occupant load of the assembly space. If the actual occupant load of the space is less than the capacity of the opening, then the refuge area can be designed for the smaller number. This is the more common scenario for a defend-in-place strategy where the plan is for all occupants from a compartment to be moved into the refuge area, even if there are additional exits in the compartment of origin.

[BE] 1026.4.1 Capacity. The capacity of the refuge area shall be computed based on a net floor area allowance of 3 square feet (0.2787 m^2) for each occupant to be accommodated therein. Where the *horizontal exit* also forms a *smoke compartment*, the capacity of the refuge area for Group I-1, I-2 and I-3 occupancies and Group B *ambulatory care facilities* shall comply with Sections 407.5.3, 408.6.2, 420.6.1 and 422.3.2 of the *International Building Code* as applicable.

❖ These refuge areas are meant to hold the occupants temporarily in a safe place until they can evacuate the premises in an orderly manner or, in the case of hospitals and like facilities, to hold bedridden patients and other nonambulatory occupants in a protected area until the fire emergency has ended. This is commonly referred to as a defend-in-place strategy. The size of the refuge area is based on the nature of the expected occupants. In the case of Group I-3, the area will be used to hold the occupants until deliberate egress can be accomplished with staff assistance or supervision. In other cases, it is assumed that the occupants simply wait in line to egress through the required exit facilities provided on the discharge side. Although similar language is used in describing the "area of refuge" for an accessible means of egress, Section 1009.6 specifies area requirements that are insufficient for use as a "refuge area" for a horizontal exit. Care must be taken where applying both principles to the same horizontal exit.

The requirement for 3 square feet (0.28 m^2) per occupant is based on the maximum permitted occupant density at which orderly movement to the exits is reasonable. For I-1, I-2, I-3 and Group B ambulatory care, there may be additional considerations based on the type of patients or residents that need to be relocated, so a designer needs to go to the referenced sections for refuge area sizing. For example, the requirement for 30 square feet (2.8 m^2) per hospital or nursing home patient is based on the space necessary for a bed or litter. It should be noted that 30 square feet (2.8 m^2) is not based on the total occupant load, as would be determined in accordance with Section 1004.1, but rather on the number of nonambulatory patients. The 15-square-foot (1.4 m^2) requirement for occupancies in Group I-2 facilities is based on each ambulatory patient having a staff attendant.

[BE] 1026.4.2 Number of exits. The refuge area into which a *horizontal exit* leads shall be provided with *exits* adequate to meet the occupant requirements of this chapter, but not including the added *occupant load* imposed by persons entering the refuge area through *horizontal exits* from other areas. Not less than one refuge area *exit* shall lead directly to the exterior or to an *interior exit stairway* or *ramp*.

Exception: The adjoining compartment shall not be required to have a *stairway* or door leading directly outside, provided that the refuge area into which a *hori-*

zontal exit leads has *stairways* or doors leading directly outside and are so arranged that egress shall not require the occupants to return through the compartment from which egress originates.

❖ In a single-tenant facility, any of the spaces that are constantly available (i.e., not lockable) can be used as places of refuge. However, in spaces housing more than one tenant, public refuge areas such as corridors or passageways must be provided and be accessible at all times. This requirement is necessary because if a horizontal exit connects two areas occupied by different tenants, the tenants (for privacy and security purposes) could render the necessary free access through the horizontal exit ineffective. Where the horizontal exit discharges into a public or common space, such as a corridor leading to an exit, each tenant can obtain the desired security.

Note that the capacity of exits (such as an exit stairway) from a refuge area into which a horizontal exit leads is required to be sufficient for the design occupant load of the area, and does not include those who come into the space from other areas via the horizontal exit. This is because the adjacent refuge area is of sufficient safety to house occupants during a fire or until the egress system is available.

The door through the horizontal exit and the second exit must meet the separation requirements in Section 1007.1.1. Measurement of the travel distance stops at the doorway that serves as the horizontal exit. There are no requirements for travel distance from the horizontal exit to the exit (i.e., exterior exit doorway, exit stairway or exit ramp) on the other side; however, the areas on each side need to be evaluated for all means of egress requirements individually.

Where there is one horizontal exit and two fire compartments, at least one exit from each side of the horizontal exit must go directly to the outside or an exit stairway or ramp enclosure (see Commentary Figure 1026.1). The exception allows for a central building/fire area with access to two horizontal exits and no direct exterior exit door or exit stairway/ramp enclosure as long as the refuge area on each side has access to exterior exits or exit stairways/ramps (see Commentary Figure 1026.4.2).

[BE] 1026.5 Standpipes. Standpipes and standpipe hose connections shall be provided where required by Sections 905.3 and 905.4.

❖ Standpipes are required in interior exit stairways and ramps (Section 1023.12), in exit passageways (Section 1024.8) and on each side of horizontal exits (Section 1026.5) in many types of buildings, such as buildings that are four stories or taller, underground buildings, malls, or buildings with heliports or rooftop gardens. This section does not require standpipes, but is intended as a pointer to remind designers that a standpipe may be required by Sections 905.3 and 905.4. Therefore, the areas must be designed to have space for these items without obstructing the path of travel in those areas.

SECTION 1027
EXTERIOR EXIT STAIRWAYS AND RAMPS

[BE] 1027.1 Exterior exit stairways and ramps. *Exterior exit stairways* and *ramps* serving as an element of a required *means of egress* shall comply with this section.

❖ Stairways and ramps can be exit access, exit or exit discharge elements. Exterior exit access and exit discharge stairways and ramps typically involve a change of elevation of less than a story. Exterior exit access stairways or ramps between stories must comply with Section 1019.3 and, where permitted as

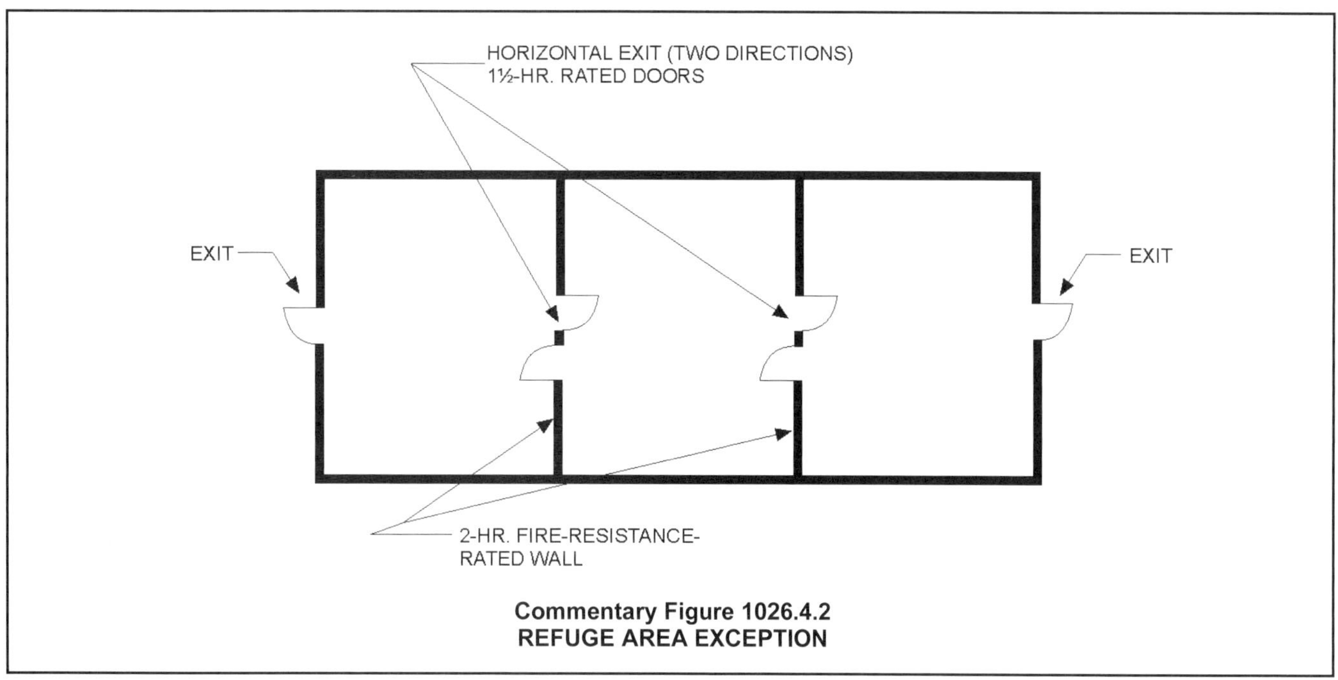

Commentary Figure 1026.4.2
REFUGE AREA EXCEPTION

part of the required means of egress, are limited by Section 1006.3. Exit stairways and ramps traverse a full story or more. Interior exit stairways and ramps must be enclosed in accordance with Section 1023. This section addresses exterior stairways and ramps that function as exit elements.

Exterior exit stairways and ramps are an important element of the means of egress system and must be designed and constructed so that they will serve as a safe path of travel. The general requirements in Section 1011 also apply to exterior stairways (for ramp provisions, see Section 1012).

Outdoor stadiums and open parking garages are examples of buildings that may appear to have exterior exit stairways, but actually have open exit access stairways (Sections 1017, 1019 and 1029).

[BE] 1027.2 Use in a means of egress. *Exterior exit stairways* shall not be used as an element of a required *means of egress* for Group I-2 occupancies. For occupancies in other than Group I-2, *exterior exit stairways* and *ramps* shall be permitted as an element of a required *means of egress* for buildings not exceeding six stories above *grade plane* or that are not *high-rise buildings*.

❖ This section specifies the conditions where exterior exit ramps or stairways can be used as required exits. Exterior exit stairways are not permitted for Group I-2 since quick evacuation of nonambulatory patients from buildings using exterior stairways is impractical. Some patients may not be capable of self-preservation and, therefore, may require assistance from staff. The period of evacuation of nonambulatory patients could become lengthy, especially in bad weather conditions. Note that steps in the exit discharge are not addressed in this requirement.

Exterior stairways or ramps are not allowed to be required exits in buildings that exceed six stories in height because of the hazard of using such a stairway or ramp in poor weather. Some persons may not be willing to use such a stairway due to vertigo. When confronted with a view from a great height, vertigo sufferers can become confused, disoriented and dizzy. They could injure themselves, become disoriented or refuse to move (freeze). In a fire situation, they could become an obstruction in the path of travel, possibly causing panic and injuries to other users of the exit.

[BE] 1027.3 Open side. *Exterior exit stairways* and *ramps* serving as an element of a required *means of egress* shall be open on not less than one side, except for required structural columns, beams, handrails and guards. An open side shall have not less than 35 square feet (3.3 m^2) of aggregate open area adjacent to each floor level and the level of each intermediate landing. The required open area shall be located not less than 42 inches (1067 mm) above the adjacent floor or landing level.

❖ An important factor in exterior exit stairways or ramps is natural ventilation. Sufficient natural ventilation is necessary so that smoke will not be trapped above the stairway or ramp walking surfaces, thereby compromising safe egress.

The exterior exit stairway or ramp must have at least one of its sides directly facing an outer court, yard or public way. This will allow the products of combustion escaping from the interior of the building to quickly vent to the outdoor atmosphere and let the building occupants egress down the exterior exit stairway or ramp. Since exterior exit stairways or ramps are partially bounded by exterior walls, a minimum amount of exterior openness is specified by the code.

The openings on each and every floor level and landing must total 35 square feet (3.3 m^2) or greater. The openings for which credit is given must occur higher than 42 inches (1067 mm) above each floor and intermediate landing level. [The bottom edge of the opening is consistent with the height requirements for guards (see Section 1015.3)]. With a standard 8-foot (2438 mm) ceiling height minus the 42-inch-high (1067 mm) guard and a typical 8-foot-wide (2438 mm) opening, the result would be $4^1/_2$ feet x 8 feet = 36 square feet (3.34 m^2). Openings of this height and area readily dissipate the smoke buildup from the exterior exit stairway or ramp (see Commentary Figure 1027.3).

[BE] 1027.4 Side yards. The open areas adjoining *exterior exit stairways* or *ramps* shall be either *yards*, *courts* or *public ways*; the remaining sides are permitted to be enclosed by the *exterior walls* of the building.

❖ This section simply specifies the type of areas that the exterior opening of the exterior exit stairway or ramp is to adjoin. These open spaces will enable the smoke to dissipate from the exterior exit stairway or ramp so it will be usable as a required exit. See Section 1027.3 for a discussion of the opening requirements. See Sections 1027.5 and 1205 for the minimum sizes of yards and courts.

[BE] 1027.5 Location. *Exterior exit stairways* and *ramps* shall have a minimum fire separation distance of 10 feet (3048 mm) measured at right angles from the exterior edge of the stairway or ramps, including landings, to:

1. Adjacent *lot lines*.
2. Other portions of the building.
3. Other buildings on the same lot unless the adjacent building *exterior walls* and openings are protected in accordance with Section 705 of the *International Building Code* based on fire separation distance.

For the purposes of this section, other portions of the building shall be treated as separate buildings.

Exception: Exterior exit stairways and ramps serving individual dwelling units of Group R-3 shall have a fire separation distance of not less than 5 feet (1524 mm).

❖ The location requirements of this section protect the users of the exterior exit stairway or ramp from the effects of a fire in another building on the same lot or an adjacent lot. The separation distance reduces the exposure to heat and smoke. If the exterior exit stairway or ramp is closer than specified, then adjacent buildings' exterior walls and openings are to be protected in accordance with IBC Section 705 so that the users of the exterior exit stairway or ramp are protected. The reason for a minimum required distance to a lot line is to provide for a future building that could be built on an adjacent lot. While buildings on the same lot can be considered one building for height and area limitations (see IBC Section 503.1.2), they must be separated by a minimum of 10 feet (3048 mm) if there is a path for exit discharge between them. The purpose of the last sentence is to clarify that an exterior exit stairway or ramp needs a minimum 10-foot separation where a building wraps around on itself, such as a U-shaped building. It is not intended that the distance be measured to an imaginary lot line between buildings on the same lot.

Requirements are the same for exterior egress balconies (Section 1021.4). For an illustration of exterior egress balconies and exterior exit stairways working together, see Commentary Figure 1027.5.

The exception for Group R-3 is to be consistent with similar types of units constructed under the IRC.

[BE] 1027.6 Exterior exit stairway and ramp protection. *Exterior exit stairways* and *ramps* shall be separated from the interior of the building as required in Section 1023.2. Openings shall be limited to those necessary for egress from normally occupied spaces. Where a vertical plane projecting from the edge of an *exterior exit stairway* or *ramp* and landings is exposed by other parts of the building at an angle of less than 180 degrees (3.14 rad), the *exterior wall* shall be rated in accordance with Section 1023.7.

Exceptions:

1. Separation from the interior of the building is not required for occupancies, other than those in Group R-1 or R-2, in buildings that are not more than two stories above grade plane where a *level of exit discharge* serving such occupancies is the first story above grade plane.
2. Separation from the interior of the building is not required where the *exterior exit stairway* or *ramp* is

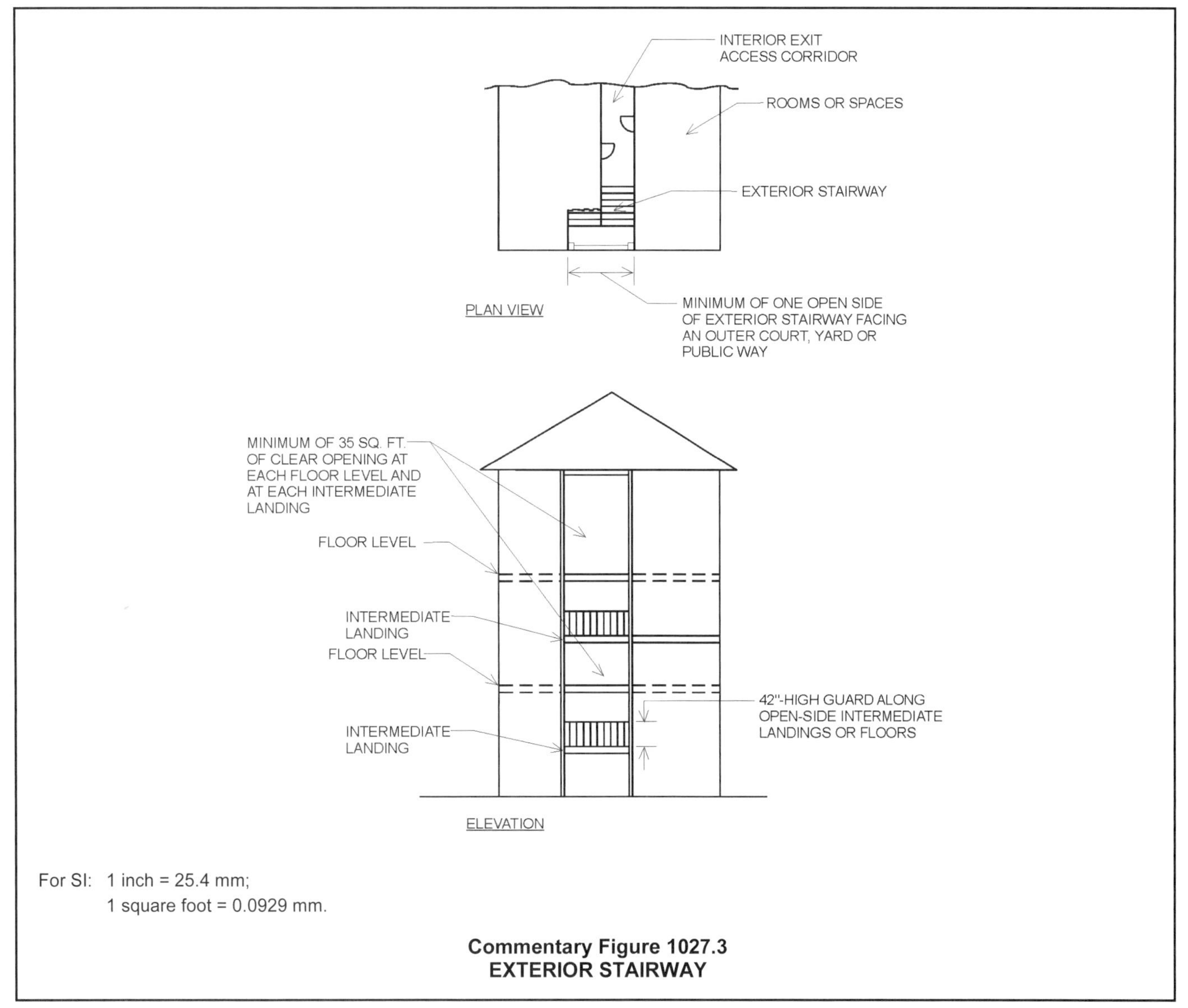

Commentary Figure 1027.3
EXTERIOR STAIRWAY

served by an *exterior exit ramp* or balcony that connects two remote *exterior exit stairways* or other approved *exits*, with a perimeter that is not less than 50 percent open. To be considered open, the opening shall be not less than 50 percent of the height of the enclosing wall, with the top of the openings not less than 7 feet (2134 mm) above the top of the balcony.

3. Separation from the *open-ended corridor* of the building is not required for *exterior exit stairways* or *ramps*, provided that Items 3.1 through 3.5 are met:

    3.1. The building, including *open-ended corridors*, and *stairways* and *ramps*, shall be equipped throughout with an *automatic sprinkler system* in accordance with Section 903.3.1.1 or 903.3.1.2.

    3.2. The *open-ended corridors* comply with Section 1020.

    3.3. The *open-ended corridors* are connected on each end to an *exterior exit stairway* or *ramp* complying with Section 1027.

    3.4. The *exterior walls* and openings adjacent to the *exterior exit stairway* or *ramp* comply with Section 1023.7.

    3.5. At any location in an *open-ended corridor* where a change of direction exceeding 45 degrees (0.79 rad) occurs, a clear opening of not less than 35 square feet (3.3 m^2) or an exterior *stairway* or *ramp* shall be provided. Where clear openings are provided, they shall be located so as to minimize the accumulation of smoke or toxic gases.

4. In Group R-3 occupancies not more than four stories in height, *exterior exit stairways* and *ramps* serving individual *dwelling units* are not required to be separated from the interior of the building where the *exterior exit stairway* or *ramp* discharges directly to grade.

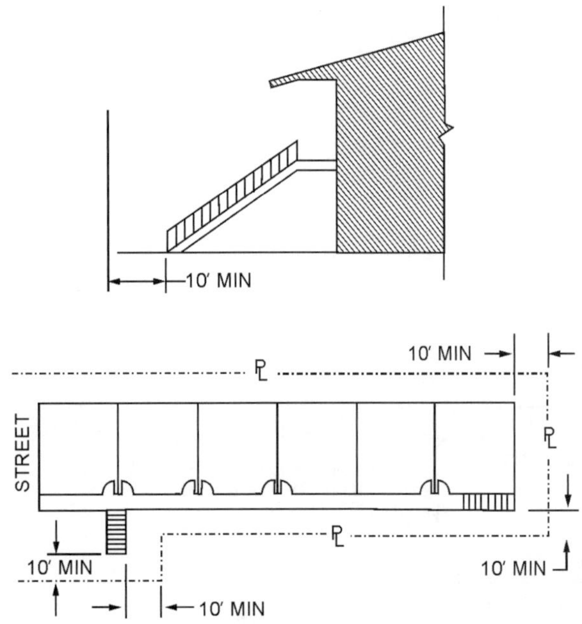

For SI: 1 foot = 304.8 mm.

Commentary Figure 1027.5
EXTERIOR BALCONY AND STAIRWAY ADJACENT TO LOT LINE

❖ Exterior exit stairways or ramps must be protected from interior fires that may project through windows or other openings adjacent to the exit stairway or ramp, possibly endangering the occupants using this means of egress to reach grade. The protection of an exterior exit stairway or ramp is to be obtained by separating the exterior exit from the interior of the building using exterior walls having a fire-resistance rating of at least 1 hour with opening protectives. If the exterior exit stairway connects four or more stories, the wall between the stairway and the inside of the building must have a fire-resistance rating of 2 hours (see Section 1023.2). Consistent with the protection required in Sections 1023.2 and 1023.7 for interior exit stairways, the fire-resistance rating must be provided for a distance of 10 feet (3048 mm) horizontally and vertically from the ramp or stairway edges, and from the ground to a level of 10 feet (3048 mm) above the highest landing.

All window and door openings within the adjacent 10-foot (3048 mm) distance must be protected with minimum $^3/_4$-hour fire-protection-rated opening protectives [see Commentary Figure 1027.6(1)]. The last sentence is similar to Section 1023.7 except that instead of measuring the angle between the building exterior walls and the unprotected walls at the exterior of the stairway or ramp, the measurement is between the building exterior walls and a vertical projection for the planes of the guard of the exterior stairway and ramp including landings.

Openings within the exterior wall between the inside of the building and the stairway must only be from normally occupied spaces. This is consistent with the requirements for interior exit enclosures (see Sections 1023.4 and 1023.5).

Exception 1 indicates that the exterior wall is not required to be rated for occupancies (other than Groups R-1 and R-2) that are two stories or less above grade where the level of exit discharge is at the lower story. The reason for this exception is that in cases of fire in low buildings, the occupants are usually able to evacuate the premises before the fire can emerge through exterior wall openings and endanger the exterior exit ramp or stairways. In hotels and apartments, however, the occupants' response to a fire emergency could be significantly reduced because they may be either unfamiliar with the surroundings or sleeping.

Exception 2 allows the exterior wall is not required to be rated where an exterior egress balcony is served by two exits and where the exits are remote from each other. Remoteness is regulated by Section 1007. This exception is applicable to all groups. In such instances, it is unlikely that the users of the exterior stairway or ramp will become trapped by fire, since they have the option of using the open balcony to gain access to either of the two available exits, and the products of combustion will be vented directly to the outside (see Section 1021 regarding egress balconies). At least one-half of the total perimeter of the egress balcony must be permanently open to the outside. The requirement for at least one-half the height of that level to be open allows for columns, solid guards and architectural or decorative elements, such as arches. With the top of the opening at least 7 feet (2134 mm) above the walking surface, products of combustion can vent, allowing occupant passage below the smoke layer [see Commentary Figures 1021.2 and 1027.6(2)].

"Open-ended corridor" is defined in Chapter 2, but another common term used for this arrangement is "breezeway." The breezeway may need to be rated as a corridor in accordance with Table 1020.1. However, Exception 3 deletes the requirement for a separation (both rated wall and opening protective) between the breezeway and the exterior exit stairway where the two elements meet. In other words, a door is not required between the open exterior stairway and the breezeway. There are additional safety requirements. An NFPA 13 or 13R sprinkler system is required in all areas of the building, including the breezeway. The

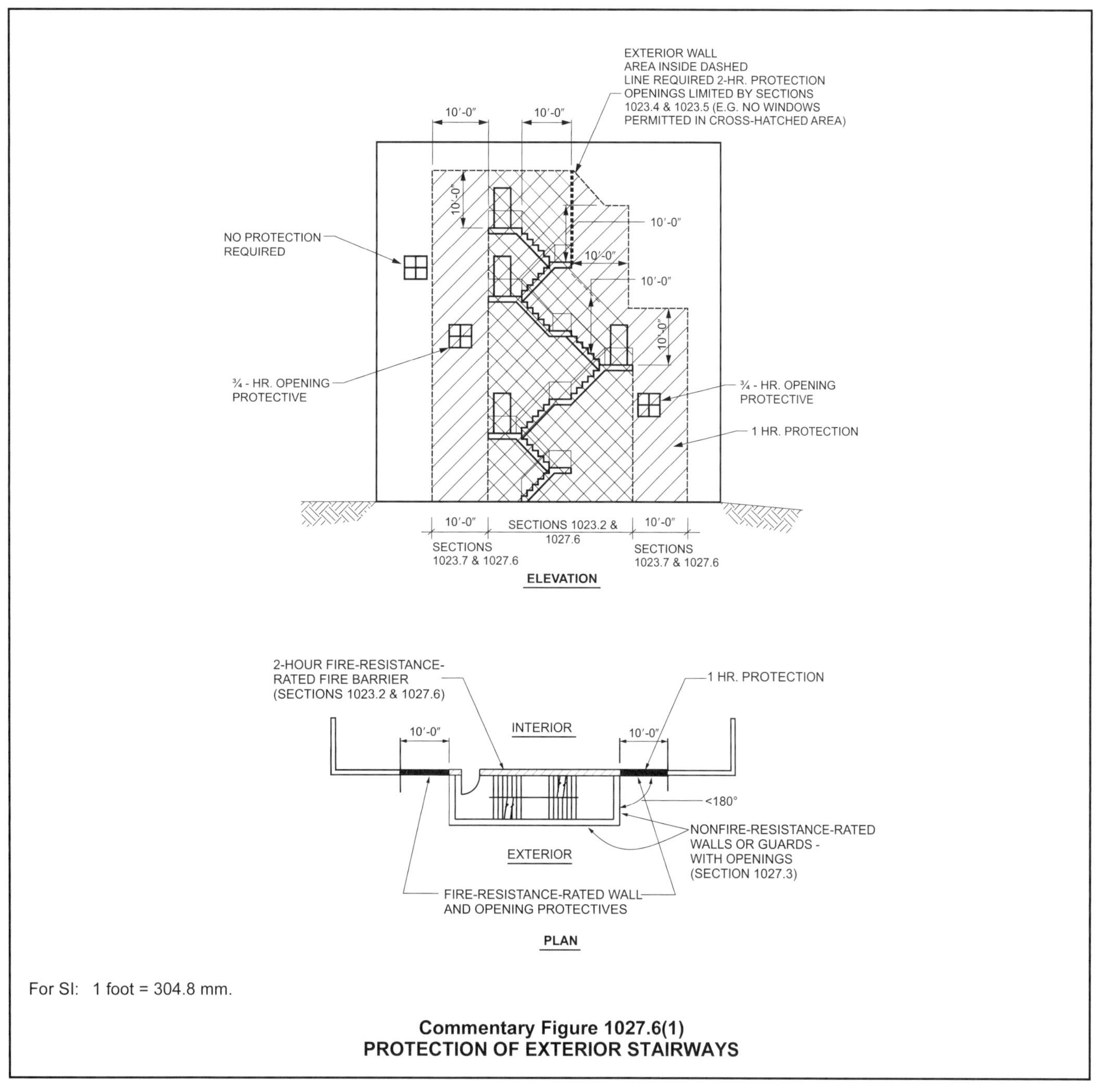

Commentary Figure 1027.6(1)
PROTECTION OF EXTERIOR STAIRWAYS

arrangements must allow for adequate cross ventilation of the breezeway so that smoke will not accumulate [see Commentary Figure 1027.6(3)]. The reference to Section 1023.7 results in any exterior walls, either directly between the exit stairway and the building or any walls that form an angle less than 180 degrees (3.14 rad) from the side of the exterior exit stairway, being protected for a distance of 10 feet (3048 mm) [see Commentary Figure 1027.6(3)]. Exit access travel distance on an open-ended corridor is measured to the first riser of an exterior stair or the beginning slope of an exterior ramp.

Section 1006.3.1, Exceptions 1 and 2, and Section 1019.3, Conditions 2 and 3, allow for open exit access stairways within Group R-3 and R-4 facilities. For consistency, per Exception 4 of this section, the exterior wall is not required to be rated between individual dwelling units and an exterior exit stairway serving them.

Separation language for exterior exit stairways is used in describing the exterior wall requirements for an exterior area for assisted rescue that is provided at an exit located on the level of exit discharge. However, steps leading from the exterior area of assisted rescue are part of the exit discharge, not exterior exit stairways as addressed in this section.

SECTION 1028
EXIT DISCHARGE

[BE] 1028.1 General. *Exits* shall discharge directly to the exterior of the building. The *exit discharge* shall be at grade or shall provide a direct path of egress travel to grade. The *exit discharge* shall not reenter a building. The combined use of Exceptions 1 and 2 shall not exceed 50 percent of the number and minimum width or required capacity of the required *exits*.

Exceptions:

1. Not more than 50 percent of the number and minimum width or required capacity of *interior exit stairways* and *ramps* is permitted to egress through areas on the *level of discharge* provided that all of the following conditions are met:
    - 1.1. Discharge of *interior exit stairways* and *ramps* shall be provided with a free and unobstructed path of travel to an *exterior exit* door and such *exit* is readily visible and identifiable from the point of termination of the enclosure.
    - 1.2. The entire area of the *level of exit discharge* is separated from areas below by construction conforming to the *fire-resistance rating* for the enclosure.
    - 1.3. The egress path from the *interior exit stairway* and *ramp* on the *level of exit discharge* is protected throughout by an *approved automatic sprinkler system*. Portions of the *level of exit discharge* with access to the egress path shall either be equipped throughout with an *automatic sprinkler system* installed in accordance with Section 903.3.1.1 or 903.3.1.2, or separated from the egress path in accordance with the requirements for the enclosure of *interior exit stairways* or *ramps*.
    - 1.4. Where a required *interior exit stairway* or *ramp* and an *exit access stairway* or *ramp* serve the same floor level and terminate at the same *level of exit discharge*, the termination of the *exit access stairway* or *ramp* and the exit discharge door of the *interior exit stairway* or *ramp* shall be separated by a distance of not less than 30 feet (9144 mm) or not less than one-fourth the length of the maximum overall diagonal dimension of the building, whichever is less. The distance shall be measured in a straight line between the exit discharge door from the *interior exit stairway* or ramp and the last tread of the *exit access stairway* or termination of slope of the *exit access ramp*.
2. Not more than 50 percent of the number and minimum width or required capacity of the interior *exit stairways* and *ramps* is permitted to egress through a vestibule provided that all of the following conditions are met:
    - 2.1. The entire area of the vestibule is separated from areas below by construction conforming to the *fire-resistance rating* of the *interior exit stairway* or *ramp* enclosure.
    - 2.2. The depth from the exterior of the building is not greater than 10 feet (3048 mm) and the length is not greater than 30 feet (9144 mm).
    - 2.3. The area is separated from the remainder of the *level of exit discharge* by a *fire partition* constructed in accordance with Section 708 of the *International* Building Code.

        Exception: The maximum transmitted temperature rise is not required.
    - 2.4. The area is used only for *means of egress* and *exits* directly to the outside.
3. *Horizontal exits* complying with Section 1026 shall not be required to discharge directly to the exterior of the building.

❖ The exit discharge is the third part of the means of egress system, which includes exit access, exit and exit discharge. The general provisions for means of egress in Sections 1003 through 1015 are applicable to the exit discharge. The basic provision is that exits must discharge directly to the outside of the building. The exit discharge is the path from the termination of the exit to the public way. Where it is not practical to

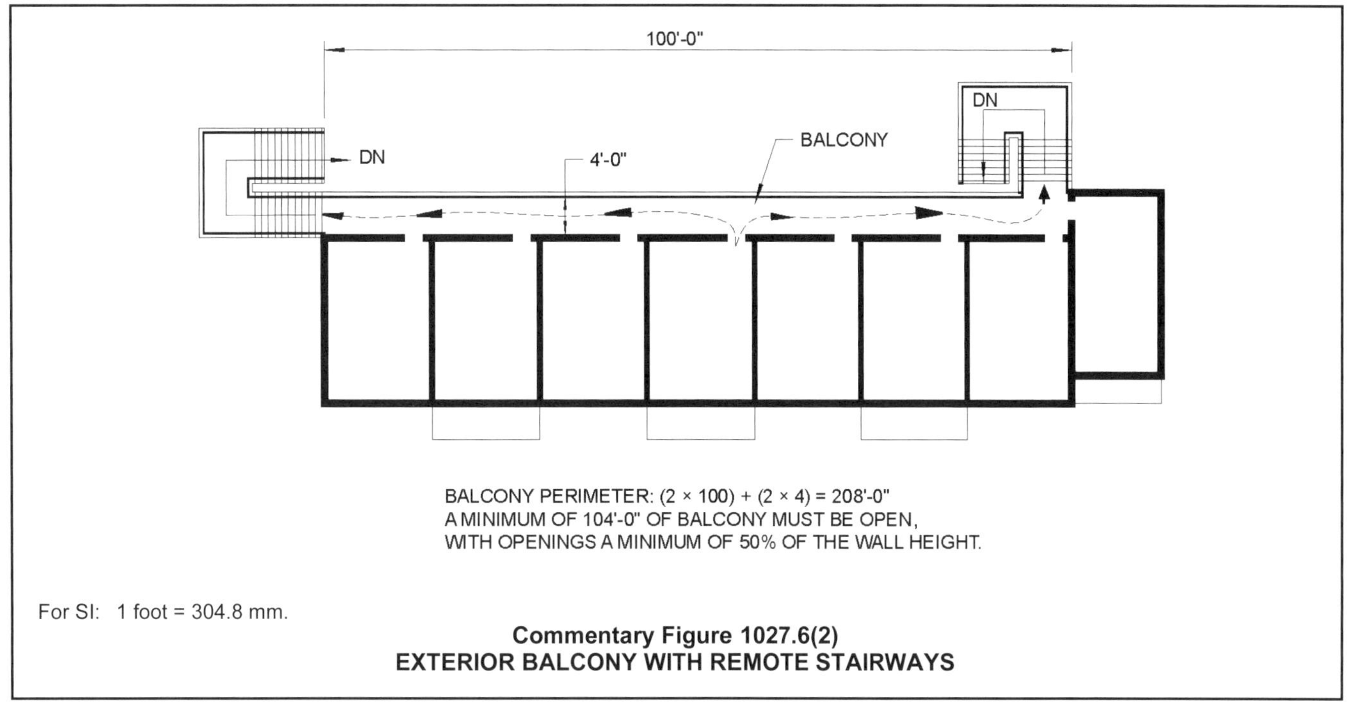

100'-0"
DN
DN
4'-0"
BALCONY
BALCONY PERIMETER: (2 × 100) + (2 × 4) = 208'-0"
A MINIMUM OF 104'-0" OF BALCONY MUST BE OPEN,
WITH OPENINGS A MINIMUM OF 50% OF THE WALL HEIGHT.

For SI: 1 foot = 304.8 mm.

Commentary Figure 1027.6(2)
EXTERIOR BALCONY WITH REMOTE STAIRWAYS

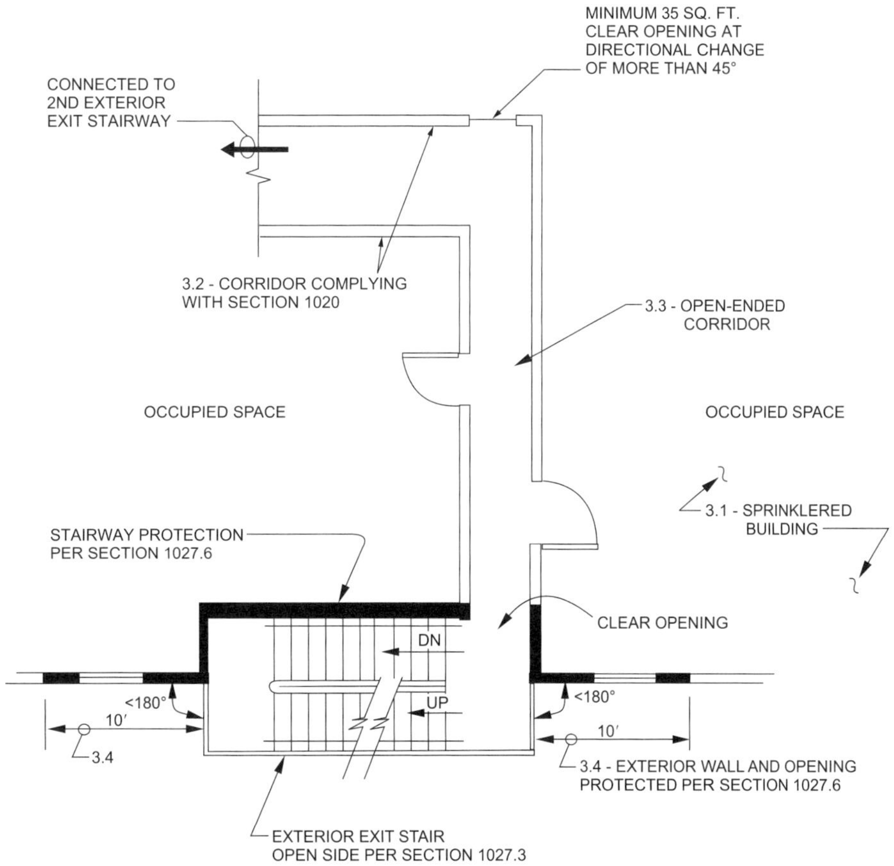

MINIMUM 35 SQ. FT. CLEAR OPENING AT DIRECTIONAL CHANGE OF MORE THAN 45°
CONNECTED TO 2ND EXTERIOR EXIT STAIRWAY
3.2 - CORRIDOR COMPLYING WITH SECTION 1020
3.3 - OPEN-ENDED CORRIDOR
OCCUPIED SPACE
OCCUPIED SPACE
3.1 - SPRINKLERED BUILDING
STAIRWAY PROTECTION PER SECTION 1027.6
CLEAR OPENING
DN
UP
<180°
<180°
10′
10′
3.4
3.4 - EXTERIOR WALL AND OPENING PROTECTED PER SECTION 1027.6
EXTERIOR EXIT STAIR OPEN SIDE PER SECTION 1027.3

For SI: 1 foot = 304.8 mm.

Commentary Figure 1027.6(3)
EXAMPLE OF EXCEPTION 3

discharge directly to the outside, there are four alternatives: an exit passageway (see Section 1024), an exit discharge lobby (see Section 1028.1, Exception 1), an exit discharge vestibule (see Section 1028.1, Exception 2) or a horizontal exit (see Section 1026 and Section 1028.1, Exception 3). While Exceptions 1 and 2 could be applicable to exit passageways and exit ramps, they are most often applied to exit stairways. Most of the commentary for Section 1028 will be limited to interior exit stairways that are enclosed in accordance with Section 1023. See Sections 1006, 1019.3 and 1028.1, Item 1.4, for exit access stairway requirements. Up to 50 percent of the interior exit stairways in a building may use either Exception 1 or 2; therefore, neither exception is viable for a single-exit building. In a two- or three-exit building, either a lobby, a vestibule or a horizontal exit can be used for exit discharge for one of the exit stairways. In a four-exit building, two of the exit stairways can use either a lobby, a vestibule or a horizontal exit for exit discharge.

An interior exit discharge lobby is permitted to receive the discharge from an exit stairway in lieu of the stairway discharging directly to the exterior. A fire door must be provided at the point where the exit stairway discharges into the lobby. Without an opening protective between the stairway and the lobby, it would be possible for the stairway to be directly exposed to smoke movement from a fire in the lobby. The opening protective provides for full continuity of the vertical component of the exit arrangement. Additionally, in buildings where stair towers must be pressurized, pressurization would not be possible without a door at the lobby level.

An exit discharge lobby is the sole location recognized in the code where an exit element can be used for purposes other than pedestrian travel for means of egress. The lobby may contain furniture or decoration, and nonoccupiable spaces may open directly into the lobby. The lobby, and all other areas on the same level that are not separated from the lobby by fire barriers consistent with the rating of the stair enclosure, must be sprinklered in accordance with an NFPA 13 or 13R system [see Commentary Figure 1028.1(1)]. If the entire level is sprinklered, no separation is required. In this case, the automatic sprinkler system is anticipated to control and (perhaps) eliminate the fire threat so as not to jeopardize the path of egress of the occupants. The lobby floor and any supporting construction must be rated the same as the stairway enclosure. If the lobby is slab on grade, this requirement is not applicable. This is consistent with the fundamental concept that an exit enclosure provides the necessary level of protection from adjacent areas. A path of travel through the lobby must be continually clear and available. The exit door leading out of the building must be visible and identifiable immediately when a person leaves the exit. This does not mean the exterior exit door must be directly in front of the door at the bottom of the stairway, but the intent is that it should be within the general range of vision. A person should not have to turn completely around or go around a corner to be able to see the way out.

Item 1.4 addresses where an exit access stairway and an exit stairway both discharge into the same lobby on the ground floor. For example, many hotels have meeting rooms on the level immediately above the lobby. This heavier occupant load, or circulation considerations, may result in an exit access stairway coming down from that second level into the same lobby that is being used for discharge from the upper floors for one of the required exit stairways. This limitation for a 30-foot (9144 mm) separation is to prevent an exit access stairway and an exit stairway from terminating too close together on the level of exit discharge. The intent is that one localized fire event in the lobby will not jeopardize the use of both means of egress components. The separation distances of 30 feet (9144 mm) or one-fourth of the overall diagonal are based on the requirements for separation of interior stairways in a high-rise building (see Section 403.5.1). This measurement is taken only at the bottom of the exit access stairway and the door to the exit enclosure. It is not required to be maintained the entire length of the stairway as required for two exit access stairways in Section 1007.1.3. The enclosure of the exit stairway offers sufficient separation protection. This is assuming that both the exit access stairway and the exit stairway are serving as required means of egress from the second level. With the limit of 50 percent of exit stairways using this exception, a third means of egress provided by an enclosed exit stairway discharging to the exterior would be required.

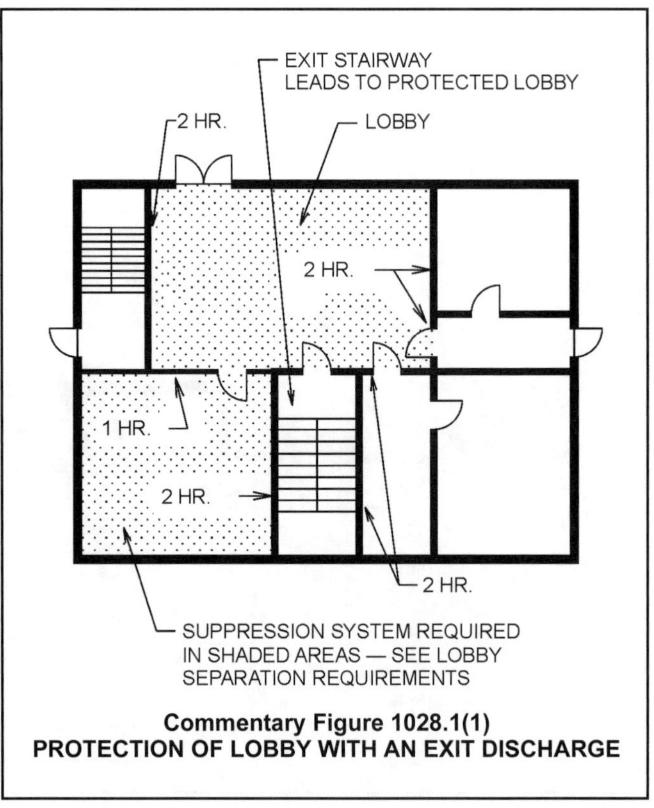

Commentary Figure 1028.1(1)
PROTECTION OF LOBBY WITH AN EXIT DISCHARGE

An exit is also allowed to discharge through a vestibule, provided it complies with the specified requirements of Exception 2. Vestibules utilizing this provision are not to be used for other purposes, such as access to closets, furniture/seating, drinking fountains, vending machines, and so on. The vestibule floor and any supporting construction must be rated the same as the stairway enclosure. If the vestibule is slab on grade, this requirement is not applicable. The size of the vestibule is limited so that it cannot be used for other activities, and the travel distance from the exit stairway to the exterior exit doorway is limited [see Commentary Figures 1028.1(2) and 1028.1(3)]. The interior walls of the vestibule must be constructed as fire partitions with a fire-protection rating of at least 1 hour. Section 708 does not reference a specific test standard for fire partitions. As such, fire partitions must comply with ASTM E119 or UL 263 per Section 703.2 (see Section 703.2 for additional commentary on the tests). ASTM E119 and UL 263 have a transmission of heat criterion for nonbearing partitions to be considered as having passed the test. The exception exempts fire partitions for the separation of a vestibule from having to comply with the transmission of heat criterion. Glass panels set in a metal frame can be used for the vestibule as long as they meet the rest of the ASTM E119 criteria.

Exception 3 acknowledges that horizontal exits offer refuge areas that will have access to an exit on the other side; therefore, a stairway that exits through a horizontal exit is not required to exit to the exterior. Many hospitals and correctional facilities use horizontal exits to defend in place rather than require an immediate building evacuation. There are exit stairways or exits available from the refuge areas, so occupants can move to the outside if needed (see Section 1026 for additional information).

[BE] 1028.2 Exit discharge width or capacity. The minimum width or required capacity of the *exit discharge* shall be not less than the minimum width or required capacity of the *exits* being served.

❖ This section specifies the exit discharge width based on minimum width and the number of occupants exiting (capacity). The exit discharge is required to be designed for the occupants from all of the exits it serves so there is not a bottleneck in the path of travel. If the exit discharge serves two exits, it is to be designed for the sum of the occupants served by both exits. Note that the capacity of the exit discharge is not required to match the total provided capacity of both exits, which is typically higher than the sum of the occupants served by both exits.

[BE] 1028.3 Exit discharge components. *Exit discharge* components shall be sufficiently open to the exterior so as to minimize the accumulation of smoke and toxic gases.

❖ An exit discharge component could be a large open space where occupants could discharge in a number of different directions or it could be limited to a narrower path by landscaping or walls (i.e., egress court). In all cases, the space must be open enough to the outside that smoke and fumes will vent upward and away from occupants evacuating the building.

EXIT STAIR LEADS TO A VESTIBULE

30′ MAX.

10′ MAX.

VESTIBULE ENCLOSURE [SEE FIGURE 1028.1(3)]

For SI: 1 foot = 304.8 mm.

Commentary Figure 1028.1(2)
VESTIBULE WITH EXIT DISCHARGE

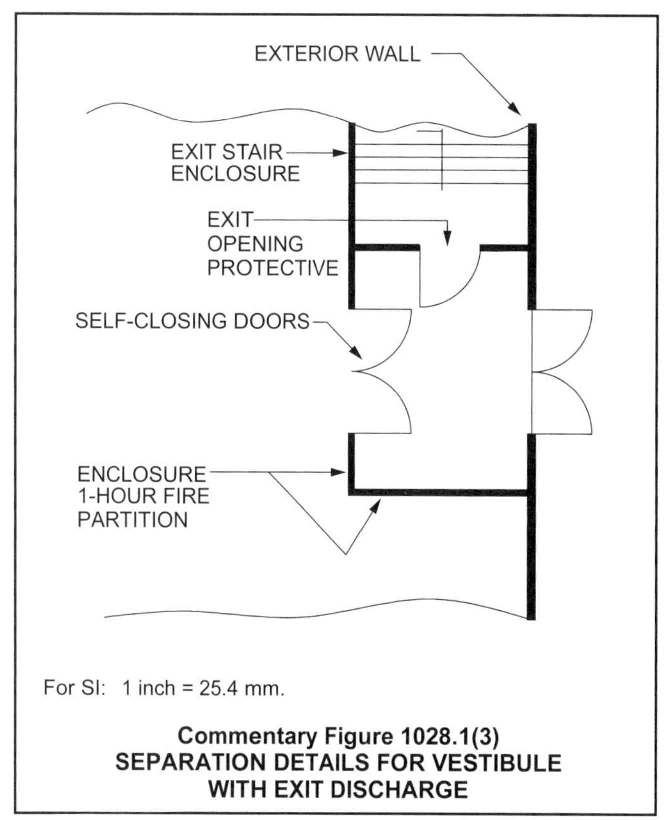

For SI: 1 inch = 25.4 mm.

Commentary Figure 1028.1(3)
SEPARATION DETAILS FOR VESTIBULE WITH EXIT DISCHARGE

[BE] 1028.4 Egress courts. *Egress courts* serving as a portion of the *exit discharge* in the *means of egress* system shall comply with the requirements of Sections 1028.4.1 and 1028.4.2.

❖ A portion of the exit discharge that is partially confined by exterior walls or other elements that confine the discharge path to a single narrow route is regulated as an egress court.

This section and the following subsections address the detailed requirements for egress courts. It is essential that exterior egress courts conveying occupants from an exit to a public way be sufficiently open to prevent the accumulation of smoke and toxic gases in the event of a fire as well as wide enough to accommodate the number of occupants leaving in that direction.

See IBC Section 1205 for additional minimum width and openness requirements where yards and courts are needed for natural light or ventilation.

[BE] 1028.4.1 Width or capacity. The required capacity of *egress courts* shall be determined as specified in Section 1005.1, but the minimum width shall be not less than 44 inches (1118 mm), except as specified herein. *Egress courts* serving Group R-3 and U occupancies shall be not less than 36 inches (914 mm) in width. The required capacity and width of *egress courts* shall be unobstructed to a height of 7 feet (2134 mm).

The width of the *egress court* shall be not less than the required capacity.

Exception: Encroachments complying with Section 1005.7.

❖ The width of an exterior court is to be determined in the same fashion as for an interior corridor. The width is to be not less than that required to serve the number of occupants from the exit or exits and not less than the minimum specified in this section (see also IBC Section 1205). The width of the court and any openings through barriers around the court must be sufficient to accommodate the number of occupants leaving the building so that the court will not become a bottleneck for the egress path.

A cross reference to Section 1005.7 in the exceptions for width in aisles (see Section 1018.1), corridors (see Section 1020.3), exit passageways (see Section 1024.2) and exit courts (see Section 1028.4.1) reinforces the fact that the protrusion limits provision is generally applicable for these types of confined routes.

[BE] 1028.4.2 Construction and openings. Where an *egress court* serving a building or portion thereof is less than 10 feet (3048 mm) in width, the *egress court* walls shall have not less than 1-hour fire-resistance-rated construction for a distance of 10 feet (3048 mm) above the floor of the *egress court*. Openings within such walls shall be protected by opening protectives having a fire protection rating of not less than $^3/_4$ hour.

Exceptions:

1. *Egress courts* serving an *occupant load* of less than 10.
2. *Egress courts* serving Group R-3.

❖ The purpose of this section is to protect the occupants served by the egress court from the building that they are exiting. If occupants must walk closely by the exterior walls of the court, the walls are required to have the specified fire-resistance rating and the openings are required to be protected as specified. This requirement is only for the first 10 feet (3048 mm) above the level of the egress court since the exposure hazard from walls and openings above 10 feet (3048 mm) is reduced. The two exceptions provide for egress courts that serve a very low number of occupants and the specified residential occupancy where the protection requirement would be located.

[BE] 1028.5 Access to a public way. The *exit discharge* shall provide a direct and unobstructed access to a *public way*.

Exception: Where access to a *public way* cannot be provided, a safe dispersal area shall be provided where all of the following are met:

1. The area shall be of a size to accommodate *not less than* 5 square feet (0.46 m^2) for each person.
2. The area shall be located on the same lot not less than 50 feet (15 240 mm) away from the building requiring egress.
3. The area shall be permanently maintained and identified as a safe dispersal area.
4. The area shall be provided with a safe and unobstructed path of travel from the building.

❖ There are instances where the path of travel to the public way is not safe or not achievable because of site constraints or security concerns. The provisions in this section specify what would constitute a safe area to allow occupants of a building to assemble in an emergency. The requirement of 5 square feet (0.46 m^2) would allow adequate space for standing persons as well as some space for persons in wheelchairs or on stretchers. Everyone who is expected to wait in this dispersal area for fire department assistance must be a minimum of 50 feet (15 240 mm) away from the building. This refuge must always remain open and not be used for parking, storage or temporary structures. A safe dispersal area is commonly found at schools or jails. Stadiums are more specifically addressed in Section 1010.2.1. Walls or fences may surround the building and part of the site due to other safety concerns. These walls and fences could stop occupants from reaching the public way.

SECTION 1029 ASSEMBLY

[BE] 1029.1 General. A room or space used for assembly purposes that contains seats, tables, displays, equipment or other material shall comply with this section.

❖ Any room that is used for assembly purposes, regardless of the occupancy of the rest of the building, must comply with this section. Spaces used for assembly seating may appear in buildings of other occupancy types; for example, a library in a school or a meeting room in an office building. This includes spaces with less than 50 occupants in other occupancies. For evaluation of the occupant load and the means of egress in these spaces, these spaces are regulated based on their function rather than their occupancy group.

Although most of the provisions in Section 1029 focus on fixed seating auditoriums or theaters, this section also addresses loose seats, tables, displays, equipment, and so on. Rooms or spaces used for assembly purposes contain elements that would affect the path of travel for the means of egress. These spaces require special consideration because of the larger occupant loads and possible low lighting (e.g., nightclubs, theaters), which can possibly lead to slower fire recognition or crowd concerns.

Since this section is extensive, here is a basic breakdown:

- Sections 1029.1.1 and 1029.1.1.1 deal with bleachers and grandstands.
- Sections 1029.2 through 1029.5 deal with number and dispersement of exits.
- Section 1029.6 and subsections discuss aisle widths based on the required capacity.
- Sections 1029.7 and 1029.8 are for travel distances and aisle accessways.
- Sections 1029.9, 1029.10 and 1029.11 deal with where aisles are required, minimum widths and layouts. This includes provisions for where stairways are a direct continuation of stepped aisles or transitions.
- Section 1029.12 discusses types of materials and walking surfaces.
- Section 1029.13 covers aisle accessways that lead to main aisles as they move through tables (Section 1029.13.1) and seating in rows (Section 1029.13.2).
- Section 1029.14 deals with slope, landings and edge protection for ramped aisles (Sections 1029.14.1 through 1029.14.1.3) as well as treads and risers for stepped aisles (Sections 1029.14.2 through 1029.14.2.4).
- Section 1029.15 discusses where seating needs to be fastened to the floor in order for aisles and accessways to be maintained.
- Section 1029.16 includes handrail provisions for ramped and stepped aisles.
- Section 1029.17 states where guards are required.

[BE] 1029.1.1 Bleachers. *Bleachers*, *grandstands* and *folding and telescopic seating*, that are not building elements, shall comply with ICC 300.

❖ On February 24, 1999, the Bleacher Safety Act of 1999 was introduced in the House of Representatives. The bill, which cites the ICC and the code, authorized the US Consumer Product Safety Commission (CPSC) to issue a standard for bleacher safety. This was in response to concerns relative to accidents on bleacher-type structures. As a result, the CPSC developed and revised the *Guidelines for Retrofitting Bleachers*. The ICC Board of Directors decided that a comprehensive standard dealing with all aspects of both new and existing bleachers was warranted and authorized the formation of the ICC Consensus Committee on Bleacher Safety. The committee was composed of 12 members, including the requisite balance of general, user interest and producer interest.

ICC 300 was completed in December 2001, and submitted to ANSI on January 1, 2002. ICC 300 was reissued with some revisions in 2007, 2012 and 2017. While the term "bleachers" is generic, the standard addresses all aspects of tiered seating associated with bleachers, grandstands, and folding and telescopic seating. These types of seating are supported on dedicated structural systems, which in turn may sit on the ground or on a building floor system (see Commentary Figure 1029.1.1). Single seats or bench seats bolted down to a stepped floor are not considered a bleacher or grandstand and should comply with Section 1029. See the definitions in Chapter 2 for "Bleachers," "Building element," "Folding and telescopic seating" and "Grandstand." While ICC 300 is consistent and also relies on Chapter 10 of the code for some provisions, the standard addresses items specific to these types of seating arrangements. For example, the minimum number of exits from a bleacher is addressed in ICC 300, Section 404.1; however, to determine the minimum number of exits from the room the bleacher is located in, Section 1006 is applicable. The bleacher standard references Chapter 11 of the code and ICC A117.1 for accessibility requirements.

ICC 300 has minimum requirements for new, alterations, repair, operation and maintenance of bleacher systems. A bleacher or grandstand is defined as "Tiered seating supported on a dedicated structural system and two or more rows high and is not a building element." The intent of the terms "dedicated structural system" and "not a building element" in the definition is to recognize that bleacher systems sit on the floor or ground and have a support system separate from the building system. However, the bleacher could rely on the building system for lateral or gravity support. The intent of "two or more rows" is so that a tiered floor system with a bench or row of seats on each tier would not be considered a bleacher.

Commentary Figure 1029.1.1
EXAMPLE OF BLEACHERS (COURTESY OF HUSSEY SEATING)

The criteria in ICC 300 include provisions for construction, means of egress within the bleacher system, inspection and maintenance for existing bleachers, and for where seating systems are relocated.

[BE] 1029.1.1.1 Spaces under grandstands and bleachers. Spaces under *grandstands* or *bleachers* shall be separated by *fire barriers* complying with Section 707 of the *International Building Code* and *horizontal assemblies* complying with Section 711 of the *International Building Code* with not less than 1-hour fire-resistance-rated construction.

Exceptions:

1. Ticket booths less than 100 square feet (9 m^2) in area.
2. Toilet rooms.
3. Other accessory use areas 1,000 square feet (93 m^2) or less in area and equipped with an *automatic sprinkler system* in accordance with Section 903.3.1.1.

❖ Sometimes spaces under grandstands are used for other purposes such as bathrooms, concession stands, storage, and so on. If that space caught on fire, it could jeopardize the safe evacuation options for persons on the bleachers. For safety, the spaces below must be separated from the bleachers by fire-resistance-rated construction. This is typically the roof and back walls of the concession stand or storage room. If the space below is either a small ticket booth or bathrooms, the potential fire load is low enough that these spaces are not required to be separated. Other accessory areas, provided that the space is sprinklered with an NFPA 13 system and has an area of 1,000 square feet (93 m^2) or less, would also be able to be located under a bleacher system without being separated. Note that Section 903.2.1.5 requires enclosed spaces with an area greater than 1,000 square feet (93 m^2) under an outdoor bleacher system to be sprinklered.

Section 304.1.3.1 recognizes that paths under bleachers for circulation and means of egress are open to the air and therefore not considered accessory areas required to be separated or sprinklered.

While the path for means of egress passing under bleachers (i.e., vomitory) is not specifically addressed in this section, where a bleacher system is outside, the capacity factors for determining minimum egress width [Table 404.5(3) of ICC 300] are based on the assumption that the egress route is essentially open to the outside and therefore has a limited chance of accumulating smoke along that route. Two of the three legacy codes specifically exempted open means of egress routes under bleachers from separation requirements.

[BE] 1029.2 Assembly main exit. A building, room or space used for assembly purposes that has an *occupant load* of greater than 300 and is provided with a main *exit*, that main *exit* shall be of sufficient capacity to accommodate not less than one-half of the *occupant load*, but such capacity shall be not less than the total required capacity of all *means of egress* leading to the *exit*. Where the building is classified as a Group A occupancy, the main *exit* shall front on not less than one street or an unoccupied space of not less than 10 feet (3048 mm) in width that adjoins a street or *public way*. In a building, room or space used for assembly purposes where there is not a well-defined main *exit* or where multiple main *exits* are provided, *exits* shall be permitted to be distributed around the perimeter of the building provided that the total capacity of egress is not less than 100 percent of the required capacity

❖ Assembly buildings, as well as buildings with spaces that function as assembly spaces (e.g., the band classroom in a school, the training room in an office, the cafeteria in a large factory), present an unusual life safety problem that includes frequent higher occupant densities and, therefore, larger occupant loads and the opportunity for irrational mass response (i.e., panic) to a perceived emergency. For this reason, the code requires a specific arrangement of the exits. Studies have indicated that in any emergency, occupants will tend to egress via the same path of travel used to enter the room and building. Therefore, the main entrance to a building or space must also be designed as the main exit to accommodate this behavior, even if the required exit capacity might be more easily accommodated elsewhere. The main entrance (and exit) must be sized to accommodate at least 50 percent of the total occupant load of the structure and must front on a large, open space, such as a street or lobby, for rapid dispersal of the occupants outside the building or space. The remaining exits must also accommodate at least 50 percent of the total occupant load from each level (see Commentary Figure 1029.2). The total occupant load includes those within the theater seating area, the foyer and any other space (e.g., ticket booth, concession stand, offices, storage and the like). Where the assembly space is within a mixed occupancy building, the intent is that the main exits from the space comply with these provisions for one-half the capacity, but not necessarily that they lead directly to the outside. Egress requirements from the building would depend on the anticipated dispersal of the assembly space occupants. For example, an office building may have a large training/conference room where the path of exit access travel from the room goes out a main exit from the space and then disseminates into the general floor egress system. The room exit access doors may need to meet the 50-percent criterion, but once the occupants leave the room and enter the general floor egress system, exit capacity can be dispersed.

The required width of the means of egress in places of assembly is more often determined by the occupant load than in other occupancies. In other occupancies, minimum required widths and travel distances will often determine the required widths and locations of exits.

This section only requires the main exit to accommodate 50 percent of the occupant load where there is a single main entrance. In contrast, a large stadium or civic center, in which there are numerous entrances (and exits), need not comply with the main entrance criteria.

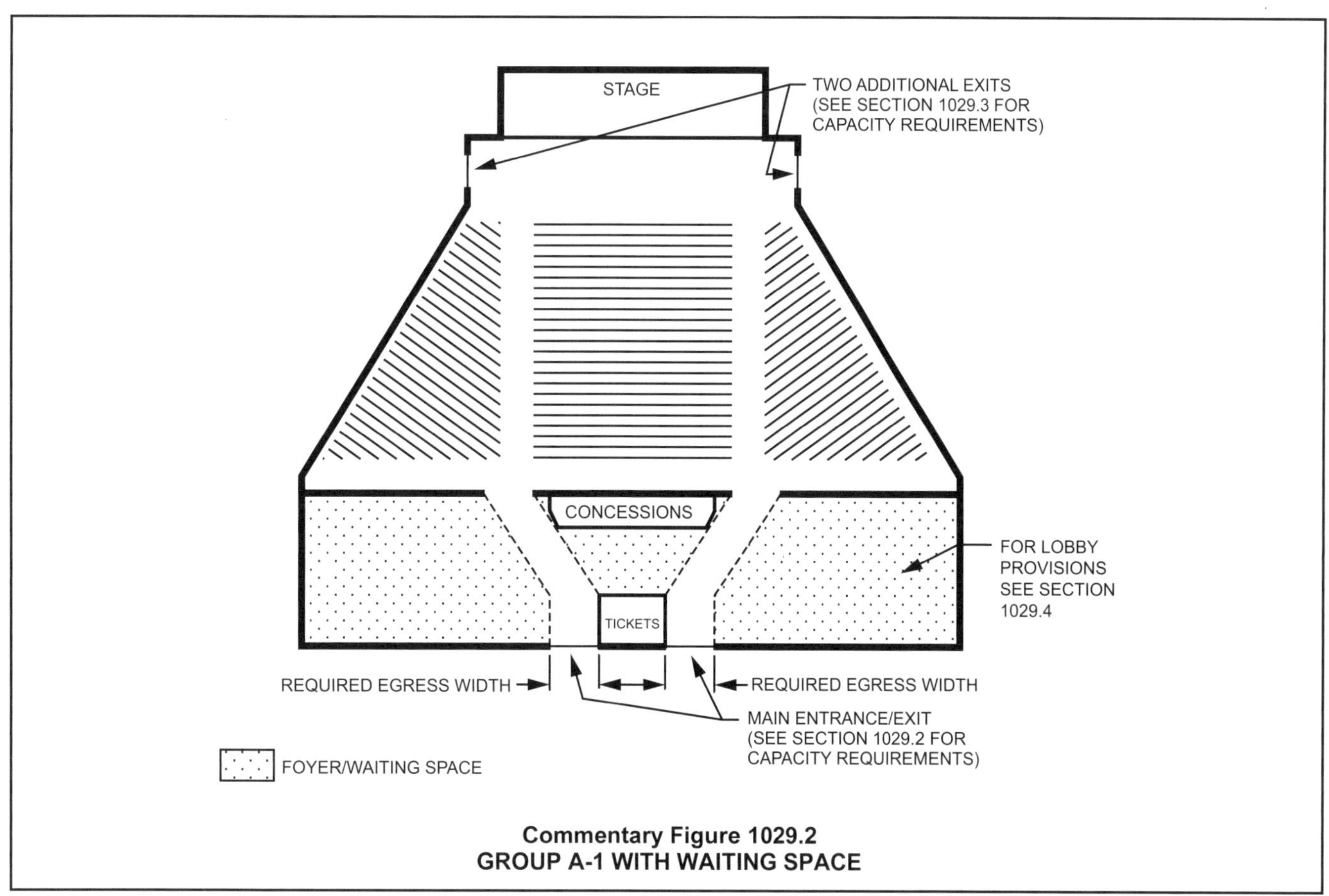

Commentary Figure 1029.2
GROUP A-1 WITH WAITING SPACE

[BE] 1029.3 Assembly other exits. In addition to having access to a main *exit*, each level in a building used for assembly purposes having an *occupant load* greater than 300 and provided with a main *exit*, shall be provided with additional *means of egress* that shall provide an egress capacity for not less than one-half of the total *occupant load* served by that level and shall comply with Section 1007.1. In a building used for assembly purposes where there is not a well-defined main *exit* or where multiple main *exits* are provided, *exits* for each level shall be permitted to be distributed around the perimeter of the building, provided that the total width of egress is not less than 100 percent of the required width.

❖ This section provides for the egress of one-half of the total occupant load by way of exits other than the main exit that is described in Section 1029.2. Assembly buildings, as well as buildings with spaces that function as assembly spaces, that are provided with multiple entrances but no single main entrance do not provide a well-defined main exit; therefore, the total required exit width needs to be distributed around the perimeter of the space or building. Examples of these assemblies would be a school gymnasium or a large stadium or civic center in which there are numerous entrances (and exits).

[BE] 1029.4 Foyers and lobbies. In Group A-1 occupancies, where persons are admitted to the building at times when seats are not available, such persons shall be allowed to wait in a lobby or similar space, provided that such lobby or similar space shall not encroach on the minimum width or required capacity of the *means of egress*. Such foyer, if not directly connected to a public street by all the main entrances or *exits*, shall have a straight and unobstructed *corridor* or path of travel to every such main entrance or *exit*.

❖ In theaters, people may arrive and wait for the next show while another group has yet to exit. This is extremely common in multiplex theater complexes. In every case, the main entrance (exit) and all other exits are to be constantly available for the entire building occupant load.

For example, because of the queuing of large crowds, particularly in theaters where a performance may be in progress and people must wait to attend the next one, standing space is often provided. For reasons of safety, such spaces cannot be located in or interfere with established paths of egress from the assembly areas. While a facility may choose to separate the route for means of egress using partitions or railings from the general lobby space to allow for easy traffic flow through the lobby to the street, it is not required to designate these areas (see Commentary Figure 1029.2).

[BE] 1029.5 Interior balcony and gallery means of egress. For balconies, galleries or press boxes having a seating capacity of 50 or more located in a building, room or space used for assembly purposes, not less than two *means of egress* shall be provided, with one from each side of every balcony, gallery or press box.

❖ This section states the threshold where not less than two means of egress are required based on the occupant load of the interior balcony, gallery or press box. Those two exits need to be dispersed. Section 1006.3.1, Exception 5, and Section 1019.3, Item 8, allow for stairways to be unenclosed exit access stairways where they are effectively part of the main seating bowl. These requirements will ensure that at least one path of travel is always available and occupants face a minimum number of hazards.

For balconies, galleries or press boxes with 50 or fewer occupants, see Section 1029.8. While balconies and galleries typically egress to stairways between floor levels, press boxes may egress directly to the assembly seating. In this situation, the occupant load would be added to the calculation for the width of aisles and aisle accessways as well as meet the common path of travel requirements. Where balconies, galleries or press boxes contain wheelchair spaces, the area must also meet the accessible means of egress requirements (Section 1009.1, Exception 2, and Section 1029.8).

[BE] 1029.6 Capacity of aisle for assembly. The required capacity of *aisles* shall be not less than that determined in accordance with Section 1029.6.1 where *smoke-protected assembly seating* is not provided, with Section 1029.6.2 where *smoke-protected assembly seating* is provided, and with Section 1029.6.3 where *open-air assembly seating* is provided.

❖ The means of egress width for spaces used for assembly is to be in accordance with this section and the referenced sections instead of the criteria specified in Section 1005 where dealing with the means of egress within seating areas. The width factors in Section 1029.6 and its subsections apply to those doorways, passageways, stepped aisles, ramped aisles and level aisles that are within the assembly seating areas.

The Board for the Coordination of Model Codes (BCMC) issued a report on means of egress dated June 10, 1985. The provisions in Section 1029 are based on this report. This report limits the application of these provisions to aisles and aisle accessways that provide exit access within the room or space within the assembly seating. This would include aisle accessways, level aisles, stepped aisles and ramped aisles. The primary concern for occupant safety would be that where the different provisions for capacity requirements in Sections 1005 and 1029 are utilized, there would not be a bottleneck in the path of travel for means of egress. For example, a common configuration at football fields is to have the seating area raised several feet above grade. Where a step or series of steps leading to grade from a raised seating area are a continuation of the stepped aisle, the width of the stepped aisle between seats and the continuation without adjacent seats should be the same. In theaters, commonly the occupants leave the seating area for a concourse or lobby area that leads to exit stairways between floor levels. In this situation, the capacity requirement in Section 1005.3 would be applicable for the exit stairway. For the many situations between these two scenarios, the decision would be based on the configuration of the seating and exit stairways between levels.

For example, in a facility without smoke protection and an occupant load of 800, doorways would need to be calculated based on 0.2 inch (5.1 mm) per occupant (see Item 4 of Section 1029.6.1). An occupant load of 800 x 0.2 inch (5.1 mm) = 160 inches (4064 mm) of egress width capacity, which translates into not less than five doors [assuming a minimum 32-inch (813 mm) clear opening for each]. This facility needs to have not less than three distinct means of egress (Section 1006.3). A main exit must accommodate not less than one-half of the occupant load (Section 1029.2). Therefore, the result would be not less than six doors: three located at the main exit and three others distributed to at least two other locations (Section 1029.3).

Different means of egress width criteria are also specified for interior assembly seating without smoke protection, interior assembly seating with smoke protection and open-air assembly seating. The egress width for smoke-protected seating and open-air seating is allowed to be less than for areas where smoke protection is not provided, since the smoke level is maintained at least 6 feet (1829 mm) above the floor of the means of egress.

[BE] 1029.6.1 Without smoke protection. The required capacity in inches (mm) of the *aisles* for assembly seating without smoke protection shall be not less than the *occupant load* served by the egress element in accordance with all of the following, as applicable:

1. Not less than 0.3 inch (7.6 mm) of *aisle* capacity for each occupant served shall be provided on stepped *aisles* having riser heights 7 inches (178 mm) or less and tread depths 11 inches (279 mm) or greater, measured horizontally between tread *nosings*.
2. Not less than 0.005 inch (0.127 mm) of additional *aisle* capacity for each occupant shall be provided for each 0.10 inch (2.5mm) of riser height above 7 inches (178 mm).
3. Where egress requires stepped *aisle* descent, not less than 0.075 inch (1.9 mm) of additional *aisle* capacity for each occupant shall be provided on those portions of *aisle* capacity that do not have a *handrail* within a horizontal distance of 30 inches (762 mm).
4. Ramped *aisles*, where slopes are steeper than one unit vertical in 12 units horizontal (8-percent slope), shall have not less than 0.22 inch (5.6 mm) of clear *aisle* capacity for each occupant served. Level or ramped aisles, where slopes are not steeper than one unit vertical in 12 units horizontal (8-percent slope), shall have not less than 0.20 inch (5.1 mm) of clear *aisle* capacity for each occupant served.

❖ This section prescribes the criteria needed to calculate the clear widths of aisles and aisle accessways in order to provide sufficient capacity to handle the occupant loads established by the catchment areas described in Section 1029.9.2. Clear width is to be measured to walls, edges of seating and tread edges.

The criteria for determining the required widths are based on analytical studies and field tests that used people to model egress situations [see Commentary Figures 1029.6.1(1) and 1029.6.1(2)].

Criterion 1 addresses the method for determining the required egress width for stepped aisles. This method corresponds with the requirements of Section 1005.3.1 for egress width per occupant of stairways in an unsprinklered building.

Criterion 2 addresses the method for determining the additional stepped aisle width required where the risers along that stepped aisle are greater than 7 inches (178 mm) high.

Criterion 3 addresses the method for determining the additional stepped aisle width where a handrail is not located within 30 inches (762 mm). With a center handrail, that would be stepped aisles wider than 60 inches (1524 mm). Side aisles have handrails along the wall. If the handrail is the top of the guard, then this requirement would apply to any side aisles

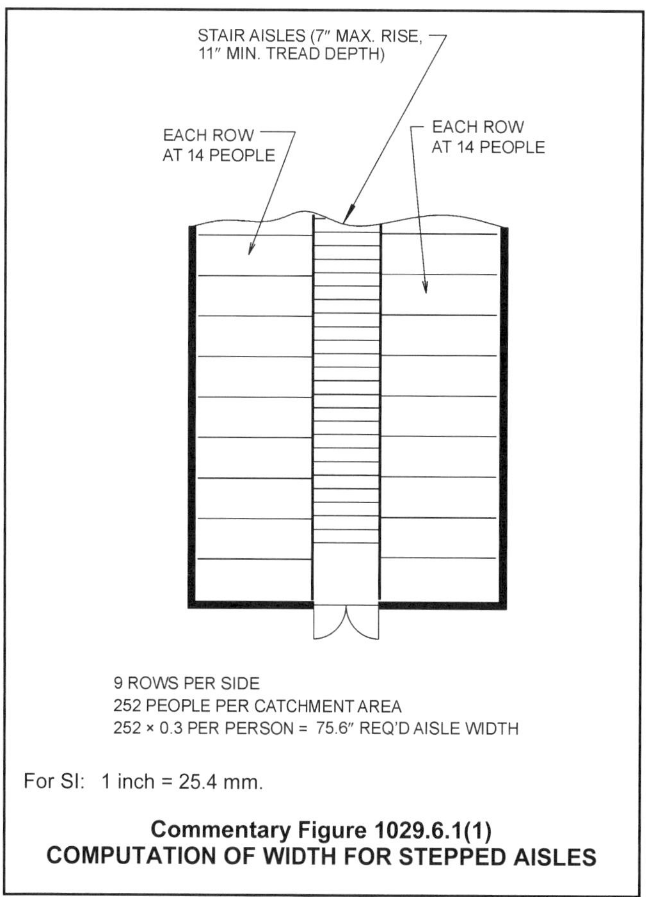

Commentary Figure 1029.6.1(1)
COMPUTATION OF WIDTH FOR STEPPED AISLES

greater than 30 inches (762 mm) wide. Because of the increased chance of falling and not being within reach of a handrail, the capacity per occupant is increased by 25 percent for the entire stepped aisle. For example, to calculate the capacity of a 72-inch-wide (1829 mm) stepped aisle, the answer would be 72 inches/0.375 inch = 192 occupants.

Criterion 4 addresses the method for determining the required widths for level or ramped and level means of egress. Where slopes are less than 1:12 (see definition for “Ramp”), the capacity requirements are also less. Level floors are quicker to negotiate than ramped surfaces for persons with limited mobility. Ramped aisle slopes are addressed in Section 1029.14.1.

These provisions are applicable within the seating area itself. When the occupants have left the seating bowl and have moved to stairways outside of the room, or have moved to cross aisles and then stairways or ramps leaving the balcony level, Section 1005.3 would be applicable. See Sections 1029.9.7 through 1029.11.2 for stairways that are a direct continuation of stepped aisles.

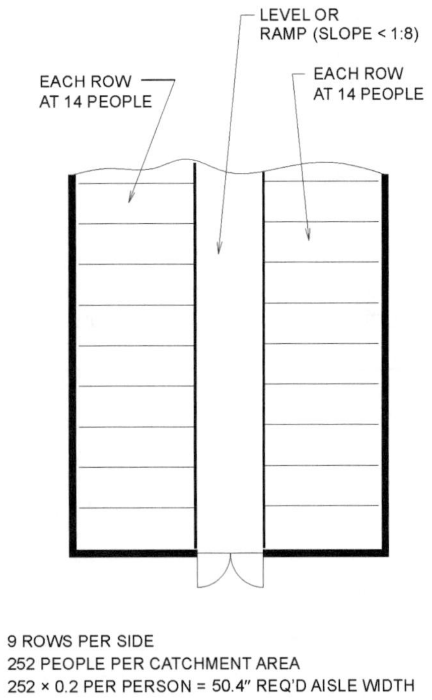

For SI: 1 inch = 25.4 mm.

Commentary Figure 1029.6.1(2)
COMPUTATION OF WIDTH FOR LEVEL, SLOPED OR RAMPED AISLES

[BE] 1029.6.2 Smoke-protected assembly seating. The required capacity in inches (mm) of the *aisle* for *smoke-protected assembly seating* shall be not less than the *occupant load* served by the egress element multiplied by the appropriate factor in Table 1029.6.2. The total number of seats specified shall be those within the space exposed to the same smoke-protected environment. Interpolation is permitted between the specific values shown. A life safety evaluation, complying with NFPA 101, shall be done for a facility utilizing the reduced width requirements of Table 1029.6.2 for *smoke-protected assembly seating*.

Exception: For *open-air assembly seating* with an *occupant load* not greater than 18,000, the required capacity in inches (mm) shall be determined using the factors in Section 1029.6.3.

❖ Special consideration is given to facilities with features that will prevent the means of egress from being blocked by smoke. Facilities to be considered smoke protected by Sections 1029.6.2.1 through 1029.6.2.3 are permitted increases in travel distance, egress capacity, and dead-end aisle and row lengths. Smoke control increases allowable egress time. Typically, model codes based on research by Dr. John J. Fruin and others recognize the need for occupants exposed to the fire environment to evacuate to a safe area within 90 seconds of notification and to reach the exterior or enclosed exit stairway within 5 minutes. With the increases permitted for smoke-protected facilities, these times are effectively doubled since the time available for safe egress also increases.

The exception is a pointer to the specific criteria for outdoor/open-air assembly seating areas. For outdoor stadiums with more than 18,000 seats, use Table 1029.6.2. This is consistent with the exception in Section 1029.6.3.

TABLE 1029.6.2. See below.

❖ This section requires the egress component to be of adequate size to accommodate the occupant load. For smoke-protected seating, the egress width per

[BE] TABLE 1029.6.2
CAPACITY FOR AISLES FOR SMOKE-PROTECTED ASSEMBLY

TOTAL NUMBER OF SEATS IN THE SMOKE-PROTECTED ASSEMBLY SEATING	INCHES OF CAPACITY PER SEAT SERVED			
	Stepped aisles with handrails within 30 inches	Stepped aisles without handrails within 30 inches	Level aisles or ramped aisles not steeper than 1 in 10 in slope	Ramped aisles steeper than 1 in 10 in slope
Equal to or less than 5,000	0.200	0.250	0.150	0.165
10,000	0.130	0.163	0.100	0.110
15,000	0.096	0.120	0.070	0.077
20,000	0.076	0.095	0.056	0.062
Equal to or greater than 25,000	0.060	0.075	0.044	0.048

For SI: 1 inch = 25.4 mm.

occupant is based on Table 1029.6.2. Typically, the larger the facility, the higher the ceiling; therefore, more space for smoke containment is associated with more time for egress. The egress width per occupant for seating without smoke protection is to be based on Section 1029.6.1 and is similar to the provisions in Section 1005.3.

Where the entire means of egress is smoke protected, the concourse and any stairways and ramps can also use the same capacity numbers (see Section 1005.3.1, Exception 2, and Section 1005.3.2, Exception 2) to determine egress width. If the concourse surrounding the smoke-protected seating bowl is not also smoke protected, the requirements in Sections 1005.3.1 and 1005.3.2 would be applicable to determine widths required for capacity of the concourse, stairways and ramps providing means of egress from the seating bowl to the exterior of the building. See Sections 1029.9.7 through 1029.11.2 for stairways that are a direct continuation of stepped aisles.

[BE] 1029.6.2.1 Smoke control. *Aisles* and *aisle accessways* serving a *smoke-protected assembly seating* area shall be provided with a smoke control system complying with Section 909 or natural ventilation designed to maintain the smoke level not less than 6 feet (1829 mm) above the floor of the *means of egress*.

❖ The means of egress (aisles and aisle accessways) within the assembly seating area are required to have some type of smoke control system that will prevent smoke buildup from encroaching on the egress path. This may be a mechanical smoke control system, designed in accordance with Section 909, or natural ventilation similar to open-air stadiums.

In either type of system, the major consideration is that a smoke-free environment be maintained at least 6 feet (1829 mm) above the floor of the means of egress for a period of at least 20 minutes.

[BE] 1029.6.2.2 Roof height. A *smoke-protected assembly seating* area with a roof shall have the lowest portion of the roof deck not less than 15 feet (4572 mm) above the highest *aisle* or *aisle accessway*.

Exception: A roof canopy in an outdoor stadium shall be permitted to be less than 15 feet (4572 mm) above the highest *aisle* or *aisle accessway* provided that there are no objects less than 80 inches (2032 mm) above the highest *aisle* or *aisle accessway*.

❖ One element of a smoke-protected assembly seating facility is that the lowest portion of the roof is required to be at least 15 feet (4572 mm) above the highest aisle or aisle accessway. The objective of this provision is to have a minimum 6-foot (1829 mm) smoke-free height to accommodate safe egress through the area. The additional 9 feet (2743 mm) of height is to provide a volume of space that will act to dissipate smoke. The measurement of the height is shown in Commentary Figures 1029.6.2.2(1) and 1029.6.2.2(2).

[BE] 1029.6.2.3 Automatic sprinklers. Enclosed areas with walls and ceilings in buildings or structures containing *smoke-protected assembly seating* shall be protected with an *approved automatic sprinkler system* in accordance with Section 903.3.1.1.

Exceptions:

1. The floor area used for contests, performances or entertainment provided that the roof construction is more than 50 feet (15 240 mm) above the floor level and the use is restricted to low fire hazard uses.

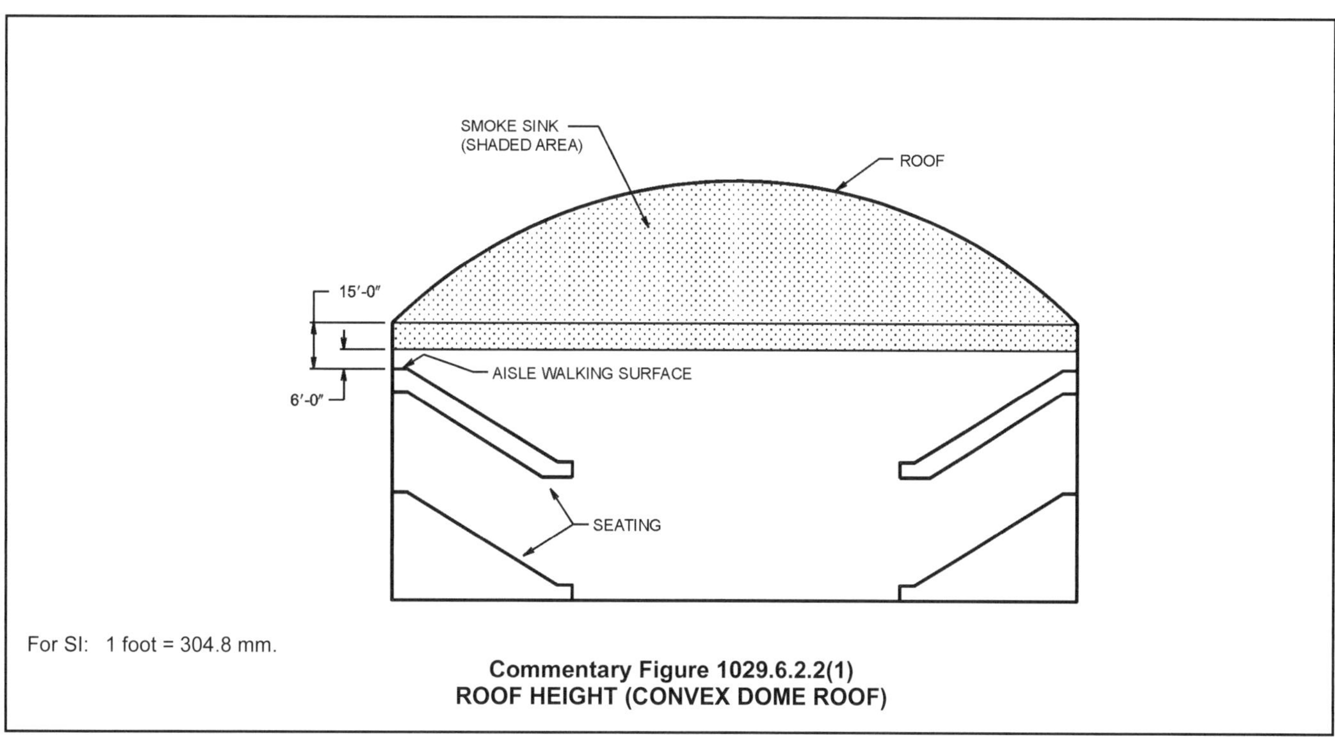

Commentary Figure 1029.6.2.2(1)
ROOF HEIGHT (CONVEX DOME ROOF)

2. Press boxes and storage facilities less than 1,000 square feet (93 m^2) in area.
3. Outdoor seating facilities where seating and the *means of egress* in the seating area are essentially open to the outside.

❖ If there are areas in the smoke-protected assembly seating structure enclosed by walls and ceilings, the entire structure is to be provided with an automatic sprinkler designed to meet the requirements of NFPA 13.

Exception 1 indicates that the area over the playing field or performance area is not required to be sprinklered if the use of the floor area is restricted. If the facility is used for conventions, trade shows, displays or similar purposes, sprinklers are required throughout, since the occupancy would no longer be a low-fire-hazard use. A characteristic of a low fire hazard occupancy is that the fuel load caused by combustibles is approximately 2 pounds per square foot (9.8 kg/m^2) or less.

In order for the contest, performance or entertainment area to be nonsprinklered, the roof over that area must be at least 50 feet (15 240 mm) above the floor in addition to the floor area meeting the low fire hazard criteria. The 50-foot (15 240 mm) criterion was selected because the response time for sprinklers at this height is extremely slow. It is estimated that the response time for standard sprinklers [50 feet (15 240 mm) above a floor with a fire having a heat release rate of 5 British thermal units (Btu) per square foot per second] exceeds 15 minutes. Therefore, it is not reasonable to install sprinklers at that height with little expectation of timely activation [see Commentary Figure 1029.6.2.3(1)]. Note that if this exception is utilized, the tradeoffs for a fully sprinklered building, such as increased height and area limitations or decreased corridor ratings, are no longer permitted.

Exception 2 indicates that automatic sprinklers are not required in small spaces in buildings. Sprinklers are required in press box and storage areas of outdoor facilities where the area exceeds 1,000 square feet (93 m^2). The primary reason for sprinklers in these areas is that both are anticipated to have a relatively large combustible load where compared to the main seating and participant areas. Additionally, in the case of storage areas, there is an increased potential for an undetected fire condition to occur [see Commentary Figure 1029.6.2.3(2)].

Exception 3 provides for outdoor seating facilities where smoke entrapment is not a safety concern.

[BE] 1029.6.3 Open-air assembly seating. In *open-air assembly seating,* the required capacity in inches (mm) of *aisles* shall be not less than the total *occupant load* served by the egress element multiplied by 0.08 (2.0 mm) where egress is by stepped *aisle* and multiplied by 0.06 (1.52 mm) where egress is by level *aisles* and ramped *aisles*.

Exception: The required capacity in inches (mm) of *aisles* shall be permitted to comply with Section 1029.6.2 for the

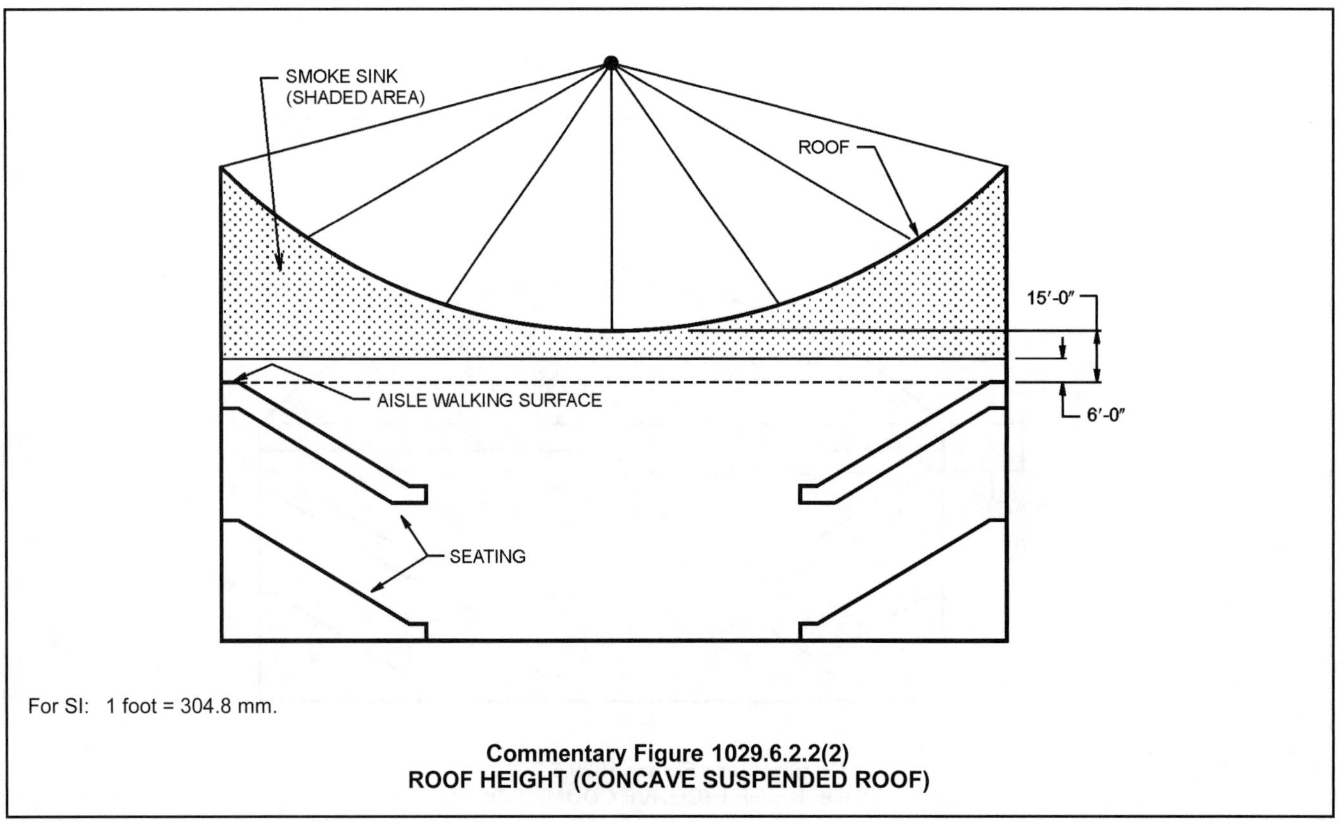

For SI: 1 foot = 304.8 mm.

Commentary Figure 1029.6.2.2(2)
ROOF HEIGHT (CONCAVE SUSPENDED ROOF)

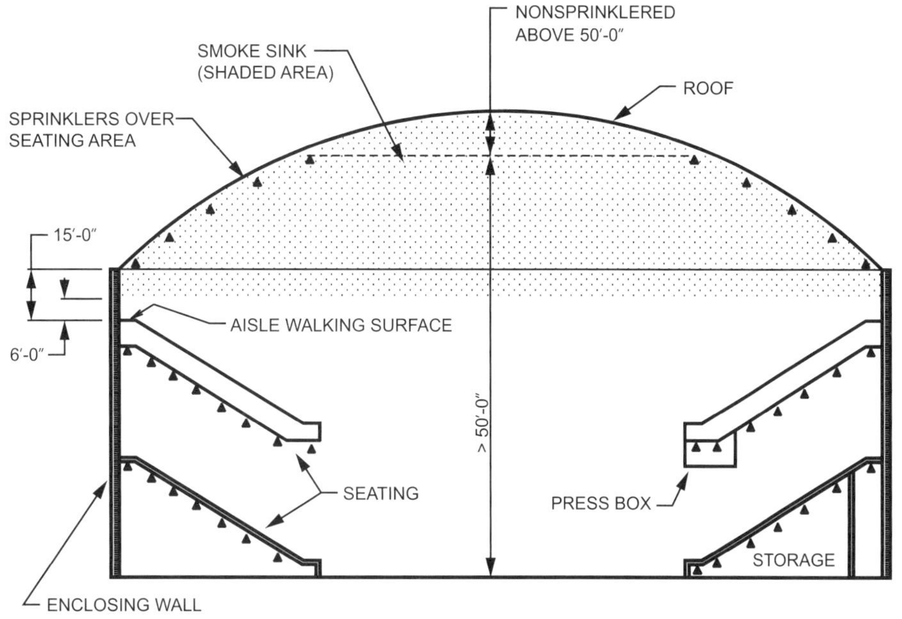

For SI: 1 foot = 304.8 mm.

Commentary Figure 1029.6.2.3(1)
INDOOR SEATING SPRINKLERED AREAS (CONVEX DOME ROOF)

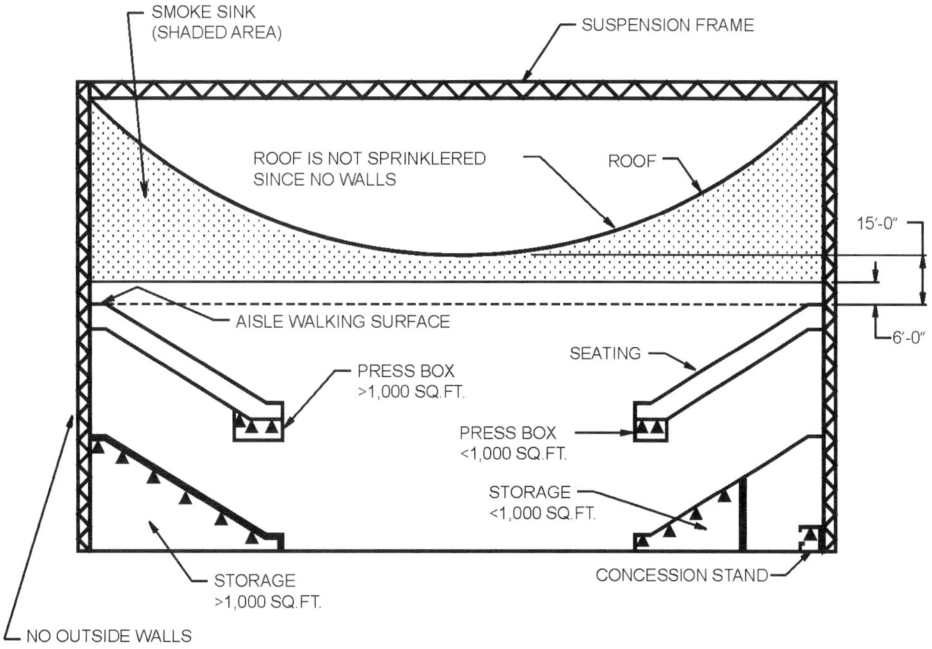

For SI: 1 foot = 304.8 mm,
1 square foot = 0.0929 m^2.

Commentary Figure 1029.6.2.3(2)
INDOOR SEATING SPRINKLERED AREAS (CONCAVE SUSPENDED ROOF)

number of seats in the *open-air assembly seating* where Section 1029.6.2 permits less capacity.

❖ This section lists the coefficients determining the width of aisles required for open-air assembly seating areas. Note that the coefficients are significantly less where compared to the values in Section 1029.6.1 for assembly areas without smoke protection. The coefficients are also less than those for smoke-protected assembly seating in Table 1029.6.2 except for very large assembly areas. The exception in this section would apply where the coefficients in Table 1029.6.2 are less than those in this section.

Low coefficients are a result of the very low hazards for open-air assembly areas and increased egress time. Where the entire means of egress is essentially open to the exterior, the concourse and any stairways and ramps can also use the same capacity numbers (see Section 1005.3.1, Exception 3, and Section 1005.3.2, Exception 3) to determine egress width. If the concourse surrounding the outdoor seating bowl is enclosed, the requirements in Sections 1005.3.1 and 1005.3.2 would be applicable to determine widths required for capacity of the concourse, stairways and ramps providing means of egress from the seating bowl to the exterior of the building. See Sections 1029.9.7 through 1029.11.2 for stairways that are a direct continuation of stepped aisles.

Generally, an outdoor assembly area meets the smoke control requirements of Section 1029.6.2 by natural ventilation and does not require an automatic sprinkler system.

[BE] 1029.7 Travel distance. The *exit access* travel distance shall comply with Section 1017. Where *aisles* are provided for seating, the distance shall be measured along the *aisles* and *aisle accessways* without travel over or on the seats.

Exceptions:

1. In facilities with *smoke-protected assembly* seating the total *exit access* travel distance shall be not greater than 400 feet (122 m). That portion of the total permitted *exit access* travel distance from each seat to the nearest entrance to a vomitory or concourse shall not exceed 200 feet (60 960 mm). The portion of the total permitted *exit access* travel distance from the entrance to the vomitory or concourse to one of the following shall not exceed 200 feet (60 960 mm).
   - 1.1. The closest riser of an *exit access stairway*.
   - 1.2. The closest slope of an *exit access ramp*.
   - 1.3. An exit.
2. In facilities with *open-air assembly seating* of Type III, IV or V construction, the total exit access travel distance to one of the following shall not exceed 400 feet (122 m).
   - 2.1. The closest riser of an *exit access stairway*.
   - 2.2. The closest slope of an *exit access ramp*.
   - 2.3. An *exit*.
3. In facilities with *open-air assembly seating* of Type I or II construction, the *exit access* travel distance shall not be limited.

❖ This section includes the travel distance limits for an assembly occupancy, which are the same as those in Table 1017.2 for Group A. The travel distance is to be measured along the same path the occupants would normally take to exit the facility using aisle accessways and aisles. For limits on length of aisles and aisle accessways, see Sections 1029.8 and 1029.9.

Exception 1 provides an extended travel distance within smoke-protected assembly seating. Basically there is 200 feet (60 960 mm) to get to a vomitory and another 200 feet (60 960 mm) to an open stairway or ramp that moves between floors or an exit (exit door, enclosed exit stairway or ramp). Measuring the travel distance to the top of an open stairway or ramp that moves between floors is similar to the allowance for open parking garages in Section 1017.3.

Exception 2 provides for an extended travel distance within open-air assembly seating since the smoke and fire hazards are very low. Assuming that the seating and the means of egress are open to the outside air, the total travel distance is 400 feet (122 m) to move through the seating or concourse to an open exit access stairway or ramp between stories or an exit (exit door, enclosed exit stairway or ramp). There is no limit for travel distance to a vomitory. Measuring the travel distance to the top of an open stairway or ramp that moves between floors is similar to the allowance for open parking garages in Section 1017.3.

Exception 3 allows for unlimited travel distance in open-air assembly seating with Types I and II construction. Typically, these large sports stadiums have multiple exits for smooth crowd movement before and after a sporting event, and there are very low smoke and fire hazards.

The allowance to use the open stairway or ramp for multiple stories is addressed in Section 1006.3.1, Exception 4, and Section 1019.3, Exception 7.

[BE] 1029.8 Common path of egress travel. The *common path of egress travel* shall not exceed 30 feet (9144 mm) from any seat to a point where an occupant has a choice of two paths of egress travel to two *exits*.

Exceptions:

1. For areas serving less than 50 occupants, the *common path of egress travel* shall not exceed 75 feet (22 860 mm).
2. For *smoke-protected* or *open-air assembly seating*, the *common path of egress travel* shall not exceed 50 feet (15 240 mm).

❖ The maximum travel distance down a single aisle accessway between rows of seating to a location where a patron would have two choices for a way out of the space is 30 feet (9144 mm). In smoke-protected or open-air seating, the common path of egress travel can be up to 50 feet (15 240 mm).

If the room or space (e.g., press box, box, gallery or balcony) has less than 50 occupants, the travel distance can be increased to 75 feet (22 860 mm). This would allow for a path of travel from a box seat, out of the box and to a main aisle or even a corridor located outside the assembly room itself.

Where this section is referenced for accessible means of egress (see Section 1009.1, Exception 2), the utilization of Exception 1 would include the entire occupant load of the seating area, box, gallery or balcony, not just the number of wheelchair spaces and companion seats. Wheelchair spaces that are integrated into the general seating would have the same 30-foot (9144 mm) common path of egress travel distance before the person needing the accessible route could choose two different paths for accessible means of egress. This provides the same level of protection for persons in accessible seating as for others within the space.

Sections 1006.2.1, 1006.3.2 and 1029.8 must be considered when determining the common path of egress travel requirements for a building. Table 1006.2.1, Note c, references Section 1029.8 for common path of egress travel within an assembly space with fixed seating. Table 1006.3.2 sets the number of ways out (means of egress via exit or exit access). Section 1029.8 regulates the distance to a decision point within a room or space used for assembly seating where a patron moves between seats (aisle accessways) and along aisles to a location where a patron would have two choices for a way out of the space.

[BE] 1029.8.1 Path through adjacent row. Where one of the two paths of travel is across the *aisle* through a row of seats to another *aisle*, there shall be not more than 24 seats between the two *aisles*, and the minimum clear width between rows for the row between the two *aisles* shall be 12 inches (305 mm) plus 0.6 inch (15.2 mm) for each additional seat above seven in the row between *aisles*.

Exception: For *smoke-protected* or *open-air assembly seating* there shall be not more than 40 seats between the two *aisles* and the minimum clear width shall be 12 inches (305 mm) plus 0.3 inch (7.6 mm) for each additional seat.

❖ In establishing the point where the occupants of a row served by a single access aisle (e.g., seating section against a wall or barrier on one end of the aisle accessways) will have two distinct paths of travel, the code allows one of those paths to be through the rows of an adjacent seating area or section (e.g., seating section with aisles on both ends of the aisle accessways). This requirement increases the row widths for the single-access seating section and the adjacent dual-access seating section. This allows the occupants to either travel down the single access aisle or readily traverse the oversized row widths to gain access to a second aisle (see Commentary Figure 1029.8.1). This exception allows a greater number of seats spaced with a minimum clearance of 12 inches (305 mm) for smoke-protected or open-air assembly seating. For the base width requirements for single- and dual-access rows, see the commentary to Sections 1029.13.2 through 1029.13.2.2.

[BE] 1029.9 Assembly aisles are required. Every occupied portion of any building, room or space used for assembly purposes that contains seats, tables, displays, similar fixtures or equipment shall be provided with *aisles* leading to *exits* or *exit access doorways* in accordance with this section.

❖ This section requires that each assembly space have designated aisles. For aisle accessway requirements, see Section 1029.13. For aisles in other occupancies, see Section 1018.

[BE] 1029.9.1 Minimum aisle width. The minimum clear width for *aisles* shall comply with one of the following:

1. Forty-eight inches (1219 mm) for stepped *aisles* having seating on both sides.

   Exception: Thirty-six inches (914 mm) where the stepped *aisles* serve less than 50 seats.

2. Thirty-six inches (914 mm) for stepped *aisles* having seating on only one side.

   Exception: Twenty-three inches (584 mm) between a stepped aisle *handrail* and seating where a stepped *aisle* does not serve more than five rows on one side.

3. Twenty-three inches (584 mm) between a stepped *aisle handrail* or *guard* and seating where the stepped *aisle* is subdivided by a mid-aisle *handrail*.

4. Forty-two inches (1067 mm) for level or ramped *aisles* having seating on both sides.

   Exceptions:

   1. Thirty-six inches (914 mm) where the *aisle* serves less than 50 seats.
   2. Thirty inches (762 mm) where the *aisle* serves fewer than 15 seats and does not serve as part of an *accessible route*.

5. Thirty-six inches (914 mm) for level or ramped *aisles* having seating on only one side.

   Exception: Thirty inches (762 mm) where the *aisle* serves fewer than 15 seats and does not serve as part of an *accessible route*.

❖ The clear widths of aisles established by the formulas given in Section 1029.6 must be not less than the minimum width requirements of this section. The development of minimum width requirements is based on the association of aisle capacity with the path of exit travel as influenced by the different features of aisle construction. The purpose is to create an aisle system that would provide an even flow of occupant egress. The minimum width of the aisles is also based on an anticipated movement of people in two directions.

Items 1, 2 and 3 deal with stepped aisles. Items 4 and 5 deal with ramped and level aisles. Items 1, 3 and 4 address aisles with seating on both sides.

Items 2 and 5 address aisles with seating on only one side. Note that each exception is applicable only to its corresponding item. For example, per Item 4, where there is seating on both sides, the minimum ramped or level aisle width is 42 inches (1067 mm). However, where that aisle serves less than 50 seats, it can be 36 inches (914 mm) wide (Exception 1) and where that aisle serves less than 15 seats, it can be 30 inches (762 mm) wide (Exception 2). In the exceptions to Items 4 and 5, there is a reminder that where the aisle also serves as an accessible route for entry or exit from wheelchair spaces, the accessible route width of 36 inches (914 mm) must be maintained.

[BE] 1029.9.2 Aisle catchment area. The *aisle* shall provide sufficient capacity for the number of persons accommodated by the catchment area served by the *aisle*. The catchment area served by an *aisle* is that portion of the total space served by that section of the *aisle*. In establishing catchment areas, the assumption shall be made that there is a balanced use of all *means of egress*, with the number of persons in proportion to egress capacity.

❖ The determination of required aisle and aisle accessway width is a function of the occupant load. In calculating the required widths, the assumption is that in a system or network of aisles and aisle accessways serving an occupied area, people will normally exit the area in a way that will distribute the occupant load throughout the system in proportion to the egress capacity of the aisles and aisle accessways. Each aisle and aisle accessway would take its tributary share (catchment area) of the total occupant load (see Commentary Figure 1029.9.2).

In addition to the provisions in this section, the requirement for the capacity of the main exit and other exits must also be considered (see Sections 1029.2 and 1029.3). While this section assumes an equal distribution, Section 1029.2 requires that where the facility has a main exit, the main exit and the access thereto must be capable of handling 50 percent of the occupant load.

[BE] 1029.9.3 Converging aisles. Where *aisles* converge to form a single path of egress travel, the required capacity of that path shall be not less than the combined required capacity of the converging *aisles*.

❖ Where one or more aisles or aisle accessways meet to form a single path of egress travel, that path must be sized to handle the combined occupant capacity of the converging aisles and aisle accessways (see Commentary Figure 1029.9.3). The reason for this requirement is to maintain the natural pace of travel

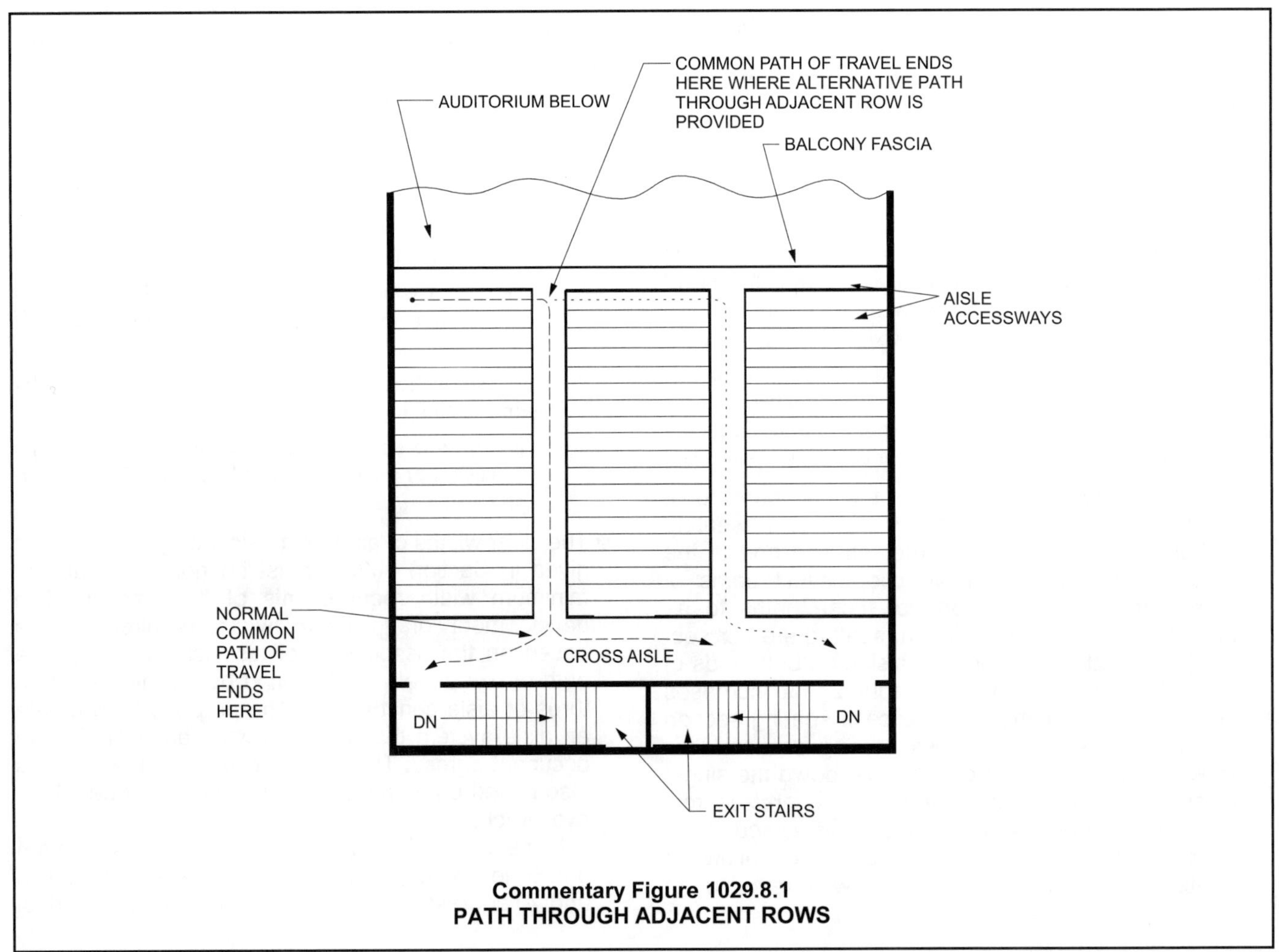

Commentary Figure 1029.8.1
PATH THROUGH ADJACENT ROWS

all the way through the aisle accessways or aisles to the exits and to minimize the queuing of occupants.

This section requires combining the required occupant capacity of converging aisles and aisle accessways, but not necessarily the required widths. For example, if two 48-inch (1219 mm) aisles converge, the result need not be a 96-inch (2438 mm) aisle unless the 48-inch (1219 mm) width of the aisles is required based on the requirements of Section 1029.6 for the actual occupant load served. However, if the 48-inch (1219 mm) width is not based on the occupant load but is required to comply with the minimum aisle width requirements of Section 1029.9.1, the resulting aisle width must be sized for the total occupant load served by the converging aisles, as determined by Section 1029.6, but not less than the minimum widths of Section 1029.9.1.

[BE] 1029.9.4 Uniform width and capacity. Those portions of *aisles*, where egress is possible in either of two directions, shall be uniform in minimum width or required capacity.

❖ Aisles that connect or lead to opposite exits must, at a minimum, be of uniform width throughout their entire lengths to allow for exit travel in two directions without creating a traffic bottleneck (see Commentary Figure 1029.9.4). They may need to be wider based on Section 1029.9.2 or 1029.9.3.

[BE] 1029.9.5 Dead-end aisles. Each end of an *aisle* shall be continuous to a cross *aisle*, foyer, doorway, vomitory, concourse or *stairway* in accordance with Section 1029.9.7 having access to an *exit*.

Exceptions:

1. Dead-end *aisles* shall be not greater than 20 feet (6096 mm) in length.
2. Dead-end *aisles* longer than 16 rows are permitted where seats beyond the 16th row dead-end *aisle* are

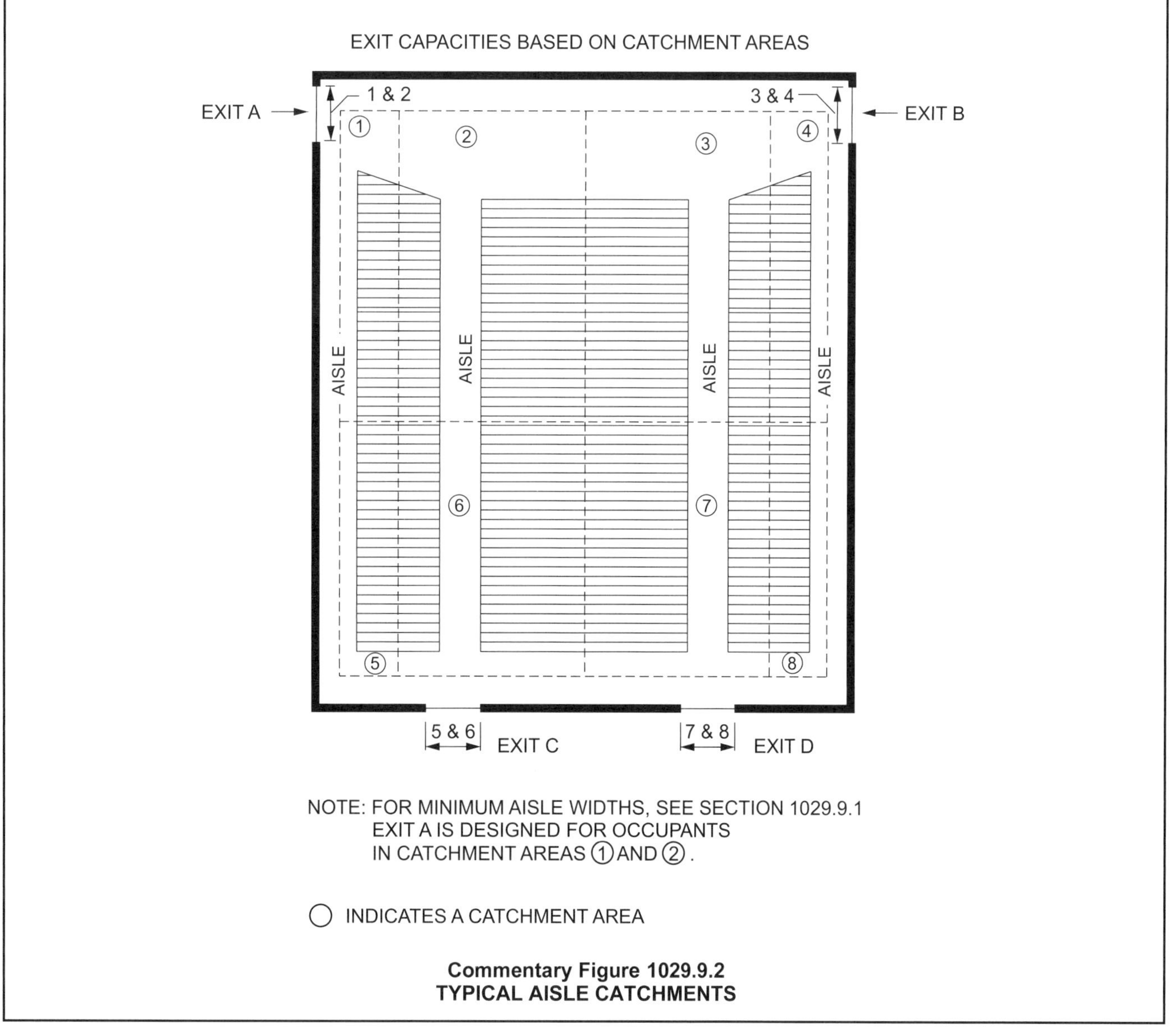

Commentary Figure 1029.9.2
TYPICAL AISLE CATCHMENTS

not more than 24 seats from another *aisle*, measured along a row of seats having a minimum clear width of 12 inches (305 mm) plus 0.6 inch (15.2 mm) for each additional seat above seven in the row where seats have backrests or beyond 10 where seats are without backrests in the row.

3. For *smoke-protected* or *open-air assembly seating*, the dead-end *aisle* length of vertical *aisles* shall not exceed a distance of 21 rows.
4. For *smoke-protected* or *open-air assembly seating*, a longer dead-end *aisle* is permitted where seats beyond the 21-row dead-end *aisle* are not more than 40 seats from another *aisle*, measured along a row of seats having an *aisle accessway* with a minimum clear width of 12 inches (305 mm) plus 0.3 inch (7.6 mm) for each additional seat above seven in the row where seats have backrests or beyond 10 where seats are without backrests in the row.

❖ Both ends of a cross aisle must terminate at either an intersecting aisle, a foyer, a doorway or a vomitory (lane) that gives access to an exit(s). Each exception allows an aisle to have a dead end of limited length. Exceptions 1 and 2 address dead-end aisles in assembly spaces with or without smoke protection. Exceptions 3 and 4 address dead-end aisles only in smoke-protected or open-air assembly seating. In accordance with Exception 1, dead-end aisles (similar to corridors and passageways) that terminate at one end of a cross aisle or at a foyer, doorway or vomitory must not be greater than 20 feet (6096 mm)

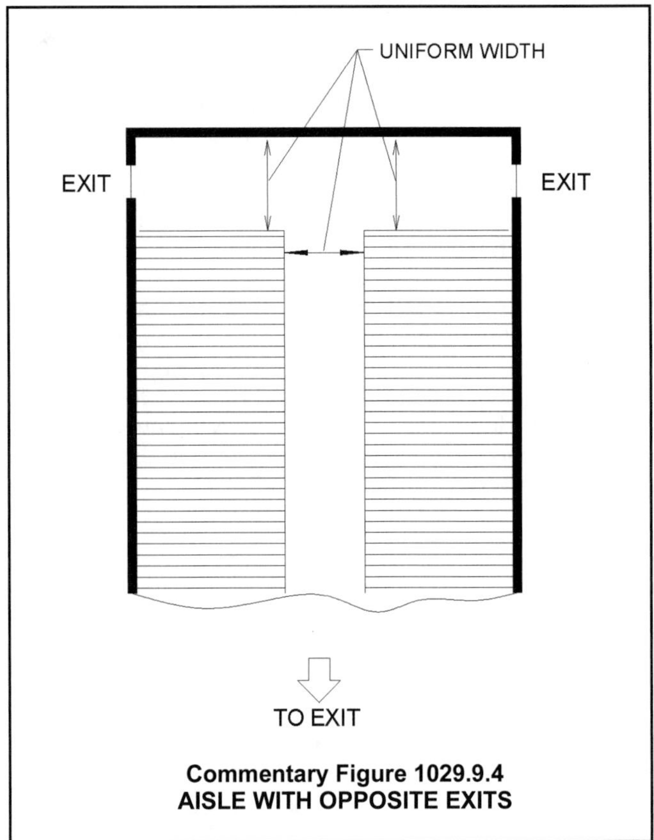

Commentary Figure 1029.9.4
AISLE WITH OPPOSITE EXITS

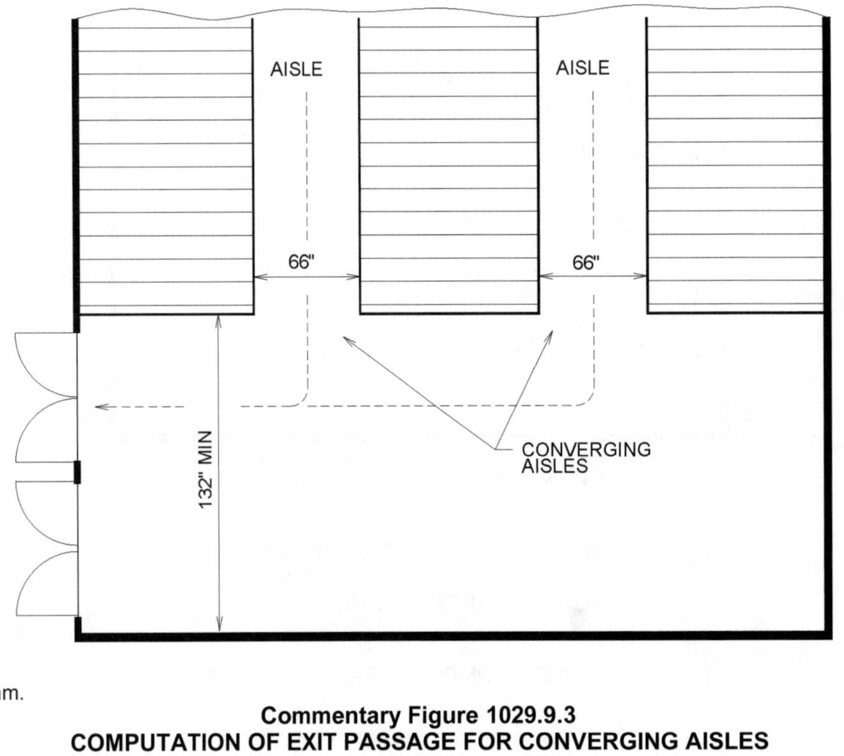

For SI: 1 inch = 25.4 mm.

Commentary Figure 1029.9.3
COMPUTATION OF EXIT PASSAGE FOR CONVERGING AISLES

in length. The intent of the row width requirements in the exceptions is to provide sufficient clear width between rows of seating to allow the occupants to pass quickly from a dead-end aisle to the aisle at the opposite end in times of emergency.

In Exception 2, the 0.6-inch (15.2 mm) increase beyond seven seats with backrests is consistent with the minimum width determined in accordance with Section 1029.13.2 for single-access rows. The code recognizes that one dead-end aisle may not be usable, thus creating a single-access row condition. There is a greater allowance for seating that looks similar to bleacher-style seating. This is consistent with ICC 300 (see Section 1029.1.1).

Exceptions 3 and 4 allow longer dead-end aisles for smoke-protected and open-air assembly seating (see Commentary Figure 1029.9.5). In Exception 4, there is a greater allowance for seating that looks similar to bleacher-style seating. This is consistent with ICC 300 (see Section 1029.1.1).

The overall purpose of this section is to provide aisle/seating arrangements that would allow the occupants to seek safe and rapid passage to exits in case of fire or other emergency.

[BE] 1029.9.6 Aisle measurement. The clear width for *aisles* shall be measured to walls, edges of seating and tread edges except for permitted projections.

Exception: The clear width of *aisles* adjacent to seating at tables shall be permitted to be measured in accordance with Section 1029.13.1.

❖ The clear width for stepped, ramped and level aisles is measured consistently with stairways and ramps to ensure a clear width for egress. The exception deals with aisles in dining areas and how to measure with loose tables and chairs.

[BE] 1029.9.6.1 Assembly aisle obstructions. There shall not be obstructions in the minimum width or required capacity of *aisles*.

Exception: *Handrails* are permitted to project into the required width of stepped *aisles* and ramped aisles in accordance with Section 1014.8.

❖ Except for handrails, aisles are required to be clear of any obstructions so that the full width is available for egress purposes. Handrails are allowed to project into the required aisle width in the same manner as handrail projections in stairways.

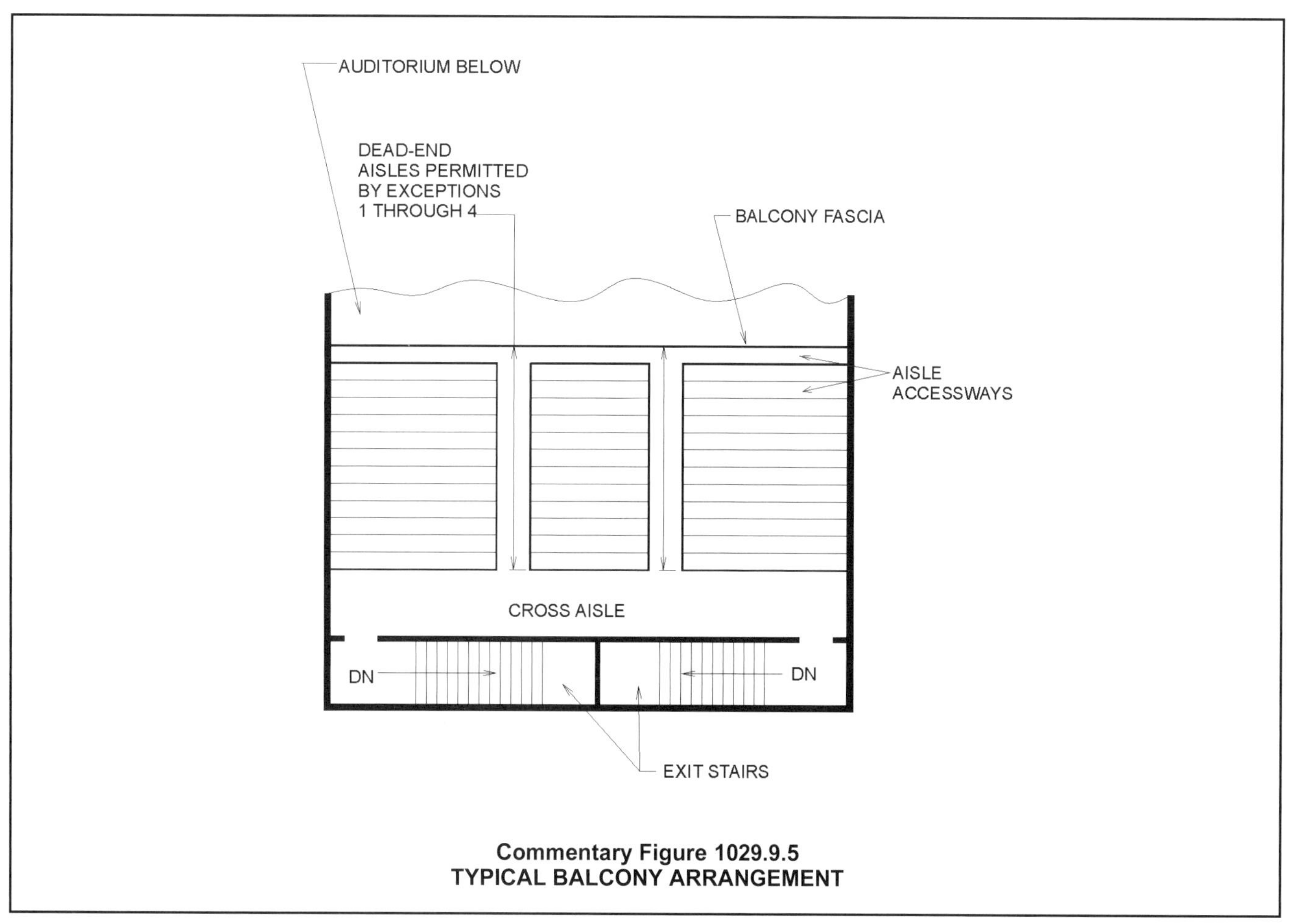

Commentary Figure 1029.9.5
TYPICAL BALCONY ARRANGEMENT

[BE] 1029.9.7 Stairways connecting to stepped aisles. A *stairway* that connects a stepped *aisle* to a cross *aisle* or concourse shall be permitted to comply with the assembly *aisle* walking surface requirements of Section 1029.14. Transitions between *stairways* and stepped *aisles* shall comply with Section 1029.10.

❖ Stairways that are a direct continuation of a stepped aisle, either at the top or bottom of the stepped aisle, and provide access to a cross aisle, shall be handled the same way as a stepped aisle for treads and risers (see Section 1029.14). For transitions between stepped aisles and stairways, see Section 1029.10. For examples, see Commentary Figures 1029.9.7(1) and 1029.9.7(2).

Commentary Figure 1029.9.7(1)
EXAMPLE OF A CONTINUATION OF A STEPPED AISLE UP TO A CROSS AISLE

Commentary Figure 1029.9.7(2)
EXAMPLE OF A CONTINUATION OF A STEPPED AISLE DOWN TO A FLOOR

[BE] 1029.9.8 Stairways connecting to vomitories. A *stairway* that connects a vomitory to a cross aisle or concourse shall be permitted to comply with the assembly *aisle* walking surface requirements of Section 1029.14. Transitions between *stairways* and stepped *aisles* shall comply with Section 1029.10.

❖ A vomitory is an entrance that pierces the back of a seating bowl of a theater or stadium that allows for entrance into the seating area. Stairways that provide a direct connection between that vomitory and an aisle or concourse shall be handled the same way as a stepped aisle for treads and risers (see Section 1029.14). For transitions between stepped aisles and stairways, see Section 1029.10.

[BE] 1029.10 Transitions. Transitions between *stairways* and stepped *aisles* shall comply with either Section 1029.10.1 or 1029.10.2.

❖ Line of sight in assembly seating is an important issue that needs to be balanced with safe egress for people seated in the assembly spaces. In order to maintain line of site, sometimes it is necessary to have a transition between stairways and stepped aisles that does not meet the standard tread, riser and landing provisions for stairways. This section replaces the standard landing requirements for stairways with a transition tread/landing.

[BE] 1029.10.1 Transitions to stairways that maintain stepped aisle riser and tread dimensions. Stepped *aisles*, transitions and *stairways* that maintain the stepped aisle riser and tread dimensions shall comply with Section 1029.14 as one *exit access* component.

❖ Where the treads and risers on the stairway and the treads and risers on the stepped aisle are the same, the whole run can be considered as one long stepped aisle.

[BE] 1029.10.2 Transitions to stairways that do not maintain stepped aisle riser and tread dimensions. Transitions between *stairways* and stepped *aisles* having different riser and tread dimensions shall comply with Sections 1029.10.2.1 through 1029.10.3.

❖ Where the stepped aisle and directly connected stairways do not have the same tread and riser dimensions, there are options for the transition between the two sections. This transition is the tread(s) between the stepped aisle and the stairway.

[BE] 1029.10.2.1 Stairways and stepped aisles in a straight run. Where *stairways* and stepped *aisles* are in a straight run, transitions shall have one of the following:

1. A depth of not less than 22 inches (559 mm) where the treads on the descending side of the transition have greater depth.
2. A depth of not less than 30 inches (762 mm) where the treads on the descending side of the transition have lesser depth.

❖ Typically, the treads on the stairway will have a smaller depth than the treads under the seating.

Assuming that is the case, where the stairway is at the high end of the stepped aisle, a transition tread of not less than 22 inches (559 mm) in depth shall be provided between the stairway and the stepped aisle [see Commentary Figure 1029.10.2.1(1)]. Where the stairway is at the low end of the stepped aisle, a transition tread of not less than 30 inches (762 mm) in depth shall be provided between the stepped aisle and the stairway [see Commentary Figure 1029.10.2.1(2)].

[BE] 1029.10.2.2 Stairways that change direction from stepped aisles. Transitions where the *stairway* changes direction from the stepped *aisle* shall have a minimum depth of 11 inches (280 mm) or the stepped *aisle* tread depth, whichever is greater, between the stepped *aisle* and *stairway*.

❖ Where the stepped aisle takes a turn and becomes a stairway, the aisle width must be maintained (see Sections 1029.6 and 1029.9.1). The transition between the stepped aisle and the turn must continue the tread depth of the stepped aisle or have a minimum depth of 11 inches (280 mm) to match the stairway treads, whichever is greater. There may be more than one transition between the stepped aisle and the turn [see Commentary Figure 1029.10.2.2].

[BE] 1029.10.3 Transition marking. A distinctive marking stripe shall be provided at each *nosing* or leading edge adjacent to the transition. Such stripe shall be not less than 1 inch (25 mm), and not more than 2 inches (51 mm), wide. The edge marking stripe shall be distinctively different from the stepped *aisle* contrasting marking stripe.

❖ At these transitions there may be a change in riser height, even if the tread depth stays the same. The stripe is to draw attention to the transition to reduce the chance of a trip or fall. This is different from the stripes required for stepped aisles in Sections 1029.14.2.2 and 1029.14.2.3.

[BE] 1029.11 Stepped aisles at vomitories. Stepped *aisles* that change direction at vomitories shall comply with Section 1029.11.1. Transitions between a stepped *aisle* above a vomitory and a stepped *aisle* to the side of a vomitory shall comply with Section 1029.11.2.

❖ Similar to Section 1029.10.2.2, where the stepped aisle takes a turn around a vomitory, the aisle width must be maintained (see Sections 1029.6 and 1029.9.1). The transition between the stepped aisle and the turn must continue the tread depth of the stepped aisle or have a minimum depth of 11 inches (280 mm) to match the stairway treads, whichever is greater. There may be more than one transition between the stepped aisle and the turn [see Commentary Figure 1029.11].

[BE] 1029.11.1 Stepped aisles that change direction at vomitories. Stepped *aisle* treads where the stepped *aisle* changes direction at a vomitory shall have a depth of not less than 11 inches (280 mm) or the stepped *aisle* tread depth, whichever is greater. The height of a stepped *aisle* tread above a transition at a vomitory shall comply with Section 1029.14.2.2.

❖ See the commentary to Section 1029.11.

[BE] 1029.11.2 Stepped aisle transitions at the top of vomitories. Transitions between the stepped *aisle* above a vomitory and stepped aisles to the side of a vomitory shall have a depth of not less than 11 inches (280 mm) or the stepped *aisle* tread depth, whichever is greater.

❖ See the commentary to Section 1029.11.

[BE] 1029.12 Construction. *Aisles*, stepped *aisles* and ramped *aisles* shall be built of materials consistent with the types permitted for the type of construction of the building.

Exception: Wood *handrails* shall be permitted for all types of construction.

❖ The construction materials permitted for stepped, ramped and level aisles are consistent with stairways and ramps.

[BE] 1029.12.1 Walking surface. The surface of *aisles*, stepped *aisles* and ramped *aisles* shall be of slip-resistant materials that are securely attached. The surface for stepped *aisles* shall comply with Section 1011.7.1.

❖ This section intends that for walking surfaces, stepped aisles will be addressed similarly to stairways (Section 1011.7.1), level aisles the same as floors (Section 1003.4) and ramped aisles the same as ramps (Section 1012.7.1). See the commentary for these sections.

[BE] 1029.12.2 Outdoor conditions. Outdoor *aisles*, stepped *aisles* and ramped *aisles* and outdoor approaches to *aisles*, stepped *aisles* and ramped *aisles* shall be designed so that water will not accumulate on the walking surface.

❖ Where stepped, ramped and level aisles are located in an outdoor situation, there is the same concern for the accumulation of ice and snow as there would be for exterior stairways or ramps. See Sections 1011.7.2 and 1012.7.2 regarding maximum slope to allow for drainage and where grated walking surfaces are permitted.

[BE] 1029.13 Aisle accessways. *Aisle accessways* for seating at tables shall comply with Section 1029.13.1. *Aisle accessways* for seating in rows shall comply with Section 1029.13.2.

❖ Aisle accessways are paths for means of egress between rows of seats or between tables. The aisle accessway leads to aisles, which in turn lead toward exits from the space. This is the same idea as moving through a room full of furniture to a corridor to reach an exit. In both situations, the path for means of egress is confined. For aisle accessway requirements in other occupancies, see Section 1018.

[BE] 1029.13.1 Seating at tables. Where seating is located at a table or counter and is adjacent to an *aisle* or *aisle accessway*, the measurement of required clear width of the *aisle* or *aisle accessway* shall be made to a line 19 inches (483 mm) away from and parallel to the edge of the table or counter.

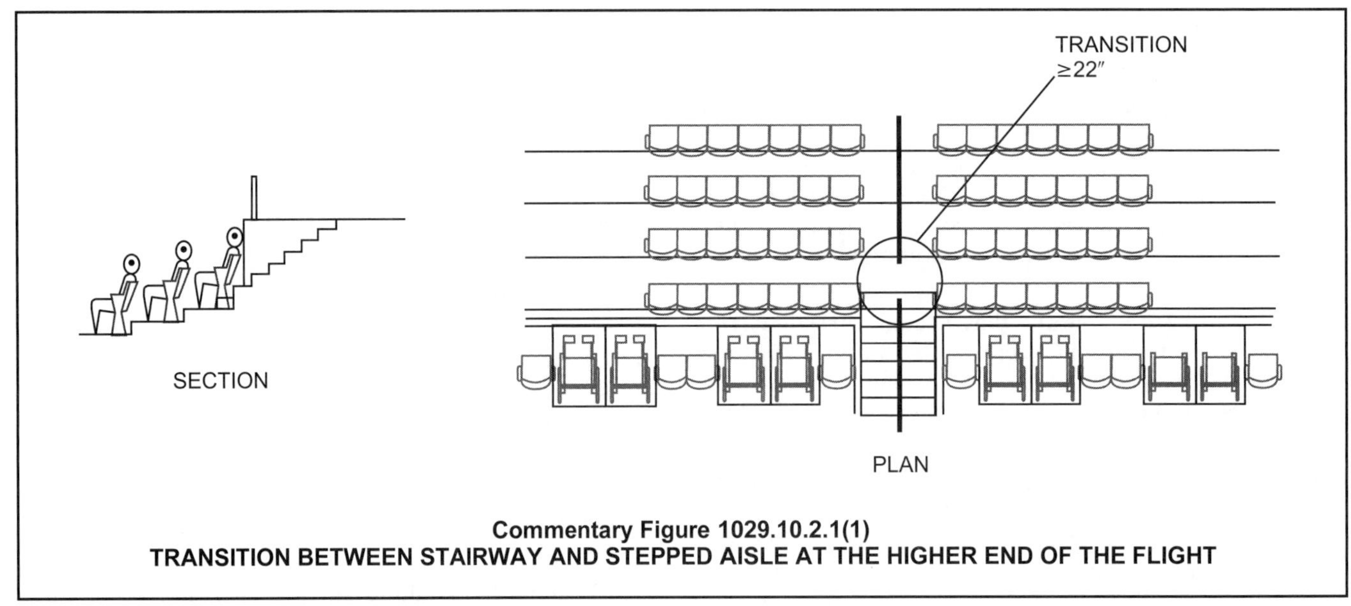

Commentary Figure 1029.10.2.1(1)
TRANSITION BETWEEN STAIRWAY AND STEPPED AISLE AT THE HIGHER END OF THE FLIGHT

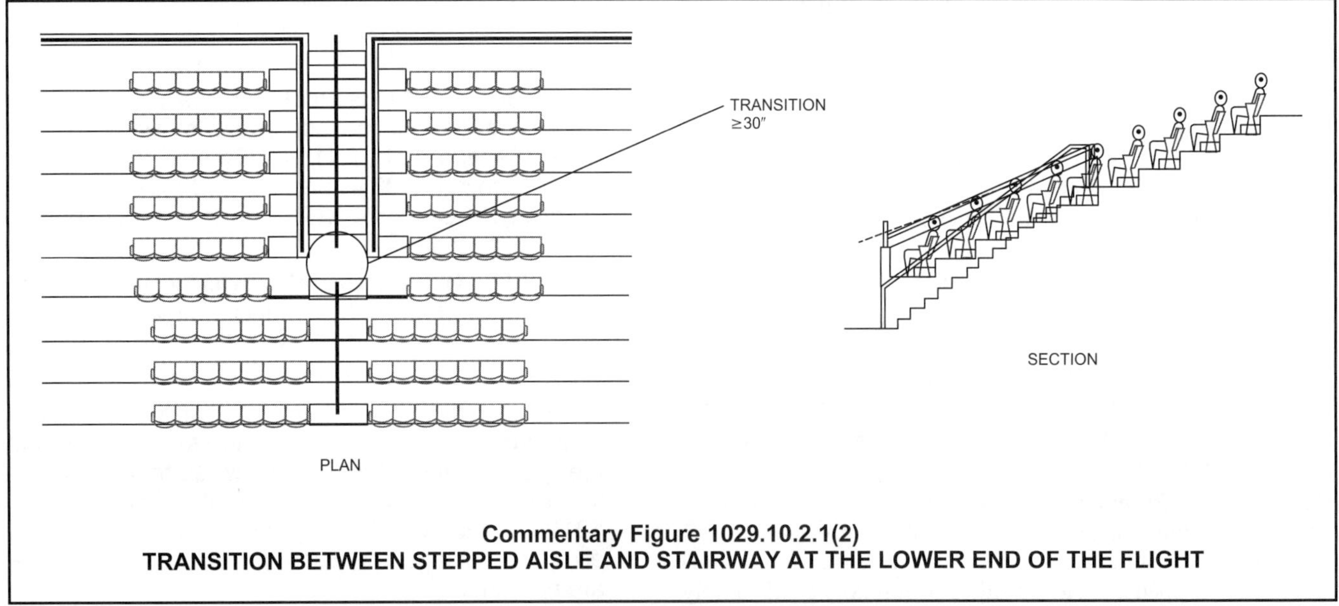

Commentary Figure 1029.10.2.1(2)
TRANSITION BETWEEN STEPPED AISLE AND STAIRWAY AT THE LOWER END OF THE FLIGHT

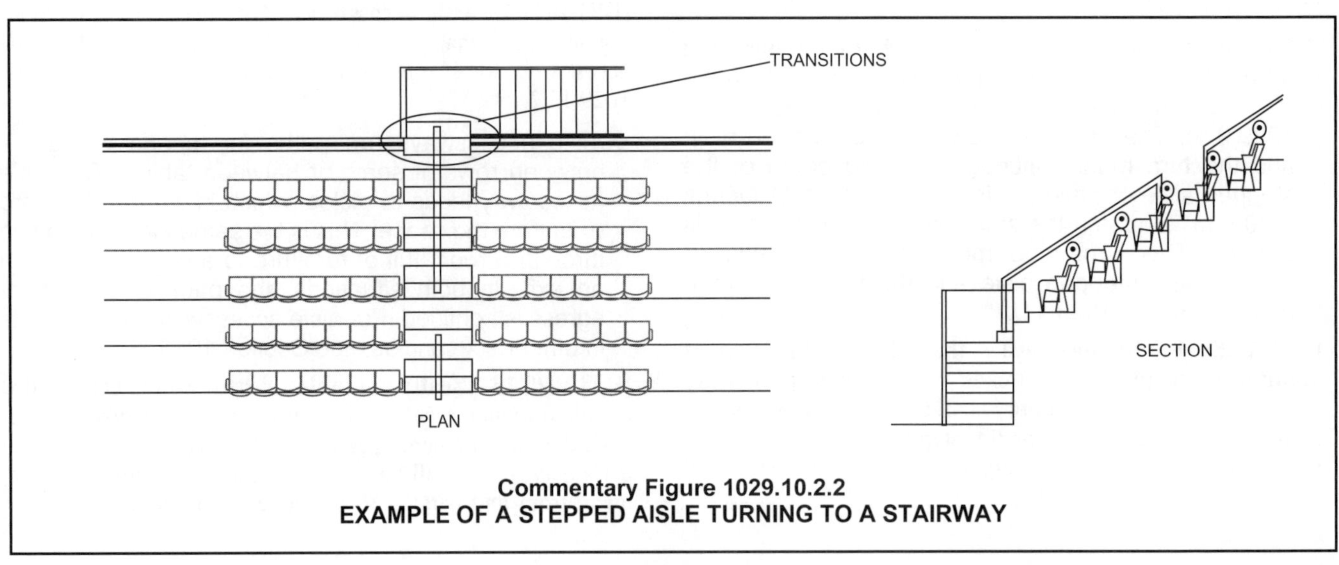

Commentary Figure 1029.10.2.2
EXAMPLE OF A STEPPED AISLE TURNING TO A STAIRWAY

The 19-inch (483 mm) distance shall be measured perpendicular to the side of the table or counter. In the case of other side boundaries for *aisles* or *aisle accessways*, the clear width shall be measured to walls, edges of seating and tread edges.

> **Exception:** Where tables or counters are served by fixed seats, the width of the *aisle* or *aisle accessway* shall be measured from the back of the seat.

❖ Most seating at tables should be adjacent to aisles or aisle accessways. In measuring the width of an aisle or aisle accessway for movable seating, the measurement is taken at a distance of 19 inches (483 mm) perpendicular to the side of the table or counter. This 19-inch (483 mm) space from the edge of the table or counter to the line where the aisle or aisle accessway measurement begins is intended to represent the space occupied by a typical seated occupant. This dimension is also considered to be adequate to accommodate seats with armrests that are too high to fit under the table where fixed seats are used. The aisle width is permitted to be measured from the back of the seat based on the exception. As indicated in Commentary Figure 1029.13.1, where seating abuts an aisle or aisle accessway, 19 inches (483 mm) must be added to the required aisle or aisle accessway width for seating on only one side and 38 inches (965 mm) for seating on both sides. Where seating will not be adjacent to the aisles or aisle passageways, as is the case where tables are at an angle to the aisle or aisle accessway, the measurement may be taken to the edge of the seating, table, counter or tread. Sections 1029.13.1.1 and 1029.13.1.2 address width and travel along aisle accessways. For aisles between tables, see the general requirements for aisles in assembly spaces.

[BE] 1029.13.1.1 Aisle accessway capacity and width for seating at tables. *Aisle accessways* serving arrangements of seating at tables or counters shall comply with the capacity requirements of Section 1005.1 but shall not have less than 12 inches (305 mm) of width plus $^1/_2$ inch (12.7 mm) of width for each additional 1 foot (305 mm), or fraction thereof, beyond 12 feet (3658 mm) of *aisle accessway* length measured from the center of the seat farthest from an *aisle*.

> **Exception:** Portions of an *aisle accessway* having a length not exceeding 6 feet (1829 mm) and used by a total of not more than four persons.

❖ This section specifies two criteria for determining the required width of aisle accessways at tables: the requirements of Section 1005.1 for capacity based on the number of occupants and the option described in this section. The aisle accessway width is to be the wider of the two requirements. The aisle accessway width between tables is determined similarly to the aisle accessway between rows of seats for viewing an event.

The relationship of tables and seating sometimes results in a situation in which it is difficult to determine which chairs are served by which aisle accessway; therefore, the width of the aisle accessway is a function of the distance from the aisle. The same minimum 12 inches (305 mm) is used and is increased $^1/_2$ inch (12.7 mm) for each additional foot of travel beyond 12 feet (3658 mm).

Recognizing that the normal use of table and chair seating will require some clearance for access and service, the exception eliminates the minimum width criteria if the distance to the aisle [or an aisle accessway of at least 12 inches (305 mm)] is less than 6 feet (1829 mm) and the number of people served is not more than four. Therefore, the first 6 feet (1829 mm) are not required to meet any minimum width criteria. After the first 6 feet (1829 mm), the requirements for an aisle accessway will apply. The length of the aisle accessway is then restricted by Section 1029.13.1.2. Where the maximum length of the aisle accessway is reached, an aisle, corridor or exit access door must be provided (see Commentary Figure 1029.13.1.1).

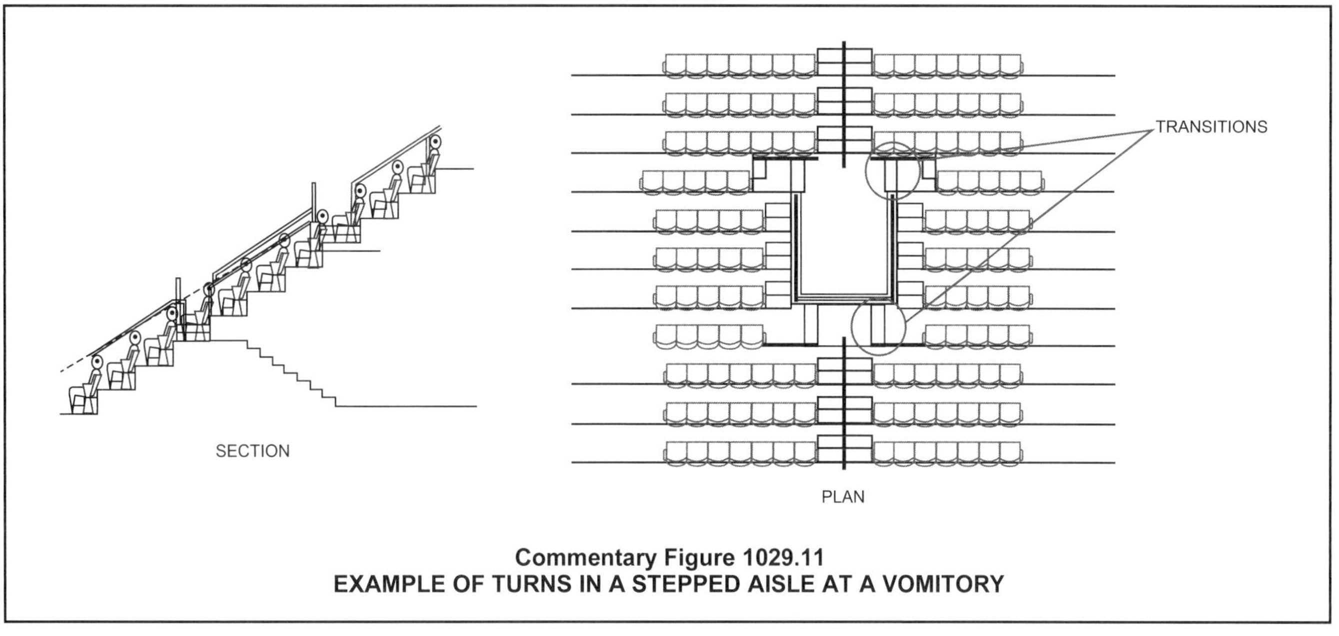

Commentary Figure 1029.11
EXAMPLE OF TURNS IN A STEPPED AISLE AT A VOMITORY

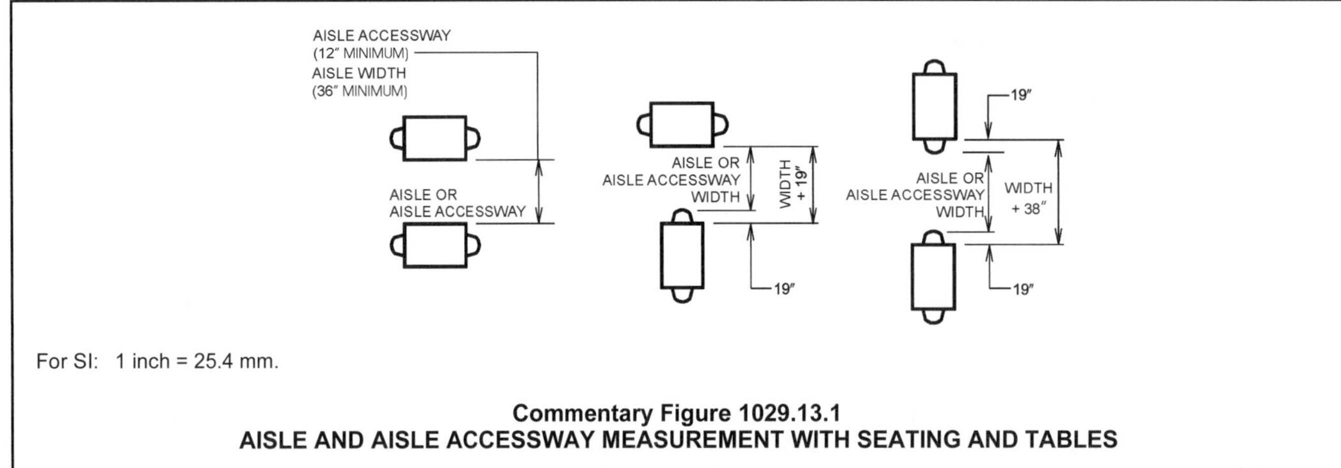

Commentary Figure 1029.13.1
AISLE AND AISLE ACCESSWAY MEASUREMENT WITH SEATING AND TABLES

[BE] 1029.13.1.2 Seating at table aisle accessway length. The length of travel along the *aisle accessway* shall not exceed 30 feet (9144 mm) from any seat to the point where a person has a choice of two or more paths of egress travel to separate *exits*.

❖ At some point in the exit access travel, it is necessary to reach an aisle complying with the minimum widths of Section 1029.9.1. Aisle accessway travel distance for seating at tables is not to exceed 30 feet (9144 mm), which may represent a dead-end condition (see Commentary Figure 1029.13.1.1).

More and more sports facilities are starting to add venues that include dining while watching the sporting event. At this time, the code does not include provisions for dining that occurs in smoke-protected areas.

[BE] 1029.13.2 Clear width of aisle accessways serving seating in rows. Where seating rows have 14 or fewer seats, the minimum clear *aisle accessway* width shall be not less than 12 inches (305 mm) measured as the clear horizontal distance from the back of the row ahead and the nearest projection of the row behind. Where chairs have automatic or self-rising seats, the measurement shall be made with seats in the raised position. Where any chair in the row does not have an automatic or self-rising seat, the measurements shall be made with the seat in the down position. For seats with folding tablet arms, row spacing shall be determined with the tablet arm in the used position.

Exception: For seats with folding tablet arms, row spacing is permitted to be determined with the tablet arm in the stored position where the tablet arm when raised manually to vertical position in one motion automatically returns to the stored position by force of gravity.

❖ The requirements of this section are applicable to theater-type seating arrangements. This includes both "continental" and "traditional" seating arrangements. Theater-type seating is characterized by a number of seats arranged side by side and in rows. In this type of seating arrangement, the potential exists for a large number of occupants to be present in a confined environment where the ability of the occupants to move quickly is limited. In order to egress, people are required to move single file within a narrow row (i.e., aisle accessway) before reaching an aisle; both the aisle and aisle accessway limit movement toward an exit. To provide adequate passage between rows of seats, this section requires that the clear width between the back of a row to the nearest projection of the seating immediately behind must be at least 12 inches (305 mm) [see Commentary Figure 1029.13.2(1)]. Where chairs are manufactured with automatic or self-lifting seats, the minimum width requirement may be measured with the seats in a raised position. Commonly used in college lecture halls, seats with built-in tablet arms are provided so that students can take notes. For an example of a type of tablet arm that complies with the exception, see Commentary Figure 1029.13.2(2).

Where chairs with tablet arms are used, the required width is to be determined with the tablet arm in its usable position. The exception allows for folding tablet arms that fall back into the stored position when a person rises out of the seat. With seats occupied and tablets raised, students egressing en masse down the row would at most encounter one tablet to move out of the way. With these types of arms, the aisle accessway can be measured for the seat or arm as indicated in Commentary Figure 1029.13.2(1).

With respect to self-rising seats, ASTM F851 provides one method of determining acceptability.

[BE] 1029.13.2.1 Dual access. For rows of seating served by *aisles* or doorways at both ends, there shall be not more than 100 seats per row. The minimum clear width of 12 inches (305 mm) between rows shall be increased by 0.3 inch (7.6 mm) for every additional seat beyond 14 seats where seats have backrests or beyond 21 where seats are without backrests. The minimum clear width is not required to exceed 22 inches (559 mm).

Exception: For *smoke-protected* or *open-air assembly seating*, the row length limits for a 12-inch-wide (305 mm) *aisle accessway*, beyond which the *aisle accessway* minimum clear width shall be increased, are in Table 1029.13.2.1.

❖ Where rows of seating are served by aisles or doorways located at both ends of the path of row travel, the number of seats that may be used in a row may be up to, but not more than, 100 (continental seating) and the minimum required clear width aisle accessway of 12 inches (305 mm) between rows of seats must be increased by 0.3 inch (7.6 mm) for every additional seat beyond 14 seats with backrests, but not more than a total of 22 inches (559 mm) (see Commentary Figure 1029.13.2.1). The increase for seating without backrests is to allow for bench seating similar to bleacher requirements in ICC 300 (see Section 1029.1.1). For example, in a row of 24 seats, the minimum clear width would compute to 15 inches (381 mm) [12 + (0.3 × 10)]. For a row of 34 seats, a clear width of 18 inches (457 mm) would be required. Increases in the clear width between rows of seats would occur up to a row of 46 seats. From 47 to 100 seats, a maximum clear width of 22 inches (559 mm) between rows would apply.

Since the row is to provide access to an aisle in both directions, the minimum width applies to the entire length of the row aisle accessway.

The exception allows more seats in a row with the minimum 12-inch (305 mm) seat spacing since safe egress time is extended for smoke-protected and open-air assembly seating.

Where a second means of egress for occupants of a single-access row is possible through an adjacent dual-access row, see Section 1029.8.1.

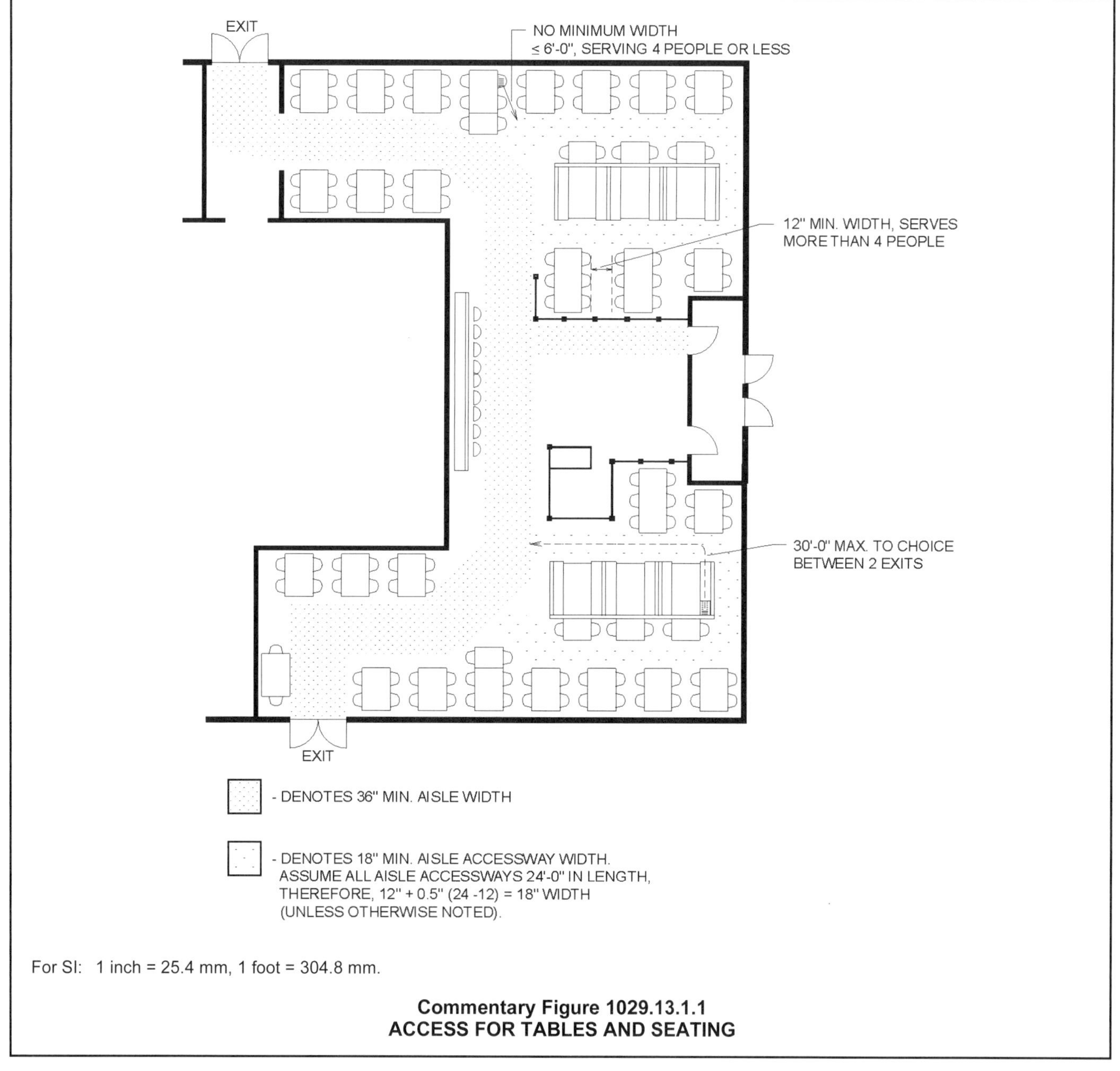

For SI: 1 inch = 25.4 mm, 1 foot = 304.8 mm.

Commentary Figure 1029.13.1.1
ACCESS FOR TABLES AND SEATING

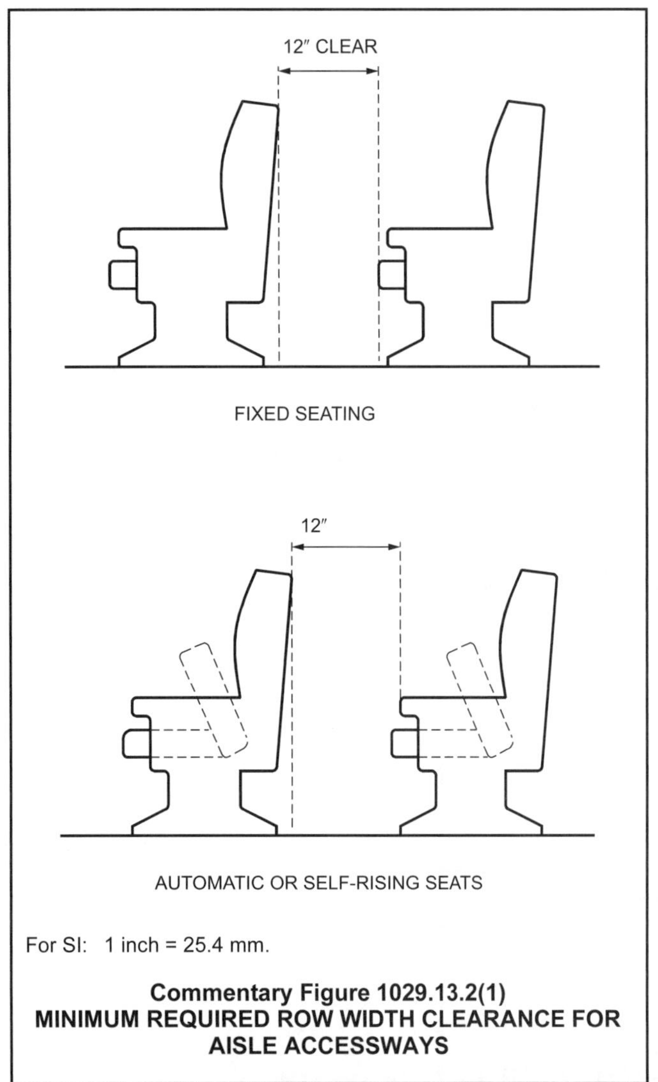

For SI: 1 inch = 25.4 mm.

Commentary Figure 1029.13.2(1)
MINIMUM REQUIRED ROW WIDTH CLEARANCE FOR AISLE ACCESSWAYS

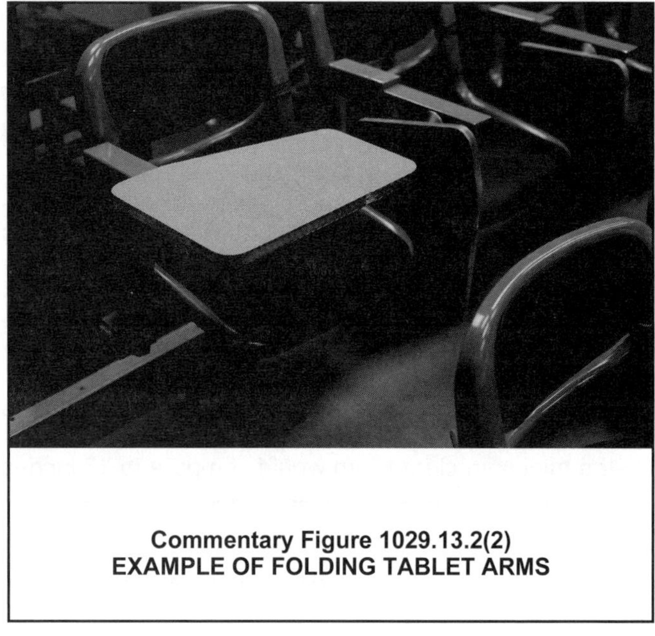

Commentary Figure 1029.13.2(2)
EXAMPLE OF FOLDING TABLET ARMS

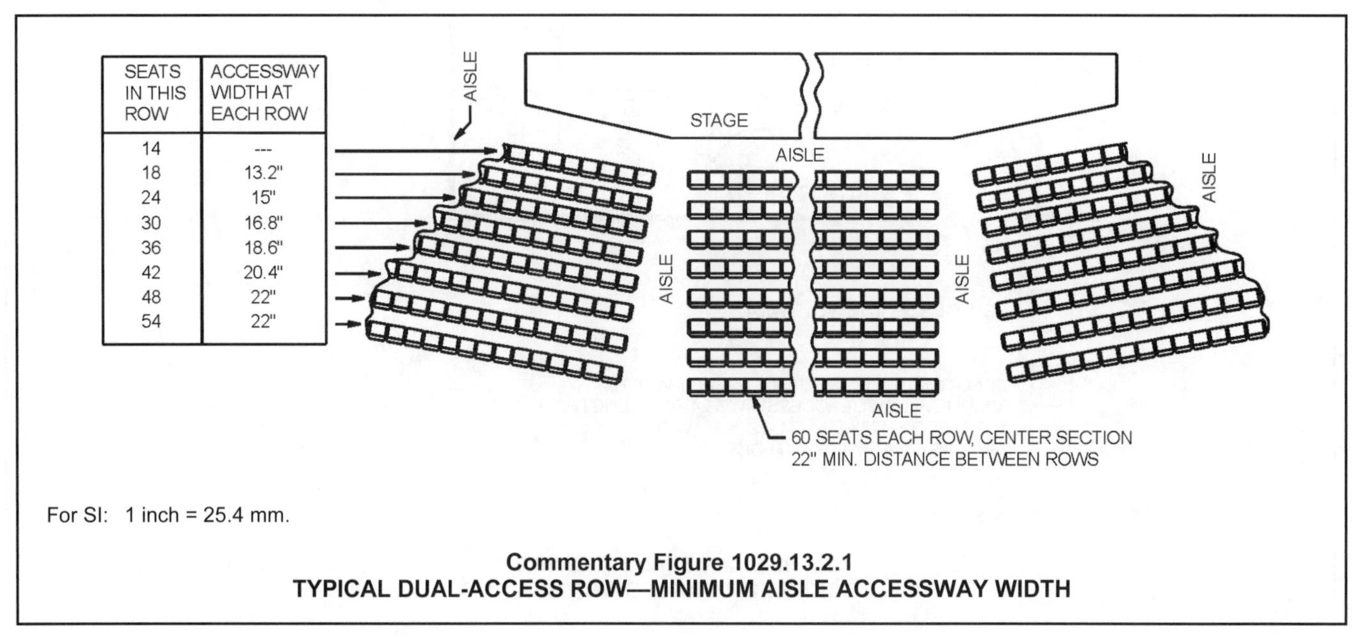

SEATS IN THIS ROW	ACCESSWAY WIDTH AT EACH ROW
14	---
18	13.2"
24	15"
30	16.8"
36	18.6"
42	20.4"
48	22"
54	22"

For SI: 1 inch = 25.4 mm.

Commentary Figure 1029.13.2.1
TYPICAL DUAL-ACCESS ROW—MINIMUM AISLE ACCESSWAY WIDTH

TABLE 1029.13.2.1. See below.

❖ Table 1029.13.2.1 recognizes the increased egress time available in smoke-protected and open-air assembly seating areas. Therefore, this table permits greater lengths for rows that have the minimum 12 inches (305 mm) of clear width in smoke-protected or open-air venues. Where a row exceeds the lengths identified in the table, the row width is to be increased in accordance with Section 1029.13.2.1 [0.3 inch (7.6 mm) per additional seat] for dual-access rows and Section 1029.13.2.2 [0.6 inch (15.2 mm) per additional seat] for single-access rows. Column one of this table is based on the total number of seats contained within the assembly space, not the seats per level. The increase for seating without backrests is to allow for bench seating similar to bleacher requirements in ICC 300 (see Section 1029.1.1).

[BE] 1029.13.2.2 Single access. For rows of seating served by an *aisle* or doorway at only one end of the row, the minimum clear width of 12 inches (305 mm) between rows shall be increased by 0.6 inch (15.2 mm) for every additional seat beyond seven seats where seats have backrests or beyond 10 where seats are without backrests. The minimum clear width is not required to exceed 22 inches (559 mm).

Exception: For *smoke-protected* or *open-air assembly seating*, the row length limits for a 12-inch-wide (305 mm) *aisle accessway*, beyond which the *aisle accessway* minimum clear width shall be increased, are in Table 1029.13.2.1.

❖ Where rows of seating are served by an aisle or doorway at only one end of a row, the minimum clear width of 12 inches (305 mm) between rows of seats must be increased by 0.6 inch (15.2 mm) for every additional seat beyond seven for seats with backrests, but not more than a total of 22 inches (559 mm) (see Commentary Figure 1029.13.2.2). The increase for seating without backrests is to allow for bench seating similar to bleacher requirements in ICC 300 (see Section 1029.1.1). While this section does not specify the maximum number of seats permitted in a row, the 30-foot (9144 mm) common path of egress travel limitation (see Section 1029.8) essentially restricts the single-access row to approximately 20 seats, based on an 18-inch (457 mm) width per seat. A row of 12 seats with backrests would compute to a

[BE] TABLE 1029.13.2.1
SMOKE-PROTECTED OR OPEN-AIR ASSEMBLY AISLE ACCESSWAYS

TOTAL NUMBER OF SEATS IN THE SMOKE-PROTECTED OR OPEN-AIR ASSEMBLY SEATING	MAXIMUM NUMBER OF SEATS PER ROW PERMITTED TO HAVE A MINIMUM 12-INCH CLEAR WIDTH AISLE ACCESSWAY			
	Aisle or doorway at both ends of row		Aisle or doorway at one end of row only	
	Seats with backrests	Seats without backrests	Seats with backrests	Seats without backrests
Less than 4,000	14	21	7	10
4,000	15	22	7	10
7,000	16	23	8	11
10,000	17	24	8	11
13,000	18	25	9	12
16,000	19	26	9	12
19,000	20	27	10	13
22,000 and greater	21	28	11	14

For SI: 1 inch = 25.4 mm.

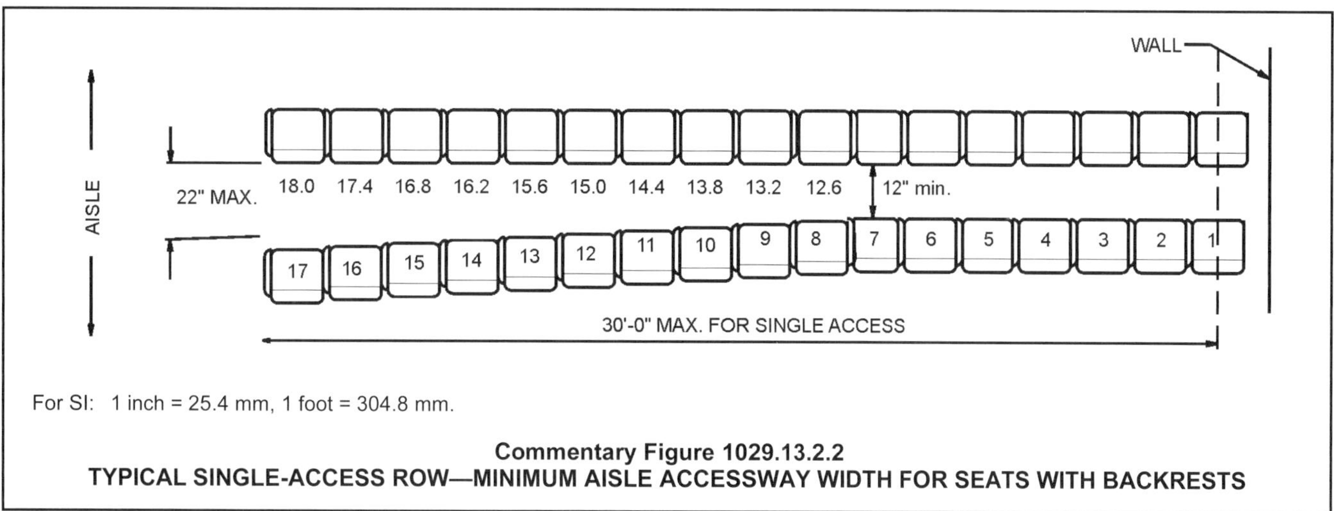

For SI: 1 inch = 25.4 mm, 1 foot = 304.8 mm.

Commentary Figure 1029.13.2.2
TYPICAL SINGLE-ACCESS ROW—MINIMUM AISLE ACCESSWAY WIDTH FOR SEATS WITH BACKRESTS

required minimum width of 15 inches (381 mm) [12 + (0.6 × 5)]. Similarly, a row of 17 seats with backrests would require a clear width of 18 inches (457 mm) and so on. Since dual access is not provided, incremental increases would be permitted in the aisle accessway width as shown in Commentary Figure 1029.13.2.2. Incremental increases in the required width would occur up to the maximum number of seats, which is determined by the 30-foot (9144 mm) dead-end limitation.

The reason for increasing the row accessway widths incrementally with increases in the number of seats per row is to provide more efficient passage for the occupants who are using the aisle accessway. As a practical matter, where dual-access (see Section 1029.13.2.1) and single-access seating arrangements are used together, the largest computed clear width dimension would normally be applied by the designer to both arrangements so that the rows of seats will be in alignment. Where a second means of egress for occupants of a single-access row is possible through an adjacent dual-access row, see Section 1029.8.1.

[BE] 1029.14 Assembly aisle walking surfaces. Ramped *aisles* shall comply with Sections 1029.14.1 through 1029.14.1.3. Stepped *aisles* shall comply with Sections 1029.14.2 through 1029.14.2.4.

❖ Assembly facilities such as theaters and auditoriums often require sloping or stepped floors to provide seated occupants with preferred sightlines for viewing presentations (for sightlines for wheelchair spaces, see Section 1108.2). Aisles must, therefore, be designed to accommodate the changing elevations of the floor in such a manner that the path of travel will allow occupants to leave the area at a rapid pace with minimal possibilities for stumbling or falling during times of emergency.

[BE] 1029.14.1 Ramped aisles. *Aisles* that are sloped more than one unit vertical in 20 units horizontal (5-percent slope) shall be considered to be a ramped *aisle*. Ramped *aisles* that serve as part of an accessible route in accordance with Sections 1009 of this code and Section 1108.2 of the *International Building Code* shall have a maximum slope of one unit vertical in 12 units horizontal (8-percent slope). The slope of other ramped *aisles* shall not exceed one unit vertical in 8 units horizontal (12.5-percent slope).

❖ Similar to the definition for "Ramp" in Chapter 2, aisles that slope 1:20 or less are considered sloped aisles, but are not ramps. Note that ramps that serve as part of an accessible route to and from accessible wheelchair spaces (Sections 1009 and 1108.2) must comply with the more restrictive requirements for ramps in Section 1012. This section requires that aisles with a gradient from 1:20 to 1:8 (12.5-percent slope) must meet the ramped aisle provisions in this section. Aisles with a gradient exceeding 1 unit vertical and 8 units horizontal (12.5-percent slope) must consist of a series of treads and risers that comply with the requirements of stepped aisles in Section 1029.14.2.

[BE] 1029.14.1.1 Cross slope. The slope measured perpendicular to the direction of travel of a ramped *aisle* shall not be steeper than one unit vertical in 48 units horizontal (2-percent slope).

❖ The limitation of 1 unit vertical in 48 units horizontal on the slope across the direction of travel is to prevent a severe cross slope that would pitch a user to one side (see Commentary Figure 1012.2).

[BE] 1029.14.1.2 Landings. Ramped *aisles* shall have landings in accordance with Sections 1012.6 through 1012.6.5. Landings for ramped *aisles* shall be permitted to overlap required *aisles* or cross *aisles*.

❖ The reference to ramp landings in Sections 1012.6 through 1012.6.5 picks up the requirements for ramps to have a landing at the top and bottom of each run and where ramps change direction. This also includes requirements for landing slope, width and length. This does not pick up the requirement for ramps to have a landing at every 30 inches (762 mm) in rise as indicated in Section 1012.4. This is in consideration of the line of sight requirements for the different venues and the ability to provide a safe and smooth transition between the ramped aisles and the adjacent aisle accessways as patrons move into and out of their rows. A cross aisle or aisle can also serve as the ramp landing as long as it meets the 1:48 maximum slope provisions for landings.

[BE] 1029.14.1.3 Edge protection. Ramped *aisles* shall have edge protection in accordance with Sections 1012.10 and 1012.10.1.

> **Exception:** In assembly spaces with *fixed seating*, edge protection is not required on the sides of ramped *aisles* where the ramped *aisles* provide access to the adjacent seating and *aisle accessways*.

❖ Where an aisle has a dropoff on either side, it needs edge protection. In a seating venue, this would typically be the ramped aisle at the perimeter of the seating. This edge protection can be a wall, a horizontal rail that prevents the passage of a 4-inch (102 mm) sphere between the ramp surface and the rail, or a minimum 4-inch-high (102 mm) curb (see Commentary Figure 1012.10.1). Edge protection is not required between the ramped aisle and adjacent seating, including wheelchair seating spaces, as this could be a tripping hazard for people coming in and out of the rows.

[BE] 1029.14.2 Stepped aisles. *Aisles* with a slope exceeding one unit vertical in eight units horizontal (12.5-percent slope) shall consist of a series of risers and treads that extends across the full width of *aisles* and complies with Sections 1029.14.2.1 through 1029.14.2.4.

❖ What must be recognized here is that stepped aisles are part of the floor construction and are intended to provide horizontal egress. Tread and riser construction for this purpose should not be directly compared to the requirements for treads and risers in conventional stairways that serve as means of vertical egress. Sometimes, because of design considerations, the gradient of an aisle is required to change from a level floor to a ramp and then to steps. In cases where there is no uniformity in the path of travel, occupants tend to be considerably more cautious, particularly in the use of stepped aisles, than they would normally be in the use of conventional stairways.

This section requires aisles with a slope greater than 1:8 to use steps. Aisles with slopes greater than 1:20 to 1:8 must comply with provisions for ramped aisles in Section 1029.14.1.

[BE] 1029.14.2.1 Treads. Tread depths shall be not less than 11 inches (279 mm) and shall have dimensional uniformity.

Exception: The tolerance between adjacent treads shall not exceed $^{3}/_{16}$ inch (4.8 mm).

❖ Depths of treads are not to be less than 11 inches (279 mm) and uniform throughout each flight. The exception states that a variance of not more than $^{3}/_{16}$ inch (4.8 mm) is permitted between adjacent treads to accommodate variations in construction. While the minimum tread depth provision is the same as the limiting dimension for treads in interior stairways (see Section 1011.5.2), it rarely applies in the construction of stepped aisles. A more common form of stepped aisle construction is to provide a tread depth equal to the back-to-back distance between rows of seats. This way the treads can be extended across the full length of the row and serve as a supporting platform for the seats. Other arrangements might require two treads between rows of seats, with each tread equaling one-half of the depth of the seat row.

In theaters, for example, the back-to-back distance between rows of fixed seats usually ranges between 3 and 4 feet (914 and 1219 mm), depending on seat style and seat dimensions as well as the ease of passage between the rows (see Commentary Figure 1029.14.2.1). The selection of single-tread or two-tread construction between rows of seats depends on the gradient and suitable riser height (see Section 1029.14.2.2), as needed for sightlines.

In comparing this section to Section 1029.14.2.2, it is significant to note the emphasis placed on the tread dimension. While not desirable, the code permits riser heights to deviate; however, tread dimensions must not vary beyond the $^{3}/_{16}$-inch (4.8 mm) tolerance.

[BE] 1029.14.2.2 Risers. Where the gradient of stepped *aisles* is to be the same as the gradient of adjoining seating areas, the riser height shall be not less than 4 inches (102 mm) nor more than 8 inches (203 mm) and shall be uniform within each *flight*.

Exceptions:

1. Riser height nonuniformity shall be limited to the extent necessitated by changes in the gradient of the adjoining seating area to maintain adequate sightlines. Where nonuniformities exceed $^{3}/_{16}$ inch (4.8 mm) between adjacent risers, the exact location of such nonuniformities shall be indicated with a distinctive marking stripe on each tread at the *nosing* or leading edge adjacent to the nonuniform risers. Such stripe shall be not less than 1 inch (25 mm), and not more than 2 inches (51 mm), wide. The edge marking stripe shall be distinctively different from the contrasting marking stripe.
2. Riser heights not exceeding 9 inches (229 mm) shall be permitted where they are necessitated by the slope of the adjacent seating areas to maintain sightlines.

❖ In stepped aisles where the gradient of the aisle is the same as the gradient of the adjoining seating area, riser heights are not to be less than 4 inches (102 mm) nor more than 8 inches (203 mm) (see Commentary Figure 1029.14.2.2). For the safety of the occupants, risers should have uniform heights, where possible, throughout each flight. However, nonuniformity of riser heights is permitted in cases where changes to the gradient in the adjoining seating area are required because of sightlines and other seating layout considerations.

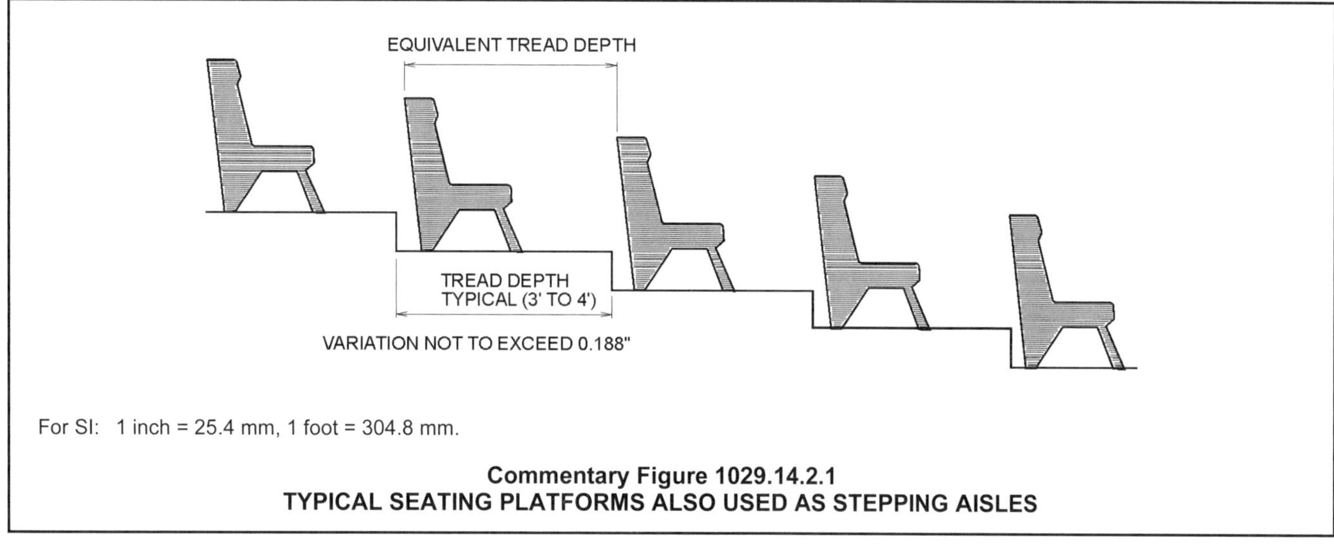

Commentary Figure 1029.14.2.1
TYPICAL SEATING PLATFORMS ALSO USED AS STEPPING AISLES

Where variations in height exceed $^3/_{16}$ inch (4.8 mm) between adjacent risers, a distinctive marking stripe between 1 inch (25 mm) and 2 inches (51 mm) wide is to be located on the nosings of each tread as a visual warning to occupants to be cautious. Frequently, this is done with "runway" lights. Note that this stripe must be different from the tread contrast marking stripes required for transitions in Section 1029.10.3 and the tread stripes in Section 1029.14.2.3. These stripes must be visible in lighted conditions; therefore, they are not required to comply with the provisions for luminous tread markings in Section 1025.

While the riser height may vary to adjust to sightlines of the associated seating, there is a maximum change for adjacent treads so that there is consistency in the flight (see Section 1029.14.2.2.1).

In comparing this section with Section 1029.14.2.1, it is significant to note the emphasis placed on the tread dimension. While not desirable, the code permits riser heights to deviate; however, Section 1029.14.2.1 does not permit tread dimensions to vary beyond the $^3/_{16}$-inch (4.8 mm) tolerance.

[BE] 1029.14.2.2.1 Construction tolerances. The tolerance between adjacent risers on a stepped *aisle* that were designed to be equal height shall not exceed $^3/_{16}$ inch (4.8 mm). Where the stepped *aisle* is designed in accordance with Exception 1 of Section 1029.14.2.2, the stepped *aisle* shall be constructed so that each riser of unequal height, determined in the direction of descent, is not more than $^3/_8$ inch (9.5 mm) in height different from adjacent risers where stepped *aisle* treads are less than 22 inches (560 mm) in depth and $^3/_4$ inch (19.1 mm) in height different from adjacent risers where stepped *aisle* treads are 22 inches (560 mm) or greater in depth.

❖ Where risers in a stepped aisle are consistent, the construction tolerance between adjacent treads allows for a maximum difference of $^3/_{16}$ inch (4.8 mm). Stairways allow for $^3/_8$ inch (9.5 mm), but this is for the flight of stairs (see Section 1011.5.4). Where the seating arrangement allows for unequal heights, the difference between adjacent risers is greater for situations with deeper treads. With a tread of 22 inches (560 mm) or greater, most people will be taking more than one step on each tread.

[BE] 1029.14.2.3 Tread contrasting marking stripe. A contrasting marking stripe shall be provided on each tread at the *nosing* or leading edge such that the location of each tread is readily apparent when viewed in descent. Such stripe shall be not less than 1 inch (25 mm), and not more than 2 inches (51 mm), wide.

Exception: The contrasting marking stripe is permitted to be omitted where tread surfaces are such that the location of each tread is readily apparent when viewed in descent.

❖ The exception provides for the omission of the contrasting marking stripe where the tread is readily apparent, such as where aisle stair treads are provided with a roughened metal nosing strip or where lighted nosings occur. In such situations, the user is aware of the treads without the marking stripe. This stripe must be different from the marking stripe required for nonuniform risers in Section 1029.14.2.3 and the tread contrast marking stripes required for transitions in Section 1029.10.3

These stripes must be visible in lighted conditions; therefore, these stripes are not required to comply with the provisions for luminous tread markings in Section 1025.

[BE] 1029.14.2.4 Nosing and profile. *Nosing* and riser profile shall comply with Sections 1011.5.5 through 1011.5.5.3.

❖ The profiles of treads and risers contribute to stepped aisle safety. The radius or bevel of the nosing eases the otherwise square edge of the tread and prevents irregular chipping and wear that can become a maintenance issue and seriously affect the safe use of the stepped aisles. Since safety considerations for stepped aisles and stairways are the same for nosing and riser profiles, the provisions in stairways are referenced for this requirement.

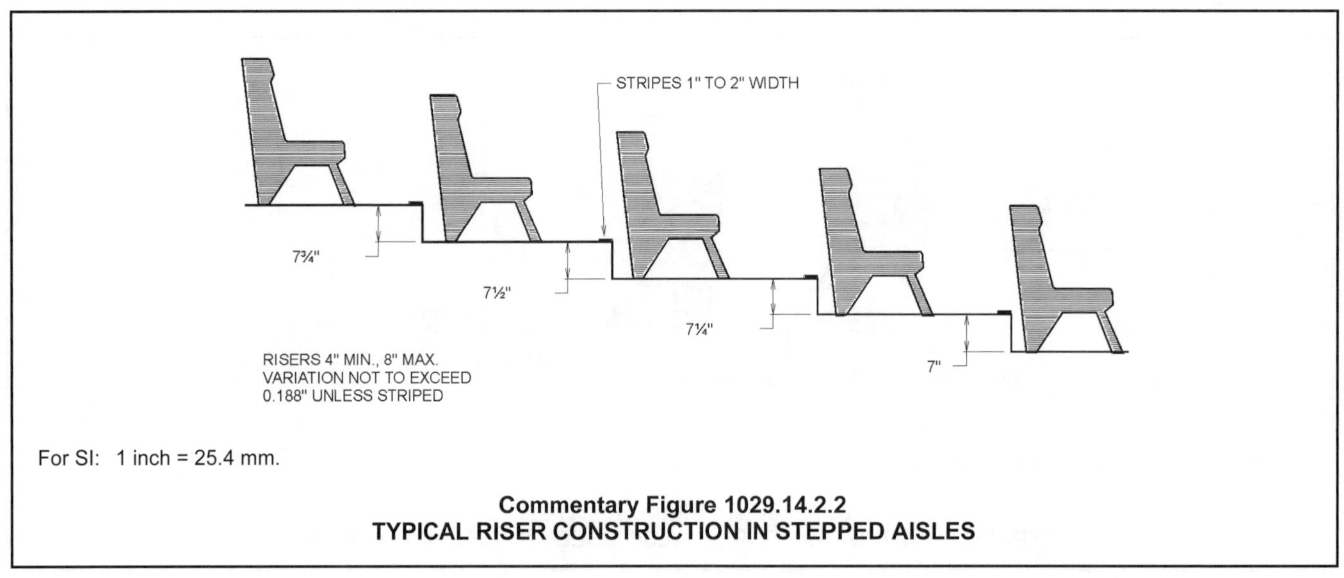

For SI: 1 inch = 25.4 mm.

Commentary Figure 1029.14.2.2
TYPICAL RISER CONSTRUCTION IN STEPPED AISLES

[BE] 1029.15 Seat stability. In a building, room or space used for assembly purposes, the seats shall be securely fastened to the floor.

Exceptions:

1. In a building, room or space used for assembly purposes or portions thereof without ramped or tiered floors for seating and with 200 or fewer seats, the seats shall not be required to be fastened to the floor.
2. In a building, room or space used for assembly purposes or portions thereof with seating at tables and without ramped or tiered floors for seating, the seats shall not be required to be fastened to the floor.
3. In a building, room or space used for assembly purposes or portions thereof without ramped or tiered floors for seating and with greater than 200 seats, the seats shall be fastened together in groups of not less than three or the seats shall be securely fastened to the floor.
4. In a building, room or space used for assembly purposes where flexibility of the seating arrangement is an integral part of the design and function of the space and seating is on tiered levels, not more than 200 seats shall not be required to be fastened to the floor. Plans showing seating, tiers and *aisles* shall be submitted for approval.
5. Groups of seats within a building, room or space used for assembly purposes separated from other seating by railings, *guards*, partial height walls or similar barriers with level floors and having not more than 14 seats per group shall not be required to be fastened to the floor.
6. Seats intended for musicians or other performers and separated by railings, *guards*, partial height walls or similar barriers shall not be required to be fastened to the floor.

❖ The purpose of this section is to require that assembly seating be fastened to the floor where it would be a significant hazard if loose and subject to tipping over. The exceptions allow loose assembly seating for situations where the hazard is lower, such as floors where ramped or tiered seating is not used; where not more than 200 seats are used; for box seating arrangements; and where a limited number of seats are within railings, guards or partial height walls.

[BE] 1029.16 Handrails. Ramped *aisles* having a slope exceeding one unit vertical in 15 units horizontal (6.7-percent slope) and stepped *aisles* shall be provided with *handrails* in compliance with Section 1014 located either at one or both sides of the *aisle* or within the *aisle* width.

Exceptions:

1. *Handrails* are not required for ramped *aisles* with seating on both sides.
2. *Handrails* are not required where, at the side of the *aisle*, there is a *guard* with a top surface that complies with the graspability requirements of *handrails* in accordance with Section 1014.3.
3. *Handrail* extensions are not required at the top and bottom of stepped *aisles* and ramped *aisles* to permit crossovers within the *aisles*.

❖ For the safety of occupants, handrails must be provided in aisles where ramps exceed a gradient of 1 unit vertical in 15 units horizontal (6.7-percent slope) (see Commentary Figure 1029.16). All stepped aisles are required to have handrails. Handrails can be on one side, both sides or in the center of the aisle. Typically, handrails are in the center of the aisle where there is seating on both sides or on one side where the aisle is adjacent to a side wall or a guard. While Sections 1011.11 and 1012.8 specify that handrails are required on both sides of stairways or ramps, the exceptions in Sections 1011.1 and 1012.1 and throughout Section 1014 allow for Section 1029.16 to be utilized for handrail location where dealing with stepped aisles, transitions and ramped aisles within assembly seating areas. This would include requiring handrails being within 30 inches (762 mm) (Section 1014.9) of the required stairway width. Safety for aisles wider than 60 inches (1524 mm) with center

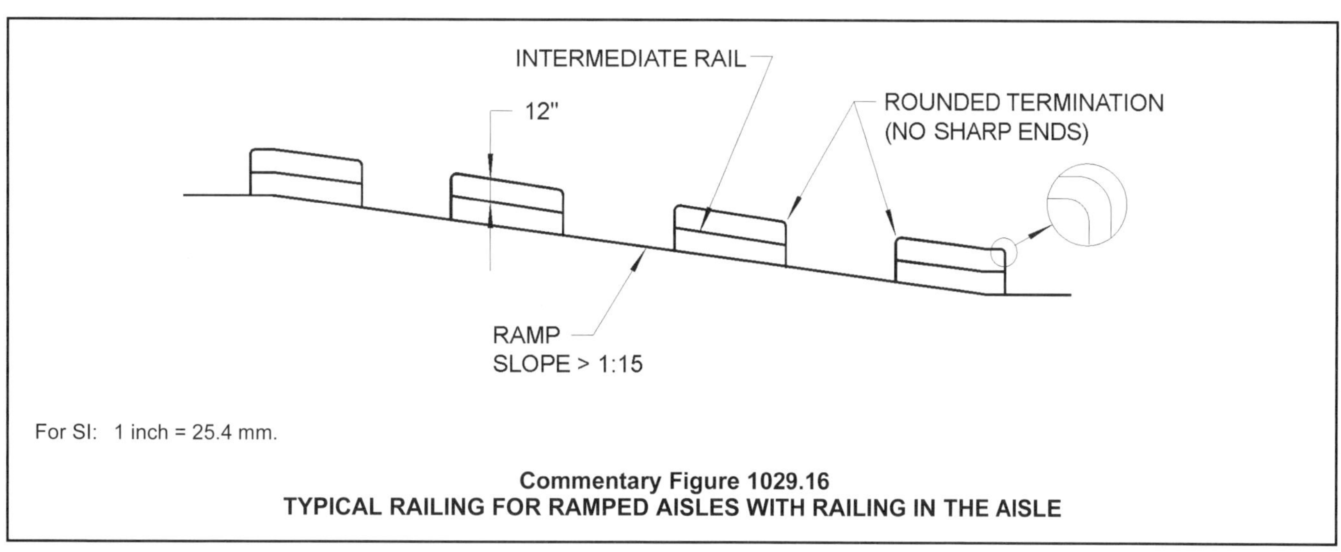

Commentary Figure 1029.16
TYPICAL RAILING FOR RAMPED AISLES WITH RAILING IN THE AISLE

handrails and side aisles wider than 30 inches (762 mm) is specifically addressed with the capacity increases in Sections 1029.6.1 and 1029.6.2. Referencing Section 1014 will require the provisions for handrail height, graspability and fittings. Continuity, extensions, clearance and projections are more specifically addressed in Section 1029.16, this section and subsequent subsections.

Exception 1 omits the handrail requirements where steeper ramped aisles have seats on both sides of the aisle, effectively reducing the fall hazard. This also allows for these ramped aisles to be wide enough for accessible routes to and from wheelchair spaces.

Exception 2 allows handrails to be omitted where there is a guard at the side of the ramped or stepped aisle with a top rail that complies with the requirements for handrail graspability (see Section 1014.3). Note that the guard must meet the height and opening requirements specified in Section 1015 or 1029.17, as applicable.

While Section 1029.16.1 allows for discontinuous handrails, and Exception 3 (as well as Section 1014.6, Exception 2) exempts handrail extensions where they could block access to the seating, the handrail must extend the full run of the stepped aisle. Stopping the handrail short of the bottom riser flight (except where permitted by Section 1029.16.3 for mid-aisle handrails) would be considered a code violation. Handrails along the wall adjacent to stepped aisles or ramps should include the handrail extensions where feasible.

[BE] 1029.16.1 Discontinuous handrails. Where there is seating on both sides of the *aisle*, the mid-aisle *handrails* shall be discontinuous with gaps or breaks at intervals not exceeding five rows to facilitate access to seating and to permit crossing from one side of the *aisle* to the other. These gaps or breaks shall have a clear width of not less than 22 inches (559 mm) and not greater than 36 inches (914 mm), measured horizontally, and the mid-aisle *handrail* shall have rounded terminations or bends.

❖ Where aisles have seating on both sides, handrails may be located at the sides of the aisles, but are typically located in the center of the aisle. (Handrails on both sides of a stepped aisle will typically either block access to the aisle accessways or not be able to meet the gap requirements. Transitions per Sections 1029.10 and 1029.11 can have handrails on both sides or mid-width.) The width of each section of the subdivided aisle between the handrail and the edge of seating is to be not less than 23 inches (584 mm) measured to the handrail centerline (see Section 1029.9.1, Item 3).

For reasons of life safety in fire situations and also as a practical matter in the efficient use of the facility, a handrail down the middle of a straight aisle should not be continuous along its entire length. The decision for using one or two handrails may change at transitions, depending on the configuration. Crossovers must be provided by means of gaps or breaks in the handrail installation. Such openings must not be less than 22 inches (559 mm) or greater than 36 inches (914 mm) wide, and must be provided at intervals not exceeding the distance of five rows of seats (see Commentary Figure 1029.16.1). All handrail terminations should be designed to have rounded ends or bends to avoid possible injury to the occupants (see Commentary Figure 1029.16).

[BE] 1029.16.2 Handrail termination. *Handrails* located on the side of stepped *aisles* shall return to a wall, *guard* or the walking surfaces or shall be continuous to the *handrail* of an adjacent stepped *aisle flight.*

❖ The purpose of return requirements at handrail ends is to prevent a person from catching an article of clothing or satchel straps or from being injured by falling on the extended end of a handrail. Where a handrail is on a wall adjacent to a stepped aisle, it can return the same as a handrail on a stairway.

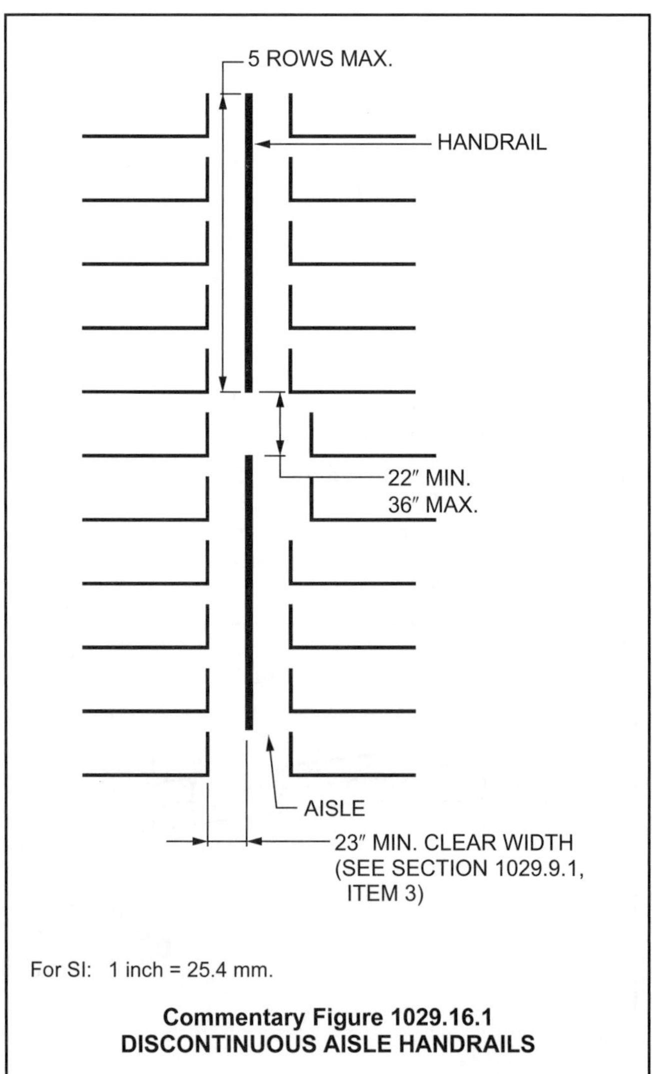

For SI: 1 inch = 25.4 mm.

Commentary Figure 1029.16.1
DISCONTINUOUS AISLE HANDRAILS

[BE] 1029.16.3 Mid-aisle termination. Mid-aisle *handrails* shall not extend beyond the lowest riser and shall terminate within 18 inches (457 mm), measured horizontally, from the lowest riser. *Handrail* extensions are not required.

Exception: Mid-aisle *handrails* shall be permitted to extend beyond the lowest riser where the *handrail* extensions do not obstruct the width of the cross *aisle*.

❖ The intent is to clarify how far a mid-aisle handrail can stop from the bottom of a stepped aisle and still allow for a person to get past the front of the rail to enter the first row of seating. Since the purpose of a handrail is to arrest a fall or provide stability for someone moving up or down the stepped aisle, the handrails should also not start so far back that someone could not reach the handrail from the cross aisle, or would have to let go too soon before they got to the cross aisle. The intent of the exception is to allow for a mid-aisle handrail to have a bottom extension if it will not block the cross aisle. However, if a designer wants to not have a handrail extension in order to provide access to the front row of raised seats, the handrail must extend to at least 18 inches (457 mm) from the nosing of the bottom riser.

[BE] 1029.16.4 Rails. Where mid-aisle *handrails* are provided in stepped *aisles*, there shall be an additional rail located approximately 12 inches (305 mm) below the *handrail*. The rail shall be adequate in strength and attachment in accordance with Section 1607.8.1.2 of the *International Building Code*.

❖ Handrail installations down the middle of an aisle must be constructed with intermediate rails located 12 inches (305 mm) below and parallel to main handrails. The rail below the handrail is to stop people from going under the handrail or swinging on the handrail (see Commentary Figure 1029.16). The lower rail is not intended to meet all handrail provisions for graspability; however, it does have to meet the same strength criteria as a handrail.

[BE] 1029.17 Assembly guards. *Guards* adjacent to seating in a building, room or space used for assembly purposes shall be provided where required by Section 1015 and shall be constructed in accordance with Section 1015 except where provided in accordance with Sections 1029.17.1 through 1029.17.4. At *bleachers, grandstands and folding and telescopic seating*, *guards* must be provided where required by ICC 300 and Section 1029.17.1.

❖ This section establishes the scope of the guard provisions within assembly seating. Depending on the event, the sightline constraints can be for a wide viewing angle. For example, to see the entire football field, a person may have to look right and left. Good design will establish a balance between safety and sight issues that will need to be evaluated on a case-by-case basis.

Some situations unique to assembly make it necessary to strike a balance between safety requirements and line of sight issues. Section 1029.17.1 addresses the guards around the outside edge of a seating area, such as a bleacher or tiered seating arrangement that is on each side of a high school football field, or along the first- and third-base lines at a baseball field. The perimeter guards are required for assembly seating addressed in Section 1029 and seating covered by ICC 300. The purpose of Section 1029.17.2 is to provide for occupant safety with guards along elevated cross aisles, typically in aisles that occupants use to move side to side across the seating bowl. If there is only an aisle accessway between the seats and the guard, typically found at the front of a balcony or raised section, then Section 1029.17.3 is applicable. If the aisle is moving down through the seating toward a dropoff, then Section 1029.17.4 is applicable.

[BE] 1029.17.1 Perimeter guards. Perimeter *guards* shall be provided where the footboards or walking surface of seating facilities are more than 30 inches (762 mm) above the floor or grade below. Where the seatboards are adjacent to the perimeter, *guard* height shall be 42 inches (1067 mm) high minimum, measured from the seatboard. Where the seats are self-rising, *guard* height shall be 42 inches (1067 mm) high minimum, measured from the floor surface. Where there is an *aisle* between the seating and the perimeter, the *guard* height shall be measured in accordance with Section 1015.3.

Exceptions:

1. *Guards* that impact sightlines shall be permitted to comply with Section 1029.17.3.
2. *Bleachers, grandstands and folding and telescopic seating* shall not be required to have perimeter *guards* where the seating is located adjacent to a wall and the space between the wall and the seating is less than 4 inches (102 mm).

❖ The intent of perimeter guards is to address the risk of falling from the side and back of a seating area. This provision is applicable for bleachers, grandstands and folding and telescopic seating addressed in ICC 300 and other assembly seating arrangements.

ICC 300 requires guards with 4-inch openings where the floor surface has an adjacent 30-inch (762 mm) dropoff (ICC 300, Section 408). The dropoff is measured from the floor rather than the seatboard because the ICC 300 committee did not believe it was appropriate to require guards in a two- or three-row bleacher system. For fixed seats and benches, the height for perimeter guards is measured from the seatboard, to address when people stand on the seats. Where seats are self-rising, the guard height would be measured from the floor. Self-rising seats have backs and are very difficult to stand on.

Exception 1 is to allow for the limited situation where guards at the sides of the seating may affect the line of sight in wide venues.

Exception 2 will permit bleacher systems constructed inside the building to use the building walls as perimeter guards if the opening between the bleacher and the wall is less than the opening permitted for guards.

[BE] 1029.17.2 Cross aisles. Cross *aisles* located more than 30 inches (762 mm) above the floor or grade below shall have *guards* in accordance with Section 1015.

Where an elevation change of 30 inches (762 mm) or less occurs between a cross *aisle* and the adjacent floor or grade below, *guards* not less than 26 inches (660 mm) above the *aisle* floor shall be provided.

> **Exception:** Where the backs of seats on the front of the cross *aisle* project 24 inches (610 mm) or more above the adjacent floor of the *aisle*, a *guard* need not be provided.

❖ The purpose of this section is to provide for occupant safety with guards along elevated cross aisles. The minimum height of the guard is a function of the cross-aisle elevation above the adjacent floor or grade below [i.e., 42 inches (1067 mm) high with more than a 30-inch (762 mm) dropoff and 26 inches (660 mm) high with a 30-inch (762 mm) or less dropoff]. Where the seatbacks adjacent to cross aisles are a minimum of 24 inches (610 mm) above the floor level of the cross aisle, they will serve as the guard (see Commentary Figure 1029.17.3 for an illustration of the requirements in this section).

[BE] 1029.17.3 Sightline-constrained guard heights. Unless subject to the requirements of Section 1029.17.4, a fascia or railing system in accordance with the *guard* requirements of Section 1015 and having a minimum height of 26 inches (660 mm) shall be provided where the floor or footboard elevation is more than 30 inches (762 mm) above the floor or grade below and the fascia or railing would otherwise interfere with the sightlines of immediately adjacent seating.

❖ The purpose of this section is to provide for occupant safety with guards along elevated seating for areas other than cross aisles, such as the front of a raised area or balcony level. The seats would only have an access aisle between the seat and the dropoff.

This section specifies a height of 26 inches (660 mm) for guards along fascias. The guard height and the dropoff are measured from the floor or footboard. This is to provide a reasonable degree of safety while improving sightlines for persons seated immediately behind a fascia or balcony edge. The guard opening configuration must comply with Section 1015.4 (see Commentary Figure 1029.17.3 for an illustration of the requirements in this section).

[BE] 1029.17.4 Guards at the end of aisles. A fascia or railing system complying with the *guard* requirements of Section 1015 shall be provided for the full width of the *aisle* where the foot of the *aisle* is more than 30 inches (762 mm) above the floor or grade below. The fascia or railing shall be not less than 36 inches (914 mm) high and shall provide not less than 42 inches (1067 mm) measured diagonally between the top of the rail and the *nosing* of the nearest tread.

❖ This section applies only where the foot end of aisles (the lower end) is greater than 30 inches (762 mm)

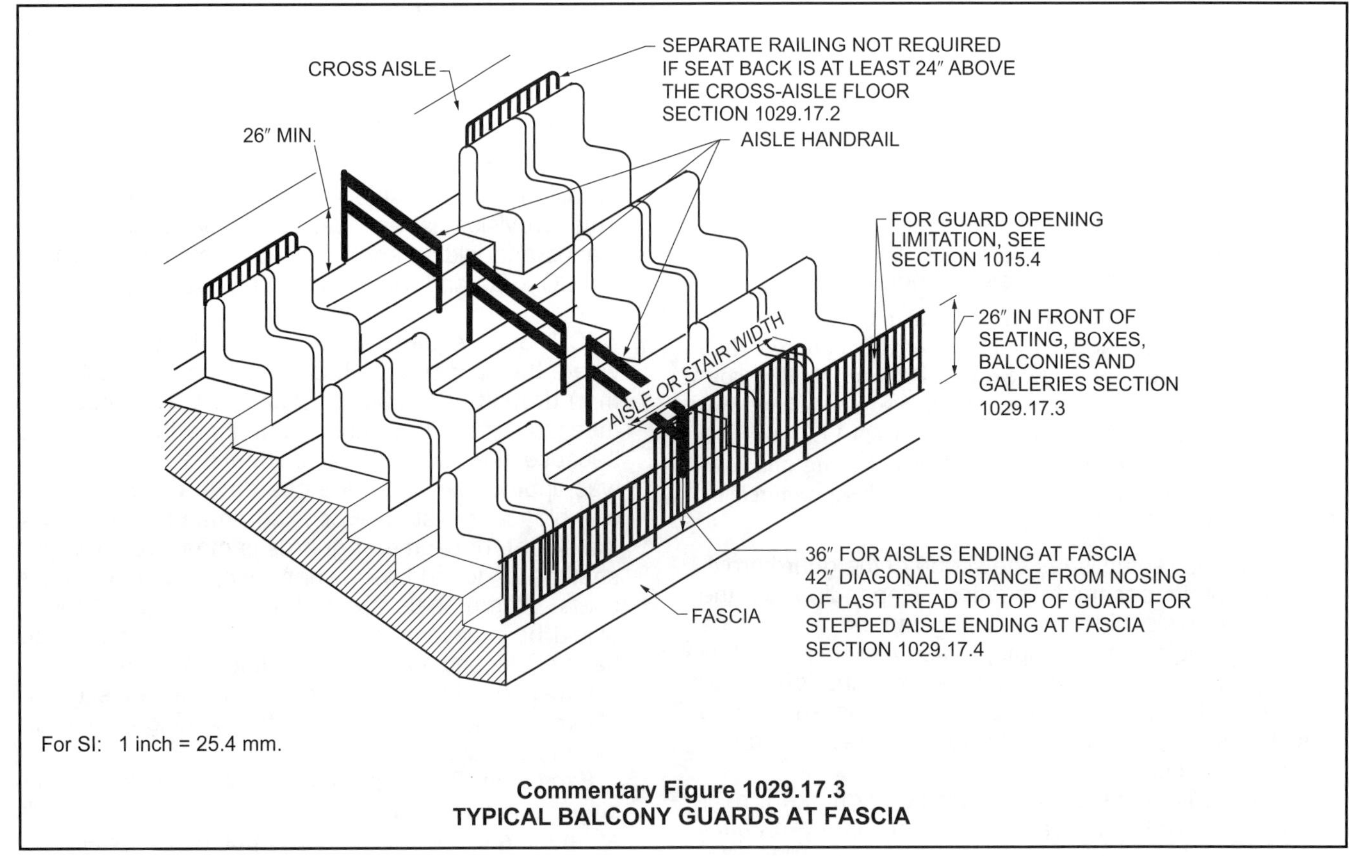

Commentary Figure 1029.17.3
TYPICAL BALCONY GUARDS AT FASCIA

above the adjacent floor or grade below. This typically occurs where aisles move down through rows of seating to the front edge of a balcony or raised seating area. The guard must satisfy both of the specified height requirements to provide safety for persons at the end of the aisle in case someone trips moving down the stepped or ramped aisle. The 36-inch (914 mm) minimum height is measured from the floor vertically to the top of the guard. The minimum 42-inch (1067 mm) diagonal dimension from the nosing of the nearest stair tread to the top of the fascia or guard provides sufficient height to arrest a fall from the nearest aisle riser (see Commentary Figure 1029.17.3 for an illustration of the requirements in this section). The end result could be a guard with a vertical height of more than 36 inches (914 mm).

SECTION 1030 EMERGENCY ESCAPE AND RESCUE

[BE] 1030.1 General. In addition to the *means of egress* required by this chapter, *emergency escape and rescue openings* shall be provided in the following occupancies:

1. Group R-2 occupancies located in stories with only one *exit* or access to only one *exit* as permitted by Tables 1006.3.3(1) and 1006.3.3(2).
2. Group R-3 and R-4 occupancies.

Basements and sleeping rooms below the fourth story above *grade plane* shall have not fewer than one exterior *emergency escape and rescue opening* in accordance with this section. Where *basements* contain one or more sleeping rooms, *emergency escape and rescue openings* shall be required in each sleeping room, but shall not be required in adjoining areas of the *basement*. Such openings shall open directly into a *public way* or to a *yard* or *court* that opens to a *public way*.

Exceptions:

1. *Basements* with a ceiling height of less than 80 inches (2032 mm) shall not be required to have *emergency escape and rescue openings*.
2. *Emergency escape and rescue openings* are not required from *basements* or sleeping rooms that have an *exit* door or *exit access* door that opens directly into a *public way* or to a *yard*, *court* or exterior exit balcony that opens to a *public way*.
3. *Basements* without *habitable spaces* and having not more than 200 square feet (18.6 m^2) in floor area shall not be required to have *emergency escape and rescue openings*.
4. Within individual *dwelling* and *sleeping units* in Groups R-2 and R-3, where the building is equipped throughout with an *automatic sprinkler system* installed in accordance with Section 903.3.1.1, 903.3.1.2 or 903.3.1.3, sleeping rooms in *basements* shall not be required to have *emergency escape and rescue openings* provided that the *basement* has one of the following:
   - 4.1. One *means of egress* and one *emergency escape and rescue opening*.
   - 4.2. Two *means of egress*.

❖ Emergency escape and rescue openings (EERO) are required in single-exit Group R-2 apartment and congregate residence buildings and all Group R-3 and R-4 dwellings where occupants may be sleeping during a potential fire buildup. Group R-2 apartment buildings permitted to have a single exit from a story are required to have EERO by Table 1006.3.3(1), Note a. Group R-2 congregate residences permitted to have a single exit are required to have an EERO by Table 1006.3.3(2), Note a.

All basements and each bedroom/sleeping room are to be provided with an exterior window or door that meets the minimum size requirements and is operable for emergency escape by methods that are obvious and clearly understood by all users. Sleeping rooms four stories or more above grade are not required to be so equipped, since fire service access at that height, as well as escape through such an opening, may not be practical or reliable. Since single-exit apartment buildings are limited to three stories and most Group R-3 and R-4 buildings are two or three stories, this limit is not applicable very often. Section 1019.3, Item 2, limits Groups R-3 and R-4 to four stories where using a single open exit access stairway.

The provision for basements is in recognition that they typically have only a single means of egress without alternative routes through standard windows. Many times a basement is finished at a later time; therefore, as a safety precaution, at least one EERO is required in every basement. If bedrooms are provided within the basement, the location and number of EERO are determined by the bedrooms.

It is important to note that this window is only an element of escape and is not part of the means of egress required from the story unless it is a door conforming to normal egress requirements.

Exceptions 1 and 3 are intended to exempt basements that would not likely be finished as living space since this lessens the chance of such spaces having sleeping rooms.

The intent of Exception 2 is to permit sleeping rooms with a door that has direct access to an exterior-type environment, such as a street or exit balcony, to not have an EERO. The open atmosphere of the escape route would increase the likelihood that the means of egress would be available even with the delayed response time for sleeping residents. This would also exempt walk-out basements that did not include bedrooms.

Exception 4 is applicable in buildings sprinklered throughout with an NFPA 13, 13R or 13D system. In Group R-2, if there are two, three or four units in the basement, this exception is considered for each unit separately. In recognition of this addition protection, each bedroom in a basement is not required to have an EERO if the basement as a whole has one exit stairway/exterior door and one EERO or the occupants have access to either two exit stairways and/or doors. The overall effect is that in a sprinklered dwelling unit, an EERO can be anywhere in the basement instead of within the bedroom.

[BE] 1030.1.1 Operational constraints and opening control devices. *Emergency escape and rescue openings* shall be operational from inside the room without the use of keys or tools. Window-opening control devices complying with ASTM F2090 shall be permitted for use on windows serving as a required *emergency escape and rescue opening*.

❖ If security grilles, decorations or similar devices are installed on escape windows, such items must be readily removable to permit occupant escape without the use of any tools, keys or force greater than that required for the normal operation of the window. This would include any window fall prevention devices and window-opening control devices required by Section 1015.8.

[BE] 1030.2 Minimum size. *Emergency escape and rescue openings* shall have a minimum net clear opening of 5.7 square feet (0.53 m^2).

Exception: The minimum net clear opening for grade-floor *emergency escape and rescue openings* shall be 5 square feet (0.46 m^2).

❖ The net clear opening area and minimum dimensions are intended to provide a clear opening through which an occupant can pass to escape the building or a fire fighter (in full protective clothing with breathing apparatus) can pass to enter the building for rescue or fire suppression activities. Note, this is the clear opening size, not the size of the window.

Since the emergency escape windows must be usable to all occupants, including children and guests, the required opening dimensions must be achieved by the normal operation of the window from the inside (e.g., sliding, swinging or lifting the sash). It is impractical to assume that all occupants can operate a window that requires a special sequence of operations to achieve the required opening size. While most occupants are familiar with the normal operation by which to open the window, children and guests are frequently unfamiliar with any special procedures that may be necessary to remove or tilt the sashes. The time spent in comprehending the special operation unnecessarily delays egress from the bedroom and could lead to panic and further confusion. Thus, windows that achieve the required opening dimensions only through operations such as the removal of sashes or mullions are not permitted. It should be noted that the minimum area cannot be achieved by using both the minimum height and minimum width specified in Section 1030.2.1 (see Commentary Figure 1030.2).

[BE] 1030.2.1 Minimum dimensions. The minimum net clear opening height dimension shall be 24 inches (610 mm). The minimum net clear opening width dimension shall be 20 inches (508 mm). The net clear opening dimensions shall be the result of normal operation of the opening.

❖ Note that both the minimum dimensions in this section and the minimum area requirements in Section 1030.2 apply. Thus, a grade floor window that is only 24 inches (610 mm) in height must be 30 inches (762 mm) wide to meet the 5-square-foot (0.46 m^2) area requirement of Section 1030.2 for grade floor openings (see Commentary Figure 1030.2). Note, this is the clear opening width, not the size of the window.

[BE] 1030.3 Maximum height from floor. *Emergency escape and rescue openings* shall have the bottom of the clear opening not greater than 44 inches (1118 mm) measured from the floor.

❖ This section limits the height of the bottom of the clear opening to 44 inches (1118 mm) or less such that it can be used effectively as an emergency escape (see Commentary Figure 1030.2). Note that this dimension is to the bottom of the actual window opening, not the sill height of the rough opening.

[BE] 1030.4 Window wells. An *emergency escape and rescue opening* with a finished sill height below the adjacent ground level shall be provided with a window well in accordance with Sections 1030.4.1 and 1030.4.2.

❖ Emergency escape and rescue openings that are partially or completely below grade need to have win-

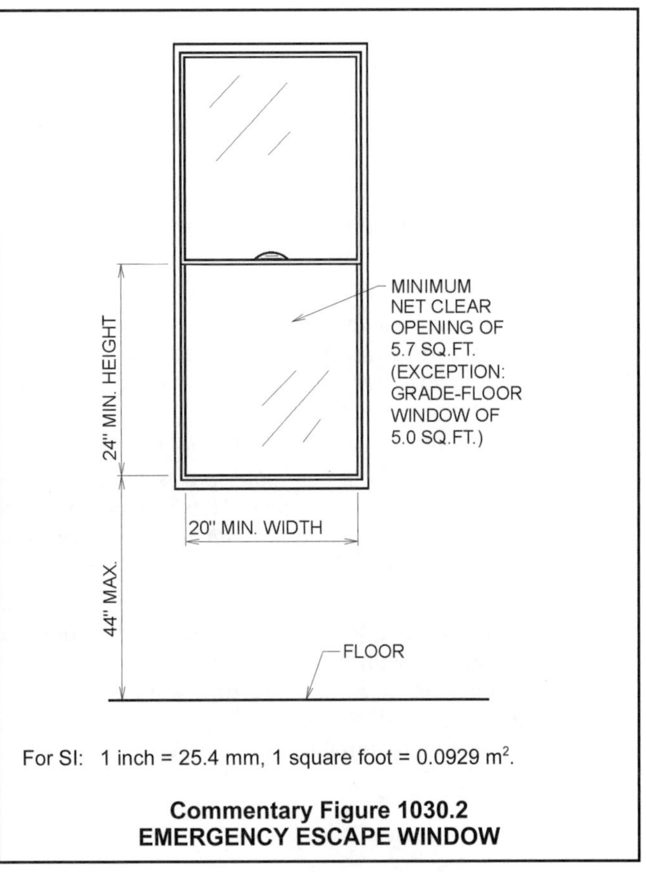

**Commentary Figure 1030.2
EMERGENCY ESCAPE WINDOW**

dow wells so that they can be used effectively (see Commentary Figure 1030.4).

[BE] 1030.4.1 Minimum size. The minimum horizontal area of the window well shall be 9 square feet (0.84 m^2), with a minimum dimension of 36 inches (914 mm). The area of the window well shall allow the *emergency escape and rescue opening* to be fully opened.

❖ This section specifies the size of the window well that is needed for a rescue person in full protective clothing with breathing apparatus to use the rescue opening. The required 9 square feet (0.84 m^2) is the size of the window well. Thus, the window well must project away from the plane of the window at least 3 feet (914 mm), as well as 3 feet (914 mm) along the plane of the window along the wall (see Commentary Figure 1030.4).

[BE] 1030.4.2 Ladders or steps. Window wells with a vertical depth of more than 44 inches (1118 mm) shall be equipped with an *approved* permanently affixed ladder or steps. Ladders or rungs shall have an inside width of not less than 12 inches (305 mm), shall project not less than 3 inches (76 mm) from the wall and shall be spaced not more than 18 inches (457 mm) on center (o.c.) vertically for the full height of the window well. The ladder or steps shall not encroach into the required dimensions of the window well by more than 6 inches (152 mm). The ladder or steps shall not be obstructed by the *emergency escape and rescue opening*. Ladders or steps required by this section are exempt from the *stairway* requirements of Section 1011.

❖ This section specifies that a ladder or steps be provided for ease of getting into and out of window wells that are more than 44 inches (1118 mm) deep.

Usually, ladder rungs are embedded in the wall of the window well. The 44-inch (1118 mm) dimension is the depth of the window well, not the distance from the bottom of the window well to grade. For example, if the floor of a window well is 40 inches (1016 mm) below grade, but the wall of the window well projects above grade by 6 inches (152 mm), steps or a ladder are required since the vertical depth is 46 inches (1168 mm).

It is important that the ladder not obstruct the operation of the emergency escape window (see Commentary Figure 1030.4).

[BE] 1030.5 Bars, grilles, covers and screens. Bars, grilles, covers, screens or similar devices are permitted to be placed

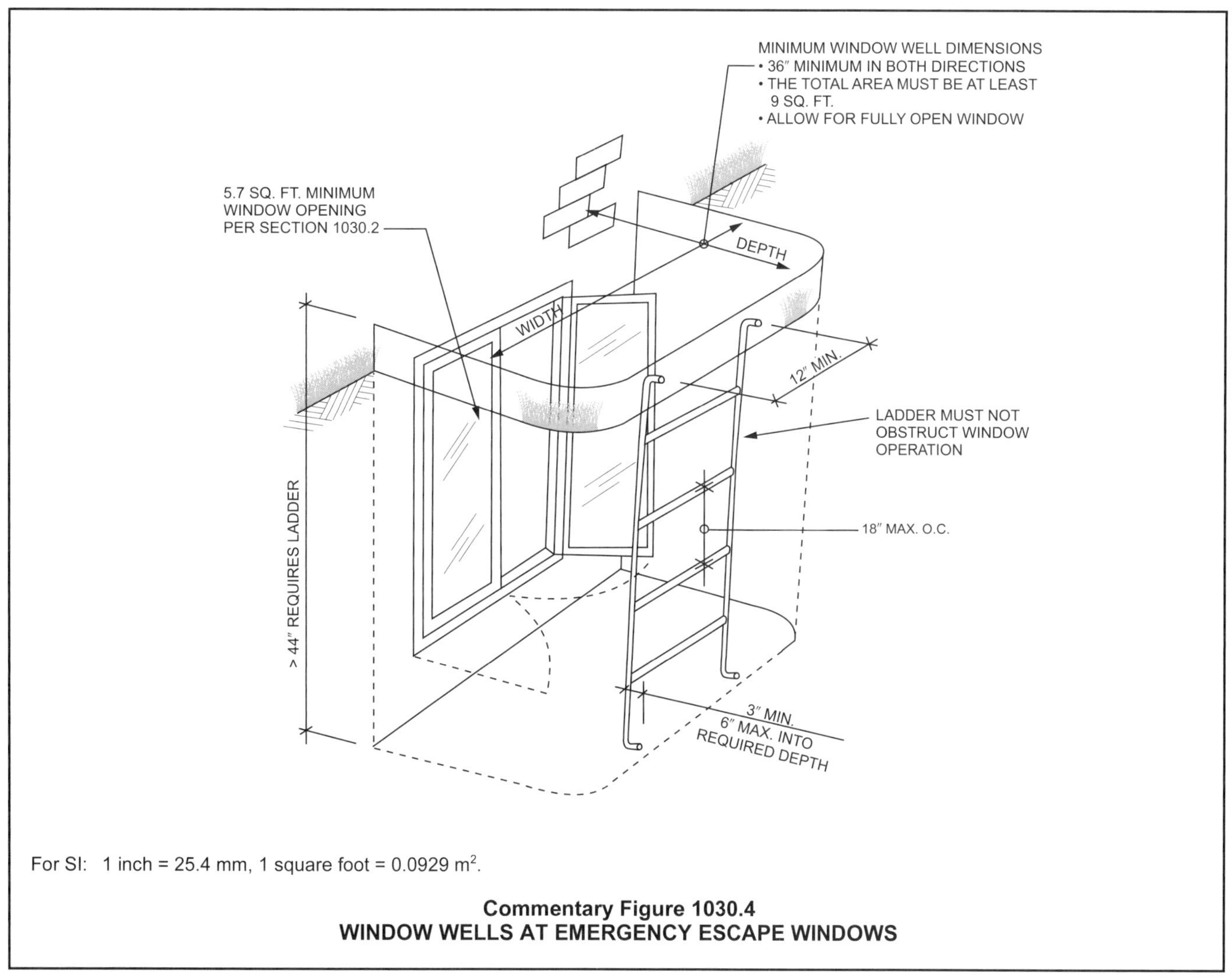

Commentary Figure 1030.4
WINDOW WELLS AT EMERGENCY ESCAPE WINDOWS

over *emergency escape and rescue openings,* bulkhead enclosures, or window wells that serve such openings, provided that the minimum net clear opening size complies with Sections 1030.1.1 through 1030.4.2 and such devices shall be releasable or removable from the inside without the use of a key, tool or force greater than that which is required for normal operation of the *emergency escape and rescue opening.* Where such bars, grilles, covers, screens or similar devices are installed in existing buildings, they shall not reduce the net clear opening of the *emergency escape and rescue opening* and *smoke alarms* shall be installed in accordance with Section 907.2.10 regardless of the valuation of the *alteration.*

❖ Where bars, grilles, grates or other devices that prevent full operation of the window are placed over the emergency escape and rescue opening, it is important that they are easily removable. The requirements for ease of operation are the same as those required for windows.

Windows in Group R-2, R-3 and R-4 dwelling units may also have to meet window opening limitations because of concerns about child falls (see Section 1015.8). Only some of the window-opening control devices will also work for emergency escape and rescue openings.

Where smoke alarms are not already provided and where items that could possibly slow the opening of emergency escape and rescue windows are installed in existing buildings, smoke alarms must also be installed. Smoke alarms are necessary to provide advance warning of a fire for safety purposes.

SECTION 1031 MAINTENANCE OF THE MEANS OF EGRESS

1031.1 General. The *means of egress* for buildings or portions thereof shall be maintained in accordance with this section.

❖ This section introduces the provisions for the maintenance of the means of egress in all buildings and structures.

1031.2 Reliability. Required *exit accesses, exits* and *exit discharges* shall be continuously maintained free from obstructions or impediments to full instant use in the case of fire or other emergency where the building area served by the *means of egress* is occupied. An *exit* or *exit passageway* shall not be used for any purpose that interferes with a *means of egress.*

❖ It is important for safety that the pathway from any point in a building to the exit discharge be kept clear so that occupants can exit the building at any time without obstructions in the egress path. Such obstructions could include storage in the means of egress, which is specifically regulated by Section 315.3.2. Similarly, handrails, stair treads, flooring materials, door hardware and other fixtures and finishes must be maintained in such a way as to prevent them from becoming hazards themselves.

The last sentence of this paragraph provides correlation with Sections 1022.1, 1023.1 and 1024.1, which, in new buildings, prohibit the use of exits, interior exit stairway and ramp enclosures and exit passageways, respectively, for any purpose other than a means of egress. However, it is important that an exit, interior exit stairway or ramp enclosure or an exit passageway not be used for any purpose other than as a means of egress throughout the life of the building, not just when the building is built. For example, there is a tendency to use stairway enclosures for storage, furniture, vending machines, copy machines, displays and similar purposes. Such a situation can obstruct the path of exit travel. Further, if the contents consist of combustible materials or ignition sources, the use of the stairway as a means of egress may be jeopardized, creating a hazard to life safety. Note, however, that the restriction is not limited to situations where the contents are combustible because of the potential for obstruction and the inherent difficulties in limiting the materials to noncombustibles (see also commentary, Sections 1022.1, 1023.1 and 1024.1).

It is not the intent of this requirement to prohibit occupants from using the stairway, ramp or exit passageway as a circulation route during normal operation.

1031.2.1 Security devices and egress locks. Security devices affecting *means of egress* shall be subject to approval of the *fire code official.* Security devices and locking arrangements in the *means of egress* that restrict, control, or delay egress shall be installed and maintained as required by this chapter.

❖ In our society, security is an ever-growing concern, and often the solutions to enhancing the security of buildings conflict with the life-safety concerns of building and fire codes. This section gives the fire code official an important measure of control over the installation or modification of security devices that could adversely affect the egress system of a building. See the commentary to Section 1010 for specifics on the different security hardware options permitted.

While this section focuses on physical impediments or obstructions to exit use, there are also security devices that emit smoke, mist or other confusing or debilitating media that could obscure exits, temporarily disable innocent occupants or result in mistaken false alarms (from passersby seeing the smoke or mist and thinking the building is on fire), which could affect fire fighter egress and safety. See the commentary to Section 316.5 for a discussion of such devices.

[BE] 1031.2.2 Locking arrangements in educational occupancies. In Group E occupancies, Group B educational occupancies and Group I-4 occupancies, egress doors from classrooms, offices and other occupied rooms shall be permitted to be provided with locking arrangements designed to keep intruders from entering the room where all of the following conditions are met:

1. The door shall be capable of being unlocked from outside the room with a key or other approved means.

2. The door shall be openable from within the room in accordance with Section 1010.1.9.
3. Modifications shall not be made to existing listed panic hardware, fire door hardware or door closers.
4. Modifications to fire door assemblies shall be in accordance with NFPA 80.

❖ Unfortunately, active shooter incidents in schools are a threat in modern society and have resulted in the need to quickly secure classrooms and other occupied areas to keep unwanted intruders from entering. Many unlisted devices are being used to secure the doors from being opened. Many of these devices have not been evaluated to ensure they operate properly and do not impair door operation. These devices are being deployed in periodic lockdown drills and present the potential for students or unauthorized personnel to secure doors so rooms cannot be entered. This section allows key-actuated deadbolts or other locks to be provided on classroom doors, where the teacher can choose to lock the door and provide shelter-in-place in the classroom. This section also requires the door to be able to be unlocked from the opposite side in cases where the school administrator or responders wish to enter the room without having to make a forcible entry. Door hardware is currently available that allows classrooms to be provided with lockdown capabilities that comply with applicable Chapter 10 requirements. However, the costs of retrofitting doors with such hardware far exceed the cost of retrofitting with a simple deadbolt lock. This is a significant issue for school systems that are continually facing budget restrictions.

1031.3 Obstructions. A *means of egress* shall be free from obstructions that would prevent its use, including the accumulation of snow and ice.

❖ Blocked exits are among the most common egress problems. Obstructions, impediments and storage or placement of articles in a manner that prevents access to or reduces the effective width of egress elements are prohibited. Such impediments may be movable or fixed. Maintenance of safe egress conditions implies keeping exits free of storage, decorations and debris that obstruct access or visibility. Complex egress paths may also violate the intent of this requirement by confusing or obscuring the path of egress travel. When inspecting, extra care should be taken to follow the egress path occupants must take in the event of an emergency from a number of points in the same manner. Holding open an egress door, thus giving fire unimpeded access to the path of egress, may pose an even greater hazard than blocking an exit.

Accumulations of snow and ice could prevent timely exiting from the building in the case of fire or other emergencies. Generally, if the exit is used regularly, the exit doorway area is kept free of ice and snow. Where a required exit is not used regularly, it may be necessary to protect the exit doorway area from the accumulation of ice and snow, either by construction of overhangs or enclosures, heated slabs or, where approved by the fire code official, by a reliable snow removal program that is aggressively enforced.

1031.3.1 Group I-2. In Group I-2, the required clear width for *aisles*, *corridors* and *ramps* that are part of the required *means of egress* shall comply with Section 1020.2. The facility shall have a plan to maintain the required clear width during emergency situations.

Exception: In areas required for bed movement, equipment shall be permitted in the required width where all of the following provisions are met:

1. The equipment is low hazard and wheeled.
2. The equipment does not reduce the effective clear width for the *means of egress* to less than 5 feet (1525 mm).
3. The equipment is limited to:
    3.1. Equipment and carts in use.
    3.2. Medical emergency equipment.
    3.3. Infection control carts.
    3.4. Patient lift and transportation equipment.
4. Medical emergency equipment and patient lift and transportation equipment, when not in use, are required to be located on one side of the corridor.
5. The equipment is limited in number to not more than one per patient sleeping room or patient care room within each smoke compartment.

❖ This is a procedural requirement. In a Group I-2 occupancy where patients are moved in beds, the minimum corridor width is 8 feet. It is recognized that certain movable pieces of equipment will be present in the corridor during normal operations of patient care units. This section limits the types and number of such pieces of equipment and the restrictions the equipment may impose on the means of egress. During emergencies, facilities must have an emergency management plan addressing the steps that must be taken by the facility and responding staff to ensure that the required 8-foot-wide corridor is kept clear of movable obstructions (see IBC Section 407). The terminology is consistent with NFPA 101.

[BE] 1031.4 Exit signs. Exit signs shall be installed and maintained in accordance with the building code that was in effect at the time of construction and the applicable provisions in Section 1104. Decorations, furnishings, equipment or adjacent signage that impairs the visibility of exit signs, creates confusion or prevents identification of the *exit* shall not be allowed.

❖ The scoping provisions of Section 1001.1 restrict the applicability of Section 1013 to new construction. This section provides needed application of the provisions of Section 1013 to existing buildings as well. Exit signs are intended to stand out from their immediate background. Clutter and obstructions in the form of drapes, decorations, partitions and other signs may distract attention from properly placed exit signs. Careful attention should be paid to how occupants will view the sign from where they must begin the egress sequence. Certain lighting conditions can obscure the direct viewing and ready identification of exit signs.

1031.5 Nonexit identification. Where a door is adjacent to, constructed similar to and can be confused with a *means of egress* door, that door shall be identified with an *approved* sign that identifies the room name or use of the room.

❖ Many times doors have the appearance of being exit doors but do not lead to an egress path. In many cases, these doors only open into rooms with no other way out. In such cases, this section requires that the door be provided with "nonexit" door signage to warn occupants that it is not part of the means of egress. The exact name or use of the room should be indicated, such as "storage," "mechanical room," "electrical room" or similar verbiage. Note that this section is not specifically included in the new construction requirements for a building because it is difficult to determine potentially confusing nonexit doors during the plan review process. It is intended for use by the fire code official during maintenance inspections when the confusion becomes apparent.

1031.6 Finishes, furnishings and decorations. Means of egress doors shall be maintained in such a manner as to be distinguishable from the adjacent construction and finishes such that the doors are easily recognizable as doors. Furnishings, decorations or other objects shall not be placed so as to obstruct *exits*, access thereto, egress therefrom, or visibility thereof. Hangings and draperies shall not be placed over exit doors or otherwise be located to conceal or obstruct an *exit*. Mirrors shall not be placed on *exit* doors. Mirrors shall not be placed in or adjacent to any *exit* in such a manner as to confuse the direction of exit.

❖ Similar to Section 1010.1, this section establishes that existing egress doors need to be easily recognizable for immediate use in emergency situations throughout the life of the building. Thus, the code specifies that doors are not to be hidden in such a manner that a person would have trouble seeing where to egress. Displays, furnishings, finishes and decorations are frequently intended to create a mood or atmosphere; however, they often make familiar places confusing even to those who normally occupy them. Bright lights, vivid colors, mirrors and hanging material may significantly reduce contrast, impede visibility or confuse direction. It is not uncommon for a building owner to refinish the interior of an occupancy and paint or otherwise apply a matching finish to a door and the surrounding wall, making the door indistinguishable. This commonly occurs with murals that are painted on walls of corridors.

Tables, chairs, display cases, coat racks and similar movable objects placed in corridors or aisles may reduce required egress capacity or may require substantial effort to remove or negotiate quickly. Anything that slows egress may also impede access, particularly to fire fighters who may be called to rescue occupants or fight the fire. Similarly, anything that obscures the visibility of exit signs is prohibited by Section 1031.4.

1031.7 Emergency escape and rescue openings. Required *emergency escape and rescue openings* shall be maintained in accordance with the that was code in effect at the time of construction, and both of the following:

1. Required *emergency escape and rescue openings* shall be operational from the inside of the room without the use of keys or tools.
2. Bars, grilles, grates or similar devices are allowed to be placed over *emergency escape and rescue openings* provided that the minimum net clear opening size complies with the code that was in effect at the time of construction and such devices shall be releasable or removable from the inside without the use of a key, tool or force greater than that which is required for normal operation of the *emergency escape and rescue opening*.

❖ In new construction, Section 1030.1 requires that in Group R-2 buildings with a single exit or in Group R-3 and R-4 dwellings, every sleeping room below the fourth story must have at least one operable window or exterior door approved for emergency escape or rescue. This section provides the necessary maintenance and utilization requirements for emergency escape openings.

Maintenance requirements are provided to increase the reliability of emergency escape elements. Included are allowances to provide emergency escape elements with security devices that retain the usability of the window or door while allowing a measure of security for the building occupants from intruders. Note that these provisions are applicable only to emergency escape openings required by the applicable building code in force when the building was constructed, in accordance with Section 1104.1.

The same blocking, locking and maintenance restrictions that apply to egress doors apply to emergency escape windows and doors. These egress components are frequently found blocked by furniture, fans and window air conditioners, especially in residential sleeping rooms. Inspections of other means of egress elements should include a look at basement escape windows and doors as well. Mechanical parts of exterior doors and windows are particularly susceptible to wear and tear and should be the subject of frequent inspections and periodic preventive maintenance. Hinges must swing and handles must turn at all times so that they are ready to function when needed.

Since emergency escape windows must be usable to all occupants, including children and guests, the required opening dimensions must be achieved by the normal operation of the window from the inside (e.g., sliding, swinging or lifting the sash). It is impractical to assume that all occupants can operate a window requiring a special sequence of operations to achieve the mandated opening size. While most occupants are familiar with the normal operation by which to open the window, children and guests are frequently unfamiliar with special procedures necessary to remove the sashes. The time spent in comprehending the special operation unnecessarily delays egress from the bedroom and could lead to panic and further confusion; thus, windows that achieve the required opening dimensions only by performing operations such as the removal of sashes or mullions are not permitted.

Not only are security devices or accessories frequently added to emergency escape windows to prevent entry, but too often the windows themselves are replaced with others that provide inadequate clearance or improper locking arrangements. Security grille designs are available to deter entry without compromising egress. Security bars, grilles or screens placed over emergency escape windows must also be releasable or removable from the inside without the use of a key, tool or force greater than what is required for normal operation of the window.

1031.8 Inspection, testing and maintenance. Two-way communication systems for *areas of refuge* shall be inspected and tested on a yearly basis to verify that all components are operational. Where required, the tests shall be conducted in the presence of the *fire code official*. Records of inspection, testing and maintenance shall be maintained.

❖ Since these components are part of the fire protection features of a building, two-way communication systems should be tested in order to verify their operation. Communication is paramount for the occupant using the area of refuge; therefore, it is reasonable to verify the operation of the communication system just as is done for any other fire protection equipment. Many of these systems utilize an "acknowledge" light, and yearly testing would help to eliminate a potential failure of the communication system for something as critical, yet unassuming, as a burned-out bulb. See the commentary to Sections 1009.6.5 and 1009.8 for further discussion of these systems.

1031.9 Floor identification signs. The floor identification signs required by Sections 1023.9 and 1104.24 shall be maintained in an *approved* manner.

❖ This section provides correlation with Sections 1023.9 and 1104.24. The requirement for the maintenance of signs designating floor levels in interior stairway exit enclosures has equal importance in existing buildings. See the commentary to Section 1023.9 for further discussion of these signs.

1031.10 Emergency lighting equipment inspection and testing. Emergency lighting shall be maintained in accordance with Section 1008 and shall be inspected and tested in accordance with Sections 1031.10.1 and 1031.10.2.

❖ This section provides the requirements for regular testing of emergency lighting equipment installed in accordance with Section 1008. While Section 1203.4 requires that emergency power systems be inspected and tested in accordance with the referenced standards, NFPA 111 Section 1.1.4.1, Item 4, specifically exempts battery unit equipment from being covered by the maintenance provisions of that standard and NFPA 110 does not apply. These sections fill that gap in maintenance coverage by providing for the testing of the most common type of emergency lighting found in smaller buildings, i.e., battery unit emergency lighting equipment (see Commentary Figure 1031.10).

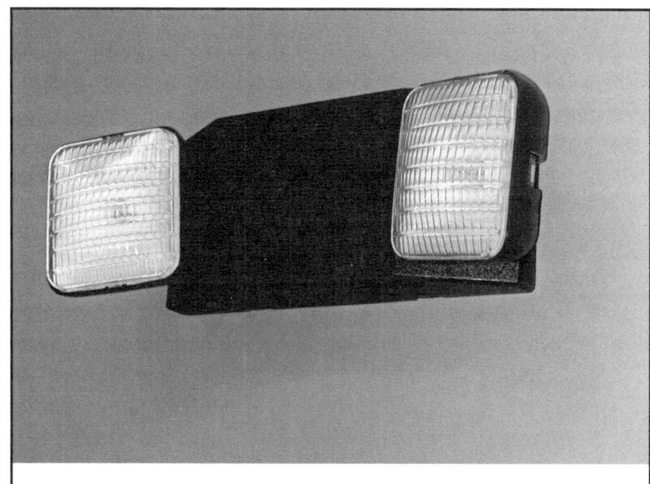

Commentary Figure 1031.10
TYPICAL BATTERY UNIT EMERGENCY LIGHTING

1031.10.1 Activation test. Emergency lighting equipment shall be tested monthly for a duration of not less than 30 seconds. The test shall be performed manually or by an automated self-testing and self-diagnostic routine. Where testing is performed by self-testing and self-diagnostics, a visual inspection of the emergency lighting equipment shall be conducted monthly to identify any equipment displaying a trouble indicator or that has become damaged or otherwise impaired.

❖ This section requires a monthly 30-second function test of the battery unit emergency lighting equipment to verify that the unit is holding a charge, that all connected bulbs or luminaires are operational and that the transfer switch functions properly. This test must be conducted by turning off the normal power supply circuit that serves the unit, not by simply pressing the "test" button on the unit. It is important to note that since NFPA 70 typically requires a lock-on device to be provided on branch circuit breakers powering unit equipment, those lock-ons must be reinstalled upon completion of the test.

1031.10.2 Power test. Battery-powered emergency lighting equipment shall be tested annually by operating the equipment on battery power for not less than 90 minutes.

❖ Section 1008.3.4 requires that emergency lighting for means of egress has a duration of 90 minutes. This section complements that requirement by requiring a 90-minute operational test of battery units annually to verify the condition of the battery, unit-powered bulbs or luminaires, and unit circuitry. As with the activation test in Section 1031.10.1, this test should be conducted by turning off the normal power supply to the unit. The determination of whether the unit remains "sufficiently illuminated" for the full 90-minute test should be based on the performance requirements for emergency lighting for means of egress established in Section 1008.3.5.

Bibliography

The following resource materials were used in the preparation of the commentary for this chapter of the code:

24 CFR, *Fair Housing Accessibility Guidelines* (FHAG). Washington, DC: Department of Housing and Urban Development, 1991.

28 CFR Parts 35 and 36 Final Rule, *2010 Standards for Accessible Design*. Washington, DC: U.S. Department of Justice, September 15, 2010.

36 CFR Parts 1190 and 1191 Final Rule, *The Americans with Disabilities Act (ADA) Accessibility Guidelines; Architectural Barriers Act (ABA) Accessibility Guidelines*. Washington, DC: Architectural and Transportation Barriers Compliance Board, July 23, 2004.

Appendix B to Part 36, *Analysis and Commentary on the 2010 ADA Standards for Accessible Design*. Washington, DC: Department of Justice, September 15, 2010.

Architectural and Transportation Barriers Compliance Board, 42 USC 3601-88, *Fair Housing Amendments Act (FHAA)*. Washington, DC: United States Code, 1988.

ASME A17.1-2016/CSA B44-16, *Safety Code for Elevators and Escalators*. New York: American Society of Mechanical Engineers.

ASME A18.1-2014, *Safety Standard for Platform Lifts and Stairway Chairlifts*. New York: American Society of Mechanical Engineers.

ASTM D2047-04, *Standard Test Method for Static Coefficient of Friction Polish-coated Flooring Surfaces as Measured by the James Machine*. West Conshohocken, PA: ASTM International.

ASTM E119-16, *Standard Test Methods for Fire Tests of Building Construction and Materials*. West Conshohocken, PA: ASTM International.

ASTM E2072-14, *Standard Specification for Photoluminescent (Phosphorescent) Safety Markings*. West Conshohocken, PA: ASTM International.

ASTM F851-87 (Reapproved 2015), *Standard Test Method for Self-rising Seat Mechanisms*. West Conshohocken, PA: ASTM International.

DOJ 28 CFR, Part 36 (Appendix A)-91, *ADA Accessibility Guidelines for Buildings and Facilities*. Washington, DC: U.S. Department of Justice, 1991.

DOJ 28 CFR, Part 36-91, *Americans with Disabilities Act* (ADA). Washington, DC: U.S. Department of Justice, 1991.

Final Report of the HUD Review of the Fair Housing Accessibility Requirements and the 2003 International Building Code (IBC). February 18, 2005 (Docket No FR-4943-N-02).

Final Report of the HUD Review of the Fair Housing Accessibility Requirements and the 2006 International Building Code (IBC). May 31, 2007 (Docket No FR-5136-N-01).

Fire Modeling Analysis Report. July 20. 2011, and *The Report to the California State Fire Marshal on Exit Access Travel Distance of 400 Feet* by Task Group 400, December 20, 2010, by Aon Fire Protection Engineering. The complete report can be found on the California State Fire Marshal's website at: http://osfm.fire.ca.gov/codedevelopment/pdf/2010interimcodeadoption/Part-9_ISOR_Attachment_A_rev20110720comp.pdf

HUD 24 CFR, Part 100, *Federal Fair Housing Accessibility Guidelines*. Washington, DC: U.S. Department of Housing and Urban Development.

NIST IR 4770-92, *Report on Staging Areas for Persons with Mobility Limitations*. Washington, DC: National Institute of Standards and Technology, 1992.

"Review of Fall Safety of Children Between the Ages of 18 months and 4 Years in Relation to Guards and Climbing in the Built Environment," prepared for the National Ornamental & Miscellaneous Metals Association (NOMMA). Upper Marlboro, MD: NAHB Research Center, Inc., 2007.

UL 10C-09, *Positive Pressure Fire Tests of Door Assemblies—with Revisions through February 2015*. Northbrook, IL: Underwriters Laboratories, Inc.

UL 305-2012, *Panic Hardware—with Revisions through August 2014*. Northbrook, IL: Underwriters Laboratories, Inc.

UL 924-06, *Standard for Safety Emergency Lighting and Power Equipment—with Revisions through April 2014*. Northbrook, IL: Underwriters Laboratories. Inc.

UL 1994-04, *Standard for Luminous Egress Path Marking Systems—with Revisions through May 2015*. Northbrook, IL: Underwriters Laboratories, Inc.

Chapter 11: Construction Requirements for Existing Buildings

General Comments

This chapter first appeared in the 2009 edition of the code, as Chapter 46. It brings many of the retroactive existing building fire protection and life safety requirements previously found in Chapters 7, 9 and 10 to one location for a more convenient and user-friendly enforcement tool. Requirements for premises identification of buildings remain in Chapter 5 and the existing building interior finish requirements remain in Chapter 8.

Excluding the general provisions and definitions, Chapter 11 is divided into four sections. Section 1103 addresses fire safety requirements for existing buildings. This includes protection of vertical openings in shafts and openings for escalators. Section 1103 also contains provisions requiring automatic sprinkler, standpipe, and fire alarm and detection systems in existing buildings. Section 1104 specifies the minimum means of egress requirements for existing buildings and is based on materials once found in Chapter 10. Section 1105 establishes construction requirements for existing Group I-2 occupancies. Section 1106 sets forth the requirements for fire department access to outdoor storage of tires, which is retroactive to any existing storage conditions.

Note that Section 1101.4 provides a level of reasonableness for enforcement of this chapter. It is not intended that existing conditions be immediately fixed, rather a process and timeline is worked through with the owner.

Purpose

The purposes of this chapter are to provide minimum construction requirements for existing buildings and to provide them in one place. Many newer buildings may already meet these requirements and no further action will be necessary. Those that do not meet these minimal construction requirements will need to address those deficiencies. It should be noted that interior finishes for existing buildings are dealt with separately in Chapter 8.

SECTION 1101 GENERAL

1101.1 Scope. The provisions of this chapter shall apply to existing buildings constructed prior to the adoption of this code.

❖ This section introduces Chapter 11 and indicates that it is applicable to all buildings constructed prior to the code's date of adoption.

1101.2 Intent. The intent of this chapter is to provide a minimum degree of fire and life safety to persons occupying existing buildings by providing minimum construction requirements where such existing buildings do not comply with the minimum requirements of the *International Building Code.*

❖ This chapter provides a single location for such requirements. Included is a quick-reference table (see Table 1103.1) to determine whether there are any requirements that would be applicable as the inspector is conducting the inspection. Each provision in the code that refers to retroactive requirements now has a reference to this chapter.

Historically, there has been confusion as to when the construction provisions of Section 102.1 could be applied to an existing building. It has been said that in every case the fire code official must declare a "distinct hazard"; however, this is not correct. There are specific construction requirements for existing buildings provided by International Code Council® (ICC®) membership to address distinct hazards. Since the determination of a hazard is already accomplished, it is not necessary for the fire code official to repeat the process. Therefore, all of the requirements in Chapter 11 will apply to existing buildings.

Section 102.1, Item 3, also indicates that the retroactive construction provisions referred to are located in Chapter 11, thus clarifying which provisions in the code are actually construction provisions that should be applied to an existing building. Since only the provisions listed in this chapter would apply to an existing facility, all of the other construction provisions in the code apply to new construction. However, as has always been the case, the code official can still exercise judgment and declare a distinct hazard under Section 102.1, Item 4, for other items or operations not addressed in Chapter 11. See the commentary to Section 102.1 for further information.

Section 1104.1 makes it clear that existing buildings must still comply with the code under which the building was built or the minimum egress requirements in Section 1104, whichever is more restrictive.

In this fashion, a building will not be allowed to reduce the egress system protection or design from the original approval. Section 1104 is not as restrictive as requirements for new construction and allows for the continued use of existing buildings when the egress is at an acceptable standard, but not in complete compliance with the *International Building Code®* (IBC®).

1101.3 Permits. Permits shall be required as set forth in Sections 105.6 and 105.7 and the *International Building Code.*

❖ See the commentaries to Section 105.7 and IBC Section 105.

1101.4 Owner notification. When a building is found to be in noncompliance with this chapter, the *fire code official* shall duly notify the *owner* of the building. Upon receipt of such notice, the *owner* shall, subject to the following time limits, take necessary actions to comply with the provisions of this chapter.

❖ See the commentaries to Sections 110.3 and 110.3.2.

1101.4.1 Construction documents. *Construction documents* necessary to comply with this chapter shall be completed and submitted within a time schedule *approved* by the *fire code official.*

❖ See the commentaries to Section 105.4 and its subsections.

1101.4.2 Completion of work. Work necessary to comply with this chapter shall be completed within a time schedule *approved* by the *fire code official.*

❖ See the commentaries to Section 105.3.1 and IBC Section 105.3.2.

1101.4.3 Extension of time. The *fire code official* is authorized to grant necessary extensions of time where it can be shown that the specified time periods are not physically practical or pose an undue hardship. The granting of an extension of time for compliance shall be based on the showing of good cause and subject to the filing of an acceptable systematic plan of correction with the *fire code official.*

❖ See the commentary to Section 105.3.2.

SECTION 1102 DEFINITIONS

1102.1 Definitions. The following terms are defined in Chapter 2:

DUTCH DOOR.

EXISTING.

❖ Definitions of terms can help in the understanding and application of the code requirements. This section directs the code user to Chapter 2 for the proper application of the indicated terms used in this chapter. Terms may be defined in Chapter 2 or in another International Code® (I-Code®) as indicated in Section 201.3, or the dictionary meaning may be all that is needed (see also commentaries, Sections 201 through 201.4).

SECTION 1103 FIRE SAFETY REQUIREMENTS FOR EXISTING BUILDINGS

1103.1 Required construction. Existing buildings shall comply with not less than the minimum provisions specified in Table 1103.1 and as further enumerated in Sections 1103.2 through 1103.10.

The provisions of this chapter shall not be construed to allow the elimination of *fire protection systems* or a reduction in the level of fire safety provided in buildings constructed in accordance with previously adopted codes.

Exceptions:

1. Where a change in fire-resistance rating has been approved in accordance with Section 501.2 or 802.6 of the *International Existing Building Code.*
2. Group U occupancies.

❖ This section reinforces the provisions of Section 1101.1 and points to the table that provides a tabular summary of the requirements of this chapter and how they apply to the various occupancy groups. With respect to existing fire protection systems, this section reinforces the provisions of Section 901.4, which emphasizes the principle that systems installed and maintained in compliance with the codes and standards in effect at the time they were placed in service must remain operational at the same level at all times.

The first exception recognizes an allowance provided in the *International Existing Building Code®* (IEBC®). Sections 501.2 and 802.6 of the IEBC allow reductions in fire-resistance-rated construction if an automatic sprinkler system is added to a building. These reductions are required to be consistent with what is required in the IBC and also include extensive documentation and approval from the code official.

The second exception correlates with Table 1103.1. That table does not include provisions for Group U occupancies (as defined in Section 202 and IBC Section 312), which are generally miscellaneous structures that do not pose the same life safety hazard as occupancies that are not classified in Group U.

1103.1.1 Historic buildings. Facilities designated as historic buildings shall develop a fire protection plan in accordance with NFPA 914. The fire protection plans shall comply with the maintenance and availability provisions in Sections 404.3 and 404.4.

❖ Section 102.6 generally does not require compliance with the code for historic buildings. However, that same section states that such buildings have a fire protection plan as required by this section. This plan will provide minimal ongoing safety for the occupants. This section also references back to the maintenance and availability requirements found in Chapter 4 to make sure the plans remain current and available to occupants and code officials.

TABLE 1103.1
OCCUPANCY AND USE REQUIREMENTS[a]

SECTION	USE				OCCUPANCY CLASSIFICATION																		
	High-rise	Atrium or covered mall	Under-ground building	Tire storage	A	B	E	F	H-1	H-2	H-3	H-4	H-5	I-1	I-2	I-3	I-4	M	R-1	R-2	R-3	R-4	S
1103.2	R	R	R	—	R	R	R	R	R	R	R	R	R	R	R	R	R	R	R	R	—	—	R
1103.3	R	—	R	—	R	R	R	R	R	R	R	R	R	R	R	R	R	R	R	R	—	—	R
1103.4.1	R	—	R	—	—	—	—	—	—	—	—	—	—	—	R	R	—	—	—	—	—	—	—
1103.4.2	R	—	R	—	R	R	R	R	R	R	R	R	R	R	—	—	R	R	R	R	—	—	R
1103.4.3	R	—	R	—	R	R	R	R	R	R	R	R	R	R	—	—	R	R	R	R	—	—	R
1103.4.4	—	R	—	—	—	—	—	—	—	—	—	—	—	—	—	—	—	—	—	—	—	—	—
1103.4.5	—	—	—	—	—	R	—	—	—	—	—	—	—	—	—	—	—	R	—	—	—	—	—
1103.4.6	—	—	—	—	R	—	R	R	R	R	R	R	R	R	R	R	R	—	R	R	R	R	R
1103.4.7	—	—	—	—	R	—	R	R	R	R	R	R	R	R	R	R	R	—	R	R	R	R	R
1103.4.8	R	—	R	—	R	R	R	R	R	R	R	R	R	R	—	—	R	R	R	R	R	R	R
1103.4.9	R	—	—	—	—	—	—	—	—	—	—	—	—	—	R	—	—	—	—	—	—	—	—
1103.4.10	—	—	—	—	R	R	R	R	R	R	R	R	R	R	R	R	R	R	R	R	R	R	R
1103.5.1	—	—	—	—	R[c]	—	—	—	—	—	—	—	—	—	—	—	—	—	—	—	—	—	—
1103.5.2	—	—	—	—	—	—	—	—	—	—	—	—	—	—	R	—	—	—	—	—	—	—	—
1103.5.3	—	—	—	—	—	—	—	—	—	—	—	—	—	—	R[b]	—	—	—	—	—	—	—	—
1103.5.4	—	—	—	—	R	R	R	R	R	R	R	R	R	R	R	R	R	R	R	R	R	R	R
1103.6.1	R	—	R	—	R	R	R	R	R	R	R	R	R	R	R	R	R	R	R	R	—	—	R
1103.6.2	R	—	R	—	R	R	R	R	R	R	R	R	R	R	R	R	R	R	R	R	—	—	R
1103.7.1	—	—	—	—	—	—	R	—	—	—	—	—	—	—	—	—	—	—	—	—	—	—	—
1103.7.2	—	—	—	—	—	—	—	—	—	—	—	—	—	R	—	—	—	—	—	—	—	—	—
1103.7.3	—	—	—	—	—	—	—	—	—	—	—	—	—	—	R	—	—	—	—	—	—	—	—
1103.7.4	—	—	—	—	—	—	—	—	—	—	—	—	—	—	—	R	—	—	—	—	—	—	—
1103.7.5	—	—	—	—	—	—	—	—	—	—	—	—	—	—	—	—	—	—	R	—	—	—	—
1103.7.6	—	—	—	—	—	—	—	—	—	—	—	—	—	—	—	—	—	—	—	R	—	—	—
1103.7.7	—	—	—	—	—	—	—	—	—	—	—	—	—	—	—	—	—	—	—	—	—	R	—
1103.8	—	—	—	—	—	—	—	—	—	—	—	—	—	R	—	—	—	—	R	R	R	R	—
1103.9	R	—	—	—	—	—	—	—	—	—	—	—	—	R	R	—	R	—	R	R	R	R	—
1103.10	—	—	—	—	—	—	—	—	—	—	—	—	—	R	R	—	—	—	—	—	—	—	—
1104	R	R	R	—	R	R	R	R	R	R	R	R	R	R	R	R	R	R	R	R	R	R	R
1105	—	—	—	—	—	—	—	—	—	—	—	—	—	—	R	—	—	—	—	—	—	—	—
1106	—	—	—	R	—	—	—	—	—	—	—	—	—	—	—	—	—	—	—	—	—	—	—

R = The building is required to comply.
a. Existing buildings shall comply with the sections identified as "Required" (R) based on occupancy classification or use, or both, whichever is applicable.
b. Only applies to Group I-2, Condition 2 occupancies as established by the adopting ordinance or legislation of the jurisdiction.
c. Only applies to Group A-2 occupancies where alcoholic beverages are consumed.

1103.2 Emergency responder radio coverage in existing buildings. Existing buildings other than Group R-3, that do not have approved radio coverage for emergency responders in the building based on existing coverage levels of the public safety communication systems, shall be equipped with such coverage according to one of the following:

1. Where an existing wired communication system cannot be repaired or is being replaced, or where not approved in accordance with Section 510.1, Exception 1.
2. Within a time frame established by the adopting authority.

Exception: Where it is determined by the fire code official that the radio coverage system is not needed.

❖ This section specifies the requirements for emergency responder radio coverage in existing buildings other than Group R-3 occupancies. The reason Group R-3 occupancies were exempted from this requirement was based on the fact that it was not reasonable to require retroactive systems for occupancies that are essentially one- and two-family dwellings. Where radio coverage is not adequate, Section 510.1, Exception 1 allows for the installation of a wired communication system. However, in existing buildings that have such a system or may have taken that exception, in the event the wired communication system becomes inoperative and cannot be repaired or is undergoing extended repair or replacement, this section allows the fire code official to require the installation of an acceptable system.

Where an existing building is determined to have inadequate radio coverage based on the requirements of Section 510.4, Item 2 of this section allows the fire code official to establish a time frame for compliance with Section 510.1. There are times when prior to construction it will be difficult to confidently assure that radio coverage will not be affected by the building itself. That is the reason these requirements are also applicable to existing facilities.

1103.3 Existing elevators. In other than Group R-3, existing elevators, escalators and moving walks shall comply with the requirements of Sections 1103.3.1 and 1103.3.2.

❖ The following two sections provide retroactive requirements that apply to existing elevators and, to a certain extent, escalators and moving walkways. Note that Section 606 also deals with the ongoing operation and maintenance of elevators in buildings. That section also has requirements related to fire service keys.

1103.3.1 Elevators, escalators and moving walks. Existing elevators, escalators and moving walks in Group I-2, Condition 2 occupancies and serving ambulatory care facilities shall comply with ASME A17.3.

❖ This section is specific to Group I-2, Condition 2 occupancies (hospitals) and ambulatory care facilities. Not only are existing elevators required to comply with ASME A17.3, but escalators and moving walks must also comply. Note that Section 3001.3 of the IBC would require ongoing maintenance of all elevators and conveying systems. This section specifies compliance with ASME A17.3, *Safety Code for Existing Elevators and Escalators,* for such maintenance.

The healthcare industry has historically been required to comply with regulations set forth by accreditation and certification agencies, such as The Joint Commission. ASME A17.3 has been referenced by guidelines adopted by The Joint Commission for over a decade and this requirement provides correlation of the code with the mandated healthcare industry standard.

The reference to ASME A17.3 requires that existing elevators, escalators, moving walks and their related operating equipment in Group I-2, Condition 2 occupancies and ambulatory care facilities to comply with a minimum level of safety. Because the occupants of these types of facilities are often incapable of self-preservation, it is essential to provide ASME-mandated features for occupant safety including escalator and moving walk emergency stop buttons and automatic skirt obstruction stop features.

1103.3.2 Elevator emergency operation. Existing elevators with a travel distance of 25 feet (7620 mm) or more above or below the main floor or other level of a building and intended to serve the needs of emergency personnel for fire-fighting or rescue purposes shall be provided with emergency operation in accordance with ASME A17.3.

Exceptions:

1. Buildings without occupied floors located more than 55 feet (16 764 mm) above or 25 feet (7620 mm) below the lowest level of fire department vehicle access where protected at the elevator shaft openings with additional fire doors in accordance with Section 716 of the *International Building Code* and where all of the following conditions are met:

   1.1. The doors shall be provided with vision panels of approved fire protection rated glazing so located as to furnish clear vision of the approach to the elevator. Such glazing shall not exceed 100 square inches (0.065 m^2) in area.

   1.2. The doors shall be held open but be automatic-closing by activation of a fire alarm initiating device installed in accordance with the requirements of NFPA 72 as for Phase I Emergency Recall Operation, and shall be located at each floor served by the elevator; in the associated elevator machine room, control space, or control room; and in the elevator hoistway, where sprinklers are located in those hoistways.

   1.3. The doors, when closed, shall have signs visible from the approach area stating: WHEN THESE DOORS ARE CLOSED OR IN FIRE EMERGENCY, DO NOT USE ELEVATOR. USE EXIT STAIRWAYS.

2. Buildings without occupied floors located more than 55 feet (16 764 mm) above or 25 feet (7620 mm) below the lowest level of fire department vehicle access where provided with *automatic sprinkler systems* installed in accordance with Section 903.3.1.1 or 903.3.1.2.

3. Freight elevators in buildings provided with both *automatic sprinkler systems* installed in accordance with Section 903.3.1.1 or 903.3.1.2 and not less than one ASME 17.3-compliant elevator serving the same floors.

Elimination of previously installed Phase I emergency recall or Phase II emergency in-car systems shall not be permitted.

❖ This section establishes requirements for existing elevators. Existing elevators that travel 25 feet (7620 mm) or more above or below the main level must, as a minimum, be equipped with emergency operation capabilities that comply with ASME A17.3. New elevator installations are held to more restrictive guidelines for increased cost effectiveness and must have both emergency recall (Phase I) and emergency in-car operation (Phase II) systems to comply with ASME A17.1 for any amount of travel distance, as required by Section 606.1. The ASME standards are safety codes for elevators and escalators: ASME A17.3 for existing elevators and ASME A17.1 for new elevator installations. Automatic fire detection devices provided for Phase I emergency recall operation must be installed in accordance with Section 907.3.3.

There are several exceptions based on the expense of providing Phase I recall and Phase II emergency operation for existing elevators. ASME A17.3, Rule 211.3 (Firefighters' Service—Automatic Elevators) states, "All automatic (nondesignated attendant) operation elevators having a travel of 25 ft (7.62 m) or more above or below the designated level shall conform to the requirements of this Rule."

These changes are needed because of the excessive expense of compliance for many of these retrofits. Application of the mandatory Phase I and Phase II retrofits required by A17.3 triggers complete replacement of the elevator machinery at costs running into the hundreds of thousands of dollars. What is a relatively inexpensive fire safety feature in a new elevator installation can be unreasonably onerous when applied to existing elevators. It is therefore reasonable to codify alternate methods for building owners to meet the intent of the codes. It is important to note that the 25-foot travel threshold for an ASME A17.3 emergency operation retrofit is not mitigated by occupant load; number of stories; elevator use; building fire or smoke compartment conditions; the presence of sprinklers; or any building-specific operational fire-fighting considerations. For elevators installed prior to the adoption of newer elevator emergency operations features, many existing three-story buildings require retrofits: elevators in nonatmospherically segregated spaces such as low-rise atriums require retrofits; vintage freight elevators, regardless of maintenance condition or the ability of building occupants to access them, require retrofits. The problem of inflexible compliance options is magnified by the division of professional jurisdictions because elevator authorities typically do not have the expertise to assess fire risk on a total building basis; hence there is a need for the code to scope retroactive fire safety provisions.

By allowing for more affordable or effective alternatives to the Phase I and Phase II retrofits, less opposition should exist to adoption of ASME A17.3 and its other retroactive safety requirements such as safety bulkheads for hydraulic elevators and door restrictors, thereby enhancing overall elevator safety.

Phase I emergency recall is intended to prevent elevator users from being discharged at a floor that is engaged in a fire; to prevent occupants from accessing an elevator during a fire; and, in a detected fire condition, to return the elevator car to a designated floor for fire-fighter access for operations and rescue.

Phase II emergency in-car operation is intended to provide fire fighters the ability to operate the elevator for fire-fighting operations.

Exception 1 meets the intent of the code by:

- Providing an additional fire door, with a vision panel, between elevator occupants and a fire engaged floor. This protects occupants from car and hoistway doors automatically opening directly to a fire event. The vision panel lets occupants view fire risk and select another floor to travel to for egress. This door provides an additional barrier to smoke and water contamination of the hoistway and improves building compartmentation.

- Providing additional signs on the added door immediately at the elevator opening telling building occupants to not use the elevator when the door is closed. In other words, if you can read the sign you shouldn't use the elevator.

- Recognizing that common fire-fighting operations policy requires fire fighters to use the stairs to address any fire on the sixth floor or lower in a building; meaning that in low-rise buildings immediate fire-fighter access to the elevators is not as critical. The sixth floor of a building typically corresponds to the code's definition of a high-rise building as one with "an occupied floor located more than 75 feet (22 860 mm) above the lowest level of fire department vehicle access." This is broadly recognized as the elevation at which a compromise is achieved between the inherent hazard of using an elevator in a structural fire response and the need to respond in a timely way to the fire.

Exception 1 also tacitly acknowledges that these elevators were never "intended to serve the needs of emergency personnel for fire-fighting or rescue purposes," as the charging section states.

Locations of fire alarm-initiating devices used to initiate door closing are identical to those used to initiate Phase I operations via reference to NFPA 72 by ASME A17.3.

Exception 2 recognizes that there is no documented loss of life while in an elevator during a structural fire in a building protected with automatic fire sprinklers. It is reasonable that if an owner has already provided superior fire safety features in an existing building he or she will not be required to retrofit expensive fire safety features of limited value.

For buildings otherwise within the scope of the exception, Exception 2 provides an incentive to provide fire sprinklers.

The references to Sections 903.3.1.1 and 903.3.1.2 mean that only a fire sprinkler system installed in accordance with the appropriate technical standard (NFPA 13 or NFPA 13R) will permit relaxation of the Phase I and Phase II emergency operations requirements.

Fifty-five feet was selected as the upper limit for the floor height of buildings for a couple of reasons. It was suggested that a height limit of roughly four stories would be preferable when considering response factors associated with ascertaining elevator occupant locations and conditions. Since 55 feet is the elevation at which automatic sprinkler protection is triggered, and since it roughly corresponds to four stories, it is offered as a suitable threshold.

Exception 3 recognizes that buildings having another elevator equipped with Phase I and Phase II emergency operations already meet the intent of Phase II fire-fighter operations provisions. The fire sprinkler requirement and the limited passenger use of freight elevators means that the likelihood of life loss in the freight elevator is very low. For buildings without fire sprinklers, this provision provides an incentive to install fire sprinkler systems.

The final paragraph of this section clarifies that previously installed Phase I emergency recall and Phase II emergency in-car operations are not to be removed.

1103.4 Vertical openings. Interior vertical openings, including but not limited to *stairways*, elevator hoistways, service and utility shafts, that connect two or more stories of a building, shall be enclosed or protected as specified in Sections 1103.4.1 through 1103.4.10.

❖ Vertical openings that are not properly protected can act as a chimney for smoke, hot gases and products of combustion. Unprotected floor openings have been a major contributing factor in many large loss-of-life fires. This section retroactively requires the enclosure of vertical openings between floors with approved fire barriers. The intent is to increase the level of safety in all buildings by enclosing unprotected floor openings and, thus, removing the avenue for unimpeded fire and smoke spread. In particular, the code is intended to ensure that means of egress in existing multiple-story buildings are given a reasonable level of protection.

Vertical communication between floors (including stairways, escalator openings, elevator hoistways, trash and laundry chutes, and other types of building service and mechanical shafts) can contribute significantly to fire and smoke spread because of "stack effect" (see Commentary Figure 1103.4). This section and Sections 1103.4.1 through 1103.4.8 require that interior shafts be enclosed with fire barriers of the fire-resistance rating indicated. These assemblies must be constructed and protected as required by the IBC. The allowance for sprinklers in the various sections recognizes the value of automatic sprinkler systems conforming to Section 903.3.1.1 (NFPA 13 system) or 903.3.1.2 (NFPA 13R system), as applicable.

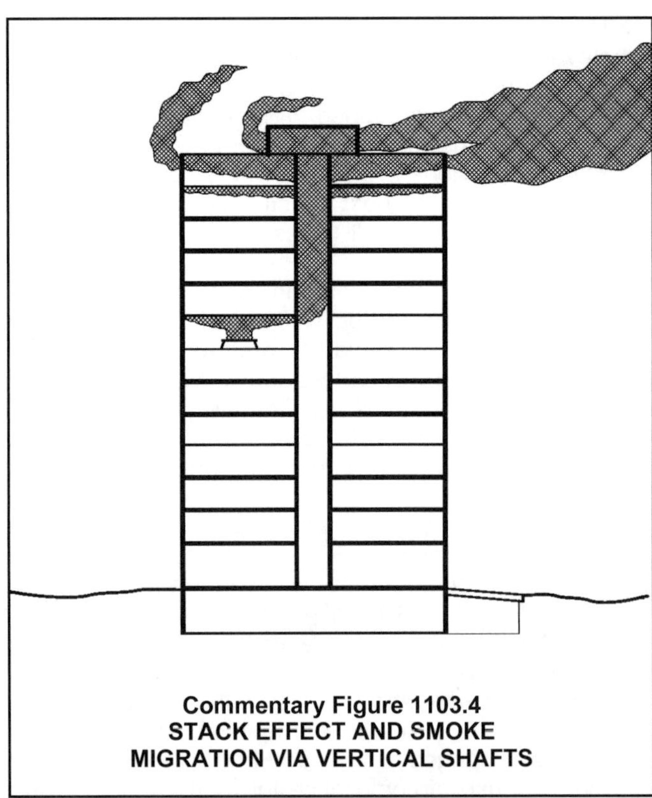

Commentary Figure 1103.4
STACK EFFECT AND SMOKE MIGRATION VIA VERTICAL SHAFTS

1103.4.1 Group I-2 and I-3 occupancies. In Group I-2 and I-3 occupancies, interior vertical openings connecting two or more stories shall be protected with 1-hour fire-resistance-rated construction.

Exceptions:

1. In Group I-2, unenclosed vertical openings not exceeding two connected stories and not concealed within the building construction shall be permitted as follows:
   - 1.1. The unenclosed vertical openings shall be separated from other unenclosed vertical openings serving other floors by a smoke barrier.
   - 1.2. The unenclosed vertical openings shall be separated from corridors by smoke partitions.

1.3. The unenclosed vertical openings shall be separated from other fire or smoke compartments on the same floors by a smoke barrier.

1.4. On other than the lowest level, the unenclosed vertical openings shall not serve as a required means of egress.

2. In Group I-2, atriums connecting three or more stories shall not require 1-hour fire-resistance-rated construction where the building is equipped throughout with an *automatic sprinkler system* installed in accordance with Section 903.3, and all of the following conditions are met:

2.1. For other than existing approved atriums with a smoke control system, where the atrium was constructed and is maintained in accordance with the code in effect at the time the atrium was created, the atrium shall have a smoke control system that is in compliance with Section 909.

2.2. Glass walls forming a smoke partition or a glass-block wall assembly shall be permitted where in compliance with Condition 2.2.1 or 2.2.2.

2.2.1. Glass walls forming a smoke partition shall be permitted where all of the following conditions are met:

2.2.1.1. Automatic sprinklers are provided along both sides of the separation wall and doors, or on the room side only if there is not a walkway or occupied space on the atrium side.

2.2.1.2. The sprinklers shall be not more than 12 inches (305 mm) away from the face of the glass and at intervals along the glass of not greater than 72 inches (1829 mm).

2.2.1.3. Windows in the glass wall shall be nonoperating type.

2.2.1.4. The glass wall and windows shall be installed in a gasketed frame in a manner that the framing system deflects without breaking (loading) the glass before the sprinkler system operates.

2.2.1.5. The sprinkler system shall be designed so that the entire surface of the glass is wet upon activation of the sprinkler system without obstruction.

2.2.2. A fire barrier is not required where a glass-block wall assembly complying with Section 2110 of the *International Building Code* and having a $^{3}/_{4}$-hour fire protection rating is provided.

2.3. Where doors are provided in the glass wall, they shall be either self-closing or automatic-closing and shall be constructed to resist the passage of smoke.

3. In Group I-3 occupancies, exit *stairways* or ramps and *exit access stairways* or *ramps* constructed in accordance with Section 408 in the *International Building Code*.

❖ This section specifically addresses vertical openings only for Group I-2 and I-3 occupancies. In nursing homes, hospitals and jails, the first response to a fire is to defend in place or move residents, patients or detainees to an adjacent smoke compartment. To maintain the separation needed to limit the spread of smoke, an increased level of protection is required. There are three exceptions to the requirement for 1-hour enclosure of vertical openings (for vertical openings in other occupancies, see Section 1103.4.8).

Exceptions 1 and 2 are applicable for Group I-2 occupancies (nursing homes and hospitals). Exceptions 1 and 2 are intended to more appropriately address floor openings in existing construction. Without these exceptions, the IBC would allow construction of a floor opening without a 1-hour fire barrier in certain specific cases. This also impacts all historical nonrated floor openings that have been reviewed, approved and maintained. Unrated vertical openings had been allowed in hospitals and nursing homes previously. Atriums have been installed with various types of smoke venting and removal systems over the past few decades. These exceptions attempt, while maintaining an appropriate level of protection, to address general requirements that have been broadly used throughout older editions of the building codes. These exceptions are consistent with federal regulations governing hospitals and nursing homes. It should be remembered that these provisions are retroactive. They apply regardless of whether an alteration is to be undertaken.

Exception 3 provides consistency with Exception 1 to Section 1023.2, which allows interior exit stairways in Group I-3 occupancies to be in accordance with Section 408.3.8 of the IBC.

Being able to see into and out of a stairway enclosure is an important security feature.

1103.4.2 Three to five stories. In other than Group I-2 and I-3 occupancies, interior vertical openings connecting three to five stories shall be protected by either 1-hour fire-resistance-rated construction or an *automatic sprinkler system* shall be installed throughout the building in accordance with Section 903.3.1.1 or 903.3.1.2.

Exceptions:

1. Vertical opening protection is not required for Group R-3 occupancies.
2. Vertical opening protection is not required for open parking garages.
3. Vertical opening protection for escalators shall be in accordance with Section 1103.4.5, 1103.4.6 or 1103.4.7.
4. *Exit access stairways* and *ramps* shall be in accordance with Section 1103.4.8.

❖ See the commentary to Section 1103.4. The exceptions are consistent with the exceptions to the shaft enclosure requirements of the IBC. Exception 1 exempts single-family dwellings and small congregate residences from vertical opening enclosures because of occupant familiarity with the premises and the relatively small occupant load. Exception 2 recognizes that it would be impractical and unnecessary to enclose shafts in parking occupancies where open ramps are a fundamental design element. Exception 3 addresses escalator openings and refers to the applicable code sections that apply. Exception 4 recognizes that exit access stairways and ramps have various allowances that would not require enclosure. These allowances are consistent with Chapters 7 of the IBC and 10 of this code (see Section 1103.4.8).

1103.4.3 More than five stories. In other than Group I-2 and I-3 occupancies, interior vertical openings connecting more than five stories shall be protected by 1-hour fire-resistance-rated construction.

Exceptions:

1. Vertical opening protection is not required for Group R-3 occupancies.
2. Vertical opening protection is not required for open parking garages.
3. Vertical opening protection for escalators shall be in accordance with Section 1103.4.5, 1103.4.6 or 1103.4.7.
4. *Exit access stairways* and *ramps* shall be in accordance with Section 1103.4.8.

❖ See the commentary to Section 1103.4. The exceptions are consistent with the exceptions to the shaft enclosure requirements of the IBC. Exception 1 exempts single-family dwellings and small congregate residences from vertical opening enclosures because of occupant familiarity with the premises and the relatively small occupant load. Exception 2 recognizes that it would be impractical and unnecessary to enclose shafts in parking occupancies where open ramps are a fundamental design element. Exception 3 addresses escalator openings and refers to the applicable code sections that apply. Exception 4 recognizes that exit access stairways and ramps have various allowances that would not require enclosure. These allowances are consistent with Chapters 7 of the IBC and 10 of this code (see Section 1103.4.8).

1103.4.4 Atriums and covered malls. In other than Group I-2 and I-3 occupancies, interior vertical openings in a covered mall building or a building with an atrium shall be protected by either 1-hour fire-resistance-rated construction or an *automatic sprinkler system* shall be installed throughout the building in accordance with Section 903.3.1.1 or 903.3.1.2.

Exceptions:

1. Vertical opening protection is not required for Group R-3 occupancies.
2. Vertical opening protection is not required for open parking garages.
3. *Exit access stairways* and *ramps* shall be in accordance with Section 1103.4.8.

❖ See the commentary to Section 1103.4. The exceptions are consistent with the allowances for atrium and mall enclosure requirements of the IBC. Exception 1 exempts single-family dwellings and small congregate residences from vertical opening enclosures because of occupant familiarity with the premises and the relatively small occupant load. Exception 2 recognizes that it would be impractical and unnecessary to enclose shafts in parking occupancies where open ramps are a fundamental design element. Exception 3 recognizes that exit access stairways and ramps have various allowances that would not require enclosure. These allowances are consistent with Chapter 7 of the IBC, Chapter 10 of this code, and Sections 402 and 404. Escalators within a mall are addressed in Sections 1103.4.5, 1103.4.6 and 1103.4.7 (see Section 1103.4.8).

1103.4.5 Escalators in Group B and M occupancies. In Group B and M occupancies, escalators creating vertical openings connecting any number of stories shall be protected by either 1-hour fire-resistance-rated construction or an *automatic sprinkler system* in accordance with Section 903.3.1.1 installed throughout the building, with a draft curtain and closely spaced sprinklers around the escalator opening.

❖ This section addresses escalator openings in Group B and M occupancies and provides the option of either enclosing the vertical opening with 1-hour construction or equipping the building throughout with an NFPA 13 sprinkler system with the vertical opening protected by draft curtains and closely spaced sprinklers. Section 8.15.4.2 of NFPA 13 provides specifications on the construction and installation of the draft curtains ("draftstops" in NFPA 13) and Section 8.15.4.3 provides installation criteria for the automatic sprinklers for protecting the opening. There is no limit to the number of stories connected by vertical openings protected by either option in this section. IBC Section 712.1.3 contains similar, but more stringent, requirements for escalator openings in new buildings.

1103.4.6 Escalators connecting four or fewer stories. In other than Group B and M occupancies, escalators creating vertical openings connecting four or fewer stories shall be protected by either 1-hour fire-resistance-rated construction or an *automatic sprinkler system* in accordance with Section 903.3.1.1 or 903.3.1.2 shall be installed throughout the building, and a draft curtain with closely spaced sprinklers shall be installed around the escalator opening.

❖ In other than Group B and M occupancies, escalators creating vertical openings connecting four or fewer stories shall either be protected by 1-hour fire-resistance-rated construction or an *automatic sprinkler system* in accordance with Section 903.3.1.1 or 903.3.1.2 shall be installed throughout the building and a draft curtain with closely spaced sprinklers shall be installed around the escalator opening.

This section addresses escalator openings connecting a maximum of four stories in other than Group B and M occupancies. Similar to Section 1103.4.5, it provides the option of either enclosing the vertical opening with 1-hour construction or equipping the building throughout with an NFPA 13 or 13R sprinkler system with the vertical opening protected by draft curtains and closely spaced sprinklers. Section 8.15.4.2 of NFPA 13 provides specifications on the construction and installation of the draft curtains ("draftstops" in NFPA 13) and Section 8.15.4.3 provides installation criteria for the automatic sprinklers for protecting the opening (also see commentary, Section 1103.4). IBC Section 712.1.3.1 contains similar, but more stringent, requirements for escalator openings in new buildings.

1103.4.7 Escalators connecting more than four stories. In other than Group B and M occupancies, escalators creating vertical openings connecting five or more stories shall be protected by 1-hour fire-resistance-rated construction.

❖ This section addresses escalator openings connecting five stories or more in other than Group B and M occupancies and provides no option to enclosing the vertical opening with 1-hour construction (see commentary, Section 1103.4). IBC Section 712.1.3 contains similar, but more stringent, requirements for escalator openings in new buildings.

1103.4.8 Occupancies other than Groups I-2 and I-3. In other than Group I-2 and I-3 occupancies, floor openings containing *exit access stairways* or *ramps* that do not comply with one of the conditions listed in this section shall be protected by 1-hour fire-resistance-rated construction.

1. *Exit access stairways* and *ramps* that serve, or atmospherically communicate between, only two stories. Such interconnected stories shall not be open to other stories.
2. In Group R-1, R-2 or R-3 occupancies, *exit access stairways* and *ramps* connecting four stories or less serving and contained within an individual *dwelling unit* or *sleeping unit* or live/work unit.
3. *Exit access stairways* and *ramps* in buildings equipped throughout with an *automatic sprinkler system* in accordance with Section 903.3.1.1, where the area of the vertical opening between stories does not exceed twice the horizontal projected area of the *stairway* or *ramp*, and the opening is protected by a draft curtain and closely spaced sprinklers in accordance with NFPA 13. In other than Group B and M occupancies, this provision is limited to openings that do not connect more than four stories.
4. *Exit access stairways* and *ramps* within an atrium complying with the provisions of Section 404 of the *International Building Code*.
5. *Exit access stairways* and *ramps* in open parking garages that serve only the parking garage.
6. *Exit access stairways* and *ramps* serving open-air seating complying with the exit access travel distance requirements of Section 1029.7 of the *International Building Code*.
7. *Exit access stairways* and *ramps* serving the balcony, gallery or press box and the main assembly floor in occupancies such as theaters, places of religious worship, auditoriums and sports facilities.

❖ Vertical openings in Group I-2 and I-3 occupancies are specifically addressed in Section 1103.4.1. This section addresses vertical openings in other occupancies. There are many provisions for new construction in Chapter 10 that permit exit access stair floor openings without a fire-rated enclosure. Without this section, many of these permitted floor openings would be required to be fire rated by this chapter. In addition, a building constructed under this code in full compliance with Chapter 10 would be in violation of Sections 1103.4 through 1103.4.8 upon issuance of the certificate of occupancy if these allowances were not provided. Clearly it was not the intent for Chapter 11 to contradict Chapter 10. This section notes all of the current conditions that allow an unenclosed exit access stair or ramp. All of these conditions originate from Section 1019. It is important to note that this section and these conditions only apply to exit access stairways and ramps. This section does not apply to exit stairways. Exit stairways are not exempted from enclosure.

1103.4.9 Waste and linen chutes. In Group I-2 occupancies, existing waste and linen chutes shall comply with Sections 1103.4.9.1 through 1103.4.9.5.

❖ This section is intended to clarify the allowable use and construction of chutes and incinerators in Group I-2 occupancies (hospitals and nursing homes). These items are used as integral parts of the operation of a healthcare facility, especially the waste or linen chutes. Some incinerators are still in use, but the requirements found in Sections 1103.4.9.1

through 1103.4.9.5 seek to separate them from other vertical openings, especially a trash chute, by requiring a separate discharge room from the incinerator. Waste and linen chutes in other occupancies are addressed in Section 1103.4.8.

1103.4.9.1 Enclosure. Chutes shall be enclosed with 1-hour fire-resistance-rated construction. Opening protectives shall be in accordance with Section 716 of the *International Building Code* and have a fire protection rating of not less than1 hour.

❖ At minimum, chutes must be enclosed with 1-hour fire-resistance-rated construction. This is consistent with Section 713.4 of the IBC for shaft enclosures for chutes connecting three stories or less. Openings other than chute access doors addressed in Section 1103.4.9.2 must meet IBC Section 716 requirements.

1103.4.9.2 Chute intakes. Chute intakes shall comply with Section 1103.4.9.2.1 or 1103.4.9.2.2.

❖ This section focuses on where chutes can be accessed throughout a building. There are two configurations addressed. The first, in Section 1103.4.9.2.1, addresses access from the corridor. Section 1103.4.9.2.2 then addresses chute intakes accessed from a chute intake room.

1103.4.9.2.1 Chute intake direct from corridor. Where intake to chutes is direct from a *corridor*, the intake opening shall be equipped with a chute-intake door in accordance with Section 716 of the *International Building Code* and having a fire protection rating of not less than 1 hour.

❖ In facilities that predate current requirements, some chute doors open into corridors. As it is not practical to reconstruct such chutes to meet modern standards, this section aims to directly address that situation by defining requirements for the chutes' safe maintenance. This configuration has a more direct effect on the safety of the occupants than those chute intakes addressed in Section 1103.4.9.2.2. Therefore, the opening must be in accordance with Section 716 of the IBC and be rated for at least 1 hour.

1103.4.9.2.2 Chute intake via a chute-intake room. Where the intake to chutes is accessed through a chute-intake room, the room shall be enclosed with 1-hour fire-resistance-rated construction. Opening protectives for the intake room shall be in accordance with Section 716 of the *International Building Code* and have a fire protection rating of not less than $^3/_4$ hour. Opening protectives for the chute enclosure shall be in accordance with Section 1103.4.9.1.

❖ This configuration provides a layer of protection to the building occupants by first entering a room that is protected with 1-hour fire-resistance-rated construction. The door rating is only required to be $^3/_4$ hour versus 1 hour as required in Section 1103.4.9.2.1. The door for the chute intake itself would still be required to be 1 hour.

1103.4.9.3 Automatic sprinkler system. Chutes shall be equipped with an *approved automatic sprinkler system* in accordance with Section 903.2.11.2.

❖ This section would retroactively require compliance with Section 903.2.11.2 for sprinkler placement within the chute.

1103.4.9.4 Chute discharge rooms. Chutes shall terminate in a dedicated chute discharge room. Such rooms shall be separated from the remainder of the building by not less than 1-hour fire-resistance-rated construction. Opening protectives shall be in accordance with Section 716 of the *International Building Code* and have a fire protection rating of not less than 1 hour.

❖ This section provides minimal requirements for protection of the chute discharge room. This provides a minimal separation requirement for existing chute discharge rooms. This is consistent with the requirements in Section 713.13.4 of the IBC for shafts connecting three stories or less in new construction. The rating of the door must also be 1 hour.

1103.4.9.5 Chute discharge protection. Chute discharges shall be equipped with a self-closing or automatic-closing opening protective in accordance with Section 716 of the *International Building Code* and having a fire protection rating of not less than 1 hour.

❖ This section requires that the chute discharge room continue the protection of the enclosure through opening protection. The discharge must also have a 1-hour fire protection rating and be self- or automatic-closing. This is consistent with the requirement of IBC Section 713.13.4 that the opening protection have the same rating as the enclosure. The opening must also be self-closing or automatic-closing.

1103.4.10 Flue-fed incinerators. Existing flue-fed incinerator rooms and associated flue shafts shall be protected with 1-hour fire-resistance-rated construction and shall not have other vertical openings connected with the space other than the associated flue. Opening protectives shall be in accordance with Section 716 of the *International Building Code* and have a fire protection rating of not less than 1 hour.

❖ Because of regulation from the EPA and other entities, flue-fed incinerators are frequently found abandoned or otherwise unused in existing buildings. This requirement is intended to separate and protect any potential hazard of inactive incinerator systems from the rest of the building.

1103.5 Sprinkler systems. An *automatic sprinkler system* shall be provided in existing buildings in accordance with Sections 1103.5.1 through 1103.5.4.

❖ This section introduces the retroactive sprinkler requirements of Sections 1103.5.1 through 1103.5.4.

1103.5.1 Group A-2. Where alcoholic beverages are consumed in a Group A-2 occupancy having an occupant load of 300 or more, the fire area containing the Group A-2 occupancy shall be equipped with an *automatic sprinkler system* in accordance with Section 903.3.1.1.

❖ This requirement implements Recommendation 1 of the NIST *Report of the Technical Investigation of The Station Nightclub Fire* (NIST NCSTAR 2: Vol. I). Recommendation 1 states: "Model codes should require sprinkler systems for all new and existing nightclubs regardless of size." Group A-2 occupancies involve conditions such as large occupant loads, high occupant density, significant fuel loading and moveable furnishings and decorations. Group A-2 occupancies also include the potential for reduced lighting levels, high noise levels, combustible decorations, strobe and flashing lights, alcohol consumption, and confusing egress paths. Each of these alone can be a significant issue, but when combined they lead to the inability of the occupants to promptly and safely exit the building under fire conditions.

This proposal does not reach as far as the recommendation from NIST. While the NIST proposal recommends fire sprinklers in all facilities, this section requires the existing Group A-2 occupancy fire area with an occupant load in excess of 300 where alcoholic drinks are consumed to be equipped with an automatic sprinkler system. The section does not require fire areas containing A-2 occupancies less than 300 to be protected, nor does it require the entire floor to be protected. Setting the threshold at 300 occupants will place the requirement where the higher potential for loss of life exists.

Additionally, this section focuses on Group A-2 occupancies that serve alcoholic beverages. This is felt to be more in line with the NIST recommendations that were made following the Station Nightclub fire, recognizing that the intoxication of patrons plays a significant role in the potential risk of injury or loss of life in the event of a fire. In addition, limiting the scope of the change to only those occupancies where alcoholic beverages are consumed allows a connection to licensing laws that jurisdictions typically have in place for sale of such beverages. Such licensing laws, where they apply, will provide significant leverage for jurisdictions to be able to effectively enforce the requirement for an automatic sprinkler system as a condition of being code compliant and issuance of a license.

Note that Section 903.2.1, which addresses new Group A-2 occupancies, requires an automatic sprinkler system throughout the story containing the group A-2 occupancy and all stories below where the fire area exceeds 5,000 square feet, has an occupant load of 100 or more or is located on a story other than the level of exit discharge. Installing automatic sprinklers in a new building is much more efficient and cost effective. The automatic sprinkler requirements for new Group A-2 occupancies include anything that qualifies as Group A-2, whether or not alcohol is served. This is more reasonable to ask of new construction. In existing construction, this section is aimed at the higher-risk Group A-2 occupancies in recognition of the difficulty in requiring sprinklers in existing buildings.

1103.5.2 Group I-2. In Group I-2, an *automatic sprinkler system* shall be provided in accordance with Section 1105.9.

❖ This section is merely a pointer to the sprinkler requirements for Group I-2 occupancies found in Section 1105.9. Section 1105.9 requires that an automatic sprinkler system be provided on the floor containing the Group I-2 occupancy, all floors between that level and the level of exit discharge, and all floors below the level of exit discharge. This requirement is less restrictive than what is found in Section 1103.5.3, since Section 1103.5.3 requires the entire building to be equipped throughout with an automatic sprinkler system. Note that I-2 occupancies include nursing homes and hospitals. Section 1103.5.3 only addresses hospitals.

1103.5.3 Group I-2, Condition 2. In addition to the requirements of Section 1103.5.2, existing buildings of Group I-2, Condition 2 occupancy shall be equipped throughout with an *approved automatic sprinkler system* in accordance with Section 903.3.1.1. The *automatic sprinkler system* shall be installed as established by the adopting ordinance. **[DATE BY WHICH SPRINKLER SYSTEM MUST BE INSTALLED].**

❖ This section is specific to hospitals and is more restrictive than the requirements of Sections 1103.5.2 and 1105.9. Instead of requiring the installation of an automatic sprinkler system from the story containing the Group I-2, Condition 2 occupancy to the level of exit discharge and below the level of exit discharge, this section requires the building to be equipped throughout with an automatic sprinkler system. This requirement, however, is based on the adopting ordinance establishing a date by which the automatic sprinkler system will be installed. Sprinkler systems are a vital safety system that protects building systems and components.

To ensure continuous operation in healthcare facilities, the installation of automatic sprinkler systems needs to be carefully planned so as to not adversely affect patient health. Accessing and exposing ceiling spaces can create conditions leading to infection and possibly death to patients with compromised immune systems. In many situations, hospitals may not be able to appropriately retrofit the installation of a fire suppression system; in those situations, a time frame is needed to replace facilities. The period for adoption of this proposed requirement has been left to the local authority having jurisdiction. Coordinating the time frame for adoption with federal requirements is recommended. It is currently anticipated that the Centers for Medicaid and Medicare (the federal authority having jurisdiction) will require retroactive installation of automatic sprinkler systems in hospitals by the year 2021. However, the exact time frame was uncertain at the time of development of this requirement. Facilities will require lead time to meet this standard without adversely affecting the health of patients and disrupting patient care. These are the same factors that a jurisdiction should consider when choosing a date for adoption.

It should be also clear that this change is a separate measure that must be taken in addition to the current requirement. It is not intended to allow a facility to have a time frame for installing the current requirement (although jurisdictions may choose to do this). Nor is it intended to imply that the entire building containing a hospital should install an automatic sprinkler system immediately. At a minimum, a 3-year time frame is recommended for implementation of this requirement. This considers the process planning, capital approval, regulatory approval, design and installation of the sprinkler system. The capital-planning piece of a large-scale initiative such as a building-wide sprinkler system, normally spans multiple fiscal years.

1103.5.4 Pyroxylin plastics. An *automatic sprinkler system* shall be provided throughout existing buildings where cellulose nitrate film or pyroxylin plastics are manufactured, stored or handled in quantities exceeding 100 pounds (45 kg). Vaults located within buildings for the storage of raw pyroxylin shall be protected with an *approved automatic sprinkler system* capable of discharging 1.66 gallons per minute per square foot (68 L/min/m^2) over the area of the vault.

❖ This section requires an approved automatic fire-extinguishing system in existing buildings used for the manufacture and storage of pyroxylin plastics. Cellulose nitrate (pyroxylin) plastics pose unusual and substantial fire risks. Pyroxylin plastics are the most dangerous and unstable of all plastic compounds. The chemically bound oxygen in their structure permits them to burn vigorously in the absence of atmospheric oxygen. Although these compounds produce approximately the same amount of energy as paper when they burn, pyroxylin plastics burn at a rate as much as 15 times greater than comparable common combustibles. When burning, these materials release highly flammable and toxic combustion byproducts. Consequently, cellulose nitrate fires are very difficult to control. Although this section specifies a sprinkler threshold quantity of 100 pounds (45 kg), the need for additional fire protection should be considered for pyroxylin plastics in any amount.

Although the code includes cellulose nitrate "film" in its requirements, cellulose nitrate motion picture film has not been used in the United States since the 1950s. All motion picture film produced since that time is what is typically called "safety film." Consequently, the only application for this section relative to motion picture film is where it may be used in laboratories or storage vaults that are dedicated to film restoration and archives. The protection of these facilities is addressed in Sections 306.2 and 6504.2.

Even though this section would permit an approved fire-extinguishing system in existing structures containing pyroxylin plastics, vaults must be protected by an approved automatic sprinkler system with a density of 1.66 gpm/ft^2 (68 L/min/m^2) over the entire area of the vault. The high sprinkler density recognizes the need to immerse the pyroxylin plastics in water to counteract the vigorous burn rate of these materials.

Note that in Table 1103.1, on the row for Section 1103.5.4, an "R" appears for all occupancy groups since pyroxylin plastics may be found in any occupancy.

1103.6 Standpipes. Existing structures shall be equipped with standpipes installed in accordance with Section 905 where required in Sections 1103.6.1 and 1103.6.2. The *fire code official* is authorized to approve the installation of manual standpipe systems to achieve compliance with this section where the responding fire department is capable of providing the required hose flow at the highest standpipe outlet.

❖ This section recognizes that some existing buildings do not have a standpipe system and introduces the minimum requirements for existing buildings. In place of a standpipe system that has a water supply capable of supplying the system demand automatically, this section would permit the fire code official to approve the use of a manual standpipe system in an existing building if adequate hose flow is available when the fire department charges the system. The standpipe system may be either a manual dry or a manual wet system.

1103.6.1 Existing multiple-story buildings. Existing buildings with occupied floors located more than 50 feet (15 240 mm) above the lowest level of fire department access or more than 50 feet (15 240 mm) below the highest level of fire department access shall be equipped with standpipes.

❖ Although it would be inappropriate to require a standpipe system in an existing building to be designed based on the requirements of Section 905.3 for new construction, this section establishes a maximum height limitation for existing buildings regardless of occupancy beyond which a standpipe is required. The system is to be installed in accordance with Section 905. Many existing buildings may also not be equipped with an automatic sprinkler system. This section will, at least, provide some means of manual fire suppression in buildings where exterior fire department access is limited.

1103.6.2 Existing helistops and heliports. Existing buildings with a rooftop helistop or heliport located more than 30 feet (9144 mm) above the lowest level of fire department access to the roof level on which the helistop or heliport is located shall be equipped with standpipes in accordance with Section 2007.5.

❖ A heliport or helistop on a new or existing building is a distinct hazard that can involve flammable fuels and combustible cargo and present an immediate rescue situation. In the event of an emergency, rapid deployment of hand hose lines will be necessary to attack a resulting fire, effectuate rescue and to protect exposures and the remainder of the building. This section specifies that when existing buildings have a helistop or heliport on a rooftop location more than 30 feet

(9144 mm) above the lowest level of fire department vehicle access, a standpipe system is required throughout the building, not just a hose connection at the roof level. This is critical in fire-fighting operations because, many times, the connection below the rooftop level may be needed to gain access to the roof. If the only connection is on the roof, it is of no use if the fire fighters cannot get to it. Additionally, a heliport includes fueling operations. It is entirely possible for a spill to not only affect the rooftop, but also floors below as the liquid fuel spreads. The standpipe system will again be utilized in these situations. Note that this section refers to Section 2007.5 for design and standpipe hose connection location for the rooftop heliport or helistop. See the commentary to Sections 905.3.6 and 2007.5 for further information.

1103.7 Fire alarm systems. An *approved* fire alarm system shall be installed in existing buildings and structures in accordance with Sections 1103.7.1 through 1103.7.6 and provide occupant notification in accordance with Section 907.5 unless other requirements are provided by other sections of this code.

Exception: Occupancies with an existing, previously *approved* fire alarm system.

❖ This section specifies the occupancy conditions where an approved fire alarm system is retroactively required in an existing building. These systems must, upon activation, provide occupant notification throughout the area protected by the system unless other alternative provisions, such as an emergency voice/alarm communication system, are allowed.

The exception recognizes the infeasibility of requiring existing, previously approved fire alarm systems to conform to current code requirements. The existing fire alarm system must be adequately tested and maintained in accordance with Section 901.6 and shown not to create a hazard.

A common concern in the application of the exception is in the scoping of the condition. Where the building is in use and continues in use as it was before, the exception is quite clear that no modifications are required if the existing system has been previously approved, regardless of how long ago that may have been. If there is an addition to the building, the addition must meet the requirements for new work and tie into the existing system if the existing system is capable of adequately handling the new devices. The addition is only adding devices and does not require the existing system to be upgraded.

If the building is altered, the alarm system must be altered in accordance with its original installation. For example, if the existing system does not include visual notification devices and the alteration includes remodeling to existing toilet rooms, there is no requirement for installing visual devices in the remodeled toilet rooms. If, on the other hand, the existing system is not capable of receiving new devices or relocated existing devices, then the replacement of the existing panel must be considered since the altered system would be less effective than before the alteration.

1103.7.1 Group E. A fire alarm system shall be installed in existing Group E occupancies in accordance with Section 907.2.3.

Exceptions:

1. A manual fire alarm system is not required in a building with a maximum area of 1,000 square feet (93 m^2) that contains a single classroom and is located not closer than 50 feet (15 240 mm) from another building.
2. A manual fire alarm system is not required in Group E occupancies with an *occupant load* less than 50.

❖ Group E occupancies are limited to educational purposes through the 12th grade. Because of the typical age and maturity of the occupants, more time may be needed to safely evacuate the building. The requirement for retroactive installation of, at least, a fire alarm system recognizes that many existing, previously approved nonsprinklered educational facilities would most likely require sprinklers under current code provisions (see Section 903.2.3).

Although not limited to this use condition, Exception 1 recognizes the current use of mobile trailer-type facilities on site as additional educational classroom facilities. This exception does not exempt the main building, but it would exempt these auxiliary buildings of limited size that do not present an exposure hazard because of the required separation distance.

Exception 2 would exempt small day care centers that serve children older than 2 years of age, a small Sunday school classroom at a church or similar limited educational use areas (see commentary, Section 907.2.3).

1103.7.2 Group I-1. An automatic fire alarm system shall be installed in existing Group I-1 facilities in accordance with Section 907.2.6.1.

Exception: Where each sleeping room has a *means of egress* door opening directly to an exterior egress balcony that leads directly to the *exits* in accordance with Section 1021, and the building is not more than three stories in height.

❖ Group I-1 facilities are assumed to have more than 16 occupants who, because of their age, mental disability or other reasons, must live in a supervised environment 24 hours a day. This section would require existing Group I-1 occupancies to have an approved fire alarm system as required by Section 907.2.6.1.

The exception recognizes the increased degree of life safety resulting from having direct access to the exterior from the sleeping rooms. The occupants are not forced to evacuate through the interior of the building during a potential fire. The exterior egress balconies must be sufficiently open to the atmosphere and constructed to minimize the accumulation of smoke and toxic gases.

1103.7.3 Group I-2. In Group I-2, an automatic fire alarm system shall be installed in accordance with Section 1105.10.

❖ This section is simply a pointer to the specific requirements for Group I-2 occupancies found in Section 1105. Section 1105.10 addresses the need for a fire alarm system. See the commentary to Section 1105.10.

1103.7.4 Group I-3. An automatic and manual fire alarm system shall be installed in existing Group I-3 occupancies in accordance with Section 907.2.6.3.

❖ Because occupants may be restrained, leading to difficulties in evacuating, an approved fire alarm system is required in existing Group I-3 occupancies. The system must comply with Section 907.2.6.3 (see commentary, Section 907.2.6.3).

1103.7.5 Group R-1. A fire alarm system and smoke alarms shall be installed in existing Group R-1 occupancies in accordance with Sections 1103.7.5.1 through 1103.7.5.2.1.

❖ This section introduces the retroactive fire alarm system and smoke alarm requirements for Group R-1 transient occupancies such as hotels, motels, and boarding houses.

1103.7.5.1 Group R-1 hotel and motel manual fire alarm system. A manual fire alarm system that activates the occupant notification system in accordance with Section 907.5 shall be installed in existing Group R-1 hotels and motels more than three stories or with more than 20 *sleeping units.*

Exceptions:

1. Buildings less than two stories in height where all *sleeping units,* attics and crawl spaces are separated by 1-hour fire-resistance-rated construction and each *sleeping unit* has direct access to a *public way, egress court* or yard.
2. Manual fire alarm boxes are not required throughout the building where the following conditions are met:
   - 2.1. The building is equipped throughout with an *automatic sprinkler system* installed in accordance with Section 903.3.1.1 or 903.3.1.2.
   - 2.2. The notification appliances will activate upon sprinkler water flow.
   - 2.3. Not less than one manual fire alarm box is installed at an *approved* location.

❖ This section specifies the conditions where a fire alarm system is required in existing Group R-1 hotels and motels. The two main criteria are independent of each other in that a fire alarm system is required if the building is more than three stories above grade, regardless of the number of sleeping units, or contains 20 sleeping units, regardless of the number of stories. Occupants of these types of Group R-1 facilities are assumed to be more transient than the occupants of Group R-1 boarding and rooming houses regulated by Section 907.2.8.

Exception 1 recognizes the increased level of life safety afforded by adequate compartmentation using 1-hour fire-resistance-rated construction between sleeping units and direct exterior access for egress.

Exception 2 does not omit fire alarm systems but, rather, permits them to be initiated automatically by sprinkler system water flow switches in lieu of manual fire alarm boxes. The sprinkler system is to be equipped with local audible alarms that can be heard throughout the building and at least one manual fire alarm box installed at an approved location.

The exceptions do not affect the independent provision in Section 1103.8 for single- or multiple-station smoke alarms.

1103.7.5.1.1 Group R-1 hotel and motel automatic smoke detection system. An automatic smoke detection system that activates the occupant notification system in accordance with Section 907.5 shall be installed in existing Group R-1 hotels and motels throughout all interior *corridors* serving sleeping rooms not equipped with an *approved,* supervised *automatic sprinkler system* installed in accordance with Section 903.

Exception: An automatic smoke detection system is not required in buildings that do not have interior *corridors* serving *sleeping units* and where each sleeping unit has a *means of egress* door opening directly to an *exit* or to an exterior *exit access* that leads directly to an *exit.*

❖ This section requires an automatic smoke detection system within interior corridors serving unsprinklered sleeping rooms. Such systems make use of smoke detectors for alarm initiation, in accordance with Section 907.4.3, with one exception.

The exception provides that automatic smoke detection is not required in motels and hotels that do not have interior corridors and in which sleeping units have a door opening directly to an exterior exit access that leads directly to the exits. The exception is intended to ensure that the exit access from the sleeping unit door be exterior and not require reentering the building prior to entering the exit. Since the exit access is outside, the need for detectors other than in sleeping units is greatly reduced. Unlike Exception 1 to Section 1103.7.5.1, exit balconies and exterior stairs serving sleeping units are allowed.

1103.7.5.2 Group R-1 boarding and rooming houses manual fire alarm system. A manual fire alarm system that activates the occupant notification system in accordance with Section 907.5 shall be installed in existing Group R-1 boarding and rooming houses.

Exception: Buildings less than two stories in height where all *sleeping units,* attics and crawl spaces are separated by 1-hour fire-resistance-rated construction and each *sleeping unit* has direct access to a *public way, egress court* or yard.

❖ Group R-1 boarding and rooming houses are still assumed to be transient residential occupancies even though the functional use of a boarding and rooming house is different from that of a typical hotel or motel. Boarding and rooming houses tend to have more extended living arrangements and border on being classified as Group R-2 facilities. For this reason, this section requires Group R-1 boarding and rooming houses to be equipped with a manual fire alarm system regardless of the height of the building or number of sleeping rooms.

The exception recognizes the increased level of life safety afforded by adequate compartmentation using 1-hour fire-resistance-rated construction between sleeping units and direct exterior access for egress.

1103.7.5.2.1 Group R-1 boarding and rooming houses automatic smoke detection system. An automatic smoke detection system that activates the occupant notification system in accordance with Section 907.5 shall be installed in existing Group R-1 boarding and rooming houses throughout all interior *corridors* serving *sleeping units* not equipped with an *approved,* supervised sprinkler system installed in accordance with Section 903.

Exception: Buildings equipped with single-station smoke alarms meeting or exceeding the requirements of Section 907.2.10.1 and where the fire alarm system includes not less than one manual fire alarm box per floor arranged to initiate the alarm.

❖ This section requires an automatic smoke detection system within interior corridors serving unsprinklered sleeping rooms. Such systems make use of smoke detectors for alarm initiation, in accordance with Section 907.4.3, with one exception.

The exception provides that automatic fire detectors are not required in boarding and rooming houses where single-station smoke alarms complying with the minimum requirements of Section 907.2.10.1 and at least one manual fire alarm box per floor are installed. The single-station smoke alarms give the desired early warning notification to occupants and the manual fire alarm box is an additional means to activate the occupant notification system.

1103.7.6 Group R-2. A manual fire alarm system that activates the occupant notification system in accordance with Section 907.5 shall be installed in existing Group R-2 occupancies more than three stories in height or with more than 16 *dwelling* or *sleeping units.*

Exceptions:

1. Where each living unit is separated from other contiguous living units by *fire barriers* having a *fire-resistance rating* of not less than $^3/_4$ hour, and where each living unit has either its own independent *exit* or its own independent stairway or ramp discharging at grade.
2. A separate fire alarm system is not required in buildings that are equipped throughout with an *approved* supervised *automatic sprinkler system* installed in accordance with Section 903.3.1.1 or 903.3.1.2 and having a local alarm to notify all occupants.
3. A fire alarm system is not required in buildings that do not have interior *corridors* serving *dwelling units* and are protected by an *approved automatic sprinkler system* installed in accordance with Section 903.3.1.1 or 903.3.1.2, provided that *dwelling units* either have a *means of egress* door opening directly to an exterior *exit access* that leads directly to the *exits* or are served by open-ended *corridors* designed in accordance with Section 1027.6, Exception 3.
4. A fire alarm system is not required in buildings that do not have interior *corridors* serving *dwelling units*, do not exceed three stories in height and comply with both of the following:
    - 4.1. Each *dwelling unit* is separated from other contiguous *dwelling units* by *fire barriers* having a *fire-resistance rating* of not less than $^3/_4$ hour.
    - 4.2. Each *dwelling unit* is provided with hard-wired, interconnected smoke alarms as required for new construction in Section 907.2.10.

❖ This section specifies the conditions where a manual fire alarm system is required in existing Group R-2 apartment buildings based on height or the number of dwelling or sleeping units. Occupants of Group R-2 facilities tend to be more permanent than those in Group R-1 facilities.

Exception 1 recognizes the increased degree of life safety afforded by compartmentation using fire-resistance-rated construction and independent means of egress (see Section 907.2.9).

As indicated in Exception 2, existing buildings that are fully sprinklered in accordance with NFPA 13 or 13R do not need a manual fire alarm system if local alarms will sound upon activation of the sprinkler system. The exception essentially eliminates the need for manual fire alarm boxes if evacuation alarms can still be heard throughout the building upon sprinkler system water flow. Other alarm-initiating devices would similarly not be required if the water flow device will initiate the appropriate alarm. This exception does not affect the independent provisions in Section 907.2.10.

Exception 3 mirrors Section 907.2.9, Exception 3, and recognizes the superior fire record of sprinklered multiple-family occupancies by allowing omission of a fire alarm system where a building is fully sprinklered, has no interior egress corridors and provides direct exterior egress from each dwelling unit. Note that in such buildings, rated fire separations are still required between units.

Exception 4 provides a reasonable alternative to retrofitting a manual fire alarm system in existing Group R-2 occupancy buildings not exceeding three stories in height and having exits that lead directly to the outside. Fire risk in apartments tends to be greatest for occupants inside the dwelling unit where a fire originates, and money spent to retrofit fire safety equipment in apartments is better spent within dwelling units, as opposed to common areas.

Countless existing apartment buildings have only a single smoke alarm in the common area. The code does not require retrofitting sleeping rooms with smoke alarms where such alarms weren't required at the time of construction. The lack of smoke alarms in bedrooms, and particularly the lack of interconnecting alarm signals, increases the risk of injury or death in a unit of fire origin and other units that experience smoke infiltration. An additional consequence may be delayed recognition of a fire event, which increases the risk of harm to other building occupants and may delay notification of the fire department. This exception also requires minimal separation from other units.

1103.8 Single- and multiple-station smoke alarms. Single- and multiple-station smoke alarms shall be installed in existing Group I-1 and R occupancies in accordance with Sections 1103.8.1 through 1103.8.3.

❖ This section introduces the requirements for the installation of smoke alarms in existing Group I-1 and R occupancies. These requirements recognize the benefit of installing smoke alarms in existing structures, but provide several exceptions for buildings that are not undergoing substantial renovations. These provisions also correlate with Section 704.6 of the *International Property Maintenance Code®* (IPMC®) for single- or multiple-station smoke alarm requirements for existing Group R dwellings.

1103.8.1 Where required. Existing Group I-1 and R occupancies shall be provided with single-station smoke alarms in accordance with Section 907.2.10. Interconnection and power sources shall be in accordance with Sections 1103.8.2 and 1103.8.3, respectively.

Exceptions:

1. Where the code that was in effect at the time of construction required smoke alarms and smoke alarms complying with those requirements are already provided.
2. Where smoke alarms have been installed in occupancies and dwellings that were not required to have them at the time of construction, additional smoke alarms shall not be required provided that the existing smoke alarms comply with requirements that were in effect at the time of installation.
3. Where smoke detectors connected to a fire alarm system have been installed as a substitute for smoke alarms.

❖ This section requires that Group I-1 and R occupancies be provided with single-station smoke alarms where they are not already provided. Reference is made to the new building requirements of Section 907.2.10 for the primary requirements; however, interconnection and power supply are more specifically addressed for existing buildings in Sections 1103.8.2 and 1103.8.3. Therefore, the basic requirement is that smoke alarms must be provided in all locations required by Section 907.2.10, but several modified requirements related to interconnection of alarms and power supply are provided, recognizing the impracticality of such installations in existing conditions. Three exceptions are also provided to address possible scenarios where smoke alarms have already been installed but the installation does not meet the current code requirements, recognizing that the code is intended to permit existing smoke alarm installations to continue unchanged where they meet the code that was in effect at the time they were installed.

Exception 1 indicates that smoke alarms installed and maintained in accordance with the applicable code at the time of construction can continue unchanged. Exception 2 indicates that smoke alarms that were not required by the code at the time of construction, but were later installed can continue where they meet the requirements of the applicable code at the time of installation. Exception 3 indicates that smoke detectors connected to a fire alarm system may be used in lieu of smoke alarms.

In summary, this section requires the installation of smoke alarms in Group I-1 and R occupancies that do not currently have any smoke alarms. It does not require compliance with the current smoke alarm requirements if the building already has smoke alarms meeting requirements that were applicable when they were installed. The focus here is not to have the owner replace or revise his or her smoke alarms any time the code requirements for new construction change.

1103.8.2 Interconnection. Where more than one smoke alarm is required to be installed within an individual *dwelling* or *sleeping unit,* the smoke alarms shall be interconnected in such a manner that the activation of one alarm will activate all of the alarms in the individual unit. Physical interconnection of smoke alarms shall not be required where listed wireless alarms are installed and all alarms sound upon activation of one alarm. The alarm shall be clearly audible in all bedrooms over background noise levels with all intervening doors closed.

Exceptions:

1. Interconnection is not required in buildings that are not undergoing *alterations*, repairs or construction of any kind.
2. Smoke alarms in existing areas are not required to be interconnected where *alterations* or repairs do not result in the removal of interior wall or ceiling finishes exposing the structure, unless there is an attic, crawl space or *basement* available that could provide access for interconnection without the removal of interior finishes.

❖ This section, like Section 907.2.10.5, requires that where multiple-station smoke alarms are present, they are to be interconnected and be audible over back-ground noises. This section also includes language that would allow listed wireless alarms to substitute for wired interconnection of the smoke alarms in both new and existing construction, making it clear that listed wireless systems comply with the code. Historically, while some code officials have not recognized wireless interconnection of smoke alarms as meeting the code requirement for interconnection, most have accepted such interconnection as its use has proliferated and its reliability has been demonstrated. See the commentary to Section 907.2.10.5 for further information on interconnection.

Exception 1 does not require interconnection where the building is not undergoing any construction or repairs. Exception 2 clarifies to what extent the building must be undergoing construction before interconnection is required. Generally, the exceptions try to be reasonable based on the practicality of such installations; therefore, unless areas such as attics or crawl spaces can still be utilized while the interior finishes are being removed (e.g., drywall removed, exposing the studs), interconnection would not be required. Such renovations may only be limited to portions of a structure; therefore, complete interconnection may not be practical or possible. The intent is that additional walls, etc., should not be removed solely to interconnect the smoke alarms. Battery-powered alarms, as allowed by Section 1103.8.3, may be interconnected where a building is not supplied by a commercial power source.

1103.8.3 Power source. Single-station smoke alarms shall receive their primary power from the building wiring provided that such wiring is served from a commercial source and shall be equipped with a battery backup. Smoke alarms with integral strobes that are not equipped with battery backup shall be connected to an emergency electrical system. Smoke alarms shall emit a signal when the batteries are low. Wiring shall be permanent and without a disconnecting switch other than as required for overcurrent protection.

Exceptions:

1. Smoke alarms are permitted to be solely battery operated in existing buildings where construction is not taking place.
2. Smoke alarms are permitted to be solely battery operated in buildings that are not served from a commercial power source.
3. Smoke alarms are permitted to be solely battery operated in existing areas of buildings undergoing *alterations* or repairs that do not result in the removal of interior walls or ceiling finishes exposing the structure, unless there is an attic, crawl space or *basement* available that could provide access for building wiring without the removal of interior finishes.

❖ This section requires both a primary power supply from the building wiring, as well as a supervised battery backup. Wiring must be permanent and supplied from a circuit that is properly overcurrent-protected, but without any on-off switching capability. Currently, there are some smoke alarms on the market that have an integral visual alarm notification component (a strobe light) but do not have a built-in battery for the strobe. Thus, if the power for the building fails, the smoke detection and audible signal of the device may still operate, but the strobe will not. It is critical for rooms that may house those with hearing impairments and are equipped with these smoke alarms that the strobe be as reliable as the audible signal element. This section resolves that concern by requiring such smoke alarms to be connected to an emergency electrical system for backup power in accordance with Section 1203.

This section is very similar to Section 907.2.10.6. The primary differences are the exceptions.

Exception 1 allows the use of batteries as the sole power source if no construction or related repairs are occurring in the building.

Exception 2 allows the use of batteries as the sole power source if there is no other power source available (i.e., the building is without an electric utility connection).

Exception 3 clarifies to what extent the building must be undergoing construction before connection to the building wiring is required. Generally, the exceptions try to be reasonable based on the practicality of such installations; therefore, unless areas such as attics or crawl spaces can be utilized for interstitial access for wiring while the interior finishes are being removed (e.g., drywall removed, exposing the studs), connection to the building wiring would not be required. Such renovations may only be limited to portions of a structure; therefore, adding permanent wiring may not be practical or possible. The intent is that additional walls, etc., should not be removed solely to connect the smoke alarms to the building wiring.

1103.9 Carbon monoxide alarms. Carbon monoxide alarms shall be installed in existing dwelling units and sleeping units where those units include any of the conditions identified in Sections 915.1.2 through 915.1.6. The carbon monoxide alarms shall be installed in the locations specified in Section 915.2 and the installation shall be in accordance with Section 915.4.

Exceptions:

1. Carbon monoxide alarms are permitted to be solely battery operated where the code that was in effect at the time of construction did not require carbon monoxide detectors to be provided.
2. Carbon monoxide alarms are permitted to be solely battery operated in dwelling units that are not served from a commercial power source.
3. A carbon monoxide detection system in accordance with Section 915.5 shall be an acceptable alternative to carbon monoxide alarms.

❖ This section requires CO alarms in accordance with the requirements of Section 915 in dwelling and sleeping units. Most carbon monoxide poisoning fatalities in buildings occur in dwelling units with fuel burning appliances or attached garages. Requiring carbon monoxide alarms in these existing dwellings addresses this problem. Section 915 provides very specific requirements on placement. This recognizes the need for and the practicality of providing such protection in existing buildings. Also note that Section 915 addresses Group E occupancies. This section does not address Group E occupancies. The first and second exception acknowledge that allowing battery-powered units to be provided is a relatively low-cost solution in existing buildings where carbon monoxide alarms were not initially required or where dwelling units and sleeping units are not connected to a commercial power source. The third exception provides the option of using a CO detection system in place of individual CO alarms. See the commentary to Section 915 for more details on alarm requirements and placement.

1103.10 Medical gases. Medical gases stored and transferred in health-care-related facilities shall be in accordance with Chapter 53.

❖ This section requires compliance with Chapter 53 compressed gases where medical gases are stored and transferred in existing health-care-related facilities. This will address several different types of occupancies including Group I-2 and ambulatory care facilities but can also address facilities such as a small dentist office. It was considered necessary to make sure that all existing facilities comply with these requirements to meet CMS guidelines. A general reference was made since the medical gas requirements of Section 5306 are only one aspect of the regulation of compressed gases.

SECTION 1104 MEANS OF EGRESS FOR EXISTING BUILDINGS

1104.1 General. *Means of egress* in existing buildings shall comply with the minimum egress requirements where specified in Table 1103.1 as further enumerated in Sections 1104.2 through 1104.25, and the building code that applied at the time of construction. Where the provisions of this chapter conflict with the building code that applied at the time of construction, the most restrictive provision shall apply. Existing buildings that were not required to comply with a building code at the time of construction shall comply with the minimum egress requirements where specified in Table 1103.1 as further enumerated in Sections 1104.2 through 1104.25.

❖ The primary concept of this section is to require existing buildings to comply with the specific means of egress requirements for new buildings except as modified by this section. Where an item is specifically addressed by Section 1104, the requirements of this section allow existing buildings to not fully meet the requirements for new buildings in Sections 1003 through 1030.

For example, the guard height requirements in Section 1104.6 include exceptions for the guard height requirement for new buildings in Section 1015.2. The requirements for existing buildings in Section 1104 are intended to be the same or less stringent than the comparable provisions for new buildings in Sections 1003 through 1030.

This section applies to most existing buildings. Though the code does not specifically state, where a building has been built to meet the requirements of the building code in effect at the time of construction and, in the opinion of the fire code official, the means of egress is not hazardous, the building would satisfy this section. As such, none of the specific requirements in this section would apply.

In the absence of any evidence of compliance with a building code at the time the building was constructed, all provisions of Sections 1104.1 through 1104.25 apply. See Chapter 13 of the IEBC for a performance-based compliance alternative analysis regimen for existing buildings, especially Sections 1301.6.11 through 1301.6.15, which deal with the means of egress analysis. Chapter 19 of the *International Code Council Performance Code®* (ICCPC®) also provides a performance approach to means of egress evaluation.

1104.2 Elevators, escalators and moving walks. Elevators, escalators and moving walks shall not be used as a component of a required *means of egress*.

Exceptions:

1. Elevators used as an *accessible means of egress* where allowed by Section 1009.4.
2. Previously *approved* elevators, escalators and moving walks in existing buildings.

❖ This section is the same as Section 1003.7, except Exception 2 is added. Thus, an escalator or moving walk could be used as part of the required means of egress in an existing building if it had been previously approved by the fire code official.

1104.3 Exit sign illumination. Exit signs shall be internally or externally illuminated. The face of an exit sign illuminated from an external source shall have an intensity of not less than 5 foot-candles (54 lux). Internally illuminated signs shall provide equivalent luminance and be *listed* for the purpose.

Exception: *Approved* self-luminous signs that provide evenly illuminated letters shall have a minimum luminance of 0.06 foot-lamberts (0.21 cd/m^2).

❖ This section is the same as Section 1013.3 for new buildings, except that Section 1013.3 includes an exception to illumination for tactile signs. The same exception should apply for existing buildings.

1104.4 Power source. Where emergency illumination is required in Section 1104.5, exit signs shall be visible under emergency illumination conditions.

Exception: *Approved* signs that provide continuous illumination independent of external power sources are not required to be connected to an emergency electrical system.

❖ This section requires that exit signs serving the occupancies listed in Section 1104.5 be illuminated during the use of emergency power for the means of egress. The comparable section for new buildings is Section 1013.6.3. Exit signs for all new building occupancies must be illuminated at all times and have an emergency power source.

1104.5 Illumination emergency power. Where *means of egress* illumination is provided, the power supply for *means of egress* illumination shall normally be provided by the premises' electrical supply. In the event of power supply failure, illumination shall be automatically provided from an emergency system for the following occupancies where such occupancies require two or more *means of egress*:

1. Group A having 50 or more occupants.

   Exception: Assembly occupancies used exclusively as a place of worship and having an *occupant load* of less than 300.

2. Group B buildings three or more stories in height, buildings with 100 or more occupants above or below a *level of exit discharge* serving the occupants or buildings with 1,000 or more total occupants.

3. Group E in interior *exit access* and *exit stairways* and *ramps*, *corridors*, windowless areas with student occupancy, shops and laboratories.

4. Group F having more than 100 occupants.

   Exception: Buildings used only during daylight hours and that are provided with windows for natural light in accordance with the *International Building Code*.

5. Group I.

6. Group M.

   Exception: Buildings less than 3,000 square feet (279 m^2) in gross sales area on one story only, excluding mezzanines.

7. Group R-1.

   Exception: Where each *sleeping unit* has direct access to the outside of the building at grade.

8. Group R-2.

   Exception: Where each *dwelling unit* or *sleeping unit* has direct access to the outside of the building at grade.

❖ Section 1008.3 requires emergency power for emergency egress lighting in all new buildings along aisles, corridors and exit access stairways leading through or from spaces where two or more means of egress are required. This section requires emergency power for emergency egress lighting only for the listed occupancy conditions for existing buildings.

1104.5.1 Emergency power duration and installation. Emergency power for *means of egress* illumination shall be provided in accordance with Section 1203. In other than Group I-2, emergency power shall be provided for not less than 60 minutes for systems requiring emergency power.

❖ A 90-minute emergency power duration for emergency egress lighting is required by Section 1008.3 for new buildings. The emergency power system for emergency egress lighting in existing buildings in other than Group I-2 occupancies, however, is to provide power for at least 60 minutes. This duration is consistent with Section 1104.1.

1104.6 Guards. Guards complying with this section shall be provided at the open sides of *means of egress* that are more than 30 inches (762 mm) above the floor or grade below.

❖ Where guards are required in this section, the requirements are the same as in Section 1015 for new buildings (see commentary, Section 1015.1). Sections 1104.6.1 and 1104.6.2 do provide allowances for the height and opening limitations that are less than required for new construction.

1104.6.1 Height of guards. Guards shall form a protective barrier not less than 42 inches (1067 mm) high.

Exceptions:

1. Existing guards on the open side of exit access and exit *stairways* and *ramps* shall be not less than 30 inches (760 mm) high.
2. Existing *guards* within *dwelling units* shall be not less than 36 inches (910 mm) high.
3. Existing *guards* in assembly seating areas.

❖ Guard height in new construction is typically 42 inches (1067 mm) minimum. In the legacy codes, there were allowances for guards to have the top rail at the height required for handrails where the guard was along a stairway or ramp (except for Group E). Exception 1 is in recognition of those allowances. Exceptions 2 and 3 are in recognition of the lower guard heights allowed within dwelling units (Section 1015.3, Exceptions 1, 2 and 3) and with assembly seating (Section 1029.17) for new construction.

1104.6.2 Opening limitations. Open *guards* shall have balusters or ornamental patterns such that a 6-inch-diameter (152 mm) sphere cannot pass through any opening up to a height of 34 inches (864 mm).

Exceptions:

1. At elevated walking surfaces for access to, and use of, electrical, mechanical or plumbing systems or equipment, guards shall have balusters or be of solid materials such that a sphere with a diameter of 21 inches (533 mm) cannot pass through any opening.
2. In occupancies in Group I-3, F, H or S, the clear distance between intermediate rails measured at right angles to the rails shall not exceed 21 inches (533 mm).
3. *Approved* existing open guards.

❖ Generally, this section allows maximum openings of 6 inches (152 mm) versus the maximum openings of 4 inches (102 mm) allowed by Section 1015.4. Exception 1 mirrors Section 1015.4, Exception 3, and Exception 2 mirrors Section 1015.4, Exception 4.

1104.7 Size of doors. The required capacity of each door opening shall be sufficient for the *occupant load* thereof and shall provide a minimum clear opening width of 28 inches (711 mm). Where this section requires a minimum clear opening width of 28 inches (711 mm) and a door opening includes two door leaves without a mullion, one leaf shall provide a clear opening width of 28 inches (711 mm). The minimum clear opening height of doorways shall be 80 inches (2032 mm).

Exceptions:

1. The minimum and maximum width shall not apply to door openings that are not part of the required *means of egress* in occupancies in Group R-2 and R-3 units that are not required to be an Accessible Type A unit or Type B unit.
2. Door openings to storage closets less than 10 square feet (0.93 m^2) in area shall not be limited by the minimum clear opening width.
3. The width of door leaves in revolving doors that comply with Section 1010.1.4.1 shall not be limited.
4. The maximum width of door leaves in power-operated doors that comply with Section 1010.1.4.2 shall not be limited.
5. Door openings within a *dwelling unit* shall have a minimum clear opening height of 78 inches (1981 mm).
6. In dwelling and sleeping units that are not required to be Accessible units, Type A units or Type B units, exterior door openings, other than the required *exit* door, shall have a minimum clear opening height of 76 inches (1930 mm).
7. *Exit access* doors serving a room not larger than 70 square feet (6.5 m^2) shall have a minimum door leaf width of 24 inches (610 mm).
8. The minimum clear opening width shall not apply to doors for nonaccessible showers or sauna compartments.
9. The minimum clear opening width shall not apply to the doors for nonaccessible toilet stalls.
10. Door closers and door stops shall be permitted to be 78 inches (1980 mm) minimum above the floor.

❖ Generally, this section requires doors to provide a minimum clear opening of 28 inches (711 mm) versus the minimum clear opening of 32 inches (813 mm) for new construction in Section 1010.1.1. The other provisions and exceptions in this section are the same as those in Section 1010.1.1 for new construction. Exceptions 2, 8, 9 and 10 of Section 1010.1.1 are not included in this section. Exception 2 is not needed since these provisions for existing buildings only require a 28-inch clear opening (711 mm) door. Exception 8 relates to accessibility requirements that are not intended to be retroactively applied except within the context of the IEBC. Exceptions 9 and 10 are newer exceptions that have not been addressed in these retroactive provisions.

1104.7.1 Group I-2. In Group I-2 occupancies, means of egress doors where used for the movement of beds shall provide a minimum clear opening width of $41^1/_2$ inches (1054 mm).

Doors serving as means of egress doors and not used for movement of beds shall provide a minimum clear opening width of 32 inches (813 mm).

❖ In Group I-2 occupancies, the need to move patients in beds requires a clear opening of $41^1/_2$ inches, consistent with new construction requirements. As with Ambulatory Care occupancies in Section 1104.7.2, other doors within Group I-2 occupancies could use the 28-inch clear opening allowance.

This requirement was previously found within Section 1104.7 but removed to separate the more general requirements from the more specific for Group I-2 occupancies.

1104.7.2 Ambulatory care. In ambulatory care facilities, doors serving as means of egress from patient treatment rooms shall provide a minimum clear opening width of 32 inches (813 mm).

❖ The 32-inch clear width for patient treatment or sleeping within ambulatory care facilities is based on the nature of the activities within the space (see Section 1104.7.2). As with Group I-2 occupancies in Section 1104.7.1, other doors within ambulatory care facilities could use the 28-inch clear opening allowance.

Prior to the 2018 code, this requirement was found within Section 1104.7, but was moved to separate the more general requirements from the more specific for ambulatory care facilities.

1104.8 Opening force for doors. The opening force for interior side-swinging doors without closers shall not exceed a 5-pound (22 N) force. The opening forces do not apply to the force required to retract latch bolts or disengage other devices that hold the door in a closed position. For other side-swinging, sliding and folding doors, the door latch shall release when subjected to a force of not more than 15 pounds (66 N). The door shall be set in motion when subjected to a force not exceeding 30 pounds (133 N). The door shall swing to a full-open position when subjected to a force of not more than 50 pounds (222 N). Forces shall be applied to the latch side.

❖ This section is similar to Section 1010.1.3. The allowance for fire doors to have a greater opening force in new construction has a broader context in this section, which allows for all doors with closers to not meet the 5-pound opening force. The maximum door-operating force in this section is less restrictive than that required in Section 1010.1.3 for new construction.

1104.9 Revolving doors. Revolving doors shall comply with the following:

1. A revolving door shall not be located within 10 feet (3048 mm) of the foot or top of *stairways* or escalators. A dispersal area shall be provided between the *stairways* or escalators and the revolving doors.
2. The revolutions per minute for a revolving door shall not exceed those shown in Table 1104.9.

3. Each revolving door shall have a conforming side-hinged swinging door in the same wall as the revolving door and within 10 feet (3048 mm).

Exceptions:

1. A revolving door is permitted to be used without an adjacent swinging door for street-floor elevator lobbies provided that a stairway, escalator or door from other parts of the building does not discharge through the lobby and the lobby does not have any occupancy or use other than as a means of travel between elevators and a street.
2. Existing revolving doors where the number of revolving doors does not exceed the number of swinging doors within 20 feet (6096 mm).

❖ This section is comparable with Section 1010.1.4.1 for new buildings. The capability of collapsing to a width of 36 inches (914 mm) in Condition 2 of Section 1010.1.4.1 for new construction does not apply to existing revolving doors. The two exceptions in this section are not allowed for new construction.

TABLE 1104.9
REVOLVING DOOR SPEEDS

INSIDE DIAMETER (feet-inches)	POWER-DRIVEN-TYPE SPEED CONTROL (rpm)	MANUAL-TYPE SPEED CONTROL (rpm)
6-6	11	12
7-0	10	11
7-6	9	11
8-0	9	10
8-6	8	9
9-0	8	9
9-6	7	8
10-0	7	8

For SI: 1 inch = 25.4 mm, 1 foot = 304.8 mm.

❖ Table 1008.1.4.1 for new construction has a wider range of door sizes and often has a slower maximum speed allowance than this table.

1104.9.1 Egress component. A revolving door used as a component of a *means of egress* shall comply with Section 1104.9 and all of the following conditions:

1. Revolving doors shall not be given credit for more than 50 percent of the required egress capacity.
2. Each revolving door shall be credited with not more than a 50-person capacity.
3. Revolving doors shall be capable of being collapsed when a force of not more than 130 pounds (578 N) is applied within 3 inches (76 mm) of the outer edge of a wing.

❖ This section is similar to Section 1014.1.4.1.1 for new construction.

1104.10 Stair dimensions for existing stairways. Existing *stairways* in buildings shall be permitted to remain if the rise does not exceed $8^{1}/_{4}$ inches (210 mm) and the run is not less than 9 inches (229 mm). Existing *stairways* can be rebuilt.

Exception: Other *stairways approved* by the *fire code official.*

❖ This section includes a much less stringent criterion for stairway treads and risers than that in Section 1011.5.2. This section also allows existing stairways to be rebuilt. The tread and riser dimensions of the rebuilt stairway have additional allowances in Section 1104.10.1.

1104.10.1 Dimensions for replacement stairways. The replacement of an existing *stairway* in a structure shall not be required to comply with the new *stairway* requirements of Section 1011 where the existing space and construction will not allow a reduction in pitch or slope.

❖ This section is consistent with Section 503.1 of the IEBC. This section is intended to allow that, where an existing stairway was built with a steeper rise/run ratio than permitted in the current code, the stairway can be replaced with its original configuration. Enlarging the opening to achieve the current rise/run ratio and headroom would be considered technically infeasible. The principle is that not allowing for this option could result in stairways that were not maintained because they could not be brought up to current codes.

1104.11 Winders. Existing winders shall be allowed to remain in use if they have a minimum tread depth of 6 inches (152 mm) and a minimum tread depth of 9 inches (229 mm) at a point 12 inches (305 mm) from the narrowest edge.

❖ In new construction, winders are only permitted within dwelling units and along curved or spiral stairways (Sections 1011.5.3, 1011.9 and 1011.10). The tread size allowances for existing stairways are smaller than permitted for curved stairways.

1104.12 Curved stairways. Existing curved *stairways* shall be allowed to continue in use, provided that the minimum depth of tread is 10 inches (254 mm) and the smallest radius shall be not less than twice the width of the *stairway*.

❖ For other than certain residential occupancies, this section has fewer requirements than Section 1011.9 for new construction. The relaxed requirements of the exception to Section 1011.9 apply to Group R-3 occupancies and individual dwelling units in Group R-2 occupancies.

1104.13 Stairway handrails. *Stairways* shall have *handrails* on at least one side. *Handrails* shall be located so that all portions of the *stairway* width required for egress capacity are within 44 inches (1118 mm) of a *handrail*.

Exception: *Aisle stairs* provided with a center *handrail* are not required to have additional *handrails*.

❖ Handrails are required on both sides, with certain exceptions, for new construction. This section requires rails on one side. The 44-inch (1118 mm) dimension in this section is an increase from the 30-inch (762 mm) dimension in Section 1014.9 for new construction. Handrails for assembly occupancies in new construction are covered in Section 1029.16. See Section 1014 for handrail requirements for new construction.

1104.13.1 Height. *Handrail* height, measured above *stair* tread nosings, shall be uniform, not less than 30 inches (762 mm) and not more than 42 inches (1067 mm).

❖ The allowable range of handrail height installation in this section is broader than the 34 inches (834 mm) up to 38 inches (965 mm) allowed for new construction in Section 1014.2. This is in recognition of previous allowances for the handrail to be the top rail of a guard. This is still permitted for new construction in assembly seating (see Section 1029.16, Exception 2).

1104.14 Slope of ramps. *Ramp* runs utilized as part of a *means of egress* shall have a running slope not steeper than one unit vertical in 10 units horizontal (10-percent slope). The slope of other *ramps* shall not be steeper than one unit vertical in eight units horizontal (12.5-percent slope).

❖ The slope of means of egress ramps for new construction in Section 1012.2 is a maximum of 1:12. The steeper ramps of 1:8 slope in assembly aisles, as permitted by Section 1029.14 for new construction, should also apply to existing construction.

1104.15 Width of ramps. Existing *ramps* are permitted to have a minimum width of 30 inches (762 mm) but not less than the width required for the number of occupants served as determined by Section 1005.1. In Group I-2, *ramps* serving as a *means of egress* and used for the movement of patients in beds shall comply with Section 1105.6.3.

❖ Ramps for new construction in Section 1012.5.1 are required to have a minimum clear width of 36 inches (914 mm) between handrails. This section requires a 30-inch (762 mm) minimum ramp width (see commentary, Section 1012.5.1). This section also references the more specific requirements for Group I-2 occupancies in Section 1105.6.3. The minimum width required by that section is 48 inches. See the commentary to Section 1105.6.3.

[BE] 1104.16 Fire escape stairways. Fire escape *stairways* shall comply with Sections 1104.16.1 through 1104.16.7.

❖ This section and the referenced sections provide detailed requirements for fire escape stairways. Fire escape stairways are allowed as a required means of egress only in an existing building, according to Section 504 of the IEBC. Sections 1104.16.1 through 1104.16.7 of this code are similar to Sections 504.1 through 504.5 of the IEBC.

[BE] 1104.16.1 Existing means of egress. Fire escape *stairways* shall be permitted in existing buildings but shall not constitute more than 50 percent of the required *exit* capacity.

❖ Fire escapes are limited to serving 50 percent of the required exit capacity because they have minimum usability and are not appropriate for use by persons with limited physical capability.

[BE] 1104.16.2 Opening protectives. Doors and windows within 10 feet (3048 mm) of fire escape *stairways* shall be protected with $^{3}/_{4}$-hour opening protectives.

> **Exception:** Opening protectives shall not be required in buildings equipped throughout with an approved *automatic sprinkler system.*

❖ It is important that doors and windows in the vicinity of a fire escape be protected so that the fire escape will be usable during a fire. The exception for an automatic sprinkler system takes into account the ability of the sprinkler system to control the fire and reduce the need for opening protectives.

[BE] 1104.16.3 Dimensions. Fire escape *stairways* shall meet the minimum width, capacity, riser height and tread depth as specified in Section 1104.10.

❖ The riser height and tread depth requirements are the same as for existing stairways. The limits are specified in Section 1104.10; however, the minimum width and occupant capacity are not specified.

[BE] 1104.16.4 Access. Access to a fire escape *stairway* from a *corridor* shall not be through an intervening room. Access to a fire escape *stairway* shall be from a door or window meeting the criteria of Section 1005.1. Access to a fire escape *stairway* shall be directly to a balcony, landing or platform. These shall not be higher than the floor or window sill level and not lower than 8 inches (203 mm) below the floor level or 18 inches (457 mm) below the window sill.

❖ This section establishes the arrangement of the fire escape to the building so that the fire escape can be easily reached. Access is not permitted through a room because the room could pose an unacceptable hazard or be locked. The elevation limits of the exterior landing, balcony or platform are to make the fire escape easily accessible.

[BE] 1104.16.5 Materials and strength. Components of fire escape *stairways* shall be constructed of noncombustible materials. Fire escape *stairways* and balconies shall support the dead load plus a live load of not less than 100 pounds per square foot (4.78 kN/m^2). Fire escape *stairways* and balconies shall be provided with a top and intermediate *handrail* on each side.

❖ The noncombustible construction requirement is so that the fire escape will be available for use during a fire. The loading of 100 pounds per square foot (psf) (4.78 kN/m^2) anticipates that a number of persons will be using the fire escape at the same time. To verify the ongoing viability of fire escape stairways, Section 1104.16.5.1 requires tests or field surveys to validate the capacity.

[BE] 1104.16.5.1 Examination. Fire escape *stairways* and balconies shall be examined for structural adequacy and safety in accordance with Section 1104.16.5 by a registered design professional or others acceptable to the *fire code official* every 5 years, or as required by the *fire code official*. An inspection report shall be submitted to the *fire code official* after such examination.

❖ Fire escape stairways are typically prohibited in new construction but do constitute a means of egress component in many existing, multistory buildings. Neither the IBC nor this code contain a specific definition as to what actually constitutes fire escape stairways, and in previous editions of the codes no frequency for their inspection was established. This section establishes an inspection frequency for fire escape stairways and balconies erected on existing buildings. By design, fire escape stairways present a concern to code officials because the stairways, ladders, balconies and mechanical fasteners are commonly constructed of carbon or galvanized steel, which will rust, and this reduces their strength if they are not properly maintained. The evaluation is necessary to confirm that this exterior stairway egress component satisfies a minimum design load requirement prescribed in Section 1104.16.5; is properly maintained; and is available for service in the event of an emergency that requires the occupants to egress the building.

Unless otherwise specified by the fire code official, an inspection of fire escape stairways and their balconies is required every 5 years to verify compliance with the structural requirements of Section 1104.16.5. The individual evaluating fire escapes is required to be a registered design professional as defined in Chapter 2 or an individual approved by the fire code official, and a report of the inspection must be provided to the fire code official.

[BE] 1104.16.6 Termination. The lowest balcony shall not be more than 18 feet (5486 mm) from the ground. Fire escape *stairways* shall extend to the ground or be provided with counterbalanced *stairs* reaching the ground.

Exception: For fire escape *stairways* serving 10 or fewer occupants, an *approved* fire escape ladder is allowed to serve as the termination.

❖ This section controls the elevation of the lowest fire escape balcony. For fire escapes that serve 10 or fewer people, a ladder from the lowest balcony to the ground is permitted. In all other cases, the lower balcony is to be served by fire escape stairways. The counterbalance keeps the fire escape stairway up and off ground level when not in use.

[BE] 1104.16.7 Maintenance. Fire escape *stairways* shall be kept clear and unobstructed at all times and shall be maintained in good working order.

❖ This section prohibits using the fire escape for outdoor storage or any other activity that could block its full and instant use. Fire escapes must be kept in good condition so they will be available for use (also see Section 1031.7 for emergency escape and rescue openings).

1104.17 Corridor construction. Corridors serving an occupant load greater than 30 and the openings therein shall provide an effective barrier to resist the movement of smoke. Transoms, louvers, doors and other openings shall be kept closed or be self-closing. In Group I-2, corridors in areas housing patient sleeping or care rooms shall comply with Section 1105.5.

Exceptions:

1. *Corridors* in occupancies other than in Group H, that are equipped throughout with an *approved automatic sprinkler system.*
2. *Corridors* in occupancies in Group E where each room utilized for instruction or assembly has not less than one-half of the required *means of egress* doors opening directly to the exterior of the building at ground level.
3. *Corridors* that are in accordance with the *International Building Code.*

❖ This section relates to Section 1020.1 for new construction. This section requires the corridors to be an effective barrier to resist the movement of smoke. Section 1020.1 for new construction requires that corridors have a fire-resistance rating. Generally, solid walls and doors that would resist smoke migration are the focus of this section. The walls or doors need not have a fire-resistance rating.

A pointer is provided to the requirements for Group I-2 occupancies in areas where such occupancies contain patient sleeping and care. Section 1105.5 provides specific requirements related to the separation requirements, allowable openings. See the commentary to Section 1105.5.

1104.17.1 Corridor openings. Openings in *corridor* walls shall comply with the requirements of the *International Building Code.*

Exceptions:

1. Where 20-minute fire door assemblies are required, solid wood doors not less than 1.75 inches (44 mm) thick or insulated steel doors are allowed.
2. Openings protected with fixed wire glass set in steel frames.
3. Openings covered with 0.5-inch (12.7 mm) gypsum wallboard or 0.75-inch (19.1 mm) plywood on the room side.
4. Opening protection is not required where the building is equipped throughout with an *approved automatic sprinkler system.*

❖ This section makes reference to the IBC requirements for corridor openings. Section 1020.1 specifies that corridors required to be fire-resistance rated are to be constructed according to Section 708 of the IBC for fire partitions. Section 708.6 of the IBC refers to Section 716 of the IBC for protected openings in smoke partitions. Thus, Section 716 of the IBC applies to existing buildings where a fire-resistance-rated corridor would be required for new construction, except where one of the exceptions in this section applies. The exceptions in this section provide a number of practical alternatives for existing buildings.

1104.18 Dead ends. Where more than one exit or exit access doorway is required, the *exit access* shall be arranged such that dead ends do not exceed the limits specified in Table 1104.18.

Exceptions:

1. A dead-end *corridor* shall not be limited in length where the length of the dead-end *corridor* is less than 2.5 times the least width of the dead-end *corridor*.
2. In existing buildings, existing dead-end corridors shall be permitted to comply with lengths established in Section 805.6 of the *International Existing Building Code*. Any newly constructed dead-end corridors within an existing building shall be limited to the lengths allowed by the *International Building Code*.

❖ This section references Table 1104.18 for the dead-end corridor limits for existing buildings. The dead-end limit for new construction is in Section 1020.4. Exception 3 in Section 1020.4 matches Exception 1 in this section. With regard to that exception, dead-end corridors are not a concern because travel is not limited to a single path due to the excessive width of the corridor. The second exception recognizes existing dead-end corridors, which are permitted by the IEBC but may exceed the limitations set forth in Table 1104.18. This exception would require that any newly created dead-end corridors to meet the requirements for new construction. Generally, the dead-end travel limits in Table 1104.18 are more liberal than those in Section 1020.4 for new construction. Note that Table 1104.18 refers to Section 1105.6.5 for Group I-2 occupancies with regard to dead-end corridor limits.

TABLE 1104.18. See page 11-25.

❖ This table contains the existing building limits for common path of travel, dead-end limit and travel distance limits. See the commentaries to Sections 1104.18, 1104.19 and 1104.20 for a discussion regarding the table.

1104.19 Exit access travel distance. *Exits* shall be located so that the maximum length of exit access travel, measured from the most remote point to an *approved exit* along the natural and unobstructed path of egress travel, does not exceed the distances given in Table 1104.18.

❖ This section references Table 1104.18 for the exit access travel distance limits for existing buildings. The travel distance limits for new construction are in Section 1017.1. Generally, the travel distance limits in Table 1104.18 for existing construction are the same as those in Table 1017.2 for new construction, except for Group H and I occupancies.

1104.20 Common path of egress travel. The *common path of egress travel* shall not exceed the distances given in Table 1104.18.

❖ This section refers to Table 1104.18 for the common path of egress travel for existing buildings. The common path of egress travel limits for new construction are in Section 1006.2.1. Generally, the limits in Table 1104.18 for existing construction are the same as in Section 1006.2.1 for new construction.

1104.21 Stairway discharge identification. An interior *exit stairway* or *ramp* that continues below its *level of exit discharge* shall be arranged and marked to make the direction of egress to a *public way* readily identifiable.

Exception: *Stairways* that continue one-half story beyond their *levels of exit discharge* need not be provided with barriers where the *exit discharge* is obvious.

❖ The requirements of this section are less stringent than the discharge identification requirements for new construction in Section 1023.8. The new construction provisions require that a barrier be placed within the stairway to prevent persons from unintentionally continuing into the levels below the exit discharge. The exception in this section is also not included in the requirements for new construction.

1104.22 Exterior stairway protection. *Exterior exit stairways* shall be separated from the interior of the building as required in Section 1027.6. Openings shall be limited to those necessary for egress from normally occupied spaces.

Exceptions:

1. Separation from the interior of the building is not required for buildings that are two stories or less above grade where the *level of exit discharge* serving such occupancies is the first story above grade.
2. Separation from the interior of the building is not required where the exterior *stairway* is served by an exterior balcony that connects two remote exterior *stairways* or other *approved exits*, with a perimeter that is not less than 50 percent open. To be considered open, the opening shall be not less than 50 percent of the height of the enclosing wall, with the top of the opening not less than 7 feet (2134 mm) above the top of the balcony.
3. Separation from the interior of the building is not required for an exterior *stairway* located in a building or structure that is permitted to have unenclosed interior *stairways* in accordance with Section 1023.
4. Separation from the open-ended corridors of the building is not required for exterior *stairways* provided that:
   4.1. The open-ended *corridors* comply with Section 1020.

TABLE 1104.18
COMMON PATH, DEAD-END AND TRAVEL DISTANCE LIMITS (by occupancy)

OCCUPANCY	COMMON PATH OF EGRESS TRAVEL LIMIT		DEAD-END LIMIT		EGRESS ACCESS TRAVEL DISTANCE LIMIT	
	Unsprinklered (feet)	Sprinklered (feet)	Unsprinklered (feet)	Sprinklered (feet)	Unsprinklered (feet)	Sprinklered (feet)
Group A	75	20/75	20[a]	20[a]	200	250
Group B[h]	75[g]	100	50	50	200	300
Group E	75	75	20	50	200	250
Group F-1, S-1	75[g]	100	50	50	200[c]	250[c, h]
Group F-2, S-2	75[g]	100	50	50	300	400
Group H-1	25	25	0	0	75	75
Group H-2	50	100	0	0	75	100
Group H-3	50	100	20	20	100	150
Group H-4	75	75	20	20	150	175
Group H-5	75	75	20	50	150	200
Group I-1	75	75	20	50	200	250
Group I-2	Notes d, e, f	Notes d, e, f	Note e	Note e	150	200[b]
Group I-3	100	100	NR	NR	150[b]	200[b]
Group I-4	NR	NR	20	20	200	250
Group M	75	100	50	50	200	250[i]
Group R-1	75	75	50	50	200	250
Group R-2	75	125	50	50	200	250
Group R-3	NR	NR	NR	NR	NR	NR
Group R-4	NR	NR	NR	NR	NR	NR
Group U	75[g]	100	20	50	300	400

NR = No Requirements.

For SI: 1 foot = 304.8 mm, 1 square foot = 0.0929 m^2.

a. See Section 1029.9.5 for dead-end aisles in Group A occupancies.

b. This dimension is for the total travel distance, assuming incremental portions have fully utilized their allowable maximums. For travel distance within the room, and from the room exit access door to the exit, see the appropriate occupancy chapter.

c. See Section 412.7 of the *International Building Code* for special requirements on spacing of doors in aircraft hangars.

d. Separation of exit access doors within a care recipient sleeping room, or any suite that includes care recipient sleeping rooms, shall comply with Section 1105.5.6.

e. In smoke compartments containing care recipient sleeping rooms and treatment rooms, dead-end corridors shall comply with Section 1105.6.5.

f. In Group I-2, Condition 2, care recipient sleeping rooms or any suite that includes care recipient sleeping rooms shall comply with Section 1105.7.

g. Where a tenant space in Group B, S and U occupancies has an occupant load of not more than 30, the length of a common path of egress travel shall not be more than 100 feet.

h. Where the building, or portion of the building, is limited to one story and the height from the finished floor to the bottom of the ceiling or roof slab or deck is 24 feet or more, the exit access travel distance is increased to 400 feet.

i. For covered and open malls, the exit access travel distance is increased to 400 feet.

4.2. The open-ended *corridors* are connected on each end to an *exterior exit stairway* complying with Section 1027.

4.3. At any location in an open-ended *corridor* where a change of direction exceeding 45 degrees (0.79 rad) occurs, a clear opening of not less than 35 square feet (3 m^2) or an exterior *stairway* shall be provided. Where clear openings are provided, they shall be located so as to minimize the accumulation of smoke or toxic gases.

❖ The exterior stairway requirements of this section are similar to those for new construction in Section 1027.1, except for Exception 1. Exception 1 in this section applies to all two-story buildings where the level of the exit discharge is the first story above grade. In new buildings, Group R-1 and R-2 occupancies would not be allowed to apply this exception. Exception 3 has been deleted from the new construction requirements. Exception 4 does not have requirements for the building to be sprinklered or a reference to Section 1023.7 for exterior walls.

1104.23 Minimum aisle width. The minimum clear width of *aisles* shall comply with the following:

1. Forty-two inches (1067 mm) for stepped aisles having seating on each side.

   Exception: Thirty-six inches (914 mm) where the stepped *aisle* serves fewer than 50 seats.

2. Thirty-six inches (914 mm) for stepped *aisles* having seating on only one side.

   Exceptions:

   1. Thirty inches (760 mm) for catchment areas serving not more than 60 seats.
   2. Twenty-three inches (584 mm) between a stepped aisle *handrail* and seating where a stepped *aisle* does not serve more than five rows on one side.

3. Twenty inches (508 mm) between a stepped *aisle handrail* or *guard* and seating where the *aisle* is subdivided by a mid-aisle *handrail*.
4. Forty-two inches (1067 mm) for level or ramped *aisles* having seating on both sides.

   Exceptions:

   1. Thirty-six inches (914 mm) where the *aisle* serves fewer than 50 seats.
   2. Thirty inches (760 mm) where the aisle serves fewer than 15 seats and does not serve as part of an accessible route.

5. Thirty-six inches (914 mm) for level or ramped *aisles* having seating on only one side.

   Exception: Thirty inches (760 mm) for catchment areas serving not more than 60 seats and not serving as part of an accessible route.

6. In Group I-2, where *aisles* are used for movement of patients in beds, *aisles* shall comply with Section 1105.6.7.

❖ Items 1 through 5 in this section provide the minimum clear width of aisles for assembly seating. Similar requirements for new construction are in Section 1029.9.1. Several of the exceptions in this section allow for narrower aisles than permitted in Section 1029.9.1; thus, the requirements for existing buildings are less stringent than those for new construction. Item 6 of this section is a pointer to the specific aisle requirements for Group I-2 occupancies where aisles are used for movement of people. See the commentary to Section 1105.6.7.

1104.24 Stairway floor number signs. Existing *stairways* shall be marked in accordance with Section 1023.9.

❖ This section requires that existing stairs be marked in the same manner as new stairways (see commentary, Section 1023.9). The signage includes important information for people evacuating the building as well emergency responders.

1104.25 Egress path markings. Existing high-rise buildings of Group A, B, E, I, M and R-1 occupancies shall be provided with luminous *egress* path markings in accordance with Section 1025.

Exception: Open, unenclosed stairwells in historic buildings designated as historic under a state or local historic preservation program.

❖ This section requires that luminous exit path markings be provided in existing buildings on the same basis as in new buildings to facilitate rapid egress and assist in full building evacuation. The text is based on Recommendations 17 and 18 of the National Institute of Standards and Technology's (NIST) report on the World Trade Center (WTC) tragedy. In New York City, after the first bombing of the WTC, requirements were instituted to require exit path markings in vertical exit enclosures in new and existing buildings. This section is taken directly from those requirements.

The marking requirement is only applicable to those buildings having occupied floors more than 75 feet (22 860 mm) above the lowest level of fire department vehicle access. The cost impact on existing buildings is minor when considering the life safety benefit. Therefore, it is logical and affordable to provide existing high-rise buildings with the same protections afforded new high-rise structures.

Historically, code requirements for high-rise buildings were written under the assumption that the building would be evacuated floor by floor. In most instances, in a building with a full suppression system, only the floor where the fire is located and the floors immediately above and below would be evacuated. Acts of terrorism and accidental incidents, such as power failures, have made it necessary to consider design for full building evacuation that is as rapid as possible. This may be made necessary in response to events both within and outside the building. This provision is intended to facilitate the most rapid possible full building evacuation. See the commentary to Section 1025 for a more complete discussion of luminous egress path markings.

The exception takes into account the aesthetics and possible natural light in an open, unenclosed stairway in a historic building. Also, since the requirement is only applicable to high-rise buildings, the requirement would have limited application in historic structures.

SECTION 1105
CONSTRUCTION REQUIREMENTS FOR EXISTING GROUP I-2

1105.1 General. Existing Group I-2 shall meet all of the following requirements:

1. The minimum fire safety requirements in Section 1103.
2. The minimum mean of egress requirements in Section 1104.
3. The additional egress and construction requirements in Section 1105.

Where the provisions of this chapter conflict with the construction requirements that applied at the time of construction, the most restrictive provision shall apply.

❖ This section provides minimum requirements for existing Group I-2 occupancies. The intent is to increase the minimum safety requirements because of the fragile and sensitive populations within these facilities. These requirements are meant to be applied retroactively. These provisions align with the current approach by the Center for Medicaid and Medicare Services (CMS), the federal authority having jurisdiction. Hospitals are required by CMS to have a life safety survey on a regular basis. If the facility does not meet certain life safety minimums, they are required to upgrade their existing facility. This code change will align the code with those CMS minimum requirements and will hopefully lead to industry consolidation. These retroactive requirements are provided to assist code officials and surveyors during the ongoing regular inspection of hospital facilities and are consistent with the inspections required by federal laws for certification and reimbursement. The requirements reflect consideration of the minimum previously approved construction methods and provide jurisdictions the ability to adopt minimum retroactive provisions that have been vetted by the industry as well as code officials. In addition, these provisions are consistent with current national standards used by the federal government, providing a more uniform level of safety and eliminating many of the current code conflicts for existing facilities.

Several sources were reviewed to determine what the appropriate minimum bar should be, including the current building and fire codes, current CMS guidelines, and previous versions of the model codes. On all issues, enforcement agencies and the regulated facilities weighed in to ensure that these requirements were both necessary and achievable.

This particular section provides scoping for these provisions. Areas in hospitals and nursing homes not in patient care areas will use the general provisions in Sections 1103 and 1104. More restrictive provisions for hospitals or nursing homes are listed in Section 1105. As stated in the general comments at the beginning of this chapter and the commentaries to Sections 1101.2 and 1103.5.3, where the buildings must upgrade, consideration of allowable time frames and procedures will need to be worked out between the authority having jurisdiction and those responsible for repairs and alterations in the nursing homes and hospitals.

1105.2 Applicability. The provisions of Sections 1105.3 through 1105.8, 1105.10 and 1105.11 shall apply to the existing Group I-2 fire area.

❖ This section addresses the federal requirement for a separation between Group I-2 occupancies that comply with the requirements in this section and those that do not. Since a building could be several different occupancies, it is reinforcing the need for separation between portions of the building that are compliant with Chapter 11 for Group I-2, and other portions of the buildings. This would require a fire separation between the Group B portion of an existing building that does not comply with all of the minimum retroactive standards of this chapter.

1105.3 Construction. Group I-2, Condition 2 shall not be located on a floor level higher than the floor level limitation in Table 1105.3 based on the type of construction.

❖ Section 1105.3 is a retroactive limitation for the allowable height based on construction type because it is a key component of the regulatory approval for a health care facility. While most, if not all, existing hospitals were built to comply with these minimum construction requirements, many were built using methods that predated the current construction type matrix. The allowance for the occupancies, as stipulated in Table 1105.3, are less than that for new construction and are consistent with what is currently mandated for licensing for healthcare facilities.

1105.4 Incidental uses in existing Group I-2. Incidental uses associated with and located within existing single-occupancy or mixed-occupancy Group I-2 buildings and that generally pose a greater level of risk to such occupancies shall comply with the provisions of Sections 1105.4.1 through 1105.4.3.2.1. Incidental uses in Group I-2 occupancies are limited to those listed in Table 1105.4.

❖ Incidental use area provisions are applicable to new construction in Section 509 of the IBC; however, similar provisions are needed for existing Group I-2 occupancies since the hazards posed by such rooms or spaces are no different for existing buildings than for new. Section 1105.4 and Table 1105.4 are very similar to and based on IBC Section 509 and Table 509, except that references to occupancies other than Group I-2 are not included. The basic requirements proposed for incidental uses in existing healthcare occupancies rely on the provisions of the IBC for specifics of construction and protection. Sections 1105.4.1 through 1105.4.3.2.1 are based on IBC Sections 509.2 through 509.4.2.1. These provisions will provide correlation with not only the IBC but also with the operational and CMS program standards for existing Group I-2 occupancies.

This specific section establishes the scope of Section 1105.4 and its applicability to Group I-2 occupancies. Incidental uses are rooms or areas that constitute special hazards or risks to life safety that are not typically addressed by the provisions for the occupancy group in which they occur, even though such rooms or areas may functionally be an extension of the primary use. Only those rooms or areas indicated in Table 1105.4 are to be regulated as incidental uses. Incidental uses can be located within both single-occupancy and mixed-occupancy buildings. The concern is that those areas designated as incidental uses pose a risk to the remainder of the building, and as such, some degree of protection is required. The nature of these incidental uses is such that they are small areas not frequented by building occupants, in which a fire could get underway and go unnoticed for a longer time than in a more frequently occupied part of the building.

TABLE 1105.3
FLOOR LEVEL LIMITATIONS FOR GROUP I-2, CONDITION 2

CONSTRUCTION TYPE	AUTOMATIC SPRINKLER SYSTEM	ALLOWABLE FLOOR LEVEL[a]			
		1	2	3	4 or more
IA	Note b	P	P	P	P
	Note c	P	P	P	P
IB	Note b	P	P	P	P
	Note c	P	P	P	P
IIA	Note b	P	P	P	NP
	Note c	P	NP	NP	NP
IIB	Note b	P	P	NP	NP
	Note c	NP	NP	NP	NP
IIIA	Note b	P	P	NP	NP
	Note c	P	NP	NP	NP
IIIB	Note b	P	NP	NP	NP
	Note c	NP	NP	NP	NP
IV	Note b	P	P	NP	NP
	Note c	NP	NP	NP	NP
VA	Note b	P	P	NP	NP
	Note c	NP	NP	NP	NP
VB	Note b	P	NP	NP	NP
	Note c	NP	NP	NP	NP

P = Permitted; NP = Not Permitted.

a. Floor level shall be counted based on the number of stories above grade.

b. The building is equipped throughout with an automatic sprinkler system in accordance with Section 903.3.1.1.

c. The building is equipped with an automatic sprinkler system in accordance with Section 1105.8.

TABLE 1105.4
INCIDENTAL USES IN EXISTING GROUP I-2 OCCUPANCIES

ROOM OR AREA	SEPARATION AND/OR PROTECTION
Furnace room where any piece of equipment is over 400,000 Btu per hour input	1 hour or provide automatic sprinkler system
Rooms with boilers where the largest piece of equipment is over 15 psi and 10 horsepower	1 hour or provide automatic sprinkler system
Refrigerant machinery room	1 hour or provide automatic sprinkler system
Hydrogen fuel gas rooms, not classified as Group H	2 hours
Incinerator rooms	2 hours and provide automatic sprinkler system
Paint shops not classified as Group H	2 hours; or 1 hour and provide automatic sprinkler system
Laboratories and vocational shops, not classified as Group H	1 hour or provide automatic sprinkler system
Laundry rooms over 100 square feet	1 hour or provide automatic sprinkler system
Patient rooms equipped with padded surfaces	1 hour or provide automatic sprinkler system
Physical plant maintenance shops	1 hour or provide automatic sprinkler system
Waste and linen collection rooms with containers with total volume of 10 cubic feet or greater	1 hour or provide automatic sprinkler system
Storage rooms greater than 100 square feet	1 hour or provide automatic sprinkler system
Stationary storage battery systems having a liquid electrolyte capacity of more than 50 gallons for flooded lead-acid, nickel cadmium or VRLA, or more than 1,000 pounds for lithium-ion and lithium metal polymer used for facility standby power, emergency power or uninterruptable power supplies	2 hours

For SI: 1 square foot = 0.0929 m^2, 1 pound per square inch (psi) = 6.9 kPa, 1 British thermal unit (Btu) per hour = 0.293 watts, 1 horsepower = 746 watts, 1 gallon = 3.785 L.

1105.4.1 Occupancy classification. Incidental uses shall not be individually classified in accordance with Section 302.1 of the *International Building Code*. Incidental uses shall be included in the building occupancies within which they are located.

❖ Consistent with the IBC, this section expressly states that incidental uses are not considered as separate and distinct occupancy classifications but, rather, are classified the same as the occupancies in which they are located. As an example, a waste and linen collection room in a hospital would be classified as a portion of the Group I-2 occupancy even though it may present a level of hazard more akin to a Group S-1 occupancy.

1105.4.2 Area limitations. Incidental uses shall not occupy more than 10 percent of the building area of the story in which they are located.

❖ The proposed floor area limitation of 10 percent for incidental uses emphasizes the ancillary nature of such rooms and areas and correlates with the IBC. Each incidental use would be limited to a maximum floor area of 10 percent of the floor area of the story in which it is located. Where there are two or more tenants located on the same story, the 10-percent limitation is based on the floor area of each individual tenant space rather than that of the entire story. The application of the limit on a tenant-by-tenant basis is consistent with the concept of incidental uses typically being ancillary only to a portion of the building (i.e., the specific tenant occupancy).

1105.4.3 Separation and protection. The incidental uses listed in Table 1105.4 shall be separated from the remainder of the building or equipped with an *automatic sprinkler system*, or both, in accordance with the provisions of that table.

❖ In addition to identifying those rooms or areas that warrant regulation as incidental uses, Table 1105.4 also indicates the required degree of protection or separation. The requirements identified in Table 1105.4 vary, depending on the incidental use. In some cases, a specific type of separation and/or protection is required, while in others there is an option.

1105.4.3.1 Separation. Where Table 1105.4 specifies a fire-resistance-rated separation, the incidental uses shall be separated from the remainder of the building in accordance with Section 509.4.1 of the *International Building Code*.

❖ Where a fire-resistance rated separation is required, the incidental use must be separated from other portions of the building in accordance with assemblies complying with the IBC.

1105.4.3.2 Protection. Where Table 1105.4 permits an *automatic sprinkler system* without a fire-resistance-rated separation, the incidental uses shall be separated from the remainder of the building by construction capable of resisting the passage of smoke in accordance with Section 509.4.2 of the *International Building Code*.

❖ In this section, where Table 1105.4 allows protection by an automatic sprinkler system without a fire-resistance-rated separation, the construction enclosing the incidental use still must resist the passage of smoke. Construction details for resisting the passage of smoke are provided in the IBC. Note that this requirement is not specifying a smoke partition. The smoke partition requirements in IBC Section 710 are specific requirements that must be directly referenced.

1105.4.3.2.1 Protection limitation. Except as otherwise specified in Table 1105.4 for certain incidental uses, where an *automatic sprinkler system* is provided in accordance with Table 1105.4, only the space occupied by the incidental use need be equipped with such a system.

❖ This section makes it clear that the sprinkler systems stipulated in Table 1105.4 would be required for the incidental use area only.

1105.5 Corridor construction. In Group I-2, in areas housing patient sleeping or care rooms, *corridor* walls and the opening protectives therein shall provide a barrier designed to resist the passage of smoke in accordance with Sections 1105.5.1 through 1105.5.7.

❖ The focus of this section is specifically for corridor construction in patient care and sleeping room areas in Group I-2 occupancies. The construction of corridors is intended to provide protection that will resist the passage of smoke. The provisions address the type of materials required, fire-resistance-rating requirements, opening protection and corridor wall continuity.

Existing corridor construction should primarily be evaluated for its ability to resist or limit the transfer of smoke, regardless of the code at the time of construction. This is consistent with the defend-in-place scenario for patient protection during a fire event (see Section 405). Corridor walls, even if they were built 60 years ago, should be regularly assessed to confirm that they minimize the transfer of smoke. This section describes some criteria by which this can be assessed.

1105.5.1 Materials. The walls shall be of materials permitted by the building type of construction.

❖ This section simply requires that the materials used to construct the corridors be consistent with the type of construction. If it is a noncombustible construction (Type I or II), the walls must be constructed in accordance with Table 601 of the IBC unless Section 603 of the IBC provides any exceptions.

1105.5.2 Fire-resistance rating. Unless required elsewhere in this code, corridor walls are not required to have a fire-resistance rating. Corridor walls that were installed as fire-resistance-rated assemblies in accordance with the applicable codes under which the building was constructed, remodeled or altered shall be maintained unless modified in accordance with the *International Existing Building Code*.

❖ The key with corridor walls is more about the resistance of the passage of smoke and less about the fire resistance. This section clarifies that these walls are not required to be fire-resistance rated unless another requirement, such as for a smoke barrier or incidental use area separation, would prompt such fire-resistance rating. Also, if the corridor was originally constructed as a fire-resistance-rated assembly as required at the time it was constructed, those corridor walls must be maintained unless the IEBC allows a reduction. Sections 501.2 and 802.6 of the IEBC allow a reduction in fire-resistance-rated assemblies based on an overall analysis of the building. The concept is that once a building without sprinkler protection has been sprinklered throughout, whether due to renovations or retroactive code application, the designer should be permitted to take advantage of some of the sprinkler trade-offs that are allowed for new construction, such as the allowance for healthcare corridors to be smoke partitions instead of needing to be fire partitions. Corridors in I-2 occupancies were required to be fire partitions for decades in nonsprinklered hospitals, and also in sprinklered hospitals built to one of the legacy codes. A proper review by the building code official must be performed to ensure that such reductions are consistent with the level of safety provided by the current building code. This proposal attempts to provide a mechanism for that process by adding a reference to the *International Existing Building Code*.

It should be noted that, according to the NFPA "Report on Fires in Health Care Facilities" published November 2012, between 2006 and 2010, Sprinklers were present in only 55 percent of reported health care fires. Although those statistics for fires 5 to 10 years ago may not precisely gauge the exact proportion of healthcare facilities without sprinklers today, the fact remains that a substantial number of existing Group I-2 occupancies are not sprinklered throughout. Revising this code article to lay out a clear path for reducing the required fire-resistance rating of corridors can only assist in incentivizing older hospitals to have sprinklers retrofitted as soon as possible. See also commentary for Section 1103.5.2, 1103.5.3 and 1105.9.

1105.5.3 Corridor wall continuity. *Corridor* walls shall extend from the top of the foundation or floor below to one of the following:

1. The underside of the floor or roof sheathing, deck or slab above.
2. The underside of a ceiling above where the ceiling membrane is constructed to limit the passage of smoke.
3. The underside of a lay-in ceiling system where the ceiling system is constructed to limit the passage of smoke and where the ceiling tiles weigh not less than 1 pound per square foot (4.88 kg/m^2) of tile.

❖ As discussed in Section 1105.5.2, providing a barrier is the key to corridor effectiveness. Section 1105.5.2 does not require a fire-resistance rating for existing corridors, but the separation that the corridor provides must be continuous to a point where the separated spaces are protected. This section provides three solutions to achieve this. The first focuses simply on extending all the way to the floor or roof sheathing, deck or slab above. The other options allow the separation to stop at the finished ceiling. Ending the separation at the ceiling membrane is conditioned on the ceiling being able to resist the passage of smoke. In the case of lay-in ceilings, they must also meet the minimum weight requirement to increase the likelihood that they will stay in place.

1105.5.4 Openings in corridor walls. Openings in *corridor* walls shall provide protection in accordance with Sections 1105.5.4.1 through 1105.5.4.3.

❖ Openings in corridor walls present the largest failures of such separations. This section addresses both windows and doors located in corridor walls. Again, these provisions are intended to address the condition of existing walls and may not be consistent with new construction.

1105.5.4.1 Windows. Windows in *corridor* walls shall be sealed to limit the passage of smoke, or the window shall be automatic-closing upon detection of smoke, or the window opening shall be protected by an automatic closing device that closes upon detection of smoke.

Exception: In smoke compartments not containing patient sleeping rooms, pass-through windows or similar openings shall be permitted in accordance with Section 1105.5.4.3.

❖ Windows must effectively employ one of the three following methods to resist the passage of smoke:

- Proper sealing.
- Automatic closing on detection of smoke (smoke detection system).
- Automatic closing by automatic closing device (single-station smoke detector).

The exception addresses lower risk areas where no patient sleeping rooms are present.

1105.5.4.2 Doors. Doors in *corridor* walls shall comply with Sections 1105.5.4.2.1 through 1105.5.4.2.3.

❖ This section addresses various different issues related to doors in corridor walls. These provisions provide some basic safety while providing flexibility in existing hospitals. As with the other provisions, these requirements and allowances are consistent with federal compliance requirements.

1105.5.4.2.1 Louvers. Doors in *corridor* walls shall not include louvers, transfer grills or similar openings.

Exception: Doors shall be permitted to have louvers, transfer grills or similar openings at toilet rooms or bathrooms; storage rooms that do not contain storage of flammable or combustible material; and storage rooms that are not required to be separated as incidental uses.

❖ Louvers, transfer grilles or similar openings present an increased risk of smoke passing into protected spaces. Therefore, these openings are generally prohibited. The exception addresses spaces where passage of smoke presents a reduced risk as such spaces are not typically occupied or their occupancy is limited.

1105.5.4.2.2 Corridor doors. Doors in *corridor* walls shall limit the transfer of smoke by complying with the following:

1. Doors shall be constructed of not less than $1^3/_4$ inch-thick (44 mm) solid bonded-core wood or capable of resisting fire not less than $^1/_3$ hour.

   Exception: Corridor doors in buildings equipped throughout with an automatic sprinkler system.

2. Frames for side-hinged swinging doors shall have stops on the sides and top to limit transfer of smoke.
3. Where provided, vision panels in doors shall be a fixed glass window assembly installed to limit the passage of smoke. Existing wired glass panels with steel frames shall be permitted to remain in place.
4. Door undercuts shall not exceed 1 inch (25 mm).
5. Doors shall be positive latching with devices that resist not less than 5 pounds (22.2 N). Roller latches are prohibited.
6. Mail slots or similar openings shall be permitted in accordance with Section 1105.5.4.3.

❖ This section provides the list of necessary requirements that existing doors in corridors must meet. Often the criteria provide some allowances not given for new construction. All criteria must be addressed if applicable.

Item 1 requires a door to be of substantial construction in nonsprinklered buildings. Either a $^1/_3$-hour fire-rated door is required or an equivalent door is prescribed. The exception allows no rating for the door in buildings equipped throughout with an automatic sprinkler system.

Item 2 requires frames to have stops on the sides and top to minimize the transfer of smoke on swinging doors.

Item 3 addresses vision panels. This item allows wired glass panels in steel frames to continue to be used where they would not be allowed in new construction.

Item 4 minimizes door undercuts to 1 inch to prevent additional smoke passage.

Item 5 addresses how such doors are required to latch. Roller latches are prohibited as they may be compromised during a fire event and lead to the door opening.

Item 6 is consistent with Section 1105.5.4.3 and allows mail slots or similar openings under certain conditions for doors in corridors.

1105.5.4.2.3 Dutch doors. Where provided, dutch doors shall comply with Section 1105.5.4.2.2. In addition, dutch doors shall be equipped with latching devices on either the top or bottom leaf to allow leaves to latch together. The space between the leaves shall be protected with devices such as astragals to limit the passage of smoke.

❖ Dutch doors have been used in health care facilities for many years for various necessary operational reasons. While the IBC does not specifically speak of dutch doors, their use is not prohibited but must meet the requirements contained in IBC Section 407.3, including positive latching and limiting the transfer of smoke. This section provides clarity for existing installations by giving specific guidance on the minimum acceptable requirements, including positive latching and smoke transfer, for their use in corridor walls. A definition is provided in Section 202 for further clarity.

1105.5.4.2.4 Self- or automatic-closing doors. Where self- or automatic-closing doors are required, closers shall be maintained in operational condition.

❖ This section is provided to make sure that self- or automatic-closing doors continue to be operational. If automatic-closing doors that are no longer operational are propped open, the function of the corridor is reduced. It is important to note that this section does not require self-closing or automatic-closing doors; it simply requires that they be maintained.

1105.5.4.3 Openings in corridor walls and doors. In other than smoke compartments containing patient sleeping rooms, mail slots, pass-through windows or similar openings shall not be required to be protected where the aggregate area of the openings between the *corridor* and a room are not greater than 80 square inches (51 613 mm^2) and are located with the top edge of any opening not higher than 48 inches above the floor.

❖ This section is essentially an exception for existing mail slot, pass-through and similar openings that are commonly found in hospitals. These are needed for privacy, medication security and other operational needs. The restrictions on their location are consistent with federal requirements.

1105.5.5 Penetrations. The space around penetrating items shall be filled with an *approved* material to limit the passage of smoke.

❖ Penetrations, though smaller than door and window openings, can create locations for smoke to pass through and must be addressed. Group I-2 occupancies often have many pipes penetrating walls that must be addressed. Many smaller openings can lead to a larger overall area of smoke passage.

1105.5.6 Joints. Joints shall be filled with an *approved* material to limit the passage of smoke.

❖ Similar to penetrations, joints that are formed at the intersections of walls and floor/ceiling assemblies and roof assemblies can create other avenues of smoke passage. If not addressed, these small openings can lead to a hazard during building fires.

1105.5.7 Ducts and air transfer openings. The space around a duct penetrating a smoke partition shall be filled with an *approved* material to limit the passage of smoke. Air transfer openings in smoke partitions shall be provided with a smoke damper complying with Section 717.3.2.2 of the *International Building Code*.

Exception: Where the installation of a smoke damper will interfere with the operation of a required smoke control system in accordance with Section 909, approved alternative protection shall be utilized.

❖ Anytime a duct penetrates a wall, the space around the duct must be minimally protected to prevent smoke passage during fire. Group I-2 occupancies may have complex HVAC systems that can lead to a multitude of ducts passing through walls. Air transfer openings through corridor walls need to be protected with smoke dampers in accordance with IBC Section 717.3.2.2 unless such dampers will affect the performance of a smoke control system.

1105.6 Means of egress. In addition to the *means of egress* requirements in Section 1104, Group I-2 facilities shall meet the *means of egress* requirements in Sections 1105.6.1 through 1105.6.7.

❖ These provisions are intended to provide minimal means of egress requirements specific to Group I-2 occupancies, where these occupancies work on a defend-in-place strategy and the needs are unique. Sections 1105.6.1 through 1105.6.7 address a variety of issues, such door size, corridor width, dead ends and exit separation.

1105.6.1 Size of door. Means of egress doors used for the movement of patients in beds shall provide a minimum clear width of $41^1/_2$ inches (1054 mm). The height of the door opening shall be not less than 80 inches (2032 mm).

Exceptions:

1. Door closers and door stops shall be permitted to be 78 inches (1981 mm) minimum above the floor.
2. In Group I-2, Condition 1, existing means of egress doors used for the movement of patients in beds that provide a minimum clear width of 32 inches (813 mm) shall be permitted to remain.

❖ This section is consistent with Section 1104.7. It follows the format and requirements of Section 1010.1.1. There are two exceptions that allow the door closers and door stops to not meet the door-opening height. This is a reasonable allowance for existing buildings and is consistent with Exception 6 to Section 1010.1.1, which allows door-opening heights in dwelling units and sleeping units to be 78 inches. The second exception provides flexibility to Group I-2, Condition 1 occupancies such as nursing homes, which do not depend on these door widths being available as frequently for bed movement.

1105.6.2 Group I-2 occupancies. In Group I-2, where a door serves as an opening protective in a fire barrier, smoke barrier or fire wall and where the door is equipped with a hold-open device, such door shall automatically close upon any of the following conditions:

1. Actuation of smoke detectors initiating the hold-open device.
2. Activation of the fire alarm system within the zone.
3. Activation of an automatic sprinkler system within the zone.

❖ This section allows doors to be held open with specific requirements as to how they are required to be released. Without this language, it was unclear whether these mechanisms would be permitted to allow doors to remain open on a regular basis. There was concern that the existing provisions in the IFC could be more restrictive than the IBC with regard allowing hold open devices. This allowance of the hold-open devices prevents damage to the door when a stretcher or supply cart moves through the barrier, providing significant operational savings by increasing the useful life of the rated door.

1105.6.3 Ramps. In areas where *ramps* are used for movement of patients in beds, the clear width of the *ramp* shall be not less than 48 inches (1219 mm).

❖ This section, which is referenced from Section 1104.15, provides the width necessary for ramps in Group I-2 occupancies where beds are being moved. Section 1104.15 only requires a 30-inch width.

1105.6.4 Corridor width. In areas where *corridors* are used for movement of patients in beds, the clear width of the *corridor* shall be not less than 48 inches (1219 mm).

❖ This section is consistent with the width required for ramps in Section 1105.6.3 and is focused on the width required for the movement of beds. The requirement of 48 inches clear width is less restrictive than that required of new construction in Section 1020.2. New Group I-2 occupancies require a 96-inch clear width.

1105.6.5 Dead-end corridors. In smoke compartments containing patient sleeping rooms and treatment rooms, dead-end *corridors* shall not exceed 30 feet (9144 mm) unless approved by the *fire code official*.

❖ The dead-end corridor requirements are specific to Group I-2 occupancies. Typically in new construction the dead-end corridor would be limited to 20 feet. This provides more flexibility but is consistent with the CMS requirements.

1105.6.6 Separation of exit access doors. Patient sleeping rooms, or any suite that includes patient sleeping rooms, of more than 1,000 square feet (92.9 m^2) shall have not less than two exit access doors placed a distance apart equal to not less than one-third of the length of the maximum overall diagonal dimension of the patient sleeping room or suite to be served, measured in a straight line between exit access doors.

❖ This requirement addresses the need for exit separation in larger patient sleeping rooms and suites. Once they become large enough, the need for two exits becomes more important. This section is less restrictive than Section 1007.1.1 by only requiring one-third the diagonal of the space versus one-half. This requirement may result in the need for an additional exit access door in such spaces.

1105.6.7 Aisles. In areas where *aisles* are used for movement of patients in beds, the clear width of the *aisle* shall be not less than 48 inches (1219 mm).

❖ This requirement is consistent with the widths established for ramps and corridors in Sections 1105.6.3 and 1105.6.4, respectively. Again, this width is associated with areas where bed movement will occur.

1105.7 Smoke compartments. Smoke compartments shall be provided in existing Group I-2, Condition 2, in accordance with Sections 1105.7.1 through 1105.7.6.

❖ Smoke compartments, used in healthcare facilities to limit the movement of smoke, are a key component of the defend-in-place strategy, a strategy where occupants are protected from fire without relocation. These compartments act as safe locations for patients by preventing the spread of smoke. Through compartmentalization, patients may remain safely in their rooms as fire suppression systems and fire responders extinguish the fire. Under severe fire conditions that threaten the immediate compartment area, patients may be evacuated horizontally to the safety of an adjacent compartment on the same floor. Being able to do this is critical since, because of the health status of many patients, their evacuation from the building might put them in danger. The proper design, construction and application of smoke compartments will provide added protection, buy valuable time and save lives of critically ill patients before a total evacuation may become necessary.

These requirements are provided to assist code officials and surveyors during the ongoing regular inspection of hospital facilities. These inspections are required by federal laws for certification and reimbursement. These requirements consider the minimum previously approved construction methods. This is consistent with the federal requirements to which these facilities are currently held. Sections 1105.7.1 through 1105.7.6 provide all the necessary elements for existing facilities.

1105.7.1 Design. Smoke barriers shall be provided to subdivide each story used for patients sleeping with an occupant load of more than 30 patients into not fewer than two smoke compartments.

❖ The defend-in-place concept is a basic minimum level of safety for these facilities. Every facility should be equipped with at least two smoke compartments for temporary relocation of patients. This section addresses acceptable configurations of smoke barrier walls and smoke barriers in existing hospitals for each story with sleeping rooms accommodating 30 or more patients.

1105.7.1.1 Refuge areas. Refuge areas shall be provided within each smoke compartment. The size of the refuge area shall accommodate the occupants and care recipients from the adjoining smoke compartment. Where a smoke compartment is adjoined by two or more smoke compartments, the minimum area of the refuge area shall accommodate the largest occupant load of the adjoining compartments.

The size of the refuge area shall provide the following:

1. Not less than 30 net square feet (2.8 m^2) for each care recipient confined to a bed or stretcher.
2. Not less than 15 square feet (1.4 m^2) for each resident in a Group I-2 using mobility assistance devices.
3. Not less than 6 square feet (0.56 m^2) for each occupant not addressed in Items 1 and 2.

Areas of spaces permitted to be included in the calculation of the refuge area are *corridors*, sleeping areas, treatment rooms, lounge or dining areas and other low-hazard areas.

❖ This section addresses adequate sizing of refuge areas. IBC Section 407.5.3 also includes requirements for sizing refuge areas. Otherwise, the provisions are fairly consistent.

1105.7.2 Smoke barriers. Smoke barriers shall be constructed in accordance with Section 709 of the *International Building Code*.

Exceptions:

1. Existing smoke barriers are permitted to remain where the existing smoke barrier has a minimum fire-resistance rating of $^1/_2$ hour.
2. Smoke barriers shall be permitted to terminate at an atrium enclosure in accordance with Section 404.6 of the *International Building Code*.

❖ Generally, compliance with the IBC is required for smoke barriers. However, the first exception is intended to bring noncompliant smoke barriers to at least a $^1/_2$-hour fire-resistance rating. Previously approved smoke barriers are not intended to be reduced to $^1/_2$ hour. Chapter 7 requires maintenance of approved construction. The second exception addresses termination of the smoke barrier. Typically, smoke barriers are required to terminate at outside walls.

1105.7.3 Opening protectives. Openings in smoke barriers shall be protected in accordance with Section 716 of the *International Building Code*. Opening protectives shall have a minimum fire protection rating of $^1/_3$ hour.

Exceptions:

1. Existing wired glass vision panels in doors shall be permitted to remain.
2. Existing nonlabeled protection plates shall be permitted to remain.

❖ This section addresses doors in smoke barriers in existing Group I-2 occupancies. This section requires compliance as applicable with Section 716. The rating of doors is required to be a minimum of 20 minutes. The first exception allows openings in doors with wired glass to remain. The second exception correlates with IBC Section 709.5, Exception 1. Smoke barrier doors are typically installed across corridors and patient treatment areas. These doors see a very high volume of gurney and bed traffic, as well as carts, wheeled equipment and transport devices. As a result, they are often damaged. Exception 2 allows the installation of a nonlabeled protective plate, usually made of steel or other resilient material, to be installed on these doors to protect them from excessive wear and damage. Due to the size of equipment being wheeled through, these protective plates need to be allowed to be greater than 48 inches high. Currently NFPA 80 would require that the protective plates on rated doors be limited to 48 inches and that they be labeled. The doors in smoke barriers do not function as true fire doors. This section contains many special directives and requirements exempting smoke barrier doors from meeting fire door requirements. Smoke barriers are intended to be substantial construction. Protective plates provide additional protection to the doors, keeping the original construction free from damage while creating a more substantial door. They do not provide the same fire-resistance rating as a true 1-hour fire barrier.

1105.7.4 Penetrations. Penetrations of smoke barriers shall comply with the *International Building Code.*

Exception: Approved existing materials and methods of construction.

❖ Penetrations, as with corridor construction, can be numerous and lead to smoke movement from one smoke compartment to another. This section requires that such penetrations be dealt with in accordance with the IBC. Sealing penetrations is a reasonable requirement to increase patient safety. There is some flexibility provided if such penetrations have already been addressed to the satisfaction of the fire code official.

1105.7.5 Joints. Joints made in or between smoke barriers shall comply with the *International Building Code.*

Exception: Approved existing materials and methods of construction.

❖ Joints formed by the intersection of smoke barriers and floor/ceiling and roof assemblies can often create gaps where smoke can spread. This simply requires compliance with the IBC to protect those joints. Similar to Section 1105.7.4 addressing penetrations, there is some flexibility provided if such joints have already been addressed to the satisfaction of the fire code official.

1105.7.6 Duct and air transfer openings. Penetrations in a smoke barrier by duct and air transfer openings shall comply with Section 717 of the *International Building Code.*

Exception: Where existing duct and air transfer openings in smoke barriers exist without smoke dampers, they shall be permitted to remain. Any changes to existing smoke dampers shall be submitted for review and approved in accordance with Section 717 of the *International Building Code.*

❖ Similar to penetrations and joints, where ducts and air transfer openings penetrate a smoke barrier they must be sealed in accordance with the IBC. IBC Section 717.5.5 requires a smoke damper unless Exception 2 to that section is met. Exception 2 to Section 717.5.5 recognizes a fully ducted system in a building equipped throughout with an automatic sprinkler system. See the commentary to IBC Section 717.5.5. The application of that exception is limited to Group I-2, Condition 2 occupancies.

The exception to this section recognizes that existing duct and air transfer openings may be permitted to remain without smoke dampers. Any modification of existing smoke dampers would have to go through the normal process for making an alteration to existing construction. The exception is not intended to allow the removal of existing smoke dampers but instead allow the continuance of existing conditions that did not require them.

1105.8 Group I-2 care suites. Care suites in existing Group I-2, Condition 2 occupancies shall comply with Sections 407.4.4 through 407.4.4.6.2 of the *International Building Code.*

❖ This proposal defines the requirements for care suites (both sleeping and nonsleeping) that are an integral design concept for many areas within a hospital. Typical uses include intensive care units, operating rooms, emergency departments and imaging departments. The suites allow for better and safer care than nonsuite options. These provisions deal with common paths of travel, separation of exit access doors, and number of doors passed through (i.e., previously intervening rooms) in suites. See the commentaries to Sections 407.4.4 through 407.4.4.6.2 of the IBC.

1105.9 Group I-2 automatic sprinkler system. An *automatic sprinkler system* installed in accordance with Section 903.3.1.1 shall be provided throughout the floor containing the Group I-2 fire area. The sprinkler system shall be provided throughout the floor where the Group I-2 occupancy is located, on all floors between the Group I-2 occupancy fire area and the *level of exit discharge,* the *level of exit discharge,* and all floors below the *level of exit discharge.*

Exception: Floors classified as an open parking garage are not required to be sprinklered.

❖ This section requires that an automatic sprinkler system be provided on the floor containing the Group I-2 occupancy, all floors between that level and the level of exit discharge, and all floors below the level of exit discharge. This is a general requirement for all Group I-2 occupancies. Automatic sprinkler protection of existing Group I-2 occupancies is of critical importance due to the nature of the occupants. In Group I-2 occupancies, the occupants are, by definition, considered not capable of self-preservation. The evacuation difficulties associated with these occupants create the need to incorporate a defend-in-place philosophy of fire protection in occupancies in Group I-2. For this reason, all such existing occupancies are to be protected with an automatic sprinkler system.

This is an especially important requirement for nursing homes. An NFPA report, *Facilities that Care for the Aged Including Nursing Homes and Residential Board and Care*, states, "The death rate per 1,000 fires was 82 percent lower when automatic suppression systems were present." The report further states, "Residents of these facilities are particularly vulnerable. The risk increases with increasing age. Consequently, the aged are considered a high-risk population. Institutional facilities that care for older adults must work diligently to prevent fires and to train staff and to equip the property (e.g., active systems) for effective response should a fire occur."

Note that Section 1103.5.3 requires that an automatic sprinkler system be installed throughout the entire building containing a Group I-2, Condition 2 occupancy. See the commentary to Section 1103.5.3 for more discussion on the intended application of that section.

1105.10 Group I-2 automatic fire alarm system. An automatic fire alarm system shall be installed in existing Group I-2 occupancies in accordance with Section 907.2.6.2.

Exception: Manual fire alarm boxes in patient sleeping areas shall not be required at *exits* if located at all nurses' control stations or other constantly attended staff locations, provided such that manual fire alarm boxes are visible, are provided with *ready access,* and travel distances required in Section 907.4.2.1 are not exceeded.

❖ Because care recipients may be incapable of self-evacuation and thus would rely on staff for assistance, an approved fire alarm system is required in existing Group I-2 occupancies. The system must comply with Section 907.2.6.2 (see commentary, Section 907.2.6.2). Note that Section 1105.9 requires sprinkler protection in existing Group I-2 occupancies and that the requirements of this section are in addition thereto. This provision is not intended to override the allowances for "private mode" in Section 907.2.6.2. Typical audible and visible alarms could be a detriment in some areas of a hospital, such as where patients are undergoing procedures.

1105.11 Essential electrical systems. Essential electrical systems in Group I-2, Condition 2 occupancies shall be in accordance with Sections 1105.11.1 and 1105.11.2.

❖ Both requirements within Sections 1105.11.1 and 1105.11.2 are specific to Group I-2, Condition 2 occupancies. This section addresses the requirements related to the needs of essential power and the reassessment to ensure that current installations will still meet the needs of the hospitals they support.

1105.11.1 Where required. Where required by NFPA 99, Group I-2, Condition 2 occupancies shall be provided with an essential electrical system in accordance with NFPA 99.

❖ This section requires existing Group I-2, Condition 2 occupancies to provide essential electrical systems where NFPA 99 would require such systems. NFPA 99 provides a risk-based approach to determine if essential power supplies are necessary. This analysis looks at the risk of failure of the system and its implications to the patients or caregivers in terms of injury or death. Specific design considerations are set based on the risk.

1105.11.2 Installation and duration. In Group I-2, Condition 2 occupancies, the installation and duration of operation of existing essential electrical systems shall be based on a hazard vulnerability analysis conducted in accordance with NFPA 99.

❖ This section requires a reassessment of the essential electrical systems based on a hazard vulnerability analysis to make sure that the systems meet the needs of the facilities for emergencies. This requirement would apply whether or not the facility is being altered or has been damaged. If "substantial improvement" of the building occurs, per the IBC and IEBC definition, ASCE 24 would require this analysis. The flood provision section addresses such concerns as the location of equipment in a flood plain.

SECTION 1106 REQUIREMENTS FOR OUTDOOR OPERATIONS

1106.1 Tire storage yards. Existing tire storage yards shall be provided with fire apparatus access roads in accordance with Sections 1106.1.1 and 1106.1.2.

❖ This section introduces the fire apparatus access provisions that follow.

1106.1.1 Access to piles. Access roadways shall be within 150 feet (45 720 mm) of any point in the storage yard where storage piles are located not less than 20 feet (6096 mm) from any storage pile.

❖ See the commentary to Section 3406.2.

1106.1.2 Location within piles. Fire apparatus access roads shall be located within all pile clearances identified in Section 3405.4 and within all fire breaks required in Section 3405.5.

❖ See the commentaries to Sections 3405.4 and 3405.5.

Bibliography

The following resource materials were used in the preparation of the commentary for this chapter of the code.

Ahrens, Marty. *Facilities that Care for the Aged Including Nursing Homes and Residential Board and Care.* Quincy, MA: National Fire Protection Association, 2006.

Complete Revision History to the 2018 I-Codes. Washington, DC: International Code Council, 2017.

Chapter 12: Energy Systems

General Comments

Chapter 12 was added to the 2018 code to address the current energy systems found in the code and serves as an introduction to a wide range of systems to generate and store energy in, on and adjacent to buildings and facilities. The expansion of such energy systems is related to meeting today's energy, environmental and economic challenges. Appropriate criteria to address the safety of such systems in building and fire codes is an important part of protecting the public at large, building occupants and emergency responders. Previously, requirements for energy systems such as standby power systems, photovoltaic (PV) systems and stationary battery systems were scattered in various locations in Chapter 6, which addresses building services and systems. However, with the addition of fuel cells and capacitor energy storage systems to the code, a chapter dedicated to such related issues was necessary. This chapter provides an appropriate location for the addition of future energy systems.

The provisions are broken into several main sections as follows:

- Section 1203. Emergency and standby power systems. These were previously located in Chapter 6 but have been relocated to this chapter to keep the concept of energy storage and generation together have been placed in this chapter. These provisions mirror those in Chapter 27 of the *International Building Code*® (IBC®).
- Section 1204. Solar photovoltaic power systems. These provisions address the needs of the fire department fighting a fire with PVs installed. The provisions focus on both providing pathways and proper signage to understand where and how the system can be shut down. There is also a general reference to the *National Electrical Code*® (NEC®) (NFPA 70) for all other applicable requirements.
- Section 1205. Stationary fuel cell power systems. These systems are becoming more prevalent in buildings and the hazards are being addressed. They often use hydrogen gas and cng as a fuel, which can pose a significant hazard if not properly managed.
- Section 1206. Energy storage systems include both stationary battery storage systems and capacitor energy storage systems. These types of systems are increasing as the technology develops.

Purpose

The purpose of Chapter 12 is to centralize energy-related issues regulated by the code to properly manage potential hazards to occupants and fire fighters. The provisions are located in a single chapter to make the requirements easier to access. Additionally, it provides the framework to address new and emerging energy systems and the related risks. For example, the battery storage system section (Section 1206.2) specifically has provisions for other types of batteries not yet recognized. They are addressed through hazard analysis and testing.

SECTION 1201 GENERAL

1201.1 Scope. The provisions of this chapter shall apply to the installation, operation and maintenance of energy systems used for generating or storing energy. It shall not apply to equipment associated with the generation, control, transformation, transmission, or distribution of energy installations that is under the exclusive control of an electric utility or lawfully designated agency.

❖ The focus of this chapter is on the energy systems as they pertain to the generation and storage of energy for use in buildings. In the case of photovoltaic systems, much of the requirements are focused on the safety of fire fighters who may need to access a roof or portions of the building containing such systems. This section specifically notes that the chapter is not focused on the distribution and transmission that would be controlled and regulated by an electric utility. The focus is on the systems as they affect the safety of occupants and fire fighters in or on the building.

1201.2 Electrical wiring and equipment. Electrical wiring and equipment used in connection with energy systems shall be installed and maintained in accordance with Chapter 12 and NFPA 70.

❖ The intention is that in addition to requirements found in this chapter, anything electrical in nature is required to comply with the NEC. This is the primary referenced standard throughout the International Codes® (I-Codes®) for all electrical issues.

1201.3 Mixed system installation. Where approved, the aggregate kWh energy in a fire area shall not exceed the maximum quantity specified for any of the energy systems in this chapter. Where required by the *fire code official*, a hazard mitigation analysis shall be provided and approved in accordance with Section 104.7.2 to evaluate any potential adverse interaction between the various energy systems and technologies.

❖ The concept of on-site energy storage and generation within or supporting a specific building is growing. The methods and types of installations are often mixed and must be looked at in terms of their overall fire risk. In some cases, this chapter already addresses this issue. For example, in Section 1206 there are specific overall kWh limitations where different battery storage systems are used in a single space. However, the fact that a fuel cell may be located in a fire area with battery storage systems would need to be addressed through this section. This section empowers the fire code official to require evaluation of the impact of such systems.

SECTION 1202 DEFINITIONS

1202.1 Definitions. The following terms are defined in Chapter 2:

BATTERY SYSTEM, STATIONARY STORAGE.

BATTERY TYPES.

Lead-acid battery.

CAPACITOR ARRAY.

CAPACITOR ENERGY STORAGE SYSTEM.

CRITICAL CIRCUIT.

EMERGENCY POWER SYSTEM.

ENERGY MANAGEMENT SYSTEMS.

FUEL CELL POWER SYSTEM, STATIONARY.

STANDBY POWER SYSTEM.

STATIONARY BATTERY ARRAY.

❖ This section lists terms that are specifically associated with the subject matter of this chapter. It is important to emphasize that these terms are not exclusively related to this chapter, but may or may not also be applicable where the term is used elsewhere in the code.

Definitions of terms can help in the understanding and application of the code requirements. The purpose for including a list within this chapter is to provide more convenient access to terms that may have a specific or limited application within this chapter. For the complete definition and associated commentary, refer back to Chapter 2. Terms that are italicized provide a visual identification throughout the code that a definition exists for that term. The use and application of all defined terms are set forth in Section 201.

SECTION 1203 EMERGENCY AND STANDBY POWER SYSTEMS

1203.1 General. Emergency power systems and standby power systems required by this code or the *International Building Code* shall comply with Sections 1203.1.1 through 1203.1.9.

❖ This section states that all required emergency and standby power systems should comply with various subsections. These subsections provide more detailed direction on required installation for such systems. These provisions are consistent with the standards referenced by the code and provide basic information to the code official.

1203.1.1 Stationary generators. Stationary emergency and standby power generators required by this code shall be listed in accordance with UL 2200.

❖ This section applies only to generator sets that are chosen and permanently installed to provide an emergency or standby power supply for the required, fixed building facilities indicated in Section 1203.2. Section 2.37 of UL 2200 defines a stationary unit as "An engine generator that is intended to be hard wired and/or permanently installed." The section would not apply to mobile units such as truck-, trailer- or skid-mounted or other nonfixed, nonpermanent units. Such nonpermanently installed units would not be approved for purposes of complying with the requirements of Section 1203. Similarly, stationary generator sets that are installed for purposes other than to supply emergency or standby power required by the code would not be required to be listed to UL 2200.

1203.1.2 Fuel line piping protection. Fuel lines supplying a generator set inside a high-rise building shall be separated from areas of the building other than the room the generator is located in by an approved method, or an assembly that has a fire-resistance rating of not less than 2 hours. Where the building is protected throughout with an automatic sprinkler system installed in accordance with Section 903.3.1.1, the required fire-resistance rating shall be reduced to 1 hour.

❖ This section is intended to require fuel lines supplying a generator set inside a building to be separated with fire-resistance-rated construction from areas of the building other than the room in which the generator is located. It mirrors the text that was approved for the 2015 IBC, Section 403.4.8.2 for high-rises.

These provisions extend the requirement to any building that has a generator that is separated from the rest of the building. It is common for diesel-fueled generators to have a day tank and resupply the day tank via remote fuel oil tanks. The fuel line piping from those remote tanks to the generator can be exposed to the same fire incident that the generator has been protected against. Loss of the fuel line due to fire exposure has the same impact as loss of the generator itself.

The language only refers to "fuel lines" to also provide protection in those cases where a gaseous fuel supply is approved for use.

1203.1.3 Installation. Emergency power systems and standby power systems shall be installed in accordance with the *International Building Code*, NFPA 70, NFPA 110 and NFPA 111.

❖ Emergency power systems are intended to provide electrical power for life safety systems, such as egress illumination, emergency communications and processes involving the handling and use of hazardous materials. In other words, emergency power is required where the loss of normal power would endanger occupants. Such systems are covered in Article 700 of NFPA 70 and one of their key features is the required response time of 10 seconds or less. The time between loss of normal power and the provision of emergency power must be kept very short to prevent putting occupants at risk. This is especially important during an emergency event such as a building fire, but is important at all times to prevent occupant confusion, which could happen if a crowded building suddenly becomes dark.

Standby power systems are covered in Article 701 of NFPA 70 and are intended to provide electrical power for loads not as critical in terms of transfer time as those requiring emergency power. Standby power loads include smoke control systems; certain elevators; certain hazardous material operations; smokeproof enclosure systems; illumination; heating, ventilating and air-conditioning (HVAC) systems; refrigeration; and sewage pumps. Standby power systems must provide power within 60 seconds of failure of primary power.

Sources of power for emergency power systems (NFPA 70, Section 701-10) include storage batteries, generators, uninterruptible power supplies and separate services. Sources of power for standby systems include those allowed for emergency systems plus a source that is taken from a point of connection ahead of the normal service disconnecting means.

NFPA 110 addresses the performance criteria and "nuts and bolts" of emergency and standby power systems and separates them into types, classes and levels relative to maximum response time, minimum required operation time and life safety importance factor, respectively. NFPA 111 addresses stored emergency power supply systems and is similar in coverage to NFPA 110. Stored energy systems typically rely on batteries that store chemical energy.

1203.1.4 Load transfer. Emergency power systems shall automatically provide secondary power within 10 seconds after primary power is lost, unless specified otherwise in this code. Standby power systems shall automatically provide secondary power within 60 seconds after primary power is lost, unless specified otherwise in this code.

❖ These provisions are consistent with NFPA 70 and provide clarity to the code official regarding one of the key differences between standby and emergency power. This is discussed in more detail in the commentary to Section 1203.1.2.

1203.1.5 Load duration. Emergency power systems and standby power systems shall be designed to provide the required power for a minimum duration of 2 hours without being refueled or recharged, unless specified otherwise in this code.

❖ In order to properly design emergency and standby power systems, the minimum load duration must be known. This section provides a default minimum 2-hour duration for systems unless another load duration is specified. For instance, emergency responder radio coverage systems are required to provide standby power for 24 hours.

1203.1.6 Uninterruptable power source. An uninterrupted source of power shall be provided for equipment where required by the manufacturer's instructions, the listing, this code or applicable referenced standards.

❖ In some cases an uninterruptable power supply is required. Uninterruptible power supplies are different from emergency and standby power supplies in that there is no transfer time allowed. This is necessary for equipment with volatile memories or that is generally sensitive to any loss of power. An uninterruptible power source must be provided if required by the equipment manufacturer's instructions; the listing of the equipment; the code; or applicable referenced standards, such as NFPA 72.

1203.1.7 Interchangeability. Emergency power systems shall be an acceptable alternative for installations that require standby power systems.

❖ An emergency power system, given its more rapid transfer time, is an acceptable substitute for a standby power system. It will result in a faster-reacting system, which will only improve performance.

1203.1.8 Group I-2 occupancies. In Group I-2 occupancies located in flood hazard areas established in Section 1612.3 of the *International Building Code,* where new essential electrical systems are installed, and where new essential electrical system generators are installed, the systems and generators shall be located and installed in accordance with ASCE 24. Where connections for hook up of temporary generators are provided, the connections shall be located at or above the elevation required in ASCE 24.

❖ This section provides a necessary link to ASCE 24, *Flood Resistant Design and Construction,* for Group I-2 essential electrical systems. There have been losses of such systems due to flooding where the standard was not properly addressed. These types of facilities, such as hospitals and nursing homes, need to have continued operation during flood events. Hurricane Katrina is a good example of such power being lost during flooding. This provision will ensure that such systems will be correctly installed in new Group I-2 occupancies or replaced in those that have been substantially damaged by a flood.

ASCE 24 provides the designer with the minimum requirements and expected performance for the design and construction of buildings and structures in flood hazard areas. It is not a restatement of all of the National Flood Insurance Program regulations, but offers additional specificity, some additional requirements, and some limitations. Buildings designed according to ASCE 24 are better able to resist flood loads and flood damage. See the commentary to Section 1612.3 of the IBC for additional information on this topic.

1203.1.9 Maintenance. Existing installations shall be maintained in accordance with the original approval and Section 1203.4.

❖ Existing generators must be properly maintained to continue to serve the purpose for which they were installed. This section ensures that maintenance. The maintenance level is linked to the original installation approval. Section 1203.4 provides detailed maintenance requirements.

1203.2 Where required. Emergency and standby power systems shall be provided where required by Sections 1203.2.1 through 1203.2.18.

❖ Fires or natural events can cause the loss of utility power as a result of either damage to equipment and wiring or from fire fighters shutting off power to eliminate sources of ignition and danger to personnel.

Sections 1203.2.1 through 1203.2.18 list locations throughout buildings and facilities where emergency or standby power is required. In some cases, the requirements are occupancy- or use-specific; in others they are system- or equipment-specific. Generally, the requirements are related to life safety-oriented systems in buildings, such as a fire alarm system or elevators used for egress for those with disabilities. Recall that emergency and standby power systems have different characteristics, and subsequent sections will require one or the other (see commentary, Section 1203.1.3).

1203.2.1 Ambulatory care facilities. Essential electrical systems for ambulatory care facilities shall be in accordance with Section 422.6 of the *International Building Code.*

❖ This section is a pointer to Section 422.6 of the IBC for requirements for essential electrical systems for ambulatory care facilities. Section 422.6 requires compliance with NFPA 99 for essential electrical systems. NFPA 99, the Healthcare Facilities Code provides an assessment tool for determining what constitutes essential electrical systems. It provides a risk-based approach to determine the need for an essential electrical system, what class system is required and general design requirements for each type of system.

1203.2.2 Elevators and platform lifts. Standby power shall be provided for elevators and platform lifts as required in Sections 606.2, 1009.4.1, and 1009.5.

❖ Elevators can be a component of an accessible means of egress in accordance with Section 1009.4 and must, therefore, be dependable at all times. Without backup power, an elevator could be a dead end for someone with physical disabilities trying to egress a building (see commentary, Section 1009.4).

Platform lifts are allowed to be used as part of an accessible means of egress only where they are allowed as part of an accessible route, in accordance with IBC Section 1109.8, Items 1 through 10. Where this is the case, the platform lift could be a dead end for someone with physical disabilities if power to the platform lift were to be lost; therefore, standby power is required, in accordance with Section 1203 or ASME A18.1.

The reference to Section 606.2 addresses how standby power is to be provided to elevators where required elsewhere. These requirements are the same as those found in Section 3003 of the IBC. Primarily, these requirements apply to high-rise buildings (see commentary, IBC Section 403.4.8.3). Also note that the IBC has specific standby power requirements in Sections 3007.8 and 3008.8 for fire service access elevators and occupant evacuation elevators, respectively. These requirements are more restrictive than those found in Section 606.2 of the code and Section 3003 of the IBC (see commentary, Section 606.2).

1203.2.3 Emergency responder radio coverage systems. Standby power shall be provided for emergency responder radio coverage systems as required in Section 510.4.2.3. The standby power supply shall be capable of operating the emergency responder radio coverage system for a duration of not less than 24 hours.

❖ Loss of power is likely during an emergency situation and, in many cases, emergency responders will require the use of their radios for an extended period of time. Note that as it relates to energy systems, standby power is required to operate the radio coverage system for not less than 24 hours.

1203.2.4 Emergency voice/alarm communication systems. Emergency power shall be provided for emergency voice/alarm communication systems as required in Section 907.5.2.2.5. The system shall be capable of powering the required load for a duration of not less than 24 hours, as required in NFPA 72.

❖ Section 907.5.2.2.5 requires that emergency voice/alarm communication systems include an emergency power source. Certain Group A occupancies and covered malls are two of the occupancies and building types that require emergency voice/alarm communication systems.

1203.2.5 Exit signs. Emergency power shall be provided for exit signs as required in Section 1013.6.3. The system shall be capable of powering the required load for a duration of not less than 90 minutes.

❖ Emergency power is warranted for exit signage illumination since guiding occupants to the exits is certainly a life safety function (see commentary, Section 1013.6.3). Note that this section specifies a time duration of not less than 90 minutes for exit sign illumination. This specific duration would take precedence over the general 2-hour duration specified in Section 1203.1.5.

1203.2.6 Gas detection systems. Emergency power shall be provided for gas detection systems where required by Sections 1203.2.9 and 1203.2.16. Standby power shall be provided for gas detection systems where required by Section 916.5.

❖ This section notes that such emergency power requirements originate both in the hazardous material provisions in Chapter 50 and associated hazardous materials chapters, such as those addressing toxic and highly toxic materials. Additionally, semiconductor facilities as addressed in Chapter 27 require gas detection for higher hazard materials such as toxic and highly toxic gases and flammable gases.

1203.2.7 Group I-2 occupancies. Essential electrical systems for Group I-2 occupancies shall be in accordance with Section 407.11 of the *International Building Code*.

❖ Emergency power systems are required to comply with NFPA 99 by the Center for Medicare/Medicaid Services (CMS) in order for a federally licensed health care facility to receive federal reimbursement funds. Section 407.11 of the IBC provides a direct reference to NFPA 99 for the design and construction of emergency power systems in Group I-2. See the commentary to Section 407.11 of the IBC.

1203.2.8 Group I-3 occupancies. Power-operated sliding doors or power-operated locks for swinging doors in Group I-3 occupancies shall be operable by a manual release mechanism at the door. Emergency power shall be provided for the doors and locks.

Exceptions:

1. Emergency power is not required in facilities where provisions for remote locking and unlocking of occupied rooms in Occupancy Condition 4 are not required as set forth in the *International Building Code*.
2. Emergency power is not required where remote mechanical operating releases are provided.

❖ In an emergency situation involving power loss, occupants in detention and correctional facilities are at the mercy of door-locking mechanisms and those who control such locks; thus, emergency power is warranted. For a discussion of Exception 1, see the commentaries to Sections 408.4.1 and 408.4.2 of the IBC. Exception 2 recognizes that the use of mechanical operating releases controlled remotely eliminates the need for emergency power.

1203.2.9 Hazardous materials. Emergency and standby power shall be provided in occupancies with hazardous materials as required in the following sections:

1. Sections 5004.7 and 5005.1.5 for hazardous materials.
2. Sections 6004.2.2.8 and 6004.3.4.2 for highly toxic and toxic gases.
3. Section 6204.1.11 for organic peroxides.

❖ Where hazardous materials and processes are housed, occupant safety could be dependent on one or more ventilation, treatment, temperature control, alarm or detection system. Thus, emergency or standby power is required, depending on the nature of the material hazard presented (see the commentaries to code sections referenced in Items 1 through 3).

1203.2.10 High-rise buildings. Standby power and emergency power shall be provided for high-rise buildings as required in Section 403 of the *International Building Code*, and shall be in accordance with Section 1203.

❖ Occupants of high-rise buildings are at greater risk due to longer egress travel times, difficult fire-fighter access and the danger of vertical spread of fire and smoke. In accordance with this chapter and Section 403.4.8 of the IBC, some loads in a high-rise building will require standby power and some will require emergency power (see the commentary to Section 403.4.8 of the IBC).

1203.2.11 Special purpose horizontal sliding doors. Standby power shall be provided for horizontal sliding doors as required in Section 1010.1.4.3. The standby power supply shall have a capacity to operate not fewer than 50 closing cycles of the door.

❖ Power-operated doors could be an obstruction to egress if the primary power supply fails; therefore, standby power is required to maintain door operation (see commentary, Section 1010.1.4.3).

1203.2.12 Hydrogen fuel gas rooms. Standby power shall be provided for hydrogen fuel gas rooms as required by Section 5808.7.

❖ Ventilation and gas detection are critical to the ongoing safe operation of a hydrogen fuel gas room. Therefore, both ventilation and gas detection systems are required by Section 5808.7 to be provided with standby power (see commentary, Section 5808.7).

1203.2.13 Laboratory suites. Standby or emergency power shall be provided in accordance with Section 5004.7 where *laboratory suites* are located above the sixth story above grade plane or located in a story below grade plane.

❖ This section correlates with requirements in Chapter 38 regarding laboratory suites. The provisions of Section 3804 permit a larger amount of hazardous materials on higher floors than would be permitted applying the maximum allowable quantities; therefore, it was felt reasonable to require standby or emergency power. Typically, if the MAQs were exceeded the requirements of Section 5004.7 would apply. Section 5004.7 provides the triggers as to when standby and emergency power are required.

1203.2.14 Means of egress illumination. Emergency power shall be provided for *means of egress* illumination in accordance with Sections 1008.3 and 1104.5.1.

❖ Emergency power for illumination is necessary so that the path of travel to all exits is illuminated to guide occupants and allow for safe egress (see commentary, Section 1008.3).

1203.2.15 Membrane structures. Standby power shall be provided for auxiliary inflation systems in permanent membrane structures in accordance with Section 2702 of the *International Building Code*. Auxiliary inflation systems shall be provided in temporary air-supported and air-inflated membrane structures in accordance with Section 3103.10.4.

❖ Air-supported and air-inflated structures would collapse on the occupants if the inflation systems failed. Section 3102.8.1.1 of the IBC requires redundant inflation equipment that would serve little purpose in the event of power failure without standby power. Emergency power is required for all exit signs in temporary tents and membrane structures (see commentary, IBC Section 3102.8.2). Note that temporary air-supported and air-inflated membrane structures require auxiliary power. However, the auxiliary power is not specifically standby power in accordance with Section 1203.1. Section 3103.10.4 sets out specific criteria as to how this is to be provided. The time it takes to provide this power is 60 seconds, which is the same transfer time required for standby power in Section 1203.1.3.

1203.2.16 Semiconductor fabrication facilities. Emergency power shall be provided for semiconductor fabrication facilities as required in Section 2703.15.

❖ Where hazardous materials are utilized in Group H-5 hazardous production materials (HPM) facilities, many systems are depended on to protect the occupants from exposure, including exhaust/ventilation systems, gas cabinet exhaust systems, gas detection systems, alarm systems and suppression systems. Loss of power would endanger the occupants; thus, emergency power is essential for these occupancies. For the complete list of required systems, see Section 2703.15 and its commentary.

1203.2.17 Smoke control systems. Standby power shall be provided for smoke control systems as required in Section 909.11.

❖ Smoke control systems are intended to maintain a tenable environment in certain buildings to allow the occupants ample time to evacuate or relocate to protected areas. As such, smoke control systems are life safety systems and must be dependable (see commentary, Section 909.11). Such systems are more likely to be needed during a power loss than typical building systems such as HVAC.

1203.2.18 Underground buildings. Emergency and standby power shall be provided in underground buildings as required in Section 405 of the *International Building Code* and shall be in accordance with Section 1203.

❖ In the event of power failure, occupants could be underground without light, ventilation and numerous required life safety systems. These structures are analogous to inverted high-rise buildings. See Sections 405.8.1 and 405.8.2 of the IBC, which require standby power and emergency power for specified loads, respectively.

1203.3 Critical circuits. Required critical circuits shall be protected using one of the following methods:

1. Cables used for survivability of required critical circuits shall be listed in accordance with UL 2196 and shall have a *fire-resistance rating* of not less than 1 hour.
2. Electrical circuit protective systems shall have a *fire-resistance rating* of not less than 1 hour. Electrical circuit protective systems shall be installed in accordance with their listing requirements.
3. Construction having a *fire-resistance rating* of not less than 1 hour.

❖ This section presents three options for the protection of critical circuits.

The first option is listing to UL 2196 with a rating of 1 hour. UL 2196 is the ANSI-approved standard for tests of fire-resistive cables. NFPA 20 (fire pumps) and NFPA 72 (fire alarms) include selective survivability requirements to ensure integrity of certain critical circuits.

The second option is an electrical circuit protective system with a fire-resistance rating of 1 hour, installed in accordance with the system's listing. NFPA 70 does not specify the applicable standard in the mandatory provisions of the code, but recognizes electrical circuit protective systems as alternatives to listed cables. An electrical circuit protective system is a field assembly of components that must be installed according to the listing requirements and manufacturer's instructions in order to maintain the listing for the system. There are more than two dozen electrical circuit protective systems listed in the UL *Fire Resistance Directory*.

The third option is simply to protect the critical circuits in 1-hour fire-resistance-rated construction. This would serve the same intent of protection as the first two options.

1203.4 Maintenance. Emergency and standby power systems shall be maintained in accordance with NFPA 110 and NFPA 111 such that the system is capable of supplying service within the time specified for the type and duration required.

❖ This section introduces requirements for maintenance of all elements of emergency and standby power systems. The two standards referenced are for emergency and standby power systems and stored electrical energy emergency and standby power systems, respectively. NFPA 110 is geared toward power sources, such as diesel-driven generators, while NFPA 111 is geared toward power supplies, such as stationary lead-acid battery systems. See also Section 1203.1.9, which requires the same system maintenance as was originally approved.

1203.4.1 Group I-2. In Group I-2 occupancies, emergency and standby power systems shall be maintained in accordance with NFPA 99.

❖ There are special requirements in NFPA 99 for the maintenance and inspection of generators installed at hospitals and nursing homes. In addition to these special requirements, NFPA 99 also references NFPA 110.

1203.4.2 Schedule. Inspection, testing and maintenance of emergency and standby power systems shall be in accordance with an approved schedule established upon completion and approval of the system installation.

❖ Standby power and emergency power are useful only if they continue to work over the life of both the building and its associated equipment; therefore, this section specifically focuses on the maintenance of such systems. The primary specifications of these secondary power supplies are that they be able to supply power within the specified length of time.

This section requires that a specific schedule be created at the completion of the installation of the power system to encourage regular maintenance.

1203.4.3 Records. Records of the inspection, testing and maintenance of emergency and standby power systems shall include the date of service, name of the servicing technician, a summary of conditions noted and a detailed description of any conditions requiring correction and what corrective action was taken. Such records shall be maintained.

❖ Documentation of maintenance is key, in that it highlights what specifically was inspected and tested and where potential problems exist. It also provides a level of accountability by providing information about the inspector and inspection agency for future reference. These documents must be made available to the fire code official on request.

As a result of a review of Recommendation 2(c) of the National Institute of Standards and Technology (NIST) Charleston, South Carolina Sofa Superstore Fire Report, changes were made to Section 108.3 along with 49 other sections (including this section), to comprehensively address record-keeping requirements. Section 108.3 provides standardized record-keeping requirements for periodic inspection, testing, servicing and other operational and maintenance requirements of the code, and states that records must be maintained on the premises or another approved location and that copies must be provided to the fire code official on request. Section 108.3 also clarifies that records must be maintained for a period of not less than 3 years unless a different time interval is specified in the code or a referenced standard, and that the fire code official is authorized to prescribe the form and format of such records (see commentary, Section 108.3).

1203.4.4 Switch maintenance. Emergency and standby power system transfer switches shall be included in the inspection, testing and maintenance schedule required by Section 1203.4.2. Transfer switches shall be maintained free from accumulated dust and dirt. Inspection shall include examination of the transfer switch contacts for evidence of deterioration. When evidence of contact deterioration is detected, the contacts shall be replaced in accordance with the transfer switch manufacturer's instructions.

❖ One of the most important features of emergency and standby power systems is the ability for the primary power to be switched to the secondary power supply within the specified time; therefore, this section pays specific attention to the long-term reliability of the transfer switches. This includes inspection for cleanliness and signs of deterioration.

1203.5 Operational inspection and testing. Emergency power systems, including all appurtenant components, shall be inspected and tested under load in accordance with NFPA 110 and NFPA 111.

Exception: Where the emergency power system is used for standby power or peak load shaving, such use shall be recorded and shall be allowed to be substituted for scheduled testing of the generator set, provided that appropriate records are maintained.

❖ This section requires that emergency power systems be tested and inspected as specified in NFPA 110 and 111. There is an exception to testing emergency power systems when they are used either for peak power periods or for standby power. Use during peak hours means that on a fairly regular basis the power supply will be tested. In terms of using emergency power for standby power, the capacity of both types of secondary power systems is the same. The two differ on when they will activate; therefore, testing the system as a standby power supply is adequate when the emergency power system is used as standby power.

1203.5.1 Group I-2. In Group I-2 occupancies, emergency and standby power systems shall be inspected and tested under load in accordance with NFPA 99.

❖ There are special requirements in NFPA 99 for the maintenance and inspection of generators installed at hospitals and nursing homes. In addition to these special requirements, NFPA 99 also references NFPA 110.

1203.5.2 Transfer switch test. The test of the transfer switch shall consist of electrically operating the transfer switch from the normal position to the alternate position and then return to the normal position.

❖ This section prescribes the specific sequence of events for testing transfer switches. The switch must move from the normal position to the alternate position and back again. Emergency power must be available within 10 seconds of the loss of primary power, whereas standby power is to be available within 60 seconds. The transfer switches, therefore, must work within the specified time.

1203.6 Supervision of maintenance and testing. Routine maintenance, inspection and operational testing shall be overseen by a properly instructed individual.

❖ This section requires a minimum level of qualifications for the testing of emergency and standby power systems. Only trained personnel should test and maintain of these systems. This is consistent with Section 108.4. See the commentary to that section.

SECTION 1204
SOLAR PHOTOVOLTAIC POWER SYSTEMS

1204.1 General. Solar photovoltaic systems shall be installed in accordance with Sections 1204.2 through 1204.5, and the *International Building Code* or *International Residential Code*. The electrical portion of solar PV systems shall be installed in accordance with NFPA 70.

❖ Solar photovoltaic (PV) power systems are among the most popular alternative energy sources. A number of US electric utility power suppliers offer incentives for the installation of PV systems on buildings because such systems offer property owners the ability to generate their own electricity and, in many cases, sell excess electricity back to the utility provider. Such an arrangement is a beneficial to the utility provider because it reduces the provider's power generation demand, which in turn can control the rates for commercial and residential customers. According to the U.S. Energy Information Administration, approximately 21,200 PV cells and modules were shipped domestically in 1999; by 2008, that number was over 524,200. As the number of PV power systems increases, economy of scale will continue to reduce the systems' costs, making them more common on commercial and residential buildings (see Commentary Figure 1204.1).

PV systems are designed to convert light energy into direct current (DC) electricity. They have no moving parts and do not contain fluids. The light-to-electricity conversion begins at the PV cell, which is commonly a semiconductor device that generates electricity when exposed to light. To be effective, PV cells are assembled into PV modules, which are then assembled into PV panels. The panels are assembled onto a frame or a flexible substrate, which then can be affixed to the roof of buildings to create a PV array. The PV array and its modules are wired together and generally operate as a series electrical circuit. PV array are required by NFPA 70 to have a fuse or other means of branch-circuit protection to prevent them from being overloaded. While not required, a PV array is commonly equipped with a blocking diode. A blocking diode is analogous to a check valve in a piping system because it limits the direction the electrons can travel. The blocking diode prevents electrical current from one power supply from finding entry into another. In PV systems, the blocking diode protects each individual PV panel if other panels fail and prevents the withdrawal of electricity from the system at night.

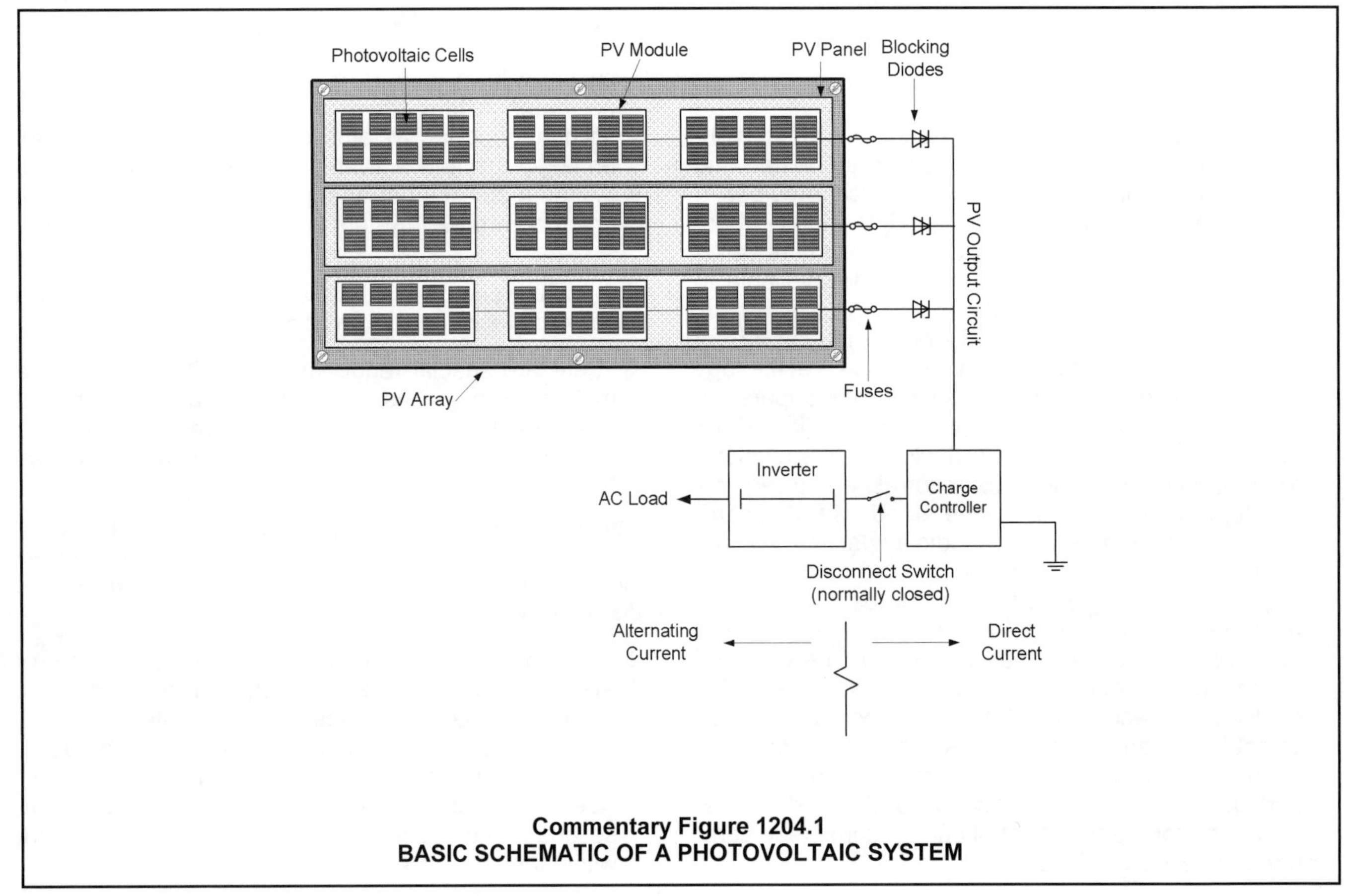

Commentary Figure 1204.1
BASIC SCHEMATIC OF A PHOTOVOLTAIC SYSTEM

The ever-increasing demand for alternative power sources poses hazards to emergency responders. The greatest danger for emergency responders operating in proximity to solar energy collection systems is the lack of knowledge needed to operate safely around these systems. Some of the potential hazards associated with PV systems are tripping and falls for fire fighters operating on the roof, earlier roof collapse due to the added dead load and electric shock. The provisions of Sections 1204.2 through 1204.5 were developed to provide for the proper installation of PV systems and to address the potential hazards to fire fighters. This section requires compliance with the IBC or *International Residential Code*® (IRC®), as applicable, and NFPA 70.

Relevant provisions are IBC Sections 1505, 1512 and 3111 and IRC Sections R324, R902, R905 and R907, as applicable.

The reference to NFPA 70 requires compliance with Section 690 of NFPA 70, which addresses requirements such as marking of equipment and the type of materials that are permitted. Section 1204.2 focuses primarily on creating pathways where fire fighters can perform manual ventilation operations on roofs.

1204.2 Access and pathways. Roof access, pathways, and spacing requirements shall be provided in accordance with Sections 1204.2.1 through 1204.3.3. Pathways shall be over areas capable of supporting fire fighters accessing the roof. Pathways shall be located in areas with minimal obstructions, such as vent pipes, conduit or mechanical equipment.

Exceptions:

1. Detached, nonhabitable Group U structures including, but not limited to, detached garages serving Group R-3 buildings, parking shade structures, carports, solar trellises and similar structures.
2. Roof access, pathways and spacing requirements need not be provided where the *fire code official* has determined that rooftop operations will not be employed.

❖ This section introduces a major requirement of PV system design: to provide access and paths so fire fighters can perform the important task of manual ventilation by cutting one or more holes in a building roof. The access also must be safe and available. The pathways need to be able to hold fire fighters, useable and free of obstructions. The provisions in Sections 1204.2 through 1204.3.3 address the placement of PV arrays on building roofs. It should be noted that these requirements do not apply to buildings regulated by the IRC. See the commentary to Section 102.5 for a discussion of the relationship between this code and the IRC.

Exception 1 recognizes that the installation of PV systems on detached Group U occupancy structures will not require ventilation and therefore does not need to be regulated by this section.

Exception 2 exempts PV arrays from the spacing requirements when the fire chief indicates that vertical manual ventilation practices will not be employed. Conditions that could be considered under this exception include, but are not limited to, proximity and type of adjacent exposures; alternative access opportunities (as from adjoining roofs); adequate ventilation opportunities beneath solar arrays that are sufficiently elevated, spaced or set back from other rooftop equipment; installation of automatic ventilation devices or new technology, methods, or other innovations that ensure adequate fire department access, pathways and ventilation opportunities. Note that a construction permit in accordance with Section 105.7.21 would still be required.

1204.2.1 Solar photovoltaic systems for Group R-3 buildings. Solar photovoltaic systems for Group R-3 buildings shall comply with Sections 1204.2.1.1 through 1204.2.1.3.

Exceptions:

1. These requirements shall not apply to structures designed and constructed in accordance with the *International Residential Code*.
2. These requirements shall not apply to roofs with slopes of 2 units vertical in 12 units horizontal or less.

❖ This section introduces the PV system access requirements for residential buildings (see Commentary Figure 1204.2.1). Note that the Group R-3 buildings focused on are typically one- and two-family dwellings that fall outside the scope of the IRC. As noted in Section 1204.1, the IRC addresses one- and two-family dwellings that fall within the scope of that code. The requirements in Section R324 are very similar to those found in Sections 1204.2.1 through 1204.2.1.3. Exception 2 exempts low-slope roofs (i.e., a slope that is 2:12 or less) because of the reduced hazards of flatter roofs. Therefore, Sections 1204.2.1.1 through 1204.2.1.3 would not apply to flat roof Group R-3 buildings.

Commentary Figure 1204.2.1
INSTALLATION OF A PV ARRAY ON AN R-3 OCCUPANCY

1204.2.1.1 Pathways to ridge. Not fewer than two 36-inch-wide (914 mm) pathways on separate roof planes, from lowest roof edge to ridge, shall be provided on all buildings. Not fewer than one pathway shall be provided on the street or driveway side of the roof. For each roof plane with a photovoltaic array, not fewer than one 36-inch-wide (914 mm) pathway from lowest roof edge to ridge shall be provided on the same roof plane as the photovoltaic array, on an adjacent roof plane or straddling the same and adjacent roof planes.

❖ Where PV arrays are installed on the roof of a Group R-3 building, a minimum of two 3-foot (914 mm) access pathways must be left from the eave to the roof ridge so fire fighters have an unobstructed area in which to cut ventilation openings. In addition, at least one of those paths must be on the street or driveway side for better access to the pathway. Finally, the last sentence is intended to ensure access to the ridge as close as possible if not on the same roof plane of the PV array.

1204.2.1.2 Setbacks at ridge. For photovoltaic arrays occupying 33 percent or less of the plan view total roof area, a setback of not less than 18 inches (457 mm) wide is required on both sides of a horizontal ridge. For photovoltaic arrays occupying more than 33 percent of the plan view total roof area, a setback of not less than 36 inches (457 mm) wide is required on both sides of a horizontal ridge.

❖ Manual ventilation is most effective when accomplished at the highest portion of the roof above the fire. This section establishes an obstruction-free zone for the roof ridge in order to optimize the area available for effective ventilation, allowing for a 2-foot (609.6 mm) trench cut. A lower setback (18 inches) is allowed for buildings with one-third or less of the roof being covered, based on the fact that other areas may be available for venting. For roofs with more than one-third of the roof covered with PV panels, the setback from the ridge is greater (3 feet). Buildings greater than 33 percent covered likely have fewer options for venting without a great setback.

1204.2.1.3 Alternative setbacks at ridge. Where an automatic sprinkler system is installed within the dwelling in accordance with Section 903.3.1.3, setbacks at the ridge shall conform to one of the following:

1. For photovoltaic arrays occupying 66 percent or less of the plan view total roof area, a setback of not less than 18 inches (457 mm) wide is required on both sides of a horizontal ridge.
2. For photovoltaic arrays occupying more than 66 percent of the plan view total roof area, a setback of not less than 36 inches (914 mm) wide is required on both sides of a horizontal ridge.

❖ This section is essentially the same as Section 1204.2.1.2, with credit provided for an automatic sprinkler system. Instead of a coverage criteria of 33 percent, it is 66 percent. The logic is that a fire is much more likely to be extinguished by the sprinklers early on, thus reducing the need to ventilate such structures and the need for room to ventilate.

1204.2.2 Emergency escape and rescue openings. Panels and modules installed on Group R-3 buildings shall not be placed on the portion of a roof that is below an emergency escape and rescue opening. A pathway of not less than 36 inches (914 mm) wide shall be provided to the emergency escape and rescue opening.

❖ This section provides the necessary pathway below emergency escape and rescue openings that are located above a portion of the roof. Without this section it is quite possible PV panels could be installed where access is necessary to emergency escape and rescue openings, thus negating their ability to serve their purpose of escape and rescue.

1204.3 Other than Group R-3 buildings. Access to systems for buildings, other than those containing Group R-3 occupancies, shall be provided in accordance with Sections 1204.3.1 through 1204.3.3.

> **Exception:** Where it is determined by the *fire code official* that the roof configuration is similar to that of a Group R-3 occupancy, the residential access and ventilation requirements in Sections 1204.2.1.1 through 1204.2.1.3 are a suitable alternative.

❖ This section introduces PV system access requirements for other than Group R-3 buildings. The exception recognizes that nonresidential buildings are often constructed in a residential configuration and authorizes the fire code official to allow the provisions for Group R-3 construction styles to be used. The access and ventilation requirements are not occupancy specific but are affected most by the construction configuration.

1204.3.1 Perimeter pathways. There shall be a minimum 6-foot-wide (1829 mm) clear perimeter around the edges of the roof.

> **Exception:** Where either axis of the building is 250 feet (76 200 mm) or less, the clear perimeter around the edges of the roof shall be permitted to be reduced to a minimum width of 4 feet (1219 mm).

❖ PV arrays installed on the roofs of nonresidential buildings must be located so they create a minimum 6-foot (1829 mm) clearance between the PV array and roof edge so fire fighters have an unobstructed area in which to move and operate when cutting ventilation openings. The exception provides some flexibility for smaller buildings where less access to the roof is needed; therefore, a reduced width of 4 feet is acceptable.

1204.3.2 Interior pathways. Interior pathways shall be provided between array sections to meet the following requirements:

1. Pathways shall be provided at intervals not greater than 150 feet (45 720 mm) throughout the length and width of the roof.

2. A pathway not less than 4 feet (1219 mm) wide in a straight line to roof standpipes or ventilation hatches.
3. A pathway not less than 4 feet (1219 mm) wide around roof access hatches, with not fewer than one such pathway to a parapet or roof edge.

❖ Pathways must be established in the design of the PV systems and meet the requirements listed in this section. The first item denotes that a straight pathway from the roof edge must be provided every 150 feet. Therefore, a 300-foot-long building would require a single pathway in the middle. Note that Section 1204.3.1 requires a 6-foot clear perimeter along the edge of the roof. Straight pathways with a 4-foot (1290 mm) clearance to tripping and other hazards help provide a safe working environment for personnel assigned to rooftop operations. Additionally, access to roof standpipes and ventilations hatches is necessary.

1204.3.3 Smoke ventilation. The solar installation shall be designed to meet the following requirements:

1. Where nongravity-operated smoke and heat vents occur, a pathway not less than 4 feet (1219 mm) wide shall be provided bordering all sides.
2. Smoke ventilation options between array sections shall be one of the following:
   - 2.1. A pathway not less than 8 feet (2438 mm) wide.
   - 2.2. Where gravity-operated dropout smoke and heat vents occur, a pathway not less than 4 feet (1219 mm) wide on not fewer than one side.
   - 2.3. A pathway not less than 4 feet (1219 mm) wide bordering 4-foot by 8-foot (1219 mm by 2438 mm) venting cutouts every 20 feet (6096 mm) on alternating sides of the pathway.

❖ This section establishes design options for providing adequate space among and around the PV arrays for safe fire department ventilation operations.

Nongravity-operated smoke and heat vents will require more intervention from the fire department; therefore, more access to those vents will be needed.

Nongravity-operated smoke and heat vents require more access by the fire department to provide ventilation and require a 4-foot width around the vent.

Note that gravity-operated smoke and heat vents are only required to provide access on one side. Gravity-operated smoke and heat vents will automatically provide ventilation if needed.

1204.4 Ground-mounted photovoltaic panel systems. Ground-mounted photovoltaic panel systems shall comply with Section 1204.1 and this section. Setback requirements shall not apply to ground-mounted, free-standing photovoltaic arrays. A clear, brush-free area of 10 feet (3048 mm) shall be required for ground-mounted photovoltaic arrays.

❖ This section applies all requirements for rooftop PV systems to ground-mounted PV systems except for the access, pathway and smoke ventilation clearance requirements since the physical hazards of a ground-mounted system are reduced. They are no longer on a roof that potentially needs to be vented. For visibility and emergency access, a clear zone is required around the arrays. This clearance also reduces the risk of a fire occurring adjacent to the arrays.

1204.5 Buildings with rapid shutdown. Buildings with rapid shutdown solar photovoltaic systems shall have permanent labels in accordance with Sections 1204.5.1 through 1204.5.3.

❖ Rapid shutdown features of solar PV systems are beneficial to fire fighters in that they can more quickly and easily reduce hazards and fight the fire. Shutting down the system more quickly reduces the live electrical aspects of the system that could injure or kill fire fighters. However, it needs to be clear what is being shut down on the system. It must be understood whether it is both the array and conductors or only the conductors. Additionally, signage in general is necessary to determine if there is more than one shut down for the system and if portions of the system are not rapid shutdown. This section is not intended to require rapid shutdown but instead to appropriately provide signage to understand where rapid shutdown capability exists. These requirements will also likely become part of NFPA 70 and are consistent with those requirements.

1204.5.1 Rapid shutdown type. The type of solar photovoltaic system rapid shutdown shall be labeled with one of the following:

1. For solar photovoltaic systems that shut down the array and the conductors leaving the array, a label shall be provided. The first two lines of the label shall be uppercase characters with a minimum height of $^3/_8$ inch (10 mm) in black on a yellow background. The remaining characters shall be uppercase with a minimum height of $^3/_{16}$ inch (5 mm) in black on a white background. The label shall be in accordance with Figure 1204.5.1(1) and state the following:

   SOLAR PV SYSTEM EQUIPPED WITH RAPID SHUTDOWN. TURN RAPID SHUTDOWN SWITCH TO THE "OFF" POSITION TO SHUT DOWN PV SYSTEM AND REDUCE SHOCK HAZARD IN ARRAY.

2. For photovoltaic systems that only shut down conductors leaving the array, a label shall be provided. The first two lines of the label shall be uppercase characters with a minimum height of $^3/_8$ inch (10 mm) in white on a red background and the remaining characters shall be capitalized with a minimum height of $^3/_{16}$ inch (5 mm) in black on a white background. The label shall be in accordance with Figure 1204.5.1(2) and state the following:

   THIS SOLAR PV SYSTEM EQUIPPED WITH RAPID SHUTDOWN. TURN RAPID SHUTDOWN SWITCH TO THE "OFF" POSITION TO SHUT DOWN CONDUCTORS OUTSIDE THE ARRAY. CONDUCTORS WITHIN ARRAY REMAIN ENERGIZED IN SUNLIGHT.

❖ Rapid shutdown can apply to both the conductors and the array or simply the conductors. Distinguishing this difference is important, as one PV system remains electrically live and all electrical is shut down for the other. There are two types of signs that can be used depending on the system.

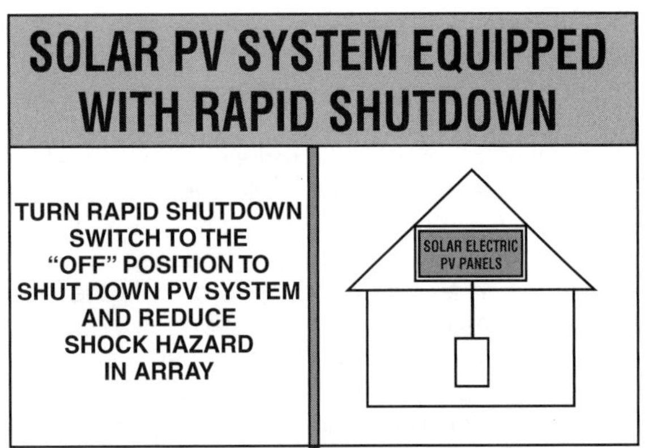

FIGURE 1204.5.1(1)
LABEL FOR SOLAR PV SYSTEMS THAT REDUCE SHOCK HAZARD WITHIN ARRAY AND SHUT DOWN CONDUCTORS LEAVING ARRAY

THIS SOLAR PV SYSTEM EQUIPPED WITH RAPID SHUTDOWN

TURN RAPID SHUTDOWN SWITCH TO THE "OFF" POSITION TO SHUT DOWN CONDUCTORS OUTSIDE THE ARRAY. CONDUCTORS WITHIN ARRAY REMAIN ENERGIZED IN SUNLIGHT

SOLAR ELECTRIC PV PANELS

FIGURE 1204.5.1(2)
LABEL FOR SOLAR PV SYSTEMS THAT ONLY SHUT DOWN CONDUCTORS LEAVING THE ARRAY

1204.5.1.1 Diagram. The labels in Section 1204.5.1 shall include a simple diagram of a building with a roof. Diagram sections in red signify sections of the solar photovoltaic system that are not shut down when the rapid shutdown switch is turned off.

❖ In addition to the signage, a diagram must also be provided. This helps to better identify through color which portions of the systems will remain live after rapid shutdown.

1204.5.1.2 Location. The rapid shutdown label in Section 1204.5.1 shall be located not greater than 3 feet (914 mm) from the service disconnecting means to which the photovoltaic systems are connected, and shall indicate the location of all identified rapid shutdown switches if not at the same location.

❖ Signage and diagrams are only helpful if located close to the disconnecting means. This section specifies a maximum distance of 3 feet that these signs can be located in association with the service disconnect. Note that buildings with multiple rapid shutdown switches need to identify where all the switches are located.

1204.5.2 Buildings with more than one rapid shutdown type. Solar photovoltaic systems that contain rapid shutdown in accordance with both Items 1 and 2 of Section 1204.5.1 or solar photovoltaic systems where only portions of the systems on the building contain rapid shutdown, shall provide a detailed plan view diagram of the roof showing each different photovoltaic system and a dotted line around areas that remain energized after the rapid shutdown switch is operated.

❖ Buildings can have two types of rapid shutdown where either the array and conductors are shut down or only the conductors. Also note it is possible to have a building with photovoltaics with some form of rapid shutdown and portions without. Due to the potential hazards to fire fighters, these differences must be provided in a detailed plan view that shows which areas are still energized.

1204.5.3 Rapid shutdown switch. A rapid shutdown switch shall have a label located not greater than 3 feet (914 mm) from the switch that states the following:

RAPID SHUTDOWN SWITCH
FOR SOLAR PV SYSTEM

❖ This section requires that the actual switch be labeled and not further than 3 feet from the rapid shutdown switch. The requirements of this section are intended to assist in providing information to fire fighters to maintain safety while fighting fires that contain photovoltaics.

SECTION 1205
STATIONARY FUEL CELL POWER SYSTEMS

1205.1 General. *Stationary fuel cell power systems* in new and existing occupancies shall comply with this section.

❖ This section deals with the regulation of stationary fuel cell power systems based on the fact that they are located in buildings, and the potential hazards they pose need to be addressed. Fuel cell power systems are being used in ever-increasing numbers to meet facility energy needs. Stationary fuel cell power systems generate power through an electrochemical process that combines hydrogen and oxygen to produce electricity. The hydrogen comes from a direct hydrogen source or from any hydrocarbon fuel such as natural gas, gasoline, diesel, or methanol if the fuel cell power system includes integral reforming. The oxygen comes from air around the fuel cell. There are several types of fuel cell systems that require different approval processes. These will be discussed further in Section 1205.3.

1205.2 Permits. Permits shall be obtained for *stationary fuel cell power systems* as set forth in Section 105.7.10.

❖ Section 105.7.10 requires a permit to allow the fire department to become familiar with and sign off on the safety of such systems.

1205.3 Equipment. *Stationary fuel cell power systems* shall comply with the following:

1. *Prepackaged fuel cell power systems* shall be listed and labeled in accordance with CSA FC 1.
2. The modules and components in a *preengineered fuel cell power system* shall be listed and labeled in accordance with CSA FC 1 and interconnected to complete the assembly of the system at the job site in accordance with the manufacturer's instructions and the module and component listings.
3. *Field-fabricated fuel cell power systems* shall be approved based on a review of the technical report provided in accordance with Section 104.7.2. The report shall be prepared by and bear the stamp of a registered design professional and shall include:
   3.1. A fire risk evaluation.
   3.2. An evaluation demonstrating that modules and components in the fuel cell power system comply with applicable requirements in CSA FC 1.
   3.3. Documentation of the fuel cell power system's compliance with applicable NFPA 2 and NFPA 853 construction requirements.

❖ Three types of fuel cell power systems are defined in Chapter 2. They include:

- Prepackaged fuel cell power systems.
- Preengineering fuel cell power systems.
- Field-fabricated fuel cell power systems.

Each of these systems has a different approach to approval. Prepackaged systems come as a complete unit and simply need to be listed and labeled in accordance with CSA FC1. These systems are ready for installation right from the factory, whereas preengineered and field-fabricated systems require more approvals during installation. The requirements for listing and labeling to CSA FC1 remove the burden to the fire code official of determining compliance with NFPA 853, which is a standard for the design, construction, and installation of stationary fuel cell power systems very similar in content to CSA FC1. Preengineered systems fall between prepackaged and field fabricated. The modules and components are listed and labeled and the system is approved but must be assembled at the job site. Again, the listing essentially demonstrates compliance with NFPA 853. In addition to listing and labeling preengineered fuel cell power systems, the manufacturer's instructions must be followed. Field fabricated is a system completely assembled at the job site and the modules are not listed or labeled. Instead, they need to meet several criteria, including demonstrating compliance with CSA FC1. This option allows for newer technologies to be used that have not been designed yet as prepackaged or preengineered. In addition to compliance with CSA FC 1, a risk analysis is necessary. Additionally, hydrogen, a common fuel used for fuel cell power systems, must meet the requirements in NFPA 2 and NFPA 853.

ANSI/CSA FC 1 is used to investigate and list the stationary fuel cells covered by this section. The construction and performance requirements in that standard address a variety of hazards, including mechanical, electrical, thermal, malfunction, erroneous human intervention and environmental. NFPA 853, *Standard for the Installation of Stationary Fuel Cell Power Systems,* includes requirements for the design, construction and installation of stationary fuel cell power systems.

1205.4 Installation. *Stationary fuel cell power systems* shall be installed and maintained in accordance with NFPA 70 and NFPA 853, the manufacturer's installation instructions, and the listing. *Stationary fuel cell power systems* fueled by hydrogen shall be installed and maintained in accordance with NFPA 2 and NFPA 70, the manufacturer's installation instructions and the listing.

❖ This section is provided to ensure that such systems are properly installed and maintained, regardless of type. Several standards are called up for this process.

1205.5 Residential use. *Stationary fuel cell power systems* shall not be installed in Group R-3 and R-4 buildings, or dwelling units associated with Group R-2 buildings unless they are specifically listed for residential use.

❖ Systems are listed for both residential and nonresidential use based on the requirements in NFPA 853 and CSA FC1. This section is provided to ensure the appropriate stationary fuel cell power system is installed.

1205.6 Indoor installations. *Stationary fuel cell power systems* installed in indoor locations shall comply with Sections 1205.6 through 1205.6.2. For purposes of this section, an indoor location includes a roof and 50 percent or greater enclosing walls.

❖ Systems are listed for either indoor or outdoor use. The 50-percent wall limitation is from NFPA 853, Section 3.3.15.2. This criteria is necessary to differentiate which installations are considered indoor versus outdoor, as the requirements vary. Section 1205.6 specifically addresses indoor installations.

1205.6.1 Listed. *Stationary fuel cell power systems* installed indoors shall be specifically listed and labeled for indoor use.

❖ The purpose of this section is to ensure that indoor systems are listed and labeled appropriately for indoor use. This makes it clear to the fire code official that what is being installed is appropriate for the location and use without requiring verification through additional documentation.

1205.6.2 Separation. Rooms containing *stationary fuel cell power systems* shall be separated from the following occupancies by fire barriers or horizontal assemblies, or both, constructed in accordance with the *International Building Code*.

1. Group B, F, M, S and U occupancies by 1-hour fire-resistance-rated construction.
2. Group A, E, I and R occupancies by 2-hour fire- resistance-rated construction.

Exception: *Stationary fuel cell power systems* with an aggregate rating less than 50 kW shall not be required to be separated from other occupancies provided that the systems comply with Section 9.3 of NFPA 853.

❖ These systems are essentially like an incidental use to the building and separations are provided for consistency with that concept. The separations are consistent with stationary storage battery systems. Systems less than 50 kW do not require additional separation, as the risk they pose is low.

1205.7 Vehicle impact protection. Where *stationary fuel cell power systems* are subject to impact by a motor vehicle, vehicle impact protection shall be provided in accordance with Section 312.

❖ The provisions in this section protect the power system from physical damage to avoid a malfunction of the equipment and the possible resulting hazards. A good example may be a fuel cell in a warehouse space where forklifts are being used (see commentary, Section 312).

1205.8 Outdoor installation. *Stationary fuel cell power systems* located outdoors shall be separated by not less than 5 feet (1524 mm) from the following:

1. Lot lines.
2. Public ways.
3. Buildings.
4. Stored combustible materials.
5. Hazardous materials.
6. High-piled stock.
7. Any portion of a designated means of egress system.
8. Other exposure hazards.

❖ The exposures are different for installations on the exterior, as there are other exposures such as adjacent buildings. The separations are based on, but not identical to, requirements in NFPA 853, Section 5.1.1.

1205.9 Fuel supply. The design, location and installation of the fuel supply for *stationary fuel cell power systems* shall comply with Chapter 53, Chapter 58 and the *International Fuel Gas Code,* based on the particular fuel being supplied to the system.

❖ This section does not address the fuel supply but instead provides references to the appropriate requirements. The primary fuels are hydrogen and CNG.

1205.10 Manual shutoff. Access to a manual shutoff valve shall be provided for the fuel piping within 6 feet (1829 mm) of any fuel storage tank serving the fuel cell and within 6 feet (1829 mm) of the power system. If the fuel tank and the *stationary fuel cell power system* are less than 12 feet (3658 mm) apart, a single shutoff valve shall be permitted. If the *stationary fuel cell power system* is located indoors, the shutoff valve shall be located outside of the room in which the system is installed, unless otherwise approved by the *fire code official*.

❖ Manual shutoff requirements are based on, but not identical to, requirements in NFPA 853, Section 6.4. Note that Section 6.4 deals with hydrogen specifically, but this section would deal with any fuel being used for the fuel cell. Fuel cells generate electricity but need a fuel source such as hydrogen or CNG. Therefore, shutoff valves must be provided in case of malfunction of the fuel supply at the fuel cell to avoid further hazards.

This section essentially is intended to provide two shutoff valves that are located within 6 feet of the fuel cell and within 6 feet of the fuel source. Some flexibility is given to systems where the fuel source and cell are less than 12 feet apart and thus can share a single shutoff valve. Indoor fuel cells must provide shutoff valves outside the room in which the fuel cell is located. This reduces the risk of entering a space with a flammable gas.

1205.11 Ventilation and exhaust. Ventilation and exhaust for stationary fuel cell power systems shall be provided in accordance with NFPA 853.

❖ Ventilation, exhaust, fire suppression and gas detection are important parts of a safe installation, and NFPA 853 is referenced for convenience. Chapter 7 of NFPA 853 addresses ventilation and exhaust. Section 7.1.1 of NFPA 853 exempts fuel cell power systems installed outdoors and listed prepackaged or preengineered and matched modular fuel cell power systems that are sealed, provide direct ventilation and exhaust in accordance with the listing and manufacturer. Outdoor installations have more air circulation to reduce the hazard of flammable gas buildup, and preengineered and prepacked installations design ventilation and exhaust into the system. The provisions focus on having separate ventilation and exhaust for the power systems and to interlock the systems in case of failure of the exhaust system.

1205.12 Fire suppression. Fire suppression for stationary fuel cell power system installations shall be provided in accordance with NFPA 853.

❖ For outdoor installations, NFPA 853 essentially requires appropriate fire hydrants be available to fight a fire. Fuel cell power systems that store flammable and combustible liquids for a fuel source require a minimum of 250 gpm for 2 hours. Where flammable and combustible liquids are not used, the existing yard or city hydrant system would be sufficient. In the case of this code, compliance with Section 507 is sufficient. Where hydrants are not available, NFPA 853 offers the option of undertaking a risk evaluation to address the suppression needs.

Indoor installations in accordance with NFPA 853 require automatic fire suppression systems within the liquid fuel pump rooms. Such suppression systems need to be interlocked with the fuel cell power system to shut down the system on activation.

1205.13 Gas detection systems. Stationary fuel cell power systems shall be provided with a gas detection system. Detection shall be provided in approved locations in the fuel cell power system enclosure, the exhaust system or the room that encloses the fuel cell power system. The system shall be designed to activate at a flammable gas concentration of not more than 25 percent of the lower flammable limit (LFL).

❖ Gas detection system requirements include detection locations from UL 853 and activation criteria that are consistent with the requirements of this code. Gas detection is critical with fuels such as hydrogen and is intended for fuel cell power systems using such fuels. The necessary locations for the detection devices will vary based on each installation and system; therefore, the term "approved" is used for their location. Note that NFPA 853 states that the detectors be located based on "leakage sources and fuel type." The intent is not to provide gas detection when liquid fuels are being used. NFPA 853 does require leak detection for liquid fuels.

1205.13.1 System activation. The activation of the gas detection system shall automatically:

1. Close valves between the gas supply and the fuel cell power system.
2. Shut down the fuel cell power system.
3. Initiate local audible and visible alarms in approved locations.

❖ The initiation of the gas detection creates three specific actions that shut off the gas supply, shut down the fuel cell and provide at least a local alarm to alert someone of the hazard. Note that such actions occur once the gas has reached 25 percent of the LFL. Again, gas detection is intended for liquefied or gaseous fuels.

SECTION 1206 ELECTRICAL ENERGY STORAGE SYSTEMS

1206.1 Scope. The provisions in this section are applicable to energy storage systems designed to provide electrical power to a building or facility. These systems are used to provide standby or emergency power, an uninterruptable power supply, load shedding, load sharing or similar capabilities.

❖ Originally this section was located in Chapter 6, and the requirements were developed in response to the concern that applying the code's generic hazardous materials requirements to battery systems was inappropriate and unnecessary. When these provisions were originally developed, they primarily addressed hazards associated with stationary lead acid battery systems used for standby and emergency power. Under the requirements of the 2015 code and earlier editions, the battery system electrolyte would have exceeded the MAQs established in Chapter 50, which would lead to battery rooms being classified as a Group H occupancy. Generally, these types of systems had a good safety record and posed a very low hazard to the building, its occupants and emergency responders. In the case of the telecommunications industry, these systems are found in buildings with very low occupant loads, such as telephone company exchanges.

Advancements in battery technologies have introduced a new generation of battery technologies, such as lithium-ion and flow batteries, each with advantages and potential hazards.

This section has been expanded to address the changing environment of energy storage systems. Section 1206 now deals with both battery storage systems and capacitor energy storage systems. "Battery system, Stationary storage" and "Capacitor energy storage system" are defined in Chapter 2.

1206.2 Stationary storage battery systems. Stationary storage battery systems having capacities exceeding the values shown in Table 1206.2 shall comply with Section 1206.2.1 through 1206.2.12.6, as applicable.

❖ As discussed, Section 1206 deals with both battery storage systems and capacitor energy storage systems. Originally the provisions of Section 1206.2 were located in Section 608. Due to the changes, advances and expanding use of battery storage systems, the requirements have increased in scope to address not only batteries provided for standby and emergency power, but also now for functions such as load shedding and load sharing. Providing protection for these new technologies and the huge amounts of energy they store is something that needs to be addressed through research, fire and fault condition testing, and the development of effective safety standards. Unfortunately, much of this work, such as determining the ability of fire suppression systems to control large fires originating within storage battery installations, still needs to be completed. These provisions are meant to manage any hazards that may exist. The provisions still accommodate the lead-acid battery systems used by the telecommunications industry with technology-specific criteria relatively unchanged from older editions of the code, as such systems continue to have a good safety track record.

The provisions of Section 1206.2 only apply to systems that meet the minimum thresholds listed in Table 1206.2. Smaller systems would not require regulation by the code.

1206.2.1 Permits. Permits shall be obtained for the installation and operation of stationary storage battery systems in accordance with Section 105.7.2.

❖ Construction permits are essential as they facilitate the necessary review process for such battery systems by the fire code official. These systems can be used in many different applications, each with their own specific hazards to be addressed based on those applications. Note that Section 105.7.2 deals with construction only.

TABLE 1206.2
BATTERY STORAGE SYSTEM THRESHOLD QUANTITIES.

BATTERY TECHNOLOGY	CAPACITY[a]
Flow batteries[b]	20 kWh
Lead-acid, all types	70 kWh
Lithium, all types	20 kWh
Nickel-cadmium (Ni-Cd)	70 kWh
Sodium, all types	20 kWh[c]
Other battery technologies	10 kWh

For SI:1 kilowatt hour = 3.6 megajoules.

a. For batteries rated in amp-hours, kWh shall equal rated voltage times amp-hour rating divided by 1000.

b. Shall include vanadium, zinc-bromine, polysulfide-bromide, and other flowing electrolyte-type technologies.

c. 70 kWh for sodium-ion technologies.

1206.2.2 Construction documents. The following information shall be provided with the permit application:

1. Location and layout diagram of the room in which the stationary storage battery system is to be installed.
2. Details on hourly fire-resistance-rated assemblies provided.
3. Quantities and types of storage batteries and battery systems.
4. Manufacturer's specifications, ratings and listings of storage batteries and battery systems.
5. Details on energy management systems.
6. Location and content of signage.
7. Details on fire-extinguishing, smoke detection and ventilation systems.
8. Rack storage arrangement, including seismic support criteria.

❖ Extensive documentation is required to obtain a permit. This helps the code official understand the extent and location of the hazard. This information is necessary for the approval of the system as well as for fire department planning purposes.

1206.2.3 Hazard mitigation analysis. A failure modes and effects analysis (FMEA) or other approved hazard mitigation analysis shall be provided in accordance with Section 104.7.2 under any of the following conditions:

1. Battery technologies not specifically identified in Table 1206.2 are provided.
2. More than one stationary storage battery technology is provided in a room or indoor area where there is a potential for adverse interaction between technologies.
3. Where allowed as a basis for increasing maximum allowable quantities in accordance with Section 1206.2.9.

❖ This section requires a hazard mitigation analysis in the form of a failure modes and effects analysis (FMEA) for certain situations. This specifically references Section 104.7.2 for proper analysis and documentation requirements. Item 1 addresses new technologies. This allows for flexibility for innovative technology with appropriate analysis and documentation.

Battery systems are being used in very different ways and applications than in the past and, in some cases, multiple types of systems may be located in a single area within a building. Item 2 requires this situation to be addressed through a hazard analysis to make sure that adverse conditions caused by mixing technologies are not realized.

In terms of Item 3, in some cases the capacity of the system surpasses that of Section 1206.2.9 and, if so, to apply the requirements of Section 1206.2 to these larger systems, a hazard mitigation analysis is necessary.

1206.2.3.1 Fault condition. The hazard mitigation analysis shall evaluate the consequences of the following failure modes, and others deemed necessary by the *fire code official*. Only single-failure modes shall be considered.

1. Thermal runaway condition in a single-battery storage rack, module or array.
2. Failure of any energy management system.
3. Failure of any required ventilation system.
4. Voltage surges on the primary electric supply.
5. Short circuits on the load side of the stationary battery storage system.
6. Failure of the smoke detection, fire-extinguishing or gas detection system.
7. Spill neutralization not being provided or failure of the secondary containment system.

❖ This section sets the criteria as to what needs to be evaluated for the analysis required in Section 1206.2.3. The language also allows the fire code official to add other failure modes to be reviewed. The provisions are only asking that a single failure be addressed for each scenario, similar to the fact that the building and fire codes have been written with the concept of a single fire start as a reasonable level of design.

1206.2.3.2 Analysis approval. The *fire code official* is authorized to approve the hazardous mitigation analysis provided that the hazard mitigation analysis demonstrates all of the following:

1. Fires or explosions will be contained within unoccupied battery storage rooms for the minimum duration of

the fire-resistance-rated walls identified in Table 509.1 of the *International Building Code*.

2. Fires and explosions in battery cabinets in occupied work centers will be detected in time to allow occupants within the room to evacuate safely.
3. Toxic and highly toxic gases released during fires and other fault conditions shall not reach concentrations in excess of Immediately Dangerous to Life or Health (IDLH) levels in the building or adjacent means of egress routes during the time deemed necessary to evacuate from that area.
4. Flammable gases released from batteries during charging, discharging and normal operation shall not exceed 25 percent of their lower flammability limit (LFL).
5. Flammable gases released from batteries during fire, overcharging and other abnormal conditions shall not create an explosion hazard that will injure occupants or emergency responders.

❖ A hazardous mitigation analysis is required under certain circumstances identified in Section 1206.2.3 to address uncertainties associated with new technologies and configurations. This section describes the acceptance criteria to judge acceptability of battery systems. This information needed by both the design professional and the fire code official.

1206.2.3.3 Additional protection measures. Construction, equipment and systems that are required for the stationary storage battery system to comply with the hazardous mitigation analysis, including but not limited to those specifically described in Section 1206.2, shall be installed, maintained and tested in accordance with nationally recognized standards and specified design parameters.

❖ Essentially, this section ensures that the storage system was designed and installed in accordance with industry practice and works with the design parameters approved for the particular installation.

1206.2.4 Seismic and structural design. Stationary storage battery systems shall comply with the seismic design requirements in Chapter 16 of the *International Building Code*, and shall not exceed the floor-loading limitation of the building.

❖ Some of these installations can become quite heavy such that they potentially affect the structural integrity of the building. Though they are technically an appliance or building system, they must be addressed from this standpoint if they cause loading issues. Also, to avoid additional failures during seismic events, the requirements of the IBC must be addressed.

1206.2.5 Vehicle impact protection. Where stationary storage battery systems are subject to impact by a motor vehicle, including fork lifts, vehicle impact protection shall be provided in accordance with Section 312.

❖ This section provides the requirements protecting the battery system from physical damage to avoid a malfunction of the systems and the possible hazards that result. This could occur for indoor or outdoor installations (see commentary, Section 312).

1206.2.6 Combustible storage. Combustible materials not related to the stationary storage battery system shall not be stored in battery rooms, cabinets or enclosures. Combustible materials in occupied work centers covered by Section 1206.2.8.5 shall not be stored less than 3 feet (915 mm) from battery cabinets.

❖ In the past, battery systems were often independent of the rest of the building and its operations. In particular, the focus had only been on applications such as telecommunications buildings. However, there are many cases now where battery storage systems are located in a variety of locations with other ongoing activities. This section requires a minimum separation from combustibles or prohibition of combustibility to reduce the risk of fire.

1206.2.7 Testing, maintenance and repair. Storage batteries and associated equipment and systems shall be tested and maintained in accordance with the manufacturer's instructions. Any storage batteries or system components used to replace existing units shall be compatible with the battery charger, energy management systems, other storage batteries and other safety systems. Introducing other types of storage batteries into the stationary storage battery system or other types of electrolytes into flow battery systems shall be treated as a new installation and require approval by the *fire code official* before the replacements are introduced into service.

❖ This section is focused on testing and maintenance of systems and any changes that occur with battery storage systems. The lack of proper testing and maintenance as required by the manufacturer could result in a hazardous situation. Also, when a battery system is altered to include other types of storage batteries, the system must be thoroughly evaluated before it is placed in service to make sure the storage battery types are compatible.

1206.2.8 Location and construction. Rooms and areas containing stationary storage battery systems shall be designed, located and constructed in accordance with Sections 1206.2.8.1 through 1206.2.8.7.4.

❖ Battery storage systems are no longer limited to standalone installations. For instance, they are sometimes installed for load shedding in high-rise buildings. These provisions address the fact that such systems are located in buildings with other activities and uses and the location and separation of such installations becomes more critical.

1206.2.8.1 Location. Stationary storage battery systems shall not be located in areas where the floor is located more than 75 feet (22 860 mm) above the lowest level of fire department vehicle access, or where the floor level is more than 30 feet (9144 mm) below the finished floor of the lowest level of exit discharge.

Exceptions:

1. Lead-acid and nickel-cadmium stationary storage battery systems.
2. Installations on noncombustible rooftops of buildings exceeding 75 feet (22 860 mm) in height that do

not obstruct fire department rooftop operations, where *approved* by the *fire code official*.

❖ In terms of location, the main concern is access for fire fighting and potential intensity of fires from certain battery systems such as lithium ion. Battery systems are becoming more common in high-rise buildings and without this section, such installations can make it much more difficult for the fire department to fight a fire. This section does not prohibit installations in high-rise buildings, but instead limits the location of such systems to the low-rise portion of the building. Likewise, underground buildings also are addressed. These restrictions were specifically added based on concerns voiced by the fire service. The same restriction is provided for capacitor energy storage systems.

Exception 1 is provided for lead-acid and nickel-cadmium storage battery systems, as they have a good safety record and further restrictions beyond that provided in previous editions are not necessary. Exception 2 allows installations on rooftops as long as they do not interfere with fire department operations.

1206.2.8.2 Separation. Rooms containing stationary storage battery systems shall be separated from other areas of the building in accordance with Section 509.1 of the *International Building Code*. Battery systems shall be allowed to be in the same room with the equipment they support.

❖ Battery storage systems are considered an accessory use and reference to Section 509.1 provides the necessary separation requirements, which are as follows:

- 1-hour separation in Group B, F, M, S and U occupancies.
- 2-hour separation in Groups A, E, I and R occupancies.

Note that the 1-hour separation is for occupancies with occupants less at risk than in Group A, E, I and R occupancies. Those occupancies tend to have more vulnerable populations due to factors such as unfamiliarity, occupants needing assistance to evacuate or occupants who may be asleep.

Allowing battery systems to be in the same room as the equipment they serve is a common practice in telecommunications offices and has proven to be safe.

1206.2.8.3 Stationary battery arrays. Storage batteries, prepackaged stationary storage battery systems and preengineered stationary storage battery systems shall be segregated into stationary battery arrays not exceeding 50 kWh (180 megajoules) each. Each stationary battery array shall be spaced not less than 3 feet (914 mm) from other stationary battery arrays and from walls in the storage room or area. The storage arrangements shall comply with Chapter 10.

Exceptions:

1. Lead-acid and nickel-cadmium storage battery arrays.
2. Listed preengineered stationary storage battery systems and prepackaged stationary storage battery systems shall not exceed 250 kWh (900 megajoules) each.
3. The fire code official is authorized to approve listed, preengineered and prepackaged battery arrays with larger capacities or smaller battery array spacing if large-scale fire and fault condition testing conducted or witnessed and reported by an approved testing laboratory is provided showing that a fire involving one array will not propagate to an adjacent array, and be contained within the room for a duration equal to the fire-resistance rating of the room separation specified in Table 509 of the *International Building Code*.

❖ In an effort to reduce the possible size and intensity of a fire or explosion, storage battery arrays are limited in size. Each array must have a fire break of essentially 3 feet from other arrays and walls. There are several exceptions. The first acknowledges the safety record of lead-acid and nickel-cadmium batteries. The second acknowledges the robustness of preengineered and prepackaged stationary storage battery systems. The third provides flexibility to base the battery array sizes on testing to determine if a fire would be contained to the room as separated as an accessory use.

1206.2.8.4 Separate rooms. Where stationary batteries are installed in a separate equipment room that can be accessed only by authorized personnel, they shall be permitted to be installed on an open rack for ease of maintenance.

❖ This section permits flexibility to access the stationary batteries and allows such batteries to be open, as only those familiar and authorized will be permitted in the room. The risk of damage to such batteries is reduced when separated from the rest of the building.

1206.2.8.5 Occupied work centers. Where stationary storage batteries are located in an occupied work center, they shall be housed in a noncombustible cabinet or other enclosure to prevent access by unauthorized personnel.

❖ In this case the batteries would be located where building occupants would be present, so some level of protection is necessary.

1206.2.8.5.1 Cabinets. Where stationary batteries are contained in cabinets in occupied work centers, the cabinet enclosures shall be located within 10 feet (3048 mm) of the equipment that they support.

❖ This reduces failure modes by reducing the risk of other hazards such as faults in the wires that connect the equipment. Placing battery system cabinets within 10 feet (3048 mm) of the equipment served by the system will limit the number of devices that can be powered by the system due to the voltage drop associated with longer or multiple conductor runs. Having a substantial clearance between the battery cabinet and powered equipment also reduces the likelihood of an ignition in the event that battery gassing has occurred within the cabinet, which could result in an explosive mixture when air is introduced upon opening the cabinet for maintenance. The clearance required by this section will also enhance the safety of personnel who may have to secure and work on equipment served by the battery system by placing the secondary power supply near enough to the powered equipment to ensure line-of-sight supervision of the secured battery system during equipment repair or maintenance.

1206.2.8.6 Signage. Approved signs shall be provided on doors or in locations near entrances to stationary storage battery system rooms and shall include the following or equivalent:

1. The room contains energized battery systems.
2. The room contains energized electrical circuits.
3. The additional markings required in Section 1206.2.12 for the types of storage batteries contained within the room.

Exception: Existing stationary storage battery systems shall be permitted to include the signage required at the time it was installed.

❖ As discussed earlier in this section, battery systems are found in many varying applications in today's world. They are not simply for standby and emergency power as they have been in the past and the types of batteries are more varied. This section identifies the need for signage to identify the hazards. The signage needs to denote both battery systems and electrical circuits. Item 3 denotes that there may be specific signage based on the type of batteries installed as is addressed in Section 1206.2.12. The exception addresses currently installed systems that were not required to have the prescribed signage at the time of installation, which often will be standalone lead-acid battery systems. These types of installations have had a good safety record and typically do not create exposure hazards based on their chemistries and the way they are used.

1206.2.8.6.1 Electrical disconnects. Where the stationary storage battery system disconnecting means is not within sight of the main service disconnecting means, placards or directories shall be installed at the location of the main service disconnecting means indicating the location of stationary storage battery system disconnecting means in accordance with NFPA 70.

❖ Stationary storage battery systems may be in various locations within buildings and may not be near the main service disconnect. Therefore, a way of communicating the disconnect for such systems is necessary at the main service disconnect. This is critical to fighting a fire and being able to disconnect all power supplies affecting fire-fighting operations. Note that to ensure reliability of the telecommunications network, batteries utilized in telecommunications power plants in central offices rarely have circuit breakers or an automatic disconnecting means in order to satisfy an FCC Best Practice designed to ensure highest reliability. Such installations are not within the scope of NFPA 70 and a disconnecting means is not required.

1206.2.8.6.2 Cabinet signage. Battery storage cabinets provided in occupied work centers in accordance with Section 1206.2.8.5 shall have exterior labels that identify the manufacturer and model number of the system and electrical rating (voltage and current) of the contained battery system. There shall be signs within the cabinet that indicate the relevant electrical and chemical hazards, as required by Section 1206.2.12.

❖ This section calls for the identification of the specific hazards associated with the battery system contained in each cabinet. Battery technologies vary and with that the hazard varies. This information will also provide the capacity of each battery system, which is essential for the safety of the occupants and first responders.

1206.2.8.7 Outdoor installations. Stationary storage battery systems located outdoors shall comply with Sections 1206.2.8.7 through 1206.2.8.7.4, in addition to all applicable requirements of Section 1206.2. Installations in outdoor enclosures or containers that can be occupied for servicing, testing, maintenance and other functions shall be treated as battery storage rooms.

Exception: Stationary battery arrays in noncombustible containers shall not be required to be spaced 3 feet (914 mm) from the container walls.

❖ Sections 1206.2.8.7.1 through 1206.2.8.7.4 address stationary storage battery systems when they are located outdoors. The focus is on separation from potential exposures or reducing the risk of being an exposure hazard. In addition, this section addresses concerns with how storage battery systems are situated with regard to means of egress from buildings. Where a building is dedicated to stationary battery storage and only entered for basic maintenance, testing and related functions, the building is treated as a battery storage room. The exception addresses the fact that where the battery arrays are in noncombustible containers, no separation is required. Section 1206.2.8.3 would typically require 3 feet of separation between arrays. In this case, the batteries are outdoors and provide passive protection through noncombustible containers.

1206.2.8.7.1 Separation. Stationary storage battery systems located outdoors shall be separated by a minimum 5 feet (1524 mm) from the following:

1. Lot lines.
2. Public ways.
3. Buildings.
4. Stored combustible materials.
5. Hazardous materials.
6. High-piled stock.
7. Other exposure hazards.

Exception: The fire code official is authorized to approve smaller separation distances if large-scale fire and fault condition testing conducted or witnessed and reported by an approved testing laboratory is provided showing that a fire involving the system will not adversely impact occupant egress from adjacent buildings, or adversely impact adjacent stored materials or structures.

❖ This section deals with the separation from exposure hazards or protecting exposures from the risk of battery system failures. A minimum separation of 5 feet is required. The exception allows a lesser separation where large-scale testing is undertaken to prove that an exposure hazard is not present.

1206.2.8.7.2 Means of egress. Stationary storage battery systems located outdoors shall be separated from any *means of egress* as required by the *fire code official* to ensure safe egress under fire conditions, but not less than 10 feet (3048 mm).

Exception: The *fire code official* is authorized to approve lesser separation distances if large-scale fire and fault condition testing conducted or witnessed and reported by an *approved* testing laboratory is provided showing that a fire involving the system will not adversely impact occupant egress.

❖ Separation from means of egress must be at least 10 feet. Similar to Section 1206.2.8.7.1, the exception allows a lesser separation where large-scale testing demonstrates that a hazard does not exist. This provides flexibility for new technologies or situations where a 10-foot separation is not possible.

1206.2.8.7.3 Security of outdoor areas. Outdoor areas in which stationary storage battery systems are located shall be secured against unauthorized entry and safeguarded in an approved manner.

❖ A large risk with outdoor installations and fire safety in general is a lack of properly secured facilities. Properly securing such installations reduces the risk of arson or vandalism, which could lead to a failure of such systems.

1206.2.8.7.4 Walk-in units. Where a stationary storage battery system includes an outer enclosure, the unit shall only be entered for inspection, maintenance and repair of batteries and electronics, and shall not be occupied for other purposes.

❖ Since these are considered outdoor installations, they must be minimally occupied. If they are used for other purposes, it would likely resemble an indoor installation and would need to comply with provisions for indoor installations. This may result in the need to comply with Section 1206.2.9, which could require a Group H occupancy classification.

1206.2.9 Maximum allowable quantities. *Fire areas* within buildings containing stationary storage battery systems exceeding the maximum allowable quantities in Table 1206.2.9 shall comply with all applicable Group H occupancy requirements in this code and the *International Building Code.*

Exception: Where approved by the *fire code official*, areas containing stationary storage batteries that exceed the amounts in Table 1206.2.9 shall be treated as incidental use areas and not Group H occupancies based on a hazardous mitigation analysis in accordance with Section 1206.2.3 and large-scale fire and fault condition testing conducted or witnessed and reported by an approved testing laboratory.

❖ Scientific research and large scale fire and fault condition testing is not available to justify allowing unlimited quantities of storage batteries to be provided in a single fire area. This section establishes a maximum 600 kWh MAQ for each fire area and 200 kWh for certain technologies for which less information is available. The MAQ of 600 kWh is equivalent to 1,250 storage batteries, each rated 12 V, 40 Ah. Quantities above this amount are only allowed in Group H occupancies.

Since this is a very quickly evolving industry with a variety of battery technologies, the exception provides the flexibility to avoid classification as Group H where a hazard mitigation analysis is undertaken to show that the risk is lower and the installation can be treated as an incidental use. Note that lead-acid and nickel-cadmium batteries are unlimited, which is consistent with their safety record and typical applications.

1206.2.9.1 Mixed battery systems. Where areas within buildings contain different types of storage battery technologies, the total aggregate quantities of batteries shall be determined based on the sum of percentages of each battery type quantity divided by the maximum allowable quantity of each

TABLE 1206.2.9
MAXIMUM ALLOWABLE BATTERY QUANTITIES

BATTERY TECHNOLOGY	MAXIMUM ALLOWABLE QUANTITIES[a]	GROUP H OCCUPANCY
Flow batteries[b]	600 kWh	Group H-2
Lead-acid, all types	Unlimited	Not Applicable
Lithium, all types	600 kWh	Group H-2
Nickel-cadmium (Ni-Cd)	Unlimited	Not Applicable
Sodium, all types	600 kWh	Group H-2
Other battery technologies	200 kWh	Group H-2[c]

For SI:1 kilowatt hour = 3.6 megajoules.

a. For batteries rated in amp-hours, Kilowatt-hours (kWh) shall equal rated battery voltage times the amp-hour rating divided by 1,000.

b. Shall include vanadium, zinc-bromine, polysulfide-bromide, and other flowing electrolyte-type technologies.

c. Shall be a Group H-4 occupancy if the fire code official determines that a fire or thermal runaway involving the battery technology does not represent a significant fire hazard.

battery type. If the sum of the percentages exceeds 100 percent, the area shall be treated as a Group H occupancy in accordance with Table 1206.2.9.

❖ Due to the changing technologies of battery storage systems, it is becoming more common to have multiple technologies in a single building. This section addresses how to determine the maximum allowable quantity when multiple battery systems are used. Note that due to the safety record of lead acid and nickel-cadmium battery systems, the maximum allowable quantities are unlimited. If, for example, there are flow batteries and sodium batteries in the same fire area, the allowable installed quantity permitted under this section of the code is determined on a percentage basis as follows:

Group H classification

Given:

450 kWh flow battery system

75 kWh other battery system

450 kWh flow battery system = 450 kWh/600 kWh = 0.75 × 100 = 75.00%

75 kWh other battery technology system = 75 kWh/ 200 kWh = 0.375 × 100 = 37.5%

75% (flow) + 37.5% (other) = 112.5% of MAQ; therefore, treat as Group H

Incidental Use Classification

Given:

250 kWh flow battery system

100 kWh other battery system

250 kWh flow battery system = 250kWh/600 kWh = 0.417 × 100 = 41.7%

100 kWh other battery technology system = 100 kWh/ 200 kWh = 0.5 × 100 = 50.0%

41.7% (flow) + 50% (other) = 91.7% of MAQ; therefore, treat as Incidental use

1206.2.10 Storage batteries and equipment. The design and installation of storage batteries and related equipment shall comply with Sections 1206.2.10.1 through 1206.2.10.8.

❖ This section deals with the specific design and installation of the storage batteries themselves. This addresses listing requirements, and the need for energy management systems, chargers, inverters and other components of the batteries. Part of these requirements is the assessment of whether the battery system generates potentially hazardous gases while charging.

1206.2.10.1 Listings. Storage batteries and battery storage systems shall comply with the following:

1. Storage batteries shall be listed in accordance with UL 1973.
2. Prepackaged and preengineered stationary storage battery systems shall be listed in accordance with UL 9540.

Exception: Lead-acid batteries are not required to be listed.

❖ This section addresses the basic listing requirements for batteries. Basically all storage batteries besides lead-acid must be listed to UL 1973. Prepackaged and preengineered systems must be listed in accordance with UL 9540, which includes compliance with UL 1973.

1206.2.10.2 Prepackaged and preengineered systems. Prepackaged and preengineered stationary storage battery systems shall be installed in accordance with their listing and the manufacturer's instructions.

❖ Preengineered and prepacked systems have been approved more as a system versus components and carry with them listings as a system. This section ensures they are installed in accordance with their listing and the manufacturer's instructions. For instance, if a system were listed for outdoor use only, it cannot be used within a building. Placement within the building would invalidate the listing.

1206.2.10.3 Energy management system. An approved energy management system shall be provided for battery technologies other than lead-acid and nickel cadmium for monitoring and balancing cell voltages, currents and temperatures within the manufacturer's specifications. The system shall transmit an alarm signal to an approved location if potentially hazardous temperatures or other conditions such as short circuits, over voltage or under voltage are detected.

❖ An energy management system is an important element of a safety system that monitors and takes actions on abnormal conditions that could lead to problems. These systems are critical as part of the risk reduction. This requirement does not apply to lead-acid and nickel-cadmium batteries due to the inherent stability of their chemistries and their safety record.

1206.2.10.4 Battery chargers. Battery chargers shall be compatible with the battery chemistry and the manufacturer's electrical ratings and charging specifications. Battery chargers shall be listed and labeled in accordance with UL 1564 or provided as part of a listed preengineered or prepackaged stationary storage battery system.

❖ Using incorrect chargers could create a failure resulting in thermal runaway or potentially fire or explosion. Therefore, specific listing and labeling is required to avoid the possibility of a battery system being charged incorrectly.

1206.2.10.5 Inverters. Inverters shall be listed and labeled in accordance with UL 1741. Only inverters listed and labeled for utility interactive system use and identified as interactive shall be allowed to operate in parallel with the electric utility power system to supply power to common loads.

❖ An inverter is an electronic device that is capable of changing direct current (DC) to alternating current (AC). Inverters need to be specifically listed and labeled to avoid using the wrong type, and subsequent system failure. Note that this section also requires a specific listing for utility interactive systems. These types of inverters allow things like automatic transfer to enable the stationary storage battery system to feed power back into the commercial power grid, or disconnect from the commercial grid when it is supposed to be de-energized due to an outage. These types of inverters must be inspected by the local electrical inspector and the power utility in most cases.

1206.2.10.6 Safety caps. Vented batteries shall be provided with flame-arresting safety caps.

❖ The types of batteries regulated by this section vent hydrogen and oxygen to the atmosphere. There are two types of vented batteries: nonrecombinant and recombinant. Essentially, a nonrecombinant battery is a storage battery in which, under conditions of normal use, hydrogen and oxygen gases created by electrolysis are vented into the air outside of the battery. A recombinant battery is a storage battery in which, under conditions of normal use, most of the hydrogen and oxygen gases created by electrolysis are converted back into water inside the battery instead of venting into the air.

Another term used for nonrecombinant batteries is "flooded" or "vented." Other terms used to denote recombinant batteries are "valve regulated" or "valve-regulated lead-acid (VRLA)." Flooded batteries vent regularly whereas valve-regulated batteries vent when the internal pressure exceeds the design pressure of their self-resealing vents, which are an integral part of their design. In case of either flooded or VRLA cells, flame-arresting vents are needed to prevent a static spark (or other flame source) outside the battery from propagating to the interior of the battery where oxygen or hydrogen may have accumulated during normal operation of the battery.

1206.2.10.7 Thermal runaway. Where required by Section 1206.2.12, storage batteries shall be provided with a listed device or other approved method to prevent, detect and control thermal runaway.

❖ This requirement is only applicable when required by the battery-specific requirements of Section 1206.2.12. When Section 1206.2.12 is referenced, it is only for valve-regulated lead-acid batteries.

Under certain extreme conditions of high ambient temperature or charging rate, or due to internal partial shorting in cells, VRLA batteries may experience a phenomenon known as "thermal runaway." This is a condition that occurs in a battery (especially valve-regulated types) when charging energy results in heat generation within the battery greater than the heat dissipated, causing an uncontrolled rise in battery temperature. Under these conditions, a battery may generate excessive heat that can cause failure through cell dryout or, in rare cases, rupture or melting of the battery. The thermal runaway management system and batteries are commonly listed in accordance with UL 1989.

1206.2.10.8 Toxic and highly toxic gas. Stationary storage battery systems that have the potential to release toxic and highly toxic gas during charging, discharging and normal use conditions shall comply with Chapter 60.

❖ This section covers battery technologies (many yet to hit the market) that may potentially produce toxic gases during charging, discharging and normal use, and triggers Chapter 60 safety requirements. There is no intent to address batteries that produce toxic gases during fires or abnormal conditions. Hydrogen and oxygen produced by vented batteries are not considered toxic or highly toxic gases.

1206.2.11 Fire-extinguishing and detection systems. Fire-extinguishing and detection systems shall be provided in accordance with Sections 1206.2.11.1 through 1206.2.11.5.

❖ This section provides the requirements for fire-extinguishing and detection systems for battery systems. This section also provides requirements for features that address the hazards of the release of flammable gases such as hydrogen and potential spills. The requirements may vary based on the type of battery system used. For instance, batteries with immobilized liquid versus those with free-flowing electrolyte require different ways to address spills and neutralization, as one is more prone to a larger spill than the other.

1206.2.11.1 Fire-extinguishing systems. Rooms containing stationary storage battery systems shall be equipped with an *automatic sprinkler system* installed in accordance with Section 903.3.1.1. Commodity classifications for specific technologies of storage batteries shall be in accordance with Chapter 5 of NFPA 13. If the storage battery types are not addressed in Chapter 5 of NFPA 13, the *fire code official* is authorized to approve the fire-extinguishing system based on full-scale fire and fault condition testing conducted or witnessed and reported by an *approved* laboratory.

Exception: Spaces or areas containing stationary storage battery systems used exclusively for telecommunications equipment in accordance with Section 903.2.

❖ This section is specific to the use of automatic sprinkler systems. Section 1206.2.11.1.1 addresses battery systems that contain water-reactive materials where water cannot be used.

Where an automatic sprinkler system can be used, the system must be designed to the specific commodity classification applicable to that battery technology. If the battery technology is not addressed by Chapter 5 of NFPA 13, then a sprinkler system may still be used where full-scale testing is undertaken to demonstrate the effectiveness of the system. Acceptance of this testing and ultimate approval of the system are the authority of the fire code official. A significant challenge facing designers and code officials is a lack of large-scale fire and fault condition test data to demonstrate that fire suppression systems can control battery fires from certain newer battery types. Until such protection arrangements are documented in NFPA 13 and other standards, this section needs to provide the option of approving suppression systems based on test data made available to the fire code official.

The exception is consistent with past editions of the code. The telecommunications industry has continually stressed the need for the continuity of telephone service, and the ability to maintain this service is of prime importance. This service is a vital link between the community and the various life safety services, including fire, police and emergency medical services. The integrity of this communications service can be jeopardized not only by fire, but also by water, from whatever the source. The telecommunications industry utilizes other means to achieve an exceptional record of fire safety and reliability. It must be recognized that the exception applies only to those spaces or areas that are used exclusively for telecommunications equipment. Historically, those spaces have a low incidence of fire events. Fires in telecommunications equipment are difficult to start and, if started, grow slowly, thus permitting early detection. Such fires are typically of the smoldering type, do not spread beyond the immediate area, and generally self-extinguish.

1206.2.11.1.1 Alternative fire-extinguishing systems. Battery systems that utilize water-reactive materials shall be protected by an approved alternative automatic fire-extinguishing system in accordance with Section 904. The system shall be listed for protecting the type, arrangement and quantities of storage batteries in the room. The *fire code official* shall be permitted to approve the alternative fire extinguishing system based on full-scale fire and fault condition testing conducted or witnessed and reported by an *approved* laboratory.

❖ Some battery systems utilize enough water-reactive material in their construction that a traditional automatic sprinkler system is not an option. It should be noted that some batteries systems such as lithium ion can be water reactive but can, in some cases, be suppressed with water effectively. This section requires that the system either be listed for such use, or that the use of the system is based on full-scale fire and fault condition testing. A significant challenge facing designers and code officials is a scarcity of large-scale fire and fault condition test data that demonstrate that fire suppression systems can control battery fires from some newer battery technologies. Therefore, with automatic sprinkler systems, the need for full-scale testing is critical.

1206.2.11.2 Smoke detection system. An *approved automatic smoke detection system* shall be installed in rooms containing *stationary storage battery systems* in accordance with Section 907.2.

❖ Many battery room fires are likely to be slow-growing and smoldering; therefore, a smoke detection system is required for early detection and warning in accordance with Section 907.2.22 where the systems exceed the threshold quantities in Table 1206.2. For example, where a lithium-ion system exceeds 20 kWh, a smoke detection system must be provided. Prior to 2018, Section 608 required smoke detection.

1206.2.11.3 Ventilation. Where required by Section 1206.2.3 or 1206.2.12, ventilation of rooms containing stationary storage battery systems shall be provided in accordance with the *International Mechanical Code* and one of the following:

1. The ventilation system shall be designed to limit the maximum concentration of flammable gas to 25 percent of the lower flammability limit, or for hydrogen, 1.0 percent of the total volume of the room.
2. Continuous ventilation shall be provided at a rate of not less than 1 cubic foot per minute (cfm) per square foot [0.00508 $m^3/(s \cdot m^2)$] of floor area, but not less than 150 cfm (4 m^3/min).

The exhaust system shall be designed to provide air movement across all parts of the floor for gases having a vapor density greater than air and across all parts of the vault ceiling for gases having a vapor density less than air.

❖ This section addresses the necessary ventilation requirements based on either the conclusion of the hazard mitigation analysis or the specific battery technology requirements. Some batteries need more ventilation than others.

Basic battery room ventilation, as with any other building area, must comply with the requirements of the IMC. In many cases, basic ventilation based on human comfort will be sufficient to adequately ventilate battery spaces. The main concern with many types of batteries is the buildup of hydrogen within an enclosed space. This is not the case for lithium-ion batteries, but is a concern for aqueous batteries, which contain water, such as lead-acid and nickel-cadmium battery types. Hydrogen has a wide flammability range and is the lightest element on the Periodic Table of Elements, having an atomic number of 1. The gas mixture is potentially explosive when the amount of hydrogen in air exceeds 4 percent by volume. To address the concern of hydrogen generation and containment in small volumes, a minimum ventilation criterion is defined. The ventilation need not be mechanical ventilation. This section provides two methods of compliance from which the designer may choose. The first is performance based and states that the maximum concentration of hydrogen must be limited to either 25 percent of the LFL or 1.0 percent of the total volume of the room. Note that this section states flammable gas more generally with reference to the LFL limit, as this could apply to other types of flammable gases. The second criteria of 1 percent is specific to hydrogen. This method requires an analysis of plausible failure scenarios to justify the ventilation rate ultimately chosen. An excellent guide for determining recommended ventilation rates to control hydrogen produced by batteries under many conditions is IEEE Standard 1635-2012 / ASHRAE 21 - IEEE/ASHRAE Guide for the Ventilation and Thermal

Management of Batteries for Stationary Applications. The second method simply requires continuous ventilation at a rate no less than 1 cubic foot per minute per square foot [1 $ft^3/min/ft^2$ or 0.0051 $m^3/(s \times m^2)$] of room area. This is an extremely conservative ventilation rate in most instances and the energy consumed with this high rate as well as conditioning of makeup air will, in many cases, make this method less attractive.

The sentence following the requirements is focusing on keeping the air moving in the most critical portion of the room depending on the flammable gas of concern. Hydrogen is lighter than air so the concern would be at the ceiling level; although extensive testing of leaking hydrogen concentrations in rooms containing fuel cells shows that while hydrogen is light, and the concentration at the ceiling is greater than the floor, because hydrogen molecules are so small, they tend to disperse rather than gather, and concentrations at the ceiling are typically no more than 10 percent higher than those at floor level.

1206.2.11.3.1 Cabinet ventilation. Where cabinets located in occupied spaces contain storage batteries that are required by Section 1206.2.3 or 1206.2.12 to be provided with ventilation, the cabinet shall be provided with ventilation in accordance with Section 1206.2.11.3.

❖ This section focuses on cabinets where storage batteries are located. The trigger is the same as for ventilation of battery systems in general, either as determined by the hazard mitigation analysis or based on the specific battery technology. The ventilation requirements are also the same (see commentary, Section 1206.2.11.3).

1206.2.11.3.2 Supervision. Required mechanical ventilation systems for rooms and cabinets containing storage batteries shall be supervised by an *approved* central station, proprietary or remote station service or shall initiate an audible and visual signal at an *approved* constantly attended on-site location.

❖ Where mechanical ventilation is utilized to keep the concentration of flammable gases, such as hydrogen, from reaching a flammable or explosive limit, some method of ensuring that the ventilation system is operational is necessary. This section provides two options, which include supervision or an audible and visual alarm at an approved location. A security desk that is operated 24 hours would be a reasonable location to meet the "constantly attended" criteria. It should be noted that according to the IEEE 1635 ventilation rates can be very low. Hydrogen is extremely small and will pass through walls and ceilings. Maintaining a concentration of hydrogen in building construction is difficult. One example of a facility exploding due to hydrogen from batteries is the Rancho Cordova, California data center explosion. The facility was unoccupied, not air-conditioned, with batteries on charge with no load. It took months for the hydrogen to build to explosive levels. When treated properly, aqueous batteries do not explode. In many cases, the normal ventilation for human comfort in accordance with the IMC is more than sufficient; however, supervision is required for the ventilation system.

1206.2.11.4 Gas detection system. Where required by Section 1206.2.3 or 1206.2.12, rooms containing stationary storage battery systems shall be protected by a gas detection system complying with Section 916. The gas detection system shall be designed to activate where the level of flammable gas exceeds 25 percent of the lower flammable limit (LFL), or where the level of toxic or highly toxic gas exceeds one-half of the IDLH.

❖ Gas detection may be a component of the ventilation system or provide an alarm should the ventilation system fail to keep the LFL at the levels required in Section 1206.2.11.3. Also, gas detection is required for the detection of toxic and highly toxic gases for certain battery chemistries. The requirement to provide gas detection is triggered in the same manner as ventilation: either by way of the hazard mitigation analysis or by the specific battery technology requirements in Section 1206.2.12. This section provides the criteria as to when gas detection should activate and Section 916 provides the requirements for the gas detection system. Gas detection is not used for most lead-acid and nickel-cadmium battery installations due to the relatively low amounts of hydrogen they produce in most operating conditions that is normally taken care of by natural and/or mechanical ventilation necessary for human occupancy.

1206.2.11.4.1 System activation. Activation of the gas detection system shall result in all the following:

1. Initiation of distinct audible and visible alarms in the battery storage room.
2. Transmission of an alarm to an approved location.
3. De-energizing of the battery charger.
4. Activation of the mechanical ventilation system, where the system is interlocked with the gas detection system.

Exception: Lead-acid and nickel-cadmium stationary storage battery systems shall not be required to comply with Items 1, 2 and 3.

❖ This section states the actions that must occur once the gas detection system activates. Simply having a detector activate and provide no further direction is of little use. Item 1 focuses on the safety of those possibly located in the battery storage room to alert them to the hazard. Item 2 provides information to someone outside the space to take necessary action as applicable. Item 3 requires the battery charger to cease charging, as continued charging will add to the hazardous situation. Finally, where the mechanical ventilation system is interlocked to the gas detection system, this section requires it to be activated. The exception is provided for lead-acid and nickel-cadmium storage battery systems as they have a good safety record and further restrictions beyond that provided in previous editions of the code are not necessary. Most telecommunications facilities utilize lead-acid and nickel-cadmium stationary storage battery systems. Due to the power architecture utilized in these applications, de-energizing the battery charger could result in a loss of telecommunications services.

1206.2.11.5 Spill control and neutralization. Where required by Section 1206.2.12, approved methods and materials shall be provided for the control and neutralization of spills of electrolyte or other hazardous materials in areas containing stationary storage batteries as follows:

1. For batteries with free-flowing electrolyte, the method and materials shall be capable of neutralizing a spill of the total capacity from the largest cell or block to a pH between 5.0 and 9.0.
2. For batteries with immobilized electrolyte, the method and material shall be capable of neutralizing a spill of 3.0 percent of the capacity of the largest cell or block in the room to a pH between 5.0 and 9.0.

❖ Spill control and neutralization is required by Section 1206.2.12 for several types of battery technologies, including:

- Lead-acid storage batteries.
- Nickel-cadmium batteries.
- Flow batteries.

Note that Section 1206.2.12.6 identifies the need for spill control and neutralization for other battery technologies. The need for this may vary based on the technology.

Batteries that contain a free-flowing liquid electrolyte pose the same containment problems as any other corrosive liquid hazardous material, but the containment and neutralization provisions in this section are performance based and neither specifically require spill control in the form of containment nor a specific method of neutralization. The quantity of neutralization material required to be available would be greater for these less-viscous electrolytes; however, because of their mobility and the rapidity with which they can spread and the potential scope of the spread.

Item 1 deals with batteries that contain free-flowing electrolyte. The requirement is fairly performance based and does not specifically require spill control in the form of containment, nor a specific method of neutralization. Instead, it states that a capability must be available to control and neutralize a spill equal to the liquid content of the largest single battery cell or block (not the whole battery) to a pH between 5.0 and 9.0. In the case of flooded lead-acid batteries, this may require initial absorption or containment followed by neutralization.

Batteries with immobilized electrolyte, such as VRLA batteries, are required to comply with Item 2. This item is also performance based and does not specifically require spill control in the form of containment, nor a specific method of neutralization. Instead, it states that a capability must be available to control and neutralize a spill equal to 3 percent of the liquid content of the largest single battery cell or block (not the whole battery) housed in the battery room to a pH between 5.0 and 9.0. Typically, either sodium-bicarbonate powder or an ammonia-based liquid buffering solution is provided within the room where lead-acid battery systems are located for use by trained personnel (NiCd battery installations will typically have on hand a dilute solution of boric acid for neutralizing the alkaline potassium hydroxide electrolyte solution).

The electrolyte in VRLA batteries is immobilized by either the addition of a gelling agent or by being absorbed in a fiberglass mat (i.e., a sponge). This immobilization creates a situation where a spill of the electrolyte is highly unlikely. A typical accident where a VRLA battery case is broken results in a slight drip or a slow ooze of material out of the battery that cannot be characterized as a spill.

1206.2.12 Specific battery-type requirements. This section includes requirements applicable to specific types of storage batteries. Stationary storage battery systems with more than one type of storage battery shall comply with requirements applicable to each battery type.

❖ This section deals with specific requirements based on the different types of battery technologies. This section is referenced in many cases in Section 1206.2 to determine which provisions are applicable. For example, spill control and neutralization are only applicable to some battery technologies such as lead acid batteries. This section includes requirements for specific battery technologies, and includes criteria that address potential hazards associated with the type of technology involved. The protection requirements are customized for the potential hazards associated with the various battery technologies.

1206.2.12.1 Lead-acid storage batteries. Stationary storage battery systems utilizing lead-acid storage batteries shall comply with the following:

1. Ventilation shall be provided in accordance with Section 1206.2.11.3.
2. Spill control and neutralization shall be in accordance with Section 1206.2.11.5.
3. Thermal runaway protection shall be provided for valve-regulated lead-acid (VRLA) storage batteries in accordance with Section 1206.2.10.7.
4. The signage in Section 1206.2.8.6 shall indicate the room contains lead-acid batteries.

❖ Lead-acid batteries were regulated previously by the code and the provisions are consistent with the nature of the hazard. Vented lead-acid batteries are a type of battery that typically requires spill control and neutralization. They also generate hydrogen and oxygen during charging; therefore, ventilation is necessary. Nickel-cadmium batteries are treated similarly.

1206.2.12.2 Nickel-cadmium (Ni-Cd) storage batteries. *Stationary storage battery systems* utilizing nickel-cadmium (Ni-Cd) storage batteries shall comply with the following:

1. Ventilation shall be provided in accordance with Section 1206.2.11.3.

2. Spill control and neutralization shall be in accordance with Section 1206.2.11.5.
3. Thermal runaway protection shall be provided for valve-regulated sealed nickel-cadmium storage batteries in accordance with Section 1206.2.10.7.
4. The signage in Section 1206.2.8.6 shall indicate the room contains nickel-cadmium batteries.

❖ The provisions for nickel-cadmium batteries were regulated previously by the code and the provisions are consistent with the nature of the hazard. Vented nickel-cadmium batteries are one of the types of batteries that typically require spill control and neutralization. They also generate hydrogen and oxygen during charging; therefore, ventilation is necessary. They are treated very similarly to lead-acid batteries.

1206.2.12.3 Lithium-ion storage batteries. The signage in Section 1206.2.8.6 shall indicate the type of lithium batteries contained in the room.

❖ Lithium-ion batteries only have provisions specific to signage, as many of the specific requirements such as ventilation, spill control and neutralization do not apply to such technology. Instead the primary provisions are those that apply to the size of battery arrays, separation, fire-extinguishing systems and smoke detection.

1206.2.12.4 Sodium-beta storage batteries. *Stationary storage battery systems* utilizing sodium-beta storage batteries shall comply with the following:

1. Ventilation shall be provided in accordance with Section 1206.2.11.3.
2. The signage in Section 1206.2.8.6 shall indicate the type of sodium batteries in the room and include the instructions, "APPLY NO WATER."

❖ Sodium beta storage batteries require ventilation due to the concern with the production of hydrogen. In addition, these batteries contain sodium, and thus are potentially water reactive and shouldn't normally be protected with an automatic sprinkler system. Some sodium-based battery systems have designs such that metallic sodium as a separate element will never exist in a case where it could be exposed to water, and thus these types of batteries could potentially be installed in a sprinklered space. The signage requirements make both the occupants and emergency responders aware.

1206.2.12.5 Flow storage batteries. Stationary storage battery systems utilizing flow storage batteries shall comply with the following:

1. Ventilation shall be provided in accordance with Section 1206.2.11.3.
2. Spill control and neutralization shall be in accordance with Section 1206.2.11.5.
3. The signage required in Section 1206.2.8.6 shall indicate the type of flow batteries in the room.

❖ Flow batteries use two different chemicals dissolved in liquids separated by a membrane. These batteries have the possibility of releasing hydrogen and therefore require ventilation. Spill control and neutralization must be addressed as there are liquids involved in these types of batteries. There are various combinations of chemicals used; therefore, the signage requirements note that the type of flow batteries needs to be indicated. One such combination is hydrogen-lithium bromate.

1206.2.12.6 Other battery technologies. *Stationary storage battery systems* utilizing battery technologies other than those described in Sections 1206.2.12.1 through 1206.2.12.5 shall comply with the following:

1. Gas detection systems complying with Section 916 shall be provided in accordance with Section 1206.2.11.4 where the batteries have the potential to produce toxic or highly toxic gas in the storage room or cabinet in excess of the permissible exposure limits (PEL) during charging, discharging and normal system operation.
2. Mechanical ventilation shall be provided in accordance with Section 1206.2.11.3.
3. Spill control and neutralization shall be in accordance with Section 1206.2.11.5.
4. In addition to the signage required in Section 1206.2.8.6, the marking shall identify the type of batteries present, describe the potential hazards associated with the battery type, and indicate that the room contains energized electrical circuits.

❖ Technology associated with battery systems is rapidly evolving. This section addresses batteries that are not specifically addressed by the provisions of Section 1206.2. This section covers all elements that may be necessary such as gas detection where such batteries have the potential to produce toxic and highly toxic gases. Ventilation is required and since liquid is involved, spill control and neutralization is needed. The signage required in Item 4 is more detailed than that required by Section 1206.2.8.6 because occupants and first responders may be unfamiliar with the technology and its associated hazards.

1206.3 Capacitor energy storage systems. Capacitor energy storage systems having capacities exceeding 3 kWh (10.8 megajoules) shall comply with Sections 1206.3 through 1206.3.2.6.1.

> **Exception:** Capacitors regulated by NFPA 70, Chapter 460, and capacitors included as a component part of other listed electrical equipment are not required to comply with this section.

❖ The U.S. Department of Energy is working with a wide range of stakeholders to encourage the development of large-scale electrical energy storage systems (ESS). ESS are needed because the amount of electricity that can be generated on the electrical grid is relatively fixed over short periods of time, although demand for electricity fluctuates throughout the day. Developing technology to store electrical energy so it can be available to meet demand is being actively pursued with a number of energy storage technologies, including battery storage systems and electrochemical capacitors, among others. This section is focused on capacitor energy storage systems that exceed a capacity of 3 kWh. Many of the requirements are similar to that of battery storage systems. As discussed in Section 202, these are regulated due to concerns similar to battery systems, including the amount of energy they store and how they may be a source of, or contribute to, a fire and pose a risk to fire fighters. These systems are being installed in new and existing buildings. The provisions of this section, however, are not aimed at regulating capacitors already addressed by NFPA 70 specifically or that are included as part of electrical equipment.

1206.3.1 Permits. Permits shall be obtained for the installation of capacitor energy storage systems in accordance with Section 105.7.3.

❖ Construction permits are essential as they provide the necessary review process for such battery systems to the fire code official. These systems can be used in many different applications, each with their own specific hazards that must be addressed.

1206.3.2 Location and construction. Rooms and areas containing capacitor energy storage systems shall be designed, located and constructed in accordance with Sections 1206.3.2 through 1206.3.2.5.

❖ Capacitor energy systems are being installed in various locations. For instance, they are sometimes installed for load shedding or load sharing in high-rise buildings. These provisions address the fact that such systems are located in buildings with other activities and uses and the location and separation of such installations becomes more critical.

1206.3.2.1 Location. Capacitor energy storage systems shall not be located in areas where the floor is located more than 75 feet (22 860 mm) above the lowest level of fire department vehicle access, or where the floor level is more than 30 feet (9144 mm) below the finished floor of the lowest level of exit discharge.

❖ In terms of location, the main concerns are access for fire fighting and potential intensity of fires from certain capacitor systems. Such systems are becoming more common in high-rise buildings and without this section such installations can make it much more difficult for the fire department to fight a fire. This section does not prohibit installations in high-rise buildings, but instead limits the location of such system to the low-rise portion of the building. Likewise, underground buildings are also addressed. These restrictions were specifically added based on concerns from the fire service. The same restriction is provided for stationary storage battery systems.

1206.3.2.2 Separation. Rooms containing capacitor energy storage systems shall be separated from the following occupancies by fire barriers or horizontal assemblies, or both, constructed in accordance with the *International Building Code*.

1. Group B, F, M, S and U occupancies by 1-hour fire-resistance-rated construction.
2. Group A, E, I and R occupancies by 2-hour fire-resistance-rated construction.

❖ Capacitor energy storage systems are treated similarly to stationary battery storage systems. They are not termed "accessory uses," but the intent is the same. The specific fire-resistance-rated separation requirements for capacitor energy storage systems are follows:

- 1-hour fire barrier or horizontal separation in Group B, F, M, S and U occupancies.
- 2-hour fire barrier or horizontal separation in Group A, E, I and R occupancies.

Note that the 1-hour separation is for occupancies with occupants less at risk than in Group A, E, I and R occupancies. In those occupancies, people tend to have more vulnerable populations due to factors such as unfamiliarity, occupants needing assistance to evacuate or occupants who may be asleep.

1206.3.2.3 Capacitor arrays. Capacitor energy storage systems shall be segregated into capacitor arrays not exceeding 50 kWh (180 megajoules) each. Each array shall be spaced not less than 3 feet (914 mm) from other arrays and from walls in the storage room or area. The storage arrangements shall comply with Chapter 10.

Exception: Capacitor energy storage systems in noncombustible containers located outdoors shall not be required to be spaced 3 feet (914 mm) from the container walls.

❖ In an effort to reduce the possible size and intensity of a fire or explosion, capacitor energy system arrays are limited in size to 50 kWh. Each array must have a fire break of essentially 3 feet from other arrays and walls. The exception addresses the fact that where the capacitor arrays are in noncombustible containers, no separation is required for outdoor installations. Outdoor containers pose less risk since it is easier to address a failure at outdoor installations and there are no building occupants at risk.

1206.3.2.4 Signage. Approved signs shall be provided on doors or in locations adjacent to the entrances to capacitor energy storage system rooms and shall include the following or equivalent verbiage and information:

1. "CAPACITOR ENERGY STORAGE ROOM."
2. "THIS ROOM CONTAINS ENERGIZED ELECTRICAL CIRCUITS."
3. An identification of the type of capacitors present and the potential hazards associated with the capacitor type.

❖ Signage is critical to emergency responders to understand the electrical hazard that exists. There are differing types of capacitor energy storage systems. Signage must identify the specific hazard as well as the best way to manage a fire that includes such technologies.

1206.3.2.5 Electrical disconnects. Where the capacitor energy storage system disconnecting means is not within sight of the main service disconnecting means, placards or directories shall be installed at the location of the main service disconnecting means identifying the location of the capacitor energy storage system disconnecting means in accordance with NFPA 70.

❖ Capacitor energy storage systems may be located in various locations within buildings and may not be near the main service disconnect. Therefore, some way of communicating the disconnect for such systems is necessary at the main service disconnect. This is critical to fighting a fire and being able to disconnect all power supplies affecting fire-fighting operations.

1206.3.2.6 Outdoor installation. Capacitor energy systems located outdoors shall comply with Sections 1206.3.2.6 through 1206.3.2.6.4 in addition to all applicable requirements of Section 1206.3. Installations in outdoor enclosures or containers that can be occupied for servicing, testing, maintenance and other functions shall be treated as capacitor storage rooms.

> **Exception:** Capacitor arrays in noncombustible containers shall not be required to be spaced 3 feet (914 mm) from the container walls.

❖ Sections 1206.3.2.6 through 1206.3.2.6.4 address capacitor energy storage systems when they are located outdoors. The focus is on separation from potential exposures or reducing the risk of being an exposure hazard. In addition, this section addresses concerns with how capacitor energy storage systems are situated with regard to means of egress from buildings. Where a building is dedicated to capacitor energy storage systems and only entered for basic maintenance, testing and related functions, it is considered a capacitor energy storage room. The exception addresses the fact that where the battery arrays are in noncombustible containers, no separation is required. Section 1206.3.2.3 would typically require 3 feet of separation between arrays. In this case, the capacitors are outdoors and provide passive protection through noncombustible containers.

1206.3.2.6.1 Separation. Capacitor energy systems located outdoors shall be not less than 5 feet (1524 mm) from the following:

1. Lot lines.
2. Public ways.
3. Buildings.
4. Stored combustible materials.
5. Hazardous materials.
6. High-piled stock.
7. Other exposure hazards.

> **Exception:** The *fire code official* is authorized to approve lesser separation distances if large-scale fire and fault condition testing conducted or witnessed and reported by an approved testing laboratory is provided showing that a fire involving the system will not adversely impact occupant egress from adjacent buildings, or adversely impact adjacent stored materials or structures.

❖ This section deals with separating systems from exposure hazards and protecting exposures from the risk of capacitor energy storage system failures. A minimum separation of 5 feet is required. The exception allows a lesser separation where large-scale testing is undertaken to prove that an exposure hazard is not present.

1206.3.2.6.2 Means of egress. *Capacitor energy storage systems* located outdoors shall be separated from any means of egress as required by the fire code official to ensure safe egress under fire conditions, but not less than 10 feet (3048 mm).

> **Exception:** The *fire code official* is authorized to approve lesser separation distances if large-scale fire and fault condition testing conducted or witnessed and reported by an approved testing laboratory is provided showing that a fire involving the system will not adversely impact occupant egress.

❖ Separation from means of egress must be at least 10 feet. Similar to Section 1206.3.2.6.1, the exception allows a lesser separation where large-scale testing demonstrates that a hazard does not exist. This provides flexibility for new technologies or situations where 10 feet of separation is not possible.

1206.3.2.6.3 Security of outdoor areas. Outdoor areas in which *capacitor energy storage systems* are located shall be secured against unauthorized entry and safeguarded in an approved manner.

❖ A large risk with outdoor installations and in general with fire safety is a lack of properly secured facilities. Properly securing such installations reduces the risk of arson or vandalism, which could lead to a failure of such systems.

1206.3.2.6.4 Walk-in units. Where a capacitor energy storage system includes an outer enclosure, the unit shall only be entered for inspection, maintenance and repair of capacitors and electronics, and shall not be occupied for other purposes.

❖ Since these are considered outdoor installations, they must be minimally occupied. If they are used for other purposes, it would likely resemble an indoor installation and would need to comply with provisions for indoor installations. This may result in the need to comply with Section 1206.3.3, which could require a Group H occupancy classification.

1206.3.3 Maximum allowable quantities. Fire areas within buildings containing *capacitor energy storage systems* that exceed 600 kWh of energy capacity shall comply with all applicable Group H occupancy requirements in this code and the *International Building Code*.

❖ Scientific research and large-scale fire and fault condition testing is not available to justify allowing unlimited size capacitor energy storage systems in mixed occupancy buildings even with the separations set out in Section 1206.3.2.2. This section establishes a maximum of 600 kWh for all types of capacitors within each fire area. Where capacitors exceed 600 kWh a Group H occupancy classification would be required.

1206.3.4 Capacitors and equipment. The design and installation of *capacitor energy storage systems* and related equipment shall comply with Sections 1206.3.4.1 through 1206.3.4.5.

❖ This section deals with the specific design and installation requirements of the capacitor energy storage systems and associated equipment. This addresses listing requirements, the need for energy management systems and charger compatibility. Part of these requirements is the assessment of whether the capacitor energy storage system generates toxic or highly toxic gases.

1206.3.4.1 Listing. Capacitors and *capacitor energy storage systems* shall comply with the following:

1. Capacitors shall be listed in accordance with UL 1973.
2. Prepackaged and preengineered stationary capacitor energy storage systems shall be listed in accordance with UL 9540.

❖ This section addresses the basic listing requirements for capacitor energy storage systems. Basically all capacitor energy storage systems must be listed to UL 1973. Prepackaged and preengineered systems must be listed in accordance with UL 9540, which includes compliance with UL 1973.

1206.3.4.2 Prepackaged and preengineered systems. In addition to other applicable requirements of this code, prepackaged and preengineered *capacitor energy storage systems* shall be installed in accordance with their listing and the manufacturer's instructions.

❖ Preengineered and prepacked systems have been approved more as a system versus components and carry with them listings as a system. This section ensures that they are installed in accordance with their listing and manufacturer's instructions. For instance, if a system is listed for outdoor use only, it cannot be used in a building. Placement in the building would invalidate the listing.

1206.3.4.3 Energy management system. An approved energy management system shall be provided for monitoring and balancing capacitor voltages, currents and temperatures within the manufacturer's specifications. The system shall transmit an alarm signal to an approved location if potentially hazardous temperatures or other conditions such as short circuits, over voltage or under voltage are detected.

❖ Energy management systems that monitor and take action on abnormal conditions that could lead to problems are an important element of a safety system. Energy management systems are critical as part of the risk reduction of capacitor energy storage systems.

1206.3.4.4 Capacitor chargers. Capacitor chargers shall be compatible with the capacitor manufacturer's electrical ratings and charging specifications. Capacitor chargers shall be listed and labeled in accordance with UL 1564 or provided as part of a listed preengineered or prepackaged *capacitor energy storage system.*

❖ Using incorrect chargers could create a failure resulting in thermal runaway or potentially fire or explosion. Therefore, specific listing and labeling is required to avoid the possibility of a capacitor energy storage system being charged incorrectly.

1206.3.4.5 Toxic and highly toxic gas. *Capacitor energy storage systems* that have the potential to release toxic and highly toxic materials during charging, discharging and normal use conditions shall comply with Chapter 60.

❖ This section covers capacitor energy storage technologies (many yet to hit the market) that may potentially produce toxic gases during charging, discharging and normal use, and triggers Chapter 60 safety requirements. There is no intent to address capacitor energy systems that produce toxic gases during fires or abnormal conditions.

1206.3.5 Fire-extinguishing and detection systems. Fire-extinguishing and smoke detection systems shall be provided in *capacitor energy storage system* rooms in accordance with Sections 1206.3.5.1 through 1206.3.5.2.

❖ This section provides the requirements for fire extinguishing and detection for capacitor energy storage systems. This section also provides requirements for other features to address hazards such as the release of flammable gases such as hydrogen and potential spills.

1206.3.5.1 Fire-extinguishing systems. Rooms containing *capacitor energy storage systems* shall be equipped with an *automatic sprinkler system* installed in accordance with Section 903.3.1.1. Commodity classifications for specific capacitor technologies shall be in accordance with Chapter 5 of NFPA 13. If the capacitor types are not addressed in Chapter 5 of NFPA 13, the *fire code official* is authorized to approve the *automatic sprinkler system* based on full-scale fire and fault condition testing conducted by an *approved* laboratory.

❖ This section is specific to the use of automatic sprinkler systems. Section 1206.3.5.1.1 addresses capacitor systems that contain water-reactive materials where water cannot be used.

Where an automatic sprinkler system can be used, the system must be designed to the specific commodity classification applicable to that capacitor technology. If the capacitor energy storage system technology is not addressed by Chapter 5 of NFPA 13, then a sprinkler system may still be used where full-scale testing is undertaken to demonstrate the effectiveness of the system. Acceptance of this testing and ultimate approval of the system are the authority of the fire code official. A significant challenge facing designers and fire code officials is a lack of large-scale fire and fault condition test data to demonstrate that fire suppression systems can control capacitor fires. Until such protection arrangements are documented in NFPA 13 and other standards, this section needs to provide the option of approving suppression systems based on test data made available to the fire code official.

1206.3.5.1.1 Alternative fire-extinguishing systems. *Capacitor energy storage systems* that utilize water-reactive materials shall be protected by an approved alternative *automatic fire-extinguishing system* in accordance with Section

904. The system shall be listed for protecting the type, arrangement and quantities of capacitors in the room. The *fire code official* shall be permitted to approve the system based on full-scale fire and fault condition testing conducted by an *approved* laboratory.

❖ Some capacitor energy storage systems cannot be protected by water so a traditional automatic sprinkler system is not an option. This section requires that the system be either listed for such use or that the use of the system be based on full-scale fire and fault condition testing. A significant challenge facing designers and code officials is a scarcity of large-scale fire and fault condition test data that demonstrate that fire suppression systems can control capacitor fires. Therefore, the option of full-scale testing is critical.

1206.3.5.2 Smoke detection system. An approved *automatic smoke detection system* shall be installed in rooms containing *capacitor energy storage systems* in accordance with Section 907.2.

❖ A smoke detection system is required for early detection and warning in accordance with Section 907.2.23.

1206.3.5.3 Ventilation. Where capacitors release flammable gases during normal operating conditions, ventilation of rooms containing capacitor energy storage systems shall be provided in accordance with the *International Mechanical Code* and one of the following:

1. The ventilation system shall be designed to limit the maximum concentration of flammable gas to 25 percent of the lower flammability limit.
2. Continuous ventilation shall be provided at a rate of not less than 1 cubic foot per minute (cfm) per square foot [0.00508 $m^3/(s \bullet m^2)$] of floor area, but not less than 150 cfm (4 m^3/min).

The exhaust system shall be designed to provide air movement across all parts of the floor for gases having a vapor density greater than air and across all parts of the ceiling for gases having a vapor density less than air.

❖ This section is not applicable to all capacitor energy storage systems; but only to capacitor energy storage systems that release flammable gases during normal conditions. The room ventilation, as with any other building area, must comply with the requirements of the IMC. Generally, the main concern is the production of hydrogen and oxygen within an enclosed space. Hydrogen has a wide flammability range and is the lightest element on the Periodic Table of Elements, having an atomic number of 1. The gas mixture is explosive when the amount of hydrogen in air exceeds 4 percent by volume. To address the concern of hydrogen generation and containment in small areas, a minimum ventilation criterion is set. This section provides two methods of compliance from which the designer may choose. The first is performance based and states that the maximum concentration of hydrogen must be limited to either 25 percent of the LFL or 1.0 percent of the total volume of the room. Note that this section states flammable gas more generally with reference to the LFL limit as this could apply to other types of flammable gases. The second criteria of 1 percent is specific to hydrogen. This method requires an analysis of plausible failure scenarios to justify the ventilation rate ultimately chosen. The second method simply requires continuous ventilation at a rate no less than 1 cubic foot per minute per square foot [1 $ft^3/min/ft^2$ or 0.0051 $m^3/(s \times m^2)$] of room area.

The sentence following the requirements is focusing on keep the air moving in the most critical portion of the room depending on the flammable gas of concern. Hydrogen is lighter than air so the concern would be at the ceiling level. However, extensive testing of leaking hydrogen concentrations in rooms containing fuel cells shows that while hydrogen is light, and the concentration at the ceiling is greater than the floor, because hydrogen molecules are so small, they tend to disperse rather than gather, and concentrations at the ceiling are typically no more than 10 percent higher than those at floor level.

1206.3.5.3.1 Supervision. Required mechanical ventilation systems for rooms containing *capacitor energy storage systems* shall be supervised by an *approved* central station, proprietary or remote station service, or shall initiate an audible and visible signal at an *approved,* constantly attended on-site location.

❖ Where mechanical ventilation is utilized to keep the concentration of flammable gases, such as hydrogen, from reaching a flammable or explosive limit, some method is necessary to ensure that the ventilation system is operational. This section provides two options, which include supervision or an audible and visual alarm at an approved location. A security desk that is operated 24 hours would be a reasonable location to meet the "constantly attended" criteria. See the discussion related to battery systems and hydrogen in the commentary to Section 1206.2.11.3.2.

1206.3.5.4 Spill control and neutralization. Where capacitors contain liquid electrolyte, *approved* methods and materials shall be provided for the control and neutralization of spills of electrolyte or other hazardous materials in areas containing capacitors as follows:

1. For capacitors with free-flowing electrolyte, the method and materials shall be capable of neutralizing a spill of the total capacity from the largest cell or block to a pH between 5.0 and 9.0.
2. For capacitors with immobilized electrolyte, the method and material shall be capable of neutralizing a spill of 3.0 percent of the capacity of the largest cell or block in the room to a pH between 5.0 and 9.0.

❖ This section only applies to capacitor energy storage systems that have liquid electrolyte. There are two types, either free flowing or immobilized. The two items deal with both types of electrolyte conditions.

Capacitors that contain a free-flowing liquid electrolyte pose the same containment problems as any other corrosive liquid hazardous material, but the containment and neutralization provisions in this section are performance based and neither specifically require spill control in the form of containment nor a specific method of neutralization. The quantity of neutralization material required to be available would be greater for these less-viscous electrolytes, however, because of their mobility and the rapidity and potential scope of the spread.

Item 1 deals with capacitors that contain free-flowing electrolyte. The requirement is fairly performance based and neither specifically requires spill control in the form of containment, nor a specific method of neutralization. Instead, it states that a capability to control and neutralize a spill equal to the liquid content of the largest single cell or block to a pH between 5.0 and 9.0 must be available.

Capacitors with immobilized electrolyte are required to comply with Item 2. This item is also performance based and neither specifically requires spill control in the form of containment, nor a specific method of neutralization. Instead, it states that a capability to control and neutralize a spill equal to the 3 percent of the liquid content of the largest single cell or block housed to a pH between 5.0 and 9.0 must be available. Typically, either sodium-bicarbonate powder or a liquid buffering solution is provided within the room where the capacitor system is located for use by trained personnel.

1206.3.6 Testing, maintenance and repair. Capacitors and associated equipment and systems shall be tested and maintained in accordance with the manufacturer's instructions. Any capacitors or system components used to replace existing units shall be compatible with the capacitor charger, energy management systems, other capacitors, and other safety systems. Introducing different capacitor technologies into the capacitor energy storage system shall be treated as a new installation and require approval by the *fire code official* before the replacements are introduced into service.

❖ This section is critical to the long-term safe and effective use of the capacitor energy storage system. This section provides the mechanism to enable such systems to be tested and maintained. More importantly, it requires that any time a different capacitor technology is being used with an existing capacitor energy storage system, that it be addressed as if it were new. This would require a full review of the requirements in Section 1206.3.

Bibliography

The following resource materials were used in the preparation of the commentary for this chapter of the code:

IEEE 1035-2012/ASHRAE 21, *Guide for the Ventilation and Thermal Management of Batteries for Stationary Applications*. Atlanta, GA: ASHRAE, 2012.

CHAPTERS 13 through 19

RESERVED

INDEX

B

C

D

E

F

G

H

I

J

K

L

M

N

P

S

T

U

Y

Z

The ICC Assessment Center (formerly known as ICC Certification & Testing) provides nationally recognized credentials that demonstrate a confirmed commitment to protect public health, safety, and welfare. Raise the professionalism of your department and further your career by pursuing an ICC Certification.

ICC Certifications offer:

- Nationwide recognition
- Increased earning potential
- Career advancement
- Superior knowledge
- Validation of your expertise
- Personal and professional satisfaction

Exams are developed and maintained to the highest standards, which includes continuous peer review by national committees of experienced, practicing professionals. ICC is continually evolving exam offerings, testing options, and technology to ensure that all building and fire safety officials have access to the tools and resources needed to advance in today's fast-paced and rapidly-changing world.

Enhancing Exam Options

Effective July 2018, the Assessment Center enhanced and streamlined exam options and now offers only computer based testing (CBT) at a test site and PRONTO. We no longer offer paper/pencil exams.

Proctored Remote Online Testing Option (PRONTO)

Taking your next ICC certification exam is more convenient, more comfortable and more efficient than ever before with PRONTO.

PRONTO provides a convenient testing experience that is accessible 24 hours a day, 7 days a week, 365 days a year. Required hardware/software is minimal – you will need a webcam and microphone, as well as a reasonably recent operating system.

Whether testing in your office or in the comfort of your home, your ICC exam will continue to maintain its credibility while offering more convenience, allowing you to focus on achieving your professional goals. The Assessment Center continues to add exams to the PRONTO exam catalog regularly.

18-15617

Checkout all the ICC Assessment Center has to offer at iccsafe.org/certification